ENVIRONMENTAL SCIENCE
A Framework for Decision Making

Also of interest from the Benjamin/Cummings Series in the Life Sciences

General Biology

N. A. Campbell
Biology (1987)

K. D. Johnson, D. L. Rayle, and H. L. Wedberg
Biology: An Introduction (1984)

Evolution, Ecology, and Behavior

F. J. Ayala and J. W. Valentine
Evolving: The Theory and Process of Organic Evolution (1979)

R. J. Lederer
Ecology and Field Biology (1984)

M. Lerman
Marine Biology: Environment, Diversity, and Ecology (1986)

D. McFarland
Animal Behavior (1985)

E. Minkoff
Evolutionary Biology (1983)

R. Trivers
Social Evolution (1985)

Plant Biology

M. G. Barbour, J. H. Burk, and W. D. Pitts
Terrestrial Plant Ecology, second edition (1987)

J. Mauseth
Plant Anatomy (1988)

Animal Biology

H. E. Evans
Insect Biology: A Textbook of Entomology (1984)

P. E. Lutz
Invertebrate Zoology (1986)

L. G. Mitchell, J. A. Mutchmor, W. D. Dolphin
General Zoology (1988)

A. P. Spence
Basic Human Anatomy, second edition (1986)

A. P. Spence and E. B. Mason
Human Anatomy and Physiology, third edition (1987)

Genetics

F. J. Ayala
Population and Evolutionary Genetics: A Primer (1982)

F. J. Ayala and J. A. Kiger, Jr.
Modern Genetics, second edition (1984)

J. B. Jenkins
Human Genetics (1983)

R. Schleif
Genetics and Molecular Biology (1986)

Microbiology

I. E. Alcamo
Fundamentals of Microbiology, second edition (1987)

R. M. Atlas and R. Bartha
Microbial Ecology: Fundamentals and Applications, second edition (1987)

M. Dworkin
Developmental Biology of the Bacteria (1985)

G. J. Tortora, B. R. Funke, and C. L. Case
Microbiology: An Introduction, second edition (1986)

P. J. VanDemark and B. L. Batzing
The Microbes (1987)

ENVIRONMENTAL SCIENCE
A Framework for Decision Making

SECOND EDITION

DANIEL D. CHIRAS

University of Colorado, Denver

THE BENJAMIN/CUMMINGS PUBLISHING COMPANY, INC.

Menlo Park, California • Reading, Massachusetts • Don Mills, Ontario
Wokingham, U.K. • Amsterdam • Sydney • Singapore
Tokyo • Madrid • Bogota • Santiago • San Juan

For Kathleen in whom all hope is born

Sponsoring Editor: Andrew Crowley
Developmental Editor: Martine Westermann
Production Editor: Karen Gulliver
Designer: Gary Head
Photo Research: Darcy Lanham
Cover photo by Dan Morrill Photographer
Photo and text credits appear after the Glossary

Library of Congress Cataloging in Publication Data

Chiras, Daniel D.
    Environmental science.

    Includes bibliographies and index.
    1. Environmental policy. 2. Environmental protection.
I. Title.
HC79.E5C485   1988   363.7   87-13906
ISBN 0–8053–2257–4

    CDEFGHIJ––MU––898

The Benjamin/Cummings Publishing Company, Inc.
2727 Sand Hill Road
Menlo Park, California 94025

Preface

The first edition of *Environmental Science: A Framework for Decision Making* reached a large audience across the United States. Feedback from users and reviewers helped me prepare this second edition. My goal for the new edition was to create a slightly shorter book that fits the one-term course, without omitting any of the coverage and features that were so well received in the first edition.

As in the first edition, I set out to write a book that is user friendly, not laden with irrelevant statistics. I wanted to continue to present important facts and concepts in a clear and exciting way and to minimize bias by presenting the pros and cons of new technologies, population control policies, pollution control measures, and so on. My objective was to write a book that helps students learn the facts behind environmental issues and solutions so that they can make up their own minds about what should be done.

This book provides a broad overview of the many environmental problems facing humanity and the solutions to these quandaries. The chapters contain important information on ecology, anthropology, evolution, earth science, biology, ethics, economics, and other areas to enable students to understand more fully the sometimes overwhelming assortment of environmental problems facing the world. The melding of these disciplines results in new ways of looking at our environmental problems and opens up many avenues for solving them.

Themes

The central theme of this book is that time for action is running short; overpopulation, resource depletion, pollution, and indifference are rapidly catching up with us.

The second major theme is that the long-term well being of this planet and its inhabitants requires the development of a sustainable society—one that conserves natural resources, recycles, relies on renewable resources whenever possible, reduces pollution, and controls population growth. Such a society, based on the lessons from ecology, may seem foreign or even unattainable, but it remains our only realistic hope for prosperity for the long term. Careful planning and implementation will usher in a sustainable future.

The third theme is that complex environmental problems require complex solutions, not simple ameliorative steps that cure only the symptoms. Political, technological, economic, indeed even ethical changes must all be brought into play to solve the world's environmental dilemmas.

Finally, this book stresses that we are all part of the problem and must therefore be part of the solution. Air pollution is not just a problem of inadequate laws or corporate neglect, but also the result of our own wasteful practices. Solving these problems need not mean reverting to old-fashioned ways or even making tremendous sacrifices. It does mean using energy and other resources much more wisely, conserving all resources, recycling all that we can, using renewable resources, and limiting our family size. Numerous suggestions are given in each chapter for such personal solutions.

Organization

This book is divided in five parts and organized around three central issues—population, resources, and pollution. Part 1 provides a base of knowledge in ecology, earth science, chemistry, biology, evolution, and human social development. Part 2 covers population growth, the impacts of population, and population control. Part 3 deals with a variety of resource issues and outlines a plan for developing a sustainable society. Part 4 discusses pollution and the legal, technical, and personal solutions for it. Part 5, the capstone of the book, places the population, resource, and pollution crisis against a social backdrop by looking at ethics, economics, and politics. It suggests ways to make the transition to a sustainable society.

Special Features

The following special features from the first edition have been retained to keep this text informative and useful and to increase student interest and involvement:

Models

One of the key features of this book is the use of conceptual models, which in this edition have been integrated in appropriate chapters. These models are easy to understand and are designed to encourage holistic thinking, emphasizing the systems approach to environmental problems. Below is a brief description of each model:

- *Population, Resource, and Pollution Model:* presents a fuller view of the human niche, and helps students see the way we affect our environment and vice versa.

- *Multiple Cause and Effect Model:* helps students analyze the causes of many of our current environmental dilemmas by exhibiting the web of cause and effect.

- *Impact Analysis Model:* shows the various impacts that we have on the environment and the ways in which we are affected by our own actions.

- *Risk Analysis Model:* examines the risks and benefits associated with today's new and existing hazards.

Chapter Supplements

Chapter supplements, found at the end of some chapters, provide more detailed coverage of important topics and provide an added degree of flexibility. Such topics of current interest include acid rain, indoor air pollution, stratospheric ozone depletion, radiation pollution, nuclear war, and environmental law.

Point/Counterpoints and Viewpoints

As might be expected, complex environmental issues often result in hotly contested debates:

- Is outer space the answer to our population and resource problems?
- Are we responsible to future generations?
- Is population growth good or bad for us?
- Does environmental protection cost us jobs?

- Are we losing the war against cancer?
- Are we playing God with nature?

These and many other important and timely issues are debated in Point/Counterpoint or discussed in Viewpoint by such luminaries as Norman Myers, Ben Bova, Garret Hardin, Julian Simon, Amory and Hunter Lovins, Frederic Krupp, and others. These editorials can stimulate individual thinking as well as classroom discussion on many complex problems.

Color Galleries

Four color galleries are included in this book to emphasize some of the key concepts and issues. They are: the earth, the biomes, endangered species, and resource misuse.

Essays

Numerous Essays present interesting findings in environmental science to pique student interest. Newsworthy stories and unique ecological solutions to a number of problems are the topics of these brief articles.

Chapter Summaries

Each chapter is followed by a succinct summary of the important concepts and terms, designed to reinforce the key points. These summaries may also be valuable study tools.

New in the Second Edition

The second edition introduces a number of new features.

The Environmental Quotient

A simple test found in the Prologue to the book offers students a way to determine their attitudes regarding environmental issues as well as their current level of action—that is, how much they are doing to reduce pollution, resource waste, and so on. This section is designed to encourage individuals to take more active roles in solving environmental problems.

Case Studies

Another new feature in the second edition is the Case Study—in-depth studies of important issues in environmental science, such as genetic engineering, protecting Antarctica, problems facing the cleanup of the Great Lakes, and the links between air pollution and Parkinson's disease.

Increased Coverage of the Basic Sciences

I've added more information from the basic sciences to help students better understand environmental issues. The formation of the earth, the evolution of life, geological processes, chemistry, and other fundamental topics are covered in Chapter 2 and integrated in other chapters.

Updated Coverage

The second edition has been thoroughly updated with new discoveries, new environmental laws, the most recent statistics on resources, population, and pollution, and new suggested readings. New essays, viewpoints, photographs, tables, and line drawings have been added as well.

Acknowledgments

This book is the offspring of a great many people, for whom a mere thanks seems terribly inadequate. First and foremost are the thousands of scholars in anthropology, biology, chemistry, demography, natural resources, political science, economics, ecology, and dozens of other disciplines. Their ideas, their research, indeed their lives, form the foundation on which this book rests. To them a world of thanks and an enormous debt of gratitude.

A warm and very special thanks to my friend and colleague, Teresa Audesirk, who reviewed the second edition and helped make it more accurate and more readable and who helped supply me with mounds of reference material needed in the update.

A genuine thanks to the staff at Benjamin/Cummings who labored over this book as if it were their own. A special thanks to Andrew Crowley, my editor, who coordinated much of the long process, who read and commented on the manuscript throughout, who infused the project with enthusiasm and creativity, and whose high standards are evident everywhere; to Martine Westermann, who took over for Andy at the beginning of the production phase, reading and commenting on the text, helping me refine the basic science material and carefully updating facts and figures; to friend, compatriot, and developmental editor, Bonnie Garmus, whose work on the first edition still shows through; to Karen Gulliver, who guided this book through the tedious production stages; to Darcy Lanham who located the new photographs for this text; to eagle-eyed copyeditor Bill Waller who smoothed out the rough spots and carefully checked over the manuscript; to first edition research assistants Dave Shugarts, Cynthia Stuart, Diane Short, and Ann Beckenhauer and second edition research assistants Rae Nelson, Carmen Bal, and Elizabeth Yerkes, who helped update the book.

Finally, an extra special word of thanks to my wife, Kathleen, who encouraged me throughout and endured complaints of tired eyes and sore back from the long hours bent over my books. To her, much more than thanks.

Many manuscript reviewers provided helpful and constructive criticism on both the first and second editions of *Environmental Science: A Framework for Decision Making*:

David M. Armstrong, *University of Colorado, Boulder*
Robert Auckerman, *Colorado State University*
Terry Audesirk, *University of Colorado, Denver*
Michael Bass, *Mary Washington College*
Bayard H. Brattstrom, *California State University, Fullerton*
Lester Brown, *Worldwatch Institute*
Ann S. Causey, *Auburn University*
Donald Collins, *Montana State University*
Sally DeGroot, *St. Petersburg Junior College*
James H. Grosklags, *Northern Illinois University*
Richard Haas, *California State University, Fresno*
William S. Hardenbergh, *Southern Illinois University*
John P. Harley, *Eastern Kentucky University*
John N. Hoefer, *University of Wisconsin, La Crosse*
Gary James, *Orange Coast College*
John Jones, *Miami Dade Community College*
Alan R. P. Journet, *Southeast Missouri State University*
Thomas L. Keefe, *Eastern Kentucky University*
Suzanne Kelly, *Scottsdale Community College*
Thomas G. Kinsey, *State University College at Buffalo*
David Lovejoy, *Westfield State College*
Timothy F. Lyon, *Ball State University*
Glenn P. Moffat, *Foothill College*
Charles Mohler, *Cornell University*
Bryan C. Myres, *Cypress College*
John H. Peck, *St. Cloud State University*
Michael Priano, *Westchester Community College*
Joseph Priest, *Miami University*
Robert J. Robel, *Kansas State University*
Jack Schlein, *York College, City University of New York*
Michael P. Shields, *Southern Illinois University*
Roger E. Thibault, *Bowling Green State University*
Leland Van Fossen, *DeAnza College*
Bruce Webb, *Animal Protection Institute*
Ross W. Westover, *Canada College*

Jeffrey R. White, *Indiana University*
Ray E. Williams, *Rio Hondo College*
Larry Wilson, *Miami Dade Community College*
Stephen W. Wilson, *Central Missouri State University*
Susan Wilson, *Miami Dade Community College*

Richard J. Wright, *Valencia Community College*
Paul A. Yambert, *Southern Illinois University*

I am very thankful for their helpful comments.

DANIEL D. CHIRAS
Denver, Colorado

Brief Contents

Detailed Contents

Prologue

In an outlying village in Ethiopia, two children are lowered into a communal grave that houses the bodies of others who have died in recent days. Villagers stare vacantly at the men who cover the bodies with dirt; to the friends and relatives of these children who watch, death has lost much of its significance. Against the constant hunger and death, few mourn another child's passing.

Worldwide, 700 people will die from starvation, extreme malnutrition, or infectious disease stemming from food shortages in the half hour it takes you to watch the evening news. This year alone, the death toll from hunger and associated diseases is estimated to be 40 million people. This is the equivalent of 300 jumbojets, each carrying 400 passengers, crashing with no survivors every day of the year. Almost half of the victims are children. Despite an outpouring of aid from the rich nations, hundreds of millions more will die in years to come.

A False Sense of Security?

For Africans of the southern Sahara, the future looks bleak. Long-term drought, overpopulation, continued misuse of the land, and political struggles all create spreading deserts that swallow farmland at an alarming rate. In this dilemma, nature dictates an extreme solution: people must die to reestablish the balance.

But what about those of us in the wealthy nations of the world? Need we worry? To many people, the answer is no. Resource shortages are a thing of the past. Newspaper headlines assure us of an "oil glut" that has forced OPEC nations to slash prices, bringing inflation under control. And there is renewed talk among politicians and business leaders of continued economic growth. Some critics believe that our sense of security is illusory. But why not feel secure; with an ally as powerful as technology, how could we not prosper?

Part of the answer may lie in the way we mistreat our soil, perhaps our greatest resource of all. In the United States, for example, farmers currently cultivate 170 million hectares (421 million acres) of land. According to recent estimates by the Department of Agriculture, nearly one-half of the United States' farmland is eroding faster than it can be replaced by natural processes. Perhaps more importantly, three of every four farmers are unaware that erosion on their property exceeds the replacement level. Making matters worse, there is very little land in reserve to replace the prime land now washing into U.S. waterways. Some experts believe that crop production could fall by 10% to 30% in the United States in the next 50 years if soil erosion continues unchecked. Costs of food will rise as good farmland is destroyed. The United States may lose its position as a leading food exporter. Grain shipments to hungry nations may be reduced as well, unless something is done . . . quickly.

Consider also one of our most valuable resources, oil, thought by many to be the lifeblood of industrial societies. Oil's economic importance to developed nations became clear in the 1970s when per-barrel prices jumped from $3.00 to over $35. A whirlwind of inflation began, perilously gripping the industrial world, nearly halting industrial production. The American economy, among others, was driven to its knees. Millions of workers were laid off as inflation brought industrial production to a near standstill.

Despite current, short-term gluts and falling prices, the long-range future of oil is dim. Estimated worldwide oil supplies will last only 70 more years at current consumption. Should consumption rise, as expected, even fewer oil years await us. Clearly, time is running out for oil.

Long before our wells run dry, however, the rich, oil-dependent nations will begin to flounder. By some estimates, somewhere around 2000 or 2010 global oil production will fall short of demand, sending prices sharply upward. The inflation of the 1970s will seem like warm spring breezes compared to the hurricane winds of global inflation.

You and I, and millions of people like us, will very likely see the end of oil within our lifetimes. The time is ripe for charting new paths, but this nation and others are sitting back, swayed by reports of an apparent oil glut, waiting.

Declining resources are only part of the threat to modern society. Industrial economies jeopardize their future by destroying croplands, forests, streams, lakes, and buildings. Pollution and development threaten to rip apart the delicate web of life. Foremost on the list of pollutants is acid rain and snow.

Today, over 230 ponds and lakes in the Adirondacks have lost their aquatic life because of acids from industry and transportation. Deposited by rain and snow, these acids kill fish, algae, and aquatic plants. In southern Sweden 20,000 lakes are without or soon to be without fish because of widespread acid deposition. In Canada, 100 lakes have met a similar fate. But the effect of acid rain is felt much wider. For instance, much of the once-rich Black Forest in Germany has been poisoned by this toxic rain. And in the United States, acid precipitation causes an estimated $5 billion worth of damage to buildings and statues. Much of the $320 million damage to the Statue of Liberty was the result of acid rain.

Compounding our problems is the growing threat of nuclear war. Besides killing millions of people, nuclear war could drastically change global climate, perhaps ushering in a nuclear winter by sweeping millions of tons of dust into the atmosphere that block sunlight and cause surface temperatures to fall. Avoiding a nuclear war ranks high on our list of priorities.

The long-term future of the world is in jeopardy. It is not just the poor of Ethiopia or Chad or Sudan who stand to lose, but also the wealthy residents who make up one-fourth of the world's population but consume 80% of its resources. The rich and the poor are locked in a crisis created by overpopulation, vanishing resources, and excessive pollution.

Tragedy of Our Times

Paul Valery once noted that the tragedy of our times is that the future is not what it used to be. In reality, though, the future is rarely what we think it will be. The tragedy of our times is that few people realize that the future has changed. We are, as a whole, going about our daily lives as if nothing has happened, lulled into complacency by old and fairly unrealistic dreams. Oil gluts, falling gasoline prices, and economic stability have given us a false sense of security at a time when we need, more than anything, three key ingredients: foresight, planning, and action—both individually and collectively.

This book examines the crisis of population, resources, and pollution that engulfs humankind. You will find it a hopeful book, filled with solutions. It views our dilemma in much the same way that the Chinese view crises. Their word for crisis is *wei-chi*. The first part means "beware of danger." The second part means "opportunity for change."

In this spirit, I invite you to look at the critical paths we are now on. You will see that the human race can survive the human race and prosper. But changes must be made—big changes in the way we think and the ways we act.

The Secrets of Nature

What alterations in our course are necessary? Experts disagree, but many believe that the key to our long-term survival lies in the widely ignored lessons of nature. Consider these facts: undisturbed ecosystems persist for decades, centuries, even millions of years. The rate of extinction in such ecosystems is low. Human society, on the other hand, now wipes out a vertebrate (backboned) species every nine months and itself faces global extinction after only a relatively short stay on earth. Why is it that nature persists while we deplete and destroy? The secret of nature is that survival hinges on a sustainable system—a system that perpetuates itself without destroying the very things that permit life to continue.

Nature capitalizes on four major strategies to meet this end. The first is recycling. The global ecosystem is a consummate recycler. Water, carbon, oxygen, nitrogen, and all other substances are used over and over. As a result, new generations are built from the old. The long-term future of humankind depends on following a similar direction.

Nature's second secret is the use of renewable resources—resources that renew themselves through natural biological or physical and chemical processes. Wood, water, and wind are examples. For millenia, humankind heated its homes with wood, reaped the riches of the biological world for food, and fashioned its goods from flax and other plant products. Only in the past 200 years has our allegiance to renewable resources wavered. Today, we depend heavily on a variety of non-renewable substances: fuel, plastics, and synthetic fabrics made from oil; metals; and so on. Our new dependency, many think, is a dangerous trap. It cannot be sustained indefinitely. Our long-term future requires a greater dependency on resources that can renew themselves. Protecting these resources is a form of self care.

Nature's third secret is conservation. A fat wildebeest or an obese ostrich do not exist in nature. For the most part, organisms use what they need—no more, no less. Modern industrial societies, on the other hand, are often gluttonous, overeating, wastefully consuming, and recklessly depleting. Ecologists warn us that we cannot do so forever with impunity.

The fourth secret of nature is population control. Through a variety of ways, populations of living things are kept from living beyond their means. Predators trim the prey populations. Diseases eliminate the weak and aged. Environmental conditions keep populations from exploding. For humans, technological advances, medicine, and sanitation have removed many of the natural barriers to human population explosion. The upshot of the rapid human population expansion is often foulsmelling skies, filthy water, and landscapes devoid of vegetation and animal life. The ecosystem is sacrificed to continue population growth. Most ecologists agree that we must learn to control our numbers to preserve the global ecosystem.

Such are the secrets of nature: recycling, renewable resources, conservation, and population control. It is ironic that today we must go back to nature to relearn these forgotten lessons. If we are to survive for thousands of years to come, we must build a sustainable society, a society that lives in harmony with nature, not a society that seeks complete domination over all living things or destroys its renewable resource base. Building a sustainable society does not mean reverting to a primitive existence, it means using resources in a pattern laid down by nature.

Frontiers

A great frontier lies ahead of us. It is not the great expanse of space or the oceanic depths that we must conquer, but rather it is ourselves. Ahead of us lies the greatest and sometimes most inaccessible frontier—that of self-understanding and self-control. Before we race further into space to satisfy our needs, we must learn to look deeper within ourselves and find ways to build a sustainable society.

We can achieve such a society within our lifetimes, but each of us must help. Individuals must do more than pay lip service to recycling, conservation, renewable resources, and population control, and they must take action now. This book looks at the problems and suggests ways to build a sustainable society. It concerns itself more with the long-term future of humankind, recognizing fully that we must make changes now to transition smoothly into sustainability. Some of you may wonder why we should worry about future generations. Shouldn't we let them fend for themselves? And why should we change our ways now? Part of the answer is that we hold the future in our hands. At no time in history has the present generation had such potential to shape the future. The decisions we make on nuclear energy, acid rain, and tropical rainforests will affect our sons and daughters and

theirs more profoundly than they will affect us. It is for this reason alone that we must rethink the past and redefine the future.

A sustainable society will not be a radical departure from our current way. In fact, many examples of sustainability are now commonplace, like bottle bills, battery recycling, water conservation, and wilderness preservation. It takes only a small effort and a little wisdom to get back on track. Abraham Lincoln said it best, "As the times are new, so we must think and act anew." Let this be our challenge: to see that the future is no longer what it used to be and to build a future that will last.

What is Your EQ?

All organisms draw from the environment the things they need to survive. Of all living things, however, we humans place the largest demands on the environment. Our advanced technologies and burgeoning numbers are cause for an enormous strain on earth's life-giving support systems. By driving our cars, watering our lawns, feeding our families, recreating, and thousands of other activities we pollute and deplete resources.

Many futurists believe that to build a lasting society humanity must be more environmentally conscious and learn to reduce its impact and resource demand. The test presented here can help achieve this goal in two ways: First, it can help each of us assess our attitudes toward the environment. Second, it can help us assess the environmental impacts of our lifestyles.

Please take a few minutes to answer the following questions. When you have finished add up your scores and compare them with the scales provided at the end. You might want to analyze areas in the second test (on actions and impacts) to see where you need work and draw up a plan to improve your score, but be careful to select a realistic goal. Retake the test at the end of the semester and compare your scores to see the progress you have made.

Environmental Quotient

Area 1: Environmental Attitudes

This section queries your attitudes toward the environment. Please answer them as honestly as possible, indicating what you really think and not what you think your professor might want to hear.

Please note that words mean different things to different people. Thus, it is difficult to find a wording that suits each person.

Circle the correct responses and total them for your attitude score.

1. Generally speaking, how strongly do you favor the environmental movement?

   Not at all 0 1 2 3 4 5 Strongly support

2. Generally speaking, would you favor environmental protection if it meant slower economic growth?

   Not at all 0 1 2 3 4 5 Very much so

3. Generally speaking, would you support a candidate for public office if he or she favored spending more to reduce pollution?

   Not at all 0 1 2 3 4 5 Very much so

4. Would you be willing to change your lifestyle (say, reduce home energy consumption or use mass transit more often) to help reduce air pollution?

   Not at all 0 1 2 3 4 5 Very much so

5. Would you favor a reduction in population growth in the United States?

   Not at all 0 1 2 3 4 5 Very much so

6. Would you support a reduction in U.S. population size?

   Not at all 0 1 2 3 4 5 Very much so

7. Would you support a reduction in population growth in Third World nations?

   Not at all 0 1 2 3 4 5 Very much so

8. Would you support a nationwide recycling bill, requiring all bottles and cans to be returned for recycling?

   Not at all 0 1 2 3 4 5 Very much so

9. Do you support the nationwide law to increase the speed limit on the nation's highways?

   Very much so 0 1 2 3 4 5 Not at all

10. Generally speaking, would you prefer to live in a nation that emphasizes conservation of energy over development of new energy supplies?

    Not at all 0 1 2 3 4 5 Very much so

11. Generally speaking, do you support wilderness protection, even if important minerals could no longer be extracted from the land?

    Not at all 0 1 2 3 4 5 Very much so

12. Do you think that humans are apart from nature and immune to its laws or a part of it and, therefore, subject to its rules?

    Apart from 0 1 2 3 4 5 A part of nature

13. Given the choice between a vehicle that gets 40 miles per gallon and one that gets 25 miles per gallon but costs $1,000 less, would you buy the low-polluting gas miser (supposing that the cars are identical in all other respects)?

    Probably not 0 1 2 3 4 5 Absolutely

14. Would you oppose a 10% increase in food prices to cut back on soil erosion to protect America's farms for future generations?

    Absolutely 0 1 2 3 4 5 Absolutely not

15. Would you support a 10% increase in the cost of all paper, books, wood and wood products if that money were to be spent on protecting tropical rainforests?

    Probably not 0 1 2 3 4 5 Absolutely

16. Generally speaking, would you support your state if it refused to sponsor the Winter Olympics, which would bring in millions of dollars of revenue, because the site would irreparably damage a popular cross-country skiing and hiking spot, as well as the habitat of an endangered species?

    Probably not 0 1 2 3 4 5 Absolutely

17. Would you voluntarily water your lawn at night or reduce the length of your daily showers to help your city/town conserve water?

    Probably not 0 1 2 3 4 5 Absolutely

18. Which should dictate the way resources are managed?

    Economics 0 1 2 3 4 5 Environmental concerns

19. Humans are superior to all other forms of life and should dominate nature?

    Absolutely 0 1 2 3 4 5 Absolutely not

20. Generally speaking, would you prefer to live in a society that conserves resources to benefit future generations if it means fewer material goods for you?

    Absolutely not 0 1 2 3 4 5 Absolutely

Environmental Attitude Scale

Your environmental attitude is	if you scored
Very strong	90–100
Strong	80–89
Moderately strong	60–79
Moderately weak	40–59
Weak	20–39
Very weak	0–19

Area 2: Actions and Impacts

This section assesses your actions and impacts. Answer each question and add up the score when you are finished.

Give yourself

1. 10 points if you plan to have 0–2 children _____

2. 5 points if you generally recycle all of your aluminum cans _____

3. 5 points if you generally recycle your newspaper _____

4. 5 points if you generally recycle your glass containers _____

5. 20 points if you drive a car that gets over 45 miles per gallon on the highway _____

6. 10 points if you drive a car that gets over 35 miles per gallon on the highway _____

7. 5 points if you drive a car that gets over 25 miles per gallon on the highway _____

8. 20 points if you walk, take a bus, carpool, or ride your bike to work or school _____

9. 5 points if you use energy-conserving lightbulbs _____

10. 10 points if you keep your heat at 68° F in the winter _____

11. 10 points if you generally donate old clothes and other goods to charitable organizations _____

12. 10 points if you have your car tuned at least once a year _____

13. 5 points if you generally turn off your TV or stereo when you leave home _____

14. 5 points if you turn off lights when you're out of a room for more than a minute _____

15. 5 points if you turn the water off while you're brushing your teeth _____

16. 5 points if you take showers shorter than 5 minutes _____

17. 5 points if you regularly obey the speed limit _____

18. 5 points if you have written a congressional representative stating your view on an environmental issue within the past year _____

19. 5 points if you regularly read an environmental publication _____

20. 5 points if you are a member of an environmental organization _____

Total score _____

Action and Impact Scale

Your rating is	if you scored
Excellent; keep up the good work	over 100
Good; but there's room for improvement	75–100
Fair; there's plenty of room for improvement	50–74
Poor; lots of room for improvement with a little effort on your part	less than 50

ENVIRONMENTAL SCIENCE
A Framework for Decision Making

PRINCIPLES OF ENVIRONMENTAL SCIENCE

Environmental Science: Meeting the Challenge

The ability of our minds to imagine, coupled with the ability of our hands to devise our images, brings us a power almost beyond our control.

JOAN MCINTYRE

"It was the best of times, it was the worst of times," wrote Charles Dickens in his classic novel *A Tale of Two Cities*. Were he alive today, Dickens might look upon the present with an equal mixture of feelings. There are many signs that humanity has reached a high point in its long cultural evolution: medical advances, worldwide communication systems, and miraculous computers. Despite this technological prowess, however, humanity is besieged by a seemingly insurmountable array of problems: war and social unrest; devastating hunger in the Third World at the same time that U.S. farmers are falling into bankruptcy; water shortages caused by farmers who pump groundwater faster than it can be replaced; plant and animal extinction on an unprecedented scale; soil erosion of epic proportions; widespread destruction of the rich tropical rain forests; acid rain and snow that threaten sensitive ecosystems; air pollution that endangers the global climate; and toxic chemical spills and abandoned waste dumps that pollute our precious groundwater.

"The optimist proclaims that we live in the best of all possible worlds," wrote James Branch Cabell, the American novelist and essayist. "The pessimist fears this is true." In truth, no time is ever uniformly prosperous for humankind or free of threat. There is room for both optimism and pessimism.

Looking back on the 20th century, historians may proclaim this to have been a period of unrivaled promise and peril. At no time, they may observe, had humanity's prospects seemed so confusing—so bright yet so gloomy.

Figure 1-1 The earth from space. This finite planet provides the materials all living things need to survive. Only energy comes from outside this closed system.

A Modern Response to the Environmental Crisis

This book focuses on the problems we now face and offers—with enthusiasm and optimism—many solutions to them. The solutions spring from a new kind of science that has emerged in recent years to deal with the complex set of problems described above. This new academic discipline is called **environmental science**. Environmental science is really just a new name for an activity that humans have been engaged in throughout time: learning how to live on this planet without damaging it unnecessarily or threatening their existence in the process.

Today, environmental science is practiced by many thousands of specialists, ranging from researchers testing new metals to naturalists searching for undiscovered plants to scientists learning how to better monitor the earth's activities from outer space (Figure 1-1).

What Is Environmental Science?

Just what is environmental science? To understand the term, take each word separately. The word *environmental* refers broadly to everything around us: the air, the water, and the land as well as the plants, animals, and microorganisms that inhabit them. To a biologist the environment consists of two basic parts of a unified whole: the

abiotic, or nonliving, components, and the **biotic**, or living, components. Biotic factors include all organisms knit together in an interconnected food web. The abiotic factors include sunlight, precipitation, and nutrient availability. (A broader discussion of the environment appears in Chapter 3.)

Science, of course, refers to a body of knowledge about the world and all its parts. We know it also as a method for finding new information. Tucked away in a laboratory the research scientist deliberately sets out on a fascinating search for new information, hoping in many cases to discover the laws that govern life and the nonliving world we live in. Science seeks exactness through measurement, insight through close observation, and foresight through its theories. How scientists go about their work is discussed in Chapter Supplement 1-1.

Mastering the Environment—and Ourselves

In early human history environmental science did not exist as a recognized endeavor. Nonetheless, our earliest ancestors were by necessity avid students of the environment. They carefully observed animals so they could better hunt them. They painstakingly studied plants so they knew where to find them and when to pick the seeds and fruits. (For more on our early ancestors see Chapter 2.)

When humans turned to farming, they continued to improve their use of animals and plants, and they learned how to follow the movements of the stars to time annual planting and harvesting. However, the vast ecological knowledge of the early hunters and gatherers began to be lost. As modern industries and nations arose, humans turned to resources such as coal and mineral ores, learning where they could be found, how they could be extracted efficiently, and how they could be made to serve our needs. In the process we became manipulators of the environment, with a power so great that we could conceivably change the destiny of our tiny planet. Caught up in marvelous new technologies that enabled us to better our lives, we temporarily forgot that the environment was our home. Much of our air turned filthy, and much of our water, brown and murky; hundreds of species vanished before we remembered what our ancient ancestors had known from the beginning: that we humans are intricately linked to the environment. What we do to the environment, we do to ourselves. Environmental science came into existence as a recognized discipline to cope with the vast problems spawned by overpopulation, resource depletion, and pollution. It has become a key tool in our survival.

Modern environmental science is aimed at helping us control our own actions in the natural world to avoid irreparable damage. In this sense, environmental science means learning to master ourselves.

Welcome to a New Kind of Science

To solve the highly complex problems mentioned above—overpopulation, depletion of resources, and pollution—requires a knowledge of many scientific fields. Environmental science calls on chemistry, biology, geology, and a great many other disciplines, including sociology, climatology, anthropology, forestry, and agriculture. Spanning this wide range of knowledge, environmental science offers an integrated view of the world and our part in it.

Environmental science takes on the colossal task of understanding complex issues in their entirety. Because of this it is an often awkward melding of science, engineering, and liberal arts that requires broadly educated men and women in an age that leans consistently toward specialization. More and more, though, human survival depends on the lessons we can learn from this broad, interdisciplinary science.

Environmental science differs from the traditional "pure," or objective, science, which seeks knowledge for its own sake. Instead, it offers a great deal of urgent advice and reaches many conclusions that challenge cherished beliefs and practices. You may find this true as you read this book. In contrast to the astronomer in a mountaintop observatory or the cell biologist in a laboratory, environmental scientists are often in the thick of things, at the heart of today's hottest debates. And what they have to say does not always please people who continue to believe that the world has an unlimited supply of resources just for us.

Environmental science is the study of the environment, its living and nonliving components, and the interactions of these components. By choice it focuses on the many ways that humans affect the environment. Crossing many traditional boundaries, it attempts to find answers to complex, interrelated problems of population, resources, and pollution, problems that threaten the welfare and long-term survival of humanity.

Outlines of a Crisis

The previous section divided the environmental crisis into three main categories, overpopulation, depletion, and pollution. Entwined throughout these three is a fourth, less tangible problem involving values and feelings; it will be discussed under the heading of the human failing.

This book takes its form around these four headings. Part 1 describes the principles and practices of environmental science; Part 2 discusses population; Part 3 deals with resources; and Part 4 covers pollution. Part 5, in many ways the capstone of this book, looks into questions of values, economics, and politics, those of the present time and those needed to build a sustainable future.

Overpopulation: Too Many People

In 1986 the world's population exceeded 5 billion, and it was swelling at a rate of 1.7% a year. This rate may not seem very high but it would mean a doubling of our numbers in only 41 years. By the time you retire, 10 billion people could inhabit the earth. Despite several decades of agricultural research aimed at increasing the food supply one of every three persons living in the poor, developing nations is unable to find enough to eat. Twelve million people die of starvation each year, and thirty million more perish from diseases made worse by hunger. Most startling, in the areas hardest hit by hunger population is doubling every 17 to 30 years!

This explosion of world population is an outgrowth of the industrial age and the rise of technology. Three key factors are to blame: increased food production, disease control, and better sanitation. These advances greatly increased the survival rate of newborns, but this great change occurred without any decrease in the number of births. As a result, populations worldwide have exploded. Most experts agree that until people start having fewer children, especially in the poorer nations, population will continue to soar, and problems of depletion and pollution will worsen.

Depletion: Eroding the Basis of Life

As world population continues to increase, many resources necessary for human survival will become scarce. Consider the example of firewood. A rural Indian peasant needs only a few pieces of wood each day for cooking. But throughout the countryside millions of people roam, all in search of the tiny ration of wood that will get them through the day; such actions add up to an alarming total. In India forests around many villages have been stripped bare. No dead limbs survive; many live trees have been cut down as well. As a result, peasants are forced to forage farther and farther from their home villages. Many spend most of their waking hours looking for fuel. Because of the shortages, many villagers burn dried cow dung, which is easier to find but ultimately robs farmland of an important source of fertilizer.

The earth's supply of **nonrenewable resources**—those that cannot be regenerated, such as oil, silver, and coal—is finite, or limited. As populations swell and demand increases, nonrenewable resources fall more quickly into short supply. Even **renewable resources**, which have the capacity to regenerate, can become scarce if the demand exceeds their replenishment. Countless examples exist. The redwoods of California today are falling faster than they can regrow to supply wood for picnic tables, decks, and lawn furniture. Numerous species of plants and animals are also being depleted because of overharvesting. Prime agricultural land is being destroyed by careless farming practices that result in soil erosion or nutrient

Figure 1-2 The Cuyahoga River in Cleveland, on fire from chemical pollutants. Considerable progress has been made in cleaning up waterways around the world, especially in the United States. Still, many invisible chemicals are found at dangerous levels.

depletion; in some cases once-rich farmland has been converted into barren desert. In others deep gullies carve up the surface of previously productive land. Huge tropical rain forests in equatorial nations are fast disappearing as the demand for wood, grazing land for beef cattle, and farmland for homeless urban refugees rises.

Pure population pressure and excess consumption lie behind resource depletion. But another important factor is wasteful industrial processes that squander resources and produce excessive pollution. Fortunately, many steps have been taken worldwide to defuse the crisis.

Pollution: Defiling the Land, Water, and Air

Air, water, and land pollution are probably familiar to more people than any other environmental problem. But pollution plagues more than just the cities or regions we live in.

In the spring of 1983 atmospheric scientists flying over the Arctic made the first measurements of a thick orange-brown layer of industrial air pollution covering an area the size of North America and extending more than 8500 meters (28,000 feet) into the atmosphere. That same year U.S. astronauts returning from a space shuttle flight deplored the filthy blanket of air encircling the earth.

As for water pollution, perhaps the most vivid case occurred in the 1960s in Cleveland. The Cuyahoga River, which cuts through the industrial sections of the city, caught fire because levels of flammable pollutants were so high (Figure 1-2). Many lakes and rivers have been cleaned up in the last two decades in the United States and abroad by placing controls on the most visible pol-

lutants, such as raw sewage and industrial effluents. However, many invisible, cancer-causing substances still pollute these waterways, in some areas causing an epidemic of cancer in fish and threatening the health of people who regularly consume fish.

One of the decade's most dramatic pollution news stories occurred in Bhopal, India. On December 3, 1984, while many people were asleep, a deadly cloud of methyl isocyanate, used to make pesticides, leaked from a storage tank at a Union Carbide Corporation plant. Within days the death toll had risen to 2500. The number injured was estimated in the tens of thousands. According to one estimate, as many as 100,000 survivors may suffer permanent injury, including sterility, blindness, and brain damage. The Bhopal disaster is considered the worst industrial accident in history. Dramatic in its outcome, it tends to draw attention away from some even more critical problems, such as acid precipitation and global carbon dioxide pollution.

The Human Failing: A Crisis of Spirit

The ecological crisis is the sum of the interconnected problems of overpopulation, resource depletion, and pollution. Throughout it lies a more subtle problem, a crisis of the human spirit, something awry in the way we perceive the world and our place in it. It arises from apathy, greed, despair, arrogance, ignorance, and many other human failings.

The crisis of the human spirit is manifest in our escape into materialistic life-styles and our view of humans as apart from nature and immune to its laws. It is found in

Is Outer Space the Answer to Our Population and Resource Problems?

No Escape from the Population Bomb

Daniel Deudney

The author is a former senior researcher at the Worldwatch Institute in Washington, D.C., where he studied and wrote on space, the "global commons" (the oceans, the atmosphere, and Antarctica), and resource issues. He is the author of several papers on space resources and coauthor of Renewable Energy: The Power to Choose (*Norton, 1983*).

Much of the recent writing about humanity's future in space has been dominated by outlandish proposals for large-scale space operations that aim to bypass the earth's resource limits, either by exporting people from the planet or by importing energy and materials from space. These include space colonies, solar-powered satellites, and asteroid mining operations. At first glance these massive undertakings have a logical appeal: the earth is limited, space is infinite.

Even though space contains vastly more "living" room, energy, and materials than the earth, this abundance cannot be brought to bear meaningfully on the earth's problems. Whatever the long-term prospect for human colonies in space, the earth's population and resource problems will have to be solved on earth in the near term.

Long a staple of science fiction writers, space colonies were among the many visionary ideas proposed by the pioneers of rocket technology in the early years of this century. In recent years space colonies have been advanced as a near-term solution to the earth's population and environmental problems by Professor Gerard O'Neill, a Princeton University physicist. In

his writings he details plans to build colonies with first 10,000 inhabitants, and later a million. Manufactured out of materials from the earth, and then the moon and asteroids, the colonies would be made completely self-sufficient by harnessing the sun for all sources of energy. Such colonies would float freely in space, circumventing the need to tame the harsh environments of other planets. Space colonization is specifically promoted as a solution to overcrowding and environmental degradation on earth. By the exporting of ever greater numbers of people into these orbiting cities, the wildlife and wilderness qualities of earth could be protected, or perhaps even expanded.

Life in space is envisioned as pastoral, pollution-free, and pluralistic—like floating garden cities. Yet in reality space habitation would probably be bleak. Thick metal shielding would be necessary to block the lethal cosmic and solar radiation. Life would be like that in a submarine—cramped, isolated, and uneventful. For at least the next several decades people will go into space to perform various specialized missions— or perhaps briefly as tourists—but they will not live there in significant numbers.

No scientific laws forbid large space colonies, but the technology to build and maintain such structures remains conjecture. Structures of the size envisioned are thousands of times larger than anything yet built for space; no doubt there will be unforeseen and even insurmountable technical problems. The ecologist Paul Erlich points out that scientists have no idea how to create large, stable ecosystems of the sort that would be needed to make space colonies self-sufficient. The key to such knowledge is, of course, much more study of the ecosystems on earth, many of which are becoming less diverse and less stable. It could be many decades before scientists know enough to understand—let alone recreate—ecosystems as complex as those now being degraded. There are also unanswered questions of human biology: Can babies be born and grow up in a weightless environment? Would the various forms of cosmic and solar radiation make the mutation and cancer rate unacceptably high?

Space colonies are not even a partial answer to the population and environmental problems of earth. At a time when 800 million people live in "absolute poverty" on earth, it makes little sense to think about building fabulously expensive habitats in space. Simply transporting the world's daily increase of about 200,000 people into space would consume the annual gross national product of the United States. Each launch of the space shuttle costs a quarter of a billion dollars, and that doesn't even include the $25 billion in research and other initial costs. Maintaining the complex life-support systems in orbit costs thousands of dollars an hour.

Population stabilization is a difficult social challenge, but it is certainly less complex than the organizational and political skills needed for large-scale colonization of space.

Solar-powered satellites, or Sunsats, are often seen as complements of large-scale space colonization and as a source of energy for earthlings. The Sunsat's principal appeal is its ability to collect virtually unlimited amounts of solar energy day and night without polluting the earth's atmosphere. The construction of Sunsat, however, would be an undertaking of unprecedented size and cost. A 1980 NASA and U.S. Department of Energy study estimated that 60 satellites, each as big as Manhattan island, would be needed to produce the current U.S. electrical usage. The cost estimates ranged from an optimistic $1.5 trillion to a more probable $3 trillion. If two Sunsats were built each year, one heavy-life rocket—seven times the largest rocket ever built—would have to be launched each day for 30 years to build and service them.

More troubling are planetary-scale environmental risks. Beaming trillions of watts of microwaves through the atmosphere for extended periods is almost certain to alter the composition of gases in unpredictable ways. Launching millions of tons of material into orbit would also release large quantities of exhaust gases into the upper atmosphere, perhaps disrupting the ozone layer which screens out ultraviolet light. An operational Sunsat system big enough to make a difference in the terrestrial energy equation would be a shot-in-the-dark experiment with our atmosphere.

The other mirage of abundance in space that has recently received attention is asteroids. These irregularly shaped rocks, which orbit the sun, range in size from as small as a grain of sand to as big as the state of Texas. Although there is probably enough metal in the asteroid belt to meet world needs for many centuries, getting them to the earth's surface would be costly and energy-intensive and would risk an accidental collision and ecological disruption on a colossal scale. Long before it becomes feasible or economical to bring rare metals from space, scientists should be able to turn the abundant clay, silicon, alumina, hydrocarbons, and iron in the earth's crust into materials that can be used to meet global needs.

In summary, large-scale space colonization and industrialization is an unworkable attempt to escape from the problems of the earth. In the struggle to protect the earth from overpopulation, ecological degradation, and resource depletion, outer space has a great, largely unfulfilled role to play. It can be valuable not as a source of energy or materials or as a place to house the world's growing population, but rather as a tool both for learning more about our planet and for assisting problem solving here on earth.

Toward a New World

Ben Bova

The author is past editor of Omni *magazine and a distinguished science and science fiction writer who has published numerous nonfiction works, short stories, and novels. His recent book,* The High Road *(Pocket Books, 1983), deals specifically with energy and mineral acquisition from space.*

We live in a solar system that is incredibly rich in energy and raw materials. In interplanetary space more wealth than any emperor could dream of is available for every human being alive. Instead of thinking of our world as a finite pie that must be sliced thinner and thinner as population swells, we must go out into space and create a larger pie so that everyone can have bigger and bigger slices of wealth.

What can we gain from the New World that begins a couple of hundred miles above our heads? Of immediate concern, there is energy in space—enormous energy from unfiltered sunlight. The sun radiates an incomprehensible flood of energy into space—the equivalent of 10 billion megatons of H-bomb explosions every second. The earth intercepts only a tiny fraction of this energy, less than .2 billionths of the total energy given off by the sun.

For the purposes of our generation, a few dozen solar-powered satellites in geostationary orbit above the equator may be sufficient. Each would beam 5 billion watts of energy to us, making a substantial contribution to our energy supplies.

Natural resources are also there in superabundance. Thanks to the Apollo explorations of the moon, we know that lunar rocks and soil contain many valuable elements such as aluminum, magnesium, titanium, and silicon.

Looking further afield, there are asteroids that sail through the solar system, especially in a region between Mars and Jupiter called the Asteroid Belt. To a miner or an industrialist they are a bonanza. An MIT astronomer, Tom McCord, estimates that there are hundreds of millions of billions of tons of nickel–iron asteroids in the belt. The economic potential of these resources is incalculably large. And mixed in with these are many other valuable metals and minerals.

This "mother lode" of riches is a long way from earth—hundreds of millions of miles—but in space, distance is not so important as the amount of energy you must expend to get where you want to go. Like sailing ships, spacecraft do not burn fuel for most of their flight; they simply coast after achieving sufficient speed to reach their destination. Space is not a barrier, it is a highway. The biggest and most difficult step in space flight is getting off the earth's surface.

The opportunity offered by space is not to export people from earth, but to import valuable resources to earth.

We will move outward into space because it is biologically necessary for us to do so. Like children driven by forces beyond our understanding, we head into space citing all the good and practical and necessary reasons for going. But in actuality we go because we are driven.

The rocket pioneer Krafft Ehricke has likened our situation on earth today to the situation in a mother's womb after nine months of gestation. The baby has been living a sweet life, without exertion, nurtured and fed by the environment in which it has been enclosed. But the baby gets too big for that environment, and the baby's own waste products are polluting that environment to the point where it becomes unlivable. Time to come out into the real world.

Our biological heritage, our historical legacy, our real and pressing economic and social needs are all pointing toward the same conclusion: It's time to come out into the real world. Time to expand into the new world of space.

our single-minded pursuit of economic wealth. It is the foundation of our general lack of concern for future generations and for the long-term well-being of our planet.

This crisis of the spirit can be blamed for much of the damage that occurs in the name of progress. Therefore, solutions to the environmental crisis lie not only in new scientific discoveries and new technologies but also in finding answers to the internal crisis. Part 5 of this book, "Environment and Society," will examine this topic of values and ethics and show how we can change our ways through fundamental changes in our beliefs.

Beyond Despair

Many experts agree that the problems of overpopulation, depletion, pollution, and the human failing have created an ecological crisis, which threatens the natural systems of which humans are a part. This threat to the **biosphere**, the living skin of planet earth, is worsened by our frequent failure to consider the link of cause and effect extending over decades or centuries. In failing to do so, we often create additional problems whose solutions may reach beyond our grasp. Consider what is happening in many African nations now actively engaged in wiping out **infectious diseases**, those caused by bacteria and viruses that are transmitted from person to person. Pesticides to eradicate vectors (animals and insects that carry diseases) and new drugs to treat infectious disease have successfully lowered the death rate in many countries, but as we have seen, no reduction in birth rate has accompanied the rapid decline in deaths. As a result the populations of

many countries have exploded, placing enormous demands on farmland, wildlife populations, and other resources. Such unanticipated, adverse effects are called **ecological backlashes**.

Consider another example: Pesticides and fertilizers are used to increase agricultural output to feed the 83 million new world residents each year. These chemicals are released into the environment, where they may poison wildlife and pollute drinking water. In some cases they have been implicated in birth defects in babies, miscarriages in pregnant women, and cancer in adults.

Many observers believe that our daunting list of problems can be solved without devastating ecological backlashes. These people see the dangers posed by overpopulation, pollution, and resource depletion as an opportunity to strike out in new directions. Such an optimistic view is not meant to minimize the severity of our predicament but, rather, to give us a refreshingly new outlook.

In his studies of societal attitudes toward the future the Dutch futurist Fred Polak showed that people's image of what is to come has the power to shape that future. This is a form of self-fulfilling prophecy. Our view of the future is much like a barometer that foretells the success or failure of a society. Polak concluded that "bold visionary thinking is in itself the prerequisite for effective social change." When pessimism abounds, the future will probably be a gloomy one, but a positive outlook increases the possibility of a bright future.

The challenge before us is immense: to create a society that can thrive within the limits of a finite planet. To do

The Aswan Dam: Ecological Backlash from Blind Cost–Benefit Analysis

The Nile River flows from its headwaters in Sudan and Ethiopia through an arid region of Egypt and eventually spills into the Mediterranean Sea. For centuries this great river carried 50 million to 100 million tons of silt each year to the land stretching along its banks and to the Mediterranean Sea. In the sea this nutrient-rich silt nourished a variety of microorganisms that, in turn, were food for thriving fish populations. On the land the silty water flooded nutrient-impoverished soil as the river spilled over its banks, enriching the soil. The nutrients robbed by agriculture were replaced by the natural floods that occurred each year in late summer and early fall, floods caused by the monsoon rains along the river's headwaters.

In the early 1960s, however, Egypt built the Aswan Dam along the Nile to provide electricity for the growing city of Cairo and to provide irrigation water for the lower Nile basin. The government, of course, had studied the proposal to build the dam, but it had looked primarily at the benefits that would result from the dam versus the economic cost of construction. Little attention was given to possible ecological backlashes.

Not long after the dam was completed and Lake Nassar began to fill, the people of Egypt and the world grew alarmed. Numerous problems began to make themselves painfully evident. First, the periodic flooding that had provided an annual fertilization of the land ceased. As a result, farmers along the Nile had to import fertilizer for their land at an exorbitant cost. Second, the sardine fishery in the eastern Mediterranean collapsed. Nutrient-rich silt that had once poured into the sea almost stopped. The sardine catch plummeted from 18,000 tons per year to 500 tons in only a few years. Third, the rising waters of Lake Nassar threatened the Ramses Temple at Abu Simbel, built over 3000 years ago. Engineers and construction workers sponsored by the United States, Egypt, and the United Nations dismantled the huge temple piece by piece and moved it to a site 60 meters (200 feet) above its original level, where it would be safe from the rising waters. The cost of this project was astronomical. Fourth, the incidence of schistosomiasis (a debilitating, sometimes fatal disease) in humans increased in Egypt as a result of the dam. The organism that causes this disease is carried by snails. Snails require a constant supply of water, which the lake and the irrigation channels provided. The spread of this disease, for which there is no known cure, is almost certain.

If a cost–benefit analysis had been done before construction of the dam began, chances are that it might not have been built. See Chapter 14 for an example of an approach you might take to making a cost–benefit analysis of the Aswan Dam.

---

so we must redirect technology, economics, industry, and government with a common goal in mind: preserving the foundation on which life depends—the land, the water, the air, and the all-important but delicate interconnection between the living and nonliving components of the biosphere. Our goal is to build a sustainable future that robs neither the earth of its beauty and strength nor its inhabitants of their place for survival (Figure 1-3).

The Population, Resource, and Pollution Model: A New Perspective

Many people find environmental issues complex and confusing. Even experts disagree on the causes of our problems and the ways to solve them. In fact, if you have ever listened to experts debate current issues, such as acid

Figure 1-3 Solar businesses in Soldiers Grove, Wisconsin. They have cut their energy bills by 90% by superinsulating their buildings and tapping the generous power of the sun.

Figure 1-4 The population segment of a world computer model, showing the interrelation of many factors. Each factor is assigned a numerical value, and the computer calculates how changes in one or more factors affect others. Pluses indicate positive feedback, in which one factor causes an increase in another. Minuses indicate negative feedback, in which one factor diminishes another.

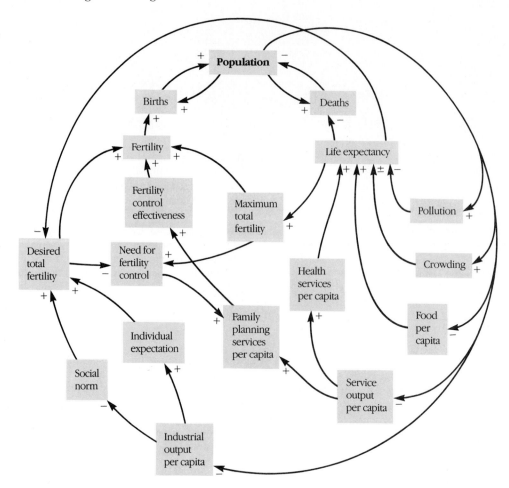

rain or nuclear energy, you have probably wondered whether civilization will ever find workable solutions.

Others find environmental problems clear-cut. "Politics are to blame," one person proclaims. "It's our attitudes toward nature," another argues. "Technology and energy waste are the roots of our troubles," a third declares. Such people often support narrow solutions, which fall short of the mark and may even create ecological backlashes and additional financial burdens on society.

This section presents a "conceptual model" to satisfy the needs of these two different groups—a need for order, on the one hand, and a need to expand understanding, on the other. Careful study of this model will reward you many times over.

Models are one of the most powerful tools of the working environmental scientist. They can be adapted to computers and used to study complex issues such as world food supply, pollution, or even plant and animal extinction. The study of complex systems with computers is called **system dynamics**.

System dynamics computer models in environmental science are computer programs that deal with many environmental problems on many different levels. The first

global model was introduced in 1970 by J. W. Forrester. He used it to study the future of human civilization by looking at some of the most pressing issues, including population growth, pollution, and the depletion of natural resources. Figure 1-4 depicts just one part (population) of an updated version of the model, showing how complex it is. Not all models need be this detailed.

Perhaps you have worked with a computer to manage your budget. This type of program, like all computer programs, is developed from conceptual models much like the one presented in Figure 1-4, above. On a home computer, budget programs can forecast the effects of variations in living expenses on your savings or spending money. In a similar manner computer models can predict the effects of pollution on human health, the effects of oil scarcity on economics and resource demand, and much more.

The Population, Resource, and Pollution (PRP) model (Figure 1-5) seems general on first glance. It shows in the most basic terms how humans interact with their environment. Don't be deceived by its simplicity. A more careful look will show that it contains a wealth of useful information.

Figure 1-5 Population, Resource, and Pollution model. Plus marks indicate positive feedback loops, and minus signs indicate negative feedback loops. Note that some activities, such as resource use, can have positive *and* negative influences on others, such as population.

Vital Links: Humans and the Environment

The Population, Resource, and Pollution model shows that human populations acquire resources from the environment to survive. Food, minerals, and timber are prime examples. Take a walk through a forest being cut for timber in the Pacific Northwest or study the air in virtually any city in the world; what you will see is that acquiring and using resources frequently pollutes our environment. The timber operation creates sediment that washes into streams; burning gasoline and coal in our cities creates sometimes apalling levels of pollution. **Pollution** is any change in the air, water, or soil that could reduce their ability to support life. Some pollution is caused by natural events; this is called **natural pollution**. The rest comes from human activities and is called **anthropogenic pol-**

lution. Pollutants may be **biodegradable**, which means that they can be broken down by living organisms, usually single-celled bacteria and fungi. Sunlight and temperature, however, may also degrade some pollutants. **Non-biodegradable** pollutants, those that are not readily broken down, can persist in the environment. Both degradable and biodegradable pollutants can cause considerable harm.

The effects of pollution vary considerably, depending on a number of factors. Three of the most important are the concentration (the amount per unit of air, water, or soil) of the pollutant, the duration of exposure (how long it stays in the environment), and its chemical nature (how reactive it is). Chapter 14 covers this topic in more detail. As you well know, pollution has widespread effects. For example, some water pollutants kill fish and the birds that feed on them. Pollution can make water unsuitable for drinking or swimming and, in some cases, can even result in serious human illness and death.

The Population, Resource, and Pollution model says that human populations acquire and use resources from the environment. In most cases these resources enhance our survival and promote population growth; this is indicated in the model by the plus signs on the arrows leading from resources to population. This response is an example of a **positive feedback loop**, where one factor leads to the growth of a second factor, which in turn stimulates the first one in a repetitive cycle. In the example given here, increasing the use of resources increases population size. The spiraling effect comes about as the rising population steps up its resource demand. Fortunately, postive feedback loops are generally rare.

More common are **negative feedback loops**, where one factor shuts off another. The furnace in your home provides an excellent example. The furnace switches on when the temperature drops below the setting on the thermostat. Heat from the furnace warms the room air until the air temperature reaches the desired level. When it does, the furnace shuts off. Negative feedback loops are the chief mechanism for controlling biological organisms on many different levels. For instance, your blood glucose levels are maintained by this type of mechanism. Figure 1-5 shows that pollution may decrease population size. Resource depletion may have similar effects. Both are examples of negative feedback loops. (Chapter 6 covers controls on population size in more detail.) Although negative feedback loops are generally beneficial and positive feedback loops are often detrimental, it is important to realize that under certain circumstances each type of feedback loop may have opposite effects.

The Population, Resource, and Pollution model takes on a greater significance when we expand its three principal factors. Table 1-1 lists some additional factors discussed in more detail throughout this book. You might want to study it briefly before reading the next section.

Studying the Interactions: Cross-Impact Analysis

The three elements of the PRP model interact with one another in so many ways that only a computer could keep track of them. We can get a glimpse of how they affect one another by using a simple technique called **cross-impact analysis**. This technique helps break down complex interactions into simpler ones that are more easily understood.

Figure 1-6 is a simplified cross-impact analysis chart. In this chart the three elements of the PRP model are lined up in two perpendicular columns. In box 1 you can describe how population factors affect resource factors,

Table 1-1 Breakdown of Factors of the Population, Resource, and Pollution Model

Population	Resources	Pollution
Size	Acquisition	Water
Distribution	Use	Land
Density	Supply	Air
Growth rate	Demand	
	Character	

such as supply, demand, acquisition, and use. In box 2 you can describe how population factors affect pollution, and so on.

Take some time to fill out the chart. You will find that you already know a great deal about the ways populations, resources, and pollution are linked. At the end of the course you may want to repeat the exercise; if you have been conscientious in your study, you will find that your knowledge has grown tremendously and that you have a deeper appreciation of the complexity of modern society.

A Glimpse of What Is to Come

Today, modern society and its underlying beliefs are under attack from all sides. One thing that this book will make clear is that modern industrial society as we know it cannot continue. Part 2 will show that the curve of population growth, growing steeper every year, must eventually stop rising. Part 3 will document how the resources we rely on—oil, metals, land, and water—are reaching or, in some cases, have already reached their limits. Part 4 will describe the facts about pollution and its effects. Part 5 will outline the attitudes and practices of both economics and politics that are fast becoming outdated, even dangerous, in a world of limits.

Column A			
Population	X	1	2
Resources	3	X	4
Pollution	5	6	X
Column B	Population	Resources	Pollution

Figure 1-6 Cross-impact analysis chart, used to compare the interactions between the three factors in the Population, Resource, and Pollution model. By comparing factors in Column A with those in Column B, you can gain a deeper understanding of environmental problems. Why not take a few minutes to test your understanding? Start by comparing ways that populations affect resources, then look at ways that populations affect pollution, and so on.

Building a Sustainable Society

Many experts agree that if human society is to endure, not just for another century but for thousands and thousands of years, we need to develop a **sustainable society** that (1) controls population size, (2) uses resources wisely, (3) recycles all nonrenewable resources, and (4) relies on renewable resources wherever possible. A growing number of scientists and world leaders have taken an active role in developing such a brave new world. A sustainable society is so profoundly different from the way we live that it cannot be achieved without considerable effort. You will learn how to build a sustainable society as you read this book, and you will also learn where you can help. You may want to jot down these ideas in a notebook for later reference.

Changing Our Ways

Perhaps the first order of business is to convince governments to look beyond immediate needs and to learn how to cooperate better internationally to control population, pollution, and resource depletion. Environmental science will continue to prove helpful in achieving these goals. This new science has already helped us recognize overpopulation as one of the roots of other pressing problems, resulting in a proliferation of population control programs throughout the world. It has already done much to expand our understanding of global resource depletion and our knowledge of ways to treat and prevent global pollution. From the knowledge of human impact may come the necessary transformations in values and institutions needed to build a sustainable society.

New values are essential to building a sustainable society. Some of the new attitudes we need are clear. The attitude that "there is always more"—labeled the **frontier mentality** in this book—must be replaced with an attitude that this world is limited: "there is not always more." Limits are all around us, set by the availability of fossil fuel energy, minerals, and land. As you will learn in the chapters on ecology, the earth is a **closed system**. All of the elements needed to maintain life come from within and are recycled over and over. The atoms that make up your body could well have been part of a dinosaur that roamed the earth millions of years ago, and they will be part of some living thing long after you have gone. This makes all organisms—past, present, and future—relatives. The recycling of living matter in the earth's closed system points out the importance of preserving the environment.

The Role of Environmental Science

Changing our ways will be a colossal task, a process that will take generations to complete. It will involve arduous work in many fields. The moon landing was a weekend home-improvement chore compared with the job ahead. The study of environmental science is a cornerstone of change.

But what has science to say to a philosopher, a public policymaker, a social leader, an economist, or a religious thinker? Aren't these people outside the sphere of science? As we will see, the boundaries between the world of science and the rest of society are being eliminated today by the problems we face. Scientific understanding is essential to all who ponder the fate of humanity and actively seek to make changes. To voters, it can be a guideline for wise decision making.

Some pessimistic thinkers believe that the human species is already doomed: that resource depletion, poisonous pollutants, radiation, and changes in global climate, alone or together, will slowly eradicate humanity. At the least, they say, things will get worse: we could lose centuries of technological and economic progress in the next few decades if trends continue. Our wonderfully diverse biological world, the product of millions of years of evolution, could be wiped out in a fraction of the history of living things.

Many other people see a glimmer of hope. They hold that the technology that got us into this mess can also get us out of it. Technological responses to current problems, or **technological fixes**, are their answer. But such "technological optimists" often paint an unrealistic picture of the future and do not always distinguish what is technologically possible from what is feasible and affordable. Carried away with technological optimism, they often see outer space as a source of new minerals, free energy, and more living space for the crowded citizenry of the world (see the Point/Counterpoint in this chapter). They propose new technologies such as nuclear fusion to solve the energy crisis. They view new pollution control technologies as the answer to our polluted waters and skies. Little emphasis is given, however, to changing life-styles, cutting back on resource demand, or stopping population growth.

Beyond the incompatible visions of these two groups, a few things are certain. The first is that time is short. Indeed, shortage of time may be our greatest shortage. Another certainty is that during your lifetime vast changes will take place; some will be bad, others good. What we do today will determine which predominate.

Humans have grown into a force rivaling nature itself; as Walt Whitman wrote, "Here at last is something in the doings of men that corresponds with the broadcast doings of the day and night." To build a sustainable society we must learn ways to treat our earth better, not to rival nature but cooperate with it to live in harmony. For that great task, environmental science is our single most important tool.

> *Life can only be understood backwards; but it must be lived forwards.*
>
> KIERKEGAARD

Summary

Environmental science is the study of the environment, its non-living and living components, and the interactions between them. The importance of environmental science is that it helps us understand and solve a growing number of problems revolving around three central issues: pollution, resources, and overpopulation. Environmental science is a new synthesis; unlike more traditional sciences it calls on dozens of disciplines—from psychology to atmospheric science—in an effort to understand the interaction between humans and the environment.

Environmental science deals with the population, resource, and pollution issues, each of which has profound effects on the others. In 1986 the world's population climbed above the 5-billion mark. If the current growth rate continues, the world population will double in 40 years. Many people—one of every three in the developing nations—do not get enough to eat now. What is the prospect for future generations?

Such unprecedented growth in human numbers springs primarily from medical and scientific developments, which have drastically cut the death rate but have not been accompanied by a fall in the birth rate. If populations continue to swell, resource shortages are bound to get worse. They may even limit future growth or cause a reduction in human numbers.

Overpopulation, excessive consumption, and wasteful practices create another problem for all nations of the world—pollution. Signs of global pollution are everywhere.

Lying beneath the environmental crisis is a more subtle problem: a failing of the human spirit manifested as apathy, greed, despair, arrogance, ignorance, feelings of insignificance, and many other symptoms. Solving our problems, therefore, requires a change in our attitudes. Knowledge of our impact on the environment may help us adopt holistic values that help us change population growth, resource acquisition and use, pollution, consumption, and technology. Such an approach will go a long way toward solving the ecological crisis and help us prevent unfortunate **ecological backlashes**.

This book views crisis as an opportunity for change and views societal attitudes toward the future as a barometer of the ultimate fate of that society. An optimistic outlook can lead to a brighter future, but it must be realistic and accompanied by action.

The **PRP model** can help us formulate a new direction by helping us understand where we are now. Illustrating the fundamental ties between populations, resources, and pollution, it can help us predict the impacts of future actions. A better understanding of these interrelationships can be gained by using **cross-impact analysis**.

Building a **sustainable society** requires four achievements: control of population growth, wise use of resources (conservation), widespread reliance on recycling, and use of renewable resources wherever possible. Environmental science can help us attain these goals by continuing to provide insight and information.

Discussion Questions

In a study group or by yourself, answer each of the following.

1. Name one of the key differences between environmental science and chemistry or other traditional sciences.

2. The environmental crisis is composed of four principal elements. Name them and describe each one.

3. Describe the Population, Resource, and Pollution model, defining the three factors that make up the model and illustrating their interaction.

4. Describe how the factors in Column A might affect those in Column B. Give examples.

A	B
Population	Resources
Resource Allocation	Pollution
Resource Use	Pollution
Pollution	Population

5. Describe the foundations of a sustainable society.

6. Give examples in the United States of activities consistent with a sustainable society. What areas need improvement?

7. Make a list of things you do that are consistent with a sustainable society. What area could use some improvement?

8. In your opinion, should we be optimistic about the future or pessimistic? Why?

9. How can optimism, or pessimism for that matter, contribute to the future of a society? Can you think of some examples?

Suggested Readings

Brown, L., Chandler, W. U., Pollock, C., Postel, S. Starke, L. and Wolf, E. C. (1985). *State of the World*. New York: Norton. Detailed account of population, resources, and pollution and efforts to build a sustainable society. Published annually.

Capra, F. (1982). *The Turning Point: Science, Society, and the Rising Culture*. New York: Bantam. Insightful book.

Hardin, G. (1980). An Ecolate View of the Human Predicament. In *Global Resources: Perspectives and Alternatives*, ed. C. N. McRostie. Baltimore: University Park Press. Brilliant essay on global sharing.

Hardin, G. (1985). *Filters against Folly*. New York: Viking. Excellent treatise on ecology, economics, and science.

Hillary, E., ed. (1984). *Ecology 2000: The Changing Face of Earth*. New York: Beaufort Books. Graphically illustrated account of world environmental problems.

Murphy, E. M. (1983). *The Environment to Come: A Global Survey*. Washington, D.C.: Population Reference Bureau. Survey of major environmental trends.

Myers, N., ed. (1984). *Gaia: An Atlas of Planet Management*. Garden City, N.Y.: Anchor Books. Comprehensive, graphic presentation of global population, resource, and pollution problems.

Tobias, M., ed. (1985). *Deep Ecology*. San Diego: Avant Books. Collection of writings discussing world environmental problems and solutions.

Western, D. (1985). The Last Stand. *Discover* 6 (10): 102–107. An excellent case study of the interactions between population and resources.

Science and the Scientific Method

To many outsiders, science is an arcane body of knowledge that has little relevance to day-to-day living. And many outsiders think that the scientist's work sounds dull and uncreative. Still others see science as a mysterious realm not easily understood by the general public.

The truth of the matter, however, is that science is an exciting field that requires tremendous creativity and insight. It is also essential to our understanding of the modern world and the many issues before us. And it is not that hard to master, once we become acquainted with its special vocabulary.

You don't need to become a scientist to understand what science is all about, but the time you spend improving your understanding of this fascinating field will pay lifetime dividends. Science may help you decide what type of house to build or what type of energy to heat your water with. It may even help you vote more intelligently on important issues. Almost without exception, the more you know about science, the better off you will be. Society as a whole benefits from science, too, as it charts a safe course into the future. Without it we could bumble from one mistake to another.

Throughout this book you will learn both some fundamental principles of science and many of the scientific facts behind the headlines. The laws of ecology, the laws of thermodynamics, and the principles of toxicology—to name a few—will make you a more informed citizen.

Values and Science

You may think of science and ethics (values) as two separate spheres without ties. Values, according to the common conception, are subjective; they dictate what is right and what is wrong, whereas science is supposed to be objective and free of values. Many an engineer or scientist has proclaimed on nationwide television, "I don't make value decisions. I'm just a scientist." To these people, science is simply a way of studying the world around us and describing how it works; society must make the decisions.

A study of history, however, shows this view to be inaccurate. Science and society have affected each other in profound ways for centuries. For example, Thomas Aquinas's view of nature reflected the feudal hierarchy that prevailed during the 13th century. Organisms, he said, are diverse but unequal. Each has a distinct obligation and role that benefits others. Furthermore, he believed that change was unlikely, just as it was unlikely for a serf to become a knight. Nature was viewed as rigidly structured and independent, unchanging. The scientific interpretation of nature was heavily tainted by the social conditions of the time.

Some scientific historians argue that even Charles Darwin's theory of evolution was greatly influenced by the social, political, and economic conditions of England as it entered the industrial age. They contend, not without considerable objection, that his theory represents nature as Darwin wanted it to be, not as it really is. Jeremy Rifkin writes that "Darwin dressed up nature with an English personality, ascribed to nature English motivations and drives, and even provided nature with the English marketplace and the English form of government." In particular, he argues, Darwin projected the values of the rising industrial society onto nature. Some men were making fortunes while others floundered and often perished. Rifkin asserts that this survival of the fittest in society was the root of Darwinian evolution. Nature became what society was.

Just as social conditions may have molded scientific thinking, so did science mold or reinforce social values. In 18th-century England, for instance, the theory of evolution was seen as a process of change that led to superior forms of life, a view that scientists now see as erroneous. To the 18th-century English, however, evolution meant that some life forms were better than others. This view of science was used to justify the prosperity of a small elite class of business owners while workers were suffering in dangerous factories. This disparity was justified as a form of the survival of the fittest. The application of the theory of evolution to social ethics is called *social Darwinism*.

This misapplication of Darwinian evolution suggests that scientific information must be carefully understood and not loosely used to justify social practices. Many scientists would agree. As this book points out, however, societal values can and should be based on laws of science, especially the practical rules of ecology. Values that do not take into account the scientific principles that govern life can be destructive and may limit the future of humanity.

The Methods of Science

The study of science is often orderly and precise. The process begins with observations and measurements of the world—the rate of oxygen consumption by cells, the growth of tree rings, or the rate of soil erosion (Figure S1-1). From observations, scientists often formulate generalizations or hypotheses. A **hypothesis** is a tentative explanation of what scientists observe—for example, an explanation of why a rattlesnake shakes its rattles or why a desert plant sheds its leaves in dry spells. Hypotheses based on observation and measurement represent a type of thinking called **inductive reasoning**.

Even though the term *inductive reasoning* may be foreign to you, you have probably been using the process for many years. It may have allowed you to solve the mystery of an anonymous love note in high school, for example, or perhaps to reason why a good friend was angry with you.

Let's look at a simple example. Suppose that you were driving your car at night. Each time you hit a bump in the road, one of your headlights flickered. But when you were on newly paved blacktop, the lights worked fine. Without being aware that you were engaged in the scientific method, your mind quickly searched for answers. Within seconds you arrived at a hypothesis: perhaps bumps in the road were jiggling the filament in the headlight, causing it to flicker. This simple exercise is inductive reasoning.

Once a hypothesis is made, it is up to the scientist—in this case, you—to determine how valid it is. To test the validity of their hypotheses, researchers perform experiments. You would no doubt do the same. For example, you might experiment by replacing the headlamp and then by taking your car out on the same roads to see if the problem had been corrected. If the headlight continued to flicker, you would conclude that your hypothesis was invalid.

In a similar fashion the results of scientific experiments either support or refute initial hypotheses. If a hypothesis is refuted, a new one is generally substituted. In your case you might conjecture that the electrical wiring was faulty. By simply wiggling the electrical wires connected to the headlight, you could test your new hypothesis. If the lights flickered, you would know that your new hypothesis was correct (and that you had wasted your money buying a new headlamp).

Scientific study is a lot more involved than finding reasons why your car stalls or your garbage disposal leaks. But the methodology is still the same. Observations lead to hypotheses, which are tested by experiments.

In many scientific experiments it is necessary to set up experimental and control groups of animals or people to test the effects of various treatments. The **experimental group** is the one that you "experiment" on, perhaps giving a new drug treatment. The second group is treated identically, except that it is not given the drug. This group is the **control** group. By setting up their experiments in this manner, scientists test the effect of a single variable, the drug. Any differences in disease rates should be the result of the experimental treatment.

Through careful study, scientists check out the validity of their own hypotheses. Other researchers might also test them by setting up the same experiment. If enough researchers arrive at the same conclusion, a hypothesis can be elevated to a new level—that of a theory. A **theory**, in scientific terminology, is a

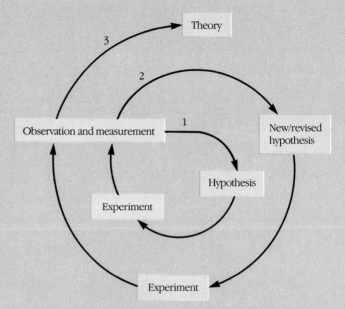

Figure S1-1 The scientific method starts with observation and measurement, from which scientists develop hypotheses, or tentative explanations. The scientist next tests the hypothesis by experimentation. If the results do not support the hypothesis, a new or modified hypothesis is created, which can then be retested and refined until a theory is formed.

hypothesis supported by enough experiments that few, if any, scientists doubt its validity. Theories are the "facts," or "principles," of science. They are consistent with the current body of scientific knowledge but are by no means immutable.

The Rise and Fall of Theories

Scientists must be open-minded about theories and must be willing to replace their most cherished ones with new ones should new information render them obsolete. As new results are published, scientists often find that different interpretations of natural events and biological processes emerge. These interpretations may replace explanations that have prevailed for decades. As a result, it is often necessary to alter or even abandon theories that have enjoyed a faithful following for many years.

New research techniques cause much of the turmoil in the scientific community. The findings from such techniques shine light on old theories and shaky hypotheses, which sometimes crumble as a result.

Perhaps the best known example of changing theory is the Copernican revolution in astronomy. The Greek astronomer Ptolemy hypothesized in A.D. 140 that the earth was the center of the solar system (the geocentric view). The moon, the stars, and the sun, he argued, all revolve around the earth. This notion held sway for hundreds of years. In 1580, however, Nicolaus Copernicus showed that the observations were better explained by assuming that the sun was the center of the solar system. Copernicus was not the first to suggest this heliocentric view.

Early Greek astronomers had proposed the idea, but it gained little attention until Copernicus's time.

The new view of the universe proposed by Copernicus was condemned as heretical by the Catholic Church. When he published his theory, it was placed on the papal index of forbidden books.

Supertheories, or Paradigms

The dominant set of assumptions that underlies any branch of science is called a **paradigm**, a word coined by the philosopher and historian of science Thomas Kuhn. A paradigm is likened to a "supertheory." It is the basic model or reality in any science. Evolution is an example from the life sciences, and atomic theory is one from the physical sciences.

Paradigms govern the way scientists think, form theories, and interpret the results of experiments. They govern the way non-scientists think, too.

Once a paradigm is accepted, it is rarely questioned. New observations are interpreted according to the paradigm; those that are inconsistent with it are often ignored. However, phenomena that fail to fit conventional wisdom may amass to a point at which they can no longer be ignored, causing scientists to rethink their most cherished beliefs and, sometimes, toss them aside. This unsettling event is called a **paradigm shift**.

The central ideas of biology, ecology, chemistry, philosophy, health, and education are all paradigms; sacred as they may seem, they are not immutable. As scientists make new observations, new theories emerge that may shake apart the foundations of a society. This book, and especially Part 5, examines the fundamental attitudes we hold toward nature (philosophical paradigms) and ways in which a shift in these attitudes could reshape human civilization.

Scientists Shouldn't Disagree— Or Should They?

Science is essential to expanding our understanding of the world we live in, but there is by no means agreement among those who practice it. How can there be so much disagreement among scientists? Aren't they trained to find the truth?

Room for disagreement among scientists is great. Paradigm shifts, discussed above, create an environment sometimes overflowing with differing views. Disagreement may also occur in the early stages of hypothesis formation, when information itself is too contradictory to form lasting hypotheses.

But why should contradictory results arise from experiments on the same phenomenon? With all the controls built into a scientific experiment, shouldn't the outcome be the same? Part of the answer is that no two experiments are the same. Even slight differences in experimental design can dramatically alter the results of a study.

Try as they may, not all scientists are successful in achieving objectivity. Bias affects the interpretation of results in sometimes subtle ways. It may even affect how a scientist sets up an experiment. Bias can be subtle and difficult to detect or extreme and easy to see. Thomas Aquinas, discussed earlier, formulated a widely accepted view of nature that mirrored the feudal system of medieval Europe. He was probably unaware that he saw nature as he saw his society, with organisms living in a hierarchy of descending importance.

Bias is an inescapable human trait. It colors the scientist's perceptions, just as it colors yours. No one is immune from it. Scientists, however, are trained to be aware of bias and to design their experiments to avoid it. Good scientists keep a vigilant watch for distortions in the lens by which they view their work and the vast body of scientific knowledge.

Scientists will always disagree. Shifts in paradigms, personal bias, and conflicting data, among other factors, generate controversy. In the meantime, we must be patient with science as it grows.

Suggested Readings

Cole, K. C. (1985). Is There Such a Thing as Scientific Objectivity? *Discover* 6 (9): 98–99. Insightful look at science and the scientific method.

Hardin, G. (1985). *Filters against Folly: How to Survive Despite Economists, Ecologists, and the Merely Eloquent*. New York: Viking. Eloquent writing on scientific bias. See Chapters 1–7.

Kuhn, T. (1970). *The Structure of Scientific Revolutions*. Chicago: University of Chicago Press. The original description of paradigms.

Rifkin, J. (1985). *Declaration of a Heretic*. Boston: Routledge and Kegan Paul. Part 1 of this book examines our modern scientific view.

Rifkin, J., and Howard, T. (1980). *Entropy: A New World View*. New York: Viking. See the first 30 pages for a controversial analysis of science and the modern view of the world.

2

New Visions of Life: Evolution of a Living Planet

Nobody knows the age of the human race, but everyone agrees that it is old enough to know better.

ANONYMOUS

Humans are unlike other animal species in many ways. One of those is our capacity to make decisions regarding right and wrong. Another is our ability to look into the future and plan. Still another is our facility to shape with our hands the images we create in our minds. Among our most important creations is transportation, ways to move about and, ultimately, populate the earth. Our newest form of transportation allows us to travel in space to explore the moon and distant planets in search of answers to the origin of our solar system and, some think, new places to live. But scientific information is not the only benefit of space journeys. As any wanderer will tell you, leaving home sometimes helps us understand and appreciate what we have taken for granted all our lives. Distance sharpens our focus, yielding striking new perspectives. Adrift in space, we have gazed back at the earth, enthralled. Our lives have been changed by what we saw.

In 1948 Sir Frederick Hoyle predicted that "once a photograph of the earth, taken from the outside, is available . . . a new idea as powerful as any in history will let loose." It was not too many years later that the first photograph of earth from outer space came to us, and Hoyle's prediction bore fruit. The earth, a sparkling red, white, and blue planet circling around the sun, came into sharp view in the minds of many people throughout the world. The vision was both breathtaking and disturbing, for it showed our home, which we had always seen as inexhaustible, as a tiny sphere alone in a mighty universe that extends beyond our imaginations. Sparkling in the sun's rays, the earth seemed exquisite, fragile, and, knowing how we have treated it, vulnerable.

The late Buckminster Fuller, well known for his contributions to environmental science, dubbed this tiny planet **Spaceship Earth**, likening it to a self-contained spacecraft whose life-support systems recycle all matter necessary for astronauts to survive. This mechanistic analogy stuck. It drove home one of the most important lessons of ecology: that all life on earth is part of an enormous recycling system. Nutrients are a common thread from the nonliving environment to the plants to animals and back again, binding together the web of life on the earth.

Subsequent journeys into space have taught us important new lessons. Lewis Thomas, a biomedical researcher and philosopher, captured one of the newest and most popular lessons when he wrote, "The astonishing thing about the Earth . . . is that it is alive." New evidence from space, presented later in this chapter, suggests that the biosphere regulates its physical and chemical environment in much the same way that organisms control their own internal environment.

The intricate control of life's essential processes may now be threatened by human civilization. Through our use of fossil fuels such as coal and oil, for example, the planet's temperature balance may be thrown out of kilter, causing a rise in global temperature that changes the earth's climate and raises the sea level. Even the powerful ozone layer that screens out harmful ultraviolet rays may be slowly eroded by air pollutants. Widespread skin cancer and serious plant damage may result.

How did we reach such a precarious place? To answer this question we will journey back in time 15 billion to 20 billion years to the beginning of the universe to trace the origin of our solar system and the emergence of life. Next we will look at the beginnings of humankind and the ways in which human society has developed.

Some Principles of Matter

Before we study the formation of the universe and its galaxies, let's take a look at matter. **Matter**, in the language of science, is anything that occupies space and has mass—wood, metals, air, water, soil. A basic unit of most matter is the **atom** (Figure 2-1).

Atoms

If you chemically break down wood or metal, you end up with atoms. With sophisticated equipment such as linear accelerators, however, you can smash atoms apart, producing even smaller units called **subatomic particles**. These particles, shown in Figure 2-1, include three types: protons, neutrons, and electrons. (Other subatomic particles exist but go beyond the scope of this book.)

An atom consists of two distinct regions. The central region is the **nucleus**; it contains positively charged par-

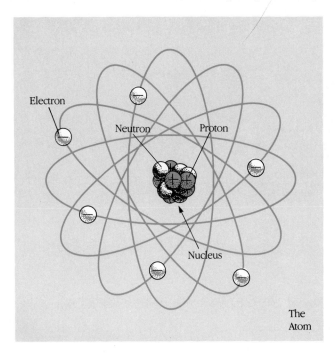

Figure 2-1 Atoms consist of a dense central region, the nucleus, containing protons and neutrons. Electrons orbit around the nucleus in the electron cloud.

ticles, called **protons**, and uncharged particles, called **neutrons**. These heavy particles (heavy on an atomic scale) are tightly packed within the nucleus and, because they have much more mass than the electrons, most of the mass of an atom (99.9%) is in the nucleus. So tiny and so heavy are they that a single cubic centimeter of tightly packed atomic nuclei would weigh 90 million metric tons.

Orbiting around the nucleus in the atom's outer region, called the **electron cloud**, are the **electrons**, negatively charged particles with almost no mass. The electrons, containing lots of energy, spin around the positively charged nucleus. The more energy an electron has, the farther it stays from the nucleus. All atoms are neutral; that is, they have no net charge, because the number of electrons is equal to the number of protons. Under certain conditions, however, an atom may gain or lose one or more electrons, thus forming a charged particle called an **ion**. A positively charged ion is called a **cation**, and is formed by the loss of one or more electrons. A negatively charged ion is called an **anion**; it is formed when an atom gains one or more electrons.

Like the star-filled universe we see on a dark night, stretching into infinity, the atom's infinitesimal size stretches our ability to comprehend. If, for example, you were to enlarge a single atom to the size of Mount Everest, its nucleus would be only the size of a football! The electrons of this enlarged atom would appear like tiny balls orbiting somewhere in that massive space. Most of the atom is space. You and I, like all other forms of matter, are largely electron fluff.

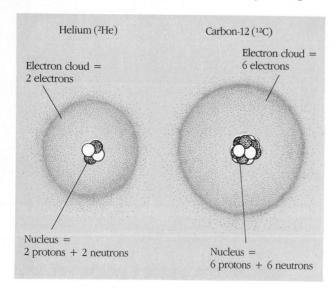

Helium (²He) Carbon-12 (¹²C)

Electron cloud =
2 electrons

Electron cloud =
6 electrons

Nucleus =
2 protons + 2 neutrons

Nucleus =
6 protons + 6 neutrons

Figure 2-2 Comparison of two common atoms, helium and carbon.

Elements

It was once thought that all physical matter consisted of four components—earth, fire, air, and water. Our knowledge of matter has since expanded considerably. The Greeks made an important contribution to our scientific knowledge by recognizing many different forms of matter, such as gold, silver, and lead. They called them the **elements**. Well known for their ability to hypothesize about scientific matters, many Greek philosophers and scientists thought that the elements were uniform throughout. A bar of gold consisted completely of a uniform mass of gold—not of separate particles. Today, scientists know that the elements are actually made up of atoms and that each of these consists of subatomic particles, as discussed above. All told there are 92 naturally occurring elements and a dozen or so that can be made in the laboratory. Each element differs from the rest, having a unique number of protons. In their neutral states, the elements also have a unique number of electrons

I	II	III	IV	V	VI	VII	VIII
1 H Hydrogen 1.0							2 He Helium 4.0
3 Li Lithium 7.0	4 Be Beryllium 9.0	5 B Boron 11.0	6 C Carbon 12.0	7 N Nitrogen 14.0	8 O Oxygen 16.0	9 F Fluorine 19.0	10 Ne Neon 20.2
11 Na Sodium 23.0	12 Mg Magnesium 24.3	13 Al Aluminum 27.0	14 Si Silicon 28.1	15 P Phosphorus 31.0	16 S Sulfur 32.1	17 Cl Chlorine 35.5	18 Ar Argon 40.0
19 K Potassium 39.1	20 Ca Calcium 40.1						

(Atomic Number / Atomic Symbol / Atomic Weight labels point to Carbon cell: 6, C, 12.0)

Figure 2-3 A simplified periodic table showing a few of the atoms found in living and nonliving matter. Note that the atoms are listed according to their atomic number and atomic weight.

equal to the number of protons. For example, the atoms of the element helium contain two protons and two electrons; the atoms of the element carbon contain six protons, six neutrons, and six electrons (Figure 2-2). No others have the same makeup. Thus, no others behave the same chemically.

Each element is represented by a symbol, a kind of chemical shorthand, consisting of one or two letters (Figure 2-3). Carbon, for instance, is designated by a "C." Oxygen is represented by an "O." The elements known to science are listed on a chart called the **periodic table of elements**. A simplified, partial chart is shown in Figure 2-3. As shown, the elements are listed on the chart by increasing **atomic numbers**, which represent the number of protons in their nuclei.

Each atom has a unique atomic number and atomic weight. The **atomic weight** is the mass of the atom, which is expressed in **atomic mass units**. Both protons and neutrons have a mass of one atomic mass unit; electrons have virtually no mass at all. The atomic weight of an atom is equal to the sum of the masses of its protons, neutrons, and electrons. Hydrogen has an atomic weight of one, because hydrogen atoms have one proton and no neutrons in their nuclei. Helium, on the other hand, has an atomic weight of four, because helium atoms have two neutrons and two protons.

Molecules

Atoms join by way of chemical bonds to form molecules. For example, two hydrogen atoms can bind to form a molecule of hydrogen, a gas at room temperature, with the chemical formula H_2. The subscript in this formula tells us that two atoms of hydrogen are linked by a chemical bond. Most atoms on the periodic table, however, do not bond to atoms of the same type; they usually form bonds with atoms of a different chemical nature. For example, two hydrogen atoms bond with one oxygen atom to form water (H_2O). Two oxygen atoms bond to one carbon atom to form carbon dioxide (CO_2).

The chemist separates molecules into two broad categories—organic and inorganic. The **organic molecules**, of which there are over a million, are the compounds of carbon, in which carbon is combined primarily with hydrogen, oxygen, nitrogen, and other carbon atoms. Examples include sucrose (table sugar) and ethanol (grain alcohol). Organic molecules are the building blocks of all living things. But just as important to life are the **inorganic molecules**: what is left—molecules such as oxygen and water. Some important molecules are listed in Table 2-1.

With the basics of chemistry in mind, let us turn our attention to the universe.

Table 2-1 Some Important Organic and Inorganic Molecules

Chemical	Type	Importance
Water	Inorganic	Primary component of all living organisms
		High heat absorbance; used for industrial cooling
		Good solvent; used for industrial cleaning; dissolves nutrients and wastes in organisms
Oxygen	Inorganic	Necessary for cells to break down foods
		Necessary for combustion
Carbon dioxide	Inorganic	Waste product of combustion and energy production in animal cells
		Pollutant that may shift global temperature balance
		Used by plants to make organic molecules such as starch and cellulose
Amino acids	Organic	Necessary for plants and animals to build proteins that form enzymes, hormones, and important structural components of cells
Carbohydrates	Organic	Source of energy for animal cells
Nucleic acids	Organic	Genetic material that controls all cellular function and heredity

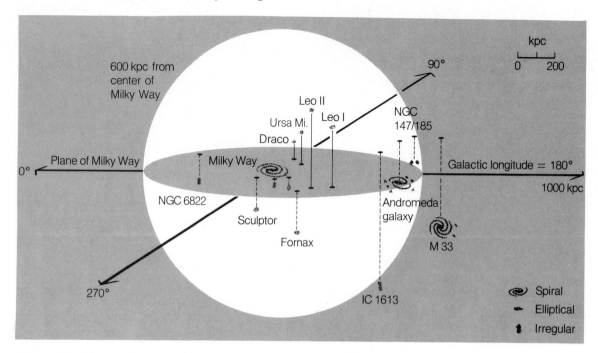

Figure 2-4   The Local Group, a cluster of galaxies, includes our solar system and its galaxy, the Milky Way, with a diameter of 100,000 light years. A light year is the distance that light travels in a year.

Origin of the Earth

Gaze out at the stars at night as far as you can see with the naked eye. Billions upon billions of stars float overhead in the dark void of space. Your eyes behold only a tiny fraction of the universe, for all stars you see are part of the Milky Way galaxy, a grouping of perhaps a trillion stars along with gas and dust. The Milky Way galaxy also houses our solar system—the sun and its nine orbiting planets (Figure 2-4). Beyond the Milky Way are countless other galaxies, a great, immeasurable sea of space and matter.

Unfathomable though they may be, the dimensions of space can be better understood by considering these facts: Light travels at a rate of 300,000 kilometers per second (186,000 miles per second). At this speed a beam of light can travel 7.5 times around the earth's equator in a second. By comparison, a supersonic jet traveling at the speed of sound (340 meters per second), would cover the same distance in 1.5 days. Now suppose you could board a spaceship traveling at the speed of light to travel across the Milky Way galaxy. This modest journey into space would take 100,000 years. Since a **light year** is defined as the distance that light travels in a year, the Milky Way galaxy is about 100,000 light years across.

The Milky Way galaxy is only one of 20 galaxies that belong to a small galaxy cluster called the **Local Group** (Figure 2-4). And the Local Group is only one of many clusters of galaxies in the universe. For your final journey suppose you decided to travel from earth to the Andro-

meda galaxy, located on the periphery of the Local Group. This journey to the edge of the Local Group would take 2.2 million years at the speed of light.

Trillions and trillions of stars clumped into galaxies—that is our universe. Among these stars, we presume, are many thousands of solar systems like ours, some likely with life. But how did the universe, galaxies, and solar systems arise?

Formation of the Universe

Astronomers believe that the universe began 15 billion to 20 billion years ago. All matter making up the universe today, they think, was compressed into an infinitely small and infinitely dense volume that exploded with a fury unknown to humankind. This explosion is appropriately called the **big bang**. Energy and matter catapulted from the place of explosion. For about a million years, however, so much energy existed in this expanding fireball that some of the subatomic particles—electrons, protons, and neutrons—thrashed about violently, unable to combine to form stable atoms.

When the universe had cooled, after a million years of continuous expansion, things began to settle down. Protons, neutrons, and electrons combined to form the first stable atoms, hydrogen and helium. These materials, over time, gave rise to the remaining elements, which ultimately formed the galaxies and solar systems, and you and me as well.

Formation of Galaxies and Stars

The universe was slow to cool after the fiery big bang. A million years afterward the universe was still 3000° C (5400° F). All matter and energy were racing from the point of explosion in a uniform flood of energy and mass. Within the expanding universe at this time, however, huge clouds of matter began forming. These clouds, called **protogalaxies**, were only slightly denser than the surrounding material. They were to give rise to the star-studded galaxies.

The fate of protogalaxies was rich and varied. Some merged with others to form supergalaxies; others simply shrank and formed dwarf galaxies. All had one thing in common: the cloud of cosmic dust condensed into a huge, swirling mass. Condensation was brought about by gravitation, the mutual attraction of matter within the cloud, which caused the cloud to contract. Over time the protogalaxies continued to contract, and as they did, they began to spin faster and faster. Spherical clouds compressed into the flattened shapes typical of many known galaxies (Figure 2-5).

Billions of years later, out of the protogalaxies stars were born. The swirling clouds of matter fragmented into smaller clumps, like lumps in your Thanksgiving gravy, which scientists call **protostars**. Collapsing under gravitation, the protostars grew denser and hotter. When a critical density was reached in the core of the protostar, the temperature became so high that nuclear fusion reactions began. Each **nuclear fusion** reaction in stars fuses four protons (hydrogen nuclei) to form a helium nucleus. In the process, some of the protons' mass is "lost," that is, converted into electromagnetic radiation such as light and heat. Many nuclear reactions every second in stars like our sun allow them to shine brightly for billions of years. Once the nuclear reactions begin, a protostar's collapse ends, and a star is born. Billions of stars formed within the swirling galactic dust, and even today new stars are being formed all the time in the galaxies.

Formation of the Solar System

Within the galaxies solar systems also formed. A **solar system** is a group of planets revolving around a star. Our solar system—consisting of the sun, a medium-sized star, and nine planets in elliptical trajectories around it—formed about 4.6 billion years ago. Astronomers now know much about the formation of our solar system because of evidence of other solar systems in formation in the Milky Way. As shown, in Figure 2-6, this process began with a spherical cloud of dust and gases in the galaxy. Many astronomers believe that an exploding star, or **supernova**, near this cloud of gas triggered the contraction and subsequent condensation of the gas and dust. In the center a star formed—the sun. Leftover materials on the periphery formed the planets by accretion of

Figure 2-5 Side view of a typical spiral galaxy.

cosmic dust, much as a snowball grows if you roll it through wet snow. The planets remain in orbit around the sun, drawn to it by gravitation. Their surface temperature is primarily determined by their distance from the sun. Were it a little closer to the sun, the earth would be too hot to support life; were it a little farther away, it would be too cold.

The Evolution of Life

The primeval earth was a spherical mass of rock and metal made molten by the condensation of matter, radioactive decay, and solar heat. Over time the earth cooled, radiating its intense heat into space. Heavy molten metals, nickel and iron, sank inward and formed the **core** (Figure 2-7). The least-dense materials remained on the surface and cooled to form a thin outer **crust**. Sandwiched between the two is the **mantle**, which is made up of materials of intermediate density. Geologists estimate the age of the earth to be 4.6 billion years.

Because of the earth's own heat and its proximity to the sun, lighter elements such as hydrogen and helium gas were driven off. There could be no atmosphere until the sun and the earth had both cooled.

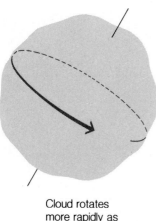 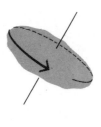 

Cloud rotates
more rapidly as
it contracts.

Cloud flattens to
pancakelike
configuration.

Planets accrete
at their present
distances from sun.

Figure 2-6   As the cloud of gas and dust that formed the solar system contracted, it rotated more rapidly. Astronomers believe that this rotation led to the formation of a rotating disk, within which protoplanets formed from subcondensation, and that the protosun acquired most of the mass of the rotating system. The contraction and subsequent condensation of the cloud may have been triggered by a supernova (exploding star).

Chemical Evolution of Life's Molecules

Over time an atmosphere emerged around the infant planet earth. It was made of small inorganic molecules—water vapor, carbon dioxide, ammonia, hydrogen—and one organic compound—methane. Many of these came from the gases emitted by volcanoes. Biologists believe that these simple molecules were all that was needed for life to begin (Figure 2-8). But how did such wondrous living things as saguaro cacti, redwoods, and blue whales emerge from such an inauspicious beginning?

For millennia as the earth and its atmosphere cooled, water fell from the skies and filled the oceans. Dissolving inorganic and organic molecules of the primitive atmosphere as it fell, rain formed the oceans and lakes, converting the earth into a melting pot for new life. Ultraviolet light from the sun, heat from volcanoes, and lightning energized the molecules dissolved in the waters, causing them to react, much as a flame from a Bunsen burner energizes a test tube reaction. As a result, the dilute inorganic soup was turned into an organic broth containing many of the key elements of life.

In the shallow pools along the margins of the seas, these organic compounds united to form simple proteins and other essential organic molecules (Figure 2-8). Piece by piece the organic chemicals needed for life began to appear.

The idea that organic compounds formed from the chemicals found in the earth's primitive atmosphere is called the **theory of chemical evolution**. A Russian scientist by the name of Oparin first proposed the theory, but it was an American chemist, Stanley Miller, who while still a graduate student set out to test this unusual notion. Miller devised a closed apparatus to which he added the chemicals thought to be found in the earth's primitive atmosphere. He provided heat and electrical sparks to simulate natural energy from volcanoes and lightning.

Figure 2-7   Cutaway model of the earth showing the crust, mantle, and core. Each of the inner planets of the solar system (Mercury, Venus, Earth, and Mars) has a differentiated structure, in which a dense, iron–rich core rests beneath a less dense mantle made primarily of silicon and oxygen. The outermost few kilometers form the rocky crust of the planet.

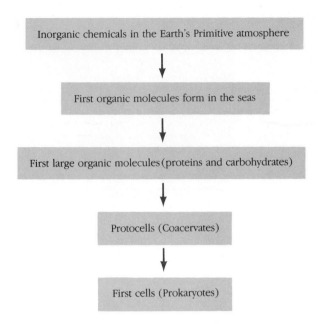

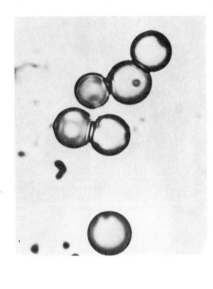

Inorganic chemicals in the Earth's Primitive atmosphere

↓

First organic molecules form in the seas

↓

First large organic molecules (proteins and carbohydrates)

↓

Protocells (Coacervates)

↓

First cells (Prokaryotes)

Figure 2-8   The Russian scientist Oparin's hypothesis on the formation of life.

Figure 2-9   Proteinoids. These protein globules were made in the laboratory under conditions that simulated the earth's primitive environment. It is thought that proteinoids or other similar globules gave rise to the first cells, and for this reason they are called protocells.

After days of energizing his chemical mixture he found that the clear mixture of gases and water had turned brown. Chemical analyses revealed the startling truth for which Miller would receive a Nobel Prize: simple organic molecules necessary for life could be formed in conditions similar to those found many millions of years ago on earth. Further experiments by other researchers showed that these molecules could be combined to form all the essential organic molecules found in living things. How cells arose from the organic stew, no one knows. But biologists believe that proteins and other polymers (long chains of molecules, also including the carbohydrates) combined to form **protocells**, small globules that looked and even acted like living organisms (Figure 2-9). Laboratory studies show that such amalgamations can grow, divide, and selectively take up materials from the environment, much like living organisms. Over millions of years, scientists believe, these simple aggregates of organic molecules took on a life of their own. They developed ways to capture energy from the sun, ways to reproduce themselves, and a way of storing genetic information: DNA.

The First Cells

The Emergence of Microbes   The first cells on earth were probably bacteria that arose at least 3.7 billion years ago, according to the latest findings (Figure 2-10). They may have lived off the organic molecules that formed earlier. An astonishing development of this exciting, but

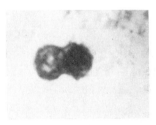

Figure 2-10   Fossil of a bacterium about 3 billion years old. Older specimens, at least 3.7 billion years old, have also been found in rocks.

little understood, period of evolutionary history was the emergence of photosynthesis. **Photosynthesis** is a series of reactions by which organic molecules, such as sugar, are made from carbon dioxide, water, and energy from the sun. Plants and algae are the principal photosynthetic organisms alive today. During the early stages of evolution photosynthesis solved an important problem facing the newly forming biological world: how to replenish the rapidly declining supplies of organic materials in the oceans, the only foodstuffs available to the early cells. Photosynthesis provided a way for organisms to make organic materials from atmospheric carbon dioxide, which was abundant but was not beingconverted fast

re 2-11 Some early
euaryotic organisms no doubt
resembled these common
aquatic organisms found today.
(*a*) The paramecium (400×).
(*b*) An amoeba taken with a
scanning electron microscope
(200×).

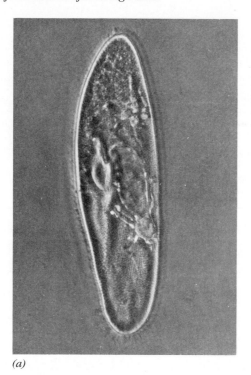

(a)

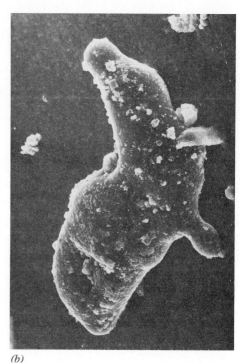

(b)

enough abiotically (through chemical evolution) to keep up with the demands of the billions of new cells inhabiting the oceans. Without photosynthesis life today would be drab indeed, most likely limited to giant bacterial colonies living along the coastlines, feeding off one another as they perished from natural causes. The land surface would be barren rock without plant or animal.

At first photosynthesis in bacteria was a relatively simple process that captured sunlight and generated organic matter. Unlike photosynthesis in plants today, it generated no oxygen. Over millions of years photosynthesis changed, however, in ways that would once again revolutionize life: it began to produce oxygen by splitting water molecules. Thus arose the blue-green algae. Before them, little free oxygen could be found in the atmosphere because it quickly reacted with chemicals. With the advent of this remarkable new process, oxygen slowly began to accumulate in the atmosphere. The first appreciable amounts were found 2.2 billion years ago.

These accumulating levels of oxygen precipitated a crisis, the first global pollution. Oxygen was probably harmful to the single-celled organisms that lived in the shallow seas. It combined with organic molecules and destroyed them. Biologists believe that many species that did not require oxygen perished over the ensuing millennia. Others sought refuge deep in muds. Still others adapted, putting this former toxin to good use and therefore giving rise to a whole host of new species.

The Emergence of Eukaryotic Cells

Out of this apparent disaster arose aerobic (oxygen-requiring) cells complete with nuclei and energy-releasing organelles (Figure 2-11). These nucleated cells are called **eukaryotes**; the first fossil remains of these cells show up in rock estimated to be 1.5 billion years old. Amoebas and paramecia are two modern forms that most closely resemble the first eukaryotic cells.

The most widely accepted explanation for the origin of eukaryotes is called the **theory of endosymbiotic evolution**. It holds that the many cellular organelles in eukaryotic cells, the tiny inclusions such as mitochondria and chloroplasts, where specific functions are carried out apart from the rest of the cell's metabolism, had once been free-living bacterial cells but were engulfed by other cells. This endosymbiotic union is thought to have enhanced the survival of both cells. In their new home the internal symbionts flourished, becoming the cell's organelles. Biologists believe that eventually a permanent relationship beneficial to both developed and persisted so that organelles could be passed from one generation to the next, ad infinitum. (For more on cells see the supplement at the end of this chapter.)

This odd relationship, like photosynthesis, was a major leap in evolution. Many new single-celled organisms arose. New and markedly different strategies for survival evolved, and out of this flood of single-celled life emerged a world of many-celled plants, animals, and fungi (Figure 2-12).

After the formation of eukaryotes the pace of evolution greatly accelerated. Three billion years had been required to make the first nucleated cells, the eukaryotes. Five hundred million years more would pass before the

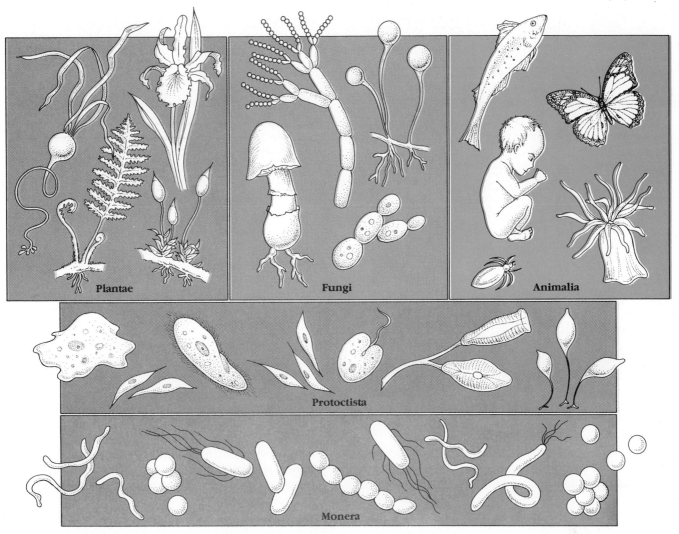

Figure 2-12 The evolutionary tree, showing biological proliferation from the earliest living organism into the "Five Kingdoms" of nature.

sponges emerged. Four hundred million years would lumber by before mollusks (such as snails) appeared. But in a flash of geologic time plants emerged from the waters and colonized the land. In even less time animals came ashore to make the earth their home. From the land animals arose the ancestors of human beings, who in a mere four million years have advanced from gathering seeds and fruits to space exploration and genetic engineering, a technology so powerful it could alter the course of evolution.

The Process of Evolution

To understand how we got here and the profound effects our species can have on the course of evolution, we must understand a little about the process of evolution. Evolution explains how life formed on the earth from a common ancestor. As George Bernard Shaw once observed,

"One touch of Darwin makes the whole world kin." Evolution also explains how life has changed over many millions of years and why it is so diverse today.

Most of what we know about the early history of life comes from fossils—preserved bones, imprints of organisms captured in rock, or even footprints of early animals. By examining these fossils embedded in rock strata whose age can be determined through various means, scientists have been able to construct a biological history of the earth. Much of that history is continuous, although some gaps do exist.

The **theory of evolution**, as Shaw points out above, is often attributed to Charles Darwin, a 19th-century British naturalist who dedicated his life to the study of the natural world (Figure 2-13). In truth, Darwin did not come up with the idea; evolution was already being widely discussed in his time, and the idea dates back to Greece. What Darwin did was to propose a believable mechanism

Figure 2-13   Charles Darwin (1809–1882) as a young man.

by which evolutionary changes could come about. This was his theory of **natural selection**, the idea that organisms best adapted to their environment are most likely to survive and reproduce, as discussed in more detail below.

Darwin's ideas on natural selection were controversial at the time he arrived at them, for they opposed a prevalent religious belief that God had given us the diverse array of living creatures. Consequently, Darwin delayed publishing his theory until 1859, more than 20 years after he had first proposed the idea of natural selection, and then went ahead—as rumor has it—only because Alfred Russell Wallace was about to publish a virtually identical theory.

Like many other great ideas natural selection took many years to be understood and appreciated. Not until the 1940s did Darwin's and Wallace's ideas on natural selection become widely accepted, nearly a hundred years after the men had developed this revolutionary concept. Even today the ideas of evolution and natural selection have their critics.

Mutation and Variation   Evolution, strictly defined, is a process in which species change over time, making them better adapted to their environment. In extreme cases new species may emerge. In sexually reproducing species the process begins by mutations in the genetic material, or DNA, of the germ cells, those that produce ova in females and sperm in males. DNA is a storehouse of information needed by the cells of the body to carry out their many functions. Sections of the DNA molecule, called **genes**, regulate individual functions. Mutations in the genes may be caused by ultraviolet light or other high-energy radiation, chemicals in the environment, and cosmic rays from the sun. (For more on mutation see Chapter 14.) Many mutations are repaired by the cells. Some may be harmful and may lead to the death or impairment of offspring. Other germ cell mutations are neutral; that is, they have no effect at all. Still others, which provide the basis for evolutionary change, increase survivability of the offspring—for example, by improving an organism's ability to escape predators, tolerate cold temperatures, or find food. Genetically based characteristics such as these, which increase an organism's chances of surviving and passing on its genes, are called **adaptations**. Genetic changes may also arise during production of ova or sperm cells, known as gametes. During the production of germ cells, genetic material may be shifted from one chromosome (long strand of DNA with associated protein) to another. The result is new genetic combinations, some of which may provide a selective advantage to the offspring.

Beneficial genetic mutations and crossing over lead to **variation** in populations, a broader genetic base that results in differences in structure, function, and behavior among individuals. This variation provides more leeway to cope with changing environmental conditions, resulting in some members that are better adapted to environmental conditions than others and hence more likely to survive and reproduce. For these reasons biologists refer to variation as the "raw material of evolution." (For more on genetics see the supplement at the end of this chapter.)

Favorable mutations and crossing over may give an organism an advantage over other members of the same species, called a **selective advantage**. It translates into a higher survival rate and more successful reproduction. The offspring of the more successful organisms gradually increase in a population and, over time, come to predominate. In time the genetic composition of the population, or the **gene pool**, will shift. If it changes significantly, a new species may form.

Variation is surely the raw material of evolution. But what molds these raw materials into new life forms?

Adaptation   The molding or driving force of evolution is natural selection. Darwin described natural selection as the process in which slight variations, if useful, are preserved. It is important to note that the environment does not in any way *direct* these changes in the genetic material; the mutations are spontaneous. The environment only preserves ("selects") those organisms in a population with new traits that confer some advantage over the rest. Natural selection is the mechanism that results in organisms better adapted to fit their environment. Some think of natural selection as survival of the fittest.

If the genetic changes in a species are drastic, a new species may emerge, a process call **speciation**. A **species** is a group of organisms that are similar in form, function, and behavior and that generally cannot interbreed with other species or, if they do, cannot produce fertile offspring. The rhinoceros and the water buffalo, for example, are different species. They look different, they behave differently, and they cannot interbreed.

How does speciation occur? Perhaps the most common mechanism of speciation occurs when members of a species are separated (Figure 2-14). In scientific language this is called **geographic isolation**. Geographic isolation can result from new mountain ranges or rivers forming in an organism's natural range. Separated by physical barriers and exposed to different environmental conditions, the two populations, over time, can evolve in quite different directions. Should they be separated long enough, they may lose their ability to interbreed. This is called **reproductive isolation**. When geographic isolation leads to reproductive isolation, new species are always the result. Because the new species emerge in different regions, the process is appropriately called **allopatric speciation** (*allopatric* is derived from the Greek for "other" and "fatherland"). New species may also form without geographical isolation. This is common in plants and is termed **sympatric speciation** ("same fatherland").

The fossil record illustrates another important aspect of the process of evolution, called **adaptive radiation**, in which one ancestral group evolves into many new species that occupy diverse environments. As shown in Figure 2-15, ancient reptiles evolved into terrestrial, aquatic, and flying forms. So did the mammals. This diversification process may occur on a large scale, as in the case of the radiation of reptiles; a medium scale; or a much smaller scale. Darwin saw evidence of adaptive radiation on a small scale when his travels took him to the Galápagos Islands, off the coast of Ecuador. Here he found 14 species of finches that probably arose from a single species of mainland finch (Figure 2-16). Occupying different islands, the mainland finch evolved into new species, diverging to make best use of the varying food sources.

Unrelated species adapt to similar environments in similar ways—for example, bats and flying dinosaurs, lions and carnivorous tyrannosauruses, as in Figure 2-15. Evolutionary biologists call this tendency for organisms to develop the same types of adaptations in response to similar environmental conditions **convergent evolution**.

Figure 2-14 Geographical isolation. When a population is split because of a new geographic barrier, new populations may arise over time because the two groups are subjected to different selective forces. This illustration shows how a mountain range could split the population of long-eared squirrels, over time creating two new species.

Applied Evolution Why study evolution in a course on environmental science? For one, it helps us understand just how our rich natural resources—trees, wildlife,

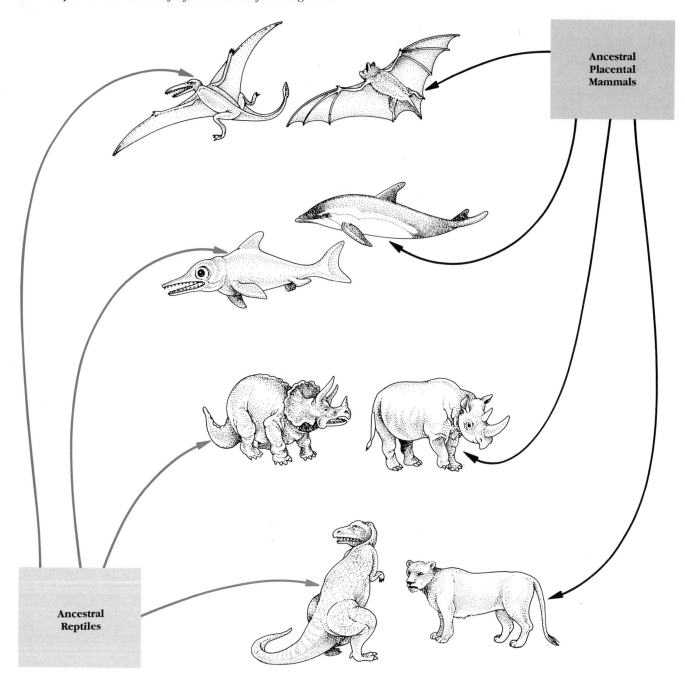

Figure 2-15 Adaptive radiation occurs as organisms evolve to fill ecological niches, making best use of available resources. The drawing shows the niches first filled by dinosaurs and later in evolution by placental mammals.

fish, and the like—got here and how long it would take nature to evolve replacements. Second, it helps us understand the importance of our impacts on other living things. Consider, for example, the evolution of penicillin-resistant bacteria.

Penicillin was the wonder drug of the 1940s and 1950s, introduced to treat bacterial infections. Today, however, 90% of the staphylococci, common and troublesome bac-

teria, are resistant to this drug. What has happened? Over the years, continued use created superstrains of penicillin-resistant staphylococci, just as a natural environmental factor selects favorable adaptations. Penicillin kills off sensitive bacteria but has no effect on those that are resistant. Over time the resistant forms predominate. Higher doses might work, but genetically resistant forms will persist, eventually producing a superstrain of bacteria that will

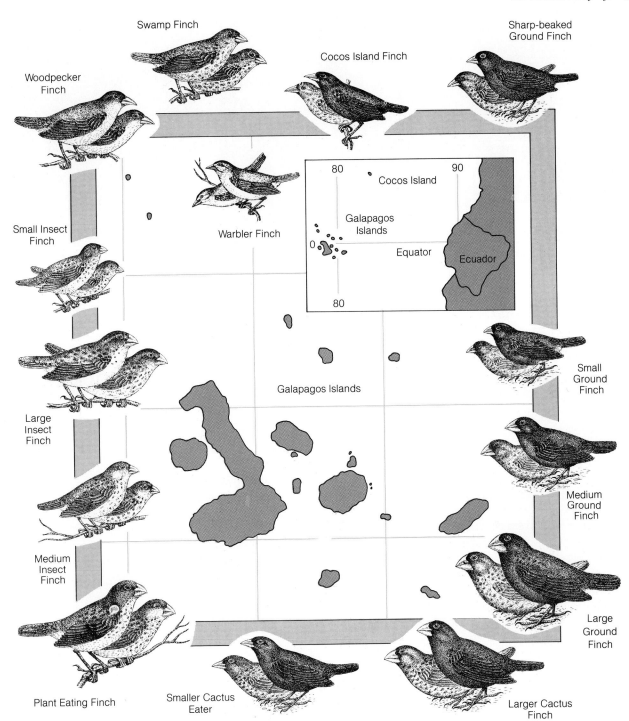

Figure 2-16 The finches of the Galápagos Islands are found nowhere else on earth, although other finch species do inhabit the mainland of South America. The Galápagos finches are not uniformly distributed over all the islands. Only the warbler finch is found on all the islands, while the medium insect finch is found only on one island. Adaptation has given rise to different species of Galápagos finches that fill the ecological niches of hummingbirds, flycatchers, and woodpeckers elsewhere in the world.

(a)   (b)   (c)

Figure 2-17 (*a*) Tarsier, (*b*) lemur, and (*c*) monkey. Notice the front-facing eyes characteristic of all primates.

render the drug nearly ineffective. More than a hundred new antibiotics have been developed in recent years to combat this problem, but each of these faces the same problem: growing genetic resistance. Resistant strains develop almost as fast as the pharmaceutical companies turn out new antibiotics.

Another example, with equally disturbing implications, is genetic resistance to pesticides, among them DDT. DDT was used widely in the years after World War II to combat malaria-carrying mosquitoes. In Sri Lanka, for example, over a million cases of malaria were reported each year in the 1940s. Widespread spraying of homes to control mosquitoes and the use of several drugs to treat victims of malaria drastically reduced the incidence of the disease. In recent years, however, several epidemics have broken out, with as many as a half a million cases. Today the incidence of malaria is on the rise. The reason is twofold. First, DDT-resistant mosquitoes have emerged through natural selection. Second, the malarial parasite (plasmodium) carried by the mosquito has also developed a resistance to the drugs used to treat victims.

These two examples illustrate the three key principles of evolution:

1. There are inheritable variations among individual organisms—in this case, variation in drug and pesticide resistance.
2. Which organisms survive to reproduce is determined by these inherited variations.
3. Natural selection is a process by which the environment—in this case, the chemical environment we make—determines which ones survive and reproduce, thus passing the trait on to their offspring.

How rapidly a species evolves is the subject of much debate. For many years evolutionists believed that such changes occurred gradually over many millions of years. They coined the term **gradualism** as a result. If this were true, paleontologists reasoned, the fossil record should contain many intermediate forms of organisms, a sort of geological recording of the gradual transformation. With few exceptions, however, the fossil record shows few intermediate stages. This gap led two noted paleontologists, Stephen Gould of Harvard University and Niles Eldredge of the American Museum of Natural History, to propose a slightly different theory: that the history of life has been characterized by long, fairly quiet periods punctuated by times of fairly rapid change. This theory is called **punctuated equilibrium**. It accounts for the lack of geological evidence to support gradualism.

Human Evolution

Our Biological Roots

The humorist Willy Cuppy wrote, "All modern men are descended from a wormlike creature, but it shows more in some people." If the truth be known, it is actually thought that humans evolved from a tree shrew that lived 80 million years ago in Africa. With handlike paws the shrew moved about the trees at night, feeding on insects. Over 50 million years the shrews evolved into tree-dwelling primates similar to modern-day tarsiers, lemurs, and monkeys with further refinements in their hands and front-facing eyes to give them binocular vision and better depth perception (Figure 2-17).

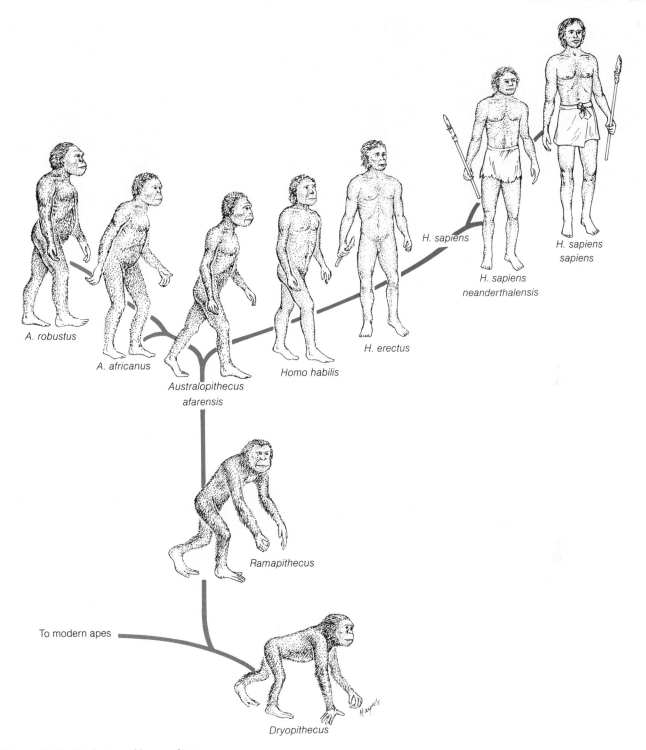

Figure 2-18 Evolution of human beings.

From the monkey line evolved the dryopithecines, the ancestors of the great apes and hominids, humans and their fossil relatives. Their emergence is estimated at roughly 20 million to 30 million years ago. Dryopithecines walked on all four limbs, much like modern apes. From them sprang the first hominids, **australopithecines** (Figure 2-18). Living in southern Africa some 4 million years ago, australopithecines roamed the grasslands, walking upright in search of food and shelter. Roughly 2 million years ago *Homo habilis* emerged. The first tool and weapon makers, they spread from Africa to Europe and Asia.

The Forgotten People

The term *endangered species* suggests the problem of plants and animals destroyed or threatened by habitat alteration, hunting, and pollution. But certain human populations—tribal peoples—are also threatened with extinction. About one out of every 25 humans alive today is an Eskimo, Pygmy, Bushman, Indian, aborigine, or some other tribal member. These people live the way their ancestors did thousands of years ago, as hunters and gatherers or subsistence-level farmers.

Tribal peoples have been uprooted in the name of progress to develop farms, mineral deposits, timber, dams, and reservoirs. Often driven from their homeland, they are forced into an area unlike that in which they have lived for centuries. In Paraguay, for example, the remnants of the Toba-Maskoy tribe have been moved to an arid region where their survival is in doubt.

Those who are allowed to stay are susceptible to new diseases brought by the developer. Brazil's Indian population has shrunk from 6 million to 200,000 since the first Portuguese explorers arrived in the early 1500s. Although war was responsible for some of the deaths, diseases brought from foreign lands were, and still are, the greatest killers. The director of Survival International (an organization dedicated to the protection of tribal people), Barbara Bentley, says,

Bushwoman from the Kalahari Desert, in Namibia, resting on her digging stick.

"The easiest way to dispose of these isolated tribal people is by sneezing."

Some tribes have been "assimilated" into the invading culture with disastrous results. Having suddenly been catapulted two or three centuries in time, they become lost, frightened, and confused by modern technology. Often, they return to their homeland only to find it destroyed. Loss of homeland and traditional values can lead to fatal psychic trauma: from Brazil to Australia, alcoholism, severe depression, and destitution take their toll. Once-skilled hunters are often reduced to begging.

The stories go on: copper mining in Panama threatens thousands of Guaymi Indians; Kalinga tribes in the Philippines fight the construction of hydroelectric dams that would flood their rice terraces; 300,000 Chilean Mapuche Indians have recently been told that their land will be opened for timber cutting; in Peru, the long-isolated Amuesha Indians are threatened by a new highway that would link them to civilization.

The elimination of these cultures will mean not only the end of age-old languages, myths, and social customs but also the irreversible loss of knowledge, including information on medicinal plants, dyes, and diet. Tribal peoples are responsible for discovering more than 3000 plant species with antifertility properties, a boon for birth control research. Some of their plant materials give promising clues to cancer prevention and cure.

The question of whether we can afford to allow these tribal people a continued existence is changing. Now the question is, Can we afford to live without them?

Five hundred thousand years later a new form arose, *Homo erectus*. With a brain slightly smaller than ours, *Homo erectus* made more sophisticated tools and weapons such as hand axes and spears. Anthropologists have found evidence in China that *Homo erectus* used fire to cook, to warm their caves, and to frighten away predators.

Evidence of *Homo sapiens'* emergence is scanty. Paleontologists believe that somewhere around 200,000 years ago our species came into being. One of the best-known examples is the European inhabitant, the Neanderthal. Like their predecessors, Neanderthals lived in caves, cooked their food on fires, and hunted animals with tools. But Neanderthals stood fully erect, had slightly larger brains than we do today, and even buried their dead. Paleontologists have found bear skulls in burial sites along with food and flowers, which they believe are a form of offering left in a ritual performed by clans that roamed the land in search of food.

Modern humans, or Cro-Magnons, emerged 30,000 years ago, perhaps in Africa. They rapidly replaced the

Table 2-2 Classification of Human Social Systems

Social System	Features
Hunting and gathering	1. The people were nomadic or semipermanent.
	2. They benefited from their intelligence and ability to manipulate tools and weapons.
	3. They were knowledgeable about the environment, and skilled at finding food and water.
	4. On the whole, they were generally exploitive of their resources.
	5. The environmental impact was generally small because of low population density and lack of advanced technology.
	6. They lived healthy lives, were well fed and experienced low disease rates.
	7. Their widespread use of fire may have caused significant environmental damage.
Agriculture	1. Farmers were generally either subsistence level or urban based.
	2. They benefited from new technologies to enhance crops and resource acquisition needed for their survival.
	3. They were knowledgeable about domestic crops and animals.
	4. They were highly exploitive of their resources.
	5. The impact of subsistence-level farming was significant, but because population size was small, damage was minimized. The impact of urban-based agriculture was much larger because of new technologies, trade in food products, increasing population, and lack of good land-management practices.
	6. Disease was more common among city dwellers because of increased population density.
	7. Poor agriculture, overgrazing, excessive timber cutting caused widespread environmental damage.
Industry	1. Industry includes early and advanced forms.
	2. It relies on new technologies, energy, new forms of transportation, tremendous input of materials, and reduced number of workers.
	3. Mass production and modern technology were transferred to the farm.
	4. Industry is highly exploitive, more so than earlier societies; devoted to maximum material output and consumption.
	5. Impact is enormous and includes pollution, species extinction, waste production, dehumanization.
	6. Humans become subject to infectious disease and new industrial-age diseases including ulcers, heart disease, and mental illness.
	7. Widespread environmental damage results from industry, agriculture and population growth.

Asiatic and European Neanderthals, for reasons still unknown. Characterized by domed heads, smooth eyebrows, and prominent chins, they perfected the stone and bone tools of their ancestors. Anthropologists believe that Cro-Magnons had a fully developed language.

At the end of the last great glacial age, Cro-Magnons spread across Siberia to the New World. Sweeping across North America, they may have been responsible for the extinction of many animal species, starting a trend that continues unabated today. Ten thousand years ago, anthropologists estimate, there were about 10 million people living on the earth. Today our numbers have swollen to over 5 billion, a 500-fold increase.

Homo habilis, present some 2 million years ago, had roughly the same form we have today. Although we know nothing of their skin, hair, or facial expression, these hominids were probably not much different from you or me.

The most drastic changes in our evolution occurred millions of years ago as we evolved from shrews to dryopithecines; the physical refinements since the emergence of australopithecines have been relatively slight. Thus, the changes that brought us to the industrial age came through cultural evolution—through learned behavior and changes in the way we tap the earth's renewable and nonrenewable resources. A closer look at these changes will help us understand where we have gone wrong and where we need to go if we are to build a sustainable society.

Human Society and Nature: The Changing Relationship

Anthropologists recognize three major social groupings of human societies: hunting-and-gathering, agricultural, and industrial (Table 2-2). Regardless of their differences, all interact with the environment in fundamentally the

(a)

(b)

Figure 2-19 Hunting-and-gathering societies wander the land in search of food and water. (*a*) The men hunt. (*b*) The women are the primary food gatherers, foraging for roots, berries, bark, and other plant products.

same way. As illustrated in the Population, Resource, and Pollution model in Chapter 1, human societies, regardless of their form, all require resources whose acquisition and use often result in pollution and depletion. The level of pollution and the extent of depletion depend on how big the population is, the population's demand for resources, and the type of resources it relies on. Such discrepancies, combined with fundamental attitudinal differences, set these three societies apart from one another in ways worth studying, ways that will give us a better understanding of the environmental crisis we now face.

Hunting-and-Gathering Societies Hunting-and-gathering societies were the dominant form of social organization throughout most of human history. It is only in the last few fleeting moments in geological time that we

have taken up agriculture and then industry as ways of life.

Hunting-and-gathering societies made a living doing just that: hunting animals and gathering numerous varieties of seeds, fruits, vegetables, and other plant matter, depending on the season (Figure 2-19). New anthropological evidence suggests that these people may have been much less skilled at hunting large animals than we commonly think. Pat Shipman, an anthropologist at Johns Hopkins University, asserts that hunters and gatherers probably gained a substantial amount of their meat by scavenging—picking the bones of animals that had been killed by others or had died from natural causes.

In any event, members of these societies had a profound knowledge of the environment. Experts in survival, they knew where to find water, edible plants, and animals;

how to predict the weather; and what plants had medicinal properties. This profound ecological knowledge is evident today in surviving hunting-and-gathering societies. The Bushmen of southern Africa, for example, can find water in the desert where most others would fail. The Australian aborigines can locate and catch a variety of lizards, insects, and grubs far better than trained field biologists.

Studies of present-day hunters and gatherers also suggest that, contrary to popular conception, our early ancestors did not live with the constant threat of starvation and did not spend the greater part of their lives in search of food. Studies also suggest that they were healthy and well nourished and suffered from few diseases.

Many hunters and gatherers were nomads—wanderers—who foraged for plants and captured a variety of animals using only primitive weapons. Because their technology did not give them a great advantage over other species, their populations never grew very large.

Judging from existing hunting-and-gathering societies, anthropologists argue that our ancient ancestors probably had a deep reverence for the environment and the plants and animals they ate. But they were by no means environmentally benign. Hunters and gatherers, for example, may have ignited grass fires to drive animal herds over cliffs for slaughter, killing many more than they needed. Such a wasteful action does not fit the image of a wise steward of the land. The plains tribes of Canada were sophisticated users of fire. They burned clearings regularly to keep them open to maintain the preferred habitat of deer. Today, Canada is dotted with large open meadows; ecologists believe that without the fires of native tribes it would be covered with unbroken coniferous forests.

Hunters and gatherers fashioned tools of sticks, stones, and animal bones to enhance their survival. On the whole they presented little danger to wild species. Even so, many scientists believe that humans were responsible for killing off many species of large animals in prehistoric times, most notably the cave bear, giant sloth, mammoth, giant bison, mastodon, giant beaver, saber-toothed tiger, and Irish elk. They killed these animals directly, drove them out of their preferred habitat, and may have wiped them out by killing their prey. Some hunters and gatherers developed semipermanent life-styles, setting up homes near rich hunting or fishing grounds that could provide a year-round supply of food. These groups were more likely to cause noticeable damage.

On balance, the hunting-and-gathering societies had little impact on the environment. Their small numbers, their generally nomadic life-style, their inefficient technology, and very possibly their reverence for the life-giving earth kept them from depleting the renewable resource base on which they depended.

Agricultural Societies Anthropologists believe that **agricultural societies** emerged between 10,000 and 6000 B.C. The roots of agriculture can be traced to Southeast Asia (Figure 2-20). Here in the moist rain forests, early humans practiced **slash-and-burn farming**. In slash-and-burn agriculture farmers cleared small jungle plots to plant their crops. They harvested and planted the same plot for several years; because the jungle soils were poor in nutrients, however, crops failed after several years, and plots were abandoned for new clearings. Native species invaded, returning the land to its original state. Damage to the jungle was negligible.

The early agricultural societies of Southeast Asia also domesticated many animals, such as the pig and fowl. These became vital food sources, greatly supplementing their crops.

Seed crops originated in a wide region extending from India and China to eastern Africa (Figure 2-20). The first farmers cleared woodlands, known for their rich soils. But a new development, the plow, opened up the fertile grassland soil, which had previously been too difficult to cultivate because of the heavy sod and thick roots of native grasses. Cultivating the grassland soil dramatically increased productivity. A variety of domesticated animals, such as goats, sheep, and cows, supplemented the human diet.

The domestication of animals and plants gave agricultural societies the means to greatly increase the productivity of the land. As a result, they achieved a greater degree of control over their subsistence, marking an important shift in the human–environment interaction. For the first time human populations could by manipulating their environment expand beyond the limits previously set by the natural food supply.

At least two major changes happened. First, the human population began to swell. Fewer people were needed to provide food, so many left the farms and moved to villages and cities, where they took up crafts and small-scale manufacturing. Second, cities grew and eventually became centers of trade, commerce, government, and religion. The face of civilization changed for good.

The plow marks a pivotal point in our cultural evolution. It is the beginning of modern technology, and with it came a dramatic shift in our demands on the environment. The growth of population and small-scale industry, in many ways caused by the plow's success, placed greater demands on the environment for wood, metals, and stone. Heightened exploitation accompanied by poor land management resulted in widespread destruction of the natural environment. Many fertile areas were destroyed by overgrazing, excessive timber cutting, and poor agricultural practices.

The shift to mass-produced food had a potentially more harmful effect: it severed, in large part, the link to nature.

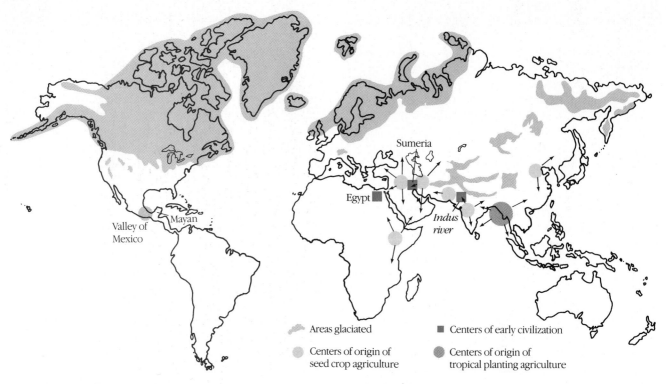

Figure 2-20 Roots of agriculture. The areas where tropical planting and seed crop agriculture originated.

Farmers concentrated on a small number of plants and animals to provide food. The profound knowledge of the environment characteristic of the hunters and gatherers all but vanished. Agriculture became an activity to dominate nature, replacing the cooperation and understanding that had marked earlier cultures.

The large centralized population whose fate hinged on successful crops found it necessary to gain more control over agricultural production. Ensuring human survival became a central preoccupation, which meant only one thing: increasing control over the environment. Thus shifted the balance of nature. Thus began a trend that continues today.

The environmental impact of the agricultural societies and their large urban centers was enormous. Archaeological and historical records show us that overgrazing, widespread destruction of forests, and poor farming practices changed many fruitful regions into barren landscapes (Figure 2-21). Ancient civilizations perished as a result, either directly as their crops failed or indirectly as other displaced peoples invaded.

This decline was especially evident in the Middle East, North Africa, and the Mediterranean from 5000 B.C. to A.D. 200. As an example, the Babylonian Empire once occu-

Figure 2-21 This ancient city was once surrounded by rich forests and grasslands. Deforestation, overgrazing, and poor agricultural practices denuded the land, turning it into desert.

Understanding the Earth

The late Buckminster Fuller coined the term "Spaceship Earth" to describe our watery planet. The earth, like a spaceship, is a closed system capable of recycling the materials necessary for life. Similar to a spaceship, the earth is vulnerable to disruptions of its life-giving systems.

In the 1970s, the British scientist J. E. Lovelock began to consider the earth as a living entity rather than a spaceship, for the earth in many ways behaves like an organism. It maintains a constant temperature, monitors the chemical composition of its lakes and oceans, and regulates its atmospheric gases in much the same way that an organism maintains its internal constancy.

Although this notion, known as the Gaia Hypothesis, has drawn much criticism, it nonetheless is an elegant metaphor that underscores a key principle of ecology: that all living things operate together. The sequoia and the gazelle, the lion and the rosebush—all are integral parts of a system as interdependent as the cells in your brain and kidneys.

This gallery takes a glimpse at the processes of earth. It shows the active building and tearing down of land, the delicate energy balance, and the oceanic and wind currents that affect life in innumerable ways.

1 The view of earth from the moon initially led to the notion of the earth as a spaceship, capable of recycling its life-sustaining materials. This metaphor has now largely been replaced by the Gaia Hypothesis of the earth as similar to an organism.

1

2 The earth's water participates in an enormous recycling system—the hydrological cycle. Heated by the sun, water evaporates from the earth's surface into the skies where it forms clouds. Falling back to earth, much of the water evaporates again while the rest flows back to the oceans along rivers and lakes. A small fraction seeps into the earth's surface and migrates slowly as groundwater.

Rain wears at the earth's surface, removing soil and washing it into the sea and lakes. People worsen erosion by stripping the land of its vegetation. Some 20 billion tons of farmland topsoil is washed away each year by wind and rain, often because of poor land management.

The earth's energy balance is as important as the hydrological cycle.

About 30% of the sunlight reaching the earth is reflected by the atmosphere, while approximately 70% is absorbed by the earth's surface and atmosphere and radiated back into space as heat. Water vapor and gases such as carbon dioxide in the atmosphere block much of the outgoing heat and radiate it back to earth, keeping the earth habitable. Unfortunately, modern civilization has added billions of tons of carbon dioxide and other gases to this thermal blanket, causing a gradual rise in global temperature. Some scientists predict that as pollution continues this warming of the earth could eventually melt enough ice to flood nearly 20% of the earth's land surface, with disastrous results for agriculture and our food supply.

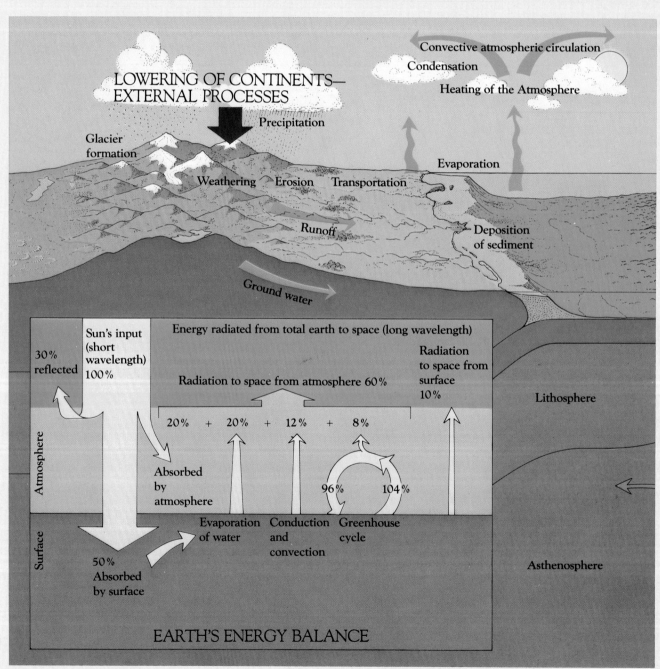

Erosion is to some extent counterbalanced by internal geological processes that build up the land. The action of tectonic plates in this respect is explained on the next page. Lava from volcanoes also adds to the buildup.

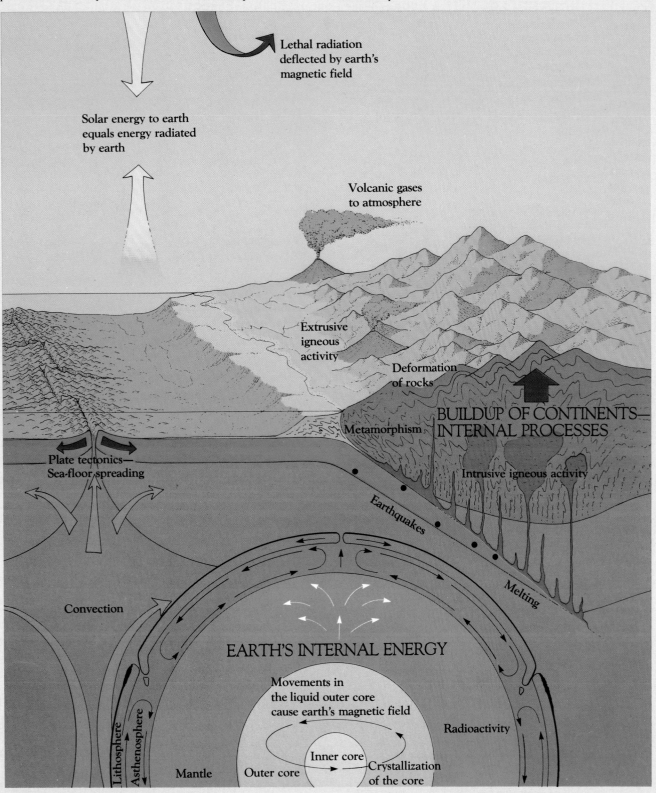

Lethal radiation deflected by earth's magnetic field

Solar energy to earth equals energy radiated by earth

Volcanic gases to atmosphere

Extrusive igneous activity

Deformation of rocks

Metamorphism

BUILDUP OF CONTINENTS— INTERNAL PROCESSES

Plate tectonics— Sea-floor spreading

Intrusive igneous activity

Earthquakes

Melting

Convection

EARTH'S INTERNAL ENERGY

Movements in the liquid outer core cause earth's magnetic field

Radioactivity

Lithosphere

Asthenosphere

Mantle

Outer core

Inner core

Crystallization of the core

3 The earth's crust consists of about ten huge movable plates, called tectonic plates, eight of which are shown here. The plates are propelled by convection of the earth's molten interior. Where they pull apart, molten rock can flow upwards and form new ocean floor. Plates that slip under others cause the buildup of continents through mountain formation. Although new crust and new minerals are formed as the earth's crust regenerates itself, the minerals are largely out of reach of modern civilization.

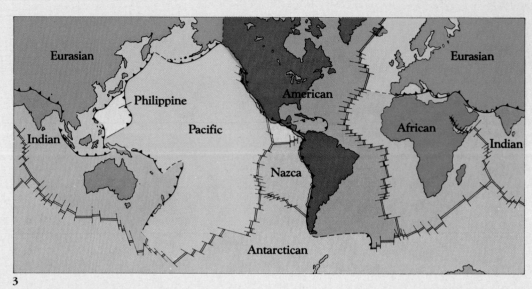

3

4 As the earth orbits the sun, the planet spins on its axis, causing large swirling currents in the earth's atmosphere. These prevailing winds are also generated by the uneven heating of the earth's surface, which leads to differences in atmospheric pressure. Wind occurs when air moves from regions of high pressure to low-pressure zones. For example, hot air rising at the equator causes the low-pressure region known as the doldrums. The northeast and southeast trade winds blow to the equator from the colder high-pressure regions at 30 north and south latitude, respectively. The westerlies blow strongly from the subtropical highs to the so-called subpolar lows at 60 north and south latitude, cooling the climate in those regions.

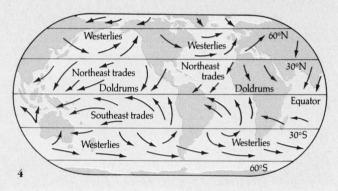

4

5 The major ocean currents are determined by the earth's rotation, by the force of the prevailing winds, and by the location of landmasses that block the currents. The flow of the warm (red) and cold (blue) currents influences regional climates. Because of the presence of the continents the currents move in loops known as gyres. The gyres flow clockwise in the northern hemisphere and counterclockwise in the southern hemisphere, due to the earth's rotation. The Gulf Stream, for example, carries warm water from the equator to the British Isles, keeping them warmer than expected at that latitude. The Humboldt Current, in contrast, brings cold water from the Antarctic to the equator, cooling the western coast of South America.

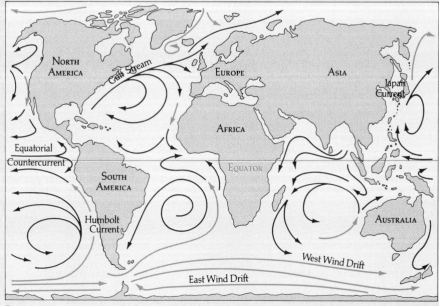

5

Figure 2-22 The Industrial Revolution marked a new day for human societies. Populations grew, resource demands skyrocketed, and pollution became widespread.

pied most of what is now Iran and Iraq. At the outset this land was covered with productive forests and grasslands. Huge herds of cattle, goats, and sheep overgrazed the grasslands, however, and eventually destroyed the natural vegetation. Forests were cut to provide timber and create more pasture. The loss of grassland and forest vegetation decreased rainfall and eventually parched the land. Sediment washed from the barren soils, robbing them of nutrients and filling irrigation canals. These changes and a succession of invading armies eventually destroyed this once-great empire.

This story has been repeated all around the Mediterranean Sea. Throughout Saharan Africa in what are now dry and uninhabitable regions, for example, remnants of once wealthy cities can be found buried in the sand.

The hunter and gatherers were benign by comparison with the agriculturists, who had lost much of their earlier reverence for nature; had powerful new tools to manipulate the elements; saw their numbers swell because of their great success in farming; watched the emergence of cities and their industry, both of which placed additional demands on resources; and witnessed the emergence of economics, which began to see the natural world in a different light, as a source of wealth.

The Industrial Society The **industrial society** is a recent phenomenon in human history brought on by the **Industrial Revolution**, a drastic change in manufacturing marked by a shift from small-scale production by hand to large-scale production by machine. Starting in England in the 1700s and in the United States in the 1800s, the Industrial Revolution brought about further changes in society, which continued to strain the once-close ties between humans and nature.

With the advent of coal-powered machines manufacturing—once carried out by hand, as the word implies—became more capital- and energy-intensive and less labor-intensive (Figure 2-22). People came to matter less than machines and production. With the increase in machine labor came a dramatic escalation in energy demand and a need for new means of transportation to move goods to and from the city. As industries grew, the influx of materials—fuel, food, minerals, and timber—into the city rose sharply.

The shift to machine production changed the working environment, the city, and the surrounding countryside that supplied the resources. The new manufacturing technologies were the fruit of scientific and engineering advances. They were complex, often made work mean-

Figure 2-23 Modern agriculture depends heavily on machinery, energy, and additional resources. Large fields are worked to achieve maximum output.

ingless and boring, and produced large quantities of smoke, ash, and other wastes (Figure 2-22).

Mechanization also swept our farms (Figure 2-23). Technological advances such as Jethro Wood's cast-iron plow with interchangeable parts and Cyrus McCormick's reaper brought on a rapid increase in agricultural production. Perhaps one of the most significant advances was the invention of the internal-combustion engine, which made horse-drawn implements obsolete. The motor-powered tractor alone could plow as much land in a week as our forebears could work in a lifetime using hand tools. Because of more efficient farming methods, fewer farm workers were needed. Unemployed workers migrated to cities, swelling their populations.

Other significant advances include the development of fertilizers, which allowed an increase in agricultural productivity without increasing the amount of land cultivated, and plant breeding, which produced higher-yield crops that were drought- and disease-resistant.

New medicines and better control of infectious disease through insecticides and improved sanitation also grew out of the Industrial Revolution. These important developments enhanced human survival. People began to live longer, and the human population began its rapid ascent.

Population growth, the agricultural transformation, the rise of industry, the rising demand for resources, and the further isolation from nature had tremendous environmental repercussions. Pollution became more widespread. Increased agricultural output destroyed wildlife habitat, depleted soils, and caused severe soil erosion, which polluted waterways. Dredging new harbors destroyed productive fishing grounds and shellfish beds. Mine waste, city sewage, and industrial discharges pol-

luted waters and wiped out native fish populations, such as the Atlantic salmon.

The shift to an industrial society further distorted the human view of nature. Industrial societies sought more control over the environment, ultimately to ensure their own survival. Industrial people came to view themselves as more and more apart from nature and superior to it. The prevailing attitude today can be traced back to the 17th-century English philosopher John Locke, who argued that the purpose of government was to allow people the freedom to exercise their power over nature to produce wealth. "The negation of nature," Locke argued, "is the way toward happiness." People must become "emancipated from the bonds of nature." These notions of disassociation and superiority have been passed from generation to generation throughout the industrial age. Locke also preached unlimited economic growth and expansion, with the belief that individual wealth was socially important for a harmonious society, an idea that has also persisted.

Industrial societies were swept up in a battle with nature. New medicines to combat disease, an arsenal of chemicals to fight pests, and new technologies to extract resources more efficiently were the key weapons. On the whole, people ate better, lived better, and began to live longer. But there was a price to be paid in environmental deterioration, which cannot go on for long without serious backlashes.

Advanced industrial societies arose in the period after World War II. Several major features distinguish this new form of society: (1) a marked rise in production and consumption, (2) a shift toward synthetics such as plastics and nonrenewable resources such as oil and metals, and (3) huge increases in energy demand for farming, industry, and day-to-day living.

The advanced industrial society, caught in an ever-escalating production–consumption cycle, has only begun to awaken to the costs of environmentally irresponsible behavior. Domination of nature continues as the central theme of modern industrial societies, economic growth remains its hallmark, and progress, its vague but commanding allure, despite evidence that these three features threaten the long-term future of our tiny planet.

One threat of considerable importance is the synthetic substances used by people living in the advanced industrial societies. Among them are plastics, nylon, and chemical pesticides, which are all derived from petroleum. Synthetics can create problems in nature, because the bacteria in soil and water, which normally decompose natural materials, are frequently unable to break synthetics down. Thus, synthetics may persist in the environment for decades. If they are biologically harmful, they can have significant environmental effects. The persistent insecticide DDT, for example, can accumulate in the fatty tissues of birds and disrupt reproduction. (See Chapters 14 and 17 for a more thorough discussion of this phenomenon.) Finally, synthetics are generally derived from nonrenewable petroleum resources; plastics, for instance, are derived from nonrenewable petroleum, and metals are made from nonrenewable ores.

Another threat is carbon dioxide, released from combustion sources such as cars, jet aircraft, factories, and power plants. As discussed further in Chapter 15, carbon dioxide released in large quantities now threatens to change the global climate in ways that will disrupt agriculture and radically change where we live. Oil depletion, acid rain, species extinction, and deterioration of the ozone layers are additional threats that round out the environmental crisis.

Twentieth-century technology and industry and the underlying belief that human beings have dominion over the world and are apart from nature have brought us to the present environmental crisis. Advances in technology, increasing control over our environment, rising population, and our growing isolation from nature have all contributed greatly. One thing that this book will make clear is that modern society as we know it cannot continue. Part 2 will show that the population growth curve must eventually stop rising and that we can halt the upward trend in population if only we want to. Part 3 will document how the resources we rely on are reaching their limits or, in some cases, are already at them. It will point out ways in which we must change. Part 4 will describe the facts about pollution and its effects and will show how we can keep from poisoning our planet. Finally, Part 5 will outline attitudes and practices of both economics and politics that are outdated, even dangerous, in a finite world and will suggest alternatives that may allow us to achieve a more peaceful coexistence with the living and giving planet.

New Visions: A Final View from Outer Space

We started this journey in outer space with a cataclysmic explosion that gave birth to the universe. It is only fitting that we end in space, too, hoping that another explosion, this one of our own making, will not steal from us the time needed to mend the damage we have wrought on the tiny, fragile planet we call home.

Traveling through space at 107,000 kilometers per hour (66,000 miles per hour), this watery planet is more than a spaceship, supporting life through its vast recycling networks. The earth is, as alluded to earlier, like a living thing. Just as you and I do, the earth regulates its temperature within a fairly narrow range and has, geologists believe, done so for several million years. The earth creates and maintains a unique chemical atmosphere conducive to life and entirely different from what scientists predict based on the earth's chemistry.

The British scientist James Lovelock coined the term **Gaia** (pronounced GAY-a) **hypothesis**, after the Greek goddess of the earth, to describe this ability of the planet to maintain constant physical and chemical conditions necessary for life. As a metaphor it goes beyond the concept of spaceship earth, for it emphasizes a lifelike unity of all things that make up the biosphere. This key principle of ecology may humble our self-centered view of human existence and help us build a sustainable society that protects the living fabric of which we are a part.

Measure your health by your sympathy with morning and spring.

Henry David Thoreau

Summary

Sometimes it is necessary to leave home to fully understand and appreciate what we have. Pictures taken during our voyages into space have helped us reshape how we think about the planet and given rise to the concept of the **spaceship earth**, a vessel carrying millions of passengers and sustained by intricate recycling mechanisms. More recent voyages have given rise to a new metaphor, that of the earth as a living thing. This is called the **Gaia hypothesis**.

Our beginnings can be traced back to the big bang 15 to 20 billion years ago. At that time, scientists speculate, all matter that makes up the universe was compressed in an infinitely small and dense volume that then exploded. The universe, made up of matter and energy, rapidly expanded. It took a million years for the universe to cool enough for stable atoms to form. **Atoms**, a basic unit of much matter, formed as **electrons**, **protons**, and **neutrons** united. Atoms consist of a central, dense **nucleus** consisting of protons and neutrons. Circling around the nucleus are the negatively charged electrons. They are found in the **electron cloud**. Atoms unite by various chemical bonds to form **molecules**.

Within this universe of atoms and subatomic particles slightly more dense clouds of immense size formed; these **protogalax-**

ies contracted under gravitation—the mutual attraction of all matter. Swirling in space the protogalaxies formed smaller clouds of matter that eventually gave rise to stars and planets.

The primeval earth was a spherical mass of rock and metal made molten by the condensation of matter, radioactive decay, and solar heat. Over time the earth cooled, forming a thin **crust** of lighter elements. The heaviest elements sank to the **core**, and intermediate-weight elements remained in the intervening **mantle**.

An atmosphere of carbon dioxide, methane, ammonia, hydrogen, and water vapor formed as the earth continued to cool. Water vapor condensed during this cooling and filled the oceans, dissolving inorganic and organic molecules from the atmosphere. Ultraviolet light from the sun energized these molecules in the dilute oceans and caused them to react with one another. Gradually, organic molecules necessary for life accumulated. These simple sugars and amino acids combined to form proteins, the genetic material DNA, and many other compounds. Larger molecular-weight compounds, scientists think, united in small globules known as **protocells**, which looked and acted like living organisms. Over millions of years these simple aggregates took on a life of their own as they developed metabolic pathways and ways to reproduce.

The first real cells to emerge from the protocells were probably bacteria that lived by absorbing nutrients from the waters. Soon they were joined by photosynthesizing cells capable of making their own organic molecules from carbon dioxide and sunlight energy. Photosynthetic bacteria evolved a more complex biochemistry that began releasing oxygen.

As oxygen accumulated in the atmosphere, new cells evolved. These **eukaryotes** were nucleated cells; that is, they contained genetic material in membrane-bound nuclei. Eukaryotes contained cellular organelles, distinct structures specialized to carry out many functions of a cell, such as energy production. The **theory of endosymbiotic evolution** describes how these organelles arose. It states that organelles were once free-living organisms that became incorporated in other cells and there set up a permanent relationship, beneficial to both host and internal symbiont. At this point in evolution the pace of change quickened. From the unicellular eukaryotes evolved the plants, fungi, and animals.

Evolution describes how life formed here on earth and how it has changed over many millions of years. It explains why life is so diverse today. But evolution also tells of a common ancestry and a common strategy for life.

Evolution results in genetic changes within a species that may lead to the formation of new species. A **species** is a group of organisms that are different anatomically, physiologically, and behaviorally from all others and generally cannot interbreed with other such groups. Evolution can be summarized as follows: There is variation in all traits, or **adaptations** to the environment, in populations of organisms. New adaptations arise from random **mutations**, changes in the genetic material, and **crossing over**, the exchange of DNA during gamete formation. Whether an organism survives in a changing environment depends on its inherited adaptations. **Natural selection** is the process by which the environment determines which ones survive and reproduce; in other words, the environment selects for the organisms in a population with the most favorable adap-

tations. If, over time, a species' genetic makeup shifts because of shifting climate, a new species may form.

The origin of the human race can be traced back to tree shrews that lived in Africa 80 million years ago. They gave rise to monkeylike creatures over the next 50 million years, which in turn evolved into the first animals with a distinctly human form, the **australopithecines**, arising about 4 million years ago. From this point humans changed very little, anatomically. Throughout most of our 4-million-year history we have made a living by hunting and gathering. It was not until 10,000 B.C. that humans turned to agriculture, a way of life that persisted until the 18th and 19th centuries. Agricultural societies were quickly replaced by industrial societies.

The shift from hunting-and-gathering societies to industrial societies involved several major changes. First, our control over the environment increased, gradually at first and then, once industry started, at a rocket speed. Knowledge of science and technology brought about this revolution in our control over the environment. Second, we became less attached philosophically and morally to the earth. We became powerful, almost godlike, in our manipulation of the world around us. More and more we saw ourselves as apart from, rather than a part of, nature. Third, our control and our emotional severance led to widespread depletion and pollution. Today, domination continues as a central theme of modern society; economic growth remains its hallmark, and progress, its vague but commanding allure.

A new vision of the earth may set us straight so we can return to a position more likely to be sustained. That vision, growing out of our search for life on other planets, is called the Gaia hypothesis. It holds that the earth is like a living thing, capable of maintaining its own environment, much the same way your body controls blood pressure, body temperature, and dozens of other functions. As a metaphor it emphasizes the unity of the biosphere, a key philosophical realization that may guide us on our way to building a sustainable society.

Discussion Questions

1. Describe in detail the formation of the universe, galaxies, stars, and our solar system. In what ways are the formations of galaxies, stars, and solar systems similar?

2. How would you set up an experiment to test the theory of chemical evolution?

3. What features did protocells have to acquire to become bacteria?

4. Define the theory of endosymbiotic evolution.

5. Describe the theory of evolution using the following terms in your discussion: Charles Darwin, natural selection, species, mutation, variation, gene pool, adaptation, speciation, geographic isolation, allopatric speciation, adaptive radiation, and convergent evolution.

6. Describe each of the major forms of society—hunting-and-gathering, agricultural, and industrial. How were they similar, and how were they different? How did the human–environment interaction shift over time?

7. List things that your body maintains in a relatively constant state—for example, body temperature. Make a parallel list of things for the earth. From your experience is it safe to conclude that the earth behaves like an organism?

Suggested Readings

Carter, V. G., and Dale, T. (1974). *Topsoil and Civilization*. Norman: University of Oklahoma Press. An in-depth account of the impacts of early societies on soils.

Clapham, W. B. (1981). *Human Ecosystems*. New York: Macmillan. Lengthy account of the stages of cultural development and the impact of societies on the environment.

Commoner, B. (1976). *The Poverty of Power: Energy and the Economic Crisis*. New York: Bantam. Insightful coverage of the economic and energy problems of industrial societies.

Foster, R. J. (1982). *Earth Science*. Menlo Park, Calif.: Benjamin/Cummings. A good beginning book on the earth sciences.

Goldsmith, D. (1985). *The Evolving Universe*. Menlo Park, Calif.: Benjamin/Cummings. Eloquently written treatise on the evolution of the universe, galaxies, and solar systems.

Isaacs, J. (1980). *Australian Dreaming: 40,000 Years of Aboriginal History*. Sydney, Australia: Lansdown Press. A wonderfully illustrated book on the hunters and gatherers of Australia.

Rifkin, J. (1985). *Declaration of a Heretic*. Boston: Routledge and Kegan Paul. Important, controversial reading on the advanced industrial society.

Russell, P. (1983). *The Global Brain*. Los Angeles: Tarcher. Superbly written view of possible evolutionary changes that could radically reshape our society. A must.

Shipman, P. (1985). Silent Bones, Broken Stones. *Discover* 6 (8): 66–69. Insightful look at how anthropologists study earlier societies, bias, and some new insights into human evolution.

Van Matre, S. and Weiler, B. (1983). *The Earth Speaks*. Warrenville, Ill.: Institute for Earth Education. Good collection of writing on the earth by poets and scientists. See especially the essay by Loren Eiseley for a beautiful description of evolution.

Genetics and the Biology of Cells

Imagine a world of ocean and barren rock without plants or animals. No springy moss underfoot or sprawling maples overhead. Imagine, too, a sea without fish or without great whales bursting to the surface for air. This was the world of 3.7 billion years ago. The first living creatures could be seen only with a microscope: tiny single-celled bacteria, immersed in the shallow waters of the sea.

The emergence of the first cellular inhabitants laid the foundation for life as we know it today. Our evolutionary history hinges on their development. From these single-celled beginnings came over 50 million species of fungi, plants, animals, and microorganisms. Most of them have perished, changing into new forms or dying out completely, leaving no descendants.

Even today every living organism begins as a single cell budded from its parent or formed by the union of two parental cells, called **gametes**.

The Cell: Some Key Concepts

The cell is the fundamental unit of life in many ways. Many organisms exist as single cells. The simplest of these is the bacterium (Figure S2-1).

Bacteria

Bacteria live in air, water, and soil. They are found inside and on the surfaces of other organisms. Unquestionably the most numerous organisms around, bacteria have a relatively simple structure. As shown in Figure S2-1, they consist of a cell wall, cell membrane, cytoplasm, and a **nucleoid**, a region containing the genetic material, DNA. Because their nuclear DNA is not bound by a membrane, bacteria are called **prokaryotes** ("before nuclei").

Bacteria divide by **binary fission**, a splitting of the organism into identical halves. Their lives are dictated by the supply of nutrients: in times of abundance they proliferate wildly; in times of shortage they all but perish. As simple as they may seem, bacteria are still complex biochemical machines. They break down organic molecules in an elaborate series of chemical

reactions to generate cellular energy, and they synthesize complex protein molecules in the blink of an eye.

Eukaryotes

Bacteria gave rise to a whole host of single-celled organisms with a more complex structure (Figure S2-2). Called **eukaryotes**, because they contain true, or membrane-bound, nuclei, these cells carry out many of their functions in cellular organelles, tiny compartments that isolate important cellular functions in much the same way that a company isolates its mail room and assembly workers for greater efficiency. Instead of producing energy in their cytoplasm as their bacterial ancestors did, for example, the eukaryotes sequester most energy production in **mitochondria**, whose structure is shown in Figures S2-2 and S2-3. (The origin of organelles is discussed briefly in Chapter 2.) The mitochondrion, discussed below, produces cellular energy from food molecules. Perhaps one of the cell's most important organelles is the **nucleus**. It houses the DNA, which contains all the information a cell needs to carry out its many functions. Within the nucleus new DNA is made prior to cell division.

The eukaryotic cell is delimited by a **cell membrane** made of fats (lipids) and protein. The cell membrane holds the cell's contents in place and also regulates the flow of materials into and out of the cell.

The apparently amorphous substance within the cell is called the **cytoplasm**. The cytoplasm consists of a solution of water with dissolved ions and many types of molecules. The cytoplasm fills the cells between the nucleus and cell membrane. Floating in it are numerous cellular organelles.

Some Cellular Organelles

Many of the cell's organelles are bound by membranes similar to the cell membrane. These membrane-bound organelles include the mitochondria, chloroplasts (in plants), endoplasmic reticulum, Golgi, and nucleus. Other organelles are not membrane-bound. They will not be discussed here for the sake of brevity.

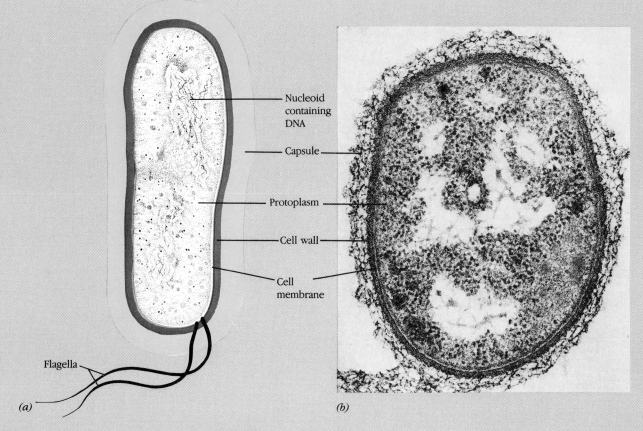

Nucleoid
containing
DNA

Capsule

Protoplasm

Cell wall

Cell
membrane

Flagella

(a)

(b)

Figure S2-1   A typical bacterium, probably the first type of cell to evolve.

The **mitochondrion**, shown in Figure S2-3, has two membranes—an outer limiting membrane and an inner membrane, thrown into folds called **cristae**. The mitochondrion is the power plant of the cell; it breaks down organic foodstuffs, derived mainly from glucose, into carbon dioxide and water. During this breakdown, energy originally stored in the covalent bonds of glucose is released. In the mitochondrion some energy is released in the form of heat, and some is converted into cellular energy in the form of a high-energy molecule that, when broken down later, provides energy to power various cellular functions, such as movement, transport of molecules across cell membranes, and protein synthesis.

The **chloroplast** in plant cells, shown in Figure S2-4, also consists of two membranes. It has odd-looking structures called **grana**, which contain **chlorophyll** and other pigments that absorb sunlight and capture its energy for carbohydrate synthesis. Outside the grana in the **stroma** of the chloroplast are the many enzymes needed to produce glucose and other carbohydrates from sunlight energy, atmospheric carbon dioxide, and water during photosynthesis.

The **endoplasmic reticulum** is a network of membranous channels extending throughout the cytoplasm. In protein-producing cells part of the endoplasmic reticulum is studded with small particles, known as **ribosomes** (a nonmembrane-bound

organelle). Together, the ribosomes and endoplasmic reticulum form the **rough endoplasmic reticulum**. This is the cellular site for making extracellular protein—that is, protein that will be released outside the cell. Some examples of extracellular protein are the pancreatic enzymes, which are made in cells in the pancreas but released into tiny ducts that transport them to the small intestine where digestion takes place, and the pituitary hormones, which must travel through the bloodstream to distant tissues.

Protein is synthesized on the surface of the rough endoplasmic reticulum, migrates inside, and then moves to another organelle, the **Golgi complex**. There it is packaged into membrane-bound sacs, called **secretory granules**, which store the protein until it is needed outside the cell. The Golgi lies near the nucleus and consists of a stack of flattened membranes, resembling pancakes.

The largest of all organelles, the **nucleus**, is bound by two membranes, forming the **nuclear envelope**. Small pores in the nuclear envelope allow materials to pass freely in and out. The nucleus houses the **DNA**, short for **deoxyribonucleic acid**. Stored in the DNA is all the information that controls cellular metabolism, growth, and structure. DNA is a self-replicating molecule; that is, it is able to reproduce itself. It also acts as a template for RNA synthesis, which is described below.

Figure S2-2 A typical eukaryotic cell.

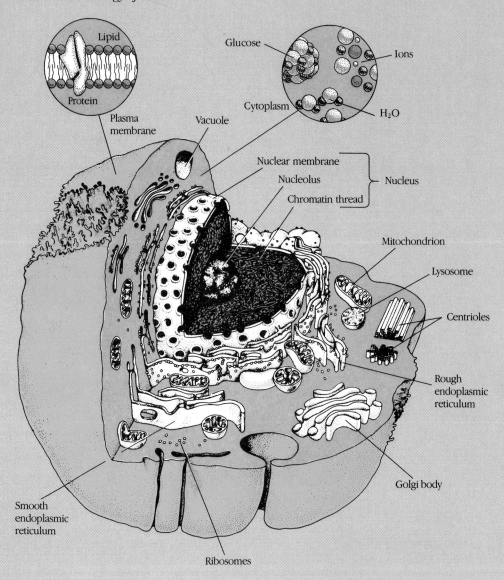

Some Principles of Genetics

Until the early 1950s biologists had only a general understanding of heredity. They knew that individual traits—eye color, skin color, and the like—were controlled by DNA, a long complex molecule found in the cell's nucleus in strands called **chromosomes**. But biologists did not know how that remarkable molecule could determine the structure of the cell's proteins or how it could regulate the more than 4000 chemical reactions taking place in typical cells. Francis Crick and James Watson discovered the secret when they unlocked the chemical structure of DNA. Their work revolutionized our understanding of biology and has opened up countless new avenues for research. Perhaps one of the most important, with direct relevance to environmental science, is genetic engineering (discussed in more detail in Chapter 7).

DNA's Structure

DNA, the researchers found, is a double-stranded molecule, as shown in Figure S2-5, shaped like a spiral staircase. They called it a double helix. Each strand of the double helix has a backbone made of alternating sugars and phosphate groups. These molecules attach to one another like beads on a necklace. Bonded to each sugar is an organic molecule called a base. Four different bases fall into two categories: purine and pyrimidines. In DNA there are two purines—adenine and guanine—and two pyrimidines, cytosine and thymine. As shown in Figure S2-5 the two DNA strands are held together by weak bonds, called **hydrogen bonds**, that form between the purine and pyrimidine bases. The twisting of the two strands forms the double helix.

The sequence of bases in the DNA is the language of the cell—the simple but elegant way it stores all the information it needs to regulate cell structure and function. It is a code that is preserved by its exact replication each time a cell divides. Thus it is passed from generation to generation more or less unchanged.

Mutations

Sometimes the base sequence of the DNA molecule does change. This is a natural biological event, called a **mutation**,

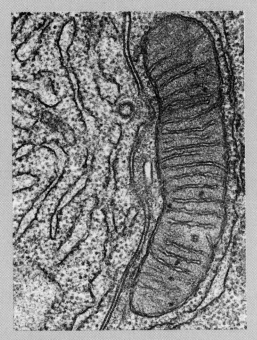

Figure S2-3 Electron micrograph of a mitochondrion.

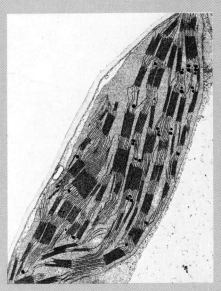

Figure S2-4 Electron micrograph of a chloroplast.

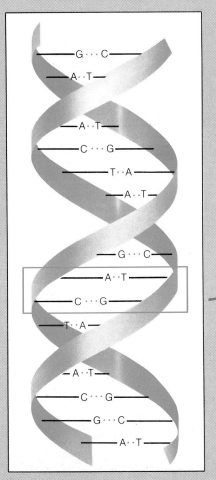

(a)

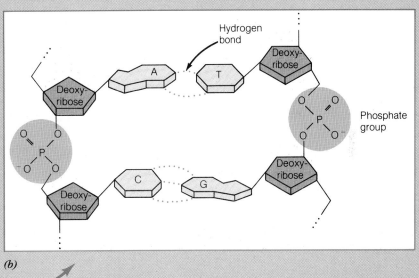

Hydrogen bond

Deoxy-ribose

A — T

Phosphate group

Deoxy-ribose

C ··· G

Deoxy-ribose

(b)

Key to the bases:

A = Adenine
T = Thymine
C = Cytosine
G = Guanine

Figure S2-5 The DNA molecule. (*a*) The ribbons represent sugar–phosphate backbones, and the bases (A, T, C and G) are oriented toward the core. Note how the complementary strands twist around one another to form a helix. (*b*) Detail of two base pairs. A is bonded to T by two hydrogen bonds, and C and G share three hydrogen bonds.

which may result from ultraviolet light or other naturally occurring radiation. Mutations also result from medical radiation, chemical pollutants, and other causes directly linked to human society. In addition, some mutations result from rare errors in the process of DNA replication, as described below. Mutations can alter a cell's structure and function in profound ways, in much the same way that a change in a set of blueprints can alter the final form—and even the function—of a building. Although cells quickly repair many mutations, some cannot be fixed. These do not always cause harm because some affect segments of the DNA that are not used by the cell. Some mutations, however, are deleterious. In extreme cases they can kill cells in which they occur. In others they may result in cancer. Still others may benefit a cell, providing it with new properties that help it better cope with its environment—giving it an advantage over others. A bacterial cell, for example, might become better adapted to survive ultraviolet radiation. Mutations are the basis of evolution, which is discussed in detail in Chapter 2. In sexually reproducing organisms beneficial mutations in germ cells are necessary to produce adaptations in offspring. These confer a selective advantage over other members of the same species and will spread throughout the population in time. This process or genetic change may lead to a new species.

DNA Replication

The double helix is held together by fairly weak hydrogen bonds, mentioned above. As a cell prepares for division, it must duplicate all of its genetic material, so that each daughter cell has a full complement of genetic material to carry on its functions. To replicate, the DNA must unwind. A special enzyme causes the DNA to pull apart like a zipper opening. The individual strands are then used as templates to make new double-stranded molecules of DNA. In biology a template is a molecule on which another is formed. The DNA template (the original strand) dictates the sequence of bases on the new strand. This results from a simple biological fact: adenine bonds only with thymine and cytosine bonds only with guanine. Thus, when an adenine is present on the original strand, a thymine will be added to the growing new strand. When thymine is present on the original, an adenine will be added, and so on with guanine and cytosine. Because of this precise base pairing, the new strand is complementary to the original strand, and DNA's structure is preserved from generation to generation. Only mutations change the sequence. Each time a cell divides, the DNA molecule is replicated. The exact genetic information is passed from cell to cell, thus preserving the genetic code needed to operate the remarkable cellular factory.

How does the nucleus control cellular structure and function? The answer is simple: by regulating the production of proteins—both enzymes and structural proteins, those used to make parts of the cell such as the cell membrane. DNA is a blueprint for protein structure. All of the information required to make the 10,000 proteins your body needs is housed in it. Protein structure is held in the genetic code, determined by the sequence of bases in the DNA molecule.

The cell makes protein in its cytoplasm, but the DNA never escapes from its storage site, the nucleus. Therefore, to make a protein in the cytoplasm, another molecule must be used,

one that can carry the genetic information to the cytoplasm. That molecule is **RNA**, or **ribonucleic acid**. RNA is much like DNA; it contains a backbone of sugar and phosphates and contains bases, but it is single-stranded and able to leave the nucleus. RNA is produced in the nucleus on the DNA. DNA unwinds, just as it does when it replicates, but makes RNA on the template. In this way the genetic code housed in the nuclear DNA is transferred to a molecule appropriately named "messenger RNA," or mRNA. The synthesis of mRNA is called **transcription**. Just as you transcribe notes in a lecture, coverting the oral message into a written one, the RNA transcribes the information needed to make protein, from DNA to RNA.

Proteins are made of small molecules called **amino acids**, of which over 20 are known to science. Their general structure is shown in Figure S2-6. When many amino acid molecules are linked together in a chain, they form a polypeptide, and a protein consists of one or more polypeptides. Each protein has a unique sequence of amino acids; the sequence of amino acids in hemoglobin, for instance, is very different from the sequence of amino acids in muscle protein. Slight changes in the DNA base sequence can result in slight changes in a protein's amino acid sequence. Such changes may have profound effects on a protein's function and in many cases make proteins nonfunctional. The effects can be devastating in a cell.

As mentioned above, the sequence of amino acids in all proteins and polypeptides is determined by the sequence of bases in the mRNA (and, originally, the DNA). Protein is produced following the mRNA code in the cytoplasm. One amino acid is positioned along the mRNA at a time, until the entire protein is made. But this process is remarkably fast. Proteins with 200 or 300 amino acids can be assembled on mRNA molecules in a minute.

Thousands of mRNA molecules flow from the nucleus when a cell is actively producing protein. Some of the protein produced on the mRNA is used to make the parts of the cell, such as protein in the cell membrane; many other proteins are **enzymes**, molecules that speed up cellular reactions. Ultimately, these enzymes control the thousands of biochemical reactions that take place in cells.

But how does the cell control enzyme production? Basically, there are two feedback mechanisms that operate on the DNA. (Feedback was discussed in Chapter 1.) In some metabolic pathways enzyme production is increased when intracellular supplies of a necessary biochemical fall below required levels. Through an elaborate process the genetic material switches on and produces the necessary enzymes to catalyze the reaction that will yield the needed product. This keeps concentrations at required levels. Other metabolic pathways do just the opposite. When levels of an important biochemical build up, mRNA production is halted, and so is enzyme production. This allows the cell to use up the excess material. In either case the cell maintains enzyme production to give it optimal levels of all necessary biochemicals.

Genes

DNA is found in chromosomes. Figure S2-7, taken from a cell just before cellular division, shows them as dark-staining bodies. Throughout most of the cell's life cycle, however, chromosomes

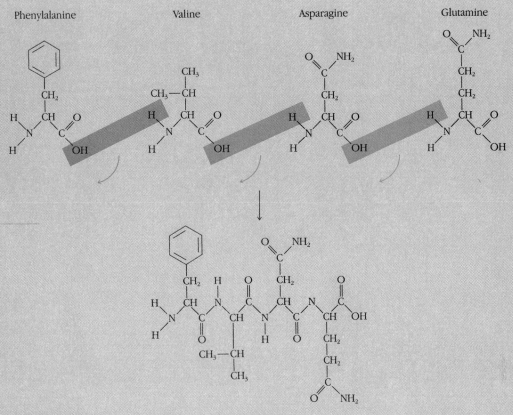

Phenylalanine   Valine   Asparagine   Glutamine

Figure S2-6 Amino acids are linked by covalent bonds, called peptide bonds, to form a protein.

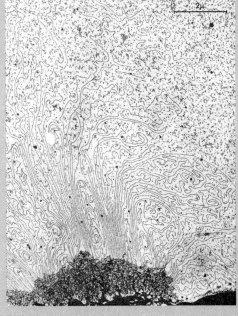

Figure S2-7 Electron micrographs of a chromosome (*a*) just before cellular division, and (*b*) unraveled.

are found unraveled in the nucleus in thin strands made of DNA and closely associated protein (Figure S2-7). In the unraveled form the chromosomes can unzip to form RNA and DNA. They are only visible with powerful electron microscopes.

Each unraveled chromosome contains a double-stranded DNA molecule which codes for thousands of proteins. A segment of the DNA that codes for a specific protein is called a **structural gene**. Each DNA strand contains thousands of structural genes, each containing the information for a different protein. All told there are an estimated 100,000 genes in each of our cells.

Structural genes are controlled by segments of the DNA called **regulatory genes**. Therefore, both regulatory and structural genes work together. Chemical substances turn the genes on and off. In a bacterial cell, for example, an increase in the concentration of lactose (a type of sugar) turns on the regulatory genes, causing the cell to make enzymes needed to break lactose apart and get out its energy.

Genes and Evolution

The first cells to emerge on earth were probably bacterialike. Simple when compared with a cell in your body, bacteria nonetheless represented a major evolutionary breakthrough. Bacteria have one chromosome—one strand of DNA in circular form. That strand holds the secret of life. It provides a way for life to proceed in an ordered fashion, to make more of itself accurately and reliably.

Consider the protocells that gave rise to the bacteria, discussed in Chapter 2. They were amalgamations of large molecules that formed globules and acted like cells. When one grew to a certain size, it split and broke into two new parts that grew and divided. In time, DNA must have arisen. That chance happening, many millions of years in the making, revolutionized the evolutionary process. No longer was the organism a mere passive blob of biochemicals that could survive only if the proper chemicals were available to it. With the advent of DNA life found a mechanisim to control its structure and function. It could now fashion itself from the environment. Life became an active process. The success of a species was locked in its DNA, not totally dependent on what was available from the environment.

DNA represented life's first real successful effort to control the environment. By random mutations, the code of life can change and get better, but only with the helpful hand of natural selection. So here arose a biological proving ground—tests and retests to fit an organism into the environment and allow new species to form to meet changing conditions. Through this interaction of genes and the environment evolution continues something that began billions of years ago: that inexorable flourishing of life on a once-barren land mass.

Suggested Readings

Campbell, Neil A. (1987). *Biology*. Menlo Park, CA: Benjamin/Cummings.

Principles of Ecology: Ecosystem Structure and Function

Never does nature say one thing, and wisdom another.

Juvenal

An urban dweller awakens to the buzz of his alarm clock, eats a hurried breakfast, and heads to the concrete, steel, and glass towers of Downtown, U.S.A. Bumper to bumper on the ten-lane highway, encased in his shiny automobile, he listens to the radio to quell his mounting tension. After half an hour on the freeway he parks his car and rides the elevator to his 15th-floor office.

Sitting back in his chair, looking out at the skyscrapers and the paved arteries bringing more office workers like him to the city, he entertains only vague notions of nature. To him, ecology may mean recycling aluminum cans or turning off the lights to save energy, activities he hasn't the time or the inclination to do. His connection with the environment is obscured by business reports to prepare, bills to pay, college educations to plan for, and a myriad of annoying chores around his suburban home. He does not think of himself as a part of the natural environment, subject to the rules and constraints that govern all living organisms. Why should he? Everything around him—his air-conditioned office, the city skyline, his home, even the carefully tended park across the street—bespeaks human mastery over nature.

Albert Camus wrote, "Man is the only creature that refuses to be what he is." It is too tempting to think of ourselves as apart from, and even above, nature. It is too easy to think that technology has made us immune to the rules that govern all living organisms. In the words of the ecologist Raymond Dasmann, however, "A human apart from environment is an abstraction—in reality no such thing exists." We humans are very much a part of the environment. Our lives are rooted in the soil and dependent on the air, water, plants, and algae. They are subject to the ecological rules that govern all the earth's living things.

This book will show how dependent we are on the earth and the myriad forms of life that share the planet with us. This chapter and the next, which examine ecology, can help you understand the danger of breaking the rules of nature.

Strictly speaking, **ecology** is the study of living organisms and their relationship to one another and to the environment. Ecology takes the entire living world as its domain, in an attempt to understand all organism–environment interactions. Given the vast number of organisms in the world, the realm of ecology is immense.

How Is the Living World Organized?

Our study of ecology will begin with a look at the way life is organized on earth, starting on a grand scale and successively focusing in on the smaller organizational patterns.

The Biosphere

The part of the earth that supports life is called the **biosphere**, or **ecosphere**. As shown in Figure 3-1, the biosphere extends from the floor of the ocean, approximately 11,000 meters (36,000 feet) below the surface, to the tops of the highest mountains, about 9000 meters 30,000 feet) above sea level. If the earth were the size of an apple, the biosphere would be a thin layer only about as thick as its skin.

Life forms are scarce at the far extremes of the biosphere: on the highest mountaintops only inert spores of bacteria and fungi can be found, and on the deep ocean floor few organisms can survive. Life evolved under more moderate conditions than the biospheric extremes, and it is in these conditions that most species thrive. The zone of abundance is a narrow band extending less than 200 meters (660 feet) below the surface of the ocean to about 6,000 meters (20,000 feet) above sea level.

Life exists mostly at the intersection of land (lithosphere), air (atmosphere), and water (hydrosphere), as shown in Figure 3-2. And from these vast domains come the ingredients that make life possible—minerals from the soil, oxygen and carbon dioxide from the air, and water from oceans and lakes. Put these ingredients in a test tube, however, and you have simply a mixture of air, water, and soil. But when these molecules are uniquely organized in living things they produce a fascinating array of shapes and forms that—among other things—grow, reproduce, and respond to various stimuli.

The biosphere—this living skin of planet earth—is, in many ways, like a sealed terrarium. If carefully set up with soil, water, plants, and a snail or two, a terrarium operates without interference with the lid sealed shut; water is reused over and over, as are minerals. Plant growth is trimmed back by hungry snails, who also consume the oxygen the plants release. Carbon dioxide from the snails is taken up by plants and used in photosynthesis to make more plant life. In short, the terrarium is a sustainable system, less complicated but much like the biosphere, which recycles water, oxygen, carbon, and other substances over and over, in a perpetual cycle. Only one thing must come from the outside for life to continue, in the terrarium and in the biosphere: sunlight.

Because the biosphere recycles all matter, it is called a **closed system**. The closed nature of the biosphere makes all species throughout all time cousins of sorts; the muscle tissue in your arm may contain carbon atoms that were part of the muscle of Julius Caesar or a plant growing in his garden. The tear in your eye may have been a tear in Napoleon's eye at Waterloo or a raindrop that fell on ancient hunters and gatherers. Those same atoms may be part of the great leaders or ordinary citizens of a society living centuries in the future.

The first law we glean from our study of ecology is that life on earth is possible only because of recycling. It is a lesson no species must learn except human beings. It is a rule, many ecologists believe, that we humans break at our peril and the peril of those yet to come.

Biomes

The terrestrial portion of the biosphere is divided into **biomes**, enormous regions characterized by climate, vegetation, animal life, and general soil type. A dozen biomes spread over millions of square kilometers and span entire continents (Figure 3-3).

Climate, the average weather conditions in a given region, determines the boundaries of a biome and the abundance of plants and animals found in it. Climatic conditions also determine the adaptations found in all living things within a biome. The most important climatic factors are precipitation and temperature (Figure 3-4). (For more details on biomes see Chapter Supplement 3-1.)

Aquatic Life Zones

The sea is also divided into more or less distinct zones, including coral reefs, estuaries, the deep ocean, and con-

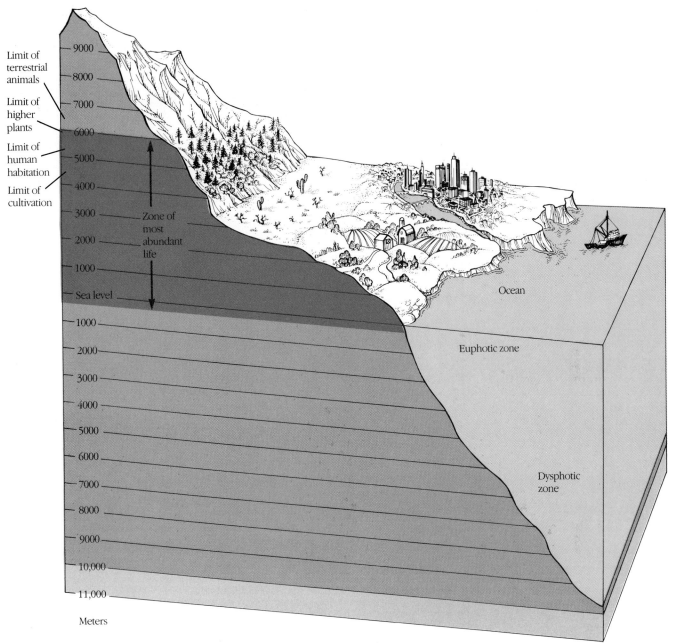

Figure 3-1 Vertical dimensions of the biosphere. Life exists in a broad band extending from the highest mountain peaks to the depths of the ocean. However, life at the extremes is rare, and most organisms are restricted to the narrow zone shown here.

tinental shelves. These are regions of different plant and animal life. The major differences among them can be traced back to levels of dissolved nutrients, water temperature, depth of sunlight penetration, and other environmental factors.

The aquatic life zones vary widely in their abundance and diversity of life. The richest areas in the ocean are generally those where land and sea meet, the **estuarine zone**. This zone includes **estuaries**, the mouths of rivers or inlets where salt and fresh water mix, and **coastal wetlands**, including mangrove swamps, salt marshes, and lagoons. In the estuarine zone nutrients from upstream soil erosion support a rich and diverse group of microorganisms, insects, and fish. So rich is this region that it is often likened to the tropical rain forest. (For more information on estuaries and wetlands see Chapter Supplement 10-1). The open ocean, in contrast, is relatively barren and is sometimes likened to the deserts.

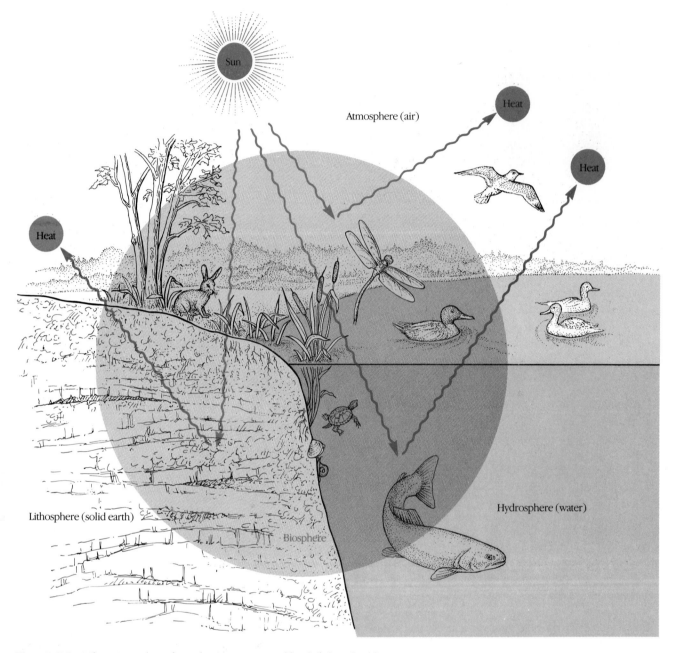

Figure 3-2 Life exists primarily at the intersection of land (lithosphere), air (atmosphere), and water (hydrosphere). As shown here, the biosphere is energized by sunlight.

Ecosystems

Ecologists invented the word **ecosystem**, an abbreviated form of **ecological system**, to describe a network consisting of organisms, their environment, and all of the interactions that exist in that environment. In short, the ecosystem is an interdependent and dynamic (ever-changing) biological, physical, and chemical system.

The biosphere is a global ecosystem. Because it is too complex to study, ecologists generally limit their view to smaller regions, setting up more manageable boundaries. For the sake of simplicity an ecosystem might be a pond, a cornfield, a river, a field, a terrarium, or a small clearing in the forest. Accordingly, ecosystems vary considerably in complexity, too. Some may be quite simple—for example, a rock with lichens growing on it. Others, like the

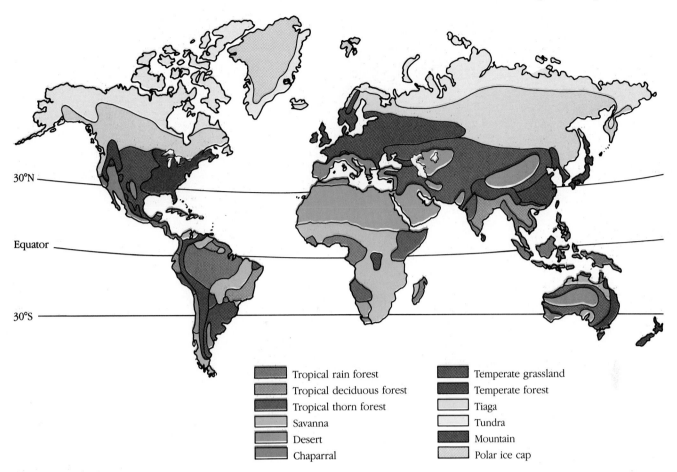

30°N

Equator

30°S

Tropical rain forest
Tropical deciduous forest
Tropical thorn forest
Savanna
Desert
Chaparral

Temperate grassland
Temperate forest
Tiaga
Tundra
Mountain
Polar ice cap

Figure 3-3 The earth's major biomes.

tropical rain forests, are quite complex. They contain an abundance of living organisms and a wide variety of species as well.

On your walks through forests and fields or even your drives in the country, you have probably noticed that adjacent ecosystems merge with one another, often without clear boundaries. For example, the edge of many mountain meadows is a zone that is half forest and half meadow, creating a unique mixture of plant and animal species. These transition zones, found between virtually all adjoining ecosystems, are called **ecotones**. Animals and plants of adjacent ecosystems intermingle in the ecotone. In addition, the ecotone supports many species not found in either of the adjacent ecosystems. These species are uniquely adapted to the conditions found there. As a result, ecotones generally have a greater number of species than surrounding areas and deserve special protection.

To gain a better understanding of the ecosystem, let us look at the two major components of all ecosystems: abiotic and biotic.

Abiotic Factors The **abiotic**, or nonliving, **factors** of an ecosystem are its physical and chemical components, for example, rainfall, temperature, sunlight, and nutrient supplies. Each of the earth's many organisms is finely tuned (through adaptations) to its environment and operates within a range of chemical and physical conditions, the **range of tolerance** (Figure 3-5). When the upper or lower limits of this range are exceeded, survival becomes difficult and often impossible. Fish, for example, generally tolerate a narrow range of water temperature. If the water cools below the lower limits of their range of tolerance, they will die or escape to warmer water. Water temperatures exceeding their upper limits of tolerance may also cause death or flight.

Even though organisms are affected by all of the chemical and physical factors of their surroundings, one factor usually outweighs the others in determining growth. It is, therefore, called a **limiting factor**. The concept of limiting factors was introduced in 1840 by the German scientist Justus von Liebig, who was studying the effects of chemical nutrients on plant growth. The limiting factor

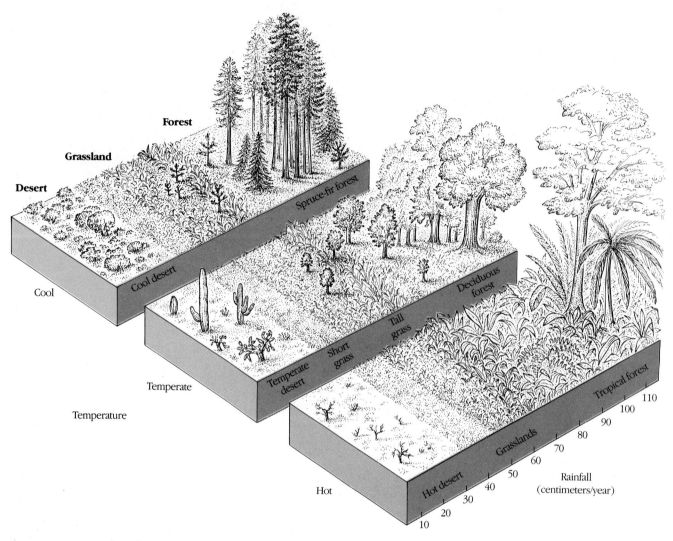

Figure 3-4 The relationship between rainfall, temperature, and vegetation. Rainfall determines the basic type of vegetation, and temperature is responsible for alterations in this basic type.

is the primary determinant of growth in an ecosystem, because it easily falls below the range of tolerance of key organisms. In certain aquatic ecosystems, for instance, phosphorus is a limiting factor. It is the first nutrient to be used up. When phosphorus is reduced, the growth of algae is impaired. Nitrate can also be a limiting factor in water or soil. A clean body of water can turn green overnight with algae, for instance, if nitrate-containing detergents from a sewage treatment plant flow into it.

The limiting factor is analogous to the slowest elephant in an African expedition. The entire party's pace through the jungle is set by this slowest elephant. In the same fashion, the entire structure of an ecosystem is determined by the limiting factor. Should the slowest elephant die, a new pace would be set by the second-slowest one. This same is true in ecosystems. An increase in the avail-

ability of a limiting factor allows accelerated growth, but new limits are invariably set by another factor.

For most terrestrial ecosystems rainfall is *the* limiting factor. As we saw in Figure 3-4, rainfall determines whether land is covered by forest, grassland, or desert. If annual rainfall exceeds 70 to 80 centimeters (27 to 31 inches), for example, forests develop. Slightly drier climates support grasslands, and the driest regions are always desert.

Differences in temperature are responsible for variations on these three basic themes (Figure 3-4). Take the wettest ecosystems as an example. Warm, wet climates support tropical rain forests with huge trees reaching 60 meters (200 feet) into the air. Slightly cooler regions are characterized by deciduous forests. In areas that are even cooler, coniferous forests grow.

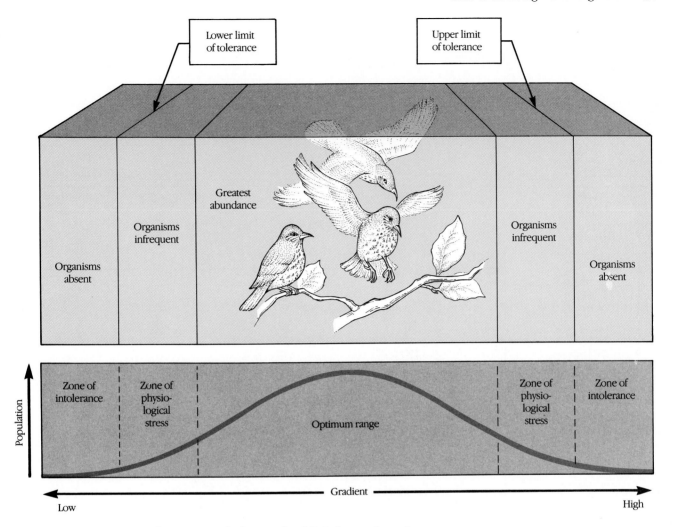

Figure 3-5 Each organism has a range of tolerance for abiotic factors. It survives within this range and can be killed by shifts below or above the range.

Biotic Factors The **biotic components** of an ecosystem are its living things—fungi, plants, animals, and microorganisms (Figure 3-6). Organisms live in **populations**, groups of the same species occupying a given region. Populations are dynamic groups, changing in size, age structure, and genetic composition in correspondence to changes in the environment.

When several populations live together, they form a **community**, a mix of species interacting on many different levels (Figure 3-6). Some organisms form predator–prey relationships. Other work together, each benefiting from the association.

Habitat and Niche

If you were to describe yourself to a foreigner, you would probably begin with where you live. Then you might tell what you do, who your friends (and enemies) are, how you interact with others, and what you do in your spare time. If you asked an ecologist studying armadillos to describe them, she would probably follow a similiar approach, first telling you where these armored minitanks live and then what they do. Where an organism lives is its **habitat**. Where it lives and how it fits into the ecosystem are its **ecological niche**, or simply its **niche**. To describe an organism's niche requires that we tell what it eats, what eats it, where it lives, and how it interacts with other living and nonliving components of the ecosystem. It's no easy task.

No two species occupy the same niche, but similar species living in the same habitat often have similar lifestyles. Consider the red-tailed hawk and the great horned owl. On the surface these species may seem quite similar, maybe identical. Hawks and owls both prey on mice and·

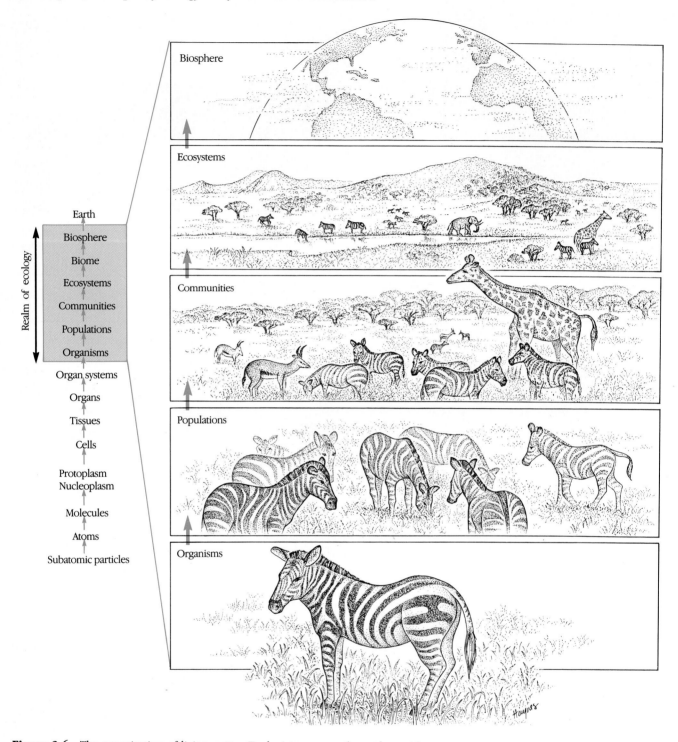

Figure 3-6   The organization of living matter. Ecologists concern themselves with the study of individual organisms, populations, and communities as well as ecosystems and the biosphere.

other rodents. They live in trees. But owls generally live in dense forests and come out at night to feed, whereas hawks prefer daytime hunting. Despite their apparent similarities, therefore, these species occupy slightly different niches. The evolution of species to fit different

niches has two beneficial effects: First, it reduces competition for limited resources by members of different species (**interspecific competition**). Second, it makes full use of environmental resources.

Because no two species occupy the same niche, two

(a)

(b)

Figure 3-7 *(a)* The koala is a specialist, for it eats only the leaves of eucalyptus trees. A loss of this food source would result in its extinction. *(b)* The coyote is a generalist. Like humans, it is an opportunist, capable of eating a wide variety of foods. Its existence is not so delicately balanced.

similar species can coexist in a given habitat without threatening each other's survival. For example, elk and deer live in the same habitat in the Rocky Mountains. But elk feed primarily on grasses and herbaceous plants, whereas deer feed primarily on shrubs.

The practical lesson of the **exclusion principle**, as it is called, is that two species cannot occupy the same niche without drastic consequences. This is another important law of ecology with important implications for wildlife officials, who in seeking to increase hunting opportunities may introduce species into an environment that come in direct conflict with existing species because of identical or extensively overlapping niches. Such species are called **ecological equivalents**.

In general, an organism's niche may be generalized or specialized. Take the koala of Australia and the coyote of North America as examples. The koala is a specialist that feeds exclusively on eucalyptus leaves. Without them it would surely perish (Figure 3-7a). The coyote, on the other hand, feeds on a wide variety of animals—rodents, rabbits, ground-nesting birds, snakes, and an occasional sheep (Figure 3-7b). The coyote occupies a wide range of habitats, too, unlike the koala. Because of its versatility the coyote is considered a generalist. Human beings, like coyotes, are generalists in many ways. We live in diverse climates and eat a wide variety of plants and animals.

Generalists tend to be less subject to changes in the abiotic and biotic environment and, therefore, are less apt to become extinct. Should a food source disappear, a generalist will not suffer. Specialists, on the other hand, walk a tightrope. Their existence may easily be threatened by the loss of a single food supply. Today the giant panda of China is threatened by a loss of its sole food source, the bamboo.

Although humans are generalists, our recent evolutionary history has been marked by increasing specialization. Today, for example, we depend on a handful of metals, a relatively small number of crops and livestock species, and a few energy sources. If supplies of any of these should be cut off, catastrophe could follow. Avoiding such hardship, many experts believe, requires us to build a future less dependent on nonrenewable (depletable) resources. Almost certainly renewable substitutes must be found to provide energy, building materials, and raw materials for the many chemicals we use. Avoiding hardship also requires us to protect our vast biological resources, for example, the genetic stock of the tropics, from which many of our important cultivated crops once came (Chapters 7 and 8). It requires us to manage our forests and grasslands well, and to protect commercial fish species (Chapter 9). More than ever we are learning that protecting these biological resources means reducing air and water pollution (Chapters 14–18).

How Do Ecosystems Work?

In this section we turn our attention to how ecosystems function. We will see how producers and consumers are related in an ecosystem and how energy and chemical nutrients flow through the biosphere.

◄ *Viewpoint*

Ecology or Egology?

Peter Russell

The author has been closely involved with the development of the Learning Methods Group, an international organization that helps people make fuller use of their mental potential. His books include The TM Technique, The Brain Book, Meditation, *and* The Global Brain, *which presents an optimistic vision of our long-term future.*

The environmental sciences usually focus on understanding the many intricate relationships and interdependencies that have evolved between the millions of living systems inhabiting the earth. Rather than looking further into the many facets of these sciences, I wish to explore this question: "Why are such studies necessary in the first place? Why is it that one species out of millions can disrupt the natural balance in so many ways and with such dire consequences?"

The rapid and liberal development of technology is clearly part of the problem. *Homo sapiens* has always been a manipulative species. A million years ago, long before civilization appeared, our opposable thumbs and large brain would have singled us out as the creature most capable of modifying its environment. In more recent history technology has amplified this capacity, and to such an extent that today one person's decision may have global repercussions.

Yet it is also clear that technological might is not the sole cause of environmental mismanagement. It is ultimately human beings who choose how to use technology, and they initiate the actions that result in ecological disturbances. In some cases the disturbance is totally unforeseen. In other cases we may already realize that a certain approach could lead to trouble. But somehow those concerned are able to ignore the warning or, worse, seek evidence to the contrary, displaying an apparent lack of care for other species, the biosystem as a whole, and, paradoxically, their own long-term welfare. How is it that people can adhere to policies that by nearly all projections look suicidal?

Such behavior stems from individuals' not seeing beyond their short-term welfare and from their perceiving their interests to be different from the interests of humanity as a whole. For most people an immediate personal fulfillment is more attractive than some distant long-term benefit, and so they naturally go for the former. Education and social controls may help curb the pull of immediate gratification, but the pull is so strong that these are unlikely to be sufficient. But what is it that makes us want to satisfy our short-term needs to the detriment of our long-term welfare? The answer appears to lie deep within our psyche.

In the more developed nations—and it is these nations that are responsible for the major environmental issues of today—the basic needs for food, clothing, shelter, and health care are fairly well attended to. What emerges then is the need for psychological welfare, in particular, the need to be liked. For many of us the major source of our personal identity lies in our interactions with other people. We need people to recognize and reaffirm our worth, and we spend considerable time and effort fulfilling this need. Much of our activity is really a search for personal reinforcement (what are often termed "positive psychological strokes"). Some psychologists estimate that as much as 80% of all our actions may be motivated by this search. And when people stand back and listen to themselves, they often find that as much as 90% of their casual conversation is prompted by this need for approval. The need to be liked has become one of our most powerful drives.

One of the most common ways we try to win approval and prestige is through material possessions. We collect many of the various accoutrements of modern living—new cars, fashionable clothes, expensive furniture, gourmet (and gourmand) diets—not because we need them physically but because we need them psychologically.

This might not be so bad if our various possessions satiated our psychological needs; but they don't. Our insecurity is rooted far deeper in our psyche than that. Instead of spotting the obvious flaw, we search for yet more things in the outer world that we hope might fill the inner gap.

Some implications of this for the way we treat the environment are obvious. We gobble up irreplaceable resources, with little regard for the long-term future, partly because the various products they are transformed into may briefly satisfy our search for identity. Thus, the consumers are as much exploiters of the environment as are the corporations who reflect the market needs.

Yet there is more to it than that. We do have choices in how we satisfy our misguided search for material well-being. We might even be able to do so in ecologically sane ways. Ultimately there are people somewhere making decisions to exploit this or that particular resource, initiate industrial processes with various environmental effects, and set in motion other activities that in one way or another upset the ecological balance. And such people are usually motivated by similar needs for approval and recognition from their peers, by the need to play the game they have chosen without losing face, and by the mistaken belief that financial security brings inner security. They are caught in the same trap as everyone else. The only difference is that they are more visible.

Another profound consequence of our inner insecurity is a lack of true caring and compassion, either for others or for the environment. Each of us, at our core, is a compassionate being capable of deep empathy and caring. If we can get back in contact with this deeper self, we can begin to experience compassion not only for other people but also for the rest of the world.

One way we block compassion is through arrogance, and one of the most dominant forms of arrogance in the Western world is scientific. The very rapid growth of a diversity of sciences has resulted in the belief that we now know how the world works and can therefore apply our considerable manipulative might with safety. Yet in most cases we have foreseen only a tiny proportion of the long-term effects of our actions. There is probably no way we as individual human beings can fully understand the complex workings and intricate balances of all the living systems on this planet. Letting go of our self-gratifying patterns of behavior, we find not only compassion but humility. We rediscover respect for the unfathomable complexity of life on earth and for all its many species.

To summarize, the environmental sciences, laudable as they are, will remain incomplete until they take account of the human psychology that gives rise to their necessity. We need to consider not just the totality of all the systems constituting the biosphere but also the larger system that includes the human psyche and its current shortcomings. The only approach that will be successful in the long term is one that attends both to the external environment and to the internal environment, the system we call "I."

Food Chains and Food Webs

In the biological world you are one of two things, either a producer or a consumer. (Only rarely can you be both). **Producers** are the organisms that support the entire living world through photosynthesis. Plants, algae, and cyanobacteria are the key producers of energy-rich organic materials. They are also called **autotrophs** (from the Greek root "troph"—to feed, nourish), because they literally nourish themselves photosynthetically—that is, by using sunlight and atmospheric carbon dioxide to make the food materials they need to survive. **Consumers** feed on plants and other organisms and are called **heterotrophs**, because they are nourished by consuming other organisms.

Consumer organisms that feed exclusively on plants are called **herbivores**. Cattle, deer, elk, and tomato hornworms are examples. Those consumers that feed exclusively on other animals, such as the mountain lion, are **carnivores**. Those consumers, such as humans, bears, and raccoons, that feed on both plants and animals are **omnivores**.

The interconnections among producers and consumers are visible all around us. Mice living in and around our homes, for example, eat the seeds of domestic and wild plants and, in turn, are preyed on by cats and hawks.

A series of oranisms, each feeding on the preceding one, forms a **food chain** (Figure 3-8). Two basic types of food chains exist in nature: grazer and decomposer. **Grazer food chains**, like the one discussed above, are so named because they start with plants and with grazers, organisms that feed on plants. Figure 3-8 illustrates familiar terrestrial and aquatic grazer food chains.

In the second type—the **decomposer**, or **detritus**, **food chain**—organic waste material is the major food source (Figure 3-9). This waste comes from plants and animals and is consumed on two levels. In the grasslands of Africa, for instance, a wildebeest that dies of old age is consumed by vultures, hyenas, and the larvae of various flies. These are called **detritus feeders**. The actual process of decomposition is carred out primarily by microscopic bacteria and fungi, known as **microconsumers**. All of these organisms, microscopic or not, derive energy and essential organic building blocks from detritus. In the process they liberate carbon dioxide, water, and other nutrients needed by plants to make more plant material and maintain the perpetual cycle.

Food chains are conduits for the flow of energy and nutrients through ecosystems. The sun's energy is first captured by plants and stored in organic molecules, which then pass through the grazer and decomposer food chains. In addition, plants incorporate a variety of inorganic materials such as nitrogen, phosphorus, and magnesium from the soil. These **chemical nutrients** become part of the plant's living matter. When the green plant is consumed, these nutrients enter the food chain. They are eventually returned to the environment by the decomposer food chain.

Classifying Consumers Biologists are avid namers, happiest when things are categorized, tagged, and dissected. The study of ecology has not been spared this obsession. For instance, ecologists categorize consumers by their position in the food chain (Figure 3-10). In a grazer food chain, for example, herbivores are called **primary consumers**, since they are the first organisms to consume the plants. Organisms that feed on primary consumers are **secondary consumers**, and so on.

The feeding level an organism occupies in a food chain is called the **trophic level**. The **first trophic level** marks

Figure 3-8   Examples of grazer food chains occurring on land and in water.

the beginning of the food chain and is made up of the producers or autotrophs (self-feeders). Primary consumers occupy the **second trophic level**, and secondary, tertiary, and quaternary consumers occupy the third, fourth, and fifth trophic levels, respectively. All consumers are heterotrophs. Figure 3-10 shows an example of a food chain broken down into trophic levels.

Food chains exist only on the pages of ecology texts;

(a) Decomposer Food Chain

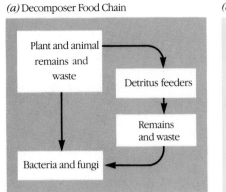

(b) Grazing Food Chain   Decomposer Food Chain

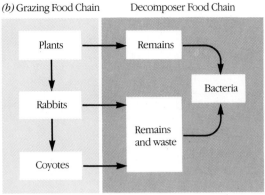

Figure 3-9 (*a*) Decomposer food chain. Bacteria and other organisms feed on plant and animal remains. (*b*) Link between the grazer and the decomposer food chains.

in reality, virtually all food chains are woven into a much more complex network called a **food web**. The food web gives a complete picture of who eats whom (Figure 3-11).

Trophic levels can be assigned in food webs just as in food chains; in a food web, however, many species occupy more than one trophic level. As illustrated in Figure 3-12, a grizzly bear feeding on berries and roots is acting as a primary consumer; it occupies the second trophic level. When feeding on marmots, an animal similar to the woodchuck, however, the grizzly is considered a secondary consumer and occupies the third trophic level. In other instances a grizzly may feed on insect-eating chipmunks. It thus occupies the fourth trophic level.

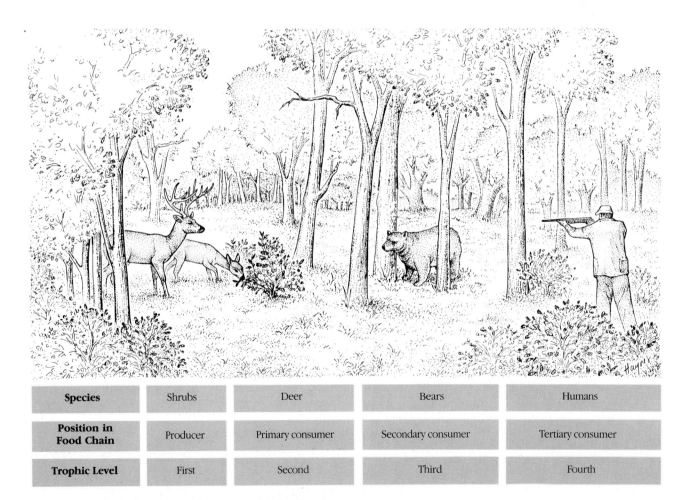

Species	Shrubs	Deer	Bears	Humans
Position in Food Chain	Producer	Primary consumer	Secondary consumer	Tertiary consumer
Trophic Level	First	Second	Third	Fourth

Figure 3-10 Grazer food chain, showing trophic levels.

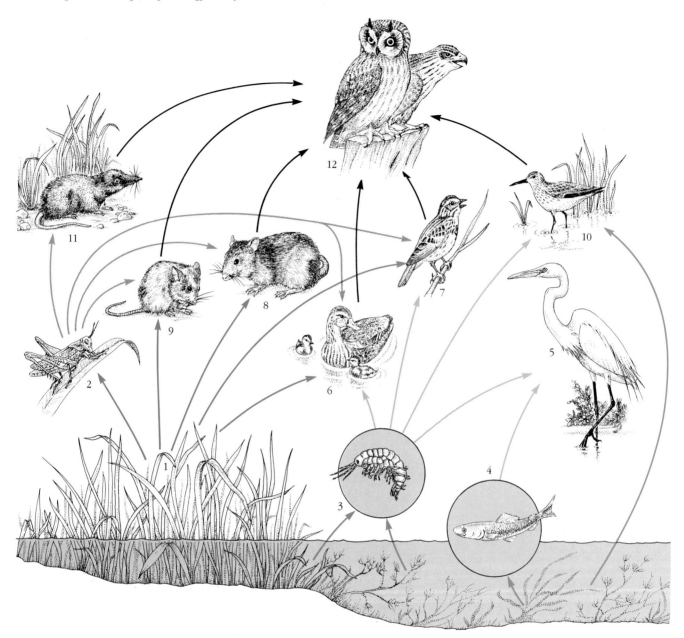

Figure 3-11 A simplified food web, showing the relationships between
producers and consumers. In a salt marsh (San Francisco Bay area), producer
organisms (1) terrestrial and salt marsh plants, are consumed by herbivorous
invertebrates, represented by the grasshopper and the snail (2). The marine plants
are consumed by herbivorous marine and intertidal invertebrates (3). Fish,
represented by smelt and anchovy (4) feed on vegetative matter from both
terrestrial and marine environments. The fish in turn are eaten by first-level
carnivores, represented by the great blue heron and the common egret (5).
Continuing through the food web, we have the following omnivores: clapper rail
and mallard duck (6); savannah and song sparrows (7); Norway rat (8); California
vole and salt marsh harvest mouse (9); and eastern and western sandpipers (10).
The vagrant shrew (11) is a first-level carnivore, while the top carnivores (second
level) are the marsh hawk and the short–eared owl (12).

Grizzly

Elk

Grasses

Berries
Roots

Chipmunk

Insects

Marmot

Grass

Figure 3-12 The grizzly eats widely from the food web. When individual food chains are drawn separately, this becomes evident.

Trophic level

Fourth			Grizzly
Third		Grizzly	Chipmunk
Second	Grizzly	Elk Marmot	Insects
First	Berries and Roots Grasses	Grasses	Grasses

The Flow of Energy and Matter through Ecosystems

In the previous section we saw that photosynthetic organisms such as plants are the starting point of all food chains, because they alone are capable of tapping the sun, the ultimate source of energy for all ecosystems. But plants capture very little of the energy that the sun transmits to earth—only 1% or 2% (Figure 3-13). Still, on this small fraction of the sunlight is built the entire living world. In this section we study the flow of energy and matter through ecosystems. But first let's take a brief look at energy.

What Is Energy? Energy and love. We are all familiar with the terms, but we still stumble when trying to define them. One of the reasons is that, like *amour*, energy comes in many forms. Heat, light, sound, electricity, coal, oil, natural gas, mechanical energy, geothermal energy, wind, nuclear power, hydroelectric power, and magnetic energy are some of the more familiar ones. As different as these forms of energy are, however, they have one thing in common: the capacity to do work. To a physicist, then, **energy** is defined as the capacity to do work. **Work** is performed on an object—be it a mountain or a mole hill—when it is moved over some distance.

All forms of energy fall into two groups: potential and kinetic. **Potential energy** is stored energy—energy stored in coal, oil, or even the food you eat. When released, it can perform work. **Kinetic energy**, in contrast, is the energy possessed by objects in motion. A falling rock and a swinging hammer can do work and, therefore, are said to possess kinetic energy.

All forms of energy follow basic laws, called the **laws of thermodynamics**. Understanding these laws will help you understand ecology and many current environmental issues.

Figure 3-13 Distribution of incoming solar radiation. Note that plants absorb only a small fraction.

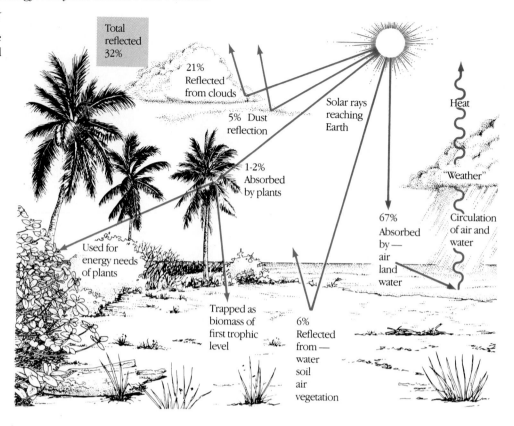

Total reflected 32%

21% Reflected from clouds

5% Dust reflection

Solar rays reaching Earth

Heat

"Weather"

Circulation of air and water

1-2% Absorbed by plants

67% Absorbed by — air land water

Used for energy needs of plants

Trapped as biomass of first trophic level

6% Reflected from — water soil air vegetation

The First Law The **first law of thermodynamics** is often called the law of **conservation of energy**. It states that energy can be neither created nor destroyed but only be transformed from one form to another.

Let's look at a familiar example. The gasoline in your car contains an enormous amount of potential energy that, when released in combustion, speeds your car—of course, not over 55 miles per hour—down the highway. As you drive along, the gas gauge shows how much gasoline you have burned. Contrary to what you may think, however, you have not destroyed that energy. Instead, you have converted it into other forms—electricity to run your radio and windshield wipers, heat to keep you warm and defrost your windows, light to show you where you are going, and, of course, mechanical movements that propel your car along the highway. Careful measurement of the amount of energy your car was consuming and the amount of energy being produced in these various forms would show that the two were equal. In simple terms, energy input is equal to energy output.

The first law has some important implications in our lives. Most importantly, it opens our eyes to a simple fact: it takes energy to get energy. In an oil-shale operation, for example, a third of a barrel of oil is needed to produce a single barrel of shale oil. In any system, whether it is a car or coal mine, energy input and output are equal. But some of the energy output is in an unusable form—heat.

In the case of oil shale what we get out of the system is exactly equal to what we put into it. Energy was not created, nor was it destroyed. However, only two-thirds of what we get out is in a usable form—oil. To some ecologists the first law says, "You can't get something for nothing."

The Second Law The first law deals with energy conversion and involves quantities—energy inputs and outputs. The second law also deals with energy conversion, but it involves a different aspect of energy—its quality.

More specifically, the **second law of thermodynamics** explains what happens to energy quality when energy changes from one form to another. The law simply states that energy is "degraded" during such conversions (Figure 3-14). Another way of saying this is that energy goes from a concentrated to a less concentrated form during a transformation. For example, when gasoline is burned in an automobile, it is converted from a very concentrated form to much less concentrated heat, which is no longer available for useful work. Concentrated energy forms are said to have a great deal of **available work**. The less concentrated forms have a lower capacity and are said to have less available work.

The second law of thermodynamics has many implications for our lives. It tells us that when we burn fossil fuels, our supply of highly concentrated energy (our finite

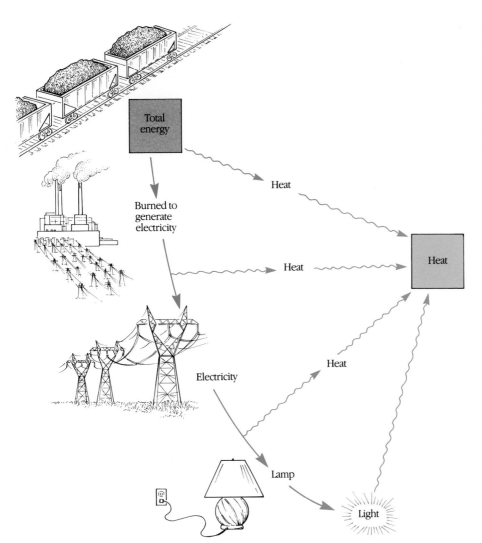

Figure 3-14 Second law of thermodynamics. During energy transformations the amount of useful work diminishes as we go from high-quality (concentrated) energy forms to low-quality (less concentrated) energy forms.

fossil fuel reserve) shrinks. It tells us also that we cannot recycle high-quality energy, because when it is burned it is dissipated into heat and lost into space. And it warns us not to waste this precious resource; the source we now tap is all that we have.

Biomass and Ecological Pyramids The laws of thermodynamics go much further. They rule the living world, from the tiniest bacterium to the largest whale. They limit ecosystems, as you will soon see, and can be used to guide us along a sustainable pathway. They can bring common sense to our politics and help us avoid foolish economic mistakes. Let us look at the implications of these laws from an ecological perspective. We will begin with the concept **biomass**.

Biomass is organic matter created by plants and other photosynthetic organisms and passed up the food chain. The biomass at the first trophic level in almost all ecosystems represents a large amount of potential (chemical) energy and tissue-building materials for the second trophic level. Studies of ecosystems show, however, that not all of the biomass of the first trophic level is converted into biomass in the second trophic level (Figure 3-15). In other words, not all plant matter becomes animal matter. Several reasons can be given for this fact. The first is that only a small part of the plant matter in any given ecosystem is eaten by organisms of the next higher level, a shown in Figure 3-15. Second, not all of the biomass eaten by the herbivores is digested; some passes through the gastrointestinal tract unchanged and is excreted. Third, most of what is digested is broken down into carbon dioxide, water, and the energy used to move about, to breathe, and to maintain body temperature. The second law of thermodynamics tells us that this energy is converted into heat, which is dissipated into the environment and is eventually lost into space.

Because of these factors the biomass of the second trophic level is greatly reduced. In fact, only 5% to 20% of the first trophic level's biomass is passed to the second trophic level. Subsequent transfers of biomass to succes-

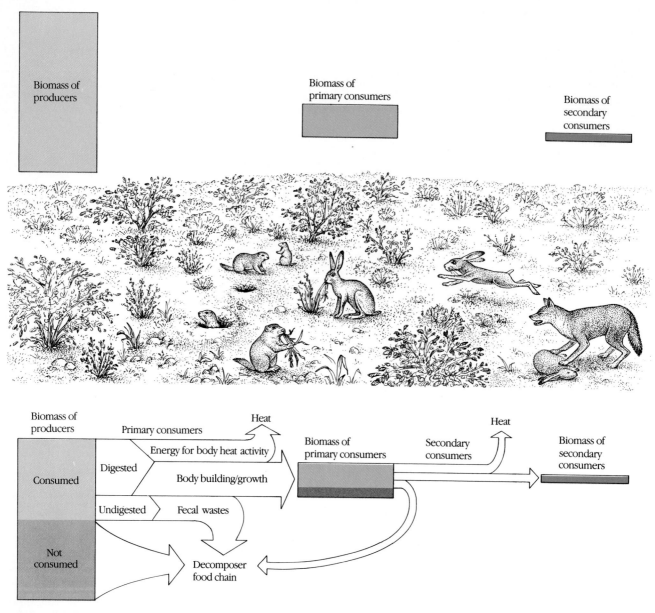

Figure 3-15   Energy and nutrient flow through the ecosystem. Note that a large fraction of the biomass of the first trophic level is not consumed. Also note the losses from one trophic level to the next.

sively higher trophic levels follow a similar pattern. Graphically represented, biomass at the different trophic levels forms the **pyramid of biomass** (Figure 3-16).

Biomass is the substance that makes up living things. The chemical bonds that hold the organic compounds of biomass together contain enormous amounts of stored, or potential, energy. This energy can be released when organic matter burns or when it is broken down by cells in plants, animals, and microorganisms. If the energy content of biomass is graphed as the biomass was, it, too, forms a pyramid, called the **pyramid of energy** (Figure 3-17).

What are the implications of the ecological pyramids? First, because biomass decreases and because organisms tend to be larger in the upper trophic levels, fewer organisms can be supported at these higher levels. The decrease in numbers forms a **pyramid of numbers**. The second implication is an extension of the first: more organisms can be supported in an ecosystem if they can feed at lower trophic levels. As illustrated in Figure 3-18, over twice as many herbivores (trophic level two) can be supported in a grassland biome as carnivores (trophic levels three and four).

Practically speaking, the ecological pyramids tell us that

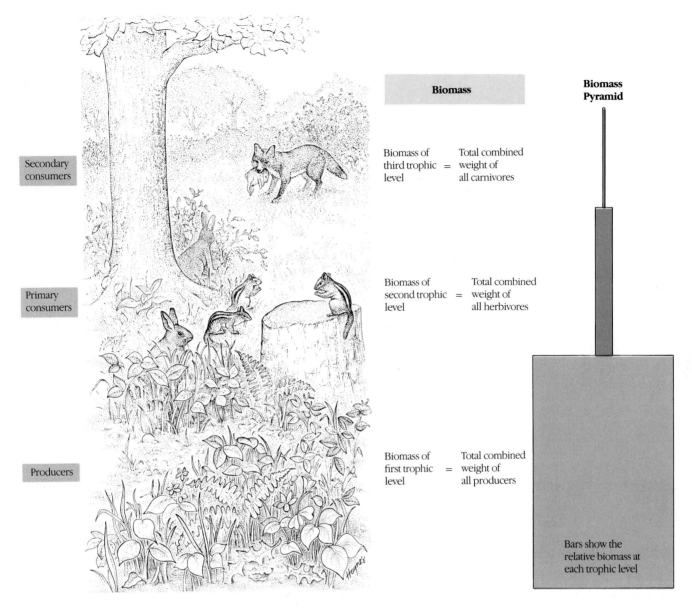

Figure 3-16 Biomass pyramid. Note that the pyramid corresponds to a single food chain at successive trophic levels.

consuming meat is much more wasteful of solar energy than eating plants, calorie for calorie. If 20,000 kilocalories worth of corn were fed to a steer, for example, 2000 kilocalories of beef would be produced (using a 10% conversion). This would feed only one person (assuming that a person can survive on 2000 kilocalories per day). If the 20,000 calories of corn were eaten directly, however, it would feed ten people for a day. In improving food supply, then, it makes more sense to increase supplies of grain rather than meat, which is generally the approach most countries take. (Chapter 7 offers additional solutions to world hunger.)

The third implication is that the loss of biomass from one trophic level to the next sets limits on the length of the food chain. Food chains usually have no more than four trophic levels, because the amount of biomass at the top of the trophic structure is not sufficient to support another level.

Productivity We measure output in factories and mines in terms of productivity: how much steel is produced and how much coal is mined per hour of labor. In ecosystems, ecologists measure productivity in a similar way. The most common measure is kilocalories of

Figure 3-17 Pyramid of energy. Note the rapid decrease in potential energy as we ascend the food chain.

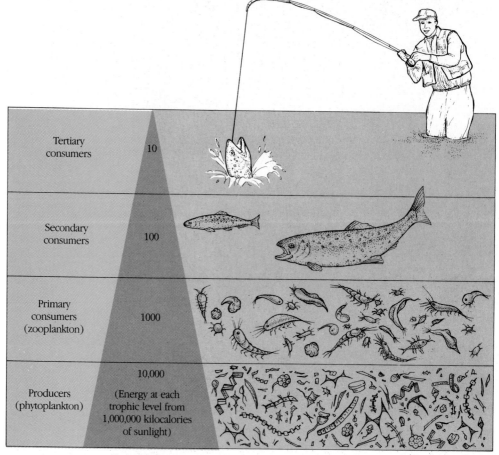

Pyramid of energy

biomass produced in a year, usually per square meter of surface area (kcal/m²/year). One **kilocalorie** is the amount of heat energy it takes to raise the temperature of one liter of water 1° C. A kilocalorie is the same as the **calorie** used by dieters in the battle of the bulge. In an ecosystem, then, productivity is the rate at which sunlight energy is converted into the potential energy of biomass. The overall rate of biomass production is called the **gross primary**

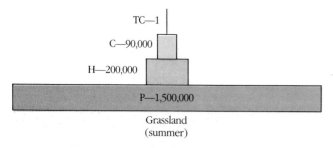

Figure 3-18 — Grassland (summer):
TC—1
C—90,000
H—200,000
P—1,500,000

Figure 3-18 Pyramid of numbers for a grassland community in the summer. The numbers represent individuals per 1000 square meters. P = producers, H = herbivores, C = carnivores, TC = top carnivores (highest consumer in a food chain).

productivity (GPP). Like a worker's gross pay, the GPP is subject to some deductions. For plants the chief deduction comes in the form of energy used to meet their own needs. Therefore, by subtracting the biomass broken down to release energy, which is called cellular respiration (R), ecologists arrive at the **net primary productivity** (NPP). Much like your net pay, the NPP is what's left over after deductions. The simple mathematical equation for net primary productivity is NPP = GPP − R.

Studies of biomass production in the earth's biomes reveal some important results: Estuaries and coral reefs are the richest areas of the ocean (Table 3-1). On land, moist temperate forests, agricultural land, and tropical forests have the highest gross primary productivity. Protecting these areas is important for the well-being of our planet and ourselves, reaffirming a fundamental law of ecology—that planet care is self-care.

How important each biome is to total global biomass production, however, depends on the total area it occupies. Taking into account both productivity and surface area, the largest producers of biomass are the open oceans, grasslands and pastures, and tropical forests (Table 3-1).

Essay 3-1

Benign Neglect in Texas: An Ecological Solution to a Perennial Problem

Texas highway officials and taxpayers have found that "benign neglect" is both economically and ecologically the best way to conduct roadside maintenance along the state's 71,000 miles of highways.

Fifty years ago the Lone Star state began sowing wild flower seeds along its nearly 800,000 acres of roadside, encouraging the brightly colored blossoms of the state's 5000 native wild flowers.

Texas is the leader in this ecological solution to roadside maintenance, which elsewhere has typically involved the planting of delicate grasses, regular mowing, irrigation, fertilization, and spraying with insecticides and herbicides—all for roadside lawns as well-groomed as a golf course. In Texas road crews mow a few times a year to help spread the flower seeds, but that's about the extent of roadside maintenance.

Besides beautifying the landscape, the hardy flowers reduce erosion and provide habitat for native species. More importantly, native wildflowers require only the water that falls naturally from the sky, and they need little if any fertilizer and care.

They resist drought, insects, and freezing weather, because they inhabit the land they have evolved over millions of years to live in.

Benign neglect makes good sense and reminds us of the words of Montaigne: "Let us permit nature to have her way; she understands her business better than we do."

Source: Adapted from McCommon, M. (1983), "A Blooming Boom in Texas." *National Wildlife* 21 (5): 4–5.

Table 3-1   Estimated Annual Gross Primary Productivity of the Biosphere and Major Ecosystems

Ecosystem	Area (10^6 km^2)	Gross Primary Productivity (kcal/m^2 year)	Worldwide Annual Gross Primary Production (10^{16} kcal)
Marine			
Open ocean	326.0	1,000	32.6
Coastal zones	34.0	2,000	6.8
Upwelling zones	0.4	6,000	0.2
Estuaries and reefs	2.0	20,000	4.0
Marine total	**362.4**		**43.6**
Terrestrial			
Deserts and tundras	40.0	200	0.8
Grasslands and pastures	42.0	2,500	10.5
Dry forests	9.4	2,500	2.4
Boreal coniferous forests	10.0	3,000	3.0
Cultivated lands with little or no energy subsidy	10.0	3,000	3.0
Moist temperate forests	4.9	8,000	3.9
Fuel-subsidized (mechanized) agriculture	4.0	12,000	4.8
Wet tropical and subtropical (broadleaved evergreen) forests	14.7	20,000	29.0
Terrestrial total	**135.0**		**57.4**
Biosphere total (round figures, not including ice caps)	**500.0**	**2,000**	**100.0**

Source: Odum, E. (1971). *Fundamentals of Ecology* (3rd ed.). Philadelphia: Saunders.

Environmental Phase   **Organismic Phase**

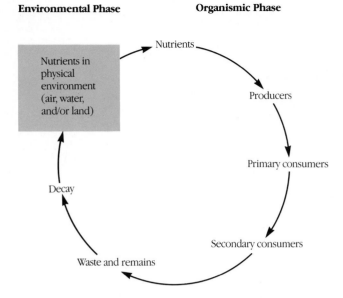

Figure 3-19 Nutrient cycles have two basic phases: environmental and organismic.

Nutrient Cycles

The economy of a country is based, in large part, on the flow of goods from agricultural and industrial producers to the people, the consumers. The "economy" of the living world is very similar. For instance, biomass and inorganic matter move from plants, the producers, to animals, the consumers. In nature these nutrients flow in a cyclic fashion so materials can be reused. Modern industrial societies flagrantly violate this fundamental rule by discarding materials, taking them out of the natural cycles so they cannot be reused easily.

Nutrients flow in cycles, but energy is an entirely different matter. It flows through the biosphere from producer to consumer but cannot be recycled, as implied by the second law of thermodynamics. Thus, as we have seen, all of the energy that enters a food chain is eventually lost as heat. This low-quality energy is dissipated into space and cannot be reused.

The cycles that move nutrients through the biosphere are called **biogeochemical cycles**, or **nutrient cycles**. As shown in Figure 3-19, the nutrient cycles involve two general phases: the **environmental phase**, in which the chemical nutrient is in the soil, water, or air, and the **organismic phase**, in which the nutrient becomes part of the living tissue of organisms.

Of the 92 naturally occurring elements, about 40 are essential to life. Six of these elements—carbon, oxygen, hydrogen, nitrogen, phosphorus, and sulfur—form 95% of the mass of all plants, animals, and microorganisms. These elements, and a few others needed in relatively large quantities, are called **macronutrients**. Others such as iron, copper, zinc, and iodine are required in only small amounts and are called **micronutrients**.

This chapter examines three nutrient cycles: carbon, nitrogen, and phosphorus. The water cycle is discussed in Chapter 10.

The Carbon Cycle   A simplified version of the carbon cycle is shown in Figure 3-20. Atmospheric carbon dioxide enters terrestrial and aquatic ecosystems. Within plants, carbon dioxide molecules react to form organic molecules such as glucose. Energy for these reactions comes from sunlight. This process, called **photosynthesis**, can be written as follows:

$$\text{carbon dioxide} + \text{water} + \text{sunlight} \longrightarrow \text{glucose} + \text{oxygen}$$

$$6\,CO_2 + 6\,H_2O + E \longrightarrow C_6H_{12}O_6 + 6\,O_2$$

The organic molecules produced during photosynthesis are passed throughout the food web. Thus, carbon flows from the atmosphere into and through the organismic phase of the cycle.

Carbon returns to the atmosphere in several ways. In plants and animals, for instance, some of the organic molecules are broken down to generate cellular energy. This process, called **cellular respiration**, results in the production of usable energy, heat, carbon dioxide, and water. It can be written as follows:

$$\text{glucose} + \text{oxygen} \longrightarrow \text{carbon dioxide} + \text{water} + \text{energy}$$

$$C_6H_{12}O_6 + 6\,O_2 \longrightarrow 6\,CO_2 + 6\,H_2O + E$$

The carbon released as carbon dioxide gas reenters the environmental phase of the cycle for reuse.

Carbon can also return to the atmosphere through the decomposer food chain. Here, decomposers consume organic wastes from plants and animals and convert it into living tissue and energy, while liberating carbon dioxide through cellular respiration. Carbon also returns when plant materials are burned by natural causes such as lightning and forest fires or as a result of human activities such as combustion of wood and coal or deliberately set fires.

Humans intervene in the global carbon cycle in two major ways: (1) by removing forests and vegetation that use atmospheric carbon dioxide to make organic molecules and (2) by liberating carbon dioxide during the combustion of coal, oil, and natural gas—carbon sources that were once isolated deep beneath the earth's surface. Combined, such activities have increased the global carbon dioxide concentrations by at least 11% since 1870. Further increases could have a devastating effect on global climate and life. (For more details see Chapter 15.)

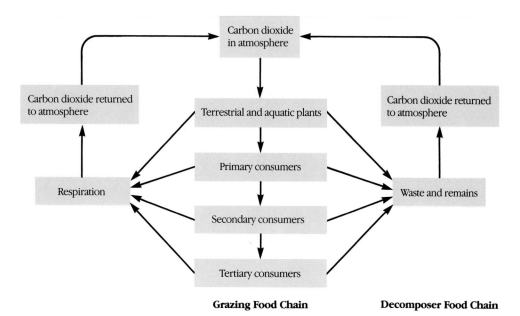

Figure 3-20 The carbon cycle.

Grazing Food Chain   **Decomposer Food Chain**

The Nitrogen Cycle Nitrogen forms part of many essential organic molecules—notably, amino acids, the building blocks of proteins, and the genetic materials RNA and DNA (Chapter Supplement 2-1). Fortunately for plants and animals nitrogen is an abundant element; approximately 79% of the air is nitrogen gas (N_2). However, plants and animals cannot use nitrogen in this form. To be usable it must first be converted into ammonia (NH_3) or nitrate (NO_3) (Figure 3-21).

The conversion of atmospheric nitrogen into nitrate and ammonia is called **nitrogen fixation**, and it occurs mainly in certain bacteria in the soil and water. One nitrogen-fixing bacterium, called *Rhizobium*, invades the roots of a group of plants called **legumes**, which include beans, peas, alfalfa, clover, and others. The roots respond by forming tiny nodules that serve as sites for nitrogen fixation. Formed either in the soil or in the root nodules, the nitrogen compounds are taken into plants and there used to synthesize amino acids, proteins, DNA, and RNA. Animals, in turn, receive the nitrogen they need by eating plants (and other animals).

Nitrogen is returned to the soil by the decay of detritus (Figure 3-21). Within the soil certain species of bacteria and fungi decompose the nitrogen-rich wastes from plants and animals. Nitrogen is released in the form of ammonia and ammonium salts. Ammonia is further converted into nitrites and then into nitrates.

The ammonium salts, nitrates, and nitrites may all be incorporated by the roots of plants and reused. Some nitrite is converted into a gas, nitrous oxide (N_2O), and released into the atmosphere.

In various forms nitrogen travels from air to soil to plant to animal and then back to soil and atmosphere in a never-ending cycle. Human farming practices, discussed in Chapter 7, greatly affect the nitrogen cycle. For example, some crops such as corn absorb large amounts of nitrogen from the soil; if nitrogen is not replaced in alternate years, the soil may become unproductive. Farmers may replace soil nitrogen by applying artificial fertilizers. Frequently used in excess, these nitrates may wash into streams, causing serious water pollution (Chapter 16).

The Phosphorus Cycle Phosphorus, found in living organisms as phosphates (PO_4), is an important part of RNA and DNA. (See Chapter Supplement S2-1.) Phosphorus is also found in fats (phospholipids) in cell membranes.

Phosphate is slowly dissolved (leached) from rocks by rain and melting snow and is carried to waterways (Figure 3-22). Dissolved phosphates are incorporated by plants and then passed to animals in the food web. Phosphorus reenters the environment in at least two ways: (1) some is excreted directly by animals, and (2) some is returned when detritus decays.

Each year large quantities of phosphate are washed into the oceans, where much of it settles to the bottom and is incorporated into the marine sediments. Sediments may release some of the phosphate needed by aquatic organisms. The rest may become buried and taken out of circulation.

Phosphate is a major component of fertilizer. By applying excess fertilizer farmers may alter the phosphorus cycle. Since phosphorus is a limiting factor in aquatic ecosystems, excesses entering from farmland runoff may cause rapid growth in algae and other aquatic plants. This phenomenon is discussed in more detail in Chapter 7.

Figure 3-21 The nitrogen cycle.

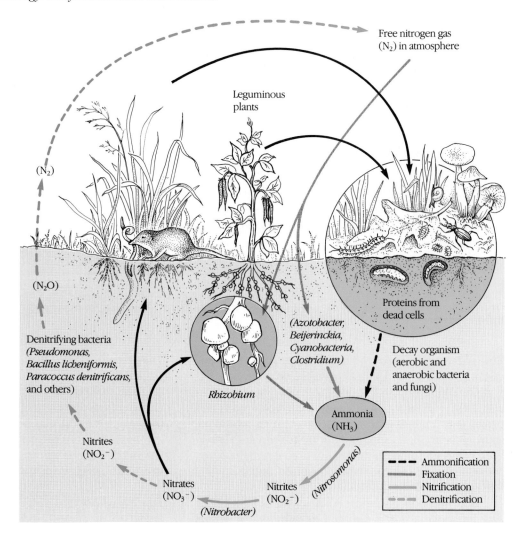

This chapter has discussed the structure of the living world, starting with the largest of all biological subdivisions, the biomes, and focusing on smaller and smaller units, including ecosystems, communities, and populations. We've seen how ecosystems are organized and have briefly examined the way ecosystems work, gaining a better understanding of how human populations alter them. With this background let us turn our attention to ecosystem balance, paying particular attention to the forces that help achieve balance. From the discussion of balance, you will see how ecosystems are altered by natural events and human intervention.

Nothing can survive on the planet unless it is a cooperative part of larger global life.

BARRY COMMONER

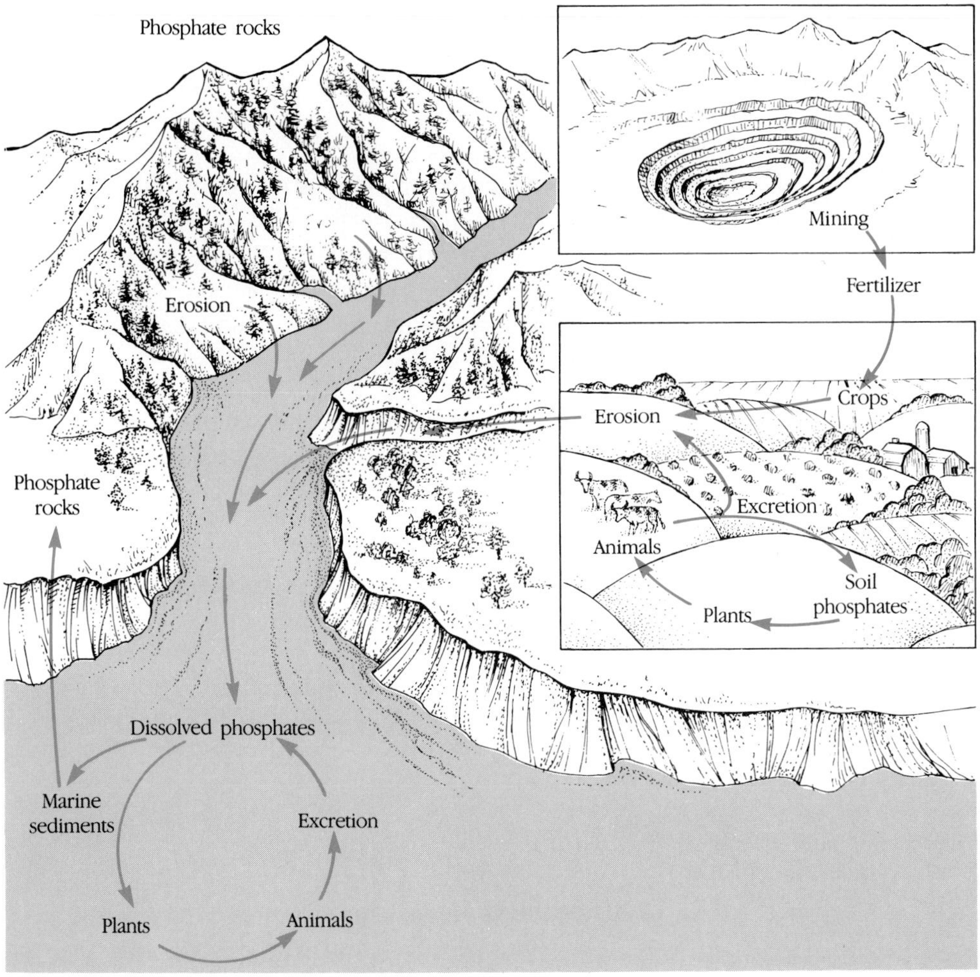

Figure 3-22 The phosphorus cycle.

Summary

Ecology is the study of the interactions between organisms and their environment. It takes the entire living world as its domain in an attempt to understand the complex web of life in the **biosphere**. The biosphere, like a sealed terrarium, is a **closed system**. All of the materials essential to life come from within it and must be recycled over and over for life to continue.

The biosphere is divided into regions, called **biomes**, each with unique plant and animal life. The boundaries of a biome are determined by the **climate**, the average of the weather conditions over long periods of time. Precipitation and temperature are the most important climatic factors.

Ecological systems, or **ecosystems**, are networks consisting of organisms, their environment, and all the interactions that exist between them. Ecosystems consist of **biotic** (living) and **abiotic** (nonliving) components. The abiotic components are physical and chemical factors needed for life.

Each organism operates within a range of chemical and physical factors called its **range of tolerance**. When the upper or lower limits of this range are exceeded, survival is threatened. In all ecosystems one abiotic factor usually limits growth and is therefore called a **limiting factor**.

The organisms are the **biotic** components of the ecosystem. Groups of organisms of the same species occupying a specific region form a **population**. The populations of plants, animals, and microorganisms in an ecosystem form a **community**. Each organism within a community occupies a specific region, its **habitat**. It also occupies a specific **niche**, which includes its habitat and all its relationships with abiotic and biotic components of the environment. No two species occupy the same niche in the same ecosystem.

Organisms may be specialists or generalists. **Generalists** occupy many different habitats and eat a wide variety of foods. **Specialists** generally live in one habitat and consume one or only a few organisms, making them more susceptible to changes in the habitat and more prone to extinction.

The living web is held together by **food chains**, a series of organisms each feeding on the preceding one. The **grazer food chain** is the nutrient and energy pathway starting with plants that are consumed by grazers. The **decomposer food chain** is a nutrient and energy pathway that starts with **detritus**. Individual food chains are part of more complex **food webs**.

The terms *primary, secondary, tertiary,* and *quaternary* are applied to consumers in the food chain. **Primary consumers** are the first level of consumers; they feed on plants in the grazer food chain and on detritus in the decomposer food chain. **Secondary consumers** feed on primary consumers (herbivores).

The feeding level an organism occupies in a food chain is called the **trophic level**. Producers form the first trophic level. Primary consumers form the second trophic level, and secondary, tertiary, and quaternary consumers occupy the third, fourth, and fifth levels, respectively.

Energy is defined as the capacity to do work. Organic matter in living organisms contains **potential energy**. Energy of motion is called **kinetic energy**. Energy is governed by the **laws of thermodynamics**. The **first law** states that energy is neither created nor destroyed but only converted from one form to another. The **second law** states that when energy is converted from one form to another, there is a loss of available work; thus, energy has been degraded or converted from a more concentrated to a less concentrated form. The laws of thermodynamics have many implications in ecology and everyday life.

Organic matter produced by living things is called **biomass**. It is a form of potential energy passed from one trophic level to the next in an ecosystem. As biomass "flows" through a food chain from one trophic level to the next, it decreases. Graphically represented, biomass at the different trophic levels forms a **pyramid of biomass**. Since biomass contains energy, the amount of potential energy at higher trophic levels also decreases and forms a **pyramid of energy**. Finally, the number of organisms decreases from one trophic level to the next higher one; this forms a **pyramid of numbers**.

Productivity is the measure of biomass production. Regions with high productivity, such as tropical rain forests, are important to humans because they supply many valuable resources.

Organic and inorganic matter move within ecosystems in **nutrient cycles**. Examples are the carbon, nitrogen, and phosphorus cycles. These cycles are essential for life and can be altered by human activities.

Discussion Questions

1. What is ecology?
2. Define the term *biosphere*. Why is the biosphere considered a closed system?
3. Define the term *biome*. What determines the type of vegetation in a biome? After studying the biome map in this chapter, name the biomes that you have visited in your lifetime.
4. Define the term *ecosystem*.
5. Discuss the concept *range of tolerance*.
6. What is a limiting factor? What is the most important limiting factor in terrestrial ecosystems?
7. How are a *niche* and a *habitat* different?
8. In what ways are humans specialists? In what ways are we generalists?
9. What is a food chain? What are the two major types? How are they different? How are they similar?
10. Sketch several simple food chains and indicate all producers and consumers. Also indicate the trophic level of each organism. Can one organism occupy several different trophic levels? Give an example.
11. Why does biomass decrease as we ascend the food chain?
12. What are the implications of decreasing biomass in the food chain?
13. Draw a detailed picture of the carbon cycle, and describe what happens during the various parts of the cycle.

Suggested Readings

Attenborough, D. (1979). *Life on Earth*. Boston: Little, Brown. Superb study of life.

Clapham, W. B. (1983). *Natural Ecosystems* (2nd ed.). New York: Macmillan. Advanced treatise on ecology.

Colinvaux, P. (1973). *Introduction to Ecology*. New York: Wiley. An excellent textbook of basic ecology.

Kormondy, E. J. (1969). *Concepts of Ecology*. Englewood Cliffs, N.J.: Prentice-Hall. Excellent introduction.

Lederer, R. J. (1984). *Ecology and Field Biology*. Menlo Park, Calif.: Benjamin/Cummings. Intermediate-level coverage of basic ecology.

Rodgers, C. L., and Kerstetter, R. E. (1974). *The Ecosphere: Organisms, Habitats, and Disturbances*. New York: Harper and Row. A good account on biomes and human disturbance.

Smith, R. L. (1976). *The Ecology of Man: An Ecosystem Approach* (2nd ed.). New York: Harper and Row. Advanced readings on ecology and environmental problems.

Smith, R. L. (1980). *Ecology and Field Biology*. (3rd ed.). New York: Harper and Row. A comprehensive textbook.

The Biomes

Look outside the window. You probably see tree-lined streets, homes or campus buildings, neatly tended lawns, or possibly a parking lot. The vegetation growing around you is probably not "natural" at all. Grasses may have been imported from Kentucky. The trees may come from Norway or the Soviet Union. Even some of the birds, such as starlings and house sparrows, are aliens, brought in from England. To get a glimpse of the natural vegetation, you may have to journey outside your town. There you may find grassland, forest, or desert that resembles the environment before humanity began to reshape it.

Grasslands, deserts, and forests are three of the relatively homogeneous zones called biomes. Biomes, as we have seen, are large regions each with its own distinctive climate, plant and animal life, and soil type. A dozen biomes spread over millions of square kilometers, spanning entire continents. This supplement looks at some of the major world biomes and the ways humans have altered them.

Tundra

The **tundra** is a vast, virtually treeless region on the far northern borders of North America, Europe, and Asia (Gallery 2, Figure 11). It lies between a region of perpetual ice and snow to the north and a band of coniferous forests (the tiaga) to the south. It is one of the largest biomes, covering about one-tenth of the earth's surface.

The tundra receives very little precipitation (less than 25 centimeters, 10 inches, per year), most of it during the summer. Contrary to popular belief very little snow falls during the long, cold winter.

The tundra is a gently rolling landscape dominated by herbaceous plants (grasses, sedges, rushes, and heather), mosses, lichens, and dwarf willows. Deep-rooted plants such as trees cannot grow there, because much of the subsoil remains frozen year-round, hence the name **permafrost**. Most tundra plants are stunted because of the short growing season, the annual freeze–thaw cycle, which tears and crushes roots and impairs growth, and windblown ice and snow, which abrade vegetation.

The summer days are long and warm, and the land becomes dotted with thousands of shallow lakes, ponds, and bogs. Millions of birds come north to nest and feed on the tundra's abundant insects.

In North America musk ox, caribou, and a variety of small rodents and mammals inhabit the tundra year-round. They share their habitat with snowy owls and ptarmigan (ground-dwelling birds similar to grouse).

The tundra is an extremely fragile biome, containing few species, a condition believed to make it more vulnerable to change (Chapter 4). Vegetation takes decades to grow back after it has been destroyed by vehicles. Large-tired "rolligons" and new vehicles that ride on a layer of air are now being used experimentally and may help us reduce our impact on the tundra (Figure S3-1).

Figure S3-1 "Rolligons" are being used in Alaska to carry heavy equipment across the tundra with minimal damage. Specially designed tires spread the weight over a large surface.

Taiga

South of the tundra, extending across North America, Europe, and Asia, is a broad band of coniferous (evergreen) forests. This biome is called the **taiga** (Gallery 2, Figures 6 and 7). The average annual precipitation in the taiga is higher than in the tundra, as is the average daily temperature.

With a growing season of 150 days and a complete thawing of the subsoil, the taiga supports an abundance of life forms. Conifers are the dominant form of plant life, for they are well adapted to the long, cold, and snowy winters. Water loss is minimized by waxy coatings on their needles. Reduced evaporation is critical in the winter, when water transport from the root systems halts. The flexible limbs are an adaptation that allows conifers to bend without breaking when covered with snow. Some deciduous trees (ones that shed their leaves each year) inhabit the taiga in localized regions, particularly in areas that are recovering after fires or heavy timber cutting.

Animal life is abundant and diverse. Bears, moose, wolves, lynx, wolverines, martens, porcupines, and numerous small rodents inhabit the forests, along with a variety of birds such as grouse, ravens, hairy woodpeckers, and great horned owls. Insects, such as mosquitoes, also thrive during the warm summer months. Over 50 species of insects that feed on conifers live in the taiga, including the spruce budworm, pine beetle, tussock moth, and pine sawfly. These can cause widespread damage to trees during droughts, which weaken trees' resistance.

Numerous lakes, ponds, and bogs spot the landscape. In North America trappers once traveled by boat into the interior of the taiga on the interconnected waterways in quest of beaver and other fur bearers. The taiga has long been of interest to the logging industry. Through past practices loggers have stripped large sections of land by **clear-cutting** forests. Until recently little or no effort was made to replant denuded areas, resulting in severe soil erosion, destruction of wildlife habitat, and pollution of streams and lakes with sediment.

Temperate Deciduous Forest

The **temperate deciduous forest** biome is located in the eastern United States, Europe, and northeastern China. A region with a warm, mild growing season and abundant rainfall, the temperate deciduous forest supports a wide variety of plants and animals (Gallery 2, Figure 8). The dominant vegetation consists of broadleafed deciduous trees such as maple, oak, and hickory. However, the dominant plant species can vary from region to region, depending on the amount of precipitation.

Temperate deciduous forests support a variety of organisms, including white-tailed deer, opossums, raccoons, squirrels, chipmunks, foxes, rabbits, black bears, mice, shrews, wrens, downy woodpeckers, and owls. During the summer, warblers and other bird species migrate into and nest in the rich green forests.

Deciduous trees act as "nutrient pumps," drawing inorganic chemical nutrients from the subsoil up through the roots to the leaves. When the leaves fall and decay, they add valuable organic and inorganic nutrients to the superficial layers of soil. These nutrients are important for plant growth.

The temperate deciduous forest biome has been extensively exploited by humans. In North America this biome once extended from the Mississippi River to the Atlantic Coast. Now, however, only about .1% of the original forest remains; most has been cleared away for farms, orchards, and cities. Early settlers often failed to practice good soil conservation methods on their farms, letting the land erode. Farmers then moved westward into virgin territory, where they often continued the same practices. Soil erosion continues today on America's farmland (Chapter 7).

Grassland

Grasslands exist in both temperate and tropical regions where rainfall is relatively low or uneven. The temperate grasslands in North America occupy an extensive region from the Rocky Mountains to the Mississippi River known as the Great Plains. Moist regions of the Great Basin, lying between the Sierra Nevada and the Rockies, also support grasslands. Temperate grasslands are found in South America, Australia, Europe, and Asia; tropical grasslands exist in Africa and South America.

Temperate and tropical grasslands are remarkably similar in appearance (Gallery 1, Figures 12 and 13). Both experience periodic drought and are characterized by flat or slightly rolling terrain. Large grazers such as the bison in North America and the zebra in Africa feed off the lush grasses in this biome. The native grasses are well adapted to drought, as their roots penetrate deep into the subsoil where they can always find water.

Because their soils are rich in inorganic and organic nutrients, grasslands have been widely used for agriculture. As discussed in Chapter 7, wind and rain take their toll on grassland soils that are farmed improperly.

Desert

Deserts are found throughout the world. The Sahara, the largest in the world, stretches across the African continent and is nearly as large as the United States. In North America deserts lie primarily on the downwind side of mountain ranges. The reason is that warm, moist air flowing toward the mountains is propelled upward as it comes in contact with the mountain range; as the moist air ascends, it is cooled, and water vapor in the air condenses, forming droplets too large to remain in suspension. These droplets form rain, which falls mostly on the windward side, leaving the downwind side dry. When rain does fall in a desert, it is often intense and frequently results in flash floods and severe soil erosion. Water evaporates quickly from the soil because the vegetation is sparse and because of the high temperatures reached on the desert floor in the summer (Gallery 2, Figure 2).

Contrary to the view held by many people, most deserts are not lifeless lands. A surprising variety of plants and animals have adapted to the unique environmental conditions. Plants include cacti, other succulents, and shrubs (mesquite, acacia, greasewood, and creosote bush). Small, fast-growing annual herbs are also found. Many of these are wildflowers that bloom only in the spring or after drenching rains. Such sudden bursts of growth can turn the desert into a colorful landscape almost overnight. (Gallery 2, Figure 3.)

Plants have developed a number of adaptations to cope with the dry conditions of the desert. These include (1) thick, waterproof outer layers, which reduce water loss; (2) an absence of leaves or a reduction in leaf size, both ways to reduce the surface area from which water can evaporate; (3) hairs and thorns, which reflect sunlight and shade the plants; (4) the ability to drop leaves (a strategy used by the ocotillo) when moisture levels are low; (5) extensive, shallow root systems to absorb as much water as possible during cloudbursts; (6) deep taproots, which penetrate into groundwater; (7) succulent water-retaining tissues to store water; (8) recessed pores (stomata), which reduce water loss; (9) wide spacing between plants to reduce competition for available water; and (10) short life spans, which allow plants to develop to maturity quickly following rainstorms.

A surprising number of animals also live in the desert. Like the plants, they have evolved a number of strategies to survive in the harsh climate. Many animals such as the ring-tailed cat are active only at night or during the early and late hours of the day when the heat is less intense. Snakes have thick scales that prevent water loss. The kangaroo rat conserves body moisture by excreting a solid urine containing nitrogen wastes (in the form of uric acid). Some species obtain water from vege-

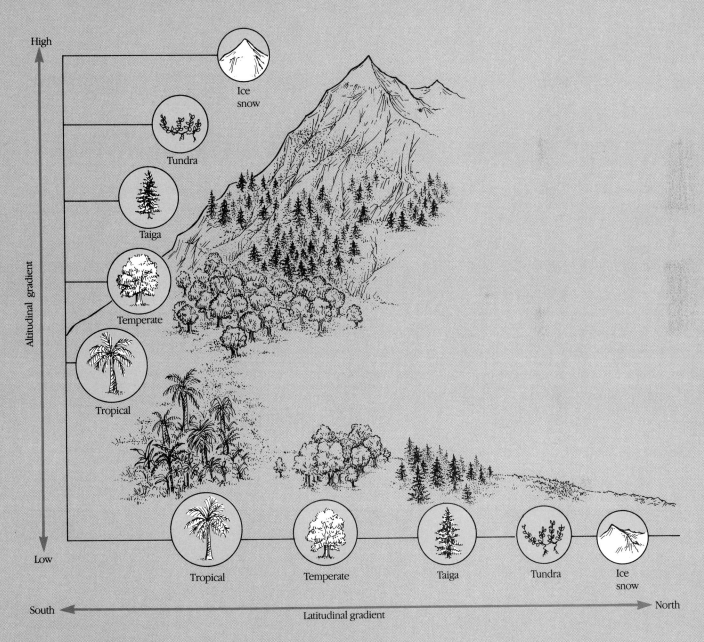

Figure S3-2 Vegetation varies with altitude in any given region. Altitudinal gradients mirror latitudinal gradients.

tation, and others from the blood and tissue fluids of their prey. Gila monsters combat the heat by remaining underground during the hottest daylight hours.

Large cities have sprung up in the American desert. Farmers have plowed the poor soil to plant their crops, but the desert soil contains little of the organic matter needed to retain moisture and contains only small amounts of the nitrogen required for plant growth. Consequently, crops are successful only if nitrogen and water are provided. City dwellers and farmers now compete for the limited water in the American West. With rising population and years of irrigation, water supplies have begun to decline, forcing many farms to shut down.

Human populations have expanded the borders of the world's deserts by allowing livestock to overgraze, deforesting lands, and following poor agricultural practices. The Sahara's southern boundaries are spreading into the Sahel region because of intense grazing in bordering grassland. Each year millions of acres of land are engulfed by spreading deserts.

Tropical Rain Forest

Tropical rain forests are located near the equator on several continents and islands. With an average annual temperature of approximately 18° C (64° F) and rainfall of 200 to 400 centimeters (80 to 160 inches) per year, the tropical rain forest is one of the richest and most complex biomes.

The dominant vegetation consists of trees that tower as high as 50 to 60 meters (165 to 200 feet) above the forest floor (Gallery 2, Figure 4). The tops of these trees interlace and form a dense canopy, which blocks out much of the sunlight. Smaller trees further reduce light penetration. Only 1% of the sunlight reaches the forest floor, and therefore only a few plants adapted to low light can grow on the ground.

The tropical rain forest is well known for its species diversity. As many as 100 tree species can be found whereas a northern coniferous forest would have only 2 or 3. The rain forest supports a diverse array of insects, birds, and other animals, too. There are as many species of butterflies (500 to 600) on a single tropical island as there are in the entire United States.

Since the ground is bare, many of the animals and insects live in the treetops, where the food is. The treetops are without a doubt the most heavily and diversely populated regions of the tropical rain forest.

Woody vines grow in the rain forest, and a large number of plants, called **epiphytes**, live dangling among the branches of the taller trees where sunlight is available. Epiphytes, like Spanish moss, which grows in the southern United States in temperate deciduous forests, gather moisture and nutrients from the humid air. They have no roots and need no soil.

Trees of the tropical rain forest have shallow root systems, because most of the nutrients are near the surface and because rainfall is abundant, which makes deep root systems unnecessary. Since their root systems are so shallow, many trees develop wide bases (known as buttresses) to prevent them from toppling over.

The soils of the tropical rain forests are thin and extremely poor in nutrients. In fact, almost all of the inorganic and organic nutrients found in this biome are tied up in the vegetation. Plant and animal wastes are rapidly decomposed on the forest floor in the decomposer food chain; organic matter does not build up, as it does in deciduous forests and grasslands. Minerals returned during decomposition are rapidly absorbed by the roots of trees or are leached from the soil by rain and carried to the groundwater, where they are often unavailable to plants.

Because they are nutrient-poor, rain forest soils are not suitable for conventional agriculture. In addition, many of the soils in tropical rain forests are composed of a red clay known as **laterite** (from the Latin *later*, "brick"), which forms an impenetrable crust one or two years after the forest is cleared to make farmland. A third problem is that once trees are removed to make room for farms, soils are easily washed away by the frequent rains. Despite these major drawbacks people throughout the world still clear tropical rain forests for farming, grazing, and timber production. An area the size of Georgia is deforested each year.

Destruction of tropical rain forests is so extensive that ecologists project that this biome, which constitutes about half the world's forest, will be gone or at least severely damaged by the year 2000. With it, they assert, thousands of animals species will vanish. (For more see the Point/Counterpoint "Deforestation of Tropical Rain Forests," in Chapter 9.)

Altitudinal Biomes

If you've ever hiked or driven through the Rocky Mountains, the Sierra Nevada, or the Cascade Mountains, you will have noticed that life zones vary with altitude (Figure S3-2; see previous page). The reason is that temperature and rainfall vary with altitude, and thus so does the plant and animal life. In the high Rockies climatic conditions are similar to those of the arctic tundra; so are the plant and animal life. Because of these similarities high mountain regions are called **alpine tundra**. As in the arctic tundra, the growing seasons are short, and the winters are cold. Annual precipitation is fairly low. Vegetation and animal life are similar to those of the far northern tundra (Gallery 2, Figures 10 and 11). Areas below the tundra resemble the taiga. The forests in these regions are dominated by spruce and fir.

Principles of Ecology: Ecosystem Balance and Imbalance

And this our life, exempt from public haunt, finds tongues in trees, books in running brooks, sermons in stones, and good in everything.

SHAKESPEARE

In 1884 the water hyacinth was introduced into Florida from South America. The hyacinth remained, for a while, simply a beautiful ornamental flowering plant in a private pond. Unfortunately, the plant accidentally entered the waterways of Florida. In these nutrient-rich waters it spread like cancer throughout the canals and rivers that lace the state. Aided by a remarkable ability to reproduce—10 plants can multiply to 600,000 in just eight months—the hyacinth now clogs waterways throughout Florida, choking out native species and making navigation impossible in some areas (Figure 4-1).

From Florida the plant has metastasized (spread) throughout much of the southern United States. Today nearly 800,000 hectares (2 million acres) of rivers and lakes from Florida to California are choked with thick surface mats of hyacinths. Florida, Louisiana, and Texas, where the problem is most severe, spend nearly $11 million a year to relieve the stranglehold these plants have on their waterways. (For a practical application of the water hyacinth, see Essay 4-1.)

For most of its existence humankind has worried about the ways in which nature affects people's lives. As this example points out, however, the danger may be not what nature will do to us but what we will do to nature (and ourselves) by unleashing some of its forces.

The story of the water hyacinth is a lesson in ecological balance or, more correctly, imbalance, a lesson in how an ecosystem can be thrown out of kilter in humankind's

Figure 4-1 The water hyacinth was introduced accidentally into Florida waters. It has proliferated at a tremendous rate, choking canals and streams and outcompeting many native species.

zeal to fashion the environment to its liking. Chapter 3 looked at the structure of ecosystems and the way energy and matter flow within them. A complete picture of ecosystems is not possible, though, until we look at ecosystem balance and imbalance to answer some important questions: How can ecosystems be altered, and in what ways can they recover from damage? How far can we push a natural community before permanently changing it?

Ecosystem Stability Defined

Before the introduction of the water hyacinth Florida's waterways were considered fairly stable ecosystems. In other words, things may have changed from day to day, but on the whole they remained more or less the same. Ecologists describe this condition as a state of **dynamic equilibrium**, or a steady state. Suppose, for sake of illustration, that you studied a mature forest ecosystem near your home each spring for an extended period, say, 20 years. If the system were stable, you would find that (1) the total number of species was fairly constant from year to year, (2) the same species were present each year, and (3) the population size of each species was approximately the same from year to year.

Stability also entails the ability of a disturbed ecosystem to return to its original condition (**resilience**). After minor changes induced by natural and human causes a stable ecosystem can "bounce back" to its previous condition. Stability is also a property of an ecosystem that causes it to resist being changed by natural events or by human interference (**inertia**). Resilience and inertia will be described in more detail later in the chapter.

What Keeps Ecosystems Stable?

Life is a continuous balancing act. Good things and bad things, income and debt, happiness and sadness, friends and enemies—all make your life what it is. Too much of the good life, and life may become meaningless. Too much sadness, and despair creeps in. The secret of life is achieving a balance between the good and the bad.

Nature, too, is a balancing act of growth and decline, predator and prey, sickness and health; the secret of living systems is achieving a balance and maintaining it. Ecosystem health, like your own health, is dependent on this precarious balance.

Population Growth and Environmental Resistance

Balance, or stability, in an ecosystem is the result of opposing forces that constantly work to regulate the size of populations. These forces can be broken down into two groups: factors that tend to increase population size, or **growth factors**, and those that tend to decrease it, called **reduction factors**. As illustrated in Figure 4-2, growth and reduction factors can be biotic or abiotic.

At any given moment population size is determined by the interplay of these factors. Since ecosystems contain many species, the entire ecosystem balance can be crudely related to the sum of the individual population balances.

The biotic factors that stimulate population growth include the ability to produce many offspring, to adapt to new or changing environments, to migrate into new territories, to compete with other species, to blend into the environment, to defend against enemies, and to find food (Figure 4-2). Certain favorable abiotic conditions also tend to increase population size. Favorable light, temperature, and rainfall, for example, all promote maximum plant growth and, because animals depend on plants, often promote increases in animal populations. The success of the water hyacinth in southern waterways is attributed, in large part, to its prolific breeding, its ability to use nutrients dissolved in surface waters, its

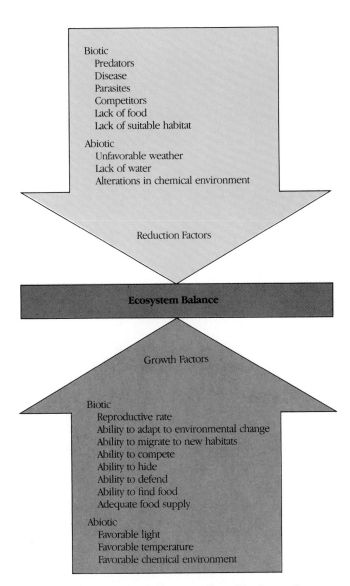

Figure 4-2 Ecosystem balance is affected by forces that tend to increase population size and forces that tend to decrease it. Growth and reduction factors consist of abiotic and biotic components.

ability to spread into new territories, and, of course, the favorable climate of the South.

Opposing the positive influence on growth are a host of abiotic and biotic factors. Ecologists describe these factors collectively as **environmental resistance**. Predators, disease, parasites, and competition by other species all effectively reduce population size, as do unfavorable weather and lack of food and water. The water hyacinth faces little environmental resistance. Even plant-eating native fish are no match for its reproductive success. Florida's waterways are out of balance; growth far exceeds environmental resistance.

Before the invention of the plow unbalanced ecosystems were a rare thing. Expansion of agriculture, urban

growth, and industrial development, discussed in Chapter 2, changed the picture entirely, making balanced ecosystems increasingly more difficult to find in many parts of the world.

On the rolling hills of eastern Kansas, however, is a reminder of the days past, for here is an example of an ecosystem operating as it has for tens of thousands of years. We will focus on a tiny portion of that ecosystem to illustrate how nature ensures its harmony.

Living in the grass-covered Flint Hills is a mouselike rodent called the prairie vole. Its population size depends on many factors such as light, rainfall, available food supply, predation by coyotes and hawks, temperature, and disease.

The prairie vole has a high reproductive capacity. When raised in the laboratory under *optimum* conditions, a pair of voles becomes remarkably prolific, producing a litter of seven pups every three weeks, month after month, for several years. The optimum conditions in a laboratory are low temperature (slightly above freezing), long days (14 hours of light a day), and plenty of water and food. Under these conditions a female will give birth to a litter and mate a few hours later. Her second litter is born about the time she weans her first. This can go on, in the laboratory, for several years. For the captive-raised vole, motherhood is no picnic.

Fortunately, in the wild, optimum conditions never completely coincide. In the summer, for instance, when food, water, and day length are optimal, the temperature is too warm. Reproduction occurs at a much more reasonable pace. In the winter, when the temperature is just right for breeding, the days are short, and the food supply is reduced. As a result, the population balance is maintained.

Resisting Change

The key word in ecosystems is **stability**. As all of us can attest, to preserve balance it is easiest to resist change in the first place. In an ecosystem this capacity is called interia. If change does occur, the second-best strategy is to recover quickly, a property called resilience.

In the living world change comes from shifts in growth and reduction factors. The introduction of new predators, a shortage of food, low rainfall, or unfavorable temperature, for example, all tend to decrease population size. Other factors, such as an abundance of food, may cause explosive growth in populations.

Changes in abiotic and biotic conditions occur with great regularity in ecosystems. Minor fluctuations are of little consequence however, for species have evolved numerous mechanisms to either resist change or to recover quickly. Prairie voles may increase their reproductive rate when a cold winter kills off a larger than

Figure 4-3 The events that follow the dumping of organic wastes into a stream.

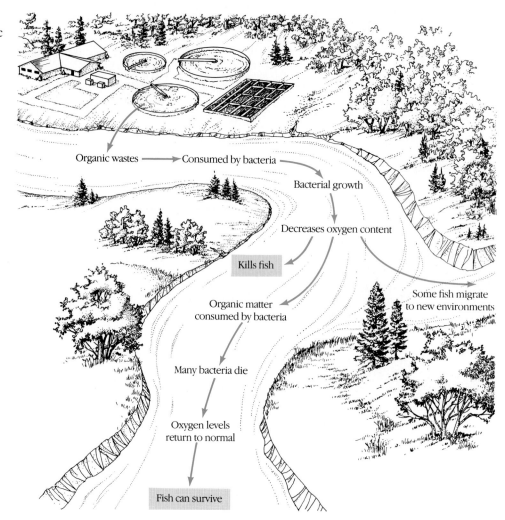

Organic wastes → Consumed by bacteria

Bacterial growth

Decreases oxygen content

Kills fish

Some fish migrate to new environments

Organic matter consumed by bacteria

Many bacteria die

Oxygen levels return to normal

Fish can survive

normal number of their population; tropical monkeys may exploit new food sources when a rainy season fails to materialize and traditional food supplies are inadequate; wolves may migrate into new territory if crowding occurs.

In many ways nature is a series of checks and balances that preserve the integrity of the whole. These checks and balances help minimize human impact, too. Sewage dumped into a stream, for example, adds organic and inorganic chemicals to the water (Figure 4-3). The organic molecules are consumed by naturally occurring bacteria whose population is normally low. The number of bacteria increases. Since bacteria use up oxygen when they consume organic materials, the level of dissolved oxygen in the stream usually drops. This decline kills fish and other organisms or forces them to migrate to new areas. In time, though, the stream will return to normal if further spills are prevented. The bacteria that proliferated after the spill will perish as the level of organic pollutants falls off. The levels of dissolved oxygen will also return to normal. Fish will return. This is an example of resilience. Chapter 16 treats this topic in detail.

Species Diversity and Stability

Ecosystem stability is significantly affected by **species diversity**, which, roughly speaking, is a measure of the number of species in a community. Species diversity is high in **mature**, or **climax**, **communities**. These are communities that have reached a definitive stage of development, such as tropical rain forests, and that will remain in this stage barring natural disaster or serious human intervention. A high level of diversity is believed to result in ecosystem stability. In support of this idea are observations that extremely complex ecosystems, such as rain forests, remain unchanged almost indefinitely if undisturbed. Simple ecosystems such as the tundra are more volatile. They can experience sudden, drastic shifts in population size. Other simplified ecosystems such as fields of wheat and corn also show extreme vulnerability to change, and they collapse if abiotic or biotic factors shift.

To see how ecologists explain this phenomenon, look at the differences in food webs in simple and complex ecosystems. As illustrated in Figure 4-4, the number of

Putting a Pest to Work: An Ecological Solution to Water Pollution

It's not often a pest makes good, but such is the case of the water hyacinth. Long infamous for clogging canals, rivers, and ponds and costing state governments millions for cleanup, the water hyacinth has been put to work as a water purifier in sewage treatment plants.

Unlike many other plants, water hyacinths need no soil. Their roots simply dangle below the surface and absorb the nutrients the plant needs to grow. The nutrients these plants need are, coincidentally, also major water pollutants—nitrates, phosphates, and potassium. Thus, the water hyacinth acts as a biological filter, removing these harmful pollutants from the water. Grown in special ponds in which wastes from sewage plants are dumped, the hyacinths provide an inexpensive alternative to conventional wastewater treatment (see Chapter 16 for more detail on this subject). As an added benefit, the water hyacinth also absorbs certain toxic wastes, pesticides, and heavy metals.

At Disney World near Orlando, Florida, officials have constructed five ponds, each roughly the size of a football field. Wastewater from the park is pumped into these ponds, purified by the water hyacinths, and then returned for reuse. San Diego is spending $3.5 million to develop a similar treatment facility.

The advantages of this approach are several. Conventional wastewater treatment is costly, requiring large amounts of electricity and numerous maintenance workers. Hyacinth treatment, in contrast, may cost about half as much because of the low energy requirements and the lack of personnel. It also allows for recycling of water, a boon to water-short regions. Also, periodic harvesting of the hyacinths yields food for livestock or fertilizer for fields. The water hyacinth provides an important ecological solution to help us build a sustainable society.

---

species in a food web in a mature ecosystem is large. So is the number of interactions among these organisms. In a complex ecosystem the elimination of one species would probably have little effect on the ecosystem balance. In sharp contrast, the number of species in the food web of a simple ecosystem is small. The elimination of one species could have repercussions on all other species.

Some ecologists believe that this link has not been adequately tested. They argue that the reason tropical rain forests are stable is that the climate is relatively uniform throughout the year. On the tundra, a relatively simple and somewhat unstable ecosystem, the climate shifts dramatically from season to season. Thus, the stability of the tropical rain forest may result not from species diversity but from its constant climate.

What is the upshot of this debate? Although it is not known for certain whether diversity creates stability, we can say that simplifying ecosystems by reducing species diversity can have deleterious effects. Several examples are discussed in this chapter.

Correcting Imbalance in Ecosystems: Succession

Small shifts in the growth and reduction factors in an ecosystem, whether brought about by natural causes or by humans, are fairly common. Ecosystems respond to these changes in a way that ensures the survival of the community. As this section points out, however, drastic shifts can seriously, sometimes irreversibly, upset ecosystem balance. Nevertheless, nature has its way of healing. This healing process is called succession.

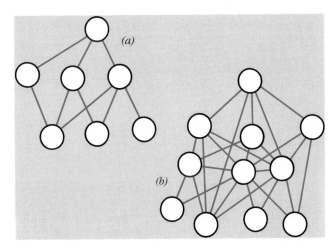

Figure 4-4 (*a*) Food web in a simple ecosystem. Circles represent organisms. Note the lack of links in the simplified web. (*b*) Food web in a complex ecosystem. Many ecologists believe that complex ecosystems are more stable because of the increased number of links, but there is no general agreement on this reason for stability in ecosystems.

Ecology: Subversive or Realistic?
The Subversive Science

William Tucker

The author, a journalist and critic of the environmental movement, has written numerous articles on environmental issues. His latest book, Progress and Privilege, *is a thought-provoking and controversial discussion of environmentalism.*

One of the key realizations of ecology is that the earth is a kind of living system governed by many self-regulating (homeostatic) mechanisms. The earth is in a state of equilibrium. If pushed too far in any one direction, the self-regulating mechanisms can become overloaded and break down, resulting in radical changes.

In its scientific aspects ecology seems to offer an extraordinary broadening of our understanding of life on the planet. Yet with its transfer into the public domain, it has become little more than a sophisticated way of saying "we don't want any more progress." Somehow this exciting discipline has been translated into a very conservative social doctrine. People have often waved the flag of "ecology" as a new way of saying that nature must be preserved and human activity minimized. Ecology has sometimes been touted as being "subversive" to technological progress. It supposedly tells us that our ignorance of natural systems is too great for us to proceed any further with human enterprise. Just as nationalistic conservatives always try to throw a veil of reverence around such concepts as "patriotism" and "national tradition," so environmentalists try to maintain the same indefinable quality around ecosystems.

The lesson environmentalists drive home is that since we do not understand ecosystems in their entirety, and never will, we dare not touch them. Our knowledge is too limited, and nothing should be done until we understand more fully the implications of our actions.

To say that ecology is the science that does not yet grasp the complex interrelationships of organisms is like trying to define medicine as the science that does not yet know how to cure cancer. Environmentalists emphasize the negative parts of the discipline because it fits their concept that we have already had enough technological progress.

The lessons of ecology tell us many things. They tell us that organisms cannot go on reproducing uncontrollably. But they also tell us that many organisms have developed behavioral systems that keep their populations from exploding. The laws of ecology tell us that we cannot throw things away into the environment without having them come back to haunt us. But they also tell us that nature evolved intricate ways of recycling wastes long before human beings appeared, and ecosystems are not as fragile as they seem.

In fact, the whole notion of "fragile ecosystem" is somewhat contradictory. If these systems are so fragile, how could they have survived this long? If ecology teaches us anything, it enhances our appreciation of how resilient nature is, and how tenaciously creatures cling to life in the most severe circumstances. This, of course, should not serve as an invitation for us to see how efficiently we can wipe them out. But it does suggest that the rumors of our powers for destruction may be exaggerated.

The environmentalist interpretation of ecology has been that ecosystems have somehow perfectly evolved, and that human intervention always leads to degradation. It should be clear that even if a particular ecosystem did represent biological perfection, that is not reason in and of itself to preserve it at the expense of human utility. Our ethical position cannot be one of completely detached aesthetic appreciation. We must first be human beings in making our ethical judgments. We cannot be completely on the side of nature.

We are not a group of imbeciles aimlessly poking into the backs of watches or tossing rocks into the gears of Creation. There is purpose to what we do, and it is essentially the same as nature's. We are trying to rearrange the elements of nature for our own survival, comfort, and welfare. We can certainly act stupidly, but we can also act out of wisdom. It is foolish to argue that everything is already perfect and must be left alone. To portray humans as meddling outsiders in an already perfected world is nonsense. In going to this extreme to reaffirm nature, we only deny that we are a part of it.

Environmental writers suggest that we practice an "ecological ethic," extending our moral concerns to other animals, plants, ecosystems, and the entire biosphere. I would accept this proposal, with one important qualification: that is, that our ethical concerns still retain a hierarchy of interest. We should extend our moral concerns to plants, trees, and animals, but not at the expense of human beings. Our first obligation is to humanity. We should avoid actions that are destructive to the biosphere, but we must recognize that at some point our interests are going to impinge upon other living things.

The Realistic Science

Daniel D. Chiras

In January 1987, crossing between the South and North islands of New Zealand, our ship overtook a Greenpeace vessel returning from Antarctica. Greenpeace is an international environmental organization renowned for its courageous—some might say radical—stands against nuclear weapons, dumping of hazardous wastes, whaling, and nuclear power.

When the captain of our ferry announced the presence of the Greenpeace ship, dozens of supporters flooded the deck to wave. The enthusiasm was not universal, however; a few passengers—presumably those who thought that Greenpeace goes too far—grumbled; a few others simply shrugged their shoulders and slouched back in their seats. The response of the crowd on board points out the wide range of public sentiment toward environmentalism.

Environmentalism, like the public's opinion of it, is a varied movement. Founded largely on lessons gleaned from ecology, it attracts a following generally interested in preserving the environment. But that means many things to many people. There is, in fact, no "typical" environmentalist. People sympathetic with the plight of the natural world have not adopted uniform values. Instead, environmentalists' values lie on a broad continuum, from the "complete preservation" philosophy, which tolerates little human intervention, to the "preserve-it-in-parks" philosophy, which seeks to protect small pieces of the environment for future generations to enjoy while developing most of the rest for human use.

Nowhere are environmentalists' beliefs more fractured than on the notion of progress. William Tucker's writings, such as the preceding essay in this Point/Counterpoint, cast environmentalists as narrow-minded obstructionists who condemn out of hand all human progress and technological development. No doubt, many businesspeople feel the same—and for good reason. Environmentalists and the science on which their movement is largely based, ecology, have threatened many a proposed housing project, dam, highway, and mine. In this narrow vein, few could deny that environmentalism is subversive to progress.

The truth, however, is not so simple. Progress is not one thing to all people. The debate over protection versus progress hinges, quite precariously, on this one fundamental statement.

To the environmentalist, progress has a meaning much broader than economic growth, faster jets, growing markets, and new gadgets to make life a little easier. Progress means prospering within the limits of nature, or, in other words, living on earth without destroying the air, water, and soil on which our lives depend. In the language of the ecologist, this means preserving the earth's carrying capacity to ensure sustainability. Progress in this light is human-centered: environmental protection ultimately means protecting people. Planet care is self-care.

Environmentalism looks forward to a better tomorrow, to progress, but with a large measure of realism. It sees that humanity cannot prosper without fundamental changes in the way we go about our day-to-day business. Toward that end, the movement and its high priests prescribe changes, but few people take the environmental message seriously.

Environmentalism seeks to restrain unprincipled avarice to prevent society from destroying the earth's generous and renewable gifts. Ecology has taught environmentalists to look to the future with their eyes wide open, rather than narrowly focused on material welfare, economic wealth, and new conveniences. Ecology tells us that we must be on the side of nature and that in attempting to rearrange the elements of nature to satisfy our needs, we must tread carefully.

Ecology and environmental science have taught us that human activities often have profound influences on the natural world and that what we do to the earth and water and sky we do to ourselves. The dust bowl days, the great deserts now spreading through Africa, and destruction of the once-rich Fertile Crescent are blatant reminders of our colossal impact, as are the threats of acid precipitation, the greenhouse effect, and stratospheric ozone depletion.

Critics of the environmental movement see the warnings it issues as unfounded pessimism. They see its opposition to new technologies or wilderness destruction as subversive to progress. Environmentalists, however, see their goal as promoting careful stewardship of our resources with one end in mind: to preserve ecosystem stability so that we may all live well. A key piece of their solution is population control.

The crux of the disagreement between the environmentalists and the "developmentalists" lies in each group's view of progress and of the importance of humankind in the natural world. Environmentalism recognizes the interdependence of all life forms and seeks to protect the rest of the living world as a means of protecting human life. There are those in the movement who see life as precious, worth preserving for its own sake. To do so requires the wholesale protection of other species—preserving the rich biological heritage we inherited from our forebears and passing it on to our descendants.

Ecology, transferred to the public domain, is a realistic science, not a subversive one. It is emerging at a time when modern society badly needs direction. It offers great hope to those people who recognize the limitations of our world. It asks, simply, that we control ourselves—a seemingly elusive form of progress far more difficult, it appears, than sending men and women into space or tapping the energy of nuclear power.

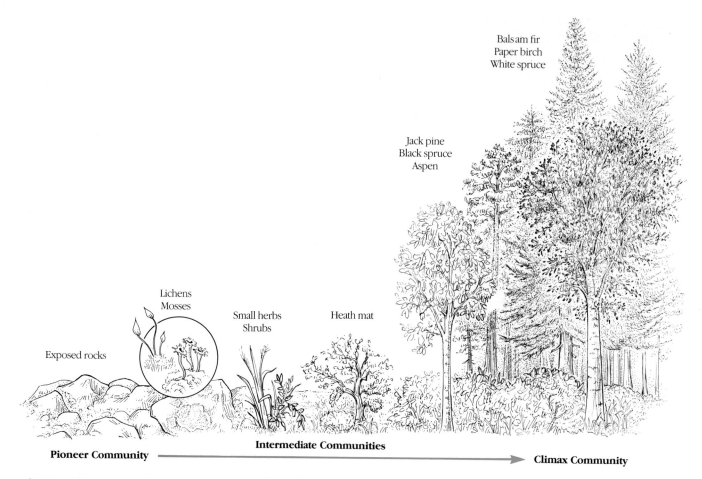

Balsam fir
Paper birch
White spruce

Jack pine
Black spruce
Aspen

Lichens
Mosses

Small herbs
Shrubs

Heath mat

Exposed rocks

Intermediate Communities

Pioneer Community ⟶ **Climax Community**

Figure 4-5   Primary succession. Here, exposed rock goes through a series of changes as one biotic community replaces another until a mature community is formed. During succession the plants of each community alter their habitat so drastically that conditions become more suitable for other species.

Walk along a forest path in the aftermath of a volcanic eruption or a forest fire sparked by lightning. Or travel the dusty path over abandoned surface mines or carelessly logged forests. Life sprouts out of the ashes or in the unstable soils; but for these places to return to their predisaster stages, years or decades must pass. If the soil washes away before nature can apply her healing craft, recovery may be impossible.

A biotic community destroyed by natural or human causes recovers in a series of changes in which one community is gradually replaced by another until the mature, or climax, community is reached. This process is called **succession**. Biotic communities can also form where none previously existed; they start out slowly but can eventually form mature communities. This is also called succession. We will take a look at both kinds of succession.

Primary Succession

Primary succession is the sequential development of a biotic community where none had existed. For instance, when the great glaciers began to retreat 15,000 years ago, large areas of barren land and rock were exposed. The exposed rock became populated with lichens (Figure 4-5). The lichens thrived for a while but were gradually replaced by mosses. The mosses were eventually replaced by ferns, grasses, and larger plants, which eventually gave way to shrubs and trees.

Understanding the process of succession requires a closer look at each plant community in this procession from barren rock to the climax community. Lichens, the first inhabitants, spread over a rock's surface. Clinging to the rock, living off moisture from the rain and organic nutrients from photosynthesis, these organisms secrete a weak acid, called carbonic acid. Carbonic acid dissolves rock, liberating nutrients and helping to make soil. Tiny insects may join the lichens, forming a **pioneer community**, the first community to become established in a once-barren environment.

The lichens and insects gradually change their environment; the consequences of such changes are dire for them. Capturing windblown dirt particles, for example, the lichens promote further soil development. Dead lichens crumble and become part of the soil, along with the remains of insects, fungi, and bacteria. Over time, enough soil develops for mosses to take root. The mosses shade the lichens and eventually kill them. Mosses, fungi, bacteria, and insects form a new community. This community, however, also brings about changes, which will eventually usher in still another community. The rise and fall of communities proceeds until the climax community forms.

Two additional examples of primary succession are the settlement of plants on a newly formed volcanic island and the conversion of a lake to a forest ecosystem. (The latter is illustrated in Figure 4-6.)

Secondary Succession

Secondary succession is the sequential development of biotic communities after the complete or partial destruction of an existing community. Usually the long, slow development of soil that takes place in primary succession is unnecessary. A climax community or intermediate community may be destroyed by natural events such as volcanic eruptions, floods, droughts, fires, and storms or by human intervention such as agriculture, intentional flooding, fire, or mining.

Abandoned farm fields provide an excellent opportunity to observe secondary succession (Figure 4-7). Former farmland is first invaded by hardy species, such as crabgrass or broom sedge, depending on the area. These plants are well adapted to survive in bare, sun-baked soil. In the eastern United States crabgrass, insects, and mice invade abandoned fields, forming pioneer communities. But crabgrass is soon joined by tall grasses and other herbaceous plants. The newcomers' shade eventually eliminates the sun-loving crabgrass. Tall grasses and other herbaceous plants dominate the ecosystem for few years along with a variety of animals, such as mice, woodchucks, rabbits, insects, and seed-eating birds.

In time, pine seeds settle in the area, and pine seedlings begin to spring up in the open field. Like crabgrass the pine trees flourish in the sunny fields. Over the next three decades pines shade out the grasses and herbs. Animals that feed on grasses, such as woodchucks, move on to more hospitable environments. Squirrels and chipmunks,

which prefer a wooded habitat, invade the new ecosystem.

Shade from the pines gradually creates an inhospitable environment for pine seedlings and a favorable environment for the growth of shade-tolerant hardwood trees such as maple and oak. As a result, hardwoods begin to take root and eventually tower over the pines; their shade gradually kills the pines, which had invaded 60 years earlier.

Succession is a race to catch the sun. Each plant stretches out its leaves to monopolize the sunlight. Succession is a process of change that is internally driven. Plants shape the environment first by making soil. The success of a plant community, however, always leads to its destruction, until the final stage is reached and a climax community is formed. At this point, the struggle to monopolize sunlight is over.

During succession, animal populations shift with the changing plant communities. The early stages in succession are characterized by a low species diversity, but the plant and animal populations rapidly expand to exploit the untapped resources of the ecosystem (Table 4-1). Because there are fewer species in the early stages of succession, food webs tend to be simple, and populations tend to be volatile. Mature biotic communities, on the other hand, have a high species diversity and stable populations. Food webs are intricate, and stability is therefore assured if changes are not too drastic.

As ecosystems become increasingly complex, the food chains become woven into more complex food webs. The grazer food chain accounts for the bulk of the biomass flow in immature or developing ecosystems. In mature ecosystems, however, most of the biomass flows through the detritus food chain. In fact, in a mature forest less than 10% of the net primary productivity is consumed by grazers.

In mature ecosystems the nutrients are cycled more efficiently with less loss. Whereas immature, or developing, ecosystems tend to lose a considerable amount of their nutrients because of erosion and other factors, mature systems are better able to entrap and hold nutrients.

Pioneer and intermediate communities are in a state of imbalance. The imbalance exists because the abiotic and biotic factors that regulate population size are constantly changing. For instance, there is initially little environmental resistance to crabgrass or lichens, so there are few limitations to growth. Thus, the growth factors such as the availability of food, favorable light, and optimum temperature stimulate a population expansion much like that seen in the hyacinth-choked waters of Florida.

During succession each community goes through a phase of increasing environmental resistance as competitors rise in number and as biotic conditions shift (Figure

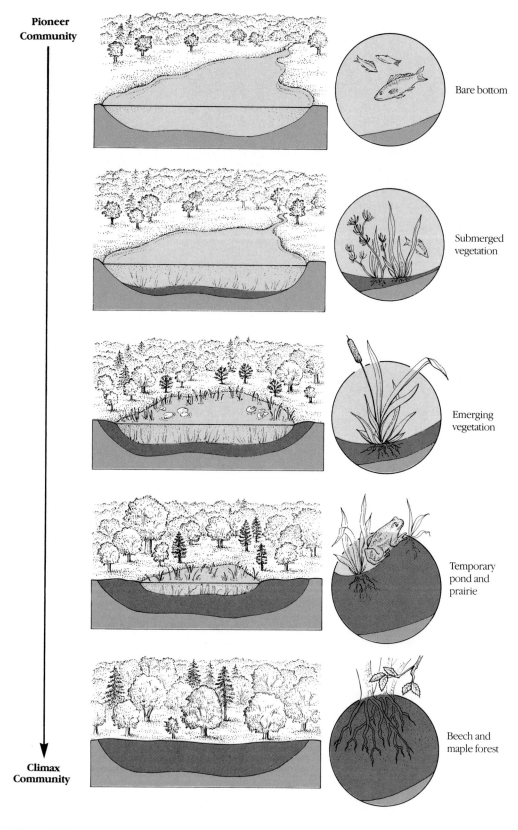

Pioneer Community

Bare bottom

Submerged vegetation

Emerging vegetation

Temporary pond and prairie

Beech and maple forest

Climax Community

Figure 4-6   Primary succession. In this example a pond is gradually converted into a forest ecosystem. Sediments accumulate on the bottom. Bottom-dwelling vegetation takes root. A series of biotic communities develops until the mature ecosystem is reached.

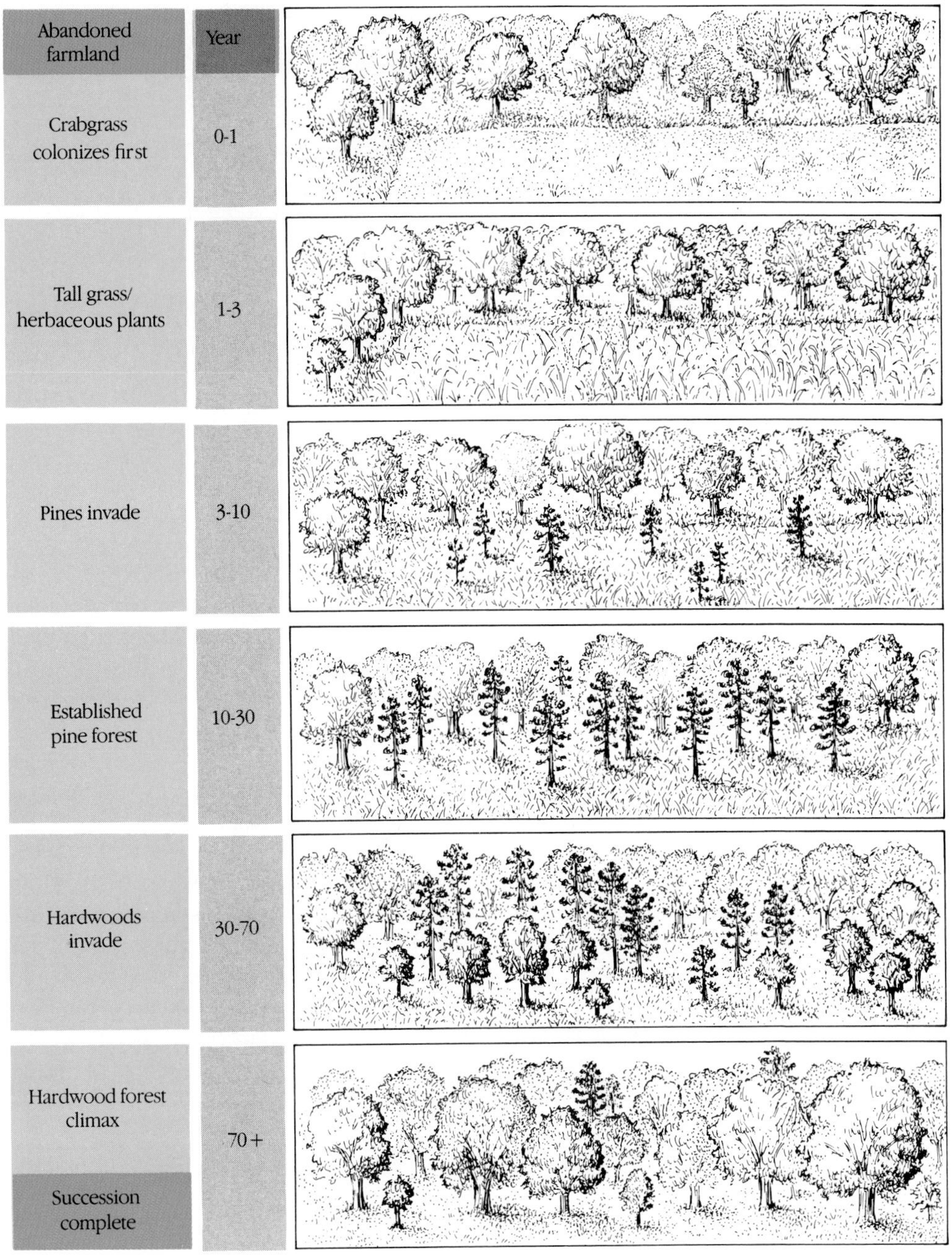

Abandoned farmland	Year
Crabgrass colonizes first	0-1

Tall grass/ herbaceous plants	1-3

Pines invade	3-10

Established pine forest	10-30

Hardwoods invade	30-70

Hardwood forest climax	70+
Succession complete	

Figure 4-7 Secondary succession. Here, abandoned eastern U.S. farmland is gradually replaced by crabgrass, which in turn gives way to other herbaceous plants. Trees move in, and over time a mature hardwood ecosystem is formed.

4-8). When environmental resistance accelerates, the population declines, and a new community establishes itself.

Human Impact on Ecosystems

Throughout human history we have used our knowledge to gain control over the environment—to shape it to our liking and enhance our survival. But our understandable search for control and security has not always produced the desired outcome. Water hyacinth–choked rivers, polluted streams, acidic rainfall, radioactive spills, energy shortages, runaway population growth, and a host of other common maladies are often the unanticipated results of our actions.

This section examines two general ways in which humans alter the biosphere: they tamper with either the biotic or the abiotic factors. This material is worth close study. What we do to the biosphere, we also do to ourselves.

Tampering with Biotic Factors

Introducing Competitors Early in the morning on June 9, 1985, Bill Wilson, who operates a front-end loader for the Chevron Corporation in southern California,

Table 4-1 Characteristics of Mature and Immature Ecosystems

Characteristic	Immature Ecosystem	Mature Ecosystem
Food chains	Linear, predominantly grazer	Weblike, predominantly detritus
Net productivity	High	Low
Species diversity	Low	High
Niche specialization	Broad	Narrow
Nutrient cycles	Open	Closed
Nutrient conservation	Poor	Good
Stability	Low	Higher

Source: Modified from Odum, E. (1969). The Strategy of Ecosystem Development. *Science* 164: 262–270. Copyright 1969 by the American Association for the Advancement of Science.

watched in amazement as a swarm of bees attacked and killed a rabbit, stinging it to death. To his further surprise, when they had finished the kill, the swarm of several thousand bees came after him. Fortunately, he was protected from the onslaught by a glass enclosure on his vehicle. The bees that had attacked Wilson were so-called killer bees, newly arrived from South America.

The killer bee is actually an African honeybee which lives in hives with 30,000 to 80,000 ill-tempered cohorts. It was brought to the New World quite intentionally. In 1956 a geneticist, Warwick Kerr, imported some African honeybees to Venezuela in an attempt to develop a successful stock of honey producers. The docile European bees used previously had fared poorly in the tropical climate. Kerr thought that interbreeding the two might yield a more successful tropical strain.

Knowing their aggressiveness, the researcher isolated the bees in screened-in hives. But in 1957 a visitor unwittingly lifted the screen, allowing 26 queens to escape with their entourage. Trouble soon began. The killer bees quickly spread, moving a remarkable 350 to 500 kilometers (200 to 300 miles) a year, interbreeding with honeybees, and destroying the honey industry in Venezuela and other countries. And that's not all. Bees assaulted people, horses, and livestock that crossed their paths.

Killer bees arrived in the United States by ship, many experts think, accompanying a load of pipe from South America. So far, California officials have located at least four colonies and have destroyed hundreds of commercial beehives to destroy any killer bees that may have mixed with the colonies.

Experts worry about the impact of the bee on the $140-million U.S. honey industry. Should it spread into northern climates and breed with its tamer cousin, the killer bee could put an end to honey production. Hives would have to be destroyed to prevent further spread and attacks. The loss of honey production would, however, be minor compared with the indirect effect of losing America's honeybees. Each year honeybees pollinate 90 major crops, worth $19 billion.

The saga of the African honeybee is one of a number of biological nightmares created by the introduction of a foreign species into a new region. But not all such intro-

Figure 4-8 A simplified graphic representation of changing population size and environmental resistance as a community develops and is eventually replaced during succession. Note that environmental resistance increases as a new community develops. Resistance is caused by unfavorable conditions created by the community itself.

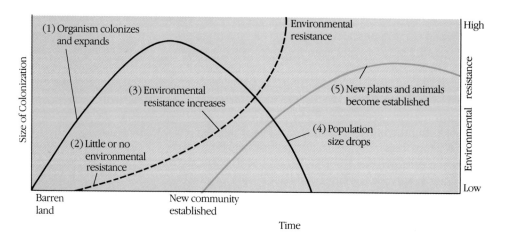

(a)

(b)

Figure 4-9 (*a*) Rabbits introduced in small numbers to Australia increased dramatically in a few years, posing a major environmental problem. They ate vegetation intended for sheep and cost the government and ranchers millions of dollars. (*b*) Widespread destruction caused by rabbits in Australia. Range on the right was protected by rabbit-proof fencing.

ductions have adverse effects. The ring-necked pheasant and chukar partridge, both aliens in this country, have done well in some areas. In other cases alien species have perished without a trace. Hardy species such as the killer bee, however, are the ones that demand our attention and remind us of the folly of careless introductions.

Consider what happened when rabbits were intentionally introduced into Australia. Twelve pairs of European rabbits were brought into the country in 1859 and released on a private ranch. In a few years the rabbits had proliferated wildly and begun eating grass intended for sheep, creating a major national environmental problem (Figure 4-9). Five rabbits eat as much grass as one sheep. Despite a major campaign to remove rabbits from Australia, by 1953 over a billion were inhabiting 3 million square kilometers (1.2 million square miles).

Plants, such as the prickly pear cactus or water hyacinth, can also reproduce uncontrollably in foreign environments. Taking over a new territory, they can wipe out native populations that compete for the same habitat. The results can be ecologically and economically disastrous.

Eliminating or Introducing Predators
Predators have never fared well in human societies. Early hunters and gatherers killed them for food and because they viewed them as competition for prey. Modern societies

have carried on this dangerous tradition, killing bears, eagles, hawks, wolves, coyotes, and mountain lions with a vengeance, often with serious ecological consequences.

One such example took place on the Kaibab Plateau, on the north rim of the Grand Canyon. In the early 1900s the state of Arizona put a bounty on wolves, coyotes, and mountain lions, which triggered their wholesale slaughter. Within 15 years virtually all of these predators had been eliminated. This intervention spawned an ecological catastrophe. Without its natural control, the deer population soared from 4000 to about 100,000 by 1924. The deer overgrazed the plateau; approximately 60,000 died from starvation in the following winters. The vegetation has still not completely recovered.

Occasionally, however, predators are introduced into areas with adverse effects. The mosquito fish, a native of the southeastern United States, has been introduced into many subtropical regions throughout the world because it eats the larvae of mosquitoes and therefore helps to control malaria, a mosquito-borne disease. Unfortunately, the mosquito fish also feeds heavily on zooplankton, single-celled organisms that consume algae. By depleting zooplankton populations the mosquito fish removes environmental resistance that curbs algal growth. This causes algae to proliferate and form thick mats that reduce light penetration and plant growth in aquatic ecosystems.

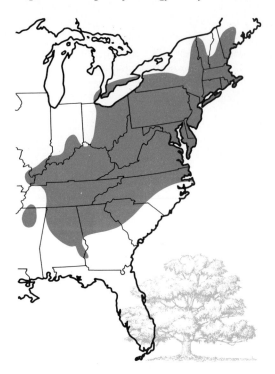

Figure 4-10 Former range of the American chestnut, a species nearly wiped out by the accidental introduction of a harmful fungus.

These examples illustrate that altering the trophic structure by introducing or eliminating predators can drastically affect ecosystems and human populations as well.

Introducing Disease Organisms Pathogenic (disease-producing) organisms are a natural part of ecosystems. Humans have unwittingly introduced pathogens into new environments where there are no natural controls. There, they have reproduced at a high rate and caused serious damage.

In the late 1800s, for example, a fungus that infects Chinese chestnuts was introduced accidentally into the United States. It had been carried in with several Chinese chestnut trees brought to the New York Zoological Park. The Chinese chestnut has evolved mechanisms to combat the fungus and is immune to it. But the American chestnut, once a valuable commercial tree found in much of the eastern United States, had no resistance at all and was virtually eliminated from this country between 1910 and 1940 (Figure 4-10). Now chestnut wood is found only in antiques, and the once-abundant American chestnut, a tasty seed commonly roasted in embers, is only a memory of our grandparents.

Tampering with Abiotic Factors

Humans also tamper with many abiotic factors by polluting the air, water, and land and by depleting resources, such as water. The consequences can be as significant as those from our manipulation of the biotic world.

Pollution Water pollution and air pollution create an unfavorable environment for many living organisms. Chlorinated compounds released into rivers from wastewater treatment plants, for example, can virtually eliminate the native fish. Oil spills on lakes, rivers, and oceans destroy fish, reptiles, and birds. Toxic pesticides eliminate birds that feed on contaminated insects and fish. Thermal pollution from power plants kills fish and many aquatic organisms on which fish feed. Possible global changes in temperature brought about by increasing atmospheric carbon dioxide could alter climate in many regions of the world, possibly eliminating thousands of species of plants and animals. In these and many other cases, human activities create an unfavorable abiotic environment that can reduce or eliminate species and upset the ecological balance.

Resource Depletion Human populations deplete or destroy resources used by other species, too. The diversion of mountain streams to supply growing cities, for instance, has left many waterways dry. Housing developments along coastlines are often made possible by filling in estuaries and marshes with dirt (Figure 4-11). Full-scale oil shale development may destroy the valuable wintering grounds of thousands of mule deer in Colorado, possibly resulting in the decimation of deer populations in the western part of the state.

Simplifying Ecosystems

Tampering with abiotic and biotic factors tends to simplify an ecosystem by reducing species diversity. A reduction in species diversity may cause ecosystem imbalance and eventual collapse.

Ecosystem simplification is best seen when natural ecosystems are converted into farmland. Grassland contains many species of plants and animals. When plowed under and planted in one crop, called a **monoculture**, the field becomes simplified and vulnerable to insects, disease, drought, wind, and adverse weather.

The reasons for this susceptibility are many. Perhaps one of the most important is that monocultures provide a virtually unlimited food source for insects and plant pathogens, especially viruses and fungi. As crops grow, food supplies increase dramatically, favoring massive growth of pest populations. Viruses, fungi, and insects become major pests. Monocultures provide little or no environmental resistance.

Figure 4-11 Parts of Miami are built on coastal areas that were once marshland.

The need to protect monocultures leads to many far-reaching problems. For instance, farmers have long used chemical pesticides to control outbreaks of pests. Chemical pesticides used to control fungi, viruses, and insects may be carried in the air or water to natural ecosystems, where they may poison beneficial organisms such as honeybees. The widespread use of DDT in the United States contaminated many terrestrial and aquatic ecosystems. Passed through the food chain, DDT reached high levels in top-level consumers, including ospreys, brown pelicans, and peregrine falcons (Figure 4-12). This poison did not kill the birds outright; rather, it interfered with the deposition of calcium in their eggshells, resulting in thinning of the shells. The fragile eggs were easily broken. Few embryos survived, and populations fell sharply, reminding us of an important biological principle: an organism lives as it breeds.

The peregrine falcon, which nests on rocky ledges throughout the United States, was nearly destroyed by DDT (Figure 4-12). By the time scientists had determined that the decline in reproduction was the result of DDT, none of the 200 known pairs east of the Mississippi River

Figure 4-12 Peregrine falcon and her chick. The peregrine, once a nearly extinct species in the United States, has made a remarkable comeback with the assistance of researchers who have incubated eggs in captivity and released birds in the wild. DDT used to protect human crops caused eggshell thinning in peregrines and other species, nearly eliminating the natural populations of these birds.

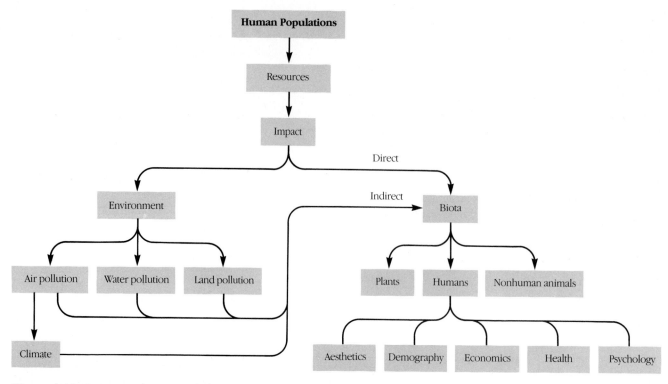

Figure 4-13   Impact Analysis model, showing the range of impacts caused by human activities.

were successfully producing young. Fortunately for the peregine falcon, DDT was banned in the United States (but still manufactured here until 1984), and a determined program was mounted that may well save these birds. By 1982 over 1000 peregrines had been raised in captivity and released into the wild by ornithologists from Cornell and Colorado State universities. The release program in the eastern United States was to end by 1987, since the population was expected to be reestablished and stable. By the early 1990s recovery should be complete in the Rockies, too.

This example shows how arduously we must work to protect simplified ecosystems such as farms and the effects that our protective measures can have. The story of the peregrine falcon, like so many other species that have been brought back from the brink of extinction, is one of personal triumph and dedication. By using ecological caution in releasing a powerful toxin into the environment, however, we could have eliminated a great deal of the cost and effort.

Impact Analysis Model

In Chapter 2 we saw how human life-styles and needs have changed over the millenia. In particular, we looked at the changing impact of human populations—how

humans have become a major molding force in the environment and how increasing technological development and increasing population size have affected the environment.

To develop a deeper understanding of human impact, let us briefly examine the model illustrated in Figure 4-13. This simplified version of the **Impact Analysis model** shows that humans have an impact on the environment—the air, water, and land—as well as the biota, the plant, animal, and microbial inhabitants of the environment. Impact analysis is far more than an intellectual exercise; it is the basis of environmental impact statements, which must be prepared for almost all major construction projects (see Chapter Supplement 21-1).

The Impact of Coal Use

To illustrate the Impact Analysis model, let us take a brief look at the mining and combustion of coal in the United States. Environmental impacts include air, water, and land pollution (Figure 4-13). Air pollution may result from mining or related activities such as trucks traveling on dirt roads near mines. Combustion of coal to generate electricity creates a much larger air pollution problem. A single 1000-megawatt coal-fired power plant, which serves roughly 1 million people, emits approximately 1500 to 30,000 metric tons (1650 to 33,000 tons) of particulates (smoke and ash) and 11,000 to 110,000 metric tons (12,000 to 121,000 tons) of sulfur dioxide gas each year.

Water pollution can also be caused by coal mining. In abandoned underground coal mines in the eastern United States, for example, certain sulfur-bearing minerals (iron pyrite) react with oxygen and water to produce highly caustic sulfuric acid. This acid drains from the mine and pollutes rivers and lakes downstream (Chapter 11).

Land pollution occurs from the actual mining of coal. In the West huge surface mines are used to reach the thick beds of coal. Large draglines rip up the surface to dig down to the coal, in the process destroying the vegetation.

Indirect Effects of Human Activities All of the forms of pollution described above affect organisms. For example, the sulfur dioxide produced by coal-fired power plants is converted to sulfuric acid in the atmosphere; carried as small droplets in the air, this acid may be washed from the sky by rain or snow. This phenomenon, acid precipitation, occurs widely in the eastern half of the United States and in Canada. In particularly susceptible regions such as southern Canada and the Adirondack Mountains of New York, acids have destroyed several hundred lakes. Lakes once known for sport fishing have turned acidic, and virtually all life has been destroyed in them. (For more on acid precipitation see Chapter Supplement 15-2).

Water pollutants affect a variety of organisms. Acid draining from coal mines in the East kills fish and aquatic plants. It corrodes bridges, locks, barges, pumps, and other metallic structures, costing millions of dollars a year for repair and replacement.

These examples illustrate a few of the many impacts of coal mining and combustion on the environment (for additional examples, see Chapter 11), showing us the indirect ways in which the environmental pollutants affect biological organisms, including humans.

Direct Effects of Human Activities Human activities may also have direct impacts on the biota. Surface mining in the West, for example, destroys the habitat of elk, pronghorn antelope, and prairie dogs. In the Yellowstone River basin, an area richly endowed with thick coal seams, about 36,440 hectares (90,000 acres) of land will be mined between 1977 and 2000. The impacts on native wildlife populations will be severe. Disturbance of land will also affect underground water supplies, requiring landowners to redrill wells that supply water for livestock and human uses.

A large increase in coal mining may result in changes in populations in nearby towns. These are called **demographic changes**. The town of Craig in northwestern Colorado, for example, experienced a rapid influx of miners

and their families between 1970 and 1980. With this came a tripling in the crime rate. Many other towns in the United States, like Craig, were hit hard by the sudden upturn in coal production in the late 1970s. In most cases they did not have enough housing for newcomers. Schools, hospitals, sewage systems, water supply systems, stores, and recreational facilities were inadequate for their swelling populations and had to be upgraded at considerable expense. As a consequence of the influx of miners, the whole social fabric of communities has changed almost overnight. Quaint agricultural towns have become noisy and crowded.

Why Study Impacts?

The Impact Analysis model is helpful when studying the effects of a particular technology, such as coal or oil shale development. It shows the areas that should be examined when making an impact analysis.

We study impact before we build roads, dams, power plants, gravel pits, and other projects, to better understand how we will affect the environment. Commonly, too little is known about the impact of human activities to make predictions concerning overall damage. As a result, we must often rely on educated guesswork or speculation.

One of the dangers of speculation is that it is imprecise. Estimates may be off by 100% or more; people forget that estimates are based on many assumptions that may not be accurate. Even though the uncertainties and assumptions are disclosed in scientific studies, people have a tendency to omit the qualifiers. Thus, what is a tentative judgment becomes an ironclad fact. The statement "Under certain weather conditions, the proposed coal-fired power plant may cause damage to neighboring crops" may be transformed into "Coal Plant Will Damage Crops." The dangers of this distortion are obvious.

Assessing the Probability of Impacts

One way of dealing with uncertainty is to carefully analyze impacts with respect to the *degree of probability* of their occurrence. Figure 4-14 illustrates how this analysis might be done. First, when analyzing a potential impact, determine the probability of its happening. For convenience, probability can be divided into four levels: high, medium, low, and unknown. High probability is indicated when the data supporting a given conclusion are strong and numerous. Medium probability is indicated when the impact is suspected but there is some uncertainty. Low probability is assigned when the impact might theoretically happen but the data do not support the contention. The fourth level of uncertainty—unknown probability—might also be added when there are no data at all showing either an impact or the absence of one.

Figure 4-14 also takes into account a much overlooked

Figure 4-14 Impact analysis chart is used for summarizing the positive and negative effects of a given technology or potential hazard. As an aid in decision making, impacts are listed according to the degree of probability of their occurrence.

Impacts		High Probability	Medium Probability	Low Probability	Unknown Probability
Air pollution	+				
	−				
Water pollution	+				
	−				
Land pollution	+				
	−				
Plants	+				
	−				
Humans	+				
	−				
Nonhuman animals	+				
	−				

variable—the fact that not all impacts are deleterious. As mentioned earlier, removing trees from forests in large numbers opens up meadows, which are used by elk for grazing. By indicating the positive as well as the negative impacts, a more balanced analysis of the impacts can be made.

For the first time in the whole history of evolution, responsibility for the continued unfolding of evolution has been placed upon the evolutionary material itself. . . . Whether we like it or not, we are now the custodians of the evolutionary process on earth. Within our own hands—or rather, within our own minds— lies the evolutionary future of the planet.

PETER RUSSELL

Summary

Mature ecosystems change with time but remain more or less the same from one year to the next. They are said to be in a state of **dynamic equilibrium**, or a **steady state**. Ecosystem stability is the ability of an ecosystem to resist change (**inertia**) or return to its original condition after it is disturbed (**resilience**).

Biotic and abiotic components of an ecosystem cause the increase and decrease of populations and ultimately determine ecosystem balance. Those that increase population size are called **growth factors**; those that depress it are called **reduction**

factors, which collectively produce **environmental resistance**.

Species diversity is considered by many ecologists to be one of the more important factors determining ecosystem stability, although direct evidence supporting this hypothesis is rare. We do know that simplifying ecosystems by reducing species diversity tends to make them more vulnerable to insects, adverse weather, and disease-producing organisms.

Small shifts in the biotic or abiotic growth or reduction factors may temporarily tip ecosystem balance, but appropriate responses within the biological community can return the system to normal. Larger shifts may result in a dramatic destabilization of the ecosystem, resulting in its collapse. A biological community destroyed by such large shifts may recover during a process known as **secondary succession**, in which new communities develop sequentially on the remains of the old until a mature, or climax, community is formed. **Primary succession**, on the other hand, is the sequential development of communities where none previously existed.

Humans cause imbalance in an ecosystem by altering its biotic or abiotic components. Introducing or eliminating competitors, predators, and pathogenic organisms, for example, can permanently disrupt ecosystem balance. Pollution and resource depletion may have the same effect. Tampering with abiotic or biotic factors in the ecosystem can reduce species diversity and simplify ecosystems. **Monocultures**, huge single-crop plantings, represent extreme ecosystem simplifications that are vulnerable to insects, disease, and adverse weather.

Discussion Questions

1. Describe ecosystem stability. Give an example of an ecosystem you are familiar with. Is it stable? Why or why not?

2. If you were to examine a mature ecosystem over the course of 30 years at the same time each year, would you expect the number of species and the population size of each species to be the same from year to year? Why or why not?

3. What is environmental resistance? What role does it play in population balance? What role does it play in ecosystem balance?

4. Give evidence that species diversity affects ecosystem stability. Is there any evidence to contradict this idea? What is it?

5. What is a mature ecosystem? What are its major features?

6. Describe temporary imbalances caused in ecosystems you are familiar with and how the ecosystems return to normal.

7. Why is one biotic community eventually replaced by another during succession?

8. What is the difference between primary and secondary succession? Give examples of both.

9. What is a pioneer community?

10. Describe how introducing competitors into an ecosystem can affect ecosystem stability. Give some examples.

11. How do humans tamper with abiotic ecosystem components? Give some examples, and trace the effect on plants and animals.

12. "Humans are like all other organisms in many respects, except they greatly simplify their ecosystem." Is this statement true? Why is it necessary for humans to simplify ecosystems? How can it be avoided? Give some examples.

13. From an evolutionary standpoint, discuss why simplified ecosystems (monocultures) are highly susceptible to fungi, viruses, and insects.

Suggested Readings

Attenborough, D. (1979). *Life on Earth*. Boston: Little, Brown. Superb study of life.

Clapham, W. B. (1983). *Natural Ecosystems* (2nd ed.). New York: Macmillan. Advanced treatise on ecology.

Colinvaux, P. (1973). *Introduction to Ecology*. New York: Wiley. An excellent textbook of basic ecology.

Kormondy, E. J. (1969). *Concepts of Ecology*. Englewood Cliffs, N.J.: Prentice-Hall. Excellent introduction.

Lederer, R. J. (1984). *Ecology and Field Biology*. Menlo Park, Calif.: Benjamin/Cummings. Intermediate-level coverage of basic ecology.

Rodgers, C. L., and Kerstetter, R. E. (1974). *The Ecosphere: Organisms, Habitats, and Disturbances*. New York: Harper and Row. A good account on biomes and human disturbance.

Smith, R. L. (1976). *The Ecology of Man: An Ecosystem Approach* (2nd ed.). New York: Harper and Row. Advanced readings on ecology and environmental problems.

Smith, R. L. (1980). *Ecology and Field Biology* (3rd ed.). New York: Harper and Row. A comprehensive textbook.

Nuclear War: Pathway to Environmental Catastrophe

Air pollution, water pollution, and resource depletion—all of these are major environmental problems facing modern civilization. Their effects, however, pale by comparison with the environmental catastrophe that would follow a nuclear war. A glimpse into the consequences of such an event provides a sometimes shocking view of the potential that humanity has for disrupting the biosphere.

The Nuclear Detonation

A nuclear explosion produces (1) enormous amounts of heat and light, (2) an explosive blast and high winds, (3) intense radiation (radiation is described Chapter Supplement 12-1), (4) a pulse of electromagnetic energy, and (5) radioactive dust called **fallout** (Figure S4-1).

Heat and Light

About a third of the energy from a nuclear explosion is released as heat and light. The light flash may produce temporary blindness in victims looking at the explosion. This is called **flash blindness** and lasts only a few minutes in most people. However, individuals gazing directly at the fireball may never completely recover their eyesight; some may be permanently blinded.

The most common injury among survivors of atomic explosions is burns resulting from the intense heat flash. Even people standing 11 kilometers (7 miles) from a 1-megaton explosion, for example, would suffer first-degree burns (similar to sunburn) on their exposed skin; 1.6 kilometers (1 mile) closer, and their exposed skin would blister from the heat. Another 1.6 kilometers closer, and their exposed skin would be charred by the heat from the blast.

Severe burns are one of the greatest threats to human life in an atomic explosion. In a major city many burn victims would die from shock soon after an explosion. The heat flash would also ignite any combustible material in its path, turning the city into an inferno and killing many other people.

Explosive Blast and Winds

Several seconds after the heat and light flashes sweep through the area surrounding a bomb detonation site, air pressure rises. This increase is called **static overpressure** and is measured in pounds per square inch (Table S4-1). Although the pressure increase is rather small, it is forceful enough to topple houses and office buildings and rupture eardrums. Tens of thousands of people would be crushed by collapsing buildings if a bomb exploded near a major city during working hours.

Accompanying the static overpressure are intense winds (Table S4-1). A bomb with the explosive power of 1 million tons of TNT (1 megaton) produces winds of 290 kilometers per hour (180 miles per hour) 6.5 kilometers (4 miles) from the detonation site. These would fan fires and damage power lines, homes, and trees. Flying debris would injure any people and animals within range.

Figure S4-1 Fireball and mushroom cloud produced by a thermonuclear blast.

Table S4-1 Blast Effects of Nuclear Explosions[1]

Distance from Explosion		1-Kiloton Weapon	150-Kiloton Weapon	1-Megaton Weapon	10-Metagon Weapon
1 mile	Overpressure: Winds:	1.4 psi 50 mph Cuts and blows from flying debris; many buildings moderately damaged	18 psi 420 mph Humans battered to death; heavy machinery dragged; reinforced concrete building severely damaged	43 psi 1700 mph Many humans killed	Above 200 psi Above 2000 mph Buried 20-centimeter-thick concrete arch destroyed
2 miles	Overpressure: Winds:	.5 psi Below 35 mph Many broken windows	6 psi 190 mph Some eardrums ruptured; bones fractured; all trees blown down; telephone lines dragged severely	17 psi 400 mph Humans battered to death; lung hemorrhage; eardrums ruptured; heavy machinery dragged severely	50 psi 1800 mph Humans fatally crushed; severe damage to buried light corrugated steel arch
5 miles	Overpressure: Winds:		1.5 psi 55 mph Cuts and blows from flying debris; many buildings moderately damaged	4 psi 130 mph Bones fractured; 90% of trees down; many buildings flattened	14 psi 330 mph Eardrums ruptured; lung hemorrhage; reinforced concrete building severely damaged
10 miles	Overpressure: Winds:	.6 psi Below 35 mph Many broken windows	1.4 psi 50 mph Cuts and blows from flying debris; many buildings moderately damaged	4.4 psi 150 mph Bones fractured; 90% of trees down; many buildings flattened	
20 miles	Overpressure: Winds:			Below 1 psi Below 35 mph many broken windows	1.5 psi 55 mph Cuts and blows from flying debris; many buildings moderately damaged
40 miles	Overpressure: Winds:				Below 1 psi Below 35 mph Many broken windows

[1]The range of effects required dictates the optimum height at which the weapon would be detonated.
Source: Goodwin, P. (1981). *Nuclear War: The Facts on Our Survival.* New York: Rutledge Press, pp. 28–29.

Table S4-2 Facts about Nuclear Explosions[1]

Weapon Yield	1-Kiloton	150-Kiloton	1-Megaton	10-Megaton	20-Megaton
Fireball maximum size	220 feet	1580 feet	3400 feet	8450 feet	11,350 feet
Minimum height of explosion for no local fallout	180 feet	1320 feet	2750 feet	6850 feet	9250 feet
Crater width (inner lip)[2]	126 feet	530 feet	950 feet	1800 feet	2300 feet
Crater depth[2]	28 feet	140 feet	210 feet	420 feet	530 feet
Range of lethal initial radiation (500 rads)	.5 mile	1.2 miles	1.6 miles	2.5 miles	3 miles
Range for skin reddening	.5 mile	5.5 miles	10 miles	24 miles	30 miles
Range for charred skin	.4 mile	3.5 miles	8 miles	18 miles	23 miles
Range for 2% of buildings gutted by fire (2-psi blast)	.8 mile	4.2 miles	8 miles	17 miles	22 miles
Range for 10% of buildings gutted by fire (5-psi blast)	.4 mile	2.2 miles	4.3 miles	9.3 miles	12 miles
Range for fatal wind drag (a human could be dragged along at 40 feet per second)	.2 mile	1.6 miles	3.3 miles	8 miles	10 miles
Duration of severe blast (4 psi)	.3 second	1.8 seconds	3 seconds	7 seconds	9 seconds
Arrival time of blast wave (4 psi)	2 seconds after flash	10 seconds after flash	20 seconds after flash	42 seconds after flash	53 seconds after flash
Range of devastation for above-ground buildings (12 psi)	.3 mile	1.3 miles	2.5 miles	5 miles	7 miles
Range of severe blast damage (4 psi)	.5 mile	2.6 miles	5 miles	11 miles	13 miles
Range at which all windows broken (1 psi)	1.3 mile	7 miles	13 miles	28 miles	36 miles

[1]The range of effects required dictates the explosion's optimum height. For example, when a 1-megaton weapon is exploded at 5000 feet there is a 1.2-mile range of devastation, compared with a 4.4-mile range when the height of explosion is 10,000 feet.
[2]Surface-burst only.
Source: Goodwin, P. (1981). *Nuclear War: The Facts on Our Survival.* New York: Rutledge Press, p. 31.

Direct Nuclear Radiation

A highly intense blast of radiation also spreads out in all directions from a nuclear explosion (Table S4-2). For large weapons the irradiated area is much smaller than the area affected by the heat or static overpressure; therefore, radiation would not be the principal cause of death. For smaller weapons, however, the range of intense radiation is greater than the range of heat and static overpressure; in such cases radiation would be the major cause of death. Some of the effects of radiation on human health are summarized in Table S4-3 and are discussed in Chapter Supplement 12-1.

Electromagnetic Pulse

Nuclear detonations create a single momentary pulse of electromagnetic radiation that spreads in all directions. This energy is similar to the electrical signal given off by lightning but much more powerful. The electromagnetic pulse would short-circuit unshielded radios, computers, and other electrical equipment, including telephone systems. The resulting blackout would occur at a time when communications would be badly needed to help coordinate rescue and health care. A single large bomb detonated in space 400 kilometers (250 miles) above Omaha, for example, could effectively cripple communications in the entire United States.

Fallout

The heat and force of a nuclear explosion thrust thousands of tons of dust into the atmosphere. In the process much of the dirt becomes radioactive. Radioactive dust particles return to the earth as fallout. Some of it may fall back immediately, landing near the site of the explosion and making the area intensely radioactive. Some fallout is carried higher into the atmosphere, only to fall back to earth many days later. Some fallout may be

Biomes

The biosphere is divided into geographically distinct land parts called biomes, each having its own specialized climate, plants, and animals. These diverse regions, made up of intricately balanced ecosystems, offer us a kaleidoscope of information on evolution and adaptation, which increases our understanding of the way the world works within the constraints of nature.

And yet, whenever we think we understand the workings of a biome (its climate, its topography, its predictability), we experience a Mt. St. Helens—a reminder from nature that life on earth is constantly in flux; changing, adjusting, adapting. Like nature, humans have altered biomes and ecosystems—but unlike nature, many of our changes have become irrevocable.

Through an understanding of the biomes we can learn about structure and function of the environment, which in turn will give us an awareness of how our world works—and, just as importantly, how it doesn't.

1 Atypical of the desert biome, the Great Sand Dunes National Monument in southern Colorado is lifeless and virtually barren.

2 The rim of the Grand Canyon in Arizona shows yet another face of the desert biome.

3 Cactus abound in the desert, blossoming briefly after the spring rains.

4 The tropical rain forest is perhaps the most diverse of all biomes. It is estimated that over 90% of the living organisms in these rain forests remain unclassified. Venezuela.

5 Rain forest in the Olympic Peninsula, Washington. Receiving over 200 inches of rain each year, this area maintains a lush growth of mosses, ferns, epiphytes, and trees.

6 The towering Alaska range overlooks the coniferous forests of the taiga, a biologically rich biome that extends across North America and much of Europe and Asia. Denali National Park, Alaska.

7 The taiga consists of large stands of one or two species of coniferous tree. Meadows occur naturally in mountain valleys, as shown here. Jasper Park, British Columbia.

8 An autumn view of the temperate deciduous forest biome.

9 Golden aspens herald autumn in the Maroon Bells-Snowmass Wilderness area, Colorado. High altitude yields a mix of coniferous and deciduous trees.

4

2

3

5

6

7

8

9

10 Alpine tundra is characterized by a short growing season, prohibiting the growth of trees or shrubs. Wildflowers, like the columbine shown here, grow densely in these areas.

11 Summery wildflowers and lichens add color to arctic tundra in the Soviet Union. Despite minimal precipitation, tundra areas remain damp from the presence of permafrost—permanently frozen soil that resists water absorption.

12 Flint Hills Preserve in Alena, Kansas, is one of the last remaining examples of the tall-grass prairie.

13 The African savannah is richly populated by grazing species that feed off trees, grass, and herbs. Kenya, Masai Mara Game Reserve.

12

10

11

13

Table S4-3 Effects of Radiation Exposure

Main Organ Involved	Distinguishing Signs	Convalescence Period	Incidence of Death	Death Occurs Within
	Above 50 rads: slight changes in blood cells			
Blood forming systems: bone marrow, lymph glands	Moderate fall in white blood cell count	Several weeks		
Blood forming systems: bone marrow, lymph glands	Severe loss of white blood cells; bleeding; infection; anemia (loss of red blood cells); loss of hair (above 300 rads)	1–12 months	0–90%	2-12 weeks
Blood forming systems: bone marrow, lymph glands		Long	90–100%	2–12 weeks
Gastrointestinal tract	Diarrhea; fever; shock symptoms		100%	2–14 days
Central nervous system	Convulsions; tremor; involuntary movements; lethargy		100%	days

Source: Goodwin, P. (1981). *Nuclear War: The Facts on Our Survival.* New York: Rutledge Press, pp. 44–45.

transported so high that it circulates in the upper atmosphere for decades, falling from the sky very gradually but exposing large areas. Radioactivity from fallout poses a threat to human health and the welfare of many other animal species.

Combined Injuries

One consequence of nuclear war that is sometimes overlooked is the effect of combined injuries. For example, victims of a nuclear exchange might be burned as well as exposed to non-lethal doses of radiation. Broken bones, cuts, and abrasions might add to their injuries. Studies on laboratory animals suggest that nonfatal injuries can add up, producing death.

Nuclear Winter

Imagine a heavy nuclear exchange in the Northern Hemisphere. Some people could survive the initial shock wave, the intense heat, the radiation, and the resulting fallout. But awaiting them, according to some experts, would be a nightmarish world of cold and darkness called **nuclear winter**.

Multiple atomic blasts would carry millions of tons of dust and soot into the atmosphere. Rising columns of smoke from

thousands of fires created by the explosions would create large, dark clouds. Dust from the explosions and smoke from the fires would block sunlight. Temperatures would plummet, with devastating effects on the biosphere.

The nuclear-winter theory was first published in 1982 by Paul Crutzen. Others, among them an American group including the renowned Carl Sagan, have arrived at similar conclusions.

No one knows for sure, but experts believe that about 40 million metric tons of soot would be required to produce a nuclear winter. Should 100 cities burn in a nuclear exchange, the world might be immersed in a dark, cold glacial age. The more smoke, the longer and more severe the winter would be.

Eventually, studies suggest, the clouds would coalesce and form a dense pall stretching from Florida to Alaska. The cloud could very easily spread south across the equator and plunge the Southern Hemisphere into a chilly twilight. Making matters worse, the smoke-laden air could absorb the sun's energy. This would cause the cloud to rise higher and thus lengthen its stay in the atmosphere.

Many scientists believe that the pall of smoke from an all-out nuclear war would plunge surface temperatures 20° to 30° C (36° to 54° F). Widespread extinction would result. Crop production throughout the world could halt. A drop in the average daily temperature of 2° or 3° C during the growing season can cut wheat production in Canada and the Soviet Union in half. Grains make up some 70% of the world's food energy; nuclear winter would, therefore, cause widespread global starvation. Climatic changes would devastate the developed countries, which are mostly in the temperate zone. According to a recent study by the International Council of Scientific Unions, however, the major environmental impacts would occur in the tropics and subtropics, where most of the Third World nations are located. Reduced temperature and rainfall in these regions would wipe out thousands of species adapted to warm, constant climates. (See Chapter Supplement 3-1 for a discussion of the tropical rain forests.)

Nuclear war by itself could also disrupt world trade of fertilizers, pesticides, and the like, resulting in further declines in farm productivity worldwide. Nuclear explosions could also create a toxic nightmare as millions of tons of potentially toxic and carcinogenic substances spewed into the atmosphere from burning cities. Asbestos, dioxins, and PCBs—among others—would spread to surrounding areas, making them even more inhospitable to life. Finally, an all-out nuclear war would also reduce the protective ozone layer, resulting in further damage, which is discussed in Chapter Supplement 15-1.

Some scientists have criticized proponents of the nuclear-winter theory for underestimating the effects. Others, such as Edward Teller, known as the father of the hydrogen bomb, argue that certain factors would "thaw" the nuclear winter, and they suggest that this new theory of doom is exaggerated. Teller and his associates, for instance, contend that fire storms would probably not generate columns of smoke that rise into the upper atmosphere; thus, the duration of the nuclear winter would be lessened. Most recently (1986) scientists at the National Center for Atmospheric Research in Boulder, Colorado have for the first time included the effects of the oceans in the computer models for a nuclear winter. These new calculations indicate that the fall in temperatures worldwide would last days, or at most weeks. In such a case, the effects of the cold would be considerably less drastic. Some scientists are speaking of a **nuclear fall**. Undoubtedly, the debate will continue for years to come.

Predicting the Effects of Nuclear War

No one can accurately predict the effects of nuclear war, because no one knows how many atomic weapons would be hurled toward warring nations, where they would explode, what the weather conditions would be, or other imponderables. Clearly, a fraction of the total nuclear arsenals of the United States and the Soviet Union could devastate the major population centers of every country in the world.

Of this we can be certain: Any nuclear explosion over an urban area would have catastrophic effects. Widespread nuclear war would have environmental and health consequences beyond our comprehension. Health care, transportation, and public sanitation would be crippled. Widespread climatic changes might grip the world in a winter or fall-like cold that would destroy plants and wildlife and grind agriculture to a stop.

Paul Warnke, former U.S. coordinator for the Strategic Arms Limitation Talks (SALT II), noted: "In this the fourth decade of the nuclear age, it is tempting to assume that a nuclear exchange won't take place and that, in any event, there is nothing the average human being can do about it. But the fact is that a nuclear war could happen and very well may happen unless we, as citizens of a threatened world, decide that we will do something."

Suggested Readings

Crutzen, P. J. (1985). The Global Environment after Nuclear War. *Environment* 27 (8): 6–11, 34–37. Excellent discussion of the nuclear-winter theory.

Ehrlich, P. R., Sagan, C., Kennedy, D., and Roberts, W. O. (1984). *The Cold and the Dark: The World after Nuclear War*. New York: Norton.

Goodwin, P. (1981). *Nuclear War: The Facts on Our Survival*. New York: Rutledge Press. Excellent coverage.

Lifton, R. J., and Falk, R. (1982). *Indefensible Weapons*. New York: Basic Books. Eloquent analysis of the nuclear age.

Riordan, M., ed. (1982). *The Day after Midnight: The Effects of Nuclear War*. Palo Alto, Calif.: Cheshire Books. Detailed account worth reading.

Russett, B. (1983). *The Prisoners of Insecurity: Nuclear Deterrence, the Arms Race, and Arms Control*. San Francisco: Freeman. Excellent discussion of the nuclear arms race.

Sagan, C. (1985). Nuclear Winter: A Report from the World Scientific Community. *Environment* 27 (8): 12–15, 38–39. Excellent overview of scientific reports on the nuclear-winter theory.

Schell, J. (1982). *The Fate of the Earth*. New York: Avon. A stirring account.

POPULATION

Population: Measuring Growth and Its Impact

One generation passeth away, and another generation cometh, but the earth abideth forever.

ECCLESIASTES 1:4

On May 24, 1985, a hurricane struck the small nation of Bangladesh, which lies just east of India along the Bay of Bengal. Winds clocked at over 160 kilometers per hour (100 miles per hour) struck the shoreline. A 5-meter (15-foot) tidal wave crashed inland, devastating homes and farms in its way. When the weather had cleared, officials surveyed the damage: A quarter of a million people were homeless; their rickety homes, built on silt islands off the shore, had been demolished by the storm. An estimated 4,000 to 15,000 people had perished. Countless livestock had died.

On the surface the disaster in Bangladesh looks like an especially severe natural disaster. On closer examination, however, it becomes clear that much of the blame can be pinned on an underlying human problem—too many people.

Bangladesh is a small country with big troubles. No larger than Wisconsin, it houses 100 million people. Rural and poor, Bangladesh is the most densely populated nation in the world and is also among the fastest growing.

The people of Bangladesh and their livestock have created an environmental disaster. Cattle have overgrazed the land. Hordes of desperate peasants have, over the years, stripped away much of the vegetation in search of food, fuel, and shelter. Denuded hillsides are stark testimony of pressure placed on the land by too many people. When the rains come, soil from the naked lands washes into streams in muddy rivulets. Brown rivers flow to the sea and deposit their silt in deltas. In search of farmland people flock to the deltas in the tens of thousands.

Almost any ecologist will tell you that deltas belong to rivers and the sea, not to people. Each year when the monsoons come, high waters flood these muddy lands, driving people away, destroying their farms and homes. Violent hurricanes wreak havoc, too, as they sweep in from the Bay of Bengal, claiming the lives of thousands who have either no way of knowing of the storm's impending arrival or nowhere to go.

In Bangladesh people are dying in a vicious circle triggered largely by **overpopulation**—too many people for the existing resources. The next section chronicles the toll of overpopulation, looking at starvation, disease, poverty, crowding, despair, illiteracy, and many other symptoms of this global disease. The following sections discuss why the human population has exploded, how to better understand the population crisis, and, finally, what the future holds for world population.

Dimensions of the Population Crisis

The population crisis can be summarized in six words: **too many people, reproducing too quickly.** This two-headed dilemma creates a myriad of problems, which are examined in the following sections.

Too Many People

"Hell is a city much like London," Shelley wrote in 1819. If he were alive today, the English poet might have put it differently: "Hell is a city much like Cairo, Calcutta, Shanghai, Bangkok, London, Los Angeles, and Mexico City." By the end of the century at least 22 cities worldwide are expected to have populations in excess of 10 million people. Sixty others will probably have exceeded the 5-million mark. Each of these urban centers will have its own unique problems, many of which may be linked to overpopulation—too many people.

The Plight of the Cities In Cairo, Egypt, lies a giant graveyard known as the City of the Dead. This particular cemetery is bustling with activity. Several hundred thousand people have set up home there because of acute housing shortages. One journalist has called it the "City of the Living Dead." Those among Cairo's 12 million inhabitants who are lucky enough to find housing don't count their blessings. Apartments are tiny. The municipal water system breaks down frequently. Sewage backs up in houses and spills onto floors, and one-third of the population lives in housing without sewage systems.

In Calcutta, India, the story is worse. More than 70% of the city's 10 million people live at or below the poverty level. At least 200,000 people are beggars. One water tap supplies, on the average, 25 slum dwellings; and about half of the homes in this beleaguered city have no indoor toilet. The streets are littered with trash and feces, and at least 600,000 people roam the city, homeless.

Shanghai, China, a well-to-do city by comparison, houses nearly 12 million people. Housing is not a problem; the government has provided for its people. But most citizens have only 2 to 3 square meters to call home—not much more than standing room. Shanghai's Huangpu River is foul with the smell of raw sewage and industrial waste. Jobs are in short supply.

Cities in the developed world are much better off, but the signs of overpopulation are still prevalent. In Los Angeles, for example, air pollution from vehicles fills the air, killing trees in the neighboring mountains, burning the eyes of visitors and residents, and blocking views. Rush-hour traffic clogs the highways (Figure 5-1). Teenage gangs rob, brawl, and vandalize. Jobless and homeless men and women rummage for food in dumpsters and garbage cans.

Crowding in urban centers has been implicated in a variety of social, mental, and physical diseases. Many social psychologists assert that social instability, divorce, mental illness, drug and alcohol abuse, high prenatal death, and rising crime rates in densely populated cities are due, at least in part, to stress from overcrowding. They call this the **inner city syndrome**. Research on humans and animals supports their contention. The most notable study was performed by the psychologist John Calhoun. In his research rats were confined to a specially built room and allowed to breed freely. As population snowballed, Calhoun observed increased violence and aggression, abnormal sexual behavior, cannibalism of young, and disruption of normal nesting and maternal behavior. The physiologist Hans Selye performed similar experiments. He observed hormonal imbalances brought about by stress. These imbalances could lead to ulcers, hypertension, kidney disease, hardening of the arteries, and increased susceptibility to other diseases. Other researchers point out that factors other than stress, such as lack of education, poverty, poor nutrition, and inadequate housing, may also contribute to the inner city syndrome.

Scientists are still unsure how crowding in cities affects human populations. But this we do know: too many people, especially in high-density urban centers, can greatly exceed the capacity of the environment to assimilate wastes. Large urban populations also place considerable demands on the outlying countryside for resources such as fuel, water, and food.

In 1986, 43% percent of the world's people lived in cities; by 2000, it is estimated, this figure will jump to

Figure 5-1 Los Angeles rush-hour traffic: a nightmare on a good day.

slightly over 60%. Crowding, and the many problems that result from it, will probably worsen.

Rural Despair A surplus of people strains the limits of rural areas as much as it does those of cities. Bangladesh, Kenya, Ethiopia, Mexico, and other countries reel under the oppressive burden of burgeoning rural populations (Figure 5-2). In Kenya, for instance, women have an average of eight children. In some rural areas eight of every ten children die. Malnutrition stunts the mental and physical development of many rural children and makes them prone to illness. Hundreds of thousands die each year.

The story is much the same in rural Ethiopia, Bangladesh, and Mexico. Overpopulation leads to unsanitary living conditions, water shortages, lack of food, death, and despair. Too many people scratching out an existence from an exhausted, abused landscape push the ecosystem beyond repair. Trees are cut down for firewood, and grasses are overgrazed. Once-fertile land becomes desert.

In an ironic twist rural overpopulation feeds the urban crisis. Dismayed peasants and their families, unable to

survive on their farms, migrate in large numbers to the cities in search of jobs and security. In Nigeria between 1962 and 1985 the proportion of people living in urban areas increased from two in ten to over six in ten. In Mexico City an estimated 1.5 million rural farmers and their families arrive each year. Nearly every major city in the world serves as a magnet for disheartened rural residents. What awaits them is often worse than what they have left.

Reproducing Too Quickly

Hunger, starvation, disease, poverty, illiteracy, pollution, unemployment, and barren landscapes are everywhere. To many observers these are signs that the human population is much too big for the earth's resources, both natural and financial. Efforts to eliminate these problems, however, have been frustrated by an immediate problem—the continued rapid growth in population. Nowhere is this trend more evident than in Africa.

Ten years ago few African nations would admit to the need to control their rapidly growing population. Growing at a rate of 3%—doubling every 24 years—the African continent fell behind in food production and economic development. Food-exporting African countries suddenly became importers. Economic development fell in arrears. Disease continued to spread. Fortunately, many leaders now recognize their plight. The predicament they face is described by Paul Ehrlich in his classic book, *The Population Bomb*. Ehrlich writes:

In order to just keep the standard of living at the present inadequate level, the food available for the people must be doubled every 24 years. Every structure and road must be duplicated. The amount of power must be doubled. The capacity of the transport system must be doubled. The number of trained doctors, nurses, teachers, and administrators must be doubled.... This would be a fantastically difficult job in the United States—a rich country with a fine agricultural system, immense industries, and access to abundant resources. Think of what it means to a country with none of these.

The world's fastest-growing areas are, in decreasing order, Africa, Latin America, and Asia. In Latin America and Asia, at least, the rate of growth is declining; further declines are still necessary if countries are to stop the mounting despair. In many African nations, however, the rate of growth is increasing; the future of this great continent is in peril.

The lesson from our survey of the overcrowded world is that we generally live as we breed. Too many of us, growing too fast, are bound to cause trouble. Ecologists warn that unless we dramatically reduce population growth, many people will fall further and further behind. Robert McNamara, president of the World Bank for 14

Figure 5-2 Overpopulation, desertification, and drought have diminished the resources available to these Nomadic people, forcing them to live in shanty towns.

years, urged that "short of nuclear war itself, population growth is the gravest issue the world faces. . . . If we do not act, the problem will be solved by famine, riot, insurrection, and war." Solving the population, pollution, and resource "trilemma" requires a substantial and immediate downturn in population growth rate. Chapter 6 discusses growth control in more detail.

The Population Explosion

In the 30 seconds it takes you to find this book on your bookshelf and turn to this page, 128 babies are born worldwide. During that same 30 seconds 50 people die; the world population increases by 78 people, a rate of 2.6 people every second!

At this rate of growth about 1.6 million people join the human population every week, approximately the number of people in Detroit. Overall, the world's population increases by 83 million people each year. In 1986 it exceeded 5 billion. By the year 2000 it may exceed 6 billion and may be growing by 100 million a year. Most of this growth takes place in the poorer nations, where three-quarters of the world's people now live.

The rapid growth of world population is a recent phenomenon. Throughout most of human history our population was quite small (Figure 5-3). During the time of Jesus, for example, there were probably fewer than 200 million people in the world. By 1850, though, world population had reached the 1-billion mark, after which it began to grow much more rapidly (Table 5-1). In the

following 80 years it doubled, reaching 2 billion by 1930. Forty-five years later it had doubled again, reaching 4 billion in 1975.

What caused the rapid upsurge in population growth starting in the 1800s?

The Survival Boom

Throughout most of human history population was kept small by disease, famine, and war. These checks on population growth are some of the reduction factors that form part of environmental resistance (see Chapter 4). In the course of human history, though, several important changes have occurred, enhancing human survival and reproduction. These include the development of tools, the agricultural revolution, the Industrial Revolution, and the opening of the New World for settlement, most of which were discussed in Chapter 2. Each has helped to unleash human population growth.

Tools played a big part in the survival of our early ancestors. New tools and technologies had an enormous effect on human population during the Industrial Revolution in the 1700s and 1800s. Population began its rapid upturn at that time.

The modern industrial society, however, has made even greater strides in increasing survival. Modern medicine stands as one of the major advances of our time. New drugs, such as penicillin, dramatically lowered the death rate. Better health care and sanitation decreased infectious diseases and increased the chances of survival. The pesticide DDT was used in the tropics to combat malaria-

Figure 5-3 Exponential growth curve depicting world population. Note the rapid upturn in world population in the last 200 years.

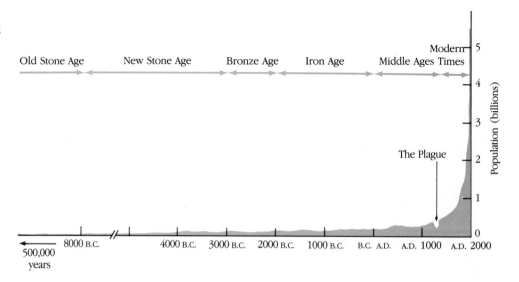

carrying mosquitoes. As a result of these developments death rates in many countries dropped precipitously (see the example of Sri Lanka in Figure 5-4) and life expectancy increased.

In 1900 the average white American female had a life expectancy of 50 years. By 1983, however, her life expectancy had climbed to 78.3 years. Life expectancy in white American males born in 1900 was about 47 years, but by 1983 it had increased to 70.9. Surprising at first, the increase in life expectancy is largely due to decreased infant mortality. Put another way, Americans live longer than their ancestors largely because more of them survive past the first year of life (Figure 5-5). Modern medicine has really helped more Americans survive those dangerous early years. Consider these statistics: between 1900 and 1978 the life expectancy for an infant increased 26 years, because more were saved in the first year; the life expectancy of a 60-year-old increased only 5.2 years.

As life expectancy increased and death rates dropped, birth rates continued at high levels in many countries (Figure 5-4). This fueled the rapid population growth that continues today.

Table 5-1 World Population Growth and Doubling Time

Population Size	Year	Time Required to Double
1 billion	1850	All of human history
2 billion	1930	80 years
4 billion	1975	45 years
8 billion (projected)	2017	42 years

A Double-Edged Sword: Expansion of the Earth's Carrying Capacity

Each of the advances cited above—tools, agriculture, medicine, and technological developments—increased the earth's **carrying capacity**—that is, the number of organisms (in this case, humans) the biosphere can support.

All ecosystems have a specific carrying capacity for each population. A hectare of grassland, for instance, may support two coyotes, ten deer, and thousands of mice. Carrying capacity fluctuates from year to year depending on climate and other factors, discussed in Chapter 3, but most organisms do little to change it. Humans are an exception to that rule: advances in tool making, agriculture, industry, and medicine allow us to extend the limits set by nature—to expand the carrying capacity.

To increase carrying capacity we tend to develop to the maximum extent possible, or maximize, single variables such as energy and agricultural production. Modern agriculture and disease control, for example, encourage population growth beyond the earth's ability to assimilate wastes. The result is polluted skies and filthy streams. We could feed even more people with further advances in agricultural technology, but the supplies of fresh water and clean air would be taxed even further. As Garrett Hardin notes, "Maximizing one [variable] is almost sure to alter the balance in an unfavorable way."

A survey of human history shows that increasing the earth's carrying capacity for our own kind has been accomplished, in many cases, at the expense of the rest of the biosphere. The price has been depleted resources, increased pollution, and the strains that accompany rapid growth. The effects of such actions on ecosystems are the subject of much of this book.

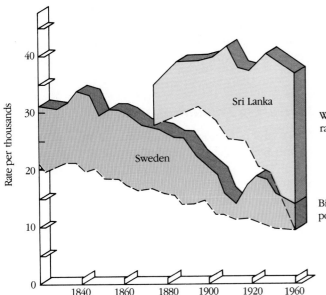

Wide difference results in rapid population growth

Birth rate and death rate nearly equal; population growth slow

Exponential Growth

Figure 5-3 showed human population growth over time. The curve is flat throughout most of human history; it is not until the last 200 years that population has veered upward. In that period population has followed a J-shaped curve called an **exponential curve**.

Exponential growth takes place when something increases by a fixed percentage every year. For example, a savings account with 5% compounded interest grows exponentially. The remarkable characteristic of all exponential growth is that early growth (in absolute terms) is quite slow. Once growth "rounds the bend," however, the thing being measured, whether money in a bank account or population, begins to increase more and more rapidly. For example, suppose that your parents opened a $1000 savings account in your name on the day you were born. This account earns 10% interest, and all the earned interest is applied to the balance, where it also earns interest. When you were 7, your account was worth $2000. By age 14, it had increased to $4000. By age 42 you will have $64,000 (Figure 5-6). If you left the money in a little longer, you'd find it growing faster and faster. At age 49 the account would be worth $128,000; at age 56 you'd have a quarter of a million dollars. Seven more years and you'd have a half a million dollars, but if you waited until

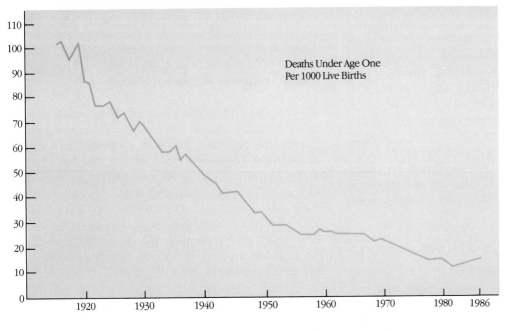

Figure 5-5 U.S. infant mortality rate, 1915–1986.

Deaths Under Age One Per 1000 Live Births

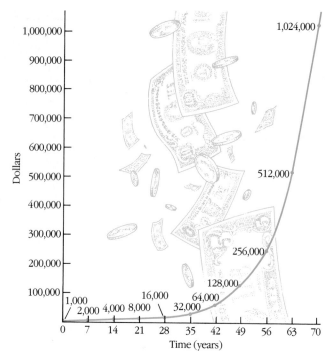

Figure 5-6 Exponential growth curve of a savings account with an initial deposit of $1000 that earns 10%.

you were 70, your account would be worth over $1 million. Looking back over your account records, you'd find that during the first 49 years it grew from $1000 to $128,000, but during the last 21 years it increased by nearly $900,000. The rate of growth was constant over the entire period, and the account doubled every seven years, but it was not until it rounded the bend of the growth curve that things began to happen quickly.

Worldwide, population has been growing in the recent past at a rate of 1.7% per year. At this seemingly slow rate of growth world population doubles every 40 years. Making our situation worse, the numbers involved have become so large that each doubling means an extraordinary increase in the number of people. Resource demand and pollution also increase exponentially. So fast has the population begun to increase in sheer numbers that civilization is hard pressed to keep up with it. As we will see in Part 3 of this book, the limits of many resources are in sight. As Part 4 shows, the atmosphere and oceans and rivers cannot assimilate all the wastes we produce.

Understanding Populations and Population Growth

The newspapers and magazines sometimes present a confusing array of statistics on population, making it difficult

for the public to understand a global issue that ranks in importance with nuclear war. With a little effort you can learn enough **demography**, or population science, to weed out the fallacies from the facts of the population debate.

Measuring Population Growth

One of the most important population measurements is growth rate, which is frequently expressed as a percentage. What does it mean when demographers report that a population is growing at a rate of 3% per year? Is this something to be thankful for or concerned about? To answer this question, let's first see how **population growth rate** is determined.

Growth Rate World population growth rate is calculated by subtracting the number of deaths in a population from the number of births. Multiplying by 100 converts the growth rate into a percentage, as shown here:

Growth Rate (%)
= (Crude Birth Rate − Crude Death Rate) × 100

Crude birth rate is the number of births per 1000 people in a population. **Crude death rate** is the number of deaths per 1000 people in a population.

The relationship between birth rates and death rates determines whether the world's population grows, shrinks, or remains the same. Some important growth rates are listed in Table 5-2.

What do the numbers in Table 5-2 really mean? A look at the growth rate of the developing nations, the earth's poorest, is instructive. The annual growth rate of these countries is 2.1%. A 2.1% growth rate means that a population is adding 2.1 persons each year for every 100 in the population. On the surface this seems rather small. These Third World nations, however, have 3.7 billion people. A 2.1% growth rate, therefore, translates into 77 million *additional* people every year!

Birth Rates The balance between birth rates and death rates in various areas determines global population growth. Each of these, however, is affected by a variety of elements. Consider birth rates first. The birth rate in a population is determined by many factors, including (1) the age at which men and women get married, (2) their educational level, (3) whether the woman works after marriage, (4) whether the couple use reliable contraceptives, (5) the number of children the woman and her husband want, (6) the couple's religious beliefs, and (7) their cultural values.

Death Rates Death rates are equally important in determining population growth. A few decades ago death

Some Demographic Surprises of the '70s

The demand for projections is insatiable. What will the population of the world be in 2000? How many children will be born? What percentage of the population will be over 65? Will the U.S. population stabilize? When? The list goes on, and for good reason: we need to project to help make the transition into the future smooth and efficient.

But if we look at the forecasts of the U.S. Census Bureau, whose experts spend their days studying the present and predicting the future of our population, we may be surprised to find that the experts are often quite wrong. For example, the bureau once projected that during the 1970s, 40 million to 49.3 million children would be born in the United States. The actual number of births was far below this—33.3 million—a sign that U.S. population growth is slowing.

The second missed guess had to do with deaths and life expectancy. The Census

Bureau projected that 21 million people would die in the 1970s, but the number dying was a little lower than expected— 19.3 million. The average life expectancy at birth was expected to increase in the 1970s, but only by about a half a year. Instead, it rose 3.4 years, because of success in reducing deaths from heart disease and stroke.

The Census Bureau also projected a slight decrease in the number of people per household. Its estimates showed that by 1980 the average household would contain 3.08 to 3.19 people. The actual value, however, was 2.76, considerably lower than estimated.

A fourth area of speculation was that of internal migration in the United States. The U.S. Bureau of Economic Analysis made projections for regional growth in a seven-volume report. It projected that the Northeast would grow by 7.6 million between 1970 and 1980; in fact, it grew

by only 1.1 million because of a much larger than expected out-migration. The West, on the other hand, was expected to grow by 4 million during the decade of the '70s. It grew by 8.3 million. The South also fooled the "experts," growing by 12.5 million instead of a projected 7.8 million.

Our need for projections is enormous, and it always will be. City planners want to know how big their population will be and the size of different age groups. Businesses are interested in future market size. Schools and colleges want to know the projected demand and supply of teachers. But from the examples cited above, healthy skepticism seems advisable. Perhaps Victor Hugo had the population experts in mind when he noted, "Caution is the eldest child of wisdom."

Table 5-2 Growth Rate and Doubling Time in 1986

Region	Growth Rate (%)	Doubling Time (years)
World	1.7	41
Developed countries	0.6	117
Developing countries	2.1	33
Africa	2.9	24
Asia	1.9	38
North America	0.7	99
Latin America	2.3	30
Europe	0.4	208
Soviet Union	1.0	68
Oceania	1.3	55

Source: Population Reference Bureau, *World Population Data Sheet, 1986.*

rates in the developing nations of the world were quite high. Few children lived past the first year. Therefore, even though birth rates were high, population growth remained low. Today, modern medicine, pesticides, and better sanitation, among other things, have reduced death

rates. Without an accompanying fall in birth rates, as we have seen, the reduction in death rates has led to an unprecedented population growth in the poorer nations. Many developed nations have stabilized their growth by lowering birth rates.

Fertility and Zero Population Growth Demographers employ dozens of measurements to assess the dynamics of the populations they study. One of the most important is the total fertility rate, which is used to predict the growth of populations. The **total fertility rate** (TFR) is the number of children women are expected to have. The total fertility rate in the United States is 1.8; that means that ten women are expected to have 18 children. In India, a much poorer nation, women have a rather startling TFR of 4.5.

One of the most encouraging population trends is that many countries have reached **replacement-level fertility**, the point at which couples produce exactly the number of children needed to replace them (Tables 5-3 and 5-4). In the United States and other developed countries replacement-level fertility is a TFR of 2.1 children. Thus, every 10 women must have 21 children to replace them-

Table 5-3   Total Fertility Rate in Mid-1986

Region		Total Fertility Rate	Population Size (Billions)
World		3.7	4.942
Developed countries		1.9	1.180
Developing countries		4.2	3.762
Africa		6.3	
Northern	5.8		
Western	6.6		
Eastern	6.8		
Middle	6.0		
Southern	5.1		
Asia		3.7	
Western	5.9		
Southern	5.0		
Southeastern	4.4		
Eastern	2.1		
(incl. China, Japan)			
North America		1.8	
U.S.	1.8		
Canada	1.7		
Latin America		4.1	
Middle	4.6		
Caribbean	3.3		
Tropical	4.2		
Temperate	3.1		
Europe		1.8	
Northern	1.8		
Western	1.5		
Eastern	2.1		
Southern	1.8		
Soviet Union		2.4	
Oceania		2.7	

Table 5-4   Countries at or near Replacement-Level Fertility in 1986

Country	Total Fertility Rate
Cyprus	2.5
Poland	2.4
Soviet Union	2.4
Czechoslovakia	2.1
Iceland	2.1
Yugoslavia	2.1
Barbados	2.0
Bulgaria	2.0
Malta	2.0
Portugal	2.0
Romania	2.0
Australia	1.9
New Zealand	1.9
Cuba	1.8
East Germany	1.8
France	1.8
Hong Kong	1.8
Japan	1.8
Spain	1.8
United Kingdom	1.8
United States	1.8
Canada	1.7
Finland	1.7
Hungary	1.7
Norway	1.7
Singapore	1.7
Sweden	1.7
Belgium	1.6
Italy	1.5
Netherlands	1.5
Switzerland	1.5
Denmark	1.4
Luxembourg	1.4
West Germany	1.3

Source: Population Reference Bureau, *World Population Data Sheet, 1986*

selves and their husbands. Why the additional child? Because one of every 21 children dies before reaching reproductive age. Replacement-level fertility is a little higher in nations with higher death rates.

The press is forever confusing the world population picture, and for good reason—an astounding number of measurements have to be understood before one can assess a population's future. Consider the confusion that arises around total fertility rate. Even though a population reaches replacement-level fertility, it does not mean that it has stopped growing. A population stops growing only when the death rate equals the birth rate (and the net migration is zero). Demographers call this **zero population growth**, or ZPG. The United States provides a perfect example. The TFR in the United States fell below replacement level in 1972, thanks in large part to modern contraception and widespread public awareness of the population dilemma. Even though the TFR has remained below replacement-level fertility since that time, the U.S. population has continued to swell. And, demographers project, at least 70 years will pass before our population stops growing. Why?

The answer is that the birth rate in the United States is also determined by the number of women in the reproductive age group of 15 to 44. If the size of the reproductive age group is expanding, as it is in the United States, so will the population. Thus, even though American women are having smaller families than their mothers did 20 years ago, more and more women keep entering the reproductive age group each year. Our current population of 242 million people will swell by 50 to 70 million because of momentum. Demographers recognize that this built-in momentum will end once the number of women in the reproductive age group stabilizes.

Population growth in the United States is not the result of American women having more children but of more women having children. In addition, about 40% of U.S. growth stems from legal and illegal immigration.

The U.S. population will stabilize only when the number of women in the reproductive age group stabilizes and only if replacement level fertility is sustained (assuming no immigration). In a sense, then, ZPG lags behind replacement-level fertility. This is called the **lag effect**. Should trends continue, the U.S. population is expected to stabilize in approximately 70 years. It could then begin to decline if the TFR remained below replacement-level fertility and immigration was reduced or halted.

A *Comparison of Growth Rates* The world is crudely divided into the haves and the have-nots—the **developed countries** and the **less developed, or developing countries** (Table 5-5). On the whole the developed countries, such as the United States, Canada, Great Britain, and the Soviet Union, grow fairly slowly, on the average about .6% per year. A number of developed countries, such as Sweden and Austria, have stopped growing altogether. Others are experiencing negative growth rates, meaning their populations are shrinking. The United States is something of an enigma among developed nations, boasting one of the fastest growth rates (1%). If this growth continued, U.S. population would double in 70 years. The developing nations, on the other hand, are growing even more rapidly—at an average of 2.1% per year. But these averages hide some dangerous trends in countries such as Kenya and Nigeria, which are growing well over 3% per year.

Doubling Time Growth rates, total fertility, and replacement-level fertility are important measurements. A better perspective on population growth can be gained by using the growth rate to calculate the time it takes a population to double. The following formula is used to determine **doubling time**:

$$\text{Doubling Time} = \frac{70}{\text{Growth Rate}}\,(\%)$$

Table 5-5 Comparison of Developed and Developing Countries

Country	Total Fertility Rate
Iceland	2.5
Hong Kong	2.4
Cyprus	2.3
Poland	2.3
Romania	2.3
U.S.S.R.	2.3
Barbados	2.2
Bulgaria	2.2
Portugal	2.2
Spain	2.2
Czechoslovakia	2.1
New Zealand	2.1
France	2.0
Malta	2.0
Yugoslavia	2.0
Cuba	1.9
East Germany	1.9
Hungary	1.9
United Kingdom	1.9
United States	1.9
Canada	1.8
Japan	1.8
Singapore	1.8
Australia	1.7
Belgium	1.7
Italy	1.7
Norway	1.7
Sweden	1.7
Finland	1.6
Netherlands	1.6
Denmark	1.5
Luxembourg	1.5
Switzerland	1.5
West Germany	1.5

Source: Population Reference Bureau, *World Population Data Sheet, 1983.*

Overall, the human population is growing at 1.7% per year. This gives a doubling time of 41 years. What is the doubling time of the developed nations (growth rate of .6%)? What is the doubling time of the less developed nations (growth rate of 2.1%)?

Migration

The previous section dealt primarily with global population, determined by the balance of death rates and birth rates. To calculate the growth of individual countries, states, or regions, demographers must take into account the number of people moving out of and into the region as well as the balance (or imbalance) between births and deaths.

The Population Debate

The Case for More People

Julian Simon

The author is a professor of economics and business administration at the University of Illinois at Champaign-Urbana. He has written several important books on population and economics, including The Economics of Population Growth *and* The Ultimate Resource.

Many technological advances come from people who are neither well educated nor well paid—the dispatcher who develops a slightly better way of deploying taxis in his ten-cab fleet, the shipper who discovers that garbage cans make excellent, cheap containers for many items, the retailer who discovers a faster way to stock merchandise, and so on. Even in science one need not be a genius to make a valuable contribution.

In the past century there have been more discoveries and a faster rate of growth of productivity than in previous centuries, when fewer people were alive. Whereas we develop new materials almost every day, it was centuries between the discovery and use of, say, copper and iron. If there had been a larger population, the pace of increase in technological practice might have been faster.

Classical economic theory has concluded that population growth must reduce the standard of living: the more people, the lower the per capita income, all else being equal. However, many statistical studies conclude that population growth does not have a negative effect on economic growth. The most plausible explanation is the positive effect additional people have on productivity by creating and applying new knowledge.

Because technological improvements come from people, it seems reasonable to assume that the amount of improvement depends in large measure on the number of people available. Data for developed countries show clearly that the bigger the population, the greater the number of scientists and the larger the amount of scientific knowledge produced.

There is other evidence of the relationship between population increase and long-term economic growth: an industry, or the economy of an entire country, can grow because population is growing, because per capita income is growing, or both. Some industries in some countries grow faster than the same industries in other countries or than other industries in the same country. Comparisons show that in the faster-growing industries the rate of increase of technological practice is higher. This suggests that faster population growth, which causes faster-growing industries, leads to faster growth of productivity.

The phenomenon economists call "economy of scale"—greater efficiency of larger-scale production where the market is larger—is inextricably intertwined with the creation of knowledge and technological change, along with the ability to use larger and more efficient machinery and greater division of labor. A large population implies a bigger market. A bigger market is likely to bring bigger manufacturing plants, which may be more efficient than smaller ones and may produce less expensive goods.

A bigger population also makes profitable many major social investments that would not otherwise be profitable—railroads, irrigation systems, and ports. For instance, if an Australian farmer were to clear a piece of land far from neighboring farms, he might have no way to ship his produce to market. He might also have trouble finding workers and supplies. When more farms are established nearby, however, roads will be built that link him with markets in which to buy and sell.

We often hear that if additional people have a positive effect on per capita income and output, it is offset by negative impacts such as pollution, resource shortages, and other problems. These trends are myths. The only meaningful measure of scarcity is the economic cost of goods. In almost every case the cost of natural resources has declined throughout human history relative to our income.

Conventional wisdom has it that resources are finite. But there is no support for this view. There is little doubt in my mind that we will continue to find new ore deposits, invent better production methods, and discover new substitutes, bounded only by our imagination and the exercise of educated skills. The only constraint upon our capacity to enjoy unlimited raw materials at acceptable prices is knowledge. People generate that knowledge. The more there are, the better off the world will be.

Is More Always Better?

Garrett Hardin

The author is a renowned environmentalist, writer, and lecturer. He has taught at several universities, and in 1980 he served as chairman of the board and chief executive officer of the Environmental Fund. He has written numerous books and articles on environmental ethics and is best known for his article "The Tragedy of the Commons."

To get at the heart of the "population problem," you should make careful measurements of the daily flow of water over Niagara Falls. You will discover that twice as much water flows over the falls during each daylight hour as during each nighttime hour. There in a nutshell you have the population problem.

Puzzled? You should be. The connection between Niagara Falls and population is not obvious. Before we can understand it we need to review a little biology.

For every nonhuman species there is an upper limit to the size of a population. Near the maximum, individuals are not so well off as they are at lower densities. Starvation appears. Crowded animals often fight among themselves and kill their offspring. Game managers and wildlife advocates agree that the maximum is not the optimum. If animals could talk, we suspect they would agree.

What about humans? Will we be happiest if our population is the absolute maximum the earth can support? Few people say so explicitly, but some argue that "more is better!"

Admittedly, we need quite a few people to maintain our complex civilization. A population the size of Monaco's, with about 25,000 people, could never have enough workers for an automobile assembly line. But Sweden, with some 8 million people, turns out two excellent automobiles. Eight million is a long way from nearly 5 billion, the approximate population of the world today.

Some say, "More people—more geniuses." But is the number of practicing geniuses directly proportional to population size? England today is 11 times as populous as it was in Shakespeare's day, but does it now boast 11 Shakespeares? For that matter does it have even one?

Consider Athens in classical times. A city of only 40,000 free inhabitants produced what many regard as the most brilliant roster of intellectuals ever: Solon, Socrates, Plato, Aristotle, Euripides, Sophocles—the list goes on and on. What city of 40,000 in our time produces even a tenth as much brilliance?

Of course, the free populace of Athens was served by ten times as many slaves and other nonfree classes. Forty thousand people free to apply themselves to intellectual and artistic matters is evidently quite enough to produce a first-rate civilization. Slaves gave 40,000 Athenians freedom to create. We are given creative freedom by labor-saving machines, certainly a more desirable form of slavery. But where are our geniuses?

Business economists are keenly aware of "economies of scale," which reduce costs as the number of units manufactured goes up. Communication and transportation, however, suffer from diseconomies of scale. The larger the city, the higher the monthly phone bill. More automobiles mean more signal lights per auto. More researchers mean more time spent in the library finding out what other investigators have done. Crimes per capita increase with city size. So do the costs of crime control. All these suggest that more may not be better.

Democracy requires effective communication between citizens and legislators. In 1790 each U.S. senator represented 120,000 people; in 1980 the figure was 2.3 million. At which time was representation closer to the ideal of democracy? To communicate with his or her constituents each senator now has an average of 60 paid assistants (versus zero in 1790). As for the president, Franklin D. Roosevelt had a staff of 37 in 1933, when the population was 125 million, whereas Ronald Reagan had a staff of 1700 in 1981, when the population was 230 million. We have to ask whether democracy can survive infinite population growth.

Let's look at another aspect of the more-is-better argument. An animal population is limited by the resources available to it. With humans, a complication arises. Though the quantities of minerals on earth are fixed, improved technology periodically increases the quantity of resources available to us. In the beginning we had to have copper ores that tested out at 20%; now we are using ores with less than 1%. Available copper has increased but not the total amount of copper on earth.

Yet it is a mistake to speak of "running out" of mineral resources. When we use copper, we don't "use it up." Abrasion of our copper artifacts ultimately disperses the metal in tiny fragments over the face of the earth, but none of the copper is destroyed. It can all be gathered together again, *but* reconcentrating it uses energy. All resource scarcity finally translates into a problem of energy. Is energy limited?

This is not an easy question to answer. The rate of energy input from the sun is strictly limited, but atomic energy is something else. In principle, atomic energy seems almost unlimited. The key question is this: can we get this energy at an acceptable environmental cost? Can we dispose of the lethal waste products safely? Can we prevent nuclear sabotage and blackmail? These questions are less scientific than trans-scientific—beyond science.

Let's return to Niagara Falls. Less water flows over the falls at night because more water is diverted to generate electricity when people aren't looking at the falls. It would be possible to use all the water to generate electricity, but then there would be no falls for us to look at. As a compromise, the volume of water "wasted" falling over the falls is reduced only at night. Therefore, the turbines and generators are not fully used 24 hours of the day, which means that local electricity costs are just a bit higher.

If the population continues to grow, the day may come when electricity is so scarce and expensive that the public will demand that Niagara Falls be shut down so that all the water can be used to generate electricity. Similar dangers face every aesthetic resource. Wild rivers can be dammed to produce more electricity, and estuaries can be filled in to make more building sites for homes and factories.

The maximum is never the optimum. With human populations, *quantity* (of people) and *quality* (of life) are tradeoffs. Which should we choose—the maximum or the optimum? This is a trans-scientific question.

Is our population now below or above the optimum? In trying to answer this I suggest that you make two lists. On one list write down all the things that you would expect to be *better* if the population doubled; on the other, all the things that would be *worse*. On which list would you put the availability of wilderness? Of theatres and museums? What about the noise level? Amount of democracy? Amount of pollution? Per capita cost of pollution control? Availability of parking spaces? Personal freedom?

When you are through, compare your list with your friends'. What value judgments account for the differences? Can these differences be reconciled? How?

Migration, technically speaking, is the movement of people across boundaries to set up a new residence. The term **immigration** refers to movements into a country; **emigration** refers to movements out. **Net migration** is the difference between immigration and emigration. Population growth in a country will stabilize if the growth rate and net migration are zero.

Immigration is one of the hottest topics today in the United States, for many reasons. One of the most important is that legal and illegal immigration into the United States accounts for 40% of the annual population growth. Efforts to stabilize U.S. population will fail unless the country brings immigration and emigration more closely into balance.

Recent public opinion polls in the United States show that a majority favors reducing immigration of all kinds. Accordingly, Congress passed a law in 1986 levying penalties against those who knowingly employ illegal immigrants and requiring job seekers to provide proof of citizenship or legal immigration status. The law is controversial, and solutions to this problem are not easy or clear-cut.

People also move *within* the boundaries of a country, often in large numbers. Such migrations can dramatically alter local economies. Figure 5-7 shows the recent migration flow in the United States. The primary flow is from the northeastern and north-central regions to the South (mostly Florida) and West (Arizona, Wyoming, Utah, Alaska, Idaho, Colorado, New Mexico, and Texas). The migration has been so dramatic in recent years that for the first time in U.S. history more than half the population lives in the West and South. This movement, called the "sunning of America," is caused by (1) expanding (sunrise) industries in the West and Southwest, especially in electronics and energy production; (2) declining (sunset) industries of the northeastern and north-central states, especially auto and steel manufacturing; (3) a desire for a warmer climate; (4) a desire for a cheaper cost of living; (5) a preference for abundant recreation; (6) an aspiration for a less hectic, less crowded life-style; and (7) the growth of retirement communities.

The massive migration to the South and West has had many important economic benefits for these regions. Overall, income has increased and unemployment has fallen. New opportunities have opened up for builders and for restaurants owners, bankers, and other members of the service sector of the economy.

Ironically, the influx of people into the Sun Belt has destroyed many of the values the migrants had sought. With growth rates in the range of 3% to 5% per year, many western cities and states have been swamped by new residents. Some major western ski areas have become so overcrowded that skiers must make reservations days in advance. Air pollution has worsened with increas-

Internal Migration

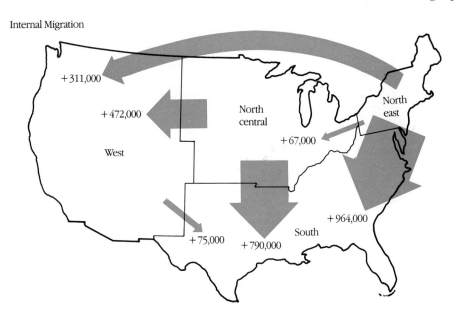

Figure 5-7 Internal migration in the United States, 1970–1975, a period of extremely frequent migration.

ing population; the clean air that many came for has disappeared. Traffic has become congested. The rapid rise in demand for housing has sent the cost of homes skyward. The breakneck speed of growth has made it difficult for local governments to provide water mains, schools, sewage treatment facilities, and the like. Spreading cities engulf smaller outlying communities and change the tempo of life.

Internal migrants affect the places they come from as well. Since many of the out-migrants are young, educated, and skilled workers, they have created a significant drain on human resources in the northeastern and north-central United States.

Seeing Is Believing: Population Histograms

Demographers use growth rates, fertility rates, and doubling times to explain the future of the human population, but few techniques shed as much light as a nicely drawn graph. The old saying "A picture is worth a thousand words" is as true in demography as it is anywhere else.

You have already seen a graph of exponential growth and pondered the consequences of such growth. What you learned was that rounding the bend of an exponential growth curve yields a remarkable growth in the population even though the growth rate remains small. Let's look at another graphic tool, the population histogram. This is a bar graph that tells a little bit about the history and a little bit about the future of a population (Figure 5-8).

The **population histogram** displays the age and gender composition of a population. The area of each horizontal bar on the histogram represents the size of a certain age and gender group. As illustrated in Figure 5-9, three gen-

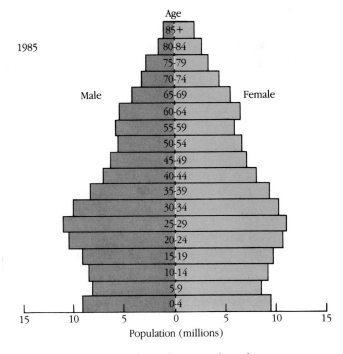

Figure 5-8 U.S. population by age and gender.

eral profiles exist: expansive, constrictive, and stationary. Mexico, a country which is expanding, has a large number of young people. If they produce more offspring than their parents did, the population will continue to expand at the base. If, on the other hand, family size decreases, the base of the histogram will begin to constrict. This is what is happening to the U.S. population. Sweden pre-

Figure 5-9 Three general types of population histogram. Expansive populations have a large percentage of young people and are expanding at the base. Constrictive populations have a tapering base, resulting from lower total fertility. Stationary or near stationary populations show no expansion or constriction. This results from couples having only the number of children that will replace them.

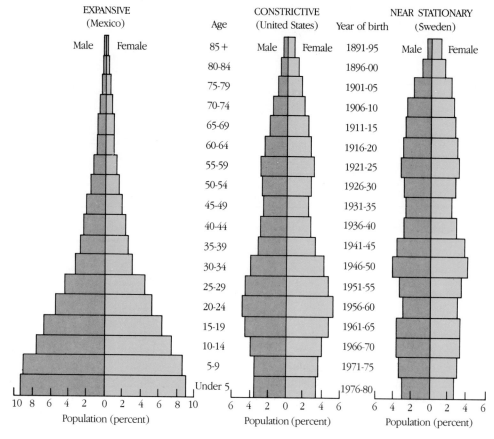

sents an entirely different picture. For many years Swedish couples have been having the same number of children as their parents had; as a result, Sweden's population is stationary.

Population histograms can change over time and, therefore, are not always reliable for making long-term predictions of future growth. Expansive populations can become constrictive, constrictive populations can become expansive, and so on.

Histograms give a snapshot view that can be used for short-term planning of schools, hospitals, retirement homes, and so on. Mexican officials, studying their histograms, might make special efforts to expand educational facilities and maternity wards. The United States might look for ways to increase retirement homes and services for the elderly.

Shifts in the population histogram can have dire consequences if ignored. In the United States the postwar baby boom, caused by an increase in fertility (seen as a bulge in Figure 5-9, a population histogram) greatly increased the number of school-age children in the 1950s and 1960s. New schools couldn't be built fast enough to keep up with the pace. Teachers were in short supply. Housing also became a serious problem as members of this age group married and searched for homes. Still larger problems loom in the early 21st century, when

those people reach retirement age. By 2030 individuals 65 and older will make up about 20% of the U.S. population, compared with 11% today. Health costs are almost certain to go higher, since people over 65 today account for nearly one-third of the nation's health bill. Gerontologists, new hospital facilities for the aged, and retirement homes will be needed to accommodate the elderly. Making matters worse, a smaller proportion of the population—including those in college today—will be supporting this large elderly group through the Social Security program.

The aging of the population also means an aging of the work force, which has positive aspects. It means that competition for entry-level positions will lessen, and it means that the labor force will, on the whole, be more experienced and will require less training. This could increase overall labor productivity—the amount of output per unit of labor.

The Future of World Population: Some Projections

Perhaps the questions most often asked of demographers are "What is the future of the world population? How big will it get? Will it really double in the next 40 years?"

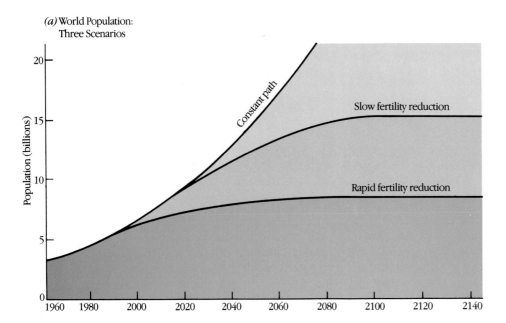

(a) World Population:
Three Scenarios

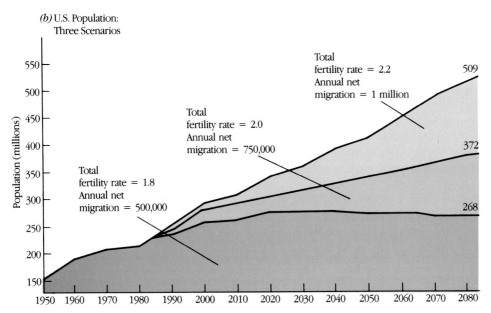

(b) U.S. Population:
Three Scenarios

Figure 5-10 (*a*) Future of world population. Constant path indicates population growth continuing at the current rate. The middle line indicates the future of world population if fertility drops off at a slow rate, the bottom line shows what might happen with a rapid decrease in fertility. As discussed in the text, the future may lie somewhere between the lower two lines. (*b*) The future of U.S. population depends on future total fertility rate and annual net migration.

The answer is that we don't know and can't know, for it is impossible to predict the future. The factors that affect future population growth, such as birth rates, fertility, and death rates, can change dramatically.

Regardless of the uncertainties involved in making estimates of future growth, many scientists have forecast growth. The world population growth rate is currently about 1.7%. If this rate continued into the future, the world population would reach 1 trillion (1,000,000,000,000) around 2300.

Long before then, demographers believe, the population growth curve will level off as a result of dropping birth rates, rising death rates, or both. Figure 5-10 plots

this and several other possibilities for the United States and the world. A slow reduction in fertility would result in a gradual decrease in population growth and a stable population by the year 2100. The population size would be about 15 billion, three times what it is today. Still another projection, based on a rapid decline in fertility, shows stabilization around 2060 at 8 billion, 3 billion more than today. Exactly where the curve levels off will depend on the persistence and success of efforts in family planning and economic development in the Third World, discussed in the next chapter.

Some demographers predict that the shortages and pollution brought about by such growth will eventually

Figure 5-11   Patterns of population growth. (*a*) Stabilization of population growth with a smooth transition to a stable population size. (*b*) Gradual dropoff caused by population exceeding the carrying capacity. (*c*) Population crash caused by irreparable change to the ecosystem. No doubt all three patterns will be seen in individual countries.

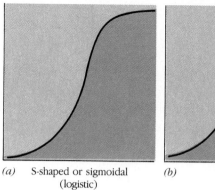

(a)   S-shaped or sigmoidal (logistic)

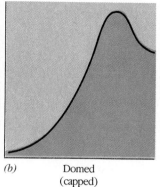

(b)   Domed (capped)

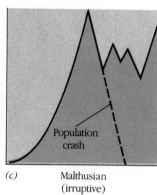

(c)   Malthusian (irruptive)

cause the human population to begin to decrease in size, producing a dome-shaped population curve instead of a **sigmoidal curve** (S-shaped, characteristic of a stabilizing population), as shown in Figure 5-11. The decrease in population size in this scenario, ecologists believe, would occur when populations exceeded the earth's carrying capacity. The introductory section of this chapter pointed out many ways in which human populations have already pushed their numbers beyond the carrying capacity. Further pollution of the air and water; further shortages of food, water, wood, grazing land, and other natural resources; or continued extinction of plants and animals could cause the population size to decrease over time— or even quite suddenly.

Still another, ominous pattern may occur. Instead of leveling off or declining smoothly the human population might suffer sudden die-offs followed by spurts of growth and further plunges. This roller coaster ride is an unstable, **irruptive** pattern caused by severe ecosystem imbalance (Figure 5-11). Finally, the human population

may plummet quite suddenly in a population crash caused by critical changes in global climate or, possibly, resource supplies. This sudden catastrophic die-off may be so severe that the human population becomes extinct or is reduced to only a fraction of its present size.

No one knows what will happen to world population. The only opinion on which the experts approach unanimity is that world population cannot grow indefinitely. Some countries will inevitably make a smooth transition to a stable state; others may experience periodic crashes caused by epidemics in crowded urban populations; others may fall to low population levels because of continued starvation and disease.

H. G. Wells once wrote that "human history becomes more and more a race between education and catastrophe." The population–resource–pollution bind we're in clearly illustrates this fact. What we decide today will have far-reaching effects that determine the kind of lives our children and theirs will have.

The doors we open and close each day decide the lives we live.

FLORA WHITTEMORE

Summary

Population growth is at the root of virtually all environmental problems, including pollution and resource depletion, and indirect social disruptions such as housing shortages, malnutrition, and inadequate health care. Rapid growth in population creates difficulties in meeting the basic needs of people. Crowding may cause mental illness, drug abuse, and various forms of antisocial behavior.

The rapid growth of world population is a recent phenomenon. Throughout most of human history our population was small, controlled by war, disease, and famine. But advances in agriculture and industry allowed us to indefinitely expand the **carrying capacity**, the number of people the earth could support.

Exponential growth, or fixed-percentage growth, follows a **J curve**. Initially, growth is slow, but once the bend of the curve is rounded, the absolute growth becomes remarkable. The environmental crisis is largely the result of our beginning to grow exponentially in recent history and then rounding the bend of the population curve.

World population growth is determined by subtracting the **crude death rate** from the **crude birth rate**. These are the number of deaths and births per 1000 people, respectively. **Doubling time**, the time it takes a population to double in size, is also used as a measure of population growth. The **developing countries**, those with low per capita income, inadequate education, and poor nutrition, contain three-fourths of the world's population and double about every 33 years. **Developed countries**, the rich, well-fed, and well-educated nations, double on the average every 117 years. Population growth in individual nations is determined by calculating the number of births minus deaths plus the **net migration**—the difference between **emigration** and **immigration**.

The most important measure of reproductive performance is the **total fertility rate** (TFR), the average number of children a woman will have. In developed countries a TFR of 2.1 is **replacement-level fertility**. Replacement-level fertility is one of the first steps toward achieving **zero population growth**.

Population histograms are an important tool for studying populations, because they show the proportion of males and females in a population in various age groups. The shape of the histogram suggests whether populations will grow, shrink, or remain stable.

The future of world population is difficult to determine, because many factors such as total fertility rate can change. Many demographers believe that world population will stabilize somewhere between 8 and 15 million and that the exponential growth curve will be converted into a **sigmoidal curve**. However, other possibilities are also likely. The exponential growth curve may be transformed into a **dome-shaped curve** as population levels fall due to overextension of the carrying capacity. Or the pattern may become **irruptive**, a series of peaks and chasms. Finally, severe damage to the environment caused by exceeding the carrying capacity could result in a devastating crash, virtually eliminating humans from the face of earth. The pattern that population will assume is largely dependent on our efforts to control it, especially in the developing nations.

Discussion Questions

1. What is the population of the world? What is the population of the United States?

2. Is the rapid growth in world population of concern to you? Why or why not? How does population growth in the United States affect your life?

3. How many years did it take the world to reach a population of 1 billion people? How quickly did we reach the second, third, and fourth billions?

4. What factors kept world population in check for so many years? Discuss the advances that have unleashed population growth in the last 200 years.

5. Define the term *exponential growth rate*.

6. What is a population histogram? Describe the three general profiles. What information do population histograms give us?

7. How is the world population growth rate calculated?

8. Define replacement-level fertility and zero population growth.

9. Discuss the pros and cons of a lenient policy toward legal and illegal immigration in the United States. Do you favor strong immigration quotas?

10. Describe internal migration patterns in the United States. What factors account for them, and what are the impacts?

11. Debate the statement "Population is the cause of all the world's problems."

Suggested Readings

Brown, L. R., McGrath, P. L., and Stokes, B. (1976). *Twenty-Two Dimensions of the Population Problem.* Worldwatch Paper 5. Washington, D.C.: Worldwatch Institute. A superb review of the impacts of population.

Brown, L. R., and Jacobson, J. L. (1986). *Our Demographically Divided World.* Worldwatch Paper 74. Washington, D.C.: Worldwatch Institute. Detailed analysis of world population. Valuable reading.

Ehrlich, P. R. (1971). *The Population Bomb.* New York: Ballantine Books. A book that startled the world, telling of the hidden dangers of overpopulation. Dated but worth reading.

Grant, L. (1983). The Cornucopian Fallacies: The Myth of Perpetual Growth. *The Futurist* 17 (4): 18–22. Important article rebutting optimists who hold that there are no limits to growth in population and resource acquisition.

Gupte, P. (1985). *The Crowded Earth.* New York: Norton. Extraordinarily readable account of overpopulation and the effects of population control. A must!

Hardin, G. (1981). An Ecolate View of the Human Predicament. *Alternatives* 7: 241–262. Superb paper on overpopulation and carrying capacity. Exceptional insights.

Haub, C., and Grant, L. (1983). *Whatever Happened to the Population Bomb?* Washington, D.C.: The Environmental Fund. Interesting answer to an important question.

Haupt, A., and Kane, T. T. (1982). *Population Handbook.* Washington, D.C.: Population Reference Bureau. A superb primer.

Huss, J. D., and Wirken, M. J. (1977). Illegal Immigration: The Hidden Population Bomb. *The Futurist* 11 (2): 114–120. An excellent article.

Mayer, J. (1984). Food, Nutrition, and Population. In *Sustaining Tomorrow: A Strategy for World Conservation and Development*, ed. F. R. Thibodeau and H. H. Field. Hanover, N. H.: University Press of New England. Good summary of overpopulation and its effects.

Myers, N. (ed.). (1984). *Gaia: An Atlas of Planet Management.* New York: Anchor Books. Good reference on population and its impacts.

Population Reference Bureau (1982). U.S. Population: Where We Are; Where We're Going. *Population Bulletin* 37 (2): 1–51. A fact-filled treatise on U.S. population past, present, and future.

Population Reference Bureau (1987). *1987 World Population Data Sheet* and *United States Population Data Sheet.* Washington, D.C.: Population Reference Bureau. Published annually with current statistics on U.S. and world population.

Simon, J. L. (1983). Life on Earth Is Getting Better, Not Worse. *The Futurist* 17 (4): 7–14. Recommended reading, along with Grant's rebuttal (above).

Webb, M., and Jacobsen, J. (1982). *U.S. Carrying Capacity: An Introduction.* Washington, D.C.: Carrying Capacity. Good overview of ways human populations have exceeded carrying capacity.

Population Control:
Key to a Sustainable Society

To rebuild our civilization we must first rebuild ourselves according to the pattern laid down by life.

ALEX CARREL

Most experts are convinced that population growth cannot continue indefinitely. This conclusion gained wide acceptance after an extensive computer study of the human future sponsored by the Club of Rome and published in the book *The Limits to Growth*. The authors found from their analysis of population growth, resources, food, pollution, and industrial output that the human population would exceed the carrying capacity of the planet within a century if exponential growth continued (Figure 6-1). According to this forecast, food supplies, industrial output, and population will grow until rapidly diminishing resource supplies put a halt to industrial growth. Population will fall later because of food shortages.

The researchers next doubled their estimated available supply of nonrenewable resources, assuming that we might be able to expand our resource base through discoveries and new technologies that improve mining efficiency (Chapter 13). They found that the human population would still overshoot the carrying capacity and crash, only a couple of decades later (Figure 6-2). The rising death rate will be due in part to increased pollution from expanded industrial output, they predicted.

In still another scenario the authors assumed that world resources were unlimited. In that study population growth was halted by rising levels of pollution. (See discussions of the greenhouse effect, depletion of atmo-

World Model Standard Run

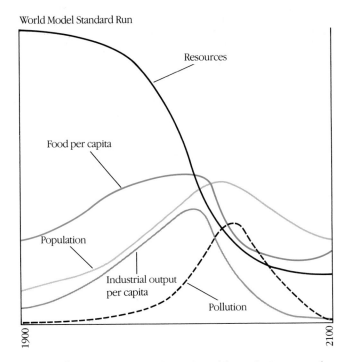

Figure 6-1 Computer analysis of world trends. Because of natural delays in the system, both population and pollution continue to increase for some time after the peak of industrialization.

World Model with Natural Resource Reserves Doubled

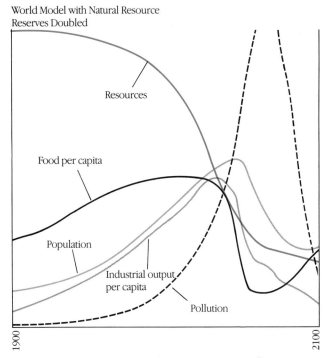

Figure 6-2 The same computer analysis as Figure 6-1, except that a doubling of natural resources in the world is assumed.

spheric ozone, and acid rain in Chapter 15.) The conclusions of the Club of Rome report were unequivocal. Any way you look at it, if human civilization continues on the same path, we will exceed the carrying capacity of the biosphere with perilous results. Can anything be done to change course?

Several computer models in *The Limits to Growth* showed that a stable world system could be reached by (1) immediately achieving zero population growth, (2) recycling, (3) pollution control, (4) soil erosion control, (5) soil replenishment, and (6) an emphasis on food production and services rather than industrial production (Figure 6-3).

Despite the warnings of scientists many political leaders remain blind to the consequences of exponential growth in population and industrial output. According to Professor D. H. Meadows and her colleagues, who collaborated on *The Limits to Growth*: "Every day of continued exponential growth brings the world system closer to the ultimate limits of . . . growth. A decision to do nothing is a decision to increase the risk of collapse." The longer we allow exponential growth to continue, the smaller the chance of achieving a sustainable future, and the greater the likelihood that we will damage the biosphere.

Stabilized World Model

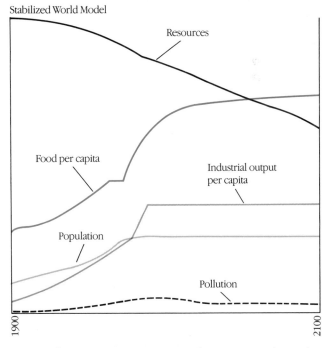

Figure 6-3 The same computer analysis as Figure 6-1, with global zero population growth, pollution control, soil management, and sustainable agriculture.

How Do We Control Population Growth?

Many experts agree that to avoid overshooting the carrying capacity and to prevent the likely population crash we should take measures now to control population growth.

Setting Our Goals

But what should our goals be—simply to allow managed growth, to reach a stable population size, or to reduce the size of the human population? The answers to these questions differ depending on who is asked, partly because many people disagree on the fundamental issue—the number of people the world can support. Some observers contend that the world can comfortably accommodate only 500,000 people; others say that a population of 100 billion would be possible. Many ecologists argue that we have already exceeded the earth's carrying capacity (ample evidence is cited in Chapter 5); thus, growth should be halted as soon as possible.

Consider the ecologists' case: Today, about one-fifth of the world's people, or about 1 billion, live in a state of extreme poverty. They are inadequately fed and sheltered. They wander the streets of Calcutta, Bangkok, Cairo, and elsewhere begging for food and stealing what they can. At night they sleep in alleyways, under bridges, or in cardboard shelters. Another 2 billion people live on the edge, with barely adequate food and shelter and few amenities. Four families live in a two-room apartment and share a water tap with 25 other families. They have no sewage disposal systems.

All told, nearly three-fifths of the world's population is in bad shape. Strenuous efforts to improve the economic condition of the world's poor, in hopes of increasing personal wealth, have failed to keep up with growth. More and more people fall into the trap of poverty each year. Thus, many observers believe that putting a stop to growth now is the best way to reduce further suffering, environmental pollution, and resource depletion. Stopping growth, reducing population size, and pursuing sensible economic plans, as discussed below, can help break the vicious circle of poverty, but the road ahead will be long and difficult.

Even if we could miraculously reach replacement-level fertility today, the enormous momentum ensures further growth to 7 to 8 billion, most of it occurring in poor nations. Following an end to growth, many experts believe, the human population should be reduced through attrition—keeping birth rates below death rates. Reducing the size of the human population throughout the world would help us live within the limits of nature and maybe ensure a better life for billions of poor people.

Population Control Strategies

How do we go about controlling population growth? For a number of years many population experts advocated a simple way—economic development. The logic was undeniably attractive: make jobs by increasing industry, farming, crafts, and services. More jobs mean more personal wealth. People could then afford decent housing, food, and education. Poverty and disease would be eliminated. As an added benefit, people would choose to have fewer children.

Demographic Transition

The idea that economic improvement in the developing nations would solve the population crisis was an appealing one for many years, and there was plenty of evidence from developed countries that it could work. The evidence came in the form of a **demographic transition**, described below. Experts reasoned that if the demographic transition worked for Europe and North America, it could work for the rest of the world as well.

The demographic transition takes place in four definable stages (Table 6-1). Countries begin in Stage 1 with high birth rates and high death rates. The population is stable at this time. Because of improvements in health care and sanitation, however, death rates begin to fall. Birth rates remain high. This is called Stage 2; it is the most dangerous stage, because the large difference between birth and death rates leads to rapid population growth. As the country develops economically, however, birth rates begin to decrease. Population growth slows. This is Stage 3. Finally, over time, birth rates and death rates come into balance. Population growth is stopped in Stage 4.

The decrease in birth rates associated with economic development can be attributed to several factors. Perhaps the most important is the shift in people's attitudes toward children. Preindustrial farmers view children as an asset. Children help with farm work and can support their parents in old age. With industrialization and the migration of families to the city, however, they become an economic liability. Given competition for living space, each child means that more money has to be devoted to food and housing. If the children do not work, they create an additional financial drain on the family. As a result, smaller families generally prevail.

Smaller families may also result from social developments like the Social Security system in the United States, which provides income for retirees, thus taking the burden off children. In addition, better sanitation and health care can contribute to smaller families by greatly increasing the chances that a child will survive the early years. Realizing this, parents voluntarily reduce the number of births. Quite simply, it is no longer necessary to have a large family to ensure the survival of a few offspring.

Table 6-1	The Stages of the Demographic Transition
Stage 1—	Preindustrial High birth rate and high death rate Little or no increase in population Example: Finland 1785–1790 Crude birth rate = 38/1000 Crude death rate = 32/1000 Natural increase = 0.6%
Stage 2—	Transitional High birth rate and falling death rate High population growth rate Example: Finland 1825–1830 Crude birth rate = 38/1000 Crude death rate = 24/1000 Natural increase = 1.4%
Stage 3—	Industrial Falling birth rate and low death rate Slower growth Example: Finland 1910–1915 Crude birth rate = 29/1000 Crude death rate = 17/1000 Natural increase = 1.2%
Stage 4—	Postindustrial Low birth rate and low death rate Slow population growth Example: Finland 1970–1976 Crude birth rate = 13/1000 Crude death rate = 10/1000 Natural increase = 0.3%

Source: Haupt, A., and Kane, T. (1978). *Population Handbook.* Population Reference Bureau.

The idea that economic development can lead to zero population growth has been a controversial topic in discussions on population control for developing countries. If factories are built and jobs are created in the cities, some argue, economic development and the newfound wealth will reduce population growth. Supporters of economic development as a means to control population growth point to the United States, Finland, Denmark, and dozens of other countries that have experienced demographic transitions. If it worked for Finland, why won't it work for Ghana, China, India, or Chad?

There are at least four reasons why not. First, the economic resources of many of the developing countries are too small to build the type of industry that took developed countries through their demographic transitions. Second, the classic transition did not take place overnight: it took Finland over 200 years to approach a balance between birth rate and death rate. The developing countries with rapid doubling times do not have this kind of time. Third, the rapid growth of population in these countries far exceeds their ability to raise the standard of living; recent

economic studies show, for instance, that a 1% growth in the labor force requires a 3% economic growth. Think of the economic growth needed to sustain populations growing at 3% and 4% per year. The fourth reason is that the fossil fuel energy sources that were essential to the demographic transition are diminishing and becoming ever more costly. Without the rich mines of England or the great oil deposits of Arabia and North America, poor nations will probably never witness economic growth like that seen in the Western world.

Many of the world's countries have entered Stage 2 of the demographic transition with high birth rates and low death rates. For the reasons given above, a demographic transition brought on by industrialization is unlikely. Thus, the demographic transition must come about in other ways, most likely through family planning and small-scale economic development.

Family Planning Family planning allows couples to determine the number and spacing of offspring. For countries stuck in Stage 2 of the demographic transition it can speed up the decline in the birth rate.

For family planning to work, information on birth control must be readily available. Birth control must also be accessible and inexpensive. People must be motivated to practice birth control, too. Strictly defined, **birth control** includes any method to reduce births, including contraception and **induced abortion**, the intentional interruption of pregnancy through surgical means or through drug treatments. A **contraceptive** is any chemical, device, or method that prevents fertilization.

Family planning programs lie on a continuum from voluntary to compulsory. **Voluntary programs** are those that make birth control available to the public at low cost. There is no pressure from the government. People choose the type of birth control and family size. Some voluntary programs are sponsored by governments (Figure 6-4), and some are run by private organizations, such as Planned Parenthood in the United States.

Family planning programs may be promoted by governments; such programs are euphemistically called **extended voluntary programs**. In these cases governmental agencies may hand out information on birth control and sterilization or sponsor posters, newspaper ads, television and radio announcements, and billboards (Figure 6-5). In Egypt, for instance, a song promoting birth control that was played with a government-sponsored commercial became so popular that it was a national hit. Payments or incentives are frequently offered by governments to couples practicing birth control or undergoing sterilization. Transistor radios, for example, are handed out in rural Egypt to couples who adopt some form of birth control. One of the key components of governmental programs is an effort to change people's thinking

Figure 6-4 Family planning in India. A doctor lectures to a group of Indian wives on various methods of birth control at a family planning clinic in New Delhi.

about family size. Varinda Vittachi, a writer from Sri Lanka, reminds us, "The world's population problem will be solved in the mind and not in the uterus." Posters in Vietnam, for example, extol the virtues of a one-child family. Informational campaigns may also attempt to change stereotypical sex roles, persuading men that masculinity and self-importance are not related to the number of their children and convincing women that the childbearing role is not the only one that makes them valuable.

Forced family planning programs involve strict governmental limitations on family size and include punishment for those who exceed quotas. These rare programs may impose sterilization after a family reaches the allotted size, limit food rations for "excess" children, or tax couples who exceed the allowed number of children. China has what many observers consider a forced family planning program. It has adopted a one-child policy to halt its rapid growth (China has one-fifth of the world's population, about 1 billion people). The one-child policy is intended to reduce China's population size, which government officials fear already exceeds the country's carrying capacity. Female workers meet regularly in small groups to discuss birth control. Government workers reportedly hound men and women with one child to undergo sterilization. Pregnant women who already have one child have reportedly been "forced" to have abortions, although authenticated cases are hard to come by, and occurrences may be rare. The Chinese government also supplements the monthly income of couples who pledge to have only one child. If a couple that has pledged to have one child has a second one, however, the government often requires repayment of the monthly bonus and cuts the monthly salary by 15%.

Figure 6-5 A familiar poster seen everywhere in India, with a smiling family and the slogan, "two or three children . . . is enough." India's Family Planning program is closely meshed into the government's health services. All doctors, nurses, and other health workers are trained and expected to provide family planning advice and assistance as part of their regular duties.

Essay 6-1

Help from the U.N. for Population Control

The world has recognized the need for population control. Hardly a nation is without a population policy. But for many Third World Nations money is a major obstacle to progress in population control.

Today, however, help is on the way. Perhaps the most important source of help is the United Nations Fund for Population Activities (UNFPA). Established in the late 1960s with several million dollars from a few donor nations, the organization has seen voluntary pledges increase to over $135 million in 1985 from 100 countries. To date the UNFPA has spent more than $1.3 billion on over 4,500 population and family planning projects in nearly 150 developing countries. The major donors are shown in the accompanying table.

The UNFPA is, to a large extent, responsible for much of the progress in population control in recent decades. It has raised international awareness of population growth through periodic censuses. It has also helped alert the world to the consequences of overpopulation and has helped many governments develop, finance, and carry out population programs. Among international agencies the UNFPA is noted for its ability to provide money for assistance that has an immediate impact.

Because of a growing concern in many developing nations over population growth, the portion of the UNFPA's budget allocated for family planning services has jumped from 35% to over 50%. In India, Indonesia, Brazil, Nigeria,

Major Donors to the UNFPA (1986)		
Country	Share of Total Contributions	Per Capita Expenditure (U.S. Dollars)
Japan	25%	$ .28
The Netherlands	15%	1.39
West Germany	13%	.29
Norway	10.5%	3.38
Canada	8%	.41
Sweden	7%	1.10
Denmark	5.5%	1.44
United Kingdom	5%	.12
Finland	4%	.99
Switzerland	2%	.50
Italy	1%	.03
Australia	1%	.05
Others	3%	—

Source: United Nations Fund for Population Activities, 1987

Bangladesh, and dozens of other countries the agency supports maternal and child health clinics, regional training in contraception, improved contraceptive distribution, and other programs. Its population experts consult with governments on the best ways to control population.

The growing commitment of most developing countries to population control, however, has created a problem in recent years. Requests for UNFPA money have exceeded the supply by about 50%.

For the most part, developed countries have responded with an outpouring of generosity. Recent substantial cutbacks by the United States, however, have severely affected the UNFPA's budget. Any further reduction in funds will seriously hamper the agency at a time when momentum for population control has peaked. (See the Population Institute Viewpoint, this chapter.) Each year of waiting worsens a problem whose solution is long overdue.

Many programs do not fit neatly into one of these categories. The government of Singapore, for instance, uses radio, billboards, and school curricula to suggest that two children per family are enough. This extended voluntary program is complemented by several coercive measures: The first two children of any family are allowed to attend local schools, but additional children must often be bused elsewhere. Furthermore, hospital costs increase for "surplus" children, and government employees who are not sterilized are given a low priority for public housing.

Small-Scale Economic Development "Family planning cannot exist in a vacuum. You can't just distribute contraceptives and tell people to go ahead and start lowering the birth rate," says Aziz el-Bindary, head of Egypt's Supreme Council for Population and Family Planning. "To have an effective family-planning program," he adds, "you also have to have an effective economy—where jobs are available, where health facilities are adequate."

Throughout the world, governments are finding that packaging together jobs for women, small-scale economic

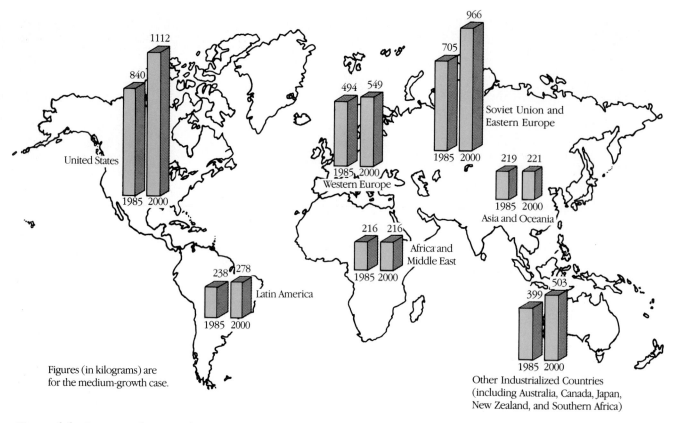

Figure 6-6   Current and projected per capita grain consumption in the world (including grain used for livestock).

development, improved education, better health care, and contraception can reduce birth rates. Many experts see this as an "enlightened approach" to population control. They believe that family planning will be successful in many places only if people want to incorporate it into their everyday lives.

With this in mind the United Nations Fund for Population Activities recently made substantial investments in clothing factories in which Egyptian women can work. Other programs are under way. The logic behind these activities is that working women often delay marriage and childbearing and thus have fewer children.

Developed Countries—What Can They Do?

Many people think that population control pertains only to the developing countries, because many of the richer, developed countries are in Stages 3 and 4 of the demographic transition. Observers point out, however, that the high per capita consumption of the developed countries has put enormous strains on the earth's carrying capacity. Widespread pollution and resource depletion are two signs that many of the developed countries have exceeded

the carrying capacity. Therefore, many ecologists argue, population size must be reduced in the developed nations if we are to build a sustainable society. Today, the populations of West Germany and a few other nations have begun to shrink because their total fertility rates have fallen below replacement-level fertility. The rest of the developed world can learn from Germany's experiences with a transition to a smaller population size, recognizing that a reduction in growth may cause immediate hardships but has many benefits as well.

According to some estimates, a single American uses 25 to 38 times more resources than a citizen of India. As shown in Figure 6-6, U.S. residents consume nearly four times as much grain as residents of Third World nations in Africa, the Middle East, Asia, and Oceania. By using less, many people argue, developed countries can make possible a more equitable sharing of the earth's resources. This redistribution may help reduce world tensions.

Sharing resources is controversial. Garrett Hardin, author of *Filters against Folly*, suggests that global sharing of resources is not the answer. The rate of growth and needs of the nearly 4 billion residents of the Third World

Table 6-2 Population Control Strategies for Developed Countries

Strategy	Rationale	Benefits
Stabilize population growth by restricting immigration, and by spending more money and time on sex education and population awareness in public schools.	High use of resources taxes the environment. Immigrants create serious strain on the economy and create social tension in conditions of high unemployment. Education helps citizens realize the importance of population control.	Limiting resource use leaves more for future generations and developing countries.
Provide financial assistance to developing countries for agriculture and appropriate industry. Aid should come from government and private sources.	Economic growth in developing countries will raise their standard of living and aid in population control.	The rich-poor gap would narrow. A decrease in sociopolitical tension and resource shortage would result.
Provide assistance to population control programs.	Better funded population programs can afford the increased technical assistance and community outreach programs necessary to provide information to the public.	Could result in faster decrease in population growth.
Make trade with less developed countries equitable and freer.	Freer trade will increase per capita income and raise standards of living with little effect on home economy.	A higher standard of living and increased job opportunities could result.
Concentrate research on social, cultural, and psychological aspects of reproduction.	Techniques available today are effective and reliable. What is needed is more motivation for population control, especially among poor countries.	Money will be better spent; research of this nature may help facilitate family planning in less developed countries.

far exceed our capacity to help, he argues. Developed countries, he contends, can assist the developing nations by sharing their knowledge of birth control, agriculture, health care, and appropriate technology. Financial assistance to help achieve a moderate rate of industrialization, using **appropriate technologies**—that is, industry that is labor intensive and uses local resources to meet local needs—can also help. Table 6-2 lists some suggestions for developed countries.

William and Paul Paddock propose a triage system to determine who gets financial and technical aid. They say that countries could be categorized in three groups: (1) those that have an adequate resource base and could survive hard times without aid, (2) those impoverished nations that would probably not survive drought and food shortage even with aid, and (3) those that can be helped. Group 1 needs no assistance. Group 2 must be given up as hopeless, for no amount of aid will help them. Group 3, if aided, could pull through a drought or other difficult

period. Therefore, they suggest, we should maximize our aid for population control, food and agricultural, and technological support and development by concentrating our efforts on Group 3. To some, this seems like an unethical approach to world assistance. Others see it as the only answer to apportion the limited aid.

Developing Countries—What Can They Do?

The less developed countries recognize the need for population control. Today 93% of the world's population lives in countries with population control policies. The International Planned Parenthood Federation, established in the 1950's, has disseminated information on birth control and provided assistance to many countries. Since the 1960's the World Bank has given financial aid to developing countries with population control policies.

Unfortunately, having a population control policy and

Table 6-3 Population Control Strategies for Developing Countries

Strategy	Rationale	Benefits
Develop effective national plan to ensure better dissemination of information and availability of contraception, and other methods of population control. Do not rely on one type of control.	Each country better understands its people and thus can design better programs to spread population control information and devices.	More effective dissemination of information and, probably, a higher rate of success.
Finance education in rural regions, emphasizing population control and benefits of reduced population growth.	Education can help make population control a reality.	Slower population growth, more effective use of contraceptives, and more incentive.
Seek to change cultural taboos against birth control and cultural incentives for large families.	Changes in culture and psychology may be needed to make population control programs effective.	Such changes will help programs succeed.
Develop appropriate industry and agriculture, especially in rural areas to reduce or eliminate the movement of people from the country to the city.	Appropriate agriculture and industry will create jobs and better economic conditions for families. A higher standard of living could translate into better health care and greater survival of young, thus destroying need for large families.	This will result in higher standard of living, better health care, and impetus for control of family size.
Seek programs of development that attain a maximum spread of wealth among the people.	Development must not help just a select few, because benefits may not trickle down to needy.	Plans of this nature yield good distribution of income and help the needy rather than select few.
Integrate population policy with economic, resource, food, and land-use policy to achieve a stable state.	Finite resources require wise allocation and use; success in the long run depends on attempts to achieve a sustainable future.	Longevity and permanence are attainable if policies are integrated and take into account the requirements of a sustainable society.
Seek funding from the United Nations and developed countries.	Developed countries have a stake in stabilizing world population growth.	Developed countries could provide significant financial support.

funding that policy are entirely different matters. Few governments today spend more than 1% of their national budget on family planning services. In addition to this monetary problem, illiteracy, rural isolation, and local taboos have hampered success. For these and other reasons, population control in developing nations has been limited. Results have been especially poor in India, Mexico, Brazil, Pakistan, and Indonesia.

Table 6-3 lists population control strategies for less developed countries. Accompanied by appropriate development, these suggestions could improve the lives of many people.

Coming to Grips with Global Overpopulation: A Case in Point

The Population Institute

The Population Institute is a nonprofit educational organization based in Washington, D.C., that evaluates facts and public policies relating to world overpopulation.

A few years ago opponents of family planning took occasional potshots at U.S. international family planning assistance. In the last few years, however, this scattershot approach has been abandoned. In its place is a vigorous, concerted attack on population programs. One of the results has been a cutoff or curtailment of U.S. funds to the International Planned Parenthood Federation and the U.N. Fund for Population Activities. The attack has been successful, and today no developing country's population program is unaffected.

For 20 years the United States has been at the forefront of efforts to convince developing countries of the vital link between population stabilization and economic progress. Today, virtually the entire developing world has accepted this premise. Many developing countries have begun programs to stabilize their population but need financial and technical assistance from the industrialized nations to make their plans work. Cutting back or cutting off assistance now is a reprehensible retreat from reality.

The implications of world overpopulation are hard to grasp for many people. The numbers, statistics, and equations may be meaningless to many of us. By any other name, overpopulation spells hunger, poverty, and unemployment on an unimaginable scale. Overpopulation is a harsh reality that spawns death and destruction. It must be confronted and overcome if we are to achieve global security, peace, and prosperity.

Nowhere is the problem of overpopulation more visible than in the cities of the world. Just after the turn of the 21st century the world will reach three monumental milestones. The globe will be inhabited by 6 billion people. A majority of the world's people will live in cities. The world population will have tripled during a single human lifespan, from 2 billion in 1930 to 6 billion in 2000.

The rapid growth of population has resulted in an increase in the number of cities and their size. Those cities with 4 million or more people are called megacities. In 1950 there were 13 megacities, with a combined population of 88 million people. By 1985 the number had grown to 42, with a total of 342 million people. By the year 2000 the number of megacities is expected to reach 66, with 600 million people.

A high proportion of the megacity growth is occurring in poor nations, those least able to cope with burgeoning populations. In 1950 nearly 65% of the megacity population was in industrialized countries, but by 2000 some 80% of the megacity population will be found in developing nations.

Urbanization has had many beneficial offshoots. But the rapid growth of megacities today strains the meager resources of the world, creating air and water pollution and widespread human suffering. Rapid urban population growth only worsens poverty. Many people are forced to live in makeshift homes in squatter cities, often on land unsuited for human habitation. Squatter cities lack such basic amenities as sewage and water systems, electricity, police and fire protection, and schools. Human excrement is everywhere; in the warm sun it dries into a fine gray powder that scatters in the wind over the entire city.

With too many people chasing too few jobs, unemployment is rampant, and wages are depressed. If an individual finds a job, he or she may earn a dollar or less for eight to ten hours of hard labor.

Without a reduction in the high fertility rate conditions are bound to get worse. During the next two decades developing countries must create 750 million new jobs to employ the large number of young people soon to reach working age. Most of these people are already born. Failure to create jobs will be disastrous.

Today, large numbers of unemployed and disaffected youths congregate in massive squatter clusters in Third World cities. They are prime candidates for extremist political groups. From the perspective of the poor, such groups offer hope. It may be false hope, but since existing systems have failed them, they are ready to search for something new.

Some people maintain that large urban regions are assets rather than liabilities. Family planning, they believe, should be halted. For the millions of people already crowded into the world's megacities and the millions more to come, such action is bound to create further hardship. It is time to come to grips with overpopulation, to support an acceleration of efforts to reduce population growth throughout the world.

Making Strategies Work

Almost any venture encounters obstacles. Population control is no exception. In fact, it is bound to face more obstacles than most projects, because it strikes at the heart of what is to many people a personal issue: the right to have children. At least three major obstacles stand in the way of population control programs: psychological inertia, lack of education, and religious beliefs.

Psychological Barriers

Large families are an asset in the developing countries, since children help with the chores and later care for

Figure 6-7   Total fertility rates of U.S. women, by level of education.

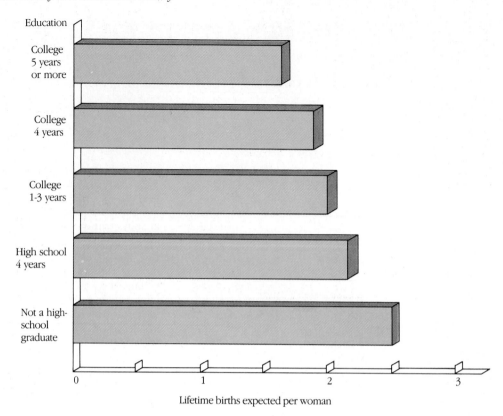

Lifetime births expected per woman

their parents. Given the high mortality rates in these countries, having many children ensures that some will survive. Even though death rates have fallen swiftly throughout the world and more children are now surviving, the traditional value of children has not been abandoned, and birth rates remain high.

Traditional views of family size often change slowly after a decline in death rates. Nowhere is this more evident than in India. In some economically developed regions, for instance, sons are still viewed in high esteem as a source of security in their parents' old age. The present government promotes small families of two or three children. Many parents see the ideal family as two sons and a daughter, to hedge their bets should one son die. In trying to reach this goal, however, couples average 4.2 children. "One son is no sons," Indians argue, still unsure of the lowered death rate. "To be sterilized is to tempt fate," another proclaims, arguing in favor of the insurance that two-son families provide. Until people begin to realize that one son is enough and that that son will probably survive, India's population growth will continue at its current rapid rate.

Having children is a self-fulfilling activity for males and females in most countries. Sociologists report that men and women are admired in many societies for the number of children they have, a view that is present in developed nations as well. The humorist and educator Bill Cosby pokes fun at this view, saying, "If a chimpanzee can have a baby, the human female [and male, I would add] should realize that the feat is something less than an entry for the *Guinness Book of World Records*."

Unfortunately, social acceptance and numerous other psychological factors result in the birth of many children who will never have adequate food, clothing, shelter, and education. In the face of such possibilities how can people continue to have large families? Citizens of developed countries tend to view children as an economic drain that detracts from their life-style. Recent studies show that it costs low-income families in the United States about $60,000 to raise a child, including education through a publicly subsidized college. Middle-income families spend about $90,000 per child. In the poor countries a child deprives the family of virtually nothing. In fact, since children represent a form of material wealth (free labor and support in old age) and satisfaction, they probably represent a net gain.

Education Barriers

U.S. Department of Commerce figures show that the higher the educational level, the lower the total fertility rate (Figure 6-7). The reason is that educated women often pursue careers, postponing marriage and child-bearing. Since the childbearing years are from 15 to 44, a woman who graduates from college at age 21, marries, but delays children until she is 30 has decreased her childbearing years by half.

Inadequate education in developing countries has several important effects on population growth. Men and women generally marry young and do not pursue careers that interfere with childbearing. Thus, the period of childbearing is much longer than that for couples in developed countries. A lack of education also makes it more difficult for people to learn about alternatives to childbearing and proper use of contraceptives. It is no wonder, then, that the birth rate is still high in rural India, where 80% to 90% of the women cannot read or write.

Religious Barriers

Religion may also be a powerful force in reproduction. In the West the Roman Catholic church has been cited as a prime cause of overpopulation. Strictly forbidding all "unnatural" methods of birth control, the Catholic church takes a dim view of the pill, the condom, the diaphragm, and abortion. In 1968 Pope Paul VI's encyclical *Humanae Vitae* condemned the use of contraceptives except the rhythm method, one of the least effective measures. Theoretically, the church provides the guidelines for the sexual practices of approximately 600 million people. Recent surveys show, however, that the use of contraceptives by Catholic women, especially in Western nations, is nearly as high as that among non-Catholics. In Latin America many priests speak out against the Vatican's official policy. Members of the Church of Jesus Christ of Latter-Day Saints don't promote birth control but favor large families.

Birth control is a generally undiscussed subject among other religions. And since many of the Eastern and Mideastern religions compete with one another for followers, birth control is not advocated.

Overcoming the Obstacles

For family planning to work, workers must understand the culture, education, and religion of a people. Programs should be tailored to meet the needs of each group. People must have access to socially acceptable birth control, and in poor countries this must be inexpensive or free and must be easy to understand and simple to use, to reduce the risk of failure. Trained individuals must be available to counsel those seeking contraceptives, abortion, or sterilization. Most importantly, attitudes toward family size must be changed if programs are to work. Perhaps the most effective way of changing attitudes is to provide work for women; to increase personal wealth; to

reduce illiteracy; and to provide better health care, sanitation, and contraception.

Ethics of Population Control

Perhaps no other issue in environmental science is so laden with ethical problems as population control. To deny the right to reproduce is to deny one of the most basic and important of all human activities. To some, population control is a violation of deep religious beliefs. To others, it is an intrusion into a private matter; and for minorities, population control has overtones of genocide. Two important ethical questions are discussed in this section as an introduction to this complex ethical issue.

Is Reproduction a Personal Right?

Some people argue that the right to reproduce at will should be curtailed when the rights of the individual interfere with the welfare of society, the collective rights of all the people. For example, in 1975 India's government, under the late Prime Minister Indira Gandhi, began a program of forced sterilization (Figure 6-8). Changes in India's Constitution placed the rights of the whole of society above the rights of the individual. This short-lived and extreme program illustrates that an important end—the welfare of an overpopulated nation's people—can prompt governments to adopt tyrannical means to achieve that end.

The other point of view was well stated in 1965 by Pope Paul in a speech to the United Nations: "You must strive to multiply bread so that it suffices for the tables of mankind, and not, rather, favor an artificial control of birth, which would be irrational, in order to diminish the number of guests at the banquet of life." To interfere with the creation of new life offends some people's deep-seated beliefs in God's role.

Individuals who support the right to reproduce freely often argue that denying such rights takes away personal freedom. Paul Ehrlich argues that we "must take the side of the hungry *billions* of living human beings today and tomorrow, not the side of potential human beings. . . . If those potential human beings are born, they will at best lead miserable lives and die young." He argues that we cannot let humanity be destroyed by a doctrine of individual freedoms conceived in isolation from the biological facts of life.

Garrett Hardin argues that the integrity of the biosphere should be the guiding principle in the debate over population control. Recognizing that the welfare of the biosphere determines the welfare of all living things, including humankind, and that we have obligations to future generations to protect the biosphere, human population control becomes a biological imperative.

Figure 6-8 Indira Gandhi, the late prime minister of India, speaks to a crowd in Calcutta about her governmental policies.

Is It Ethical Not to Control Population?

If we do not control population and instead let it run its course, will uncontrolled growth improve or worsen the world for future generations? If our actions rob from the future, can they be considered ethical?

To predict how our actions will affect the future, we can use the computer to forecast major trends in population, resources, and pollution. Such exercises, as we've seen in earlier examples, may be subject to error but nonetheless help us arrive at ethical decisions based on scientific information. *The Limits to Growth*, discussed at the beginning of this chapter, suggests that continued population growth is an invitation to disaster. The computer projections remind us that humankind comes with the same warranty that the dinosaurs had. Werner Fornos, director of the Population Institute, notes, "National leaders are recognizing that population growth without adequate resources and services results not in national strength but in national disaster."

Not controlling population, many experts agree, is unethical because it sidesteps our obligation to future generations. Critics of this viewpoint reply that technology and substitutes will be found to feed the hungry new mouths and that more people will lead to a better tomorrow. Julian Simon, an economist from the University of Illinois, is a leading advocate of this outlook. He argues that more people mean more knowledge and that knowledge is the key to a better future. This view ignores the finite nature of many resources, the ways renewable resources, such as forests, can be irreparably damaged, and the poverty that afflicts many of the world's people. (For a debate on this issue see the Point/Counterpoint in Chapter 5).

The Status of Population Control

"The world of the mid-eighties is a world of stark demographic contrasts," writes Lester Brown, a population expert of the Worldwatch Institute. Never have the differences among countries been greater. "Some populations change little in size from year to year or decline slightly," Brown notes, "while others are experiencing the fastest growth ever recorded." This section discusses the demographic contrasts, looking at areas of progress and setbacks in an effort to help us guide our future efforts.

Encouraging Trends

Developing Nations   Most of the world's developing nations see the need for programs to control population growth. Ten years ago this was not the case. Especially reluctant were Third World nations, which rallied behind the cry "Development is the best contraceptive." A decade of falling per capita food production and income and rising debt, however, has changed many leaders' minds. Today, even the World Bank, a private lending institution that has long ignored the problem, has called attention to the need for population control throughout much of the developing world. The first step in solving the population problem is awareness. The Third World countries are now aware of the problem and are trying to do something about it. In fact, for every dollar of foreign aid sent to combat population growth the developing nations spend $4.

Many nations have successful population control programs and have made phenomenal progress. The largest

Amnesty for Illegal Aliens: A Population Bomb?

Population–Environment Balance

In 1986, Congress passed legislation which could, in ten years, add 30 million people to the U.S. population. The Immigration Reform and Control Act (PL 99–603) will give permanent resident status to all persons who can prove by the end of 1987 that they arrived in this country before January 1, 1982. Population–Environment Balance supports immigration reform, but questions the wisdom of granting blanket amnesty to illegal aliens because of the long term demographic impact.

Between 6 and 12 million illegal immigrants, if not more, are already living in the United States. Government agencies expect 36% to 64% of these will apply for amnesty. This means that between 2.2 and 7.7 million people could receive amnesty and thereafter become permanent legal residents under the Immigration Reform Act.

Under immigration law, permanent residents may apply for citizenship after five years. Once they become citizens, they are free to bring in their immediate relatives—spouses, minor children, and parents. They may also petition for the admission of their brothers, sisters, and adult children. Upon entry to the United States, these relatives are classified as permanent legal residents and may apply for citizenship after five years. Once they are full citizens, they too may bring in spouses, minor children, and petition for admission of other relatives. This process, known as "chain migration," could add tens of millions of people to our population before the year 2000.

The table below shows how many new immigrants might enter the United States if the broad amnesty is followed by chain migration. The table assumes that between 2 and 8 million illegal aliens will come forward for amnesty, gain citizenship after five years, and bring in from one to four immediate family members.

Let us assume that the actual total number of family members brought in by illegal aliens given amnesty is mid-way between 2 and 32 million, the lowest and highest estimates

in the above table. This leads to the conclusion that about 18 million immigrants will enter the United States legally as a result of the amnesty. That is equivalent to adding enough people for a state the size of New York.

The United States cannot afford to allow such a massive influx of people, especially just as our economy has begun to recover from a decade of recession. The additional population would further burden our already over-extended social welfare programs and increase unemployment, making life more difficult for millions of Americans.

Besides being unfair to U.S. citizens, the amnesty for illegal aliens rewards people who knowingly violate U.S. laws and punishes those who abide by them. Millions of potential immigrants are waiting patiently for a chance to come to the United States legally. Should they not be given preference over illegal aliens? The amnesty provision in the immigration law sends a clear message to potential immigrants worldwide: it is far easier and faster to become a U.S. citizen by immigrating illegally than it is to wait for legal approval.

Another problem with the amnesty is that it sets a dangerous precedent. Believing that they might be included in a future amnesty, and hoping that not all employers will be deterred from hiring illegal aliens by the new sanctions in the immigration law, illegal aliens will continue to pour into the United States.

Population–Environment Balance advocates immigration reform and commends the effort that Congress has made towards that goal. However, we believe that granting blanket amnesty to illegal aliens is inconsistent with the main objective of the 1986 law, which is to control immigration. The amnesty will greatly increase, not decrease, immigration by setting off chain migration. The United States simply cannot afford the social, economic, and environmental degradation that will be caused by the addition of tens of millions to our population.

Chain Migration: Growth in U.S. Population Because of Amnesty

Number of Illegal Aliens Coming Forward for Amnesty	Number of Family Members Brought in After Citizenship is Obtained			
	1 Family member	**2** Family members	**3** Family members	**4** Family members
2 million	2 million	4 million	6 million	8 million
4 million	4 million	8 million	12 million	16 million
6 million	6 million	12 million	18 million	24 million
8 million	8 million	16 million	24 million	32 million

Figure 6-9 Total fertility rate is a predictive measure, telling us the number of children women will have, based on the current age-specific fertility rates. The total fertility rate in the United States has fluctuated widely with economic conditions. In the decade of the Great Depression women had a low total fertility rate. Since 1972, it has been below replacement level.

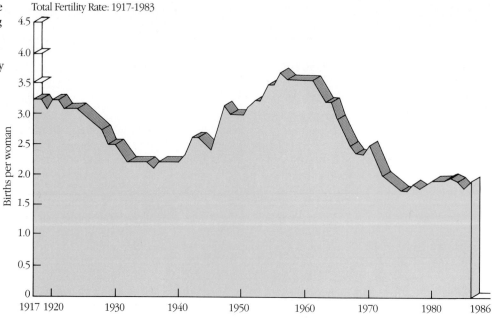

reductions in growth rate have been witnessed in China, Taiwan, Tunisia, Barbados, Hong Kong, Singapore, Costa Rica, and Egypt.

China's decline in birth rate in the 1970s is the most rapid of any country on record. It may be family planning's greatest success story. China's 2.5% annual growth rate in the 1960s (doubling time 28 years) dropped to 1% in 1986 (doubling time 70 years).

Developed Nations In the early to mid-1970s many developed countries updated their laws and policies governing family planning. A dozen countries in Europe now have stationary populations. Six more European nations are fast approaching them. Elsewhere, the United States and Japan, two of the most populous developed countries, show signs of slowing population growth. According to some demographers, the decline in growth in the developed nations is largely responsible for the large drop in the world's growth rate from over 2% in 1974 to 1.7% in 1986.

The United States exemplifies what has happened throughout much of the developed world. U.S. abortion laws were liberalized in the early 1970s, access to birth control was increased, a growing number of women entered the work force, educational opportunity for women increased, the feminist movement articulated a way of life in which motherhood was but one option, and many couples decided to remain childless. In addition, inflation and recession in the 1970s and early 1980s and soaring hospital costs no doubt helped reduce birth rates. The total fertility rate in the United States dropped to slightly below 2.1 in 1972 and since then has remained below replacement level (Figure 6-9).

Discouraging Trends

Unfortunately, the world population dilemma is far from solved; there remain some rather discouraging signs. For instance, 35% of the world's population was under the age of 15 in 1986. These children will provide a great deal of momentum for further growth as they marry and reproduce. During the 1970s death rates turned upward in many poorer countries, primarily because of hunger and malnutrition. Furthermore, food demand has now outstripped production, and world food reserves have dropped from 90 days in 1970 to 30 days in 1974 and have remained at this low level ever since. (For more on this topic see Chapter 7.)

Rapid growth is expected to continue in Africa, Latin America, and Asia, as shown in Figure 6-10. Expanded efforts are needed in these regions to avert widespread starvation, pollution, poverty, and resource depletion.

Contraceptive availability is also discouragingly low. Studies suggest that many women of reproductive age throughout the world do not want additional children but that about half of them are not using effective methods of birth control. Furthermore, whereas more than 80% of all married women in developing countries have heard of contraception, in some places such as Pakistan only one in ten women has ever used it. Another discouraging sign is the steady decline since 1960 in nonmilitary, developmental foreign aid to poor countries.

One of the most visible failures in population control is India's, even though a national birth control program has been in effect since 1951. India's program was the first of its kind in the world. The rate of growth has slowed from 2.6% in 1969 to 2.3% in 1986. India has a population of over 785 million (1986), however, and will soon exceed

Population (millions)		Change	
Now	**2000**		
Africa	513	851	65.9%
Latin America	390	564	44.6%
Asia	2,730	3,564	30.5%
Oceania	24	29	20.8%
North America	259	302	16.6%
Soviet Union	272	309	13.6%
Europe	489	511	4.5%
Total	**4,677**	**6,130**	34.1%

Figure 6-10 Projected population growth between 1984 and 2000.

China. In the next 15 years India's population is expected to swell by over 230 million, almost equal to the current population of the United States.

Population growth is a social problem. It begins with people as the cause, and ends with people as the victims. Human civilization need not decay in an explosion of people, but, many experts agree, we can improve only if we learn to live within the limits of nature. This is the lesson of ecology and demography.

In a society with a relatively short attention span, in which wars and space voyages capture our attention, we may have difficulty sustaining our interest in controlling population growth. Long-term action, lasting through the rest of this century and well into the next, can ensure a balance between human beings and the planet that will allow us to explore our full potential.

I cannot believe that the principal objective of humanity is to establish experimentally how many human beings the planet can just barely sustain. But I can imagine a remarkable world in which a limited population can live in abundance, free to explore the full extent of man's imagination and spirit.

PHILIP HANDLER

Summary

Many experts believe that the growth of population and use of resources cannot continue indefinitely without overtaxing the earth's carrying capacity. This belief is supported by elaborate computer modeling studies, which suggest that the only route to a stable, sustainable society is global zero population growth, recycling, pollution control, soil erosion control, soil replenishment, and emphasis on food production and services rather than industrial production.

Since about one-fifth of the world's population lives in a state of extreme poverty without adequate food and shelter, some population experts believe that we have already exceeded the carrying capacity. Family planning and limited economic development are ways to bring the human population back in line.

Family planning allows couples to determine the number and spacing of offspring. Programs may be voluntary, extended voluntary, or forced. Many experts believe that family planning should be part of an overall program that promotes economic development, jobs for women, health, and education.

Developed nations can contribute to a solution by reducing consumption and population size. They can assist the less fortunate with population control, agriculture, health care, and appropriate technology through financial aid and, especially, information sharing.

Many developing nations have population control programs, although funds are often inadequate. Increasing expenditures on such programs could have many long-range benefits. To be effective, programs in such countries must take into account the effects of religious beliefs, psychological factors, and educational level.

No other issue in environmental science carries with it so many ethical ramifications. To some, population control implies denial of one of the most basic and important of all human freedoms, the right to bear young. To others, it violates deep-seated religious beliefs. Still others believe that the right to reproduce should be curtailed when the rights of the individual interfere with the welfare of society; these people ask whether it is ethical *not* to control population.

Many encouraging signs of our increasing control over population have been visible in recent years. Growth rates have dropped, and world population is expected eventually to stabilize somewhere between 8 and 15 billion. Progress in population control has been remarkable in many countries, especially China, Taiwan, Tunisia, Barbados, Hong Kong, Singapore, Costa Rica, and Egypt. Unfortunately, the population problem is far from being solved. In 1986, 35% of the world's population was under 15 years of age; this group provides a great deal of momentum for further growth as it enters reproductive age. Per capita food production has barely kept pace with food consumption. In many countries only a small portion of the people practice birth control. One of the most frustrating situations is in India, which after more than three decades of attempted population control has failed to bring its population growth rate below 2%.

Discussion Questions

1. Debate this statement: "The world cannot support the people it currently has at a decent standard of living, so we should help the developing nations become industrialized. Population will fall as a result, so population control programs are not necessary."

2. Define family planning. Make a list of the three major types of family planning program. Give some specific examples of each.

3. The United Nations appoints you as head of population control programs. Your first assignment is to devise a population control plan for a developing country with rapid population growth, high illiteracy, widespread poverty, and a predominantly rural population. Outline your program in detail, justifying each major feature. What problems might you expect to encounter?

4. Describe ways in which developed countries might aid developing countries in solving the population crisis.

5. Discuss the "value" of children in less developed countries. How do these views differ from those of the developed countries? Are they similar to or different from your views?

6. Discuss reasons why the total fertility rate tends to be lower among more educated women.

7. Discuss general ways to ensure a high rate of success in population control programs.

8. Do we have the right to have as many children as we want? Should that right be curtailed? If so, under what conditions?

9. Discuss some of the encouraging and discouraging news regarding world population growth. What progress has been made? Where do we need to concentrate our efforts in the near future?

Suggested Readings

Brown, L. R. (1981). *Building a Sustainable Society*. New York: Norton. Excellent coverage of population control in Chapter 7.

Brown, L. R. (1983). *Population Policies for a New Economic Era*. Worldwatch Paper 53. Washington, D.C.: Worldwatch Institute. Informative reference.

Brown, L. R., Chandler, W. U., Flavin, C., Jacobson, J., Pollock, C., Postel, S., Starke, L., and Wolf, E. C. (1987). *State of the World 1987*. New York: Norton. See Chapters 2 and 9 for an overview of population growth and population control.

Cole, H. S. D., Freeman, C., Jahoda, M., and Pavitt, K. L. R. (1973). *Models of Doom: A Critique of "The Limits to Growth."* New York: Universe Books. A rebuttal of the computer study.

Crooks, R., and Baur, K. (1987). *Our Sexuality* (3rd ed.). Menlo Park, Calif.: Benjamin/Cummings. Excellent coverage of birth control.

Gupte, P. (1984). *The Crowded Earth: People and the Politics of Population*. New York: Norton. Superb! You must read this wonderful book on the effects of population control projects.

Hales, D. R., and Williams, B. K. (1986). *An Invitation to Health: Your Personal Responsibility* (3rd ed.). Menlo Park, Calif.: Benjamin/Cummings. Excellent coverage of contraception.

Hardin, G. (1972). *Exploring New Ethics for Survival: The Voyage of the Spaceship Beagle*. New York: Viking. A beautifully written discussion of population ethics.

Hardin, G. (1982). Some Biological Insights into Abortion. *Bioscience* 32 (9): 720–727. Important reading.

Hardin, G. (1985). *Filters against Folly*. New York: Viking. Important reading.

Jacobsen, J. (1983). *Promoting Population Stabilization: Incentives for Small Families*. Worldwatch Paper 54. Washington, D.C.: Worldwatch Institute. Excellent paper.

Kols, A., Rinehart, W., Piotrow, P., Doucette, L., and Quillin, W. F. (1982). Oral Contraceptives in the 1980s. *Population Reports* 10 (6): 190–222. Thorough analysis.

Liskin, L., and Fox, G. (1982). IUDs: An Appropriate Contraceptive for Many Women. *Population Reports* 4 (July): 101–135. Detailed analysis.

Meadows, D. H., Meadows, D. L., Randers, J., and Behrens, W. W. (1974). *The Limits to Growth* (2nd ed.). New York: Universe Books. Excellent study of population, resources, and pollution.

Mumford, S. D. (1982). Abortion: A National Security Issue. *The Humanist* 42 (5): 12–42. Some interesting and controversial insights.

RESOURCES

Feeding the World's People: Food and Agriculture

It is not in the stars to hold our destiny but in ourselves.

SHAKESPEARE

Thomas Jefferson wrote that "civilization itself rests upon the soil." The first towns, early empires, and powerful nations can all trace their origins to the deliberate use of the soil for agriculture (Chapter 2). But as R. Neil Sampson wrote, in most places on earth "we stand only six inches from desolation, for that is the thickness of the topsoil layer upon which the entire life of the planet depends."

This chapter discusses hunger, malnutrition, and many of the problems facing agriculture. It also suggests solutions that could help us develop a sustainable world agricultural system.

The Dimensions of Hunger

By various estimates hunger afflicts between 17% and 40% of the world's people, mostly in Asia, Africa, and Latin America. These people may suffer from **undernourishment**, a lack of calories, or **malnourishment**, a lack of the proper nutrients and vitamins. In the United States 10% to 15% of the population suffers from hunger, according to some experts.

Diseases of Malnutrition

Worldwide, an estimated 40 million people die each year of starvation and diseases linked to malnutrition. This is the equivalent of 300 jumbo jets, each holding around 400 passengers, crashing every day of the year. Many of the victims are children.

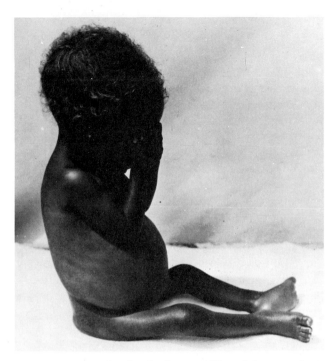

Figure 7-1 Kwashiorkor leads to swelling of the arms, legs, and abdomen. Children are stunted, apathetic, and anemic.

The most common nutritional disease of the poor is **protein–calorie malnutrition** in young children. The two main syndromes are **kwashiorkor** (resulting primarily from a lack of protein) and **marasmus** (resulting from an insufficient intake of protein and calories). Kwashiorkor and marasmus are two extremes of protein–calorie deficiency, and most individuals have symptoms of both diseases.

Kwashiorkor In the rural villages or city streets of Latin America, Asia, or Africa, children lie in their mothers' arms. Their legs and arms are wasted away, and their abdomens are swollen with fluids (Figure 7-1). They look up with sleepy eyes, moving only occasionally. These children are suffering from kwashiorkor, a protein deficiency common in children 1 to 3 years of age. This disease generally begins soon after children are weaned when they are deprived of their mothers' protein-rich breast milk and are often fed a low-protein, starchy diet.

Marasmus Other children are thin and wasted (Figure 7-2). Their ribs stick out through wrinkled skin. They suck on their hands and clothes to appease a gnawing hunger. Unlike victims of kwashiorkor, these children are alert and active. They are suffering from marasmus, a lack of protein and calories, a disease that usually strikes children who are separated from their mother while breast-feeding. Maternal death, a failure of milk production (lactation), or some milk substitutes promoted by multinational

corporations have often been to blame for this disease. Through slick advertising campaigns, some women in Third World nations were once persuaded to bottle-feed children, using powdered milk substitutes. After starting their children on the supplements, however, many women found that they could not afford them. By then, their breast milk had dried up. The children suffered. To compensate, some women diluted what milk they could afford with water from contaminated streams; their children developed diarrhea, which further reduced food intake and worsened their condition.

In the Third World countries for every clinically diagnosed case of marasmus and kwashiorkor there are hundreds of children with mild to moderate forms of malnutrition, a condition much more difficult to detect. Like the more severely malnourished children, these children are prone to infectious diseases.

Effects of Severe Malnutrition Growing evidence shows us that malnutrition early in life often leads to a permanent physical retardation. Furthermore, the more severe the deficiency, the more severe the stunting. Several studies indicate that childhood malnutrition may also impair brain development, perhaps permanently, since 80% of the brain's growth occurs before the age of 2. Victims may be mentally retarded and lack physical coordination.

Malnourished children who survive to adulthood remain mentally impaired. They become the working citizens of the poor countries. Often plagued by malnutrition their whole lives, they remain prone to infectious diseases and provide little hope for improving their nation's agriculture, literacy rate, or economic level.

Declining Food Supplies

From 1950 until 1970 improvements in agricultural production and expansion of the land area under cultivation made significant inroads into world hunger. During this period world per capita grain consumption increased by approximately 30%, resulting in a substantial improvement in the diet of many of the world's people. Since 1971, however, world food production has barely kept pace with population growth. Many experts predict that food supply will fall even further behind demand as the population continues to swell, creating even more widespread hunger and disease.

In the last two decades more and more countries have lost the ability to feed their people and have become dependent on wealthy agricultural nations such as Canada, Australia, and the United States. Food imports by the developing countries, which amounted to only a few million tons a year in 1950, are now over 100 million tons. In the long term rising energy prices may make food from agricultural nations even more expensive than it is

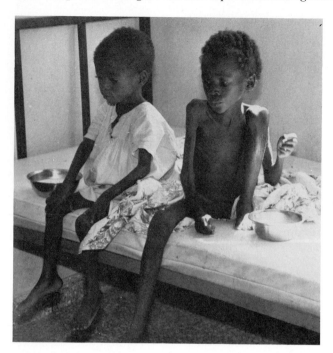

Figure 7-2 Victims of marasmus await medical attention at a hospital in Angola. Survivors of malnutrition may be left with stunted bodies and minds.

now, making it more difficult for Third World nations to buy food.

Long-Term Challenges

Many food and agricultural experts believe that unless decisive, rar-reaching steps are taken, widespread starvation is inevitable; millions will perish in the poor countries. The famine in Ethiopia, Chad, and the Sudan, in which hundreds of thousands of people have died in recent years, may foreshadow what is to come. Experts agree that the rich nations, to whom the Third World nations are highly indebted, will not be immune to the upheaval that results.

Three interrelated challenges face the world today: (1) feeding malnourished and undernourished people (the immediate problem), (2) meeting future needs for food (the long-term problem), and (3) preventing deterioration of soil and water (the continuing problem). Lester Brown of the Worldwatch Institute and other experts believe that building a sustainable worldwide agricultural system, coupled with vigorous population control programs as well as political and economic changes, could go a long way toward solving all of these problems. Before examining ways to build such a system, however, this chapter looks at the major problems facing world agriculture.

Problems Facing World Agriculture

World agriculture can be summed up this way: In the poor nations many people cannot afford food. The cropland in many of these countries is often badly managed. Torrential rains and fierce windstorms carry the soil away, reducing agricultural output. Poor farming practices also slowly rob the soils of their nutrients. Because of the decay of farmland and rising population, food supplies are falling. These countries must turn to the outside for help.

In the rich nations, in contrast, farmers turn out an abundance of food in most years, enough to feed their own people and anyone else who can afford to buy it. However, in the United States many farmers are going out of business, partly because of overproduction thanks to modern technology, fertilizers, and pest controls. Overproduction leads to lower prices, which ironically stimulate farmers to produce more in hopes that they can make their profit by high-volume production. Some government programs may also hurt farmers in the long run. For instance, government purchases of surplus grain encourage overproduction.

Modern agriculture has become a system that works best if you are a large, wealthy corporation or if you hold vast acreage. "Get big or get out" was the message of the 1970s. To stay in the business, farmers bought expensive farm machinery—tractors that cost $50,000, for instance—and land at inflated prices. High interest rates on loans in the 1970s came back to haunt American farmers in the 1980s. Crop prices plummeted, as did land values, yet the cost of the things to run farms—fuel, fertilizer, and pesticides—continued to rise. Farming, in many cases, became a losing proposition. In fact, the U.S. Department of Agriculture determined that in 1986 one farm went out of business every eight minutes.

The economics of farming also spelled trouble for the land and the long-term future of agriculture. Soil erosion, depletion of soil nutrients, and desert formation were the price unwittingly paid for mass producing cheap food. The following sections discuss many of the major problems plaguing agriculture throughout the world.

Soil Erosion

Soil erosion is the most critical problem facing agriculture today, both in the poor developing countries and in the much wealthier industrial nations. **Erosion** is the process by which rock and soil particles are detached from their original site by wind or water, transported away, and eventually deposited in another location. **Natural erosion** generally occurs at a slow rate, and new soil is usually generated fast enough to replace what is lost. **Accelerated erosion**, resulting from human activities such as over-

Figure 7-3 Soil erosion on farmland.

grazing, decreases soil fertility, causing a decline in agricultural production. In the long term accelerated erosion can destroy land permanently (Figure 7-3). Soil erosion affects distant sites. For instance, pesticides may adhere to soil particles and be transported to nearby waterways. Sediment deposited in waterways increases flooding, destroys breeding grounds of fish and other wildlife, and increases the need for dredging harbors and rivers.

The economic damage from soil erosion in the United States is estimated to be $6 billion a year. Erosion destroys about 500,000 hectares (1.25 million acres) of U.S. cropland each year. According to recent estimates, erosion exceeds replacement on nearly half of the country's farmland. Experts predict that if these trends continue, crop production will fall by 10% to 30% in the next 30 years. In the long run the U.S. agricultural system could falter. Restoring topsoil on abandoned land could take 300 to 1000 years. (See Chapter Supplement 7-1 for more on soil erosion.)

Unfortunately, little information is available on soil erosion rates throughout the world. Experts agree, however, that the problem is significant in many regions, especially in the Third World nations. Those with the fastest growing populations usually have the least money for soil conservation and the worst problems. As explained in Chapter 5, the rapid growth of population often precludes long-term care and proper management of natural resources.

Desertification: Turning Cropland to Desert

The United Nations Environmental Program recently predicted that by the end of the century one-third of the world's cropland will have turned into desert, a process called **desertification**. Few countries are immune, because virtually all countries mistreat their soils. Desertification afflicts the United States, Africa, Australia, Brazil, Iran, Afghanistan, China, and India. Worldwide, an area the size of Ohio (100,000 square kilometers, or 40,000 square miles) becomes barren desert each year (Figure 7-4).

Desertification results from many factors: drought, the inherent fragility of the ecosystem in arid and semiarid (and subhumid) regions, overgrazing, overcropping (planting too many crops per year), and plowing marginal lands. Overuse stems from overpopulation and the failure of existing socioeconomic systems to properly manage vulnerable lands.

Desertification is not new to humankind. In the ancient Middle East, for instance, the destruction of forests, overgrazing, and poor agricultural practices reduced local rainfall. Coupled with a long-term regional warming trend, the drop in rainfall turned once-productive pastureland and farmland, much of the Fertile Crescent where agriculture has its roots, into desert (Chapter 2). In more recent times the United States found itself immersed in a major environmental crisis in the famous dust bowl era of the 1930s. Farmers' fields turned dry, and huge dust storms swept the topsoil away. The dust bowl crisis was made more serious by extensive planting to supply Europe with food in the early years of World War II. When a natural drought struck, the crops failed, and heavy winds carried the soil away. Only through extensive conservation measures in the postwar years were farmers able to rebuild their soils.

Desertification, while widespread today, is especially bad in Africa. Beginning in 1968 a long-term drought in the Sahel region, coupled with overpopulation, overgrazing, and poor land management, began the rapid spread of desert southward in Ethiopia, Mauritania, Mali, Niger, Chad, and Sudan (Figure 7-5). In Ethiopia alone over 300,000 people have died of starvation and associated disease. Eight million more are on the brink of starvation. Political problems are also to blame. The Sahara

Figure 7-4 Worldwide spread of deserts. Over 37 million square kilometers (14 million square miles) are now threatened. An area of 100,000 km² becomes desert each year.

is also spreading northward, squeezing the people of North Africa against the Mediterranean. An estimated 100,000 hectares (250,000 acres) of rangeland and cropland are lost in this region each year.

Depletion of Soil Nutrients

In Chapter 3 we saw that soil nutrients are taken up by plants and incorporated into their tissues and those of the organisms that consume them. They remain in the organismic phase of the environmental cycle for some time. Eventually, most nutrients are returned to the soil through decay, entering the environmental phase of the nutrient cycle. As we saw, farming can severely disrupt nutrient cycles. By harvesting plant material, 10% of the dry weight of which is mineral matter, farmers essentially mine the soil; that is, they remove the minerals faster than they can be replaced. This problem is especially noticeable on lands planted two or three times a year and land fertilized only with artificial fertilizers.

Soil erosion also depletes the soil of nutrients, as mentioned above. The annual cost of replacing nutrients lost from erosion in the United States is about $27 billion (in 1986 dollars).

High Energy Costs and Diminishing Supplies

Few relationships are as clear as that between the cost of food and the cost of fossil fuels, such as oil and natural gas. Oil byproducts power farm equipment. Oil and natural gas run food processing plants and factories that produce farm equipment. Natural gas is converted into nitrate fertilizers. Byproducts of oil are converted into pesticides that are sprayed onto fields from airplanes and tractors. Trucks, trains, and ships, powered by oil, move food across countries and across oceans. Even the stores that sell the food to the public require oil and natural gas for heating and lighting. So high is the energy demand that modern agricultural societies invest 9 kilocalories of energy for each kilocalorie of food produced. Agriculture's dependency on fossil fuels became evident in the United States and elsewhere when petroleum prices increased from $3 a barrel to over $30 a barrel in the 1970s. Food prices climbed rapidly in tandem. Rising food prices hurt consumers in the developed nations. They also made things worse for developing countries in at least two ways: by raising domestic production costs and raising import costs.

Figure 7-5 Desertification in the Sahel region of Africa.

Oil is quickly being used up. By some estimates fewer than 70 years remain until the world runs out of oil. By 2000, demand for oil will exceed supply, driving prices up. World population and food demand are expected to be at least 50% above current levels by 2005. Unless changes are made, more of the world's people will be unable to afford food and will suffer further hunger, starvation, and disease.

Water Mismanagement

Much of the world agricultural output is dependent on irrigation. In the United States, for instance, one-eighth of all cropland is irrigated; this land produces approximately one-third of the nation's food. Since 1950 the amount of irrigated cropland has doubled. Irrigated agriculture faces several problems: (1) depletion of groundwater, (2) competition for water supplies, (3) salinization, and (4) waterlogging of soil.

Agricultural Groundwater Depletion In several regions in the United States groundwater is being depleted rapidly from **aquifers**, zones of porous material, such as sandstone, containing water (Figure 7-6). Aquifers are naturally replenished by water from rain and snow that percolates through the soil and rock from the surface in **aquifer recharge zones**.

Of major concern is the depletion of groundwater in the Ogallala aquifer, a major prehistoric water deposit that is only very slowly being recharged by natural processes. (For more details on groundwater, see Chapter 10.) The Ogallala aquifer lies under the highly productive irrigated land of Nebraska, Kansas, Colorado, Oklahoma, Texas, and New Mexico. To date over 150,000 wells have been drilled into this aquifer, mostly for agricultural irrigation. Some parts of the aquifer, which took approximately 25,000 years to fill, have been depleted in only a few decades; water levels are falling 1 meter per year in heavily used areas, compared with a 1-millimeter replenishment rate. As a result many farm wells have already been abandoned. By the end of this century, groundwater experts predict, many parts of the aquifer will be drained. Irrigated agriculture in these regions will inevitably fail.

Competition for Water Domestic and industrial use of groundwater can also deplete aquifers and reduce water available for agriculture. Already, municipal water demands in Arizona and California have made deep cuts into agricultural water use and put an end to much irrigated farming. In many western states agriculture competes with energy companies for water. Neal Jensen of Cornell University predicts that water demand by the energy industry will eventually eliminate most of the irrigated agriculture in the West.

In the long run the loss of irrigated agricultural land—whatever the cause—will lower U.S. food production, raising prices here and abroad.

Waterlogging and Salinization Irrigation has aided agriculture in many semiarid regions, but it has also created some problems. Irrigating poorly drained fields, for example, often raises the **water table**, the upper level of the groundwater. Two consequences of this practice are waterlogging and salinization (Figure 7-7). **Water-**

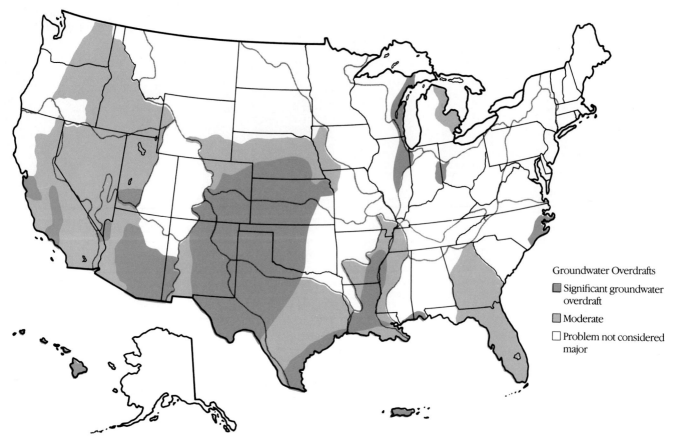

Figure 7-6   Groundwater overdraft. Areas in color indicate regions where water is being removed from aquifers by farmers, industries, and cities faster than it can be replenished.

Groundwater Overdrafts

■ Significant groundwater overdraft

▨ Moderate

□ Problem not considered major

logging occurs if the water table rises too near the surface, filling the air spaces in the soil and suffocating the roots of plants. It also makes soil difficult to cultivate. Second, water evaporates from the soil, leaving behind salts and minerals. The accumulation of these substances, called **salinization**, impairs plant growth and may make soil impenetrable.

Worldwide, one-tenth of all irrigated land suffers from waterlogging. As a result productivity has fallen approximately 20% on this 21 million hectares (52.5 million acres) of cropland, an area slightly smaller than Idaho. In the United States salinization occurs to some degree on an estimated 300,000 hectares. It is a growing problem in many other nations, including Pakistan, Iran, Iraq, Mexico, and Argentina. In Argentina alone, about 2 million hectares (5 million acres) of irrigated land has experienced a decline in productivity because of salinization.

Conversion to Nonagricultural Uses

Farmland throughout the world is being taken out of production by urbanization, energy production, trans-

portation, and other nonfarm uses (Figure 7-8). Every hour about 90 hectares (220 acres) of actual or potential farmland in the United States is converted to nonfarm uses. This is equivalent to 2160 hectares (5400 acres) per day! In addition, about 600 hectares (1500 acres) of pastureland and rangeland is lost each day. Annually, the United States loses farmland equivalent to a strip about 1 kilometer (.62 miles) wide extending from New York City to San Francisco.

Farmland conversion is a worldwide phenomenon. West Germany loses about 1% of its agricultural land by conversion every four years, and France and the United Kingdom lose about 1% every five years. Little is known about the rate of agricultural land conversion in the developing world, but it is believed to be great.

Conversion of Cropland to Fuel Farms: A Future Problem

Some experts predict that when petroleum supplies begin to fall, around the year 2000, certain crops such as sugar cane and corn will be used to make liquid fuels to

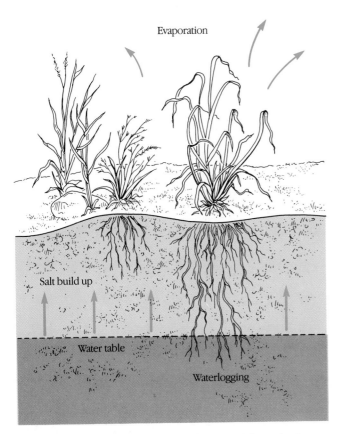

Evaporation

Salt build up

Water table

Waterlogging

Figure 7-7 Salinization and waterlogging. Salts and other minerals accumulate in the upper layers of poorly drained soil (salinization) when irrigation waters raise the water table and water begins to evaporate through the surface. The rising water table also saturates the soil and kills plant roots (waterlogging).

power automobiles and other machinery. Microorganisms convert the sugar in corn, sugar cane, and other crops into burnable ethanol. This process is called **fermentation** and is basically the same process used to make wine, whiskey, and other alcoholic beverages. Alcohol can be mixed with gasoline in a ratio of 1 part of alcohol to 9 parts of gasoline, creating **gasohol**. It can also be burned in pure form. In Brazil, for instance, cars and trucks now burn 100% ethanol.

Alcohol is a renewable energy resource, but tapping this largely ignored energy supply will have serious impacts on world agriculture. For example, Brazil eventually hopes to achieve complete self-sufficiency in automotive fuel with domestic ethanol production. Such a feat would require Brazilians to convert one-half of their farmland to fuel production, greatly reducing food exports. Should ethanol replace oil worldwide, major food producers such as Canada, the United States, and Australia will divert grain used for food to fuel production. One-fifth of the exportable corn produced in the United States would be needed to produce 2 billion gallons of ethanol, a fraction of total U.S. liquid fuel needs. As fuel farms rise in prominence, per capita food supplies could fall, along with exportable surpluses. Food prices will inevitably soar, which will affect all peoples, rich and poor. Today, most countries import some grain, and nearly a dozen countries import more than half of the grain they consume each year. Unless more countries become self-sufficient, the world's hungry will be forced to compete with the automobile fuel industry and, ultimately, the automobile users of the world for precious grain (Figure 7-9). Few people doubt who will win.

Figure 7-8 Urban sprawl, as shown here in Des Moines, Iowa, swallows up farmland at an alarming rate.

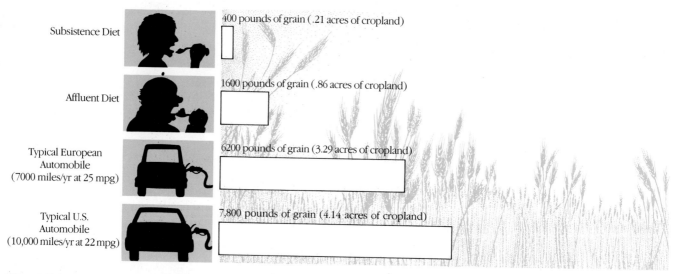

Subsistence Diet — 400 pounds of grain (.21 acres of cropland)

Affluent Diet — 1600 pounds of grain (.86 acres of cropland)

Typical European Automobile (7000 miles/yr at 25 mpg) — 6200 pounds of grain (3.29 acres of cropland)

Typical U.S. Automobile (10,000 miles/yr at 22 mpg) — 7,800 pounds of grain (4.14 acres of cropland)

Figure 7-9   Grain appetites: people versus cars. Competition for "food" is about to begin, with the wealthy car owners in a better position to pay.

Politics and World Hunger

Many of the world's food problems are political. Some agricultural experts maintain that plenty of food is produced each year but that about half of this output in the less developed countries never reaches the table. One reason is that governments, with good intentions or fraudulent ones, often become involved in the production and distribution system, reducing food availability.

In the Soviet Union, for example, government officials control the large farms. On a regional basis they decide how much fertilizer should be applied, rather than individually tailoring fertilizer demands to local needs. Such decisions ultimately reduce productivity. The failure of centralized governmental controls is underscored by the fact that private production, which takes place on about 1% of the country's farmland, yields about one-fourth of its yearly crop.

Political decisions in one country can also have tremendous impacts in other countries. In 1954, for example, the U.S. Congress enacted legislation that drove thousands of Third World farmers off their land. This law—the Farm Surplus Disposal Act, often called the Food for Peace program—authorized huge surplus grain shipments from the United States to Third World nations. This free or nearly free surplus grain entered countries with devastating consequences. Perhaps the most important effect was that Third World farmers, unable to compete with the cheap grains, were forced to abandon their farms. Ironically, Food for Peace stimulated U.S. production, but as mentioned earlier in this chapter, government support has had far-reaching effects on domestic agriculture, most notably increased production and decreased prices.

Government policies also have many subtle long-range impacts on agricultural production. A U.S. program called payment in kind (PIK), enacted during President Ronald Reagan's first term, encouraged farmers to curtail production. The ultimate goal was to reduce grain gluts that drive prices down. The program worked this way: Farmers who had cultivated a piece of land for more than two years were allowed to take it out of production; to offset possible losses the government gave them a grain payment from federal stockpiles. Grain payments amounted to 80% to 95% of their expected production. The farmer was then free to sell the grain on the market. The offshoot of this program was that land speculators got into the farm business, bought marginal land, planted it for two years, and then took it out of production so that they could collect the government grain payments. This practice was euphemistically known as "sod busting." However, much of this land was rangeland that was not well suited to farming. The already meager topsoil quickly eroded away. Through payment in kind, critics argue, the government encouraged soil erosion on good rangeland or land that could have been used for grazing or crop production in the future in conjunction with good soil conservation.

Countless examples of government interference in agriculture exist. One final example illustrates the complex problem facing Ethiopia. Here, farmers traditionally left land fallow for seven-year periods so that nutrients of this highly weathered, poor soil could be replenished by natural vegetation. This practice is now condemned

Table 7-1 Limited Diversity in American Agriculture

Crop	Varieties Available	Major Varieties in Use	Percentage of Total Production
Corn	197	6	71
Wheat	269	10	55
Soybeans	62	6	56
Rice	14	4	65
Potatoes	82	4	72
Peanuts	15	9	95
Peas	50	2	96

Source: Reichart, W. (1982), Agriculture's Diminishing Diversity, *Environment* 24(9): 6–11, 39–44.

by the Ethiopian government, which is interested in increasing farm production. If land is not cultivated within three years, it is confiscated. But not leaving it fallow will result in rapid deterioration and a long-term decrease in productivity.

Loss of Genetic Diversity

Before the advent of modern agriculture, grains and vegetables existed in thousands of varieties. Now, only a few of these varieties are commonly used; many strains have been lost forever (Table 7-1). (Numerous breeds of livestock are also being lost as ranchers throughout the world adopt breeds developed for maximum yield.) Many experts believe that this loss of variety, **genetic diversity**, could have a significant impact on world agriculture.

Before looking at those effects, consider some of the main reasons why genetic diversity is dwindling. First and foremost, the new varieties often have a higher yield on mechanized farms. Between 1903 and 1976, for instance, new varieties of wheat allowed American farmers to double their yield; new varieties of corn allowed them to quadruple output per acre. These varieties were also better suited for machine harvesting and responded well to irrigation. Finally, seed companies benefited economically by concentrating their efforts on a few varieties.

The development of high-yield varieties in the 1960s is part of a worldwide agricultural movement often called the **Green Revolution**. It began in 1944, when the Rockefeller Foundation and the Mexican government established a plant-breeding station in northwestern Mexico. The program was headed by Norman Borlaug, a University of Minnesota plant geneticist, who developed a high-yield wheat plant (Figure 7-10). Before the program

Figure 7-10 Comparison of an old variety of wheat (left and right) with a new short-stemmed high-yield variety. The first of the short-stemmed varieties was developed under the direction of Norman Borlaug.

The Promise and Peril of Genetic Engineering

No technological advance offers so much hope for a better future as genetic engineering, and none, not even the computer, promises to revolutionize so much of our society—how we treat diseases, how we grow plants and rear livestock, and how we mine for minerals and drill for oil.

When the promises of genetic engineering were first unfurled in the 1970s, however, alarm quickly grew over the possibility that new life forms would accidentally or intentionally be released into the environment. Warnings of widespread environmental disruption were sounded. Some argued that manipulating genes was morally unacceptable. Still others warned of potential misuses—a laboratory Hitler cloning superhumans or producing genetically altered biological warfare agents.

A cloud of confusion and distrust grew. Would genetic engineering expand resources and help us feed the hungry, or would it seriously endanger the human race? Nearly two decades after its inception these basic questions remain unanswered.

The Promise

Progress in genetic engineering to date shows that the promises for this new technology are very real and that the potential is much greater than once hoped. Consider these accomplishments and predictions for genetic engineering:

- Medical researchers have cloned the genes that code for human insulin, growth hormone, and one form of interferon, a potentially powerful tool against viral diseases and cancer. These chemical substances are now commercially produced by genetically engineered bacteria and are available in relatively large quantities.
- Genetic engineers are producing effective vaccines against influenza and hepatitis and are seeking vaccines against herpes, AIDS, and other dangerous viruses.
- Scientists are now implanting the gene for human growth hormone into livestock embryos in hopes of producing marketable livestock much faster than by conventional means.
- Medical researchers are developing ways to replace defective human genes with normal genes in hopes of curing previously incurable genetic disorders.
- Scientists have isolated the gene that renders certain bacteria toxic to insects and have transplanted it into a bacterium that grows on plant roots, giving some plants a new way of warding off pests.
- Geneticists have successfully introduced genes that allow plants to tolerate salty soil into oats. They have also isolated and manufactured genes that make plants resistant to herbicides so crops are not damaged by chemicals used to control weeds.
- Genetic researchers have developed a mutant bacterium that retards frost development on plants and promises to save farmers millions of dollars each year.
- Genetic engineers are trying to incorporate genes that allow plants to fix atmospheric nitrogen into nonleguminous plants, thus reducing fertilizer needs and water pollution created by excess fertilizer use.
- Genetic researchers are developing a special strain of bacteria that digests cellulose, so it can be used to make ethanol. These bacteria could help convert forest and crop residues into valuable liquid fuel as oil becomes increasingly scarce.
- Genetic engineers are developing new strains of bacteria that help extract oils and minerals. These could help increase yield as oil and mineral deposits are depleted.

The successes of genetic engineering have fostered a great deal of enthusiasm in the world business community. Dozens of new companies have formed in recent years, and billions of dollars have been invested in the fledgling industry.

The Questions

Nevertheless, safety questions remain. Will a genetically engineered bacterium like the one geneticists have created to retard frost proliferate in the wild, upsetting the ecological balance, or will it alter climate by retarding ice crystal formation in the atmosphere? And will new forms of disease be unleashed on society by accident or on purpose? Once unleashed, a new form of bacterium or virus cannot be recalled. Controlling it could prove costly.

Some individuals have criticized genetic engineering as a means of tinkering with the evolutionary process. Deliberate genetic manipulations may be different from anything ordinarily occurring during "natural" evolution. Is it right, critics ask, to interfere with the genetic makeup of living organisms and thus, the evolution of life on earth?

The Risk Debate

Recent work suggests that the dangers of genetic engineering have been blown out of proportion and that genetically engineered bacteria are not generally a threat to ecosystem stability. Most scientists agree. In one highly publicized case the U.S. Department of Agriculture came under attack for permitting the sale of a genetically engineered vaccine against pseudorabies. This disease infects 10% of America's 54 million swine, costing the pork industry, by its estimates, up to $60 million a year. The attack came from Jeremy Rifkin, a longtime critic of genetic engineering. He asserted that the department had failed to follow federal guide-

Essay 7-1

lines governing the release of genetically altered organisms (in this case, viruses) into the environment and had authorized the use of the vaccine without a proper environmental impact assessment.

Saul Kit, a Baylor University biochemist who developed the vaccine through genetic engineering, pointed out that a conventional vaccine, long used to treat the disease before the advent of his genetically engineered product, had been developed by a form of genetic engineering. The conventional vaccine, he said, was developed by growing the virus in culture dishes for thousands of generations. A weakened form with a missing gene arose by natural mutation. It was deemed safe enough to use as a vaccine to be injected into piglets. What Kit did differently was to weaken the virus by deleting part of a different gene needed to make an enzyme which is needed for the virus to reproduce. In this case, most critics agree, Rifkin's attack was misguided.

Many supporters of genetic engineering oppose attempts to halt genetic engineering. To them, the promises of this revolutionary technology far outweigh any potential damage. Feeding the world's hungry with a genetically engineered strain of supercattle, they argue, far exceeds any possible threats. Likewise gene therapy, in which defective human genes are replaced by normal ones, offers too much hope for victims of crippling diseases to be abandoned because of potential problems. Even many leading environmentalists who initially joined Rifkin and others at the outset of the battle in the 1970s have long ago switched sides. But ecologists want to see the industry properly monitored. Genetically altered species, ecologists argue, are analogous to alien species introduced into new environments. The history of such introductions has been fraught with difficulties (Chapter 8). For this reason ecologists call for careful testing before release. Rifkin, many say, is extreme, but he has raised serious questions that must be answered before widespread testing can be allowed.

Genetic engineering stands at a threshold. Still in its infancy, it offers an unparalleled opportunity for improving agriculture, animal husbandry, and medicine. At the same time this revolutionary science carries with it an unknown potential for environmental harm that worries many of its critics and much of the public as well. Which legacy will be the predominant one only time will tell, but for now many applications of genetic engineering seem to be on hold while critics and supporters work out their differences.

---

began, Mexico imported half of the wheat it consumed each year, but by 1956 it was self-sufficient in wheat production. By 1964 it was exporting half a million tons. Borlaug was later awarded a Nobel Prize for his work.

The success in Mexico led to the establishment of another plant-breeding center, in the Philippines. High-yielding rice strains were developed there and introduced into India in the mid-1960s. Again, the results were spectacular. India more than doubled its wheat and rice production in less than a decade and has become self-sufficient in wheat production.

Important as it was, the Green Revolution contributed greatly to the decrease in agricultural diversity. One of the most important concerns is the loss of genetic resistance to disease. Local varieties of plants are acclimated to their environment; natural selection has ensured this. New varieties, on the other hand, often have little resistance to insects and disease. Moreover, planting of **monocultures**, expansive fields of one genetic strain, facilitates the spread of disease and insects. As discussed in Chapter 4, simplifying ecosystems removes environmental resistance that normally keeps potential pest populations in check. The potato famine in Ireland in the 1840s is one famous example of the effects of reducing diversity. Only a few varieties of potatoes were planted in Ireland. When a fungus (*Phytophthora infestans*) began to spread among the plants, there was little to stop it and no backup supply of resistant seed potatoes. Within a few years 2 million Irish perished from hunger and disease, and another 2 million emigrated. In addition to their susceptibility to disease, high-yield hybrids are also generally less resistant to drought and flood. In 1970 the southern corn leaf blight wiped out nearly one-fourth of the U.S. corn crop. The American peanut crop, consisting of two varieties, was almost entirely destroyed in 1980 by drought and disease.

Reduced genetic diversity is a trend that began thousands of years ago during the agricultural revolution as humanity turned from hunting and gathering to an agricultural way of life (Chapter 2). That trend is worsened by a relatively new phenomenon: the destruction of tropical lands where many of the ancestors of our modern crops grow. Their fate is crucial to agriculture. Why? The future will require plants that can survive climatic changes, drought, disease, and insects. These ancient ancestors could provide the genetic material needed to improve our crops. Thus, reducing genetic diversity through deforestation and farming could have far-reaching effects on the future of agriculture. (For more on this problem see Chapters 7 and 8.)

The agricultural expert R. Neil Sampson once noted that "the progress of civilization has been marked by a trail of wind-blown or water-washed soils." Today, the destruction continues in the form of depleted soils, falling groundwater supplies, waterlogging, salinization, cropland conversion, political mismanagement, and declining agricultural diversity.

Much of the world's agricultural land is poorly managed. If the trend continues, we could conceivably destroy much of the renewable soils on which civilization rests. The population crash discussed in Chapter 5 could result from the widespread mistreatment of our agricultural land. In the following section we look at ways to convert our failing agricultural system into a sustainable system.

Building a Sustainable Agricultural System

Hunger and starvation are as much a problem of too many people as a problem of food shortages. One of the most important solutions to famine, then, is population control (Chapter 6). Beyond that, we can (1) increase agricultural land; (2) grow more on it—that is, increase productivity; (3) develop alternative foods; (4) reduce food losses to pests; and (5) increase the agricultural self-sufficiency of developing nations.

Increasing the Amount of Agricultural Land

Increasing the amount of cropland and rangeland available to us can be achieved primarily in two ways: (1) by tapping farmland reserves—that is, land not being used—and (2) by preventing loss of cropland from desertification, soil erosion, and farmland conversion.

Exploiting Farmland Reserves   For many years the United States and other agricultural nations have solved the problem of rising food demand by opening up new lands to the plow. The abundance of untapped farmland in the frontier days fostered reckless attitudes that resulted in poor land management. But the days of abundant reserves are quickly coming to an end.

U.S. farmers currently cultivate 167 million hectares (413 million acres). The cropland reserve—land that can be farmed if necessary—is a paltry 51 million hectares (127 million acres). Projected increases in foreign and domestic demand will use up this land by the year 2000. In most of the other major agricultural nations, farmland reserves are also small. If land destruction continues at the current rate, therefore, the 21st century will be marked by falling production, food shortages, and soaring prices. With fuel farms taking over farmland, the outlook for agriculture becomes dimmer. For Third World nations one inescapable conclusion can be drawn: they will have to become increasingly self-sufficient. The developed

nations won't have the food reserves to support themselves and very many developing nations. Agricultural self-sufficiency may require the developing nations to slow down and eventually stop population growth. Third World nations will also have to develop their own land, improve agricultural efficiency, reduce soil erosion and nutrient depletion, improve transportation, and conserve irrigation water.

According to the United Nations Food and Agriculture Organization, Africa and South America have large surpluses of land that could be farmed. In Africa, for example, only 21% of the potentially cultivatable land is in use. In South America only 15% is being farmed. Some experts believe that South American and African nations should develop this land, but only if the currently farmed land is protected against erosion and nutrient depletion. However, few experts believe that tropical rain forests should be developed as farmland. Soils there are poor in nutrients, easily erode in intense rains, and may become hardened when exposed to sun. (See Chapter Supplement 3-1 for more details.)

Tapping other unfarmed land may be an option, but it will severely affect many wildlife populations. Protecting wild species is important for many reasons, discussed in Chapter 8. One of the key economic reasons for preserving wildlife may be economic: it can be a major source of income because of wealthy tourists who will spend thousands of dollars to catch a glimpse of a giraffe or rhinoceros.

In other areas of the world agriculture strains the limits of land availability. In Southeast Asia, for instance, 92% of the potential agricultural land is being farmed. In southwestern Asia more land is currently being used than is considered suitable for rain-fed agriculture. Population control and improved farming practices are needed to preserve this land and ensure a sustainable system.

Reducing the Spread of Deserts   Developing new farmland is one answer to the imminent shortages of arable land. More important are measures to reduce the destruction of land currently farmed or grazed by livestock. Throughout the world people are working to stop the spread of deserts. In China agricultural officials have begun to plant a 6,900-kilometer (4,300-mile) "green wall" of vegetation to stop the spread of desert in the northern region. In Australia huge semicircular banks of earth are created in the windswept plains to catch seeds and encourage regrowth in areas denuded by livestock. In Iran migrating sand dunes are sprayed with a residue left over from oil production. The liquid dries on the surface and forms a gray mulch that retains soil moisture and facilitates the growth of drought-resistant plants. Within six years oil-mulched dunes are green with vegetation. Additional efforts worldwide include improving rangeland management, revegetating barren land, con-

Figure 7-11 Among the vegetation to the left, protected from overgrazing, are 7-year old trees, which in time will protect the land from such severe erosion.

trolling wind erosion (Figure 7-11), preventing the use of marginal lands, and irrigating.

Soil Conservation Just as important as stopping the march of deserts are efforts to cut back on soil erosion. The rich nations as well as the poor will benefit. To date, however, farmers in both the developed and developing countries have done little to reduce erosion. In the developing world farmers struggle to meet their most basic needs and have neither the time nor the means to care properly for the land. Furthermore, few can see the benefits of soil conservation, because the gains tend to materialize slowly and usually take the form of a decrease in losses rather than an increase in actual food output.

Economics impairs soil-erosion control in the developed nations (discussed in Chapter 20). Caught between high production costs and low prices for grains, farmers may ignore the long-term effects of soil erosion while synthetic fertilizers artificially help them maintain yield in the short term. Governments can promote conservation through a variety of measures, many of which are discussed in Chapter Supplement 7-1. In 1985 the U.S. Congress passed a farm bill that contains some important controls on soil erosion. The law denies any federal farm loans, subsidies, or even crop insurance to farmers who plow highly erodible land. The law also creates a land conservation program in which the federal government pays farmers to remove 16 to 18 million hectares (40 to 45 million acres) of erodible land from crop production for ten years and plant trees, grasses, or cover crops to stabilize the land and rebuild the soil.

Other Protective Measures Protecting land from desertification and soil erosion are two important steps in preserving farmland and, therefore, increasing our supply of arable land. But efforts to prevent the spread of cities, the proliferation of highways, and other nonfarm uses are also needed. Careful city planning and new zoning laws could help reduce farmland conversion by ensuring that homes, roads, airports, and businesses are not built on agricultural land. (For more on urban planning, see Chapter 22.)

Increasing the Yield of Cropland

Preserving Genetic Diversity In a forest in southwestern Mexico in 1979, four scientists discovered a few tiny patches of a wild, weedy-looking grass that could have enormous impact on corn production throughout the world. *Zea diploperennis*, a primitive near relative of modern corn whose known population numbers only a few thousand stalks, sets itself apart from all modern corns because it is a perennial; that is, unlike an annual it grows from the same root structure year after year rather than from seeds. To many people the rare corn may not seem very impressive, but to geneticists, the engineers of new corn breeds, it's the discovery of the century.

Corn, like any other crop, is only as good as the genetic "boosts" it receives—in other words, the infusions of fresh genes, which provide its resistance to disease, drought, insects, and so on. Valuable new genes come from wild plants or early varieties still grown by peasants in remote corners of the world. The new genetic vigor they confer to corn results in large harvests, and because corn accounts for one-fourth of the world's cereal grains, a large harvest is always crucial.

Genetic boosts have an enormous impact on corn production. In the last 60 years, for instance, corn harvests have more than quadrupled—from 20 bushels per hectare to 100 to 250 bushels—because of successful genetic improvements. Hence, breeders are always on the look-

Agriculture and Water: A Cost–Benefit Analysis

In this chapter we saw that agricultural irrigation water is being depleted from the Ogallala aquifer faster than it is being replenished. Annually, the net water loss is about 14 million acre-feet (1 acre-foot covers 1 acre to a depth of 1 foot). One of the proposed solutions to this problem is to divert water from the Missouri River at St. Joseph, Missouri, 850 feet (255 meters) above sea level, and pump it in a canal and pipeline to agricultural areas in western Kansas (elevation 2480 feet), eastern Colorado (3000 to 4000 feet), and Texas (3000 to 3500 feet).

Question

Do a cost–benefit analysis of this agricultural problem.

Step 1: Costs and Benefits

To balance costs and benefits, first make a list of all possible costs and benefits involved in this project. What are the major economic and environmental costs? What are the major benefits? How would you assign a numerical value to costs and benefits?

Step 2: Calculating Annual Pumping Costs

As you might have guessed, one of the chief economic costs would be incurred by pumping water uphill from St. Joseph, Missouri, to farms in Colorado, Kansas, and Texas. Let's assume that the water is going to be pumped to an average elevation of 3000 feet to make calculations easier. The electricity to pump 1 acre-foot of water up 188 feet costs about $25 (in 1979 dollars). How much will it cost to pump 14 million acre-feet from St. Joseph to 3000 feet?

Unfortunately, the cost of electricity is probably only about half the total annual cost. Repayment of loans, interest, maintenance, and personnel make up the other half. With this in mind, what is the total annual cost for pumping this water?

Step 3: Gross Returns on Corn Sales

Now that you've approximated the annual pumping costs, let's look at the approximate economic benefits. First, 14 million acre-feet of water will irrigate 8.38 million acres of land yielding 754 million bushels of corn. If corn sells for $3 per bushel (1979 dollars), what would the gross return from corn sales be? Remember, the $3 selling price does not take into account any production costs. To be accurate, you'd have to subtract the cost of seed, fertilizer, herbicides, pesticides, labor, farm equipment, land rental or mortgage and others. You might call some farmers in your area or contact an agricultural specialist at your school and find out how much profit a farmer makes per bushel of corn so you can calculate the net return.

From an economic standpoint, how feasible does this project look? What alternatives might you suggest to meeting the demand for irrigation water?

Answers

Step 1: Costs and Benefits

Costs

pumping cost
canal and pipeline construction costs
canal and pipeline maintenance
environmental costs
    reduced water flow in Missouri River
    effects on fish and wildlife
    effects on pollution concentrations
    effects on water supply for cities and farms

Benefits

continuance of irrigated agriculture
economic benefits
    profit
    jobs for farm laborers
    spinoff economic benefits—community services such as stores and farm equipment sales

Step 2: Calculating Annual Pumping Costs

2150 feet = total elevation water must be pumped
Cost to pump 1 acre-foot 2150 feet:

$$2150 \text{ feet} \times \frac{\$25}{188 \text{ feet}} = \$286/\text{acre-foot}$$

Annual cost to pump 14 million acre-feet:

$$\$286/\text{acre-foot} \times 14 \text{ million acre-feet} = \$4 \text{ billion}$$

Total cost for pumping, assuming pumping costs are only one-half of annual costs:

$$\$8 \text{ billion}$$

Step 3: Gross Returns on Corn Sales

$$754 \text{ million bushels} \times \$3/\text{bushel} = \$2.3 \text{ billion}$$

out for the very rare varieties that could help produce hardier, more resistant plants.

The primitive corn found in Mexico is also special because it is highly resistant to several diseases. The genes that provide this resistance could be introduced into conventional corn to produce a resistant perennial hybrid that grows in fields much like grass. This new plant would reduce erosion and save farmers annual costs of plowing, sowing, and cultivating. The potential savings are enormous.

New Plant and Animal Varieties Preserving the ancient relatives of modern crops is only one way to increase the yield of existing farmland. Another is to develop new plants and animals. New high-yield varieties of rice and wheat developed during the Green Revolution, for example, can produce three to five times as much grain as their predecessors when grown under proper conditions. New varieties of plants produced by breeding closely related plants to combine the best features of the parents are called **hybrids**.

As the new hybrids were introduced into many poor nations, the hopes of the Green Revolution dimmed, for farmers soon found that the hybrids required large amounts of water and fertilizer, unavailable in many areas. Without these, yields were not much greater than those of local varieties; in some cases they were even lower. The cost of the new varieties prevented many small farmers from buying them; as a result, they often went out of business as larger farms converted to the high-yield varieties. New plants were often more susceptible to insects and disease. Finally the new varieties have also contributed to the loss of genetic diversity.

The Green Revolution, written off by its critics as a failure, was the first step in a long, tedious process of plant breeding aimed at improving yield. Today, plant breeders throughout the world are developing crops with a higher nutritional value and greater resistance to drought, insects, disease, and wind. Plants with a higher photosynthetic efficiency are also in the offing. Efforts are even under way to incorporate the nitrogen-fixing capability of legumes (discussed in Chapter 3) into cereal plants such as wheat, a change that would decrease the need for fertilizers and reduce nitrogen depletion.

Some researchers are exploring the use of perennial crops for agriculture. **Perennials**, briefly described above, are those plants that produce flowers, fruit, or seeds year after year from the same root structure. Today, most agricultural crops are **annuals**, plants that must grow anew from seeds each year. Preliminary research suggests that productivity from perennials may be equal to or slightly lower than conventional annuals such as wheat, but the benefits from soil conservation, soil-nutrient retention, and energy savings may overwhelmingly favor them.

Just as new varieties of plants help increase yield, so do fast-growing varieties of fowl and livestock. Efforts are being made to improve plants and livestock by **genetic engineering**. This is a complex process involving several steps. Scientists first identify genes that give plants resistance and other important properties that might increase yield. Next they isolate the gene and chemically analyze it so they can make copies of it. Finally, the gene is inserted into seeds, which then sprout and produce cells each containing the advantageous gene. The gene can be transferred to a plant's offspring.

Genetic engineering may be used in other ways that improve agriculture. A new strain of bacteria developed by scientists at the University of California inhibits the formation of frost on plants, thus potentially offering farmers a way of reducing crop damage and increasing yield. Other scientists are working on genes that give plants resistance to herbicides used to control weeds. A group of scientists at the Monsanto Company has developed a strain of bacteria that grows on roots of corn and other plants. When eaten by insects, the bacteria release a toxic protein that kills the pest. Animal geneticists are now working on ways to improve livestock, combining genes from one species with those of another to improve efficiency of digestion, weight gain, and resistance to disease. (For more information on genetic engineering, see Essay 7-1.)

Genetic engineering is a much quicker way to produce new varieties than conventional plant breeding. However, it has generated a lot of public criticism. Much fear has been raised over its potential to create hazardous life forms that could escape into the environment, disrupting ecosystems and possibly killing people. Many scientists believe that these and a host of other concerns should not be dismissed lightly. The U.S. Environmental Protection Agency, in fact, has now developed a strict testing procedure to determine the potential risk of genetically engineered organisms.

Soil Enrichment Programs Soil conservation helps preserve farmland but can also preserve soil fertility. Other methods for maintaining soil fertility include the use of artificial or organic fertilizers and crop rotation. These methods are covered more thoroughly in Chapter Supplement 7-1, on soil management.

Improving Irrigation Efficiency Improving irrigation efficiency could help reserve the inevitable decline in irrigated farmland caused by groundwater overdrafting. Fortunately, many techniques are available to reduce water consumption on farms and in cities. (Urban water conservation is discussed in Chapter 10.) On farms, lining irrigation ditches with cement saves a lot of water (and money), as does the use of pipes (Figure 7-12a). Farmers

(a)   *(b)*

Figure 7-12   Increasing the efficiency of irrigation. (*a*) Elevated pipes reduce water loss. (*b*) Trickle systems deliver water to roots, cutting evaporation losses.

can also use drip irrigation systems to deliver water directly to the roots of the plants (Figure 7-12b). Computer systems can help conserve water by monitoring soil moisture content. These and other techniques are replacing currently wasteful practices and will probably grow in use as water supplies drop and prices for water rise.

New Foods and Food Supplements

In many countries scientists have been working to develop food supplements, using such things as algae and fish that are often rich in protein, carbohydrate, and other important nutrients. Because of consumer resistance, high costs, and other factors, supplements only slightly increase the food supply. A much more promising food source is species native to regions in need of food.

Native Species   The biosphere is an untapped biological reservoir of plants and animals, many of which may have a higher yield and better nutritional value than those we currently use. The winged bean of the tropics, for example, could be a valuable source of food, because the entire plant is edible: its pods are similar to green beans, its leaves taste like spinach, its roots are much like potatoes, and its flowers taste like mushrooms. Food scientists are looking for other plants with similar potential.

Native animals may also provide an important, sustainable food source in years to come. In Africa, for instance, native grazers are far superior to cattle introduced from Europe and America. They carry genetic resistance to disease and rarely overgraze grasslands, unlike cattle. Native grazers also generally convert a higher percentage of the plant biomass into meat and may be cheaper to raise.

Fish from the Sea   By some estimates, fish provide about 5% of the total animal protein consumed by the world's population. Although three-quarters of the fish is consumed in the developed nations, fish protein is important to the diets of many poorer countries, in many cases supplying 40% of the total animal protein consumed.

Until 1971 increasing the world fish catch was viewed as an important way to increase the world's food supply. Between 1950 and 1970 the catch tripled, reaching approximately 70 million metric tons per year. Since the early 1970s, though, the world catch has stabilized between 66 and 74 million metric tons a year, despite intensive efforts to increase yield. On a per capita basis the fish catch declined in the 1970s by about 15% and will probably continue to fall. Biologists warn that any increases could lead to the collapse of ocean fisheries. Maintaining current yields requires global cooperation to prevent overfishing and water pollution.

One method to increase fish supplies is to reduce spoilage by improving refrigeration in the entire production–consumption cycle. In the developing nations some scientists believe that this step by itself could increase the supply of fish by 40%.

(a)

(b)

Figure 7-13 (*a*) Commercial catfish farm near Monticello, Arkansas. These feeders release food pellets when a catfish nuzzles an extended rod. (*b*) Fish raised in irrigation ditches and ponds in China and other countries supply needed protein.

Commercial Fish Farms: Mariculture and Aquaculture Commercial fish farms might also help increase fish protein supplies. **Fish farms** are forms of aquatic agriculture, called **aquaculture** in fresh water and **mariculture** in salt or brackish water.

There are two basic strategies in fish farming. In the first, fish are grown in ponds; population density is high and is maintained by intensive feeding, which is costly and, therefore, not suited to developing countries (Figure 7-13a). Fish (and shellfish) can also be maintained in enclosures or ponds where they feed on algae, zooplankton, and other fish naturally found in the aquatic ecosystem (Figure 7-13b). This system requires little food and energy and is suitable for poorer countries. Worldwide, fish farms produce about 4 million metric tons of food a year. Intensified efforts could double or triple this amount.

Eating Lower on the Food Chain Many environmental science textbooks propose that wealthier citizens of the world can contribute to solving world hunger by eating lower on the food chain. The reasoning behind this idea is as follows: By consuming more grains, vegetables, and fruits—and less meat—citizens of the developed nations would free grain for the developing nations. A 10% decrease in beef consumption in the United States, for instance, would release enough grain to feed 60 million people. Chapter 3 showed that more people could be sustained off 20,000 calories of corn if it were consumed directly than if it were first fed to cattle and the meat was then fed to people. The advantages of eating lower on the food chain are clear. Beef cattle produce about 19 kilograms (43 pounds) of protein per acre per year, whereas soybeans produce nearly 200 kilograms per acre.

The problem with this apparently logical answer to world hunger is that few people respond to moral appeals. Even more important, if Americans and other wealthy world citizens were to cut back on beef consumption, thus freeing tons of grain, the developing nations still couldn't afford to buy it. Sacrifices here would most likely not translate into gains abroad. Another problem is that land suitable for grazing is often incapable of being farmed. The lesson to be learned from our study of ecology is that to feed their people, the Third World nations should concentrate on grain production rather than meat.

Reducing Pest Damage and Spoilage

Rats, insects, and birds attack crops in the field, in transit, and in storage. Conservatively, about 30% of all agricultural output is destroyed by pests, spoilage, and diseases. In the developing nations this figure may be much higher, especially in humid climates where crops are grown year-round and conditions are optimal for the spread of crop diseases and insects. Better controls on crop pests could increase the global food supply. For a detailed discussion of pest control see Chapter 17.

Inefficient transportation can delay food shipments. Meanwhile, rats, insects, birds, or spoilage may claim part of the supply. Spoilage can be prevented by refrigeration and other improvements. Grain, for instance, can be stored in dry silos or sheds to prevent the growth of mold and mildew and hold down rat populations. Technical and financial assistance from the developed countries could go a long way toward improving food storage and transportation, potentially increasing our food supply by 10% or more.

Increasing Self-Sufficiency

Increasing self-sufficiency among poorer nations is an essential part of decreasing hunger. In a world of growing interdependency a call for more self-sufficiency may seem odd. The pressures on farmland from urbanization and fuel farms in the leading agricultural export nations will force food prices up, making it increasingly difficult for poor nations to afford their food imports.

Self-sufficiency could be achieved by technical and financial aid aimed at building a sustainable agricultural system that (1) uses nonrenewable energy efficiently, (2) relies primarily on human labor, (3) conserves soil and soil nutrients, (4) uses water efficiently, (5) minimizes water pollution, (6) relies on a high level of species diversity, (7) reduces soil disruption from plowing and cultivating, and (8) uses perennial rather than annual crops.

An Integrated Approach

This chapter began by listing three problems in world agriculture: the near-term need to feed malnourished and undernourished people, the long-term need to provide food for the coming generations, and the continuing need to preserve the soil, on which our civilization depends. It should be clear that there are many ways to solve these problems. But which one is right? The answer is that not one but many of these ideas must be adopted and integrated into a policy to build a sustainable agricultural system. No single solution will suffice. Anything short of a sustainable system is, according to some observers, doomed to fail in the long run.

First and foremost, many observers believe, population growth must be brought under control. Rapid growth rates only make food shortages more difficult to solve. In the near term the developed nations may need to give food aid to the starving people of Asia, Africa, and Latin America. Some observers believe that food aid should be given only to countries committed to population control. They argue that, in the absence of population control policies, food aid only worsens the problems in the long term by promoting population growth. In the long-term, the hungry nations may need to become more self-sufficient. That can be achieved by technical assistance, education, and funding from developed nations.

Self-sufficiency could be tied to sensible economic development. Even though India is now considered self-sufficient in food production, it has hundreds of millions of malnourished people. Hunger persists because many people lack the money to pay for food. With jobs available to them, they could afford locally grown food.

Increasing the amount of cultivated land is an option open to few countries, and this option should be pursued only after vigorous efforts are made to decrease the loss of farmland from desertification, soil erosion, nutrient depletion, and urbanization. Small improvements here can pay huge dividends, including cleaner water and preservation of wildlife habitat.

The use of native plants and animals, the cultivation of newly discovered wild strains, and genetic improvements in existing crops and livestock can increase food output. Soil enrichment and carefully managed irrigation can help boost farm potential and meet the demands for food. Finally, improvements in storage and transportation could prevent the loss of food from pests and spoilage.

To a man with an empty stomach, food is God.

GANDHI

Summary

Throughout the world 40 million people die annually of starvation and diseases worsened by malnutrition. **Protein–calorie malnutrition** in children, the major nutritional disease worldwide, takes two main forms: **kwashiorkor** (protein deficiency) and **marasmus** (protein–calorie deficiency). Growing evidence suggests that malnutrition early in life leads to a permanent retardation of mental and physical growth.

Satisfying future food demand and feeding those people alive today are two of the major challenges facing agriculture. But many problems stand in the way of the goals: soil erosion, nutrient depletion, desertification, dwindling supplies of fossil fuels, groundwater depletion, waterlogging, salinization, and farmland conversion. Politics compound many of these problems.

Food experts are concerned also about the loss of species diversity, arguing that it makes our agriculture system more vulnerable to insects, disease, drought, and other natural calamities. Today, a few high-yield species have replaced a variety of species that once provided food.

Numerous strategies must be employed to meet current and future food demands. Population control is first in importance. Beyond that, we can increase the amount of agricultural land in production by exploiting currently unused farmland, by decreasing erosion on existing land, by controlling the spread of deserts, and by reducing farmland conversion.

In conjunction with these efforts food production (yield) can be increased by developing new plant and animal varieties, by soil conservation and enrichment, and by irrigation. New plant and animal varieties can be developed through artificial selection or by genetic engineering, but in order for these efforts to be successful, new varieties must not lose their resistance to disease, insects, and other natural factors that tend to reduce yield. Some agricultural researchers are exploring the use of perennial crops for agriculture. Such a system would reduce soil tillage, energy demands, and soil erosion. Careful soil enrichment programs in which natural organic wastes are used to replenish lost nutrients can be successful in retaining productivity. Finally, since much of our agricultural production comes from irrigated land and since many supplies of irrigation water are now threatened, more efficient use of water could extend production on land that otherwise might have to be abandoned.

For the most part, manufactured food supplements have proved unacceptable to people. Native species, especially grazers, may provide important protein and have many advantages over introduced species. Fish provide about 5% of the total animal protein consumed by the world's people. Increasing the fish catch, however, is unlikely and could probably be carried out only on a short-term basis before populations were depleted. A better strategy would be to reduce spoilage. Commercial fish farms might make it possible for rich and poor nations to double or triple their fish production.

Each year a large amount of food is destroyed by insects, bacteria, fungi, and rodents during production, transportation, and storage. Simple, cost-effective measures could be devised to reduce this loss.

Limits to the world's petroleum supply suggest the need for more agricultural self-sufficiency among the poor as well as the rich. Such independence can be developed by employing many of the strategies outlined in this chapter. Most important, rich and poor nations need to devise a sustainable agricultural system that uses a minimum amount of nonrenewable energy, relies on human labor, conserves soil and soil nutrients, uses water efficiently, minimizes water pollution, relies on a high level of species diversity, reduces soil tillage, and uses perennial rather than annual crops.

Discussion Questions

1. What percentage of the world's population is malnourished? What are the short- and long-range effects of malnutrition?

2. What has happened to world per capita food supply in the last two decades?

3. What is desertification, what factors create it, and how can it be prevented?

4. Discuss the statement "Soil erosion control is too expensive. We can't afford to pay for it, because our crops don't bring in enough money."

5. How does the long-term outlook for oil affect world agriculture?

6. Describe waterlogging and salinization of soils. How can they be prevented?

7. Describe the decline in agricultural diversity. How could this trend affect world agriculture? Give some examples.

8. List and discuss the major strategies for solving world food shortages. Which are most important? How would you implement them in this and foreign countries?

9. Debate the statement "Simply by practicing better soil conservation and replenishing soil nutrients we can reduce the need for developing new farmland."

10. Describe the Green Revolution, its successes and its failures. What improvements might be made?

11. Describe trends in the world fish catch. What happened to per capita yield in the 1970s? Is it likely that the annual fish catch will increase in the coming years? Why or why not?

12. Should the developing countries become more self-sufficient in agricultural production? What are the advantages of self-sufficiency for less developed countries? What are the disadvantages?

13. You have been appointed head of a U.N. task force. Your project is to develop an agricultural system in a poor African nation, which imports more than 50% of its grain and still suffers from widespread hunger. Outline your plan, giving general principles you would follow and specific recommendations for achieving self-sufficiency.

Suggested Readings

Brown, L. R. (1978). *The Worldwide Loss of Cropland.* Worldwatch Paper 24. Washington, D.C.: Worldwatch Institute. A comprehensive analysis of loss of agricultural lands.

Brown, L. R. (1980). Fuel Farms: Croplands of the Future? *The Futurist* 14 (3): 16–28. A well-written paper on one of the many threats to agricultural productivity.

Brown, L. R. (1985). Fish Farming. *The Futurist* 19 (5): 18–25. Good article.

Brown, L. R., Chandler, W. U., Flavin, C., Pollock, C., Postel, S., Starke, L., and Wolf, E. C. (1985). *State of the World 1985.* New York: Norton. Read Chapter 2, on reducing hunger.

Brown, L. R., Chandler, W. V., Flavin, C., Jacobsen, J., Pollock, C., Postel, S., Starke, L., and Wolf, E. C. (1987). *State of the World 1987.* New York: Norton. Chapter 7 summarizes important gains and further needs in agriculture.

Brown, L. R., and Wolf, E. C. (1984). *Soil Erosion: Quiet Crisis in the World Economy.* Worldwatch Paper 60. Washington, D.C.: Worldwatch Institute. Excellent.

Dudal, R. (1982). Land Degradation in a World Perspective. *Journal of Soil and Water Conservation* 37 (5): 245–249. Excellent review of potential farmland.

Gore, R., and Gerster, G. (1979). An Age-Old Challenge Grows. *National Geographic* 156 (5): 594–639. A vivid view of worldwide desertification.

Grosson, P. (1984). Agricultural Land: Will There Be Enough? *Environment* 26 (7): 16–20, 40–45. A look at farmland and soil erosion.

Reichert, W. (1982). Agriculture's Diminishing Diversity. *Environment* 24 (9): 6–11, 39–44. A superb discussion of the loss of diversity among crops and domestic livestock.

Sampson, R. N. (1981). *Farmland or Wasteland: A Time to Choose.* Emmaus, Pa.: Rodale Press. Well-written book on world agriculture.

Scoville, O. J. (1982). "Changes in Farmland: Policy Implications." *Population Bulletin* 36 (5): 1–13. A thorough analysis of the threats to U.S. agricultural production.

Solkoff, J. (1985). *The Politics of Food.* San Francisco: Sierra Club Books. Excellent account of U.S. agricultural policy.

Tanji, K., Lauchli, A., and Meyer, J. (1986). Selenium in the San Joaquin Valley. *Environment* 28 (6): 6–11, 34–39. Detailed account of the problems caused by irrigation.

Soil and Soil Management

To build may have to be the slow and laborious task of years. To destroy can be the thoughtless act of a single day.

WINSTON CHURCHILL

Throughout the world rich and poor nations alike plow their soil indiscriminately to grow food for expanding populations. They build on the soil and dig it up to get at coal and other valuable resources. Through mismanagement valuable topsoil washes into streams, where it kills aquatic life and fills in reservoirs. In short, nations treat soil as if it were an inexhaustible resource.

In the United States 500,000 hectares (1.25 million acres) of farmland are lost each year because of soil erosion. On some farms erosion is so great that two bushels of soil are lost for every bushel of corn produced (Figure S7-1). Experts predict that soil erosion may increase by 50% to 80% in the future if marginal land is brought into production to meet increased foreign demand for American-grown grains.

If agriculture is to remain productive, erosion must be controlled. This supplement discusses soil and soil formation and presents some cost-effective ways to reduce erosion and create a sustainable agricultural system.

What Is Soil?

Soil is a complex mixture of inorganic and organic materials with variable amounts of air and moisture. Clay, silt, sand, gravel, and rocks are the inorganic components of soil. Detritus, organic wastes, and a multitude of living organisms are the organic components. Soils are described according to six general features: texture, structure, acidity, gas content, water content, and biotic composition.

Soil Formation

Soil formation is a complex and often slow process, even under the best of conditions. The time it takes soil to develop depends partly on the type of **parent material**, the underlying substrate from which soil is formed. To form 2.5 centimeters (1 inch) of topsoil from hard rock may take 200 to 1200 years, depending on the climate. Softer parent materials such as shale, volcanic ash, sandstone, sand dunes, and gravel beds are converted to soil at a faster rate (in 20 years or so) if conditions are favorable.

A number of physical processes contribute to soil formation. Daily heating and cooling may cause the parent rock material to split and fragment, especially in climates such as deserts where daily temperatures can vary widely. Water entering cracks in rocks expands in freezing, causing the rock to fragment further. Rock fragments formed by heating and cooling and by freezing are slowly pulverized into smaller particles by streams or landslides, by hooves of animals, or by wind and rain.

Soil formation is facilitated by a wide range of organisms. Chapter 4 described how lichens "gnaw" away at the rock surface by secreting carbonic acid. Lichens also capture dust, seeds, excrement, and dead plant matter, which help form soil. The roots of trees and large plants reach into small cracks and fracture the rock. Roots also serve as nutrient pumps, bringing up inorganic nutrients from deeper soil layers. These chemicals are first used to make leaves and branches, which can fall and decay, thus becoming part of the soil.

Grazing animals pulverize rock and gravel under their hooves and drop excrement on the ground, adding to the soil's organic matter. The white rhinoceros, for example, produces about 30 tons of manure each year, which is deposited in its territory. A variety of insects and other creatures, such as earthworms, also participate in soil formation.

The Soil Profile

Soil is often arranged in layers of different color and composition. These layers are called **horizons**.

Figure S7-1 Areas of critical erosion in the United States. Peaks represent the highest rates of erosion.

Soil scientists recognize five major horizons (Figure S7-2). The uppermost **O horizon**, or litter layer, a thin layer of organic waste from animals and detritus, is a zone of organic decomposition characterized by a dark, rich color. Plowing mixes it in with the next layer.

The **A horizon**, or **topsoil**, varies in thickness from 2.5 centimeters (1 inch) in some regions to 60 centimeters (2 feet) in the rich farmland of Iowa. This horizon is generally rich in inorganic and organic nutrients and is economically important because it supports crops. The A horizon is darker and looser than the deeper layers. It holds moisture because of its organic material, the **humus**, and is quite porous. The A horizon is also known as the "zone of leaching," since nutrients are leached out of it as water percolates through it from the surface.

The **B horizon**, or **subsoil**, is also known as the "zone of accumulation," because it receives and collects minerals and nutrients from above. This layer is lightly colored and much denser than the topsoil because of a lack of organic matter. The **C horizon** is a transition zone between the parent material below and the layers of soil above. The **D horizon** is the parent material from which soils are derived. Not all horizons are present in all soils; in some, the layering may be missing altogether.

The soil profile is determined by the climate (especially rainfall and temperature), type of vegetation, parent material, age of the soil, and the organisms. Soil profiles tell soil scientists whether land is best for agriculture, wildlife habitat, forestry, pasture, rangeland, or recreation. They also tell us how suitable soil might be for various other uses such as home building and highway construction.

Soil Management

Soil management has two major goals: erosion control and nutrient preservation.

Erosion Control

Erosion can be controlled by a variety of techniques. This section discusses six major strategies: minimum tillage, contour farming, strip cropping, terracing, gully reclamation, and shel-

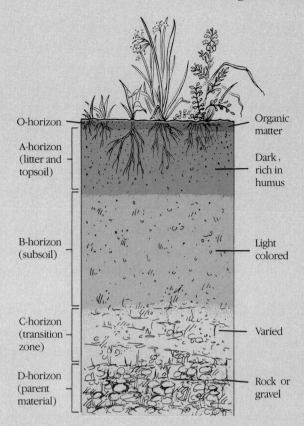

Figure S7-2 Soil profile, showing the five horizons. Not all are found in all locations.

terbelts. These measures may raise the cost of farming in the short term, but, as Chapter 20 points out, they make good economic sense in the long run.

Minimum Tillage As the name implies, **minimum tillage** is a way of farming that reduces the physical disruption of the soil caused by plowing or cultivating crops for weed control. Typically, farmers plow their fields before planting a new crop. With special implements, however, they can plant right over the previous year's crop residue.

Minimum tillage is now practiced on over 27 million hectares (67 million acres) of land in the United States (Figure S7-3). Because fields are protected much of the year by crops or crop residues, soil erosion can be decreased substantially—in some cases by as much as 90% (Figure S7-4). Minimum tillage also reduces energy consumption by as much as 80% and conserves soil moisture by reducing evaporation. Crop residues may increase habitat for predatory insects that help hold pest populations in check. This may reduce pesticide use and contamination of the environment (Chapter 17).

Despite its benefits minimum tillage has several drawbacks. For example, herbicides are often used in place of mechanical cultivation to control weeds. In addition, crop residues may harbor harmful insects that damage crops. Minimum tillage also requires new and costly farm equipment. (Figure S7-4).

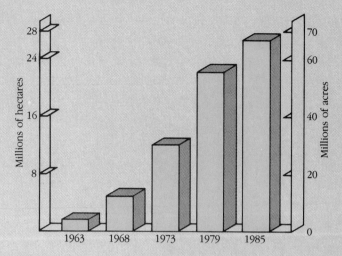

Figure S7-3 Growth in minimum (conservation) tillage in the United States.

Figure S7-4 Minimum tillage planter, designed to dig furrows in the presence of crop residue.

Contour Farming On hilly terrain, crops can be planted along level lines that follow the contour of the land. This is called **contour farming**. As illustrated in Figure S7-5, rows are planted across the direction of water flow on hilly or sloped land. This reduces the flow of water across the land, resulting in a tremendous reduction in erosion and a marked increase in water retention. In a Texas experiment water runoff from a contoured field was only 4 centimeters (1.6 inches) per year, compared with 11.6 centimeters (4.6 inches) per year for uncontoured fields. Soil erosion can be reduced by 60% to 80%.

Strip Cropping As illustrated in Figure S7-6, **strip cropping** involves planting strips of alternate crops in fields that are subject to soil erosion by wind or water. Strip cropping can be combined with contour farming to further decrease erosion. As an example, farmers may alternate row crops such as corn with cover crops such as alfalfa. Water flows more easily through row crops and begins to gain momentum, but when it meets the cover crop, its flow is virtually stopped.

Terracing For thousands of years many peoples have grown crops on terraces in mountainous terrain. Terraces have also been used in the United States for over 40 years on land with less pronounced slope (Figure S7-7).

Terracing today involves the construction of small earthen embankments on sloped cropland. These are placed across the slope to check water flow and minimize erosion. Terraces are expensive to construct and often interfere with the operation of large farm equipment; thus, farmers may prefer other, cheaper forms of soil conservation.

Gully Reclamation Gullies are a danger sign of rapid soil erosion. Some gullies can work their way up hills at a rate of 4.5 meters (15 feet) a year.

To prevent gullies from forming, farmers must reduce water flow over their land. Contour farming, strip crops, and terraces all help. Special diversion ditches can be dug in channels where water naturally flows off fields. Already formed gullies can be

Figure S7-5 This land is farmed along the contour lines to reduce soil erosion and surface runoff, thus saving soil and moisture alike.

stopped by seeding barren soils with rapidly growing plants, including trees. Small earthen dams can be built across them to reduce water flow, retain moisture for plant growth, and capture sediment, which will eventually support vegetation as erosion is reduced. Too often land with severe gullies is abandoned or haphazardly reclaimed, only to suffer worse erosion in time.

Figure S7-6 Strips of corn protect small grain plants from the effects of wind.

Figure S7-8 Shelterbelts used to protect farmland in Michigan from the erosive effects of wind.

Figure S7-7 This Iowa corn is grown on sloping land with the aid of terraces, small earth embankments that reduce water flow across the surface. The corn is planted in the stubble of last year's crop.

Shelterbelts In 1935 the U.S. government mounted a campaign to prevent the reoccurrence of the disastrous Dust Bowl days. One part of this program involved planting long rows of trees as windbreaks, or **shelterbelts**, in a north–south orientation along the margins of farms in the Great Plains (Figure S7-8). Today, thousands of kilometers of shelterbelts have been planted from Texas to North Dakota.

Shelterbelts block the wind and, therefore, decrease soil erosion and damage to crops caused by windblown dirt particles. In the winter they reduce the amount of blowing snow, thus allowing snow to build up in fields. This insulates the soil and also increases soil moisture and groundwater supplies. They can also improve irrigation efficiency by reducing the amount of water carried away from sprinklers. In addition, shelterbelts provide habitat for animals, pest-eating insects, and pollinators. Shelterbelts protect citrus groves from wind that blows fruit from trees. They have the added benefit of saving energy by reducing heat loss from homes and farm buildings.

A University of Nebraska study showed that terracing and contour farming each reduces erosion by 50%. Combined, they

can reduce soil loss by 75%. Minimum tillage is even more effective. By itself it can reduce erosion rates by 90%, but when it is combined with terracing and contour farming, soil erosion rates can be reduced by 98%.

In a sustainable agricultural system erosion control assumes a position of great importance. Inexpensive techniques that are available now can slow down the rate of erosion and help us ensure food for future generations. Regardless, many farmers are reluctant to invest in such practices. An economic explanation of this phenomenon is given in Chapter 20.

Preventing the Depletion of Soil Nutrients

Preventing soil erosion saves topsoil and also preserves soil nutrients needed to maintain food output. Several ways to prevent the depletion of soil nutrients were mentioned in Chapter 7 and are discussed in more detail below.

Use of Organic Fertilizers Organic fertilizers such as cow, chicken, and hog manure and human sewage are excellent soil supplements, which replenish organic matter and important soil nutrients such as nitrogen and phosphorus. Other organic materials may be used to build soil; especially helpful are leguminous plants such as alfalfa that are grown during the off-season and plowed under before planting crops. Referred to as "green manure," they add organic matter to the soil, retain moisture, and also reduce soil erosion during fallow periods.

Soil enrichment with organic fertilizers (1) improves soil structure, (2) increases water retention, (3) increases fertility and crop yield, (4) provides a good environment for the bacterial growth necessary for nitrogen fixation, (5) helps prevent shifts in the acidity of soil, and (6) tends to prevent the leaching of minerals from soil by rain and snowmelt. In addition, the use of human wastes on farmland could significantly reduce water pollution by waste treatment plants.

Organic wastes have been successfully applied in many areas, but this form of fertilizing, like almost anything else we do, can have some problems. One of the leading ones is transporting waste to farms, requiring pipelines or trucks. Initial investment may be high, but the long-term benefits of applying organic fertilizers could outweigh these costs. Another problem is that waste from municipal sewage treatment plants may be contaminated with pathogenic organisms such as bacteria, viruses, and parasites. Theoretically, some of these could be taken up by crops and reenter the human food chain. Toxic heavy metals, such as mercury, cadmium, and lead, are also present in municipal wastes and could enter crops. Better controls at sewage treatment plants or at the factories that produce these materials could alleviate the problem.

Use of Synthetic Fertilizers   In the United States synthetic fertilizer is the greatest source of nitrogen used by farmers. It is made by chemically combining nitrogen and hydrogen to form ammonia and ammonium salts. Some nitrates and urea are also made. Artificial fertilizers can be applied directly to the soil as a liquid, or they can be mixed with phosphorus and potassium in a dry, granular fertilizer.

Synthetic fertilizers containing nitrogen, phosphorus, and potassium—and made from natural gas—partially restore soil fertility but do not replenish organic matter or micronutrients necessary for proper plant growth and human nutrition. As a result soil is slowly degraded over years of agriculture. Excess fertilizer may be washed from the land by rains and end up in streams, causing a number of problems. (These are addressed in Chapter 16, on water pollution.)

To prevent the slow depletion of nutrients and to help develop a sustainable agricultural system, synthetic fertilizers should be supplemented by organic fertilizers. Synthetic fertilizers can probably be eliminated entirely in the developing nations or on small farms near abundant sources of organic fertilizer. Combined with programs of soil conservation and organic enrichment, synthetic fertilizers will inevitably play an important role in feeding the world's people. As fossil fuels become scarcer, however, synthetic fertilizers may become more costly.

Crop Rotation   In modern agriculture synthetic fertilizers and pesticides have allowed farmers to grow the same crop year after year on the same plot. This way farmers can concentrate their efforts on one crop that they know well. However profitable this practice might be, it is ecologically unsound, for it gradually depletes the soil of nutrients, can increase soil erosion, and often worsens problems with pests and pathogens. Crop rotation, once a common practice among farmers in the United States, could return us to a more ecologically sound and sustainable agricultural system.

Using the age-old practice of rotating crops, a farmer may plant a soil-depleting crop (corn) for one to two years and then follow it with a cover crop such as grasses or various legumes such as alfalfa. The cover crop reduces soil erosion, and legumes replenish soil nitrogen. Often, cover crops are not harvested but are simply plowed under to replenish organic matter and return nutrients to the soil.

Putting It All Together: Organic Farming   Today, thousands of farmers are running profitable farms either without chemical fertilizers and pesticides or with only small amounts of them. Called **organic farming**, this system avoids or largely excludes synthetic chemical compounds such as fertilizers, pesticides, growth regulators, and livestock food additives, relying instead on crop rotation, green manure, animal wastes, off-farm organic wastes, mechanical cultivation, and biological pest control to the maximum extent possible. Believing that a sustainable and productive agricultural system is more important than high yields alone, organic farmers concentrate on keeping their soil in top condition.

The success of organic farms baffles those who have come to think of modern agriculture as the only way to farm. The ecologist Barry Commoner compared organic and conventional farms of similar size and found that the organic farms produced nearly as well. Further research has supported this conclusion: organic farms produce about 11% fewer vegetables than a comparable "modern" farm, but the net income per hectare is about the same because of the lower costs. Organic farms require 60% less fossil fuel energy to produce corn crops with only 3% lower yields.

There are some limits to organic farming: (1) organic fertilizers may not replace all of the phosphorus and potassium drained from the soil by plants, (2) nitrogen replacement by legumes may not always be enough to give high yields of crops such as corn that have a high nitrogen requirement, (3) total production may be lower than on a conventional farm because of land devoted to soil conservation, and (4) there is a three- to five-year transition period from conventional to organic farming during which yields may be low and losses to insects and weeds may be high.

Given these drawbacks, wholesale adoption of organic farming in developed countries seems unlikely. What is more probable, though, is the adoption of many of its techniques by traditional farmers. In developing nations opportunities to develop organic farming are numerous. Considering the high cost of fossil fuels and fertilizers and the abundance of labor, organic farming may be well suited to such nations.

Achieving Cost-Effective Conservation

Controlling soil erosion and soil fertility are as much economic problems as they are resource conservation problems. Because of rising production costs, short-term profits often supersede long-term matters of fertility and erosion control. What is most urgent to the farmer is the profit needed to keep up payments on land, fertilizer, machinery, pesticides, and seed, not the long-term stability of world agriculture.

Many farmers do not view soil erosion as a major problem, because fertilizers and new high-yield seeds have boosted crop yields and masked the effects of excessive erosion. In taking the shortest path between the top and bottom line on their balance sheets, farmers ignore practices that preserve the soil at its maximum productivity.

How can we achieve cost-effective soil conservation? Below are some suggestions:

1. Target areas where erosion is the most severe (see Figure S7-1). Currently, half of all cropland erosion in the United States comes from about 10% of the total farmland. Concentrated efforts on this land could be highly cost-effective in reducing soil erosion.

2. Expand programs by governmental agencies, such as the U.S. Soil Conservation Service, to familiarize farmers with the most cost-effective ways of controlling erosion.

3. Enact agricultural zoning regulations locally to prohibit highly erodible land from being farmed.

4. Offer tax breaks to farmers to help defray the cost of soil conservation.

5. Require farmers applying for government loans, crop insurance, or aid to have an approved soil conservation program already in operation.

6. Strengthen the role of the states in soil conservation. Increase cooperation among state, local, and federal agencies involved in soil conservation.

Suggested Readings

Brock, B. G. (1982). Weed Control versus Soil Erosion Control. *Journal of Soil and Water Conservation* March/April: 73–76. A thorough study of weed control by tillage and herbicides.

Jeffords, J. M. (1982). Soil Conservation Policy for the Future. *Journal of Soil and Water Conservation* January/February: 10–13. A view of the needs of soil conservation policy in the United States.

Owen, O. S. (1980). *Natural Resource Conservation*. New York: Macmillan. Excellent sections on agriculture, soils, and land management.

Postel, S. (1985). *Conserving Water: The Untapped Potential*. Worldwatch Paper 67. Washington, D.C.: Worldwatch Institute. Detailed study of agricultural water conservation.

Sampson, R. N. (1981). *Farmland or Wasteland: A Time to Choose*. Emmaus, Pa.: Rodale Press. Well-written book on agriculture and soil conservation.

U.S. Department of Agriculture. (1969). *Windbreaks for Conservation*. Agriculture Information Bulletin 339. Washington, D.C.: Author. A detailed document on shelterbelts.

U.S. Department of Agriculture. (1980). *America's Soil and Water: Condition and Trends*. Washington, D.C.: Author. Valuable reference.

U.S. Department of Agriculture. (1980). *Soil, Water, and Related Resources in the United States*, Vols. 1 and 2. Washington, D.C.: Author. Detailed references on nonfederal soil and water resources.

U.S. Department of Agriculture. (1982). *A National Program for Soil and Water Conservation*. Summary of the 1982 Final Program Report and Environmental Impact Statement. Soil and Waters Resources Conservation Act of 1977. Washington, D.C.: Author. Outline of possible federal policy for soil conservation.

Vietmeyer, N. (1986). Lesser-Known Plants of Potential Use in Agriculture and Forestry. *Science* 232 (June 13): 1379–1384. Superb article on alternative food sources.

Wolf, E. C. (1986). *Beyond the Green Revolution: New Approaches for Third World Agriculture*. Worldwatch Paper 73. Washington, D.C.: Worldwatch Institute. Detailed assessment of agricultural prospects in developing countries.

Wildlife and Plants: Preserving Biological Diversity

The worst sin toward our fellow creatures is not to hate them, but to be indifferent to them; that's the essence of inhumanity.

GEORGE BERNARD SHAW

Stalking through the underbrush, two African peasants halt when they hear a rustling in the bushes ahead of them. Pushing back a branch, they spot the bull black rhinoceros, browsing on low branches. One of the men lifts his rifle and fires. The rhino stumbles a little, regains its footing, then races off. Another shot rings out; the rhino stumbles again, runs half a mile, and collapses in a cloud of dust.

Jubilant, the men run to the fallen beast. Their hearts beating hard, they saw off the rhino's horns and sneak into the trees, heading back to the village, where a middleman will buy the horn. The men will get $100 each, a considerable sum, for $200 will support a family for a year. Several more hunts this year and they will be wealthy men.

From Africa, rhino horns may go to Yemen or China. In Yemen they will be carved into expensive dagger handles. In China rhino horns are ground and sold as an aphrodisiac and as a fever-depressing drug costing $11,000 per kilogram (2.2 pounds).

African farmers, whose villages are doubling in size every 20 years, are plowing up grassland that was once grazing land for rhinos and other African wildlife. As the farmland spreads outward, the African rhino population is fragmented into many small groups, often with as few as 30 members. Poachers have further reduced some of these tiny groups to as few as eight animals. Interbreeding among rhinos has become a major problem.

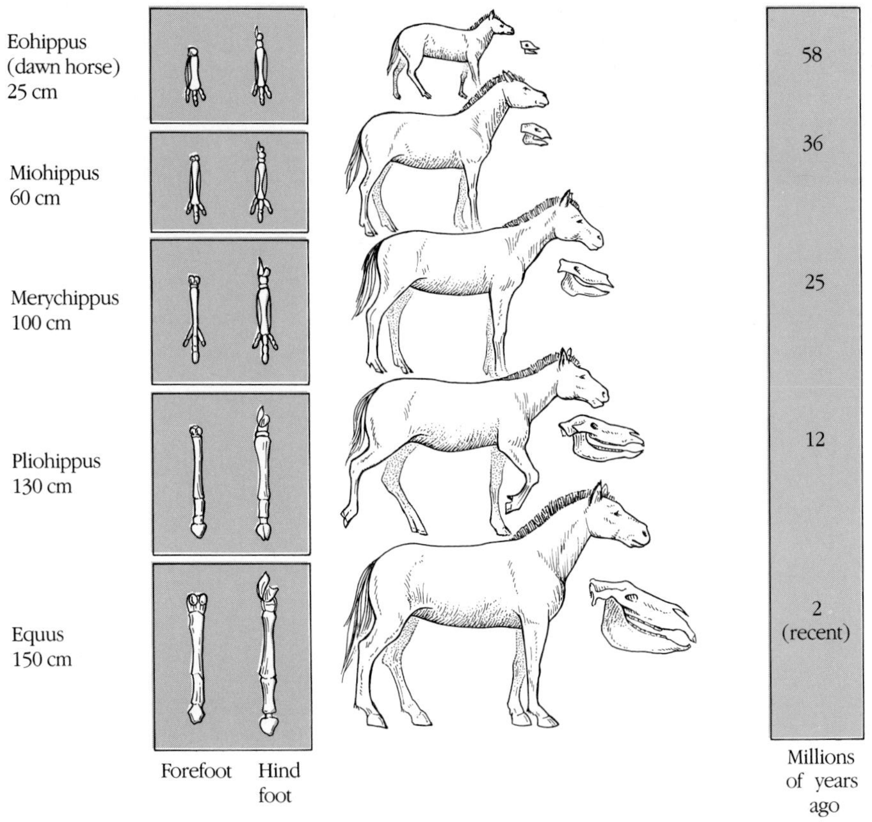

Figure 8-1 Stages in the evolutionary history of the horse.

"The rhino's demise," writes David Western, a Kenyan wildlife biologist, "stems from a jarring mix of prosperity and poverty. Asia is getting richer by the year and can afford astronomical prices for horn, while Africa is getting poorer and more desperate." Poachers, farmers, and, indirectly, wealthy Yemenis and Chinese have reduced the once-large rhino population to almost nothing. Numbering in the hundreds of thousands 50 years ago, the population of black rhinos is now estimated to be less than 8000, and it is still declining rapidly. The northern white rhino is now virtually extinct. If poaching and human population growth continue, there is little hope for the African rhino. It may be gone in five years.

This chapter examines the extinction of plants and animals, brought on by a mixture of underlying causes. It also looks at the countless benefits of wildlife to human societies and suggests the need for urgent action throughout the world.

The Vanishing Species

As many as 500 million kinds of plants, animals, and microorganisms have made this planet home since the beginning of time. Today there are 5 to 10 million species, two-thirds of which live in the tropics. Thus, 490 million species have become **extinct**, lost forever. Extinction is an evolutionary fact of life. But natural extinction differs considerably from the impending doom now facing the rhino and tens of thousands of plants and other animals. There are two reasons why natural extinction differs from the accelerated extinction now taking place.

First, during the course of millennia old species evolved into new ones (Figure 8-1). Consequently, many of the 490 million extinct species are represented today by their descendants. Modern extinctions, on the other hand, wipe out species. If the rhino should vanish, it would leave no evolutionary legacy. It would be gone forever.

Second, the rate of extinction varies considerably. Even though some species did vanish because of severe climatic changes or increasing environmental resistance created by excess predation or disease, the rate of natural extinction was slow compared with today's **accelerated extinction** (Figure 8-2). Currently, one vertebrate (backboned) species becomes extinct every nine months, compared with a natural rate of one species every 1000 years. When plants, insects, and microorganisms are added, the extinction rate climbs to one species a day. Many experts fear that we have entered a new era of extinction unparalleled in the history of the earth.

If the world's population continues to grow and nations

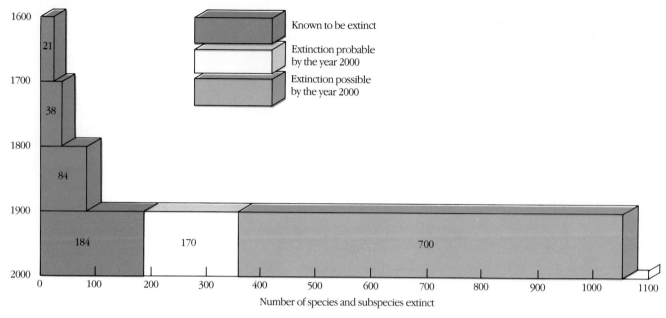

Figure 8-2 Extinction rate of vertebrate species past and projected. Notice the rapid increase in the 20th century.

continue to destroy wildlife habitat at current rates, many experts predict, an average of 40,000 to 50,000 species will be destroyed per year over the next 20 years. By the end of the 1980s we may be losing one species per hour!

Pandas, blue whales, tigers, and chimpanzees are the endangered species that make the headlines. But these species are, in fact, only a small part of the picture. Today, about 25,000 species of plants are threatened with extinction—one of every ten plant species on earth. Far more insect species teeter on the brink of extinction.

Unless we curb population growth and properly manage our resources, the biological world at the end of the century will differ radically from the world we now live in. As many as 1 million species may have vanished between 1980 and 2000. The consequences of mass extinctions, and the habitat destruction that is largely responsible for them, will be felt throughout the world.

What Causes Extinction?

Plant and animal extinction results from many underlying forces, such as economics, politics, and psychology. Figure 8-3 shows the specific activities that cause extinction and the relative importance of each. The top five, in decreasing order of importance, are: (1) habitat alteration, (2) hunting for commercial products, (3) introduction of alien and domestic species, (4) hunting for sport, and (5) pest and predator control. In Africa, extinction of the rhino stems from several of these factors, most importantly, habitat destruction and hunting for profit. In fact, multiple causation is the rule in animal and plant extinction.

Alteration of Habitat

Alteration of habitat is the most significant single factor in extinctions. Habitat is destroyed by human civilization spreading into fields, forests, oceans, and waterways. Roads, strip mines, housing projects, dams, airports, farms, and cities usurp wildlife habitat. Even recreational areas have many adverse effects on wildlife. Dams built for recreational boating and water skiing, for instance, release cold water from the bottom that threatens native fish species adapted to warmer waters. Ski resorts and the attendant condominiums and restaurants wipe out winter feeding grounds for deer, elk, and other species. For this reason Canadian biologists and environmentalists opposed the development of Mount Allan in Alberta, the site of the 1988 winter Olympic Games. They say that buildings and ski runs threaten the area's wildlife, such as grizzly bears, bighorn sheep, and elk.

Nowhere is the loss of habitat more noticeable than in the tropical rain forests. Tropical forests house about half of the earth's species. Once covering an area the size of the United States, the tropical rain forests have been cut by at least one-third. Countless species have perished as a result. (For more on tropical rain forests and their destruction see Chapter 9.)

Coral reefs, wetlands, and estuaries (the mouths of

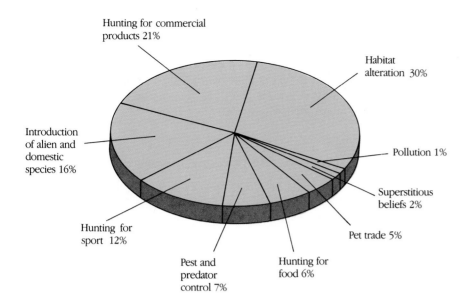

Hunting for commercial products 21%

Habitat alteration 30%

Introduction of alien and domestic species 16%

Pollution 1%

Superstitious beliefs 2%

Hunting for sport 12%

Pet trade 5%

Pest and predator control 7%

Hunting for food 6%

Figure 8-3 An approximate breakdown of the human activities that lead to extinction. More than one activity is often involved, however.

rivers) are other critical habitats now rapidly declining because of human development. Wetlands and estuaries are the home of many species (see Chapter Supplement 10-1) but are also highly prized by humankind. In Scotland, for instance, conservationists are now fighting to save several peat lands that house some of Europe's rarest birds. On the island of Islay, distillers of a famous Scotch whisky have been granted government approval to drain and harvest peat in a bog that is the winter feeding ground for 4000 white-fronted geese. If the land goes, so will this rare bird species. So far, the battle to save the bogs appears bleak. The sale of whisky is down. Agriculture is depressed. Some residents see conservationists' efforts as a threat to their economic well-being.

Commercial, Sport, and Subsistence Hunting

Animals are hunted today for profit, for food, and for sport. Collectively, these activities play a major role in species extinction.

Commercial hunting represents the biggest threat. Whale hunting is one of the most widely publicized examples. Throughout the history of whaling, men have hunted species to the brink of extinction and then moved on to other species. The result has been a severe reduction in the number of whales of many species (Table 8-1). Thanks to recent efforts by the International Whaling Commission, commercial whaling has come to a standstill. In its stead is a new industry: whale watching, with annual revenues that exceed those of the commercial whaling industry itself (Figure 8-4).

Commercial hunting is systematically reducing the populations of many other endangered species. In parts of Africa, for example, endangered male gorillas are killed by tribes seeking parts of their bodies believed to possess magical properties. The hands and head are sold to tourists. Similar poaching has caused drastic declines in elephants, rhinos, jaguars, tigers, and cheetahs. Fortunately, some of the African nations have found that wildlife can greatly enhance their appeal to tourists and have attempted to halt poaching.

Table 8-1 Whale Populations—Then and Now

Species	Number Before Commerical Whaling	Current Estimate
Blue	166,000	7,500–15,000
Bowhead	54,680	3,600–4,100
Fin	450,000	105,000–122,000
Gray	15,000–20,000	13,450–19,200
Humpback	119,000	8,900–10,500
Minke	250,000	130,000–150,000
Right	50,000	3,000
Sei (includes Bryde's)	108,000	36,800–54,700
Sperm	1,377,000	982,300

Source: From Center for Environmental Education, (1984).

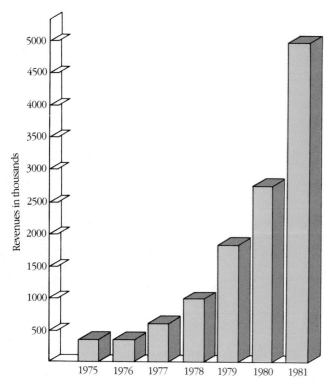

Figure 8-4 Growth in revenues from whale-watching cruises, 1975–1981.

Hunting for sport is also a factor in wildlife extinction (Figure 8-5). However, the hunting of properly managed, nonendangered species frequently benefits populations by keeping them within the carrying capacity of their habitat. It is another kind of hunting that threatens rare and sometimes endangered wildlife: trophy hunting of endangered species.

People also hunt endangered species for food. For example, Eskimos annually kill a number of endangered bowhead whales, despite scientific evidence that the population (about 2300) cannot support further killing. Continued subsistence hunting has pitted environmentalists against the Eskimos.

Introducing Foreign Species

Foreign, or **alien**, **species** introduced accidentally or intentionally into new territories often cause the extinction of native species. The water hyacinth, discussed in Chapter 4, is such an example. The English sparrow fluttering about in the bushes outside your window is another. Deliberately introduced into this country in the 1850s, the sparrow quickly spread throughout the continent. It now competes for nesting sites and food once used by bluebirds, wrens, and swallows.

Islands are especially vulnerable to new species. In Hawaii, for example, 90% of all bird species have been wiped out by human inhabitants and organisms (for example, rats) that humans have introduced. In New Zealand, half the native birds are endangered or extinct.

Florida is a showcase of alien species gone wild. Australian pines, introduced as ornamentals, have spread rapidly along coastal beaches. Their shallow roots are so dense that they destroy sandy beaches where many sea turtles lay their eggs. The Brazilian pepper, another introduced species, is growing wild in cleared land and especially mangrove swamps, the habitat of dozens of species. Worst of all is a species called the punk tree. This thirsty plant grows in swamps, creating a dense tangle of vegetation impassable to many animal species.

Figure 8-5 Sport hunting can endanger wildlife populations that are not carefully managed.

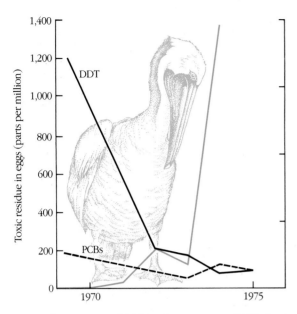

Figure 8-6 Banning of DDT and most uses of PCBs in the United States resulted in a dramatic decrease in DDT and PCB levels in brown pelican eggs and an equally dramatic increase in the number of eggs hatched.

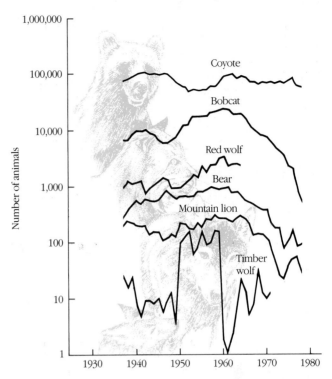

Figure 8-7 Number of predators killed by federal control programs.

Pest and Predator Control

Control of pests also influences wild populations of plants and animals. DDT and other pesticides have taken a huge toll on American wildlife (Chapter 17). The peregrine falcon disappeared in the eastern United States by the 1960s as a result of reproductive failure. DDT caused eggshell thinning and gradually wiped out the entire population of falcons east of the Mississippi River. Eagles and brown pelicans met a similar fate (Figure 8-6). Even the California condor suffered from eggshell thinning. DDT poisoning was, however, just one of many factors that spelled doom for this species. Among the others were lead poisoning (discussed above), loss of habitat from home building and farming, and fire control, which eliminated takeoff and landing areas needed by these giant scavengers, whose wings span up to 3 meters (9 feet). Especially harmful to U.S. migratory birds are the persistent pesticides, such as DDT and related compounds, that have been banned in the United States but are still produced here and sold to Latin-American countries. Birds in Latin America will also be hard hit, of course.

Predator control, once the cornerstone of wildlife management, has endangered or wiped out populations of wolves, bears, and other animals (Figure 8-7). Killing off predators creates an ecological backlash as the prey population balance is thrown out of kilter.

Collecting for Zoos, Individuals, and Research

Animals and plants are gathered in the millions throughout the world for zoos, private collectors, pet shops, and researchers. In 1983, for instance, more than 250 million fish and 4 million reptiles were imported into the United States. Each year millions of tropical birds are brought into the United States and Great Britain, but for each bird that makes it into someone's home, 10 to 50 die along the way.

Among this influx of legally imported animals come countless members of endangered, threatened, and rare species. Smuggled in, many of these animals go to private collectors. Thankfully, zoos in the United States and many other nations have banded together to stop the illegal flow of animals.

Plants are also high-ticket items. Cacti and orchids, for instance, are in high demand today and support a growing industry. Over 7 million cacti are imported each year into the United States from more than 50 countries. At home, collectors pillage Texas and Arizona deserts in search of salable cacti to adorn the lawns of their eager customers. In one area of Texas near Big Bend National Park, 25,000 to 50,000 cacti were uprooted in a single month.

Controlling the Coyote

In a quest to rid the world of pests, hardly a single species has escaped our attention. Those like the mosquito that carry disease are assaulted with poison sprays dropped from planes and helicopters (Chapter 17); pests that eat crops or weeds that crowd out domestic crop species are fought with an arsenal of sometimes deadly dusts and sprays; those that prey on livestock are shot from planes or smoked out of their dens, then shot. All in all, it has been a costly and time-consuming battle that, some say, is being lost by the newcomers, *Homo sapiens*, the technological species that is trying to carve out a niche of its own. The old guard, species like the mosquito, which have been around for hundreds of millions of years, may be winning in this war of wills. For mosquitoes and other insects genetic resistance is the weapon of choice, almost ensuring that the battle will continue ad infinitum.

Genetic resistance aside, some species exhibit a resistance to human control that boggles the mind. Take the coyote, for example. A predator and scavenger with an inherent fear of humankind, this small relative of the dog flourishes today on an ever-widening range. Where wolves once howled, the coyote now roams, feeding on insects, rodents, small birds, carrion of all sorts, and, yes, an occasional sheep or house cat or two that wanders too far from the safety of its home.

The coyote is an animal revered by some for its cunning and resistance to human extirpation. It is the environmentalist's cause célèbre. But to others, like the angry sheepmen of the West, the animal the Navajos dubbed God's Dog is a loathsome creature unfit to live. Controlling the coyote, one of the few large predators left in the United States, has become a national obsession of sorts, one that has sparked a heated debate that waxes and wanes like solar storms.

The heart of the controversy is this: Ranchers maintain that coyotes kill thousands of sheep annually, costing the industry $100 million a year. Environmentalists, on the other hand, assert that this estimate is grossly exaggerated. They put the damage at about one-tenth of that, and they argue that the environmental and economic costs of control, which exceed $18 million annually, far exceed benefits. They say, further, that we can control coyote damage at a fraction of the current cost.

Coyote populations have been "controlled" by a variety of techniques: shooting, aerial hunting, poisoning, spring-activated guns loaded with cyanide, trapping, guard dogs, and denning—burning or gassing coyotes in their dens. One of the most popular weapons before 1972 was a poison called Compound 1080, or simply 1080. Compound 1080 (sodium monofluoroacetate) is a "supertoxin." A single teaspoon of 1080 is so toxic it could kill 100 average people. A healthy adult who simply handles the meat laced with this deadly compound without gloves or precautions risks getting sick. A child who handles poisoned meat can die by licking her fingers.

For many years ranchers and government predator control agents laced meat and animal carcasses with 1080 and often dropped it from airplanes in an attempt to eradicate coyotes. Environmentalists protested. Although the poison was intended primarily for coyotes that preyed on sheep, they said, many nontarget species such as badgers, eagles, dogs, foxes, and raccoons also fed on bait and died. Such indiscriminate poisoning, environmentalists argued, was unwise.

In 1972, under heavy pressure from the environmental community, President Richard Nixon banned the use of 1080 for predator control on federal lands and in federally sponsored programs. That same year the EPA banned the chemical for commercial sale, effectively putting a stop to its use on private property as well. What convinced the EPA to remove the chemical from a long list of chemical poisons was 1080's likely role in 13 human fatalities and 6 nonfatal poisonings. The chemical, they said, was just too dangerous to humans to be used.

In February 1982, under intense pressure from the powerful livestock industry, President Ronald Reagan rescinded Nixon's ban. This left it up to the EPA to determine if 1080 could once again be used. Despite vigorous protests from the environmental community the EPA reauthorized the use of 1080 but only in sheep collars, beginning in the spring of 1986. Sheep collars contain small packets of 1080 in a liquid form and are worn around the sheep's neck, where the coyote typically strikes. When a coyote bites into the collar, it receives a lethal dose of 1080. The EPA has announced that it will sanction broader uses of 1080. For example, it may soon allow ranchers to scatter small cubes of animal fat impregnated with the poison.

Supporters of 1080 collars argue that this control measure is far more selective than other baiting techniques. It should eliminate only the troublesome coyotes, they say, and save a lot of animals that would be killed if 1080 were used more traditionally.

By all accounts, environmentalists should be happy about sheep collars, which are a far cry from the indiscriminate poisoning of days past, but they are not. Disgruntled that the poison is back on the market and that momentum is gaining for wider use, environmentalists argue these points. First, they say, scavengers such as ravens, vultures, and small mammals will feed on coyotes poisoned with 1080 as well as the tainted meat of sheep killed by coyotes. Consequently, nontarget species will continue to die. Secondly, unscrupulous ranchers could extract 1080 from the collars and use it in the old dangerous ways. Thirdly, critics are quick to point out that other less costly and less risky options are available. In Kansas, for example, only coyotes that raid sheep herds can be shot.

Case Study 8-1

As a result, Kansas supports a large population of coyotes and a healthy sheep population, and the costs of control are held to a reasonable level.

In many western states, where sheep are big business, ranchers release their flocks into pastures and mountain meadows (many in national forests) and leave them unattended throughout much of the grazing season. Managing the flocks better, say, by hiring someone to watch over them or by introducing guard dogs, could greatly cut down on coyote predation. Guard dogs have been used successfully in Europe for hundreds of years. Living with the flock, they protect sheep from marauding coyotes (see figure). The Hampshire College Farm Center in Amherst, Massachusetts, for example, has placed hundreds of its dogs in 31 states since 1978. The dogs' protective instincts are so strong that they need virtually no training. Pups are simply placed in a sheep herd early on and left with them. Exposed to sheep so early in life, scientists say, the dogs begin to consider themselves part of the flock. Lazily sunning themselves among the bleating sheep, they are quick to bound after any approaching coyote.

Guard dogs are one of the most economical and effective ways to control coyotes. A 1984 survey showed that 36% of the farms experiencing heavy predation reported no attacks after guard dogs were brought in. And because a dog can be leased for $50 a year, saving one ewe per year pays for the dog several times over. However, many ranchers do not trust dogs or are unwilling to try a new idea. And some are so used to poisons and other control methods that they look skeptically on this time-tested but forgotten solution. As a result, they continue to press for a relaxation of controls on 1080.

Guard dogs are not the only ecologically sound way to control sheep-killing coyotes. Other measures include the use of coyote-proof fences, noisemakers, and taste aversion. Taste aversion is still in the experimental phase but could prove to be effective. Ranchers inject a dead ewe or lamb with lithium chloride, a compound that produces nausea in any animal that feeds on the meat.

Many people believe that the sheep predation worsens while coyotes are raising their young. Studies show that coyotes feed on small rodents, insects, birds and other animals throughout much of the year. When there are young in the den, however, adults turn to larger prey. This means less time hunting away from the den. At this time in the coyote's life cycle sheep predation rises, for sheep are easy to kill. Control efforts should be intensified at these times.

Coyote control has frustrated American ranchers for decades because coyotes exhibit a great deal of resiliency. Following a heavy coyote "harvest," for example, females increase their litter size in the next season. The average litter of three pups can jump to seven to nine that year, thus negating control efforts.

What is needed, argue some biologists, is a way for coyotes, sheep, and humans to live peacefully side by side. That doesn't mean wiping out all coyotes with poisons or putting an end to the economically important sheep industry but, rather, a change in traditional management—most notably, a shift to more ecologically sound techniques, among them our faithful friend the dog.

Guard dogs have been used for centuries by sheepherders in Europe. This one is on duty in Colorado.

To reduce the ravaging impact of commercial cactus rustling, Arizona has made it illegal to remove 222 different plant species. With penalties up to $1000 and jail sentences up to one year, Arizona has made a small step to protect its native plants. Still, with a surface area of about 260,000 square kilometers (100,000 square miles) and only seven "cactus cops" to patrol the state, little can be done.

Researchers throughout the world use a variety of animals for their studies, many of which come from the wild. Demand is especially great for monkeys and the great apes such as chimpanzees. Taken from their homeland in Africa, as many as five chimpanzees die for every one that enters a laboratory. Fortunately, annual primate imports have dropped off rapidly in the United States and elsewhere (Figure 8-8). Despite this drop some rare and endangered species are still captured and sent to the United States. According to some sources, about 200 great apes are imported into the United States each year, further diminishing the chances of their survival in the wild.

In 1975 the United States banned the importation of all primates for pets, but it allowed continued importation for zoos and research. Because research animals often do not breed in captivity and because they have a high mortality, continual replenishment from wild populations is likely to continue.

Today, 60 primate species are on the endangered list. Researchers have exploited many of these species with little concern for their declining population or ultimate survival in the wild. Most people agree that research must continue under humane conditions but that it should not be carried out at the cost of extinction. One solution is breeding captive animals to supply zoos and researchers. Action now could stop the flow of these animals from their natural habitat and prevent the extinction of many primates.

Pollution

Pollution alters the habitat of plants and animals and thus contributes to extinction. Water pollution is especially harmful to organisms living in estuaries and coastal zones, where many economically important marine fish breed and spend their early years. Toxic wastes entering the food chain can have devastating effects, especially on the young, which are almost always more sensitive to pollutions than adults. The sources and effects of pollution are discussed in Chapters 14–18. A few examples will suffice here.

In the semiarid farmland of California's San Joaquin Valley, well-intended irrigation projects have become a major problem for wildlife. Farmers installed tile drains in their irrigated fields to prevent salinization and waterlogging (Chapter 7); water drained from farmers' fields was diverted to a series of specially built evaporation

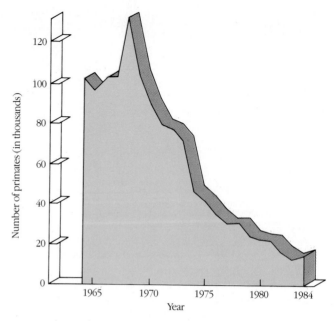

Figure 8-8 Decline in primates imported by the United States.

ponds that also serve as nesting and feeding sites for waterfowl, whose numbers, for a number of reasons, have dropped by one-third in fewer than 30 years. The Kesterson National Wildlife Refuge contains 485 hectares (1200 acres) of ponds designed to do double duty—evaporation of agricultural water and waterfowl habitat (Figure 8-9). In 1985 biologists found an unusually high incidence of abnormalities in chicks of waterfowl and wading birds at Kesterson. Chicks without eyes, beaks, wings, and legs were found, and many dead embryos were discovered. In natural conditions biologists expect a 1% deformity rate; at Kesterson the rate in some species reached 42% (Figure 8-10). Adult birds were also affected. Every day biologists recovered the bloated bodies of waterfowl. Crayfish, snakes, raccoons, and muskrats that once flourished in the rich biological community vanished. As the journalist Keith Schneider put it, "The Kesterson Refuge had become a place that killed the animals it was supposed to protect."

Water analyses quickly showed biologists the cause of the biological nightmare unfolding at the refuge. The toxic metal selenium was found in the water at levels a thousand times higher than was considered safe. The selenium (and other metals) had been leached from the soil by irrigation water and was concentrated in the pond by evaporation, wreaking havoc on the wildlife less than two years after the ponds had been built. Water quality was so bad that the Water Resources Control Board classified the refuge as a hazardous waste pit. To keep waterfowl out of the contaminated evaporation ponds, a team

Figure 8-9 The Kesterson Wildlife Refuge was built to serve a dual purpose: to provide waterfowl nesting and feeding sites, and to provide farmers a place where irrigation runoff can be evaporated. Unfortunately, toxic metals leached from the soil are poisoning the waterfowl in large numbers.

of rangers patrols them from dawn to dusk with shotguns and explosives.

The unintentional poisoning of the ducks and geese at Kesterson violated terms of the Migratory Bird Treaty signed by the United States, Canada, and Mexico. For that reason the U.S. Interior Department ordered the Federal Bureau of Reclamation to stop supplying irrigation water to 53 farms whose drainage water flows into Kesterson. Should the Interior Department stick to its decision, affected farmers would cease production of crops worth an estimated $500 million. The impacts on farm-related businesses and the general community would be staggering. The state of California is now experimenting with a small water purification plant near Kesterson, but so far the plant has proven unreliable; billions of dollars would be needed to handle the contaminated water.

Kesterson is only one of many examples of the threat that pollution poses to wildlife. Near it is an even larger refuge, known as Grasslands, where scientists have identified worrisome levels of selenium and other toxic metals. In San Francisco Bay the U.S. Fish and Wildlife Service found that two species of ducks contained selenium levels as high as those found in waterfowl in Kesterson. Selenium is believed to come from streams and possibly even aquifers draining into the San Joaquin River, which flows into the northern end of the Bay. San Francisco Bay is an important stopping-off place for migrating waterfowl. Surveys of waterfowl populations show that between 1981 and 1985 the population of surf scoters (one type of duck) fell by 80% to 90% and that of the scaup (another type

Figure 8-10 Defective killdeer embryo from the Kesterson Wildlife Refuge. Selenium and other toxic metals have resulted in a number of embryonic defects. This embryo has small eyes, a slightly twisted beak, and twisted and clenched legs and feet.

of duck) by 50%. Declining populations of striped bass and crab have also been observed. Selenium and other toxins may be largely responsible for this problem. Making matters worse, the Bureau of Reclamation is pressing Congress to fund a drainage ditch that would divert the toxic agricultural water now poisoning Kesterson Refuge to San Francisco Bay.

A recent survey by the U.S. Fish and Wildlife Service found 84 hazardous waste sites at 39 wildlife refuges and related facilities. Ten of these sites have contaminated the wildlife areas. The remaining 74 could present problems in the future.

◀ *Viewpoint*

Playing God with Nature: Do We Have Any Other Choice?

Norman Myers

The author, a wildlife expert and renowned writer, has spent 25 years advising governments on park management. He has written The Sinking Ark *and* A Wealth of Wild Species.

I still hurt to recall the first time I went out on an elephant-cropping foray. It's hard to forget the screams of terror, the fountains of blood, and the sudden silence, broken only by the clinical talk of the technicians and scientists.

In South Africa's Kruger Park, where elephant cropping is a fact of life, officials work under the seemingly arrogant notion that only humans can keep a park wild in this human-dominated world. I spent months agonizing that there must be a better way to deal with nature.

Eventually, I clawed my way to the conclusion that Kruger's approach is the right one—this arrogance, this cold-blooded dominance of nature, is our only choice—but that we must do it with great caution. Despite my realization that such management is necessary, it sticks in my throat.

When I first went to Africa almost 30 years ago, human communities tended to be islands of settlement among a sea of wildlands. Wildlife could go about untrammeled, and I could bask in the unadulterated spectacle. Today, it is the wildlands that are islands. Africa is bursting at the seams with people; population pressures threaten parks from Ethiopia to Zimbabwe, from Kenya to Senegal, making intensive management a bitter but necessary reality.

The huge Kruger Park, two and a half times the size of Yellowstone National Park, is no exception. A 950-kilometer (600-mile) fence surrounds the park, turning it into an island in an otherwise crowded land. That's where the trouble begins. Biologists theorize that islands, isolated from rejuvenating gene pools by water or fences or disturbed land, tend to have fewer species than a similar-sized portion of contiguous habitat. They are probably more susceptible to environmental change.

In fenced-off islands such as Kruger Park, wardens and scientists have concluded that they cannot allow the rich diversity of species to dwindle. To ensure diversity they have chosen to manage the park to the hilt, which is where this Viewpoint began.

The thought of the flesh of wild elephants ending up in cans in a supermarket may be incomprehensible or repellent. But that's what is happening, and for good reason—to prevent overpopulation and habitat destruction within the park. The alternative to control can be dangerous to parks, as I saw in Kenya. During the early 1970s the country was hit by drought. The elephants in Tsavo Park, already suffering from overcrowding, started to die in the thousands as food supplies shrank. People were starving, too. Yet park officials refused to allow anyone to touch the meat; they were aghast at the idea that the park's wildlife might be used to meet human needs.

Several years ago I returned to Tsavo and found that the local people were trying to acquire sections of the park for cultivation and grazing. One group of elders told me that their overall aim was to have Tsavo abolished altogether. "That park is an insult to us," one of them said. "We have a score to settle."

For their own survival, Africa's parks must take a lesson from Tsavo. Desperate, hungry people do not take pleasure in the pristine wilderness; they need food in their stomachs. Park managers must realize this. In protecting wildlife from the encroachment of humanity they can serve dual needs. Culling herds to eliminate overpopulation preserves habitat and ensures a sustainable ecosystem. In the process they can provide meat, mountains of it for neighboring peoples—reducing the animosity and making them more aware of the benefits of living side by side with wildlife.

But let us tread the path toward a human-dominated future very carefully. Once we have accepted such total management of a vast area, how long will it be before we go to extremes? Will we choose to eliminate species that aren't of any direct value to us? Will we begin to seed the savanna with "improved" grasses to increase yield, destroying native species uniquely adapted to the environment?

We established our parks as arks against a rising tide of humanity. Now we discover that it isn't enough to play Noah; willy-nilly, we are playing God. Let's do it carefully.

Outside of the refuge, birds and animals often fare even more poorly. Already, acid precipitation has devastated fish populations in southern Norway and Sweden (Chapter Supplement 15-2). Oil spills can locally touch off an ecological disaster with far-reaching effects (Chapter 16). Lead from shotgun shells is a fairly widespread toxic pollutant, which kills waterfowl by the tens of thousands each year. Hunters use more than 2,400 tons of lead shot annually. Waterfowl pick up the lead from the bottom of rivers and lakes. Others may be wounded but survive with lead embedded in body tissues. Predatory birds, such as the bald eagle, that consume waterfowl containing lead shot are also dying. Since 1966, 105 eagle deaths have been attributed to lead shot in waterfowl consumed by eagles. Because of the danger to the endangered bald eagle, a federal judge ordered the Interior Department in 1985 to ban lead shot in 22 counties in California, Illinois, Missouri, Oklahoma, and Oregon. Only nontoxic steel shot may be used in these areas. The National Wildlife Federation filed a lawsuit to force the U.S. Fish and Wildlife Service of the Interior Department to ban lead shot for waterfowl hunting in all of the lower 48 states. The ban took effect in the fall of 1987.

Lead shot in animals that are wounded by hunters and then die without being retrieved is thought to be responsible, in part, for the loss of the California condor, which once ranged from British Columbia to the southern tip of the Baja peninsula in Mexico and across the entire southern United States. Two condors in the wild died in recent years from lead poisoning; lead levels in remaining birds, now all in the San Diego Zoo, are alarmingly high.

Ecological Factors That Contribute to Extinction

Not all species are created equal. Because of peculiarities in behavior or reproduction, some are more vulnerable to extinction than others. Consider the passenger pigeon. At one time it inhabited the eastern half of the United States in flocks so large they darkened the sky. Probably the most abundant bird species to ever live, the passenger pigeon is now extinct because of widespread commercial hunting. Between 1860 and 1890 countless pigeons were killed and shipped to the cities for food. In 1878 the last nesting site in Michigan was invaded by hunters. When the guns fell silent, over 1 billion birds had been killed. By this time, the passenger pigeon was nearly extinct; only about 2000 remained. Broken into small flocks, too small to hunt economically, the birds were finally left alone. However, the number of birds dwindled year after year, until in 1914 the last bird held captive in the Cincinnati zoo died.

This tragic, oft-told story has a lesson: some species have a **critical population size** below which survival may be impossible. The passenger pigeon's population dropped below that level. The bird needed large colonies for successful social interaction and propagation of the species. Two thousand were simply not enough. This same problem faces the blue whale today.

Scientists know very little about the critical population size for many species. Overhunting, habitat destruction, and other activities discussed in this chapter can do irreparable damage before we even realize it.

Organisms can be categorized as specialists or generalists as we saw in Chapter 3. Specialists tend to become extinct more readily than generalists, who can exploit more food sources and can live in diverse habitats.

Animal size also contributes to extinction. Larger animals, like the rhino, are easier (and often more desirable) prey for hunters; they are also more likely to compete with humans for desirable resources, such as grazing land. Larger animals also generally produce fewer offspring, making it more difficult for reduced populations to recover. The large California condor, for example, lays a single egg every other year. Young condors remain dependent on their parents for about a year but are not sexually mature until age six or seven. Combined, these factors give the condor little resiliency to bounce back from pressures from human populations or natural disasters (Figure 8-11).

Another factor is the size of an organism's range. The smaller the range, the more prone it is to extinction. Finally, organisms often exhibit varying rates of tolerance to human presence. Bluejays and coyotes, for example, coexist with humans quite nicely, but grizzly bears move out when humans move into an area.

Why Save Endangered Species?

Aesthetics

As Norman Myers has written, "We can marvel at the colors of a butterfly, the grace of a giraffe, the power of an elephant, the delicate structure of a diatom. . . . Every time a species goes extinct, we are irreversibly impoverished." Wildlife, and their habitat, are in many ways a rich aesthetic resource. The sight of a female trumpeter swan gently nudging her offspring into the water for their first swim, the eerie cry of the common loon at night, the lumbering grizzly bear on a distant grassy meadow, the sputtering of a pond full of ducks, the playful antics of sea otters, the graceful dive of the humpback whale— these enrich our lives in ways no economist could figure. For the weary urbanite home from the office, the sound of migrating geese stirs deep emotions, a satisfying sense that all is well. Destroying the biological world impoverishes all of us.

Figure 8-11 The California condor is on the verge of extinction. With only 27 birds remaining, all in the San Diego zoo, the bird's future lies in the hands of scientists and zoo personnel. Hunting, habitat destruction, lead poisoning, and a low reproductive rate have resulted in the decimation of the condor population in the United States.

Ethics

Preserving endangered plants and animals is an ethical issue as well. What right, critics ask, do we have to tear apart the richly diverse biological world we live in? Don't other organisms have a right to live, too? Preserving life has become our duty, because we have acquired the means to destroy the world. With that ominous power comes responsibility.

Economics

Economically, it makes good sense to protect the rich biological diversity we inherited from our forebears. "From morning coffee to evening nightcap," writes Myers, "we benefit in our daily life-styles from the fellow species that share our One Earth home. Without knowing it, we utilize hundreds of products each day that owe their origin to wild animals and plants. Indeed our welfare is intimately tied up with the welfare of wildlife. Well may conservationists proclaim that by saving the lives of wild species, we may be saving our own."

From the biosphere we reap fish from the sea; medicines and other products from plants; important plant and animal genes needed to improve domestic crops and livestock; a wealth of wildlife for hunters, anglers, and nature lovers; and research animals that provide valuable insights into human physiology and behavior. The economic benefits of these wild resources are enormous. By some estimates, for example, half of all prescription and nonprescription drugs are made with chemicals that came from wild plants. The commercial value of these drugs is around $20 billion per year in the United States and about $40 billion worldwide. The U.S. Department of Agriculture estimates that each year genes bred into commercial crops yield over $1 billion worth of food. Similar gains can be documented for other major agricultural nations. About half of the increased productivity in corn over the last 50 years has resulted from "genetic transfusions" from wild relatives of corn or from corn's early ancestors grown now only in isolated regions.

"Wild species rank among the most valuable raw materials with which society can meet the unknown challenges of the future," writes Myers. Many developments from wild species now loom on the horizon and may offer us further financial gains and healthier lives. For example, the adhesive that barnacles use to adhere to ships may provide us with a new glue to cement fillings into teeth. A chemical derived from the skeletons of shrimps, crabs, and lobsters may help prevent fungal infections. An antiviral drug is now being developed from a Caribbean sponge. It has already proved effective against herpes encephalitis, a previously lethal brain infection that strikes thousands of people each year.

Plants and animals lost before they can be explored for possible benefits will diminish our opportunities to fight disease and increase productivity. A dozen regions located in the tropics and subtropics are the sources of virtually all commercially valuable plants and animals. They provide a reservoir of genetic material essential for the battle to fight disease, drought, and insects. Their loss would be a global tragedy with far-reaching effects on the food supply.

Ecosystem Stability

Finally, preserving species and their habitat helps ensure global ecosystem stability and, ultimately, our future. The endangered biosphere provides us with many invaluable services free of charge. It controls pests. It recycles oxygen, carbon, and dozens of important nutrients. It maintains local climate. It helps control groundwater levels and reduces flooding. Without these hidden benefits humans would be an endangered species.

Human civilization thrives as the biological world thrives. In the short term, wildlife advocates argue, a species lost here and there may be of little consequence for overall ecosystem stability, but in the long term the cumulative effect of such losses threatens our own survival.

Opposing Views

Critics of the animal protection movement argue that too much energy and money is spent on saving endangered species. Researchers and wildlife departments have spent millions of dollars to save the California condor, which still teeters on the brink of extinction (Figure 8-11). Tens of thousands of dollars will be needed to resurrect the dusky seaside sparrow, which once thrived in the marshlands of east-central Florida. A few critics argue that money would be spent more wisely on prevention. Other critics want to know why there is so much fuss over endangered species that block "human progress." Surely, a species lost here or there can have no great significance to us. The world will probably never miss the passenger pigeon or the peregrine falcon. And surely no irreparable ecosystem damage would result from the extinction of these and other species. Biologists argue, however, that if we take the attitude that each species by itself is dispensable, bit by bit we will destroy the rich biological world we live in. Somewhere the line has to be drawn: each endangered species is worth saving, because it stops the momentum toward widespread destruction. In growth-oriented societies this momentum may be difficult to slow down, much less to stop. Therefore, each hurdle put in its way becomes an important force in saving the living creatures that make up our web of life. In the words of the naturalist William Beebe, "When the last individual of a race of living things breathes no more, another heaven and earth must pass before such a one can be again."

How Can We Save Endangered Species?

Preserving species is not a simple matter; much work can be done on three overlapping levels—technical, legal, and personal.

Technical Solutions

Integrated species management is a diversified approach that attacks extinction on many fronts. Some general suggestions are:

1. Reduce habitat destruction by careful selection of urban and other development. In the United States, wetland and estuary destruction should be greatly curbed.
2. Establish preserves to protect nesting grounds and other critical habitats wherever they are needed.
3. Reduce commercial and trophy hunting when evidence shows that the hunted species is rare, threatened, or endangered and when synthetic products

can replace those acquired from these animals and plants.
4. Improve wildlife management by upgrading habitat and protecting "nongame" species.
5. Strictly control the introduction of alien species, especially on islands.
6. Design careful predator and pest control management programs so as not to indiscriminately eliminate nontarget species. Be more selective in using poisons, and eliminate them wherever possible by selecting environmental control agents (Chapter 17).
7. Reduce pollution of air, water, and land.
8. Increase public awareness of the value of wildlife and of factors causing extinction.
9. Increase public participation in habitat improvement, wildlife rescue efforts, and wildlife management (for example, by establishing hot lines and rewards for reporting poachers).
10. Increase private and governmental funding of captive breeding programs that raise endangered species for release and for habitat protection here and abroad.
11. Establish domestic breeding programs to generate research animals, rather than relying on imports. Eliminate unnecessary research on wild animals.
12. Toughen penalties and increase policing of animal and plant trade and poaching.
13. Promote international cooperation to curb the trade of endangered species.
14. Increase expenditures for all protective measures, possibly through new taxes or voluntary income tax programs under which citizens donate money to wildlife and protection.
15. Intensify research efforts to learn more about ecosystem stability and to identify critical plant and animal habitats.

The following examples illustrate some other technical solutions.

Zoos Lend a Hand Scientists at the Baltimore zoo are engaged in a unique program to save the endangered lion-tailed macaque, a monkey that has disappeared from the wild. Researchers first inject hormones that stimulate ovulation into female macaques. The hormones stimulate the release of a surplus of ova, which are flushed from the reproductive tracts of the monkeys and fertilized in petri dishes. The fertilized ova are next flown to the University of Wisconsin in Madison, where another team of researchers implants them into female rhesus monkeys, a common laboratory species. The use of surrogate mothers allow researchers to increase the number of captive monkeys and reestablish wild populations.

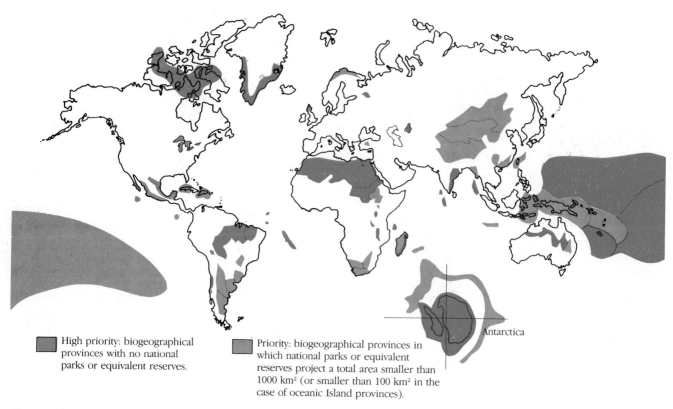

High priority: biogeographical provinces with no national parks or equivalent reserves.

Priority: biogeographical provinces in which national parks or equivalent reserves project a total area smaller than 1000 km² (or smaller than 100 km² in the case of oceanic Island provinces).

Antarctica

Figure 8-12 Regions in need of protection to preserve important wildlife and plants.

Zoos throughout the world have, for many years, been breeding endangered species in captivity to keep them from disappearing altogether and to establish populations that can be released into suitable habitat. One recent project was launched by zoos in the mainland United States in an effort to rescue three rare species of birds on the island of Guam, which are threatened by tree snakes. Eventually up to 25 zoos may participate in special breeding programs to rebuild wild populations of the Guam rail, the Micronesian kingfisher, and Mariana crow.

The future of America's remaining California condors lies in the hands of wildlife biologists and personnel of the San Diego zoo. The remaining wild condors were captured in 1986 and 1987 and transferred there, where workers are attempting to rebuild their numbers in the hope that they can be released into the wild.

Helping Third World Nations Protect Priority Areas

The world map in Figure 8-12 shows high-priority areas—that is, regions with high species diversity that are in dire need of protection. Economically, they represent our best investment in wildlife protection. Most of these regions, however, are located in Third World countries without adequate resources to protect them. Thus, a fundamental problem arises: the bulk of the earth's species and their genetic resources are in the poor devel-

oping countries, but the economically wealthy, "biologically poor" developed nations are the ones that will benefit from the genetic resources. For this reason, many experts argue that the rich should share the cost of preserving the tropics. A .1% tax on internationally traded oil would net $1 billion a year and would go a long way toward establishing and maintaining large reserves in these high-priority areas.

Beyond Habitat Protection: Germ Plasm Repositories

Preserving endangered plants and animals requires habitat protection. Wildlife, plants, and habitat are in many ways so ecologically bound together that one cannot be saved without the other. Realizing that much habitat is bound to fall to bulldozers and chain saws, biologists have been frantically searching through forests and fields to gather seeds for cold storage in **genetic repositories** (Figure 8-13). Here they can be held for future study and possible use. The U.S. Department of Agriculture currently supports the National Germ Plasm System, which has 450,000 plants in "stock" and plans to add 7,500 per year for many years to come. Third World members of the Food and Agricultural Organization of the United Nations voted in 1985 to establish a worldwide system of storing seeds, cuttings, and roots that can be used in agriculture. This system was created to thwart

Figure 8-13 Botanist replacing a seed sample in a cold storage room (0°F ±1°, or −18 to 20°C) in the NSSL where approximately 200,000 germplasm lines (individual seed samples) are stored for use by plant breeders.

Figure 8-14 Measuring only 8 centimeters (3 inches), the snail darter created a big stir between environmentalists and industry. The destruction of the snail darter by the TVA's Tellico Dam brought the multimillion-dollar project to a standstill. After years of debate, Congress ordered the dam to be completed.

"genetic imperialism" by the developed nations, which have been collecting plants and seeds from Third World nations, altering their genetic composition, and then patenting them.

However important genetic repositories are, this strategy has some major drawbacks. First, despite storage at low temperature and humidity, many seeds rot and must be replaced. Others undergo genetic mutation when stored for long periods and are no longer useful. Finally, storage systems will not work for potatoes, fruit trees, and a variety of other plants. The problems faced in germ plasm storage underscore the need to protect land containing wild relatives of our most important crops—corn, wheat, rice, sorghum, and potatoes. Such efforts will help ensure geneticists a continual supply of new genetic material.

Legal Solutions

Integrated species management requires laws that protect rare, endangered, and threatened organisms and their habitats. Today, however, poverty caused partly by overpopulation and resource shortages hinders progress in habitat protection.

In 1973, in response to the plight of wildlife and plants in the United States and abroad, the U.S. Congress passed the **Endangered Species Act**. This act (1) requires the U.S. Fish and Wildlife Service to list endangered and threatened species in the country, (2) creates federal protection of the habitat of listed species, (3) provides money to purchase this habitat, and (4) enables the United States to help other nations protect their endangered and threatened species by banning the importation of these species and by giving technical assistance.

Protection begins with the listing of an endangered or threatened species. Since 1973, 226 animals and 61 plants have been designated threatened or endangered in the United States. All federally funded or approved projects that might have an impact on endangered species must be reviewed by appropriate agencies, which can deny needed permits or ask for modifications that remove the danger.

Since the Endangered Species Act went into effect, thousands of projects have been through this process, and in most cases differences have been worked out amicably. The most renowned exception was the case of the snail darter and the Tennessee Valley Authority's Tellico Dam on the Little Tennessee River (Figure 8-14). Problems began in 1975 when an order came from a federal court to stop construction of the multimillion-dollar dam, already 90% completed, which would flood the fish's only breeding habitat.

The order was upheld in the U.S. Supreme Court. Congress soon established a committee to review requests for exemptions to the act. In 1979 the special committee refused to give the TVA an exemption, saying that the project was of questionable merit. The TVA applied more pressure on Congress, however, and later that year Congress authorized the completion of the dam. The snail darter was transplanted to several neighboring streams, where biologists believe it can live. Additional populations were discovered in several nearby streams.

The Endangered Species Act is one of the toughest and most successful environmental laws in the United States. "The real success story of the act," says Bob Davison, a National Wildlife Federation biologist, "is that there are species around today that would not have survived if the law had not forced agencies to consider the impacts of what they're doing while allowing development to proceed. . . . To a large extent, the law has succeeded in continually juggling those two competing interests."

To protect rhinos, gorillas, and other endangered species, governments throughout the world have joined in an unprecedented legal effort to stop the illegal trade in rare and endangered species. But in many cases inadequate funding makes enforcement a joke. Inspectors can be paid off by illegal traffickers of endangered species. Governmental agents can patrol only a small fraction of the poachers' range and, at least in the United States, the courts have routinely been lenient toward poachers. In 1985, however, a Montana man was sentenced to 15 years in prison for killing and selling protected eagles and grizzlies. Conservationists are hoping that this sentence, the toughest to be handed down in U.S. history, may mark a turning point.

Legal solutions can barely keep up with runaway population growth and burgeoning agricultural development. Nowhere are these trends more acute than in Africa. Without population control and strict laws to protect wildlife habitat, many of Africa's large herds will soon fade into oblivion. To help out, international wildlife organizations, most notably the World Wildlife Fund, have stepped in to help raise personal awareness and settle the conflicts between humans and wildlife. Population control programs sponsored by a number of organizations can go a long way in stemming the tide of human population that threatens wildlife throughout the world.

Personal Solutions

Millions of us walk into fast-food restaurants every day and order a hamburger and fries. In Japan, people flock to fast-food restaurants for sushi and stir-fried vegetables, which they eat with disposable wooden chopsticks. Wealthy Californians head for Catalina island for the weekend in their expensive hardwood yachts. In Central America, chain saws buzz in tropical rain forests; huge trees topple, and monkeys scurry for new homes in the outlying forests. Birds squawk and fly away, crowding into neighboring forests soon to be cut. The trees are hauled off on trucks to nearby mills, cut apart, and finally whittled down to make disposable chopsticks shipped by the millions to fast-food restaurants in Japan. Some of the wood will be fashioned into fine furniture, parquet floors, paneling, and high-quality coffins to bury the dead of the wealthy nations. On the barren forest ground ranchers

Figure 8-15 Volunteers head into an overused wilderness area in Colorado to repair badly eroded trails.

plant grasses for their cattle, raised in large part to feed the hungry hamburger crowd of North America.

The hamburger and chopstick connection illustrates the part citizens unknowingly play in the extinction of this planet's rich biological diversity. Through excessive consumerism, apathy, and unchecked population growth, we become a part of the problem. But it need not be that way. You can find out which products come from tropical forests and find alternatives. Share the information with your family and friends.

You can take a more active role, too. Members of a Denver group called Volunteers for Outdoor Colorado are working with local wildlife officials to protect habitat and joining other groups to repair badly eroded hiking trails (Figure 8-15). From Monterey, California, to Alaska volunteers are spending their free time improving salmon streams badly damaged by sediment and debris from heavily forested areas.

Join a group in your area. Contact your state fish and wildlife agency and find out what volunteer groups are up to. If none are active in your area, why not start your own? Begin with a simple project. Your wildlife officials will surely know of a few inexpensive habitat improvement projects that you can tackle in a day or two.

Since all resource extraction and processing affects wildlife, conservation can have an important effect. Shutting off lights when leaving a room, obeying the speed limit, and keeping the thermostat low in the winter will indirectly benefit wildlife. For further suggestions, check the EQ test at the beginning of the book. Your actions, combined with the actions of others like you, will cut down on pollution and land disturbance.

You can help educate others about protection of endangered species. You can join groups and spread the word through educational campaigns, lobbying, television ads, posters, books, pamphlets, and the like. Support organizations and politicians who fight against pollution, habitat destruction, commercial and trophy hunting, indiscriminate pest and predator control, and collection of animals and plants for research and home use.

Joining wildlife groups is one of the best ways to learn from dedicated experts with well-developed plans for wildlife protection. (See Appendix A for a list of organizations and their addresses). Some organizations such as the Nature Conservancy and the Trust for Public Lands purchase habitat for rare and endangered species. Others, such as the National Wildlife Federation, Sierra Club, Audubon Society, and Wilderness Society, concentrate much of their effort in the legislative arena to promote sound environmental policy.

Progress and Setbacks

There is much to be encouraged about in the battle to save endangered species. Fifteen years after the banning of DDT, many species are making a comeback. The bald eagle is perhaps the most notable. It now numbers over 2500 in the lower 48 states, and its numbers are rising. The number of brown pelicans, ospreys, and peregrine falcons are also increasing as DDT residues in the environment drop (Figure 8-6). The New York Department of Environmental Conservation reports that levels of persistent pesticides have dropped dramatically in many sport fish.

In 1982 Congress extended the Endangered Species Act for three years and added measures to ensure that species would be listed by scientific, not economic criteria. It also added tougher laws regulating activity in wetlands and requiring that all proposed development there be reviewed before approval. The Endangered Species Act was not reauthorized by Congress in 1985, but nevertheless Congress did provide new funding for the Act's measures through a Continuing Resolution. Thus, the Act is still in effect for all practical purposes.

Many species have made a dramatic comeback as a result of special breeding programs. Most notable are the Hawaiian goose (nene), peregrine falcon, and whooping crane. Protection of the sea otter in Pacific waters has revived this once highly endangered species.

Special preserves are being established worldwide to protect endangered plants. Twenty-one states have enacted voluntary tax checkoffs, which net hundreds of thousands of dollars for protecting nongame species. In Kenya wildlife officials have mounted an intensive campaign to stop the poaching of black rhinos. Several hundred rhinos will be herded into guarded sanctuaries enclosed by electric fences. Under pressure from several dozen environmental groups, the World Bank recently suspended funding for a habitat-damaging settlement project in Brazil's tropical rain forest. Funds will be disbursed only after Brazil agrees to establish protected areas and control environmental damage.

Despite these encouraging signs there are some ominous trends with possible dire consequences for wildlife. In many parts of Africa, Asia, and South America, for example, modern medicine is successfully lowering death rates, which is good for people but potentially devastating for wildlife. Oral rehydration, a new technique fast spreading in these countries, could save 5 million lives, adding to the population explosion. Further medical improvements could increase the annual growth rate in Africa by one full percentage point. For wildlife, an increase in human numbers means only one thing: increased destruction. Making matters worse for endangered wildlife and plants, many nations are developing economically; this will inevitably increase resource consumption and habitat destruction. China is a classic example with over 1 billion people; significant economic development there could have devastating effects on the ecosystem.

Despite multimillion-dollar efforts to save it, the California condor seems doomed. Destruction of swamps, coral reefs, estuaries, and rain forests throughout the world continues unabated. Lead poisoning among waterfowl continues to be a major problem. Each year 2 to 3 million ducks and geese perish from eating lead shot on the bottom of rivers and lakes.

More than ever, budgetary cuts are threatening to reverse important gains made in years past. A 22% cut in the U.S. Fish and Wildlife Service's proposed budget would precipitate drastic cuts in land acquisition, habitat protection, and maintenance at its 428 wildlife refuges. The endangered and threatened species program would be cut $5 million, significantly disrupting protection of plants and animals.

Poaching of rare and endangered animals continues throughout the world. Elephants are still killed for ivory in Africa. Cactus rustling goes on, and animal traffickers continue to deal in rare and endangered reptiles, amphibians, birds, and mammals destined for private collections, and almost certain death. This very moment in Africa a rural peasant may be taking aim at an endangered rhino. Miles away, a wealthy Yemeni proudly shows off his new rhino-handle dagger. The fight is far from over.

> *What is civilized in us is not opera or literature, but a compassion for all living things and a willingness to do more than simply care.*
>
> DANIEL D. CHIRAS

Summary

Species extinction is a natural phenomenon, which occurs during evolution as one species transforms into an entirely new one and also as a result of catastrophic climatic changes. Extinction has greatly accelerated in recent times because of human activities, including alteration of habitat; hunting for profit and sport; introduction of alien species; destruction of pests and predators; capturing species for zoos, private collections, and research; and pollution. Habitat destruction and hunting for profit are the leading causes. Today, one vertebrate species is believed to become extinct every 9 months, compared with a natural extinction rate of one species per 1000 years.

Numerous ecological factors also play a part in extinction. The **critical population size**, which is the number of organisms needed to ensure survival, varies from one species to the next. If a population is reduced below this level, survival may be impossible. Additional factors include the degree of specialization, position of an organism in the food chain, size of an organism's range, reproductive rate, and tolerance to human presence.

Ecologists argue that there are many reasons for protecting endangered species. Aesthetic considerations, animal rights, ethical responsibility, economic benefits, and ecosystem stability are all compelling ones.

We can reduce the loss of plants, animals, and microbes through **integrated species management**. Some general suggestions are to reduce habitat destruction, establish preserves, crack down on poaching and plant rustling, control the introduction of alien species, reduce pollution, fund captive-breeding programs, educate the public on the value of wild plants and animals, promote international cooperation, intensify research to learn more about ecosystem stability, and establish germ plasm centers to store seeds from wild plants that might be useful in improving the genetic stock of commercial crops.

One of the most effective tools for reducing the loss of endangered species in the United States, and to a certain extent abroad, has been the Endangered Species Act (1973). It prohibits importation of endangered species and sets out other guidelines to protect them. All federally funded projects that might have an impact an endangered species must be reviewed by the Fish and Wildlife Service or the National Marine Fisheries Service. The discovery of an endangered species only rarely results in the prohibiting of a project; in most cases only slight modifications need be made so the project can continue.

In additon to the many technical and legal solutions, numerous personal measures can be added: conserving resources, reducing waste and pollution, improving habitat, joining wildlife groups, and becoming politically active.

Discussion Questions

1. Debate the statement "Extinction is a natural process. Animals and plants become extinct whether or not humans are present. Therefore, we have little to be concerned about."

2. List and describe the factors that contribute directly to animal and plant extinction. Which ones are the most important?

3. Trophy hunters generally try to shoot the dominant males in a population. Natural predators, on the other hand, remove the sick, weak, and aged members of the population. How do trophy hunting and natural predators differ in their effects on the prey population? Use your knowledge of ecology and evolution.

4. Why are islands particularly susceptible to introduced species?

5. Discuss the "ecological" factors that contribute to species extinction.

6. Debate the argument "We must save endangered species of plants and animals."

7. Do we have a responsibility to preserve all living forms? Why or why not?

8. You are placed in a high government position and must convince your fellow executives of the importance of preserving other species. How would you do this? Outline a general plan for preserving species diversity.

Suggested Readings

Amory, C. (1974). *Man Kind? Our Incredible War on Wildlife.* New York: Harper and Row. A powerful book written by a leader in the wildlife protection movement.

Carlquist, S. (1982). The First Arrivals. *Natural History* 91 (12): 20–30. Good review on effects of alien species.

De Roy, T. (1987). When Aliens Take Over. *International Wildlife* 17 (1): 34–37. Eye-opening account of dangers of eliminating alien species once they have become established.

Domalain, J. (1977). Confessions of an Animal Trafficker. *Natural History* 87 (5): 54–57. Startling account of illegal practices in the animal trade.

Ehrlich, P., and Ehrlich, A. (1981). *Extinction: The Causes and Consequences of the Disappearance of Species.* New York: Random House. Good coverage of endangered species.

Hansen, K. (1984). South Florida's Water Dilemma: A Trickle of Hope for the Everglades. *Environment* 26 (5): 14–20, 40–42. Thorough analysis of habitat alteration in southern Florida.

Iker, S. (1985). Can We Live Up to the Law? *National Wildlife* 23 (3): 8–13. Superb look at what the Endangered Species Act has accomplished and how it works.

Jackson, P. (1986). Running Out of Room! *International Wildlife* 16 (5): 4–11. A moving tale of the effects of population pressure on Asian elephants.

Jackson, P. (1987). The Rhino's Fatal Flaw. *International Wildlife* 17 (1): 4–11. Alarming article on the fate of the rhinoceros.

Johnson, P. (1985). Smoothing the Way for Salmon. *National Wildlife* 23 (4): 31–35. Story of the work private individuals can do to help restore wildlife populations.

Laycock, G. (1966). *The Alien Animals*. Garden City, N.J.: Natural History Press. A popular account of the troubles created by species introduction.

Morell, V. (1985). Masai. A Proud People in Kenya Is on a Collision Course with Wildlife. *International Wildlife* 15 (3): 4–11. Superb account of conflicts between human civilization and wildlife.

Myers, N. (1984). The Mega-Extinctions of Animals and Plants. In *Ecology 2000: The Changing Face of Earth*, ed. Sir Edmund Hillary, pp. 82–107. New York: Beaufort Books. Well-written overview.

Myers, N. (1985). The End of the Lines. *Natural History* (February): 2, 6, 10, 11. Some new thoughts on the new age of extinction and the effects it will have on evolution.

Ola, P., and d'Aulaire, E. (1986). Lessons from a Ravaged Jungle. *International Wildlife* 16 (5): 34–41. Graphic story about the destruction of tropical rain forests and our attempts to preserve species diversity.

Owens, M., and Owens, D. (1985). *Cry of the Kalahari*. New York: Houghton Mifflin. Touching account of two wildlife biologists in Africa. Important information on behavior, ecology, and conservation.

Ralph, C. J. (1982). Birds of the Forest. *Natural History* 91 (12): 41–44. Excellent look at endangered birds on the Hawaiian islands.

Raven, P. (1985). Disappearing Species: A Global Tragedy. *The Futurist* 19 (5): 8–14. Good overview of species extinction.

Regenstein, L. (1975). *The Politics of Extinction*. New York: Macmillan. A must for all concerned with species extinction.

Schneider, B. (1977). *Where the Grizzly Walks*. Missoula, Mont.: Mountain Press. Excellent discussion of how humans contribute to extinction, especially through habitat destruction.

Schneider, K. (1985). Crisis at Kesterson. *Amicus Journal* (Fall): 22–27. Superb overview of the selenium poisonings, with an excellent look at irrigated agriculture.

Tanji, K., Lauchli, A., and Meyer, J. (1986). Selenium in the San Joaquin Valley. *Environment* 28 (6): 6–11, 34–39. Detailed account of the selenium problem at Kesterson caused by irrigation.

9

Rangeland, Forest, and Wilderness: Preserving Renewable Resources

Our duty to the whole, including the unborn generations, bids us restrain an unprincipled present-day minority from wasting the heritage of these unborn generations.

THEODORE ROOSEVELT

Space exploration has taught us a great deal about our planet and our lives. The first images of space, for instance, underscored the finite nature of the earth's resources. Humankind became more aware of its part in the web of life, a web held together by the thread of nutrients recycling over and over in this closed system.

In the early 1970s scientists pored over satellite photographs of the drought-stricken African Sahel, a band of semiarid land that borders the southern Sahara. Little did they know that another important lesson was about to be revealed. One of them noticed a bizarre piece of land amid the spreading desert. On the surface it appeared much like an oasis in the parched desert landscape. Curious to find out the reason, Norman MacLeod, an American agronomist, flew to the site. Here amid newly formed desert was a privately owned ranch of 100,000 hectares (250,000 acres). Its grasses grew rich and thick even though vegetation in the surrounding fields had long since died, exposing the sandy soil.

The secret to the success of this ranch lay in several strands of barbed wire. Stretching around the perimeter, this thin barrier held out the cattle of the nomadic tribes who had let them overgraze the surrounding communal property for decades. The ranch was divided into five sections, where a rigidly controlled number of cattle were grazed once every five years—further ensuring the ranch's survival.

Figure 9-1 Remnants of an ancient city in the Bamian Valley invaded by desert created by poor land management and drought.

The photographs of the drought-stricken Sahel reminded us of the devastation wrought by mismanaging renewable resources. "A continent ages quickly once we come," Ernest Hemingway observed. The Sahel is a case in point. But this was not the most important lesson. The most significant finding was that this semiarid grassland could remain productive despite the drought if it were well managed. Here inside the barbed-wired fence is a lesson crucial to humankind.

This chapter examines what happens to the world's **commons**, land that is shared by many people without control. It looks also at private lands, pointing out that in many cases they, too, suffer from poor management. Rangelands, forests, and wilderness areas are the key focal points of this chapter; Essay 9-1 discusses the unique problems created by off-road vehicles.

A Tragedy of the Commons

As far back as the days of ancient Greece, Aristotle recognized that property shared freely by many people often got the least care. Early civilizations toppled forests and carelessly overgrazed their cattle on their rangelands just as the tribesmen of the Sahel do today. History, however,

shows that early civilizations paid dearly for their disregard. The skeletons of buildings from ancient cities stand out in deserts that were once rich forests and grasslands of the fertile crescent (Figure 9-1). Much of Iran and Iraq, now barren desert, once supported cattle, farms, and rich forests. Greece and Rome fell, historians believe, partly because of the misuse of their lands.

Economists have debated the fate of common resources such as air, water, and land for decades. It was not until 1968, however, that much of the rest of the world became aware of the tragedy. Garrett Hardin, a prominent U.S. environmentalist, exposed the cycle of destruction in a classic paper called "The Tragedy of the Commons."

In England, Hardin noted, cattlegrowers grazed their livestock freely on fields called the commons. The commons fell into ruin, however, because of a lack of regulation. What doomed the commons was that the users became caught in a blind cycle of self-fulfillment. Individuals increased their personal wealth by increasing their herd size. Each additional cow meant more income at only a small cost, because the farmer did not have to buy new land or feed; the commons provided them. In his book *Filters against Folly*, Hardin notes that the cattlegrowers were rewarded for doing wrong. They realized that increasing their herd might lead to overgrazing and deterioration of the pasture, but they knew that the negative effects of overgrazing would be shared by all members of the community. Thus, each herdsman arrived at the same conclusion: he had more to gain than to lose by expanding his herd. This short-sighted thinking resulted in a spiraling decay of the commons. Over and over, growers increased their herd size, sharing the environmental costs with other users of the commons. Hardin summarized the situation as follows: "Each man is locked into a system that compels him to increase his herd without limit in a world that is limited." As each pursues what is best for himself, the whole is pushed toward disaster. "Freedom in a commons brings ruin to all," wrote Hardin.

The logic that compels people to abuse communal holdings has been with humankind as long as common property. Today, however, the process has begun to catch up with us. The deserts of the Middle East are a case in point, as are millions of acres of desert in the U.S. Southwest. The communal property of the Sahel is the most recent reminder. Outside the barbed-wire enclosure nomads graze their cattle on open lands. Each tribe can, according to custom, graze as many livestock as it sees fit. Heavy winds lift up huge clouds of dust, telling of the results. This chapter discusses the misuse of public forests, rangelands, and wilderness and points out ways to manage our resources more carefully. Subsequent chapters describe the problems created by the global misuse of water and air.

Hardin's analysis of the tragedy of the commons is an important contribution to environmental thinking. However, it misleads us somewhat by giving the impression that common resources stand alone in being abused. In many places private lands are no better cared for if short-term profit dictates management strategies (Chapter 20).

Today virtually all lands are gripped by the tragedy of overexploitation. A blindness to the concerns of the future is part of the frontier mentality discussed in Chapter 19. Short-term exploitation may have been permissible at one time, when the human population was small in relation to the earth's resources. Today such actions are intolerable. Too many people share this planet, and the cumulative effect of many small insults has become staggering.

Rangelands and Range Management

Rangelands are a vital component of global food, leather, and wool production. If properly managed, rangelands and the livestock they support can provide useful products indefinitely. If mistreated, rangelands, like other renewable resources, can be ruined. This section looks at problems facing rangelands and how they can be managed to ensure continued use. First, let's look at the problems created by mismanagement.

Figure 9-2 The Rio Puerco Basin of New Mexico, once a rich grassland, has turned to desert because of overgrazing.

The Navajo Indians live on a 6-million hectare (15-million-acre) reservation in Arizona, New Mexico, and Utah. Theirs is a sun-parched land, dusty and dry. Eking out an existence, the Navajos live in destitution. Making matters worse, the population has begun to skyrocket; unemployment has worsened. To feed and clothe their people, the Indians have gradually increased the size of their sheep herds. Today, the herd size exceeds the carrying capacity by at least four times. Baked by the hot summer sun and swept by fierce winter winds, the overgrazed reservation is becoming an arid dust bowl.

Southeast of the Navajo reservation lies another tract of parched desert land, the Rio Puerco Basin. Lying northwest of Albuquerque, New Mexico, it was the breadbasket of the state in the 1870s when the basin's rich grasslands supported huge herds of cattle. A century later, however, the land had crumbled under the strain of overgrazing (Figure 9-2). Erosion has formed gullies that widen by 15 meters (50 feet) a year. Wind and rain erode the soil five to ten times faster than it can be replenished naturally.

Rangeland Deterioration

Over 90 million hectares (225 million acres) of rangeland, much of it public land, have slowly turned to desert in the United States in the last 200 years. This is equivalent to an area one and a half times the size of Texas.

According to a recent study four of every ten acres of U.S. rangeland is in fair or poor condition. Figure 9-3 shows the lands that are most severely affected. The Soil Conservation Service estimates that three-fourths of all rangeland and pastureland in the country needs better management. In general, private rangeland is in worse condition than federal rangeland. The major culprit in this deterioration is overgrazing. The Navajo lands and

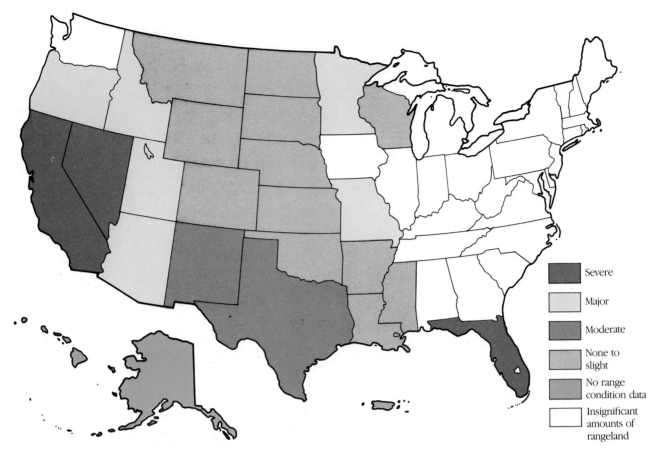

Figure 9-3 Damage to nonfederal rangeland.

the Rio Puerco Basin, discussed above, show the effects: severe erosion, a drop in groundwater, desertification, the loss of wildlife, and the invasion of weeds.

Range Management

The prospering island within the Sahel, discussed in the introduction to this chapter, provides living proof that rangeland can remain productive despite aridity. In fact, proper range management can benefit the land in many ways. Livestock, for instance, can help spread seeds and fertilize the soil.

Range management involves two basic techniques often employed simultaneously: grazing management and range improvement. Good **grazing management**, the first line of defense, requires careful control over the number of animals on a piece of land and the duration of grazing. **Range improvement** means controlling brush, revegetating barren areas, fertilizing impoverished soils, constructing fences and water holes, and similar measures to promote uniform grazing (Figure 9-4).

The key to proper range management is keeping livestock populations within the carrying capacity of the ecosystem while remaining profitable. This is often difficult, because carrying capacity varies from one year to the next depending on the weather. In dry periods the carrying capacity may be half of that in a normal year. Truly effective range management requires a willingness to cooperate with nature, benefiting from the good times and cutting back during the bad.

The **Public Rangelands Improvement Act**, passed by the U.S. Congress in 1978, promotes better range management on public land. It also calls for improvements of publicly owned rangelands currently managed by the Bureau of Land Management (BLM) and the U.S. Forest Service. Both agencies have guidelines for proper range management and attempt to manage their lands accordingly. According to some observers, however, the BLM's policy, formulated by a rancher advisory board, is not so sound as the Forest Service's, which is formulated by professional range management specialists and others.

This act also requires the BLM and Forest Service to reduce grazing where damage is evident. This strategy is not popular among ranchers, who either cannot see the benefits of improving range conditions or dispute the claims that they are overgrazing the land. One of the chief weaknesses of the Public Rangelands Improvement Act is that it does not pertain to Indian lands in the West,

Figure 9-4 Properly placed water holes help distribute cattle evenly on the range and avoid overgrazing of select areas.

where grazing reductions are badly needed. As a result of private and federal actions, U.S. rangelands seem to be gradually improving, but much more work is needed. Tremendous improvements are also needed in nations now gripped by drought.

Forests and Forest Management

Covering about one-third of the earth's land surface, forests provide many direct and indirect benefits. The most notable direct benefits are an estimated 5000 commercial products, such as lumber, paper, turpentine, and others, worth tens of billions of dollars each year. Forests also provide refuge from hectic urban life and opportunities for many forms of recreation. In many poorer nations, forests are a source of wood for cooking and heating.

Indirectly, the forests benefit us by protecting watersheds from soil erosion, thus keeping rivers and reservoirs free of silt. Forests reduce the severity of floods and facilitate aquifer recharge. Forest lands also perform many important ecological functions: they assist in the cycling of water, oxygen, nitrogen, carbon, and other nutrients and provide habitat for many species.

The United States has about 300 million hectares (740 million acres) of forest land (Figure 9-5). About two-thirds is commercial timberland, and most of this is privately held. Each year U.S. forest products sell for over $23 billion, making an important contribution to the economy.

Despite the great benefits of forests, only about 13% of the world's forest land is under any kind of management. In addition, only about 2% of the world's forests are protected in forest reserves. With world population growing and the demand for wood for fuel and goods rising, better management is badly needed to protect this renewable resource.

Worldwide Deforestation

Forestry scientists estimate that somewhere between 30% and 50% of the world's forests have already been destroyed, mostly because of clearing for agriculture, firewood production, and commercial cutting. In Nepal population pressures force farmers higher and higher up the mountainsides in search of land to plant their crops. Coupled with a rising demand for fuelwood, both for residents and for climbing expeditions that regularly visit the Himalayas, this has meant the felling of large tracts of forest, creating a serious firewood shortage.

Nepal is not alone. Africa has lost about 30% of its forests, while Brazil, the Philippines, and Europe have lost 40%, 50%, and over 70%, respectively. Besides destroying wildlife habitat, deforestation decreases sustainable fuel supplies needed for cooking and home heating. According to estimates of the Food and Agricultural Organization of the United Nations, 100 million people in 26 countries now face acute shortages of firewood. In rural Kenya some women spend up to 24 hours a week in search of wood. (See the Point/Counterpoint in this chap-

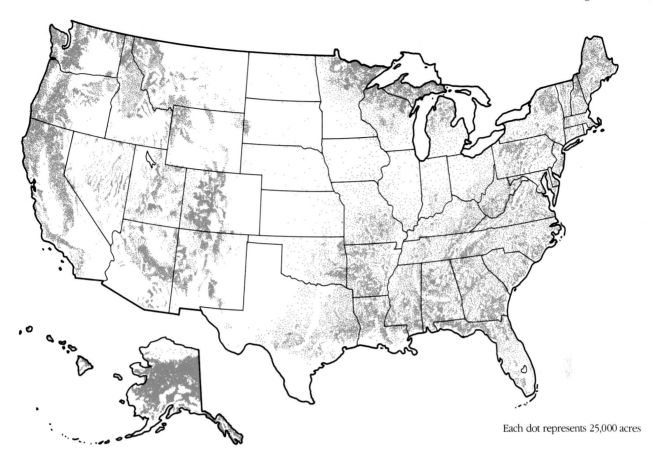

Each dot represents 25,000 acres

Figure 9-5   Distribution of forest land in the United States.

ter for a discussion of deforestation in tropical rain forests.)

The destruction of forests in exemplified by the American experience. When the first colonists arrived, forests covered about half the land surface of the United States. Soon, though, they began to clear land for farms and towns and to build ships, homes, and highways.

White pines were especially hard hit by commercial harvesting, which started in the early 1800s in New England. Proceeding westward as these trees became depleted, commercial harvesters reached Minnesota and Wisconsin in 1870. By the early 1900s the white pine had been reduced to the point that it was no longer commercially profitable to harvest. Lumber companies moved into the South to cut the slash, loblolly, and longleaf pines, but within a few decades most of the profitable stands had been felled.

Fortunately, the southern pines bounced back from heavy harvesting. The trees grow rapidly in the hot, open areas created by previous tree harvests and in abandoned cotton and tobacco fields. Today, under better management, pines support a profitable timber industry in the South.

Forest Conservation in the United States

Forests have been exploited for most of human history with little concern for long-term productivity. Commercial interests in the United States took an especially narrow economic view of the forests until after World War II, seeking monetary gain with little concern for the future. Fortunately, however, the federal government saw the need for forest protection. In 1891 President Benjamin Harrison established the first forest reserve, known as the Yellowstone Timberland Reserve.

President Theodore Roosevelt added more land to the forest reserve system. By the end of his term over 59 million hectares (148 million acres) of forest had been saved from the commercial interests. Such interests had been running roughshod over much of the public land. Many of Roosevelt's actions were at the urging of the noted conservationist and forester Gifford Pinchot. Pinchot and Roosevelt recognized that forests could be harvested without permanent damage. Carefully managed, such lands could continue to produce valuable timber for future generations.

In 1905 Roosevelt established the Forest Service as part

Essay 9-1

Off-Road Vehicles: Solving the Conflicts among Land Users

In 1947, in the bomb-shattered city of Hamamatsu, Japan, a 41-year-old college dropout and mechanic named Soichiro was rummaging through the debris when he found a surplus field generator. He took it home, strapped it to his bicycle, and with some additional tinkering had a motorbike. Soon afterward, Soichiro was designing motorbikes and motorcycles bearing his name, Honda. By 1960 Honda was selling motorcycles in the United States, and by 1976 he had captured half of the U.S. market, selling hundreds of thousands of motorcycles each year.

Honda's success was twofold. For one, the company sold well-built machines that were dependable and easy to repair. It also mounted a wide advertising campaign to clean up the image of the motorcycle user. Ads featured well-dressed, respectable-looking actors to convey the notion that decent, law-abiding Americans could also enjoy a motorcycle as transportation and a source of recreation.

The motorcycle movement grew quickly. In the early 1960s there were only 400,000 registered motorcycles in the United States, but by 1986 the number had grown to over 8 million, two-thirds of which are used off the road at some time.

Snowmobiles had a similar explosive growth. They were introduced to the public in 1959. Today there are over 2.2 million in the United States and over 1 million in Canada.

Dune buggies, four-wheel-drive vehicles, and the latest, all-terrain vehicles, join the legion of off-road vehicles meandering up mountain roads, tearing across open fields, and sloshing through muddy streams. Today there are an estimated 250,000 dune buggies and over 3 million four-wheel-drive vehicles, half of which are used off the road at some time in their life. All-terrain vehicles number over 2.5 million.

The off-road-vehicle (ORV) craze struck almost without warning, prompted by advertisements that showed drivers conquering steep slopes, charging through streams, and crashing through mud. Public land managers were surprised with the sudden explosion of off-road vehicles, and private landowners were often irate to find their property inundated by these sometimes-noisy and often-destructive machines.

Today, over 45 million Americans engage in this sport, and 50% of all off-road vehicle use occurs on federal land. As ORV popularity climbed, so did the conflicts. Private landowners, public land managers, recreationists, environmentalists, and scientists complained that the use of ORVs damaged plants and soils, conflicted with other forms of recreation, and adversely affected wildlife.

Snowmobiles

Snowmobiles damage the environment less than most other off-road vehicles, but their impact can be significant. Their noise, for example, disturbs wildlife, homeowners, and other recreationists, especially snowshoers and cross-country skiers.

Snowmobiles compact the snow they travel on. In popular snowmobiling areas in Minnesota scientists have noted that compacted snow is turned to ice and that this ice melts one week later than unpacked snow in the vicinity. This, they speculate, shortens the growing season for plants and could reduce plant growth overall. Compacted snow is also a poorer insulator than uncompacted snow; thus, in areas frequented by snowmobiles the soil freezes to a greater depth. This deep freezing may harm the roots of small plants and trees.

Tree seedlings are easily damaged by snowmobiles. Commercial tree growers report that snowmobiles break off the tops of trees, which may not kill them but often causes then to grow crooked, reducing their value for timber.

By compacting the snow, snowmobiles also impair the movement of rodents that burrow at the interface between the snow and the ground (subnivean space) during the winter in search of food. One study showed a doubling of mortality among rodents in an area used by snowmobiles. Packing snow on lakes may decrease light transmission through the ice by making the ice more opaque. This, scientists say, could reduce what little photosynthesis occurs during the winter.

Snowmobiles offer hunters and anglers access to remote areas during the winter, where they may overfish and overhunt certain species. For example, one group of 150 snowmobilers invaded a back-country lake in Minnesota and in one day removed 280 kilograms (560 pounds) of fish, nearly the entire population of the lake.

Finally, a small minority of snowmobilers harass wild animals. Chasing these cold-stressed animals can deplete their marginal energy supplies. In a weakened state they can fall prey to predators, disease, and cold.

Snowmobile damage can be reduced in a number of ways. First, users must exercise self-restraint and avoid areas that could be adversely affected, especially alpine tundra, private land, stands of new trees, and critical wildlife habitat. Second, special trails can be developed so snowmobiles will not bother other recreationists and wildlife. In Rocky Mountain National Park, for instance, snowmobilers are allowed to use the main highways, which in winter are closed to other vehicles, but they are kept apart from cross-country skiers. Third, snowmobile clubs can educate their members not to harass wildlife and to act reasonably around other recreationists. Members should be discouraged from using their snowmobiles when there is less than 15 centimeters (6 inches) of snow on the ground. Fourth, quieter snowmobiles could be developed. Everyone, including the users, will benefit (see Chapter Supplement 15-4 on noise pollution). Fifth, land managers must do a better job of regulating hunting and fishing in remote areas that are accessible to snowmobilers.

Other Off-Road Vehicles

Four-wheel-drive vehicles, dune buggies, motorcycles, and all-terrain vehicles do considerably more damage than snowmobiles, because there are more of them and because they are used at a time when there is no protective layer over the soil and vegetation.

ORVs have damaged land from Florida to Maine and from New York to California. No ecosystem has been spared. The alpine tundra of the Rocky Mountains and the Sierra Nevada and the arctic tundra of Alaska all bear their imprints. Wooded areas in Florida, Indiana, Missouri, and Colorado are scarred by inconsiderate ORV users. The grasslands of Kansas and Montana show the signs of damage. In some places the damage will be repaired naturally; in others, where damage is severe, natural repair cannot occur. Tiny trails turn into deep gullies that worsen with time.

ORVs scar land, destroy plants, accelerate soil erosion, alter the physical and chemical characteristics of soil, impair revegetation, damage wildlife habitat, destroy wildlife, and conflict with other recreationists. Especially hard hit are the wild and semiwild areas around many western cities such as Albuquerque, Phoenix, Denver, Las Vegas, San Francisco, and Los Angeles. The major problem with ORV use is that the terrain that most challenges the users and is, therefore, the most attractive to them is also most sensitive to erosion.

Large areas of the American desert, coastal sand dunes, barrier islands, forests, grasslands, and tundra are dissected and rutted by ORVs. In the tire-torn deserts of the West archaeological resources are being badly damaged. In particular, large human and animal fig-

Off-road vehicles adversely affect soil, vegetation, and wildlife.

ures, called intaglios, carved into the earth by ancient people are being badly scarred by tire tracks. Today, citizens working with the BLM are fencing off these areas to prevent further damage to these precious remnants of past cultures.

Vegetation is particularly hard hit by ORVs. Roots, seedlings, and foliage of small plants are crushed by tires. Plants are uprooted. Frames of ORVs tear limbs off larger plants. ORV damage has a ripple effect: When plants are destroyed, the soil's organic content falls, which decreases water retention and subsequent plant growth. A vicious circle sets in. In addition, destroying vegetation reduces ground cover and habitat for animals, increases soil erosion, and changes soil temperature with many long-term consequences.

Of the impacts of ORVs, soil erosion is generally the most severe. Trails used by ORVs for six years near Santa Cruz, California, are now gullies 3 meters (10 feet) deep. In other areas of California land used by ORV drivers for fewer than ten years has been so severely eroded that the bedrock is exposed. Erosion on trails removes topsoil and uproots trees and shrubs along the border of the trails. The sediment washed away by running water

is deposited downstream in river beds and on vegetation.

OVRs also compact the soil from 1 to 3 meters (3 to 10 feet) below the surface on popular trails. This compaction zone impairs root growth and impedes the penetration of water, thus diminishing plant growth and recharge of underground water supplies. Loss of shade-providing vegetation and the compaction of soil both contribute to a decrease in soil moisture in many areas; soil moisture may be decreased by 43% as deep as 3 meters below the surface on silty and clayey soils.

On hilly terrain the loss of vegetation increases water and wind erosion, often with devastating effects (see figure). ORVs destabilize sand dunes by destroying plants that naturally stabilize the sand. Moreover, once soils have begun to erode, reestablishing plants and regenerating the topsoil may become impossible. When soils can be revegetated, the costs run as high as $8,000 to $24,000 per hectare.

ORVs destroy the habitat of reptiles and mammals. Populations of ground-nesting birds, such as the California quail and snowy plover, can be wiped out. Large races with hundreds of motorcycles tearing across the deserts of the West are the most environmentally damaging of all ORV activities.

ORV Damage Control

Recognizing the impact of ORVs, President Nixon signed an executive order to limit their use on public land. President Carter amended this order with one of his own in 1977. Carter mandated closure of public lands to ORVs where they could cause damage or have caused damage to soil, vegetation, wildlife, and other values.

In response to the executive orders the Forest Service developed 150 ORV management plans for its lands. The BLM also developed regulations, but it has dragged its feet in implementing them. The BLM regulations made it possible for land managers to designate lands as either open, restricted, or closed to ORVs. Both the BLM and Forest Service regulations have made inroads into the problem of

ORV damage. In addition, ORV users have banded together and made considerable strides to educate their members on ways to reduce damage and minimize conflict with other recreationists.

But ORV damage still occurs. Some people continue to violate rules and common sense. Recent federal budget cuts will reduce governmental surveillance of sensitive areas and rehabilitation projects.

In light of declining federal budgets for land management, some experts say that ORV users themselves must patrol their activities, increase education, and learn to act more responsibly. Volunteer groups could pitch in to repair eroded trails. Increased state and federal taxes on ORVs could be used to fund management and enforcement personnel. Increased penalties for violations of ORV regulations could also help fund management and enforcement. More efforts are needed to separate ORVs from other recreationists, especially hikers and cross-country

skiers. Tighter regulations that prohibit ORV use in areas where it adversely affects wildlife, homeowners, nonmotorized recreationists, archaeological resources, vegetation, and soil are also needed. Governmental officials could develop special areas for ORVs. These could be used on a rotating basis to minimize damage and allow time for recovery. More programs are needed to educate ORV users on their impact and ways they can minimize it. Even basic lessons on the value of preserving the wild areas and maintaining ecological stability might help schoolchildren learn to act more responsibly.

ORVs are here to stay, say their supporters. They're a legitimate form of recreation. If their use can be better regulated, say some of their opponents, why not let them stay. But the price will be restraint, an exercise of common sense that reduces the damage and keeps incompatible forms of recreation well apart from one another.

---

of the Department of Agriculture. At this time the forest reserves became known as the national forests. Pinchot became the first head of the Forest Service. He favored judicious forest development over strict preservation. His ideas laid the foundation for U.S. forest management policy for decades.

Today the U.S. Forest Service controls about 76 million hectares (187 million acres) of public land in 155 national forests and 19 national grasslands. About half of the Forest Service land is open for commercial harvesting. The Forest Service lands have many uses other than commercial timber cutting, such as livestock grazing, mining, hiking, skiing, hunting, camping, and other forms of recreation. The Forest Service also conducts numerous operations—including watershed protection, recreation enhancement, forest management, range management, pest and fire control, and wildlife habitat improvement—all geared to improve the national forests.

Forest Service lands are managed by guidelines set out in the **Multiple Use–Sustained Yield Act** (1960). This law requires that national forests and grasslands be managed to achieve the *greatest good for the greatest number of people in the long term* (the **multiple use** concept). With so many interests competing for the national forests' eco-

nomic and scenic riches, numerous conflicts have arisen over this mandate. They generally involve environmentalists, on the one hand, and mining interests, timber companies, and resort developers, on the other. Central to the conflict is the question of how particular parcels of land should be used. Should a region be left for backpackers, hunters, and wildlife, or should it be leased to a ski resort developer? The controversy over wilderness designation in the next section illustrates one important example of the conflict.

Sustained yield means that the Forest Service's lands should be used so that future generations can reap the same benefits as present generations. This requires special erosion-control measures and, in some cases, reseeding to help ensure regrowth. Special controls on clearcutting, which are described below, can also increase the likelihood that forests will regrow after being cut. Many scientists believe that renewable resources in general should be managed under the sustained-yield concept.

Forest Harvest and Management

Trees are commercially harvested by three basic methods: clear-cutting, selective cutting, and shelter-wood cutting.

(a)   (b)

Figure 9-6 (*a*) Clear-cuts in the South Tongass National Forest, Alaska, and (*b*) in Kootenai National Forest, Montana.

Clear-cutting is a standard practice used primarily for softwoods (conifers), which grow in large stands with relatively few tree species. It is also used in tropical rain forests, which have tremendous species diversity. In clear-cutting operations loggers remove all the trees in 16- to 80-hectare (40- to 200-acre) plots, although on U.S. Forest Service land clear-cuts are now limited by law to 45 acres. Loggers remove the commercial timber from a plot and often burn the remaining waste. Burning this residual matter returns nutrients to the soil, facilitating regrowth and reducing the threat of fires that could damage the regenerating forest. As the new stand grows, trees are thinned to eliminate overcrowding.

Clear-cutting has numerous benefits. Perhaps most important is that it is faster and cheaper than other methods of harvesting trees. Clear-cutting also increases surface runoff, the flow of water over the ground's surface. This enhances stream flow and can increase the supply of water to cities, farms, and industry. Clear-cutting increases habitat for some species, such as deer and elk, a benefit to hunters.

Despite their many benefits, improperly sited clear-cuts can produce unsightly scars that may take years to heal (Figure 9-6). If not replanted or reseeded naturally, clear-cuts may suffer severe erosion. Erosion is especially troublesome if clear-cutting occurs on steep terrain. Eroded sediment fills streams and lakes, destroying fish habitat. Sediment also reduces the water-holding capacity of lakes and streams, which increases flooding, already more likely because of the elevated surface runoff. Erosion in clear-cut areas may deplete the soil of nutrients, thus impairing revegetation. Finally, clear-cutting destroys habitat and can contribute to the decline of many species, such as the ivory-billed and red-cockaded woodpeckers and numerous tropical species. In tropical forests clear-cutting is a prescription for ruin: soils become baked in the sun and too hard to support growth; others wash away in torrential rains. (For more on the effects of clear-cutting tropical forests see Chapter Supplement 3-1 and the Point/Counterpoint in this chapter.)

New regulations by the U.S Forest Service have greatly reduced the impact of clear-cutting in national forests, but on private lands clear-cutting is unregulated. There are 34,000 privately owned tree farms in the United States, covering approximately 30 million hectares (75 million acres). Large commercial tree farms operate much like agribusiness. Seedlings are planted, fertilized from airplanes, doused with herbicides to control less desirable species, and sprayed with insecticides and fungicides to reduce losses. When the trees reach the desirable size, they are cut down, and the cycle begins again. Here and in the tropics, large clear-cuts are the rule.

Arguing for smaller clear-cuts on private as well as federal land, E. M. Sterling, an expert on forest management, writes, "The forested mountains of the Pacific Northwest ought to be as spectacular as any in the world. Tragically, they are not. . . . For unlike those of Europe, the great mountain forests of the Northwest are being scarred by ever-increasing clear-cut logging on both private and public lands." (See Figure 9-6).

By comparison, Sterling notes, Austria harvests as much wood from its forests as does the Pacific Northwest. Yet Austrian forests show little evidence of clear-cutting, mainly because of strict forestry laws. What makes these laws unique is that they apply to public as well as private lands. Austrian law, for instance, forbids clear-cutting on all steep, erodible land. It also limits the size of clear-cuts. A private landowner may cut .6 hectares (1.5 acres) without permission, but must obtain a permit for larger clear-cuts. Seldom do clear-cuts exceed 2 hectares. Most clear-cuts are narrow strips that blend in with the terrain and ensure natural reseeding.

The lesson from Austria, environmentalists point out, is not that clear-cutting should be banned but that it can be improved in the United States to reduce erosion and the visual impact—for instance, by making cuts smaller and by blending them with the terrain. More efficient use of "waste" wood for paper or other products is needed. Restocking trees is also essential. A 1986 survey by the National Wildlife Federation showed that U.S. foresters operating on public lands in Montana had violated Forest Service regulations that require restocking within five years of harvesting. Of 600 logged sites surveyed by the federation, about 200 had not been replanted even at a minimum level.

Selective cutting is used on stands of unevenly aged trees or stands containing a number of species of different commercial value. During selective cutting, loggers individually remove only the mature trees. Hemlock, maple, beech, and a variety of other hardwood trees are well suited for selective cutting, because their seedlings require shade to grow.

Selective cutting has several disadvantages, cost and time involved being the most critical. But this technique leaves no scar, causes little or no erosion, and does little damage to wildlife habitat. Despite these benefits, forestry experts point out, it cannot be viewed as a replacement for clear-cutting.

Shelter-wood cutting is an intermediate form between clear-cutting and selective cutting. In this technique poor-quality trees are first removed. The healthiest trees are left intact. They reseed the forest and provide shade for their seedlings. Once the seedlings become established, loggers remove a portion of the commercially valuable trees. Enough are left in place to continue shading the seedlings. Finally, when the saplings are well established, the remaining mature trees are cut down.

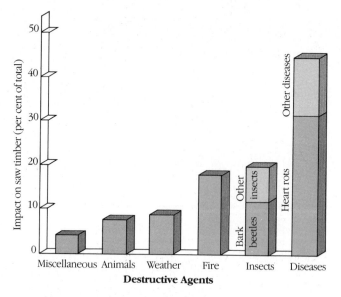

Figure 9-7 Causes of damage to U.S. forest expressed as a percentage of the total annual damage.

Shelter-wood cutting has many of the advantages of selective silviculture. It leaves no unvegetated land, minimizes erosion, and greatly increases the likelihood that the forest will regenerate. However, it is more costly than either clear-cutting or selective cutting.

Prospects for the Future: Building a Sustainable System

Between 1970 and 2000 the demand for wood in the United States is expected to double because of population growth and increased demand. By the year 2020 the demand for wood and wood products is expected to exceed the supply; clearly, something must be done. In general, two strategies can be employed: increase supply and decrease demand. Here are some specific suggestions.

Increasing Wood Supply by Protecting Forests
Protecting forests ranks among the best ways of ensuring a continued supply of wood and wood products. Clear-cutting, especially in the tropics, could be more carefully regulated on both public and private land. In particular, the clear-cuts on steep terrain could be reduced to decrease erosion that impairs regrowth. Reseeding by logging companies should also be monitored more carefully, especially on public lands. In 1986 the U.S. Congress passed an important law that prevents the U.S. Agency for International Development (AID) from funding projects in the Third World, including dams and roadways, that could lead to the destruction of tropical forests. The law

(a)　　　　　　　　　　*(b)*　　　　　　　　　　*(c)*

Figure 9-8 Benefits of forest fires. (*a*) Dense undergrowth in an Oregon pine stand results from the control of forest fires. (*b*) Controlled burning removes the undergrowth. (*c*) Periodic burning prevents disastrous fires, returns nutrients to the soil, and increases forage for cattle and wildlife.

also directs the AID to help countries find alternatives to forest colonization and requires it to support preserves and other measures to save forests and promote biological diversity.

Forests suffer from a number of natural hazards, including diseases, insects, fires, droughts, storms, and floods. As shown in Figure 9-7, diseases, insects, and fires account for most of the damage. Sound management of forest land requires that foresters use an integrated plan that maintains trees in a healthy state. This means that trees should be thinned and that soil should be protected to ensure maximum fertility and water retention. Diversity should also be encouraged, to reduce insect and disease outbreaks. Insect- and disease-resistant trees could be developed. Air pollution, which damages some trees and makes them susceptible to other environmental factors, should also be controlled. Finally, all imported trees and lumber should be carefully inspected to avoid accidentally introducing pests (Chapter 8).

Fire accounts for 17% of forest destruction, leveling .8 to 2.8 million hectares (2–7 million acres) of forest each year. According to the U.S. Forest Service, 85% of all forest fires are accidentally or deliberately started by humans. The remaining 15% are ignited by lightning. The lightning fires, generally much larger than fires started by humans, are responsible for about half of the forest damage each year.

To protect recreation, watersheds, timber, and recreational opportunities, the U.S. Forest Service and state governments attempt to reduce forest fires by posting fire danger warnings and sponsoring television and radio announcements. Each year the Forest Service spends about $100 million for fire fighting and surveillance.

Protecting forests from fire began with Gifford Pinchot in the early 1900s. It has no doubt saved billions of dollars worth of property and timber and countless animals. But ecologists and foresters now realize that strict fire control can actually be detrimental to forests. Fires are a natural event, with many benefits to the forest. For example, minor, periodic fires burn dead branches that have accumulated on the ground, returning the nutrients to the forest soil (Figure 9-8). Most animals can escape these minor **ground fires**, and living trees are generally left unharmed. Periodic ground fires also forestall intense, destructive fires.

In protected forests the story is quite different. If a fire breaks out in a forest that has been protected for one or two decades, the ample fuel supply may permit it to burn uncontrollably, spreading from treetop to treetop as a **crown fire**. Huge areas are destroyed in firestorms so hot that the soil itself is charred. Wildlife perish in large numbers. Generally, all living trees are severely burned and die as a result.

Periodic fires protect our forests from devastation. In addition, ecologists now know that many forest species require occasional fires for optimum growth. For example, the cones of the jack pine open up and release their seeds during fires. Douglas fir, sequoia, and lodgepole

>◀│   *Point/Counterpoint*

Deforestation of Tropical Rain Forests
Exaggerating the Rate and Impact of Deforestation

Sandra Brown

Ariel E. Lugo

Sandra Brown is an assistant professor of forest ecology at the University of Illinois. Her research centers on the dynamics of tropical forests and wetlands.

Ariel Lugo is project leader at the U.S. Forest Service's Institute of Tropical Forestry in Rio Piedras, Puerto Rico. He has been an associate professor at the University of Florida, an assistant secretary for the Department of Natural Resources in Puerto Rico, and a staff member of the U.S. President's Council on Environmental Quality.

There is no question that the loss of tropical forests is one of the more serious problems facing the world today. But we believe that deforestation rates and possible global impacts suggested by many popular articles are exaggerated. In this editorial we will explore the facts and fallacies of the tropical deforestation problem as well as suggesting some solutions.

Located between 23.5° N and S latitude, the tropics encompass a land area of about 4.8 billion hectares (12 billion acres) in about 80 countries. Most of these are developing nations with a high population density and rapid growth.

The tropics have more climate and soil types than any other region of the world. Rainfall varies from less than 50 centimeters (20 inches) per year to more than 1000 (400 inches). Seasonality of rainfall also varies widely. Average annual temperatures are generally hot in the lowlands but can be quite cold in the extensive mountainous regions. Using temperature, rainfall, and elevation, Holdridge classified the world into 120 life zones, of which 66 are tropical.

All ten of the soil orders are found in the tropics. It is no wonder that the tropics are reputed to have the largest number of plant and animal species in the world. The potential combinations of soil and climates are so many that an equally high number of possible ecosystems exist. For example, 32 of the 66 tropical life zones support forests, but because of the diver-

sity in soils and topography, the actual number of unique forest types is much higher. These tropical forests are not all "rain forests." Rather, almost half of them are in arid environments.

The most up-to-date assessment (1980) of tropical forests was made by J. P. Lanly of the Food and Agriculture Organization of the United Nations. He recognized two basic forest formations: closed forests, in which the various forest stories cover a high proportion of the ground; and open tree formations, which contain a dense grass layer. The closed forest formation covers about 25% of the tropical land area, and open forest formation covers about 15% of the land.

The tropical deforestation controversy centers on the moist forest, generally the "closed" broadleaf formations (97% of the total closed forests). There is reason for concern about the fate of the open forests: they have a slower rate of recovery and are important to millions of people.

Large discrepancies exist in the reported rates of deforestation and the assessments of the implications of deforestation on the environment. A report by the U.S. National Academy of Sciences and the Global 2000 report have suggested a rate of deforestation as high as 20 million hectares (50 million acres) per year, an area nearly six times the size of Rhode Island. At the other extreme, the FAO's report suggests a loss of about 7 million hectares per year (17 million acres), or twice the size of Rhode Island. People who support the high estimate predict that, except for a few remnant patches, all tropical forests will be gone by the end of the century.

The interpretation of the word *deforestation* and of the data explains some of the disagreement. By deforestation, we generally mean completely clearing a forest; selective logging does not constitute deforestation. Proponents of the high rates of forest loss, however, consider selectively logged forests in their rates because of the impact logging has on the forest structure.

The quality and interpretation of the information used in the various estimates differ significantly. We have reviewed the reports by the National Academy of Sciences and Global 2000; their reported loss is an educated guess at best. The detailed country-by-country report by Lanly is the most comprehensive and objective analysis presently available. We support his low estimate of deforestation of 7.3 million hectares (18 million acres) per year. We also point out that only about half of the clearing takes place in undisturbed forests; the rest is in already-logged forests.

Although the overall deforestation rate is much lower than many would have us believe, some countries have very high rates. Countries with small areas of tropical forests such as Costa Rica, Thailand, the Ivory Coast, and Nigeria are losing their forests at a rate of 3% to 6% a year. Unfortunately, there has been a tendency to extrapolate these rates to all countries. This is dangerous, because it ignores the fact that countries with large forest areas such as Brazil, Cameroon, and Zaire are experiencing low deforestation rates (about .2% to .4% a year). It also ignores the possibility that deforestation will decrease as the remaining forests become inaccessible or as countries undertake mitigation measures.

There is concern by many that deforestation will cause many species extinctions. Unfortunately, the relation between forest destruction and species extinction is not yet known. Whatever the relation, it follows that if deforestation is occurring more slowly, then so is species extinction.

Tropical deforestation is also blamed for increasing the global atmospheric carbon dioxide concentration and worsening the "greenhouse effect." This effect is clearly dependent on the rate of deforestation, but if the rate is lower than is often projected, there is much less to worry about. The carbon dioxide increase from the deforestation each year is less than 15% of the amount produced annually by burning fossil fuels.

It has been suggested that tropical deforestation will cause extensive changes in the rainfall of some areas. Scientists estimate that half of the rain falling on the Amazon Basin originates within the basin through a process of recycling. If the forests are greatly reduced, some say, rainfall will decrease, and areas will turn into deserts. But looking at it realistically, the average annual rainfall for much of the Amazon is about 250 centimeters (100 inches), which if reduced by half will not result in a desert.

The major effects of deforestation are felt more on the local level, especially in tropical countries where water is needed for hydroelectricity and irrigation. Deforesting watershed leads to changes in the surface runoff, increased soil erosion, siltation of reservoirs, increased flooding, and reduced stream flow.

What can be done to resolve one of the most serious problems facing civilization? The first step is to look at the problem with accurate information. Research on tropical ecology and forest management is needed. Next, management must take into consideration cultural, social, and political factors. Deforestation is as much a social and political problem as it is a biological or technical one. All sectors of society must pool efforts to solve a problem that affects them all equally.

The Demise of the Tropical Rain Forest

Alwyn Gentry

The author is associate curator of botany of the Missouri Botanical Garden. He is an active botanical researcher in Peru, Columbia, and Ecuador.

A century and a half ago the world's tropical forests covered an area twice the size of Europe. Today tropical forests have been reduced to about half that area. Many scientists believe that tropical forests are being altered at such a rapid rate—an area of tropical forest the size of Great Britain is lost each year—that they will all but disappear within our lifetime. According to a recent report by the National Academy of Sciences, the only extensive areas of undisturbed tropical forest that are likely to remain at the end of this century are patches in western Brazilian Amazonia and the Congo Basin.

The destruction of large tracts of tropical forest is a tragedy. Why? Certainly the majority of people in tropical countries consider conversion of forest to farms and pastures as "prog-

▶◀ *Point/Counterpoint (continued)*

ress." About half of the originally forested land area in the United States had been deforested and converted to cropland by 1920, yet relatively few extinctions occurred. Since 1920 the forested land area has remained at equilibrium, abandoned farms reverting to forest at about the same rate as forested lands are converted to new highways and urban development. Although one mourns the extinction of North American species such as the passenger pigeon and ivory-billed woodpecker, their loss is hardly one of the greatest tragedies of our time. Might one not expect tropical forests, too, to reach some state of sustainable equilibrium, just as temperate forests have?

The tragedy of the destruction of tropical forests stems from the fact that they are fundamentally different from temperate forests, a profound difference rarely appreciated by temperate-zone citizens. First, tropical forests contain a far greater number of plant and animal species than do temperate forests. One hectare of rich forest in the United States might include 20 or 30 tree species; a single hectare in Amazonian Peru can have over 250. Worldwide, at least two-thirds of all plant and animal species live in the tropics; only about one-sixth have been named. Second, unlike nutrients in temperate ecosystems, which are available in the soil, nutrients in tropical ecosystems are recycled in the living matter above the soil, which is often essentially a sterile substrate. Thus, most land, once cleared, cannot sustain agricultural production.

The first problem associated with deforestation is extinction. According to the recent Global 2000 Report to the President, between 1.5 million and 2 million species—15% to 20% of all species now on earth—are likely to be extinct by the year 2000, mostly due to clearing or degradation of tropical forests. Other estimates are even higher. This represents extinction on a scale unprecedented in history. Moreover, many species may become extinct without ever becoming known to science. The quality of life on earth will be diminished by a radically impoverished biota: a loss of the aesthetic beauty intrinsic in the diverse forms and intricate interactions of tropical life.

But the significance of the loss of diversity does not rest merely on arguments of aesthetics. More critically, we know nothing of the potential uses of the two-thirds of the world's tropical species. Loss of so many species is not only a tragic squandering of the earth's evolutionary heritage but also represents depletion of a significant part of the planet's genetic reservoir, a resource of immense potential economic value.

Fifteen years ago a person diagnosed as having leukemia had one chance in ten of surviving; today the chances of living are nine in ten, largely because of the chemicals vincristine and vinblastine, extracted from the vinca plant of tropical Madagascar. Vinca's cancer-curing chemicals were discovered because the plant is widely cultivated as an ornamental; how many undiscovered life-saving chemicals are being lost with each tropical plant species that becomes extinct?

Apologists for uncontrolled development like to point out that the relationship between the deforestation rate and the extinction rate is not linear—a 10% loss of forest cannot nec-

essarily be equated with a 10% loss of species. Actually, the extinction picture is much worse than the overall deforestation statistics suggest. One of the problems with predicting species extinction from deforestation statistics is that most surveys of deforestation measure tree cover, without differentiating between primary and secondary forest or between natural forest and tree plantations. Equally as many species extinctions occur from conversion of virgin forest to other kinds of tree cover as from clear-cutting, but this critical difference is not recognized by many. Only the National Academy of Sciences report cited above attempts to differentiate undisturbed forest from other types of tree cover.

Coastal Equador provides an illustration of this problem. Between 1960 and 1970 the strip of lowland wet primary forest along the base of the Andes was deforested after the first penetration of a road. Only one small patch of this forest (.8 of a square kilometer) now survives as the Rio Palenque Field Station. About 100 plant species new to science have been discovered in this tiny area, many of them represented by a single plant and, thus, bound for extinction. But perhaps 200 of the 1100 plant species of Rio Palenque would have become extinct had the field station not been created.

A second reason that the destruction of tropical forests is of global importance is the potential effect on world climate. Burning extensive forests converts their biomass to carbon dioxide, significantly increasing the world's atmospheric concentration and intensifying the well-known greenhouse effect. As a result, the earth's atmosphere could become warmer, causing glaciers and polar ice caps to melt (at least in the Antarctic) and sea levels to rise, perhaps eventually inundating coastal cities. However, the contribution to atmospheric carbon dioxide of tropical forest burning is far less than the massive conversion of fossil fuels to carbon dioxide.

On a more local scale tropical deforestation results in major changes in hydrologic balances and rainfall regimes. Clear-cutting of the forest may therefore result in a 50% decrease in rainfall in the region, converting much of the present forested area to near desert. Removing the tree cover in headwater areas also leads to rapid runoff, with increased erosion upstream and increased flooding downstream, a process that is already economically devastating in India and Pakistan and is beginning to become apparent in the Amazon and Orinoco basins.

A third problem associated with tropical deforestation is economic. In general, highly leached tropical lowland soils are incapable of supporting sustainable agricultural yields without massive infusions of costly fertilizers. Lush, high-biomass tropical forests represent the end point of a very gradual accumulation of tightly held nutrients, continually recycled through the ecosystem over millenia. Cutting and burning the forest releases sufficient nutrients for a few years of crop production before the ashes and their nutrient residue are washed away and the soil is incapable of crop production.

Small-scale slash-and-burn agriculture mimics the natural system of tree fall and regeneration from the surrounding forest. However, fallow periods of 50 or more years may be necessary before the process can be repeated profitably, making it impossible to maintain large populations permanently by this method. Available data suggest that when cutting and burning of trees is carried out intensively on a regional scale, tropical forests do not regenerate; instead, a permanent second-growth scrub may result when the soil fertility is exhausted and the fields are abandoned. Tremendous areas of the tropics have been converted to this sad state. A well-known example is the Zona Braganca south of Belém, Brazil, where hundreds of square kilometers of now-abandoned scrub provide mute evidence of the failure of the large-scale agricultural development undertaken in the 1960s. Increasing population pressures mean that this process will occur on such a large scale that forest regrowth may never be possible. The tragedy lies in the fact that tropical forests, utilized wisely, are almost certainly capable of producing far more revenue on a sustainable basis, but only when forest cover is maintained and resource harvests are controlled. Promising plans have been suggested for combinations of tree crops and small garden plots interspersed with areas of natural forest for hardwood lumber production.

Unfortunately, most of the world's tropical countries are engaged in a most shortsighted, Faustian bargain, postponing until too late the politically unpopular decision to control forest destruction. Meanwhile, temperate-zone countries have fallen far short in investing financial resources for research into tropical forest ecosystems and into eventually developing sustainable systems of land utilization that can support the burgeoning populations of tropical countries.

The global challenge to humankind posed by ever more people and fewer resources on a finite "spaceship earth" has been noted for some time. We are coming face to face with this problem in the tropical forests. The National Academy of Sciences report concludes that if tropical forest destruction continues at its present rate into the 21st century, it will lead to widespread human misery as well as fundamental alteration in the course of worldwide evolution. Relatively small investments now in research, population control, and land-use planning might well preserve this unique part of the world's biotic heritage indefinitely, with every citizen of the world demonstrably better off.

pines also require periodic fires for seed release. As we have seen, fires return nutrients to the soil and remove brush that shades seedlings. They also help reduce disease and control insect populations.

Recognizing the benefits of periodic ground fires, forest managers now let many naturally occurring forest fires burn, provided they are not a threat to human settlements. The Forest Service also starts hundreds of fires each year to remove underbrush and litter, not only to reduce the chances of potentially harmful crown fires but also to improve wildlife habitat, soil fertility, and timber production and to increase livestock forage. These **prescribed fires** are set at times when the danger of their getting out of hand is low.

Increasing Supply by Reducing Waste Waste materials such as limbs, bark, and branches can be used for fuel, paper, and a variety of paper products. Some companies grind these materials into chips that are burned for energy or used for the production of paper or chipboard (particle board). The Masonite Corporation recently installed a $6 million system to generate energy from wastewood. It paid for itself in energy savings in a mere 18 months. Less desirable trees can be converted into paper and other products that require lower quality wood. As a result, forest yield can increase by 200%.

Decreasing Demand: The Personal Connection
Recycling paper and more judicious use of wood products can help reduce future demands. Each year 1250 acres of Canadian forest are cut down to supply wood pulp for newsprint for the Sunday edition of the *New York Times*. Increased recycling of newsprint could reduce the amount of forest cut down each year.

The average American consumes over 272 kilograms (600 pounds) of wood in the form of lumber and paper. This is 4.5 times what the average European consumes and 40 times what citizens of the less developed countries use. Individuals could reduce overall consumption, for example, by recycling at home and at work, by using the backs of scrap paper for homework and notes, by carrying our own shopping bags to the store and by choosing not to use a bag for small items. The constant bombardment of advertising material can be stopped by writing companies and asking them to take you off their lists. To cut lumber use, smaller homes can be built, using 20% to 30% less wood. Earth-sheltered housing, discussed in Chapter 12, can also reduce our demand for wood while drastically cutting fuel consumption.

Wilderness

Nineteen eighty-four was a banner year for wilderness protection in the United States. President Reagan signed

Figure 9-9 Wilderness restores us. It is a vital resource in our world.

into law a bill that added 3.5 million hectares (8.6 million acres) to the **National Wilderness Preservation System**. To some people—loggers and miners, especially—designating these lands as wilderness presents a roadblock to economic progress. To others, such as hikers and backpackers, it was a sign of hope.

Wilderness, defined by U.S. law, is "an area where the earth and its community of life are untrammeled by man, where man is himself a visitor who does not remain." Wilderness provides a temporary escape from modern society (Figure 9-9). Joseph Sax, author of *Mountains without Handrails*, writes that nature "seems to have a peculiar power to stimulate us to reflectiveness by its awesomeness and grandeur." It helps us understand ourselves and the world we live in, awakening us to the forgotten interdependence of living things. "Our initial response to nature," Sax writes, "is often awe and wonderment: trees that have survived for millenia; a profusion

of flowers in the seeming sterility of the desert; predator and prey living in equilibrium. . . . [It] is also a successful model of many things that human communities seek: continuity, stability and sustenance, adaptation, sustained productivity, diversity, and evolutionary change."

But not everyone would agree. To many people, wilderness is the playground of the upper middle class, an elite group that is fighting to protect these lands and hinder the chances that others might reap some economic benefit, especially jobs created by mining and timber harvesting. Their view is probably more typical of the way most people throughout most of human history have seen undeveloped lands; historically, wilderness has been viewed as something to subdue, something to exploit for short-term gain. In early colonial and postcolonial times, American lands represented untapped wealth—an unequaled opportunity to sustain a young, growing nation. The concept of wilderness preservation, had it arisen at this time, would have seemed absurd. Today, some critics agree: wilderness designation locks up valuable resources (minerals and timber) needed by humans. Such conflicting views inevitably make compromise necessary.

Preservation: The Wilderness Act

The earliest efforts at wilderness preservation in the United States began in the 1860s. John Muir, founder of the Sierra Club and a longtime wilderness advocate, is credited with much of the early interest in saving wilderness for future generations. Further advances came in the 1930s, when the U.S. Forest Service began to set aside large tracts of forest land, called **primitive areas**, for protection. Between 1930 and 1964 the Forest Service established over 3.7 million hectares (9.1 million acres) of primitive areas in the national forests.

In 1964 Congress passed the **Wilderness Act**, establishing the National Wilderness Preservation System. The Forest Service's primitive areas were renamed **wilderness areas**, tracts of land with restricted use. The Wilderness Act forbids timber cutting, motorized vehicles, motorboats, aircraft landings, and other motorized equipment (for example, chain saws), except to control fire, insects, and diseases or where their use was already established.

The Wilderness Act sought to create an "enduring wilderness," but many unwildernesslike activities were allowed to continue: livestock grazing and mining for metals and energy fuels, if claims were filed before the end of 1983.

The Wilderness Act also directed the Forest Service, the Fish and Wildlife Service, and the National Park Service to recommend land within their jurisdictions for wilderness designation. Nearly 13 million hectares (32 million acres) of land is now protected as wilderness, mostly within the national forests. The Wilderness Act failed to consider BLM land for wilderness designation. The BLM controls vast acreages in Alaska and the West (a total of 180 million hectares, or 450 million acres). This serious omission was corrected by the **Federal Land Policy and Management Act** (1976). It calls on the BLM to submit recommendations on the wilderness suitability of its land. By 1985, however, only 147,000 hectares (369,000 acres) of BLM land had been added to the system. An additional 9.8 million hectares (24.6 million acres) had been submitted to Congress by the BLM for wilderness designation.

Controversy over Wilderness Designation

Nothing heats the waters like wilderness designation. Environmentalists continually press for more land to be set aside; the mining and timber industries generally oppose wilderness designation because it locks up valuable resources. In the battles that ensue, environmentalists are accused of being elitists who want to exclude others from profiting from the earth's riches. Wilderness protection, critics say, costs Americans jobs. Ecologists and environmentalists note, however, that wilderness experiences and the ecological benefits provided by wilderness (erosion control, habitat protection, recycling of nutrients, and so forth) cannot be translated into dollars and cents, whereas the profit from lumber and mineral ores is easily put into economic terms. This makes it difficult for the nonenvironmentalists to understand their case.

The timber industry is one of the strongest opponents of wilderness designation. Since only slightly over 8% of all government land, or about 3.5% of all land in the United States, has been given wilderness protection, environmentalists argue that the timber industry's claims that wilderness is locking up our earthly riches are unfounded. Locally, however, wilderness tracts can tie up huge parcels of land, threatening the economic well-being of communities that have long made a living by timber harvesting.

Mining interests also argue that minerals are being locked up by the National Wilderness Preservation System. If anything, many environmentalists argue, the mining interests have been catered to in excess; by allowing some mining in wilderness areas, Congress has acted against the best interests of preservation, since mining conflicts with wilderness as much as any human activity could.

Wilderness advocates are pushing for more wilderness. But should we continue to set aside wilderness, especially if it contains oil, natural gas, or minerals that could be used today? Many environmentalists believe that wildlands are more valuable than these resources, because there are no substitutes for them once they have been destroyed. And, they note, there are many ways to expand our energy and mineral resources besides additional mining. (Some of these options are discussed in Chapter 12 and 13). Environmentalists also argue that continued population growth necessitates an expansion of wilderness. But mining and timber interests validly point out that people also need minerals, wood, and wood products. Locking up the wilderness limits economic development today and in the future.

The Wilderness Curse

Lured by the thought of quiet and solitude, backpackers pour into some U.S. wilderness areas only to be dismayed by the crowds and special camping restrictions enforced by the Forest Service to protect lakes and streams from pollution. To many this overcrowding is a sign of the need for more wilderness, especially if the U.S. population is to grow by 70 million people before it stabilizes, as many demographers now predict (Chapter 5). To others it is an example of one of the major problems caused by designating an area as wilderness—people are attracted, ultimately destroying the wilderness experience for many.

Wilderness crowding and the resulting environmental degradation can be reduced or eliminated by (1) educating campers on ways to lessen their impact, (2) restricting access to overused areas, (3) issuing permits to control the number of users, (4) designating where backpackers can camp, (5) increasing the number of wilderness rangers (even volunteers) to patrol areas and also pick up garbage and monitor use, (6) disseminating information about infrequently used areas to divert campers from overused areas, and (7) improving trails to encourage use of currently underutilized areas.

Wilderness, rangeland, and forest are all part of our lives. They cater to many different needs—eating, shelter, relaxation, and escape. A world without them is almost unimaginable. A group of scientists peering through the glass of their space shuttle 100 years from now will see the evidence of our actions today. Whether they see patches of ancient desert among rich, productive land or just the opposite depends on actions and decisions we make today.

The art of progress is to preserve order amid change.

A. N. WHITEHEAD

Summary

Our land, water, and air are in many ways akin to the commons where the English once grazed their livestock. Without regulation, the commons fell into a cycle of decay. Each cattle grower increased his herd to increase personal gain, bringing ruin to the unmanaged commons. A similar fate awaits the global commons without decisive action now.

The misuse of biospheric resources is not limited to those held in common. Private land is, in many cases, treated with similar disregard.

Rangelands are a vital component of global food production. A history of overgrazing has resulted in the deterioration of both private and public rangelands, resulting in permanent loss of vegetation, erosion, desertification, wildlife extinction, invasion of weeds, and a drop in water tables. **Range management** helps us avoid these problems through two major strategies: **grazing management**, control of the number of animals on a piece of land and the duration of grazing, and **range improvement**, such as fertilizing, reseeding, and the use of techniques to encourage uniform grazing.

Forests benefit society directly by providing numerous commercially valuable products, such as wood and paper, and also by providing opportunities for recreation. Indirectly, forests benefit us by protecting watersheds from soil erosion; by reducing surface runoff; by recycling water, oxygen, carbon, and other important nutrients; and by providing habitat for a diversity of species.

Worldwide, millions of hectares of forest have been cut down. In the United States forest protection began in the late 1800s. In 1905 President Theodore Roosevelt established the Forest Service. Its first head, Gifford Pinchot, promoted careful use of forests over strict preservation. His notions of multiple and sustained use have persisted. Today the Forest Service manages lands for commercial timber cutting, grazing of livestock, mining, and recreation.

The demand for wood and wood products in the United States is expected to exceed the supply by the year 2020. To ease the crunch two strategies can be used: increasing the supply and reducing the demand. Increasing the supply means taking better care of forests and reducing forestry wastes. Decreasing the demand means recycling and cutting down on unnecessary use of wood.

Wilderness is defined by U.S. law as "an area where the earth and its community of life are untrammeled by man, where man is himself a visitor who does not remain." For some people wilderness provides an escape from hectic urban life, a chance to watch animals, exercise, or relax. To others it is an untapped resource with valuable minerals and timber. Because of such divergent views much controversy surrounds efforts to set wilderness aside.

In 1964 the U.S. Congress passed the Wilderness Act, which established **wilderness areas** within land owned by the National Park Service, Fish and Wildlife Service, and Forest Service. The law prohibits timber cutting and motorized vehicles and equipment except in certain instances. Mining can take place in designated wilderness areas as long as claims were filed before the end of 1983.

Even though many commercial interests continue to fight wilderness preservation, with local support, conservationists note that rising population and the fact that more people are turning to outdoor recreation necessitates more wilderness to avoid overcrowding and damage. Additional solutions include educating campers on ways to minimize impact, restricting access to overused areas, controlling the number of users, increasing the number of wilderness rangers patrolling areas and picking up garbage, disseminating information about infrequently used areas, and improving trails to encourage the use of underutilized regions.

Discussion Questions

1. Discuss the tragedy of the commons. Give some specific examples of "commons" and how they are mistreated.

2. What are the major problems facing rangelands in the United States? What suggestions would you make to improve the condition of American rangelands and better manage them?

3. Define the following terms as they relate forest to management: *sustained yield, multiple use*, and *clear-cutting*.

4. Why are many foresters intentionally burning forests or letting some forest fires burn?

5. List and discuss ways to satisfy the growing need for wood and wood products in the coming years. Which of your ideas are the most ecologically sound? How would you carry out your ideas if you were an elected official?

6. In what ways can you personally reduce paper and wood waste and increase recycling?

7. What are the major arguments for and against wilderness preservation?

Suggested Readings

Chiras, D. (1986). *Camp without Impact*. Denver: Wind River Publications and Volunteers for Outdoor Colorado. A pamphlet outlining ways to reduce damage to wilderness. See Appendix B for the address of the volunteer group.

Clawson, M. (1983). Reassessing Public Lands Policy. *Environment* 25 (8): 6–17. Thoughtful look at managing public lands.

Eckholm, E. (1982). *Down to Earth: Environment and Human Needs*. New York: Norton. Contains a detailed chapter on forests.

Hales, L. (1983). Who Is the Best Steward of America's Public Lands? *National Wildlife* 21 (3): 5–11. Excellent reading.

Hardin, G. (1968). The Tragedy of the Commons. *Science* 162: 1243–1248. A classic paper.

Hardin, G. (1980). Second Thoughts on "The Tragedy of the Commons." In *Economics, Ecology, Ethics*, ed. H. E. Daly. San Francisco: Freeman.

Heady, H. F. (1975). *Rangeland Management*. New York: McGraw-Hill. Excellent review.

Hughes, J. D., and Thirgood, J. V. (1982). Deforestation in Ancient Greece and Rome: A Cause of Collapse. *The Ecologist* 12 (5): 196–207. Detailed paper.

Madson, J. (1982). *Where the Sky Began: Land of the Tallgrass Prairie*. New York: Houghton Mifflin. A moving treatise.

Mathews, O. P., Haak, A., and Toffenetti, K. (1985). Mining and Wilderness: Incompatible Uses or Justifiable Compromise? *Environment* 27 (3): 12–17, 30–36. Interesting look at a sticky issue.

Nash, R. (1985). Proceed at Your Own Risk: Restoring Self-Reliance to the Wilderness. *National Parks* January/February: 18–19. Important thoughts on the value and protection of wilderness.

O'Dell, R. (1986). Alaska: A Frontier Divided. *Environment* 28 (7): 10–15, 34–37. Detailed look at preservation versus development.

Sax, J. (1980). *Mountains without Handrails: Reflections on the National Parks*. Ann Arbor: University of Michigan Press. Discusses important aspects of park and wilderness preservation.

Sheridan, D. (1981). Western Rangelands: Overgrazed and Undermanaged. *Environment* 23 (4): 14–20, 37–39. Superb account.

Spurr, S. H., and Barnes, B. V. (1980). *Forest Ecology* (3rd ed.). New York: Ronald Press. Excellent text.

Sterling, E. M. (1981). Forestry in Austria: Small Cuts and Grand Vistas. *Sierra* 66 (6): 40–42. Good comparison of U.S. and Austrian forestry practices.

Watkins, T. H. (1986). The Conundrum of the Forest. *Wilderness* 49 (172): 12–24, 34–49. Comprehensive look at U.S. management plans.

Water Resources: Preserving Our Liquid Assets

A river is more than an amenity—it is a treasure.

OLIVER WENDELL HOLMES

Roddy Hale is a farmer in trouble. In debt for $2 million to the U.S. Farmers Home Administration, he fights a losing battle to save his dry Texas farmland. Hale, like thousands of western farmers, depends on water from the rapidly falling Ogallala aquifer underlying his property. The Ogallala contains what geologists call "fossil groundwater," which has seeped into the ground over 3 million years. Because of widespread overdrafting of groundwater in the Ogallala's eight-state region, wells are running dry and once-profitable farmland is being abandoned, much of it without a protective cover of grasses.

Abandoned farmland, left to the wind and rains, is one of the many faces of a serious problem facing the United States and dozens of other countries. In Winter Park, Florida, residents return from a shopping trip to find their home, yard, and pets gone, swallowed up by the earth in one hungry gulp when the ground collapsed where the aquifer had been depleted (Figure 10-1). In California and Arizona, commuters off to work in the morning back out of their garages only to find impassable fissures in their driveways, caused by groundwater depletion. Roadways, foundations, and pipelines crack from the strain of the sinking earth.

Halfway around the world the water crisis has a different face. In Kenya, for instance, a woman and her daughter leave the village well before dawn for an 8-kilometer (5-mile) walk to the river for drinking water. They pass dry riverbeds whose mud is cracked and twisted. When the woman returns, carrying the silty water, her husband greets her with tragic news: her infant son has died of diarrhea caused by the unsanitary water they drink.

Figure 10-1 This large sink-hole developed quickly, swallowing part of a community swimming pool, parts of two businesses, a house, and several automobiles. It happened in Winter Park, Florida, on May 8, 1981.

To many it may seem as if the world is running out of water. Far from it. Today's freshwater supply is the same as it was when civilization began its ascent in the fertile valleys of the Tigris and Euphrates. In fact, enough drinkable water falls on the terrestrial portion of the biosphere each year to flood its land mass to a depth of 86 centimeters (33 inches), providing several times the amount of water each person needs to sustain a moderate standard of living.

The problem arises, in part, because water is not evenly distributed across the face of the earth: tropical rain forests are drenched with rain, whereas New York City, Los Angeles and San Diego must import water. In water-short areas human civilization has pushed well beyond the carrying capacity, exceeding the readily available supply of this renewable resource. For this transgression of ecological law it is penalized with falling water tables, sinkholes, abandoned farmland, cracked foundations, and shortages.

Water. We drink it. We wash with it. We play in, on, and underneath it. It finds a thousand uses in our factories and is a staple of food production. The abundance or lack of water often determines where we live and how well off we will be.

Despite its importance to human society water remains one of the most poorly managed resources on earth. Squandered and polluted by industry, agriculture, sewage treatment plants, and many other facilities, water is often treated as if it were of little importance to human survival.

This chapter discusses the problems of water supply and presents solutions to the problems we now face from years of mismanaging our liquid assets. Chapter 16 addresses water pollution, which affects supply in many ways.

The Hydrological Cycle

The global recycling of water is the **hydrological cycle**, or **water cycle**. It runs day and night, free of charge, busily collecting, purifying, and distributing water that serves a multitude of purposes along its path (Figure 10-2). At its heart are two processes driven by energy from the sun: evaporation and precipitation.

Water evaporates from waterways and lakes, from land, and from plants (Figure 10-2). In plants, its evaporation from leaves helps draw nutrients up the stem, much in the way that sucking on a straw draws water from a glass. The evaporative loss of water from leaves is called **transpiration**. The total loss of water from the soil and leaves is called **evapotranspiration**.

Water suspended in the clouds, except in polluted regions, is nearly pure. Collected as rainfall in rural areas, it can be used in steam irons in which distilled water is required. The reason for the purity of atmospheric moisture is that when water molecules evaporate, they leave behind dissolved impurities.

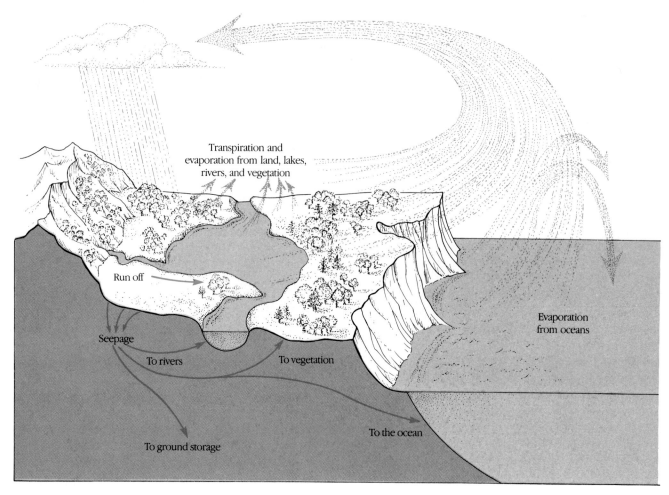

Figure 10-2   The hydrological cycle.

In the atmosphere, water is suspended as fine droplets (water vapor). The amount of moisture the air can hold depends on air temperature. The warmer the air, the more moisture it can contain. Atmospheric moisture content can be expressed as **absolute humidity**—the number of grams of water in a kilogram of dry air—or as relative humidity, the more common measurement. **Relative humidity** measures how much moisture is present in air compared with how much it could hold if fully saturated at a particular air temperature. At a relative humidity of 50%, for example, air has 50% of the water vapor it can hold at that temperature. If the relative humidity is 100%, the air is saturated.

When moisture exceeds saturation, clouds, mist, and fog form. Clouds, for example, form when moist air is raised by mountain ranges, when cold-air masses come in contact with moisture-laden air, or as warm air rises to cooler levels (Figure 10-3). For rain to form, air must contain small particles, known as **condensation nuclei**, on which the water vapor collects. Condensation nuclei may be salts from the sea, dusts, or particulates from factories, power plants, and vehicles. Over a million fine water droplets must come together to make a single drop of rain. If the air temperature is below freezing, the water droplets may form small ice crystals that coalesce into snowflakes.

Clouds move about on the winds, generated by solar energy, and deposit their moisture throughout the globe as rain, drizzle, snow, hail, or sleet. Precipitation returns water to the lakes, rivers, oceans, and land from which it came, thus completing the hydrological cycle. Water that falls on the land may evaporate again or may flow into lakes, rivers, streams, or groundwater, eventually returning to the ocean.

At any single moment 94% of the earth's water is found in the oceans, 4% is in inaccessible aquifers and 1.5% is locked up in polar ice and glaciers. This leaves about .5% of the earth's water available for human use, but most of this water is hard to reach and therefore much too costly.

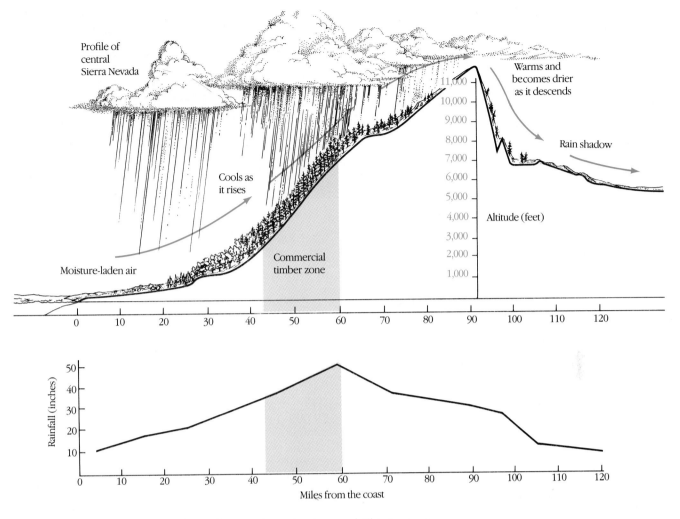

Profile of
central
Sierra Nevada

Warms and
becomes drier
as it descends

Cools as
it rises

Rain shadow

Altitude (feet)

Commercial
timber zone

Moisture-laden air

Rainfall (inches)

Miles from the coast

Figure 10-3 Mountain ranges thrust air upward, causing it to cool. This increases the relative humidity of the air, forming clouds and precipitation. Most of the precipitation falls on the windward side. As the air descends on the leeward side, it warms, and the relative humidity decreases. Leeward sides of mountain ranges are often arid.

Water Supplies and Usage

The Global Picture

Water problems face virtually every nation in the world. Despite the abundance of sparkling blue water around the Caribbean, for example, islands are plagued with freshwater supply problems. Rainwater for domestic use must be captured on rooftops and used sparingly. In many of the developing countries people spend a good part of their waking hours fetching water, frequently walking 15 to 25 kilometers (10 to 15 miles) a day to get water, often from polluted streams and rivers.

Three out of every five people in the developing nations do not have access to clean, disease-free drinking water. According to the World Health Organization, 80% of all disease in these countries results from the contaminated water that people drink and bathe in. Many countries are engaged in bitter rivalries over this precious resource. Argentina and Brazil, for instance, dispute each other's claims to La Plata River; India and Pakistan fight over the rights to water from the Indus; and Mexico and the United States have argued over the Colorado River. All told, over 150 river basins are shared by two or more countries.

The U.N. General Assembly has proclaimed the 1980s as the International Drinking Water Supply and Sanitation Decade. The goal is to provide the world's population with clean drinking water and adequate sanitation by 1990. The total cost of this ten-year project is $300 billion.

Figure 10-4 Graphic representation of water demand by continent. The bars on the left indicate 10% to 20% of the total runoff, which most countries can capture without major problems. When a country's demand exceeds these levels, it may suffer severe shortages in dry years. These graphs hide local and even regional shortages.

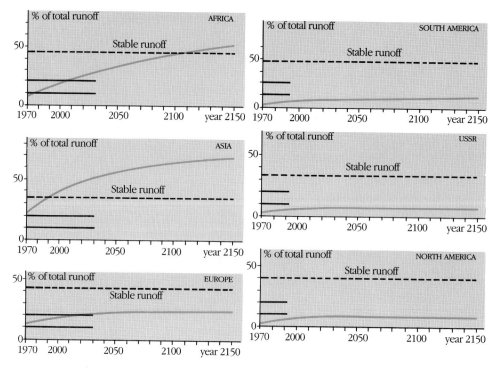

At mid-decade the prospects for meeting this goal appeared dim. To meet the goals, developing countries would need to spend at least 100 times more money than they are putting into water projects.

Water shortages are commonplace today in many parts of the globe, including parts of Peru, central Chile, many parts of Mexico, Panama, parts of Africa, New Zealand, parts of Australia, Korea, Japan, Taiwan, western India, Pakistan, most of Iran, southern Italy, Spain, and all of the Arab states except Syria. The future does not appear bright.

The world population withdraws about 9% of the potentially available freshwater runoff. Eighty-five percent of this water is used for crop and livestock production. Industrial use accounts for 7%, and domestic use makes up the rest. As a general rule it is economically feasible for most nations to withdraw up to 20% of the annual stream runoff, although some wealthy countries now withdraw almost 30%.

Irrigated land is expected to double between 1975 and 2000. Domestic and commercial use is expected to increase fivefold. Industry's water demand is expected to increase twentyfold. Rising demand almost certainly guarantees severe water shortages in the coming years. By the year 2000 water demand is expected to exceed water supply in at least 30 countries. Parts of Brazil, Mexico, many of the large Caribbean islands, East Java, Tasmania, the plains of central Thailand, half the United States, and most of Europe, India, and the Soviet Union will face this unwelcome prospect. Water shortages could limit population growth.

Figure 10-4 shows the projected water withdrawals throughout the world. The horizontal bars on the left mark 10% and 20% of the runoff, amounts that are economically feasible for most countries to withdraw. As these graphs show, Africa and Asia will require large withdrawals to meet their projected needs, far in excess of the stable runoff. **Stable runoff** is the amount of the total runoff that can be counted on from year to year. In most countries it is about 30% to 40% of the total average runoff. If a country's water demand exceeds the stable runoff, extreme water shortages can occur in dry or even moderately dry years.

Graphs and statistics can be deceiving. According to Figure 10-4, most continents should be in fairly good shape. None exceeds the stable runoff, except perhaps Asia. However, the continental averages are dangerously misleading. The graph for North America, for instance, suggests that enough water is available. Many parts of the United States, however, already tax their water supplies and suffer in dry years. The deception in these graphs stems from the fact that they lump an entire continent in one group, obscuring local supply problems. North America, for example, appears well off because the graph includes massive untapped water resources in Canada and Alaska that will probably never make their way to the U.S. Southwest.

Water Use in the United States

On the average, over 15 trillion liters (4 trillion gallons) of precipitation fall on the United States every day. Two-thirds of all this precipitation (10.5 trillion liters) evaporates. Thirty-one percent (4.9 trillion liters) finds its way

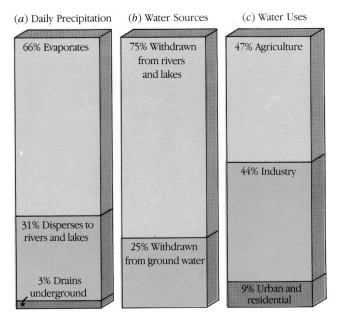

(a) Daily Precipitation   (b) Water Sources   (c) Water Uses

66% Evaporates | 75% Withdrawn from rivers and lakes | 47% Agriculture

44% Industry

31% Disperses to rivers and lakes

3% Drains underground | 25% Withdrawn from ground water | 9% Urban and residential

Figure 10-5 Disposition of precipitation, water sources, and users of water in the United States.

Table 10-1   Common Water Resource Problems
Inadequate surface water supply
Overdraft of groundwater
Pollution of surface water and groundwater
Quality of drinking water
Flooding
Erosion and sedimentation
Dredging and disposal of dredged materials
Drainage of wetlands and wet soils
Degradation of bays, estuaries, and coastal waters

to streams, lakes, and rivers, and only 3% recharges groundwater (Figure 10-5a).

Each day, billions of liters of water (an average of 1300 billion liters, or 339 billion gallons) are withdrawn from surface water and groundwater in the United States. Three-fourths of this water comes from lakes, rivers, and streams—collectively, called **surface waters**; the remainder comes from groundwater (Figure 10-5b).

Agriculture is the biggest water user in the United States. Nearly one of every two liters of water drained out of aquifers or rivers is used to irrigate crops. Industry comes a close second (Figure 10-5c). Municipal water users consume relatively little.

The average American uses about 340 liters (90 gallons) of water for domestic use each day. But just how important water is in our lives is underscored by these facts: Growing food for a family of four requires 12,000 liters (3,200 gallons) of water a day. The rayon in an average home carpet, for example, requires 190,000 liters (50,000 gallons) to make and the steel in a washing machine requires 17,000 liters (4,500 gallons) to produce. Adding all these uses together, the per capita water use in the United States is about 5,700 liters (1,500 gallons) per day.

Mismanaging Our Water Resources: Causes and Consequences

Virtually every community in the world has a problem with water (Table 10-1). In some there is too much water. Annual floods race through towns, sweeping away cars and stranding homeowners on rooftops. In others water

supply falls short of demand. Aquifers run dry because water is pumped out faster than it can be replenished. Streambeds dry up in summer months because of excessive demands for lawn watering. In many cases water is badly polluted. Resource managers believe, however, that much of our trouble stems from mismanagement. This section examines mismanagement and outlines some of the consequences.

The Numbers Game: Beyond Drought

Whether you live in New York, San Francisco, Tulsa, Key West, or Bird City, Kansas, you've probably felt the impacts of water shortage at least once in your lifetime. Water shortages stem from natural factors and mismanagement, often both.

The chief natural cause of water shortage is drought. A **drought** technically exists when rainfall is 70% below average for a period of 21 days or longer. A severe drought results in a decrease in stream flow; a drop in the water table; a loss of agricultural crops; a loss of wildlife, especially aquatic organisms; a drop in the levels of lakes, streams, and reservoirs; a reduction in range production and stress on livestock; an increasing number of forest fires; and considerable human discomfort.

Humankind has begrudgingly learned to expect and to live with droughts. More difficult to reckon with, however, is the mismanagement of urban growth and water resources. When cities grow beyond the available freshwater supply, they send their engineers far afield in search of water that can be transported to lawns, factories, and kitchens. Soon, canals and tunnels stretch out in all directions, draining rivers of their flow to support a population living well beyond the carrying capacity. When drought strikes, things can deteriorate rather quickly. Shortages arise as summer bears down on the city and the surrounding watersheds. The drier the environment, the more perilous the bargain with nature becomes.

The years 1977 and 1978 stand out in the minds of

many Californians as a time of great hardship. Normal snows and rains failed to materialize, leaving mountain reservoirs vulnerable to the heavy demand placed on them by the millions of people crowded into the area near San Francisco. Water was rationed out by the cupful, trucked in where possible. Lawns dried up. To many people the problem was a natural calamity brought on by drought. Others saw it for what it was: a drought that caused great hardship in a population living well beyond the carrying capacity of the environment.

Overdraft: Depleting Our Liquid Assets

Much of the water taken from streams and aquifers never returns to its source. For example, over 80% of the agricultural water applied to crops evaporates. Because of this, rivers flow at a fraction of their natural rates during high-use seasons. Aquifers often dry up completely, driving farmers like Roddy Hale out of business.

Rather than managing aquifers and other resources more responsibly or controlling population growth, the traditional approach has been to seek new water supplies. Expansion of water supply systems often triggers bitter conflicts among the variety of water users. New dams threaten recreational rivers (Chapter Supplement 10-1). Land developers and energy companies often find themselves grappling with farmers over water rights, as each group attempts to meet its own needs. Today, many western states have locked horns over water.

Overexploitation of existing water supplies can severely limit growth. Consider the future of Wichita, Kansas. This growing city gets most of its water from deep aquifers, the Equus beds, which are recharged at a rate exactly equal to current water withdrawal. With water demand expected to double in the next 20 years, Wichita will need to develop new sources, conserve or ration water, curtail its growth, or a combination of these.

Overexploitation of groundwater in coastal regions may lead to **saltwater intrusion** into freshwater aquifers (Figure 10-6). Taking too much water from rivers and streams may allow salt water to intrude into their estuaries, upsetting ecological balance in these important zones. This is a serious problem in Everglades National Park in Florida.

Ponds, bogs, and streams are sites that mark the intersection of aquifers and land surface. Many think of a pond as "exposed groundwater." Because of this link, groundwater overdrafting drains swamps and ponds, at times drying them up completely. Fish, wildlife, and recreation are often devastated.

To meet the growing demand, water departments around the United States wreak havoc on the natural environment. Denver, for example, has placed a number of dams throughout Colorado to capture snowmelt for summertime lawn watering, which doubles daily water

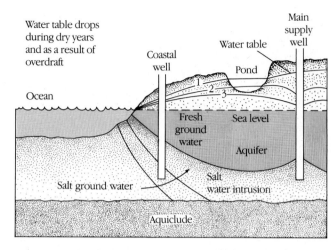

Figure 10-6 Saltwater intrusion into groundwater. Reduction of groundwater flow causes freshwater aquifer to retreat, allowing saltwater to penetrate deeper inland underground. Numbers indicate different positions of the water table and differential effects on surface water (pond). Coastal wells are first affected by falling groundwater. Inland wells pick up saltwater only after severe depletion.

consumption. Dams and reservoirs destroy the habitat of black bears, bighorn sheep, and many other animals. One dam, in Waterton Canyon near Denver, resulted in the death of one-half of the bighorn sheep population. The Denver Water Department is now actively planning a new reservoir on the same river. Many times larger, it would flood 33 miles of rapids and trout-fishing country.

In Chapter 7 we saw that groundwater overdrafting threatened the long-term prospects for irrigated agriculture in the West. In Nebraska, Kansas, Colorado, Oklahoma, and Texas, for example, 81,000 hectares (200,000 acres) of farmland on which corn had been grown were taken out of production between 1977 and 1980 because of water shortages. By 2000, Texas may lose half of its irrigated farmland, 1.2 million hectares (3 million acres).

Groundwater fills pores in the soil and thus supports the soil above the aquifer; when the water is withdrawn, the soil compacts and sinks, a process called **subsidence**. The most dramatic examples of subsidence in recent years have occurred in Florida and other southern states, where groundwater depletion has created huge **sinkholes** that may measure 100 meters (330 feet) across and 50 meters (165 feet) deep (see Figure 10-1). Subsidence has occurred over large areas in the San Joaquin Valley of California, damaging pipelines, railroads, highways, homes, factories, and canals (Figure 10-7). Southeast of Phoenix over 300 square kilometers (120 square miles) of land has subsided more than 2 meters because of groundwater overdrafting. Huge cracks have formed, some 3 meters wide, 3 meters deep, and 300 meters long.

Figure 10-7 Subsidence caused by groundwater overdrafting damaged this building and driveway in Contra Costa, California.

Are We Flooding Our Own Homes?

After shortages, the next major U.S. water problem is flooding. Despite years of flood control work, costing in excess of $8 billion, property damage is continuing to rise. Today, floods cause damage valued at over $3 billion a year.

Causes of Flooding A deceptively simple correlation can be drawn between floods and their apparent cause: heavy rainfall and snowfall. Closer examination reveals many causes that go unnoticed by most people. As illustrated in Figure 10-8, precipitation that does not evaporate must either run off or percolate into the soil. Whether it streams across the land's surface, possibly spilling over the banks of rivers, or sinks quietly into the soil to join groundwater and later discharge into streams is largely a matter of the surface features and temperature of the land, as shown in Figure 10-8. For example, major spring floods often result when snow melts before the ground has thawed. Vegetation also greatly influences surface runoff. Forest or grass cover retards water flow and promotes percolation. Heavily vegetated watersheds act as sponges. Light vegetation (for instance, in deserts) increases surface runoff and, hence, flooding. The fate of rainfall in many cases rests not so much in the hands of nature as the hands of farmers, urban planners, developers, and the like. Many activities strip vegetation from the land and increase runoff: farming, ranching, mining, off-road-vehicle use, hiking, construction, and clear-cutting on

steep terrain. Water flowing rapidly over the surface of barren land into streams causes flooding and often transports a substantial amount of soil in the process. In a vicious circle eroded sediment fills bodies of water and reduces their holding capacity. This makes flooding more likely, even after moderate rainfall.

Highways, airports, shopping centers, tennis courts, office buildings, homes, and numerous other structures greatly reduce land permeability. The devastating flood in Kansas City, Missouri, in 1980 was the direct result of a heavy rainstorm falling on thousands of acres of impermeable surface.

Figure 10-9 shows the regions of the United States that are susceptible to flooding. Many of these areas are located along the Mississippi River and its tributaries. The **floodplains** of these rivers, regions along the flanks of rivers naturally subject to flooding, are popular sites for cities, towns, and farms. Taken together, habitation along floodplains and activities that increase surface runoff ensure humankind a future of flooded basements.

Controlling Flooding When rivers flow over their banks, workers rush in with sandbags to hold back the waters. When the floodwaters recede, city engineers plan ways to stop future devastation. Traditionally, potential floods have been fought by building dams and levees (embankments to hold the water back) along river banks. Sometimes of dubious merit, these approaches only treat the symptoms of a serious and costly problem, not the

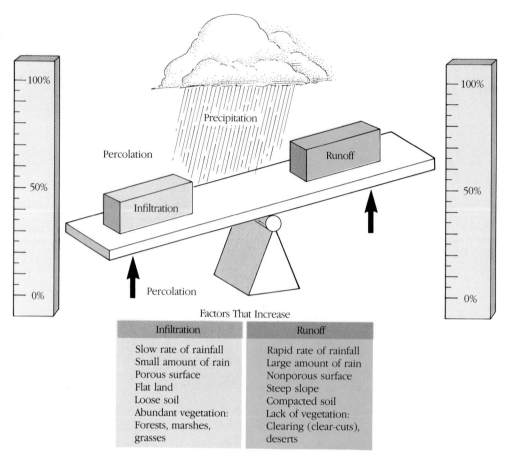

Figure 10-8 Percolation–runoff ratio. When 75% of the water flows over the surface, 25% percolates into the soil (ignoring evaporation).

Precipitation

Percolation

Runoff

Infiltration

Percolation

Factors That Increase

Infiltration	Runoff
Slow rate of rainfall	Rapid rate of rainfall
Small amount of rain	Large amount of rain
Porous surface	Nonporous surface
Flat land	Steep slope
Loose soil	Compacted soil
Abundant vegetation: Forests, marshes, grasses	Lack of vegetation: Clearing (clear-cuts), deserts

underlying causes. Watershed protection is another, perhaps more effective, approach. Watershed management is to flood control what preventive medicine is to health care. Some effective management tools include reducing deforestation and overgrazing in flood-prone regions and replanting trees, shrubs, and grasses on denuded hillsides. Consider, too, the effect of redesigning the urban environment in ways that slow down the rush of water during a rainstorm by diverting it to holding ponds or underground storage tanks or even pumping it to aquifer recharge zones. A lake in a city park could trap much of the surface flow in a rainstorm. Captured rainwater could then be released slowly to rivers or used to water lawns or recharge aquifers. Storm sewers could also divert water to special tanks that supply water to factories. Individual homeowners can divert gutter water to underground holding tanks to be used later for watering lawns and gardens and washing cars.

In some instances the wisdom of our predecessors helps in solving problems of today. But this is not always the case. Take streambed channelization as an example. **Streambed channelization** is a way, or so our ancestors thought, of reducing flooding by streamlining rivers and streams. To do this, bulldozers rip up the vegetation along a stream's banks and then deepen and straighten the channel, creating a glorified ditch that may be lined with

concrete or rock. Over the years our experience with this dubious technique has shown that it generally eases flooding in the immediate vicinity. That minor benefit is outweighed, however, by habitat destruction, increased erosion of stream banks, a loss of river recreation, and increased flooding downstream. (For a detailed look at the consequences of channelization, see Case Study 10-1.)

Streambed channelization in the United States was begun seriously in 1954, when the **Watershed Protection and Flood Prevention Act** authorized the Soil Conservation Service to drain wetlands along rivers to make more farmland and to reduce flooding. To date, 13,000 kilometers (8000 miles) of U.S. streams have been channelized. Another 13,000 kilometers have been targeted for similar "improvements." Critics argue that many projects are of dubious merit and should not be undertaken, especially when they destroy wetlands (see Chapter Supplement 10-1).

Protecting Our Liquid Assets

Many parts of the world are heading for severe water shortages in the next 20 to 30 years unless we act quickly. But what can we do?

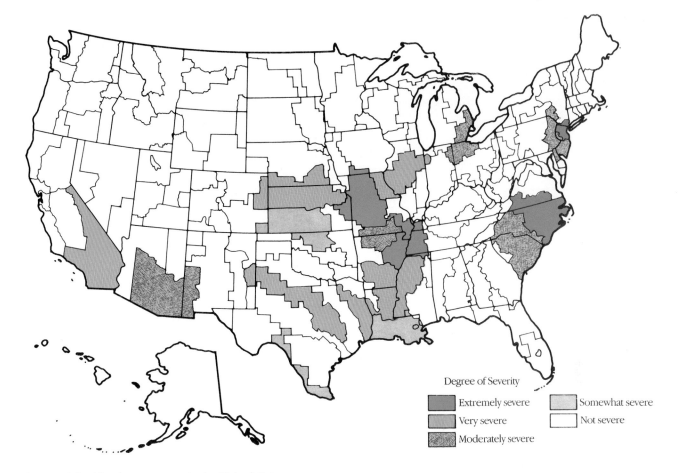

Figure 10-9 Flood-prone areas in the United States.

Population Control

Fortunately, solutions to the worsening worldwide water shortages are many. One of the most important is the control of population growth, particularly in Africa, Asia, and Latin America. Measures to control regional population growth in water-short areas in more developed countries, such as the desert Southwest of the United States, can also reduce water supply problems.

Supplementing population control are numerous technical, personal, and legal measures.

Technical Solutions: Costs and Benefits

Dams and Reservoirs Dams and reservoirs retain snowmelt and rainwater, increasing our supply of water, controlling floods, generating electricity, and increasing certain forms of recreation. They also allow the expansion of population.

Dams are no panacea, however. They are costly and may inundate towns, villages, good arable land, and wildlife habitat. Pakistan's recently completed Tarbela Dam

alone displaced 85,000 people. China's mammoth Three Gorges Dam and reservoir, to be built on the Yangtze River, will displace 2 million people and destroy nearly 100,000 acres of farmland in the world's most heavily populated and agriculturally productive river valley. Dams and reservoirs also destroy opportunities for certain forms of river recreation, including kayaking, rafting, and trout fishing (Figure 10-10). Exceptional floods can exceed the capacity of reservoirs and even destroy well-built dams.

Contrary to popular belief, dams and reservoirs do not always increase the amount of water available to some communities, because of high rates of evaporation. On Egypt's Lake Nasser, formed by the Aswan Dam, 10% of the total water supply evaporates each year.

Dams reduce stream flow into the ocean, resulting in changes in the salt concentration of estuaries, bays, and tidal waters. Reduced stream flow also reduces the nutrient inflow to coastal waters with devastating effects on the producer organisms in the aquatic food web. Because of a reduction in algal growth at the mouth of the Nile, Egypt's annual sardine catch plummeted from 16,000 metric tons per year to 450.

Figure 10-10 A kayaker paddles through turbulent white water. Dams can eliminate such recreational rapids.

Dams interrupt the natural flow of nutrient-rich sediment to floodplains, river deltas, and coastal waters. Good farmland must be abandoned or fertilized, often at a high cost. Sediments collected in reservoirs slowly fill them, making them useless. In the United States well over 2000 small reservoirs are totally clogged with sediment. Many larger reservoirs throughout the world will meet a similar fate. The $1.3-billion Tarbela Dam on the Indus River in Pakistan took nine years to build, but because of upstream soil erosion the reservoir could fill with sediment in 20 years. Lake Powell on the Colorado River will be filled in 100 to 300 years.

Dams also interfere with the migration of fish to spawning grounds. In addition, they generally release the coldest water from the bottom of the reservoir; this can make stream water exceedingly cold year round and decrease the spawning of native species. The Glen Canyon Dam on the Colorado River, for instance, releases chilly water from the reservoir's bottom and has converted the warm-water fishery below the dam to a fine rainbow trout fishery. To avoid changing stream temperature, some existing dams have been retrofitted with devices that combine warm water from the reservoir's surface with cooler deep waters. Newer dams are often fitted with multiple gates to ensure proper downstream water temperature.

Since the economic and environmental costs of dams and reservoirs are so high, caution is advised when undertaking a project of this nature to control flooding, generate electricity, or store water for later use.

Water Diversion Projects Denver, Los Angeles, Phoenix, and New York all rely on water diversion projects to supply their needs. In many cases urban water departments build small dams on distant streams and then pipe the diverted water to neighboring reservoirs, from which it flows to water treatment plants.

Because up to 80% of the annual runoff of some streams may be taken, wildlife habitat and good recreational sites may be destroyed by diversion projects. In addition, these projects usually transfer water from rural areas of low population density, often agricultural regions, to cities. This practice can create bitter conflict between urban and rural residents. Since the urban water users have a larger say in state policies, they usually win the legislative battles, leaving irrigated agriculture high and dry.

Diversion of clean, high mountain water in tributaries of the Colorado River ultimately diminishes the flow and quality of the Colorado, a source of water for over 17 million people. The lower sections of the river carry a heavy burden of sediment and dissolved salts. By removing clean water from the spring snowmelt, upstream diversions indirectly increase the concentration of salts downriver. By the time the Colorado reaches Mexico, its salt concentration is over 800 parts per million (violating a U.S.–Mexico treaty), compared with 40 parts per million at its headwaters in the Rockies.

Salts harm agricultural users as well as people who drink the water. Water with a salt concentration over 700 parts per million cannot be used for agriculture unless it is desalinated or diluted. Drinking water must have a salt concentration of 500 parts or less. A bill passed by Congress in 1973 authorized the construction of three desalination plants along the Colorado River to remove over 400,000 tons of salt from the river each year. Costing an estimated $350 million, these projects help purify water to be used in California and Mexico.

Undoing the Damage to Florida's Kissimmee River

Between 1964 and 1970 the Army Corps of Engineers hacked away at the winding Kissimmee River in Florida, hauling up mud and dumping it along the banks in a heap 5 meters (15 feet) high and 30 meters (100 feet) wide. When they had finished this huge flood-control project, a river that had once lazily meandered nearly 150 kilometers (100 miles) through the Florida landscape had been reduced to a 48-mile-long, 200-foot-wide, and 30-foot-deep canal to drain water quickly from the northern reaches of the watershed. The once-magnificent river is now referred to simply as "the Ditch." On the heels of the huge dredgers that planed the river into a straight-as-she-goes canal came the contractors, who threw up concrete dams and steel navigation locks, approximately every 10 miles. They also built huge earthen dams extending for 2 miles on either side of the locks to hold back water drained from the upper section of the watershed. From here, water could be released at a controlled rate to avoid flooding below. The dams now form five long holding ponds along the length of the canal.

Once a rich habitat for bald eagles, deer, fish, waterfowl, and alligators, the Kissimmee River has become a sterile tribute to our tireless efforts to channelize rivers to control flooding. Most scientists condemn the channelization as a major environmental catastrophe. Gone are 12,000 hectares (30,000 acres) of the original 16,000 hectares of marsh, once a major breeding ground and stopping-off place for many dozens of species of water birds. Secondary canals built by landowners along the main canal drained another 80,000 hectares. Today, the vast flocks of ducks that once rained down from the skies are gone. Gone, too, are the wading birds. By Florida Game and Fresh Water Fish Commission estimates, 90% of the waterfowl and 75% of the bald eagles have vanished from the region because of channelization. Also gone are the largemouth bass that attracted anglers from all over the nation.

Only two years after this enormous project had been completed, Florida biologists began noticing changes in Lake Okeechobee, into which the Kissimmee's clean waters once flowed. Dead fish and dying vegetation were the most blatant signs that something was awry in the lake, which provided drinking water for Miami and adjoining coastal cities. It didn't take biologists long to determine that the loss of marshlands, which purify waters and hold back sediment, was the reason for Lake Okeechobee's sudden change for the worse. The loss of the natural cleansing of wetlands and the onslaught from cattle ranches and farms that sprang up along the river's banks, releasing pesticides, fertilizer, animal wastes, and sediment, created a water-quality problem for the lake.

The waters of the Kissimmee River flow south and once fanned out across southern Florida to nourish the multimillion-hectare wetlands known as the Everglades. On the southernmost tip is Everglades National Park. To make room for farms, much of the Everglades was drained, and the water from Lake Okeechobee and the Kissimmee River basin was shunted via canals to the coast. Reduced flows have disrupted the ecology of the Everglades, seriously threatening common species as well as a number of endangered species (Chapter 8). Reduced water flows also produced an ironic backlash. Because of a lowered water table, farmland once prized because of its rich soil began to subside at a rate that some experts think could hinder farming in the region. Lower water flows have also resulted in saltwater intrusion into surface water and groundwater.

Ironically, studies after the canal was completed indicate that it provides little or none of the expected flood control north of Lake Kissimmee at the far northern end of the river. And making matters worse, it is now seen as a major threat to downstream areas. After heavy rains in central Florida, for instance, a slug of water travels rapidly southward along the canal. It can wipe out nesting waterfowl and drown unsuspecting wildlife. Under natural conditions the wetlands hold back water like a sponge, releasing it slowly with less damage.

Less than two years after the Army Corps of Engineers had trucked in the last load of cement, a special governor's conference committee released a report calling on the state to reflood the marshes that it had dried up in the channelization. Their report was only one of many to reach the same conclusion: channelizing the river had been a big mistake. And with a price tag of $30 million, it had been a costly one. Even the Army Corps of Engineers got into the action by commissioning a study to reevaluate the project and prepare recommendations for returning the river to its original state.

In 1983 Governor Robert Graham and supporters took steps to reverse the damage. In 1984 Phase 1 of the Kissimmee River Demonstration Project began. New dams were built to divert water back into the old river channel and flood the marshes along 20 kilometers (12 miles) of the river at a cost of $1.5 million. Biologists are eagerly watching to see how successful the project will be in reclaiming the marsh and rebuilding the waterfowl populations. Some are pessimistic, because the Army Corps of Engineers has insisted that navigable channels be maintained in the canal, at least through Phase 1. To satisfy the corps, 38-foot-wide, 7-foot-deep notches were left in the diversion dams. Conservationists fear that these will diminish water flow into the surrounding wetlands and reduce reflooding.

If Phase 1 is successful, state officials and conservationists hope Phase 2, filling in part of the canal, can begin soon. In an ironic twist the Army Corps of Engineers asserts that federal

Case Study 10-1 (continued)

funds cannot be used to reclaim the river. Money is available only to channelize.

Restoring the Kissimmee River is part of a major ecological experiment aimed at saving Florida's fast-vanishing wetlands. If conservationists and Florida's governor have their way, by 2000 the complex wetlands of Florida will function much as they did over 100 years ago. But at this very moment, despite the lessons learned in Florida and elsewhere, engineers and construction companies are hard at work draining enormous wetlands the world over. One of the largest lies along the Nile River. In the home of countless birds and wildlife, huge dredgers are now busily sucking up the mud and straightening the channel.

Water diversion projects will continue to be built to meet the needs of industry, agriculture, and cities. The costs and benefits of proposed projects must be thoroughly analyzed.

Desalination   The expense and ecological impact of dams and diversion projects often lead community planners to other approaches to increase their water supply. One of these is **saltwater desalination**, the removal of salts from seawater and brackish (slightly salty) water (Figure 10-11). The two main methods are evaporation and reverse osmosis. In **evaporation**, or distillation, the salt water is heated and evaporated, leaving behind the salts and minerals. The steam produced is then cooled, and pure water condenses out. In **reverse osmosis** water is forced through thin membranes whose pores allow the passage of water molecules but not the salts and minerals.

By either of these methods, seawater can be converted to drinking water or irrigation water. Since 94% of the water on earth is in the oceans, desalination might seem like the best answer to water shortages. Unfortunately, water produced by desalination is four to ten times more expensive than water from conventional sources.

Since 1977 the world's desalination capacity has increased dramatically. Nevertheless, desalination produces an insignificant proportion of the fresh water consumed by humankind. In the United States over 100 desalination plants now produce an excess of 1250 million liters (330 million gallons) per day. This is .001% of the total U.S. freshwater requirement. Most plants are located in California, Texas, Florida, and the Northeast. Desalination plants are also in operation in Saudi Arabia, Israel, Malta, and a few other countries.

Even though costs have come down in recent years, energy requirements and construction costs of desalination plants may always remain prohibitively high. For agriculture, desalination seems even more unlikely, since water-short areas are usually located far from the sea.

Desalination plants permit a further extension of the carrying capacity with potentially serious ecological impacts. For example, population growth in the Florida Keys, in part due to a new desalination plant, threatens

Figure 10-11   Desalination plant in Key West, Florida.

coral reefs and native wildlife, such as the crocodile. Construction of houses and condominiums causes erosion that pollutes coastal waters. New residents produce an increasing amount of sewage and other pollutants that can affect water quality. Large quantities of salt and minerals from desalination plants could worsen water quality.

Groundwater Management   Another technological fix for water shortages is to tap unused groundwater and to regulate withdrawal so it will not exceed recharge. In some areas groundwater can be replenished by disposing of wastewater in aquifer recharge zones. This water is cleansed as it percolates through the soil, although some of the organic waste cannot be broken down underground. Irrigation water from farm fields, storm water runoff, cooling water from industry, and treated effluents from sewage treatment plants could also be used.

Although aquifer recharge can help recharge groundwater supplies, it can also present some problems. The most significant is the cost of disposal, since many cities are far from aquifer recharge zones.

Conservation and Recycling   Two of the most direct approaches to the problem of water shortages are conservation and recycling. Since agriculture and industry are the biggest water users, efforts to recycle and conserve water in these sectors could do much to alleviate water shortages.

Agricultural water conservation is easily achievable. Open, dirt-lined ditches that deliver water to crops are only about 50% to 60% efficient, and they could be replaced with lined ditches or, better yet, pipes. Sprinklers, which often waste up to half of their water, can be replaced with drip-irrigation systems (Chapter 7), which lose only 5%. However, drip irrigation can be used for only a limited number of crops, such as fruit trees, grapevines, and some vegetables. For the vast fields of wheat and corn, more conventional methods must be used. Still, water conservation efforts such as these can help reduce water demand.

In industry, water conservation can be achieved by redesigning processes and facilities. The use of water by steam-cooled electric power plants could be cut one-fourth by using dry cooling towers (Figure 10-12), although these require more energy and are more expensive to operate than wet cooling towers.

Industry can also recycle water. Wastewater from various industrial processes can be purified and reused over and over. Municipal sewage treatment plants are a common type of water purification system, though effluents are hardly potable. Further treatment, though, could make this water pure enough to drink. In Tokyo, for example, Mitsubishi's 60-story office building has a fully automated recycling system that purifies all of the building's wastewater to drinking-water purity.

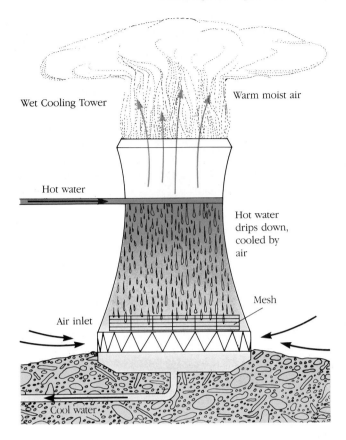

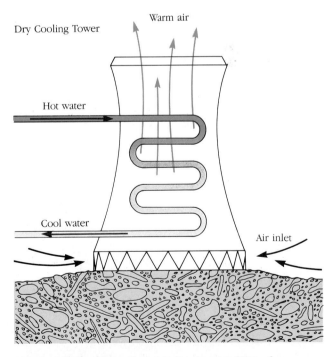

Figure 10-12   Wet and dry cooling towers. Water from electric power plants is cooled in them before being reused. Dry towers cost more to operate but conserve water.

Table 10-2 Water Savings Through Conservation

Activity	Typical Use (Liters/Use)	Efficient Use (Liters/Use)	Suggestions
Shower	77	2	Install flow restricters
		15	Shorter showers
Toilet	19	15	Bottles or bricks to displace water in tank
		13	Install low-flush toilet
		4	Install washdown toilet
Faucets	(liters/min.) 12	10	Low-flow faucets
		6	Flow restricters
Brushing teeth	20–40	2	Brushing with faucets off, then rinsing briefly
Shaving	24–48	2	Shaving with faucets off, followed by brief rinse
Washing dishes	60–80	10–20	Rinsing dishes in drainer or turning water on and off each time; using short cycle for dishwashers
Washing clothes	140	80	Front-loading washing machine
		100	Adjusting water level for each load
Outdoor watering	(liters/min.) 40	—	Nighttime watering can cut water demands in half.

As water shortages worsen and public and governmental awareness increases, recycling plants will become a necessity. Such plants decrease water demand and water pollution. Although the cost of building and maintaining large-scale recycling plants for large cities can be considerable, they may still be cheaper than new water diversion projects and dams and have added ecological benefits.

Doing Your Share: Personal Solutions

You and I can do many things to cut down on water use. Table 10-2 compares typical wasteful habits and shows how simple adjustments in our behavior translate into great water savings.

Education Solutions

Half the battle to ensure an adequate water supply can be won by education. Our children should learn the value of water and the growing demands on it; they should learn to conserve water. Such lessons may be as important as the math or history they learn. Our schools could go far toward making our youngsters resource-conscious citizens.

Legal Solutions

New laws and building codes can also help reduce household water consumption. In all areas, water-short or not, new homes could be required to use 25% to 50% less water than existing homes. This can be achieved by installing waterless or low-water toilets as well as flow restrictors for showers and faucets. Smaller lawns could be encouraged, and they could be planted with low-water grasses. Drip and root-zone irrigation systems could be required. Systems that retain rainfall and gray water (used water from showers and faucets) could be installed. Gray water is suitable for lawn and garden irrigation. Finally, municipal water agencies could charge more for water used during the daytime in the summer, when evaporation is greatest, and less for water used early in the morning or at night, when evaporation is low. This price incentive could help cut down on wasted water.

Perhaps the most serious deficiency in our regulation of water resources is poor coordination between water resource management and economic development. In many cases the two are discussed exclusively of each other. Builders put up tracts of new homes and then ask where the water will come from. City planners scramble to find water, throwing up dams and diversion projects and ruining rivers that contribute to the allure of the area.

Water development plans must be environmentally as well as economically sound. We cannot afford to assume that adequate water supplies will always be available no matter where we go and no matter what we do. In addition, we cannot blindly continue our extension of the earth's carrying capacity. Though we can make the deserts bloom, we must ask, "Should we?" Though we can pump water uphill and through tunnels under mountain ranges, we must ask about the consequences of these actions and whether there are other, ecologically sound, options. In some cases a proper analysis will cause us to abandon our plans. In others it may give us time to pursue options that make more ecological sense.

Let him who would enjoy a good future waste none of his present.

ROGER BABSON

Summary

The **hydrological cycle** is a natural system for collecting, purifying, and distributing water, which is driven by energy from the sun. At any single moment only .5% of the earth's water is available for human use.

Three-fourths of the water used in agriculture, industry, and our homes comes from **surface waters**, and the rest from groundwater. Two-thirds of the water withdrawn each day is returned to its sources, but the remaining portion is consumed—that is, it either evaporates or becomes incorporated in living tissue.

Major water supply problems include shortages, overexploitation of ground and surface water supplies, and flooding. Water shortages are brought about by a complex set of factors, including drought, overuse, waste, and overpopulation. Overexploitation of ground and surface waters occurs in many parts of the world today, creating shortages, conflict among water users, and severe economic impacts, especially for farmers. Groundwater depletion may also cause **saltwater intrusion** in coastal zones or in regions where freshwater aquifers lie near saltwater aquifers. In some regions groundwater overdrafting has caused severe **subsidence**, or sinking of the land, which results in the collapse of highways, homes, factories, pipelines, and canals.

Flooding is also a major problem. Because of natural factors and poor land management, billions of dollars worth of damage is caused by floods each year. Any human activities that increase the surface runoff and decrease percolation can potentially increase flooding. Much of the damage from flooding is our own fault, for we tend to inhabit **floodplains**, river valleys that are subject to periodic flooding. To prevent flooding, **streambed channelization** is often carried out, involving the removal of vegetation and the deepening and straightening of channels. Such actions destroy wildlife habitat, increase the rate of streambank erosion, diminish recreational opportunities, alter the aquatic environment, and often increase flooding in downstream sites.

Water problems face virtually every nation in the world. Especially hard hit are some of the less developed nations, where water is far from villages and is polluted. Polluted water supplies are responsible for 80% of all illness in these countries.

The long-term prospects for meeting water needs for industry, agriculture, and individuals are dim for many parts of the world. Africa and Asia may find adequate water supplies difficult to come by, as may many other regions within countries, even in the developed world.

There are many solutions to meeting future water demands and curbing flooding. Measures to control population growth, especially in water-short regions, are most important. In addition, numerous technological solutions can be used. The environmental impacts of each of these must be carefully considered along with long-term benefits.

Dams and reservoirs retain snowmelt and rainwater, help control floods, generate electricity, and increase certain forms of recreation. They are costly, however, often inundating wildlife habitat, farmland, and even towns. Dams also reduce stream flow into the ocean, resulting in changes in the salt concentration of estuaries, bays, and tidal waters. Dams also interrupt the natural flow of nutrient-rich sediment to coastal waters, with devastating effects on the aquatic food web. Fish migration is often impaired by dams.

Diversion projects increase water supplies in water-short regions but are often costly, reduce stream flow, destroy aquatic ecosystems, affect downstream salt concentrations, and create bitter conflicts among users.

Desalination of salt water is feasible in some places, but it is four to ten times more expensive than conventional freshwater development projects. Desalination plants produce salts that must be disposed of and encourage home and resort construction and population growth in some regions, resulting in ecosystem destruction.

In some areas it may be prudent to replenish groundwater by disposing of wastewater, industrial cooling water, storm water runoff, and water from agricultural fields in aquifer recharge zones or in special water disposal wells. Such water is purified as it percolates through the soil, but projects of this nature are feasible only if water supplies are near recharge zones.

Recycling and conservation can make important contributions to increasing water supplies in the near future. Since agriculture uses a large percentage of our water, devices to reduce irrigation losses that are inexpensive and easy to install are needed.

New laws and building codes can help reduce water consumption in and around our homes. New homes can be fitted with water-conserving toilets and shower heads, special systems to reuse gray water for lawns and gardens, or recycling systems that actually purify water from all domestic uses for reuse. Individuals can assist by reducing water consumption.

Discussion Questions

1. What is the hydrological cycle? Draw a diagram showing how the water moves through the cycle.

2. Define *transpiration, evaporation, relative humidity, absolute humidity, saturation,* and *condensation nuclei.*

3. What sector is the largest water user in the United States?

4. Define the following terms: *groundwater, water table, saltwater intrusion,* and *subsidence.*

5. Discuss the problems caused by overexploitation of ground and surface water.

6. You are appointed by the governor of your state to study floods and flood control projects. Make a list of reasons why flooding is now severe and ways to correct these problems.

7. Discuss the benefits and costs (environmental, economic, and so forth) of dams and diversion projects.

8. How can desalination of seawater help solve water shortages? What are the limitations of and the problems created by this method?

9. Describe ways in which you and your family can help conserve water. Calculate how much water your efforts will save each day. How much will they save in a year?

Suggested Readings

Abbey, E. (1984). *Beyond the Wall.* New York: Holt, Rinehart, and Winston. See Chapter 5, The Damnation of a Canyon, for a poignant view of the controversy over Glen Canyon Dam.

Ashworth, W. (1982). *Nor Any Drop to Drink.* New York: Summit Books. Excellent coverage of major water issues.

Brown, L. R., Chandler, W. U., Flavin, C., Pollock, C., Postel, S., Starke, L., and Wolf, E. C. (1985). *State of the World 1985.* New York: Norton. See Chapter 3, on water resources, for Sandra Postel's excellent analysis of freshwater supplies and demands.

Ferguson, B. K. (1983). Whither Water? The Fragile Future of the World's Most Important Resource. *The Futurist* 17 (2): 29–36. General overview of water supply problems and solutions.

Foster, R. J. (1982). *Earth Science.* Menlo Park, Calif.: Benjamin/Cummings. Excellent introductory-level coverage.

Kakela, P., Chilson, G., and Patric, W. (1985). Low-Head Hydropower for Local Use. *Environment* 27 (1): 31–38. An interesting look at the value of small dams.

Kierans, T. W. (1980). Thinking Big in North America: The Grand Canal Concept. *The Futurist* 14 (6): 29–32. Good view of the heights of technological optimism.

Maranto, G. (1984). Saving South Florida. *Discover* 5 (4): 36–40. Excellent overview of the problems created by channelization and of how Florida officials are trying to reverse the damage.

Micklin, P. P. (1985). The Vast Diversion of Soviet Rivers. *Environment* 27 (2): 12–20, 40–45. In-depth look at major water diversion projects in the Soviet Union.

Postel, S. (1985). Thirsty in a Water-Rich World. *International Wildlife* 15 (6): 32–36. Excellent article on water supplies.

Postel, S. (1986). Water for the Future: On Tap or Down the Drain? *The Futurist* 20 (2): 17–21. Superb look at water conservation.

Sheaffer, J. R. (1984). Going Back to Nature's Way: Circular vs. Linear Water Systems. *Environment* 26 (8): 10–15, 42–45. A look at ways to help solve both water shortages and water pollution.

Stokes, B. (1983). Water Shortages: The Next Energy Crisis. *The Futurist* 17 (2): 37–47. Excellent survey of world water shortages.

Udall, J. R. (1986). Losing Our Liquid Assets. *National Wildlife* 24 (1): 50–55. Exceptional account of groundwater depletion in the southwestern U.S. and its impacts.

U.S. Department of Agriculture (1980). *America's Soil and Water: Conditions and Trends.* Washington, D.C.: Author. Water use and water-related problems graphically illustrated.

Wetlands, Estuaries, Coastlines, and Rivers

From certain vantage points Chesapeake Bay resembles the vast, almost limitless ocean. For years Americans have treated it with the disrespect afforded to seemingly limitless resources. Today, however, the bay is in trouble. The rich abundance of organisms is diminishing, threatened by pollution, overfishing, and other activities.

The bay and its surrounding wetlands, in this case mostly swamps, are home to a variety of fish and shellfish, including blue crabs, oysters, and striped bass. Properly managed, the bay could provide enough food to feed Japan. However, Chesapeake Bay is much more than a food source for the 12.6 million people who live near it. It is just as much a recreational gold mine for hunters, anglers, nature enthusiasts, and boaters.

Chesapeake Bay is only 310 kilometers (195 miles) long, but its shoreline measures nearly 12,000 kilometers. In many ways the bay is a symbol of how wetlands and coastlines have been mismanaged for 200 years.

Old-timers maintain that the bay's waters once contained "wall to wall" oysters. Oyster populations have declined precipitously in the last 30 years. Bountiful harvests of striped bass may be a thing of the past, too. In 1970 the average number of bass netted per haul in seines was 30; in 1984 the count had fallen to only 4.2. Various strategies have been tried to reverse this downward trend. But the 1984 count prompted a moratorium on striped bass fishing starting January 1, 1985. Fishermen were stunned by this action.

EPA studies show that the bay's submerged vegetation, which is vital to fish populations, has dropped by 76% in the last 25 years. The EPA also notes that large **algal blooms** (bursts of algal growth resulting from certain kinds of pollution discussed in Chapter 16) now threaten the grasses. Mats of algae block sunlight from reaching the bottom.

Further damage to the bay is caused by aerobic (oxygen-requiring) bacteria, which deplete the oxygen supply when they decompose algae and organic pollutants in the water. Some oxygen depletion, or anoxia, is natural for the bay.

According to the Conservation Foundation, commercial development and population growth are the two biggest threats to the bay. The population by 2020 is projected to be 16 million. Most of the pollution comes from development—from oil spills, sewage, toxic chemicals, heavy metals, and runoff from the sur-

rounding land. The bay's extensive drainage system, an area slightly smaller than Missouri, ensures that anything added to the land will probably end up in its waters. One of the worst pollutants is nitrogen (in the form of nitrates) from commercial duck farms, municipal sewage, and farm fields.

The tragedy of neglect witnessed in Chesapeake Bay reminds us that water management involves much more than protecting humans from floods and supplying water. This supplement examines the threat to wetlands, estuaries, coastlines, and rivers and looks at ways to better manage them.

Wetlands

Wetlands, perpetually or periodically flooded lands, fall into two types. **Inland wetlands** are found along freshwater streams, lakes, rivers, and ponds. Included in this group are bogs, marshes, swamps, and river overflow lands that are wet at least part of the year. **Coastal wetlands** are wet or flooded regions along coastlines, including mangrove swamps, salt marshes, bays, and lagoons.

The Hidden Value of Wetlands

Wetlands are an extremely valuable and productive fish and wildlife habitat. Many other animal and plant species also make the wetlands their home. Deer, muskrats, mink, beavers, and otters are a few of the species that live in or around wetlands. In addition, shellfish, amphibians, reptiles, birds, and fish also call these endangered places their homes.

Aside from their importance to wildlife, wetlands also play an important role in regulating stream flow. A study in Wisconsin showed that wetlands act like sponges, holding back rainwater and reducing natural flooding. They also filter out sediment eroded from the land and therefore help reduce sedimentation in streams. Wetlands also act as traps for nitrogen and phosphorus, two common pollutants washing from heavily fertilized land. Wetland plants absorb these nutrients, preventing water pollution downstream. The sponge effect reduces flooding and has the added benefit of recharging groundwater supplies. Wet-

Figure S10-1 Wetlands in the United States.

lands are used to grow certain cash crops, including rice, cranberries, peat moss, and blueberries. Because their usefulness is not always apparent, however, they are often filled in or dredged to make way for housing, recreation, industry, and garbage dumps.

Declining Wetlands

By some estimates wetlands once covered an area the size of Texas (68 million hectares, or 170 million acres). Today, less than one-third of these rich wetlands remain, and what is left is fast heading toward oblivion. Estimates of wetlands destroyed each year range from 48,000 to 120,000 hectares (120,000 to 300,000 acres).

U.S. wetlands are shown in Figure S10-1. No matter where you look, wetlands are in trouble. Coastal wetlands are victims of huge dredgers that scoop up muck in streams and bays to make them more navigable. Dredging drains adjoining swamps. Cities often fill in swamps to make room for homes, recreational facilities, roadways, and factories. Farmers fill in swamps to expand their arable land.

Protecting Wetlands

Concern for the loss of wetlands has stirred many state governments into action. For example, Florida passed legislation in 1972 to regulate all wetland development. Strict controls in Nassau County, New York, have also slowed destruction. The federal government has assumed an increasing role in wetland protection through executive orders that prohibit all its agencies from supporting construction in wetlands when a practical alternative is available. A farm bill passed in 1985 denies farmers federal benefits, such as loans, crop insurance, and subsidies, if they drain or fill wetlands to convert them to agricultural land. The federal **Coastal Zone Management Act** (1972) calls on states to develop plans to protect coastal wetlands. Many states now have either federally approved plans or state plans that regulate their wetlands. Although a plan does not ensure protection, it is a step in the right direction.

The federal government also purchases wetlands that become part of the **National Wildlife Refuge System**. The system today contains 4 million hectares (10 million acres) of wetlands. The Fish and Wildlife Service also buys wetlands for protection. The Department of Agriculture currently pays farmers not to drain or fill in wetlands. States own additional wetland acreage. All told, a little over one-fourth of our existing wetlands are protected by these various measures. In 1986 Congress passed a measure that will raise more money for the purchase of wetlands by increasing duck stamp fees and charging admission at certain wildlife refuges.

Wetland protection laws and regulations, many critics assert, are like toothless watchdogs. In many instances little is done to enforce these important laws. Each of us can write our representatives and find out what laws exist and how they are being enforced. Local action groups can help stimulate stronger enforcement when necessary. Personal action is needed more than ever in the face of deep cuts in the federal budget. On an international scale nations can cooperate to preserve wetlands. In 1971 representatives of many nations met in Ramsa, Iran, to discuss the plight of wetlands and agreed to protect those lands within their jurisdiction. In 1986 the United States ratified the agreement. Four U.S. wildlife refuges were added to a list of wetlands of international importance.

Estuaries

Estuaries are the mouths of rivers, where saltwater and fresh water mix. Estuaries, like wetlands, are critical habitat for fish and shellfish. Together, coastal wetlands and estuaries make up the **estuarine zone**. Two-thirds of all fish and shellfish depend on this zone during some part of their life cycle.

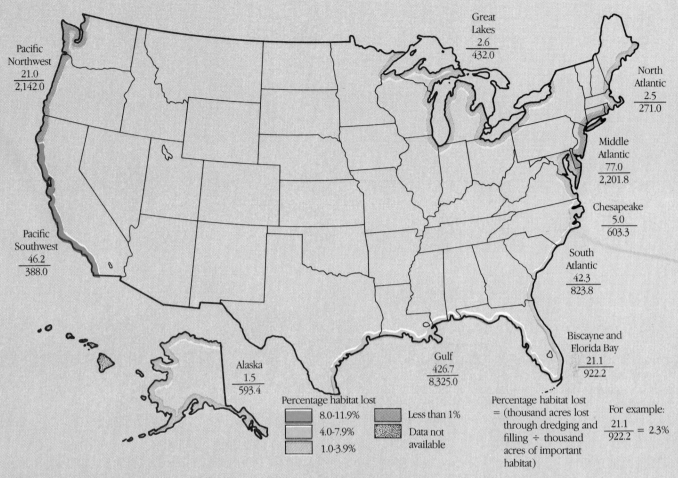

Figure S10-2 Destruction of the estuarine zone (estuaries and coastal wetlands) from dredging and filling.

The estuarine zone gets its richness from the land, eroded land. Eroded sediment, rich in nutrients, is carried in streams to the ocean, where it supports an abundance of aquatic organisms, especially algae, the base of a large and productive aquatic food web.

Estuarine zones, like wetlands, also absorb water pollutants that flow from upstream sources (sewage treatment plants, industries, cropland, and so forth). Their importance as a water purifier is underscored by estimates that 1 acre of coastal wetland is the equivalent of a $75,000 sewage treatment plant.

Damaging This Important Zone

The estuarine zone is vulnerable to a variety of assaults: pollutants from sewage treatment plants or industries; sediment from erosion that buries rooted estuarine vegetation; oil spills; and dams that can cut off the life-giving flow of nutrients from the land. Cities may withdraw so much fresh water upstream that rivers run dry. In Texas, for example, drought and heavy water demands in past years have critically reduced water flow into estuaries. The Mexican delta of the Colorado River is a remnant of its former self. Freshwater inflows are critical to maintaining the proper salt concentration in brackish water of lagoons and coastal wetlands where mollusks and other organisms dwell. Salinity may be one of the most important factors determining shellfish productivity.

Many organisms inhabit the estuarine zone, but the most sensitive to pollution are clams, oysters, and mussels. Pollution is generally thought to be one of the major factors responsible for the decline in mollusk harvests in the last 20 years. Mollusks can concentrate toxic heavy metals, chlorinated hydrocarbons, and many pathogenic organisms, including those that cause typhus and hepatitis. These pathogens may not affect the mollusks' survival, but they make them unsafe for human consumption.

The estuarine zone is a battlefield of sorts, beleaguered by pollution, water loss, sedimentation, dredging, and filling, among other invaders. Compounding the damage is the widespread problem of overharvesting of fish and shellfish. It is generally agreed that the decline in U.S. oyster production after 1950 was largely the result of overharvesting. Clams in the Northeast have likewise been severely overharvested. Chesapeake Bay is certainly a victim of heedless overfishing.

Over 40% of the U.S. estuarine zone has been destroyed. The most severe damage has occurred in California, along the Atlantic coast from North Carolina to Florida, and along the entire Gulf of Mexico (Figure S10-2). Despite state and federal laws to protect this zone, destruction continues.

Protecting the Estuarine Zone

Protecting estuaries and coastal wetlands is largely a matter of common sense and good resource management, part of an overall management strategy whose beneficial effects ripple through the biosphere just as the adverse effects do now.

Improved water pollution control (Chapter 16) is a key element of the plan. Erosion control is equally important. Water conservation to preserve vital water flow into estuaries is also needed. Restraint is the final element. Restraint means restricting dredging and filling and ending the overharvesting of fish and shellfish.

Protecting the estuarine zone presents a unique challenge in the United States, because 90% of the coastal land in the 48 conterminous states is privately owned. In 1972 Congress responded to the plight of the estuaries and coastal wetlands by passing the **Coastal Zone Management Act**. This law set up a fund to provide the 35 coastal and Great Lakes states with assistance in developing their own laws and programs. It also provided them with funds to purchase estuarine zones and estuarylike areas in the Great Lakes states. These regions are to be set aside for scientific study; as of 1983, 18 national estuarine sanctuaries had been established.

Half of the U.S. population lives in counties that are at least partly within an hour's drive of a coast, and a majority of the major cities are coastal. Discoveries of offshore oil, gas, and minerals pose new problems that require immediate answers. An abundant supply of cooling water makes the coastal zones prime candidates for new power plants and oil refineries. Because of current and potential problems the Coastal Zone Management Act is an important step in preserving U.S. coasts.

Still, according to critics, the act leaves too much discretion in the hands of the states. Some states, in fact, either have not adopted programs or enforce their programs poorly, leaving their coastal waters open to misuse.

Fifteen additional federal laws have been passed to promote coastal zone management, but they are only as good as their enforcement. Lackadaisical enforcement is almost as bad as no enforcement at all. Without further, more serious efforts to improve coastal zone management, we will almost certainly lose more of this important habitat.

Coastlines and Barrier Islands

The eastern coast of the United States and Mexico is skirted by a chain of **barrier islands**. These narrow, sandy islands are separated from the mainland by lagoons and bays (Figure S10-3). An estimated 250 barrier islands lie along the Atlantic and Gulf coasts. Many of them are popular sites for recreation. Some have been purchased by the federal government and are used for recreation (as national seashores) and wildlife habitat, but most barrier islands are under private ownership.

In the last 40 years many of these islands have been developed for vacationers. Summer homes, roads, stores, and other structures have invaded the grass-covered dunes. According to estimates of the National Park Service, in 1950 only 36,000 hectares (90,000 acres) of barrier islands had been developed, but by 1980 a total of 113,000 hectares (280,000 acres) had been devel-

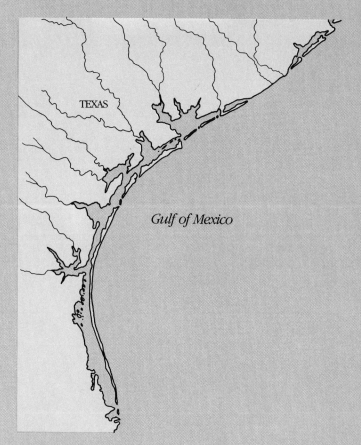

Figure S10-3 The Texas Gulf Coast is a barrier island coast. Barrier islands are moving bodies of sand that make poor sites for homes and resorts.

oped. If the current rate of development continues, by 1995 all of the remaining barrier islands will be developed.

Barrier islands and their beaches are part of a river of sand that migrates down the East Coast. The islands grow and shrink from season to season and year to year in response to two main forces. First, waves, which tend to arrive at an angle to the beach, erode the beaches, as illustrated in Figure S10-4. These waves create **beach drift**, a gradual movement of sand along the beach. In addition, the wind creates a **longshore current** parallel to the beach, which also moves sand along the beach (Figure S10-4b). Combined, beach drift and **longshore drift** are called **littoral drift**. Littoral drift causes the barrier islands to move parallel to the main shoreline. They shorten on one side and become longer on the other. Homes built on the upcurrent side of the island may collapse into the sea. Second, winter storms tend to wash over the low barrier islands and move the sand closer to the land, destroying houses, roadways, and other structures.

Home construction, attempts to stabilize the beaches and sand dunes of barrier islands, and road construction are a recipe for continued disaster. Federal actions and various relief programs have, in the past, encouraged development on barrier islands. When erosion and storm damage occurred, the government stepped in with money for disaster relief. Federal flood insurance paid for the damage, and federally subsidized construction

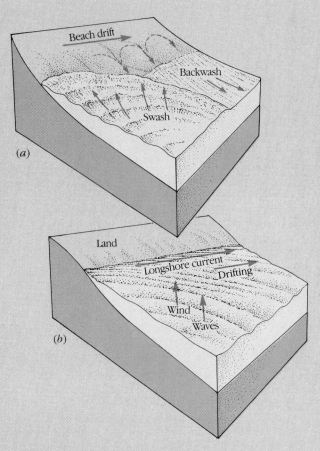

Figure S10-4 (*a*) Beach drift is caused by waves approaching obliquely. (*b*) Longshore currents are formed by offshore oblique winds and waves.

projects helped rebuild roads and stabilize the islands. A few years later other storms would devastate the islands, starting the rebuilding cycle all over again at considerable expense. Recognizing this fact, Congress passed legislation in 1982 to prohibit the expenditure of federal money for highway construction and other development on barrier islands. One of the major environmental accomplishments of the Reagan administration, the **Coastal Barrier Resources Act**, may greatly decelerate the destruction of barrier islands.

Coastal beaches are the victims of human activities. Understanding the dangers requires a look at the natural processes that affect these beaches. Coastal beaches, like barrier islands, are eroded by longshore currents. Thus, U.S. beaches are like great rivers of sand kept in constant motion by the major coastal currents. Sand lost in one area is subsequently replaced by sediment which is carried to the sea by rivers. Consequently, dams that trap sediment diminish the natural replacement of sand on coastal beaches. Pockets of coastal beach erosion plague California. According to one estimate, dams hold back nearly 40% of the sediment that once reached the mouth of the Santa Clara River north of Los Angeles. This robs California beaches of 15 million metric tons of sand each year. From New Jersey to Texas, the story is the same.

Some communities erect barriers, called jetties, to prevent erosion by longshore currents. These structures only slow down the process. Jetties are sometimes built to maintain navigable passageways in coastal harbors. In 1911, for instance, two 300-meter jetties were built on the New Jersey coast north of Cape May to prevent sand from filling in the harbor. While performing admirably in their appointed duty, the jetties have had a disastrous effect on downcurrent beaches. The beaches at Cape May grew thinner and thinner. By the 1920s the town was actively fighting back by building small jetties to keep the remaining sand from being washed away and to trap the sand flowing in the longshore currents. To the townspeople's dismay their efforts were fruitless. Beaches retreated by 6 meters (20 feet) a year. Lighthouses fell into the sea. The ocean threatened to swallow the airport. After years of anguish the town has turned to an expensive pumping system that will draw sand from above the two large jetties and move it down to the beaches.

Despite the hard lessons learned from Cape May the U.S. Army Corps of Engineers is pressing Congress to fund two 1.5-kilometer (1-mile) jetties costing $100 million to maintain a navigable channel at Orgegon Inlet in North Carolina. A pumping system would be installed to move sand across the channel to prevent downcurrent beach erosion. Critics argue that the jetties would cost six or seven times more than annual dredging.

To protect the shoreline the delicate balance between sediment flow and erosion must be maintained. Dams that retain sediment must be avoided, or rocky beaches will become common in the future. Beaches must be left alone to grow and shrink with natural cycles. Preventing their movement, which costs taxpayers millions of dollars a year, only seems to accelerate erosion and beach disappearance. Realizing that it makes more sense to cooperate with nature, many government officials on the Atlantic coast have begun to develop plans that would return developed shorelines to their natural state following destructive hurricanes. This step would begin a retreat from the shorelines, where nature probably intended humankind to be only a visitor.

Wild and Scenic Rivers

More and more people are flocking to free-flowing rivers to embark on a variety of sports—fly fishing, kayaking, rafting, inner tubing, and canoeing. This great recreational resource, however, is increasingly imperiled by dams and diversion projects (Chapter 10). Foreseeing the need to protect rivers for recreation and habitat for fish and other species, Congress passed the **Wild and Scenic Rivers Act** in 1968. It prevents the construction of dams, water diversion projects, and other forms of undesirable development along the banks of some of our remaining free-flowing rivers.

Undammed rivers offer much more than excitement for the river runner. Like wilderness, they provide unrivaled scenery and countless opportunities for relaxation and reflection. For the adventurous kayaker and rafter, they offer a taste of danger and the opportunity to test one's skills, strength, and endurance. They are home for fish and other forms of wildlife. Their canyons offer unequaled opportunity for geological study. Taken together, these opportunities make a river much more than a source of water.

Because rivers exist in varying states of development, Congress established a three-tiered classification scheme for the **Wild and Scenic River System**: **wild rivers** are relatively inaccessible and "untamed," **scenic rivers** are largely undeveloped and of great scenic value, and **recreational rivers** offer important recreational opportunities despite some development. By 1985, 61 rivers had been included in the system, totaling over 11,000 kilometers (6,900 miles).

Few things are as likely to spark controversy as a wild or scenic river designation, because so many interests vie for a river's benefits: municipal water consumers, paper manufacturers, farmers, hunters, anglers, and whitewater boaters. Competing interests are not easily compromised. A dammed river provides water for a new paper mill, water skiing, and boating, but irretrievably floods the kayakers' rapids and the fly fishermen's favorite pools.

The fight to keep free-flowing U.S. rivers free from development continues today. Much of the pressure to dam American rivers, however, has been taken off because of economic and legal forces. After years of paying for questionable dams, Congress has found that many projects return only a few cents for every dollar invested. As a result, federally subsidized water projects, often handed out as political favors, have fallen into political disfavor.

In the battle over water, compromises are inevitable, but commercial interests might better promote water conservation as a first step in meeting water needs (Chapter 10). Simple measures costing pennies can save millions of dollars. Also, smaller dams that flood only a small portion of the river should be built whenever possible. To prevent sedimentation, erosion controls in the watershed could be strengthened.

Many conservationists argue that valuable recreational rivers must be preserved just as endangered species are. When a scenic river gorge is dammed, it is gone forever. Conservationists can work with water developers to help select sites least likely to cause environmental damage.

A river is a vital resource, but dammed and diverted to water-hungry, often-wasteful consumers, that river becomes a tragic symbol of poor planning and undisciplined greed. Our goal should be to manage our rivers wisely and efficiently, minimizing waste and damage, ensuring future generations the use of treasures we now enjoy and too often take for granted.

Endangered Species

In 1978, the Supreme Court blocked the completion of the nearly finished Tellico Dam in Tennessee in order to save a small, ugly fish called the snail darter.

While many applauded the decision, some asked how we can allow a fish to stand in the way of progress. The answer is twofold: (1) Everytime we destroy a species, we destroy an intricate web of interdependency. The near-extinction of the Guam rail, for instance, has had a dramatic effect on both its prey and its predators. The altered ecosystem struggles to adapt or ceases to exist. (2) We can be certain that plants and animals contain some of the answers to the myriad of problems we have not yet been able to solve. Is the cure for cancer hidden in one of the thousands of yet unclassified plants that are being destroyed at the rate of 100,000 acres per day in the tropical rain forest? Can the rapidly disappearing gorilla teach us what we need to know about our own evolution? We can be sure that, as the diversity of the gene pool shrinks, so do our chances for answering some of humankind's more serious problems.

With the *Endangered Species Act* of 1973, the government assumed legal responsibility for vanishing plants and animals, but it has done little to fulfill this obligation. For instance, during the Reagan administration, over 3800 species were nominated, but only 36 received protection.

1 The southern sea otter lives off the Pacific coast amongst the kelp beds, which are home to its favorite food—the abalone. Widespread killings by their competitors, abalone fishermen, brought the otter to the verge of extinction. Its recent comeback is a result of legal protection.

1

2 The West Indian Manatee, now numbering only 1000, makes its home in the coastal waters of Florida. Its numbers have been reduced by habitat alteration, overhunting by humans, and injuries caused by collisions with power boats.

3 The largest living primate, the mountain gorilla has been hunted to the brink of extinction. Killed for its meat, collected for zoos, and slaughtered for body parts, the population has dwindled to about 1000.

4 The Panamanian Golden Frog lives in a three-square-mile region in Panama. Attractive to tourists in search of unusual pets, the endangered frog is now protected by law.

5 Once enjoying the largest geographic distribution on this continent, the timber wolf has been reduced to a handful of small packs in Alaska, Canada, and the Soviet Union. Probably one of the most feared and misunderstood of all animals, timber wolves were victims of widespread slaughter by humans who believed they were protecting their livestock. It is now known that wolves kill only the old or infirm in the herds.

6 The nation's symbol, the bald eagle, is endangered or threatened in most of its habitats in the United States. Habitat destruction coupled with pesticide poisonings have brought the birds' numbers down to an alarming 1300 pairs in the lower 48 states.

7 A shy animal cursed with a beautiful pelt, the snow leopard was first photographed in the wilds of Nepal in 1970. Studies indicate that as few as 16 remain today.

8 A sow grizzly will charge anything that threatens her cubs. At 1000 pounds, with a 30-inch neck and a 55-inch waist, it seems unlikely that this animal could run faster than 65 kilometers (40 miles) per hour. But she can—easily catching any human or beast that might unwittingly wander between her and her cubs. Only 800 grizzlies remain in the lower 48 states today.

9 Zoos, once contributing to the decimation of wildlife populations, have come to the assistance of endangered species. Here two zoologists introduce a motherless newborn African elephant to a lactating, and hopefully cooperative, female.

4

2

3

5

6

7

8

9

10 This California condor was hatched in the San Diego Zoo in 1983. Condor eggs are taken from nests in the Los Angeles mountains, and hatched and raised in captivity. Victims of habitat alteration, it is believed that the baby condor's chance of surviving in the wild is less than 1 in 50.

11 A zooworker feeds a hatchling using a condor puppet. The use of the puppet teaches the baby to recognize its own kind and encourages it to feed normally. It's hoped that the careful avoidance of human contact will keep the birds wild, enabling them to breed once they are set free.

12 All wild condors were captured in 1986 and 1987 and placed in captivity in southern California. Wildlife and zoo officials hope to establish a large breeding population in captivity and release birds into suitable habitats.

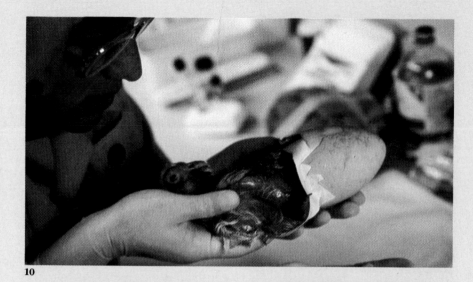

10

12

11

Energy: Winning a Dangerous Game

Our entire economic structure is built from and propelled by fossil fuels. We have invaded the long-silent burial grounds of the Carboniferous Age, appropriating the dead remains of yesteryear for the use of living today.

JEREMY RIFKIN

The year is 2000. Joanna Mills, mother of two high-school-age children, slips out of bed at 7 A.M. Tiptoeing across the cold wooden floor she turns up the thermostat to a cool 18° C (64° F). Electric current begins to flow through the baseboard heaters.

Several states west, Jacob Cowens wakes with the rising sun, pads to the window, and throws open the heavily insulated curtains. The sun pours into the main room of his passive solar home. Despite the subfreezing Wisconsin weather his house stays pretty warm at night. Sunlight and heavy-duty insulation in the ceiling and walls have been his primary "heat sources" this winter. Stored in a thick cement slab under his tile floor and interior brick walls, the heat radiates into the room day and night, keeping it warm and comfortable (Figure 11-1). Last year the Cowenses' heating bill for the entire winter was $400, compared with the Millses' $3000 bill.

Joanna Mills. Jacob Cowens. One a victim of rising energy costs, the other barely affected. One struggling to pay bills that nearly equal the house payments, the other free to send his daughter to college and invest his money in new business ventures.

Between 1973 and 1985 Americans' natural gas bills rose over 600%. A $30 monthly home heating bill in 1973 became a $210-a-month monster in 1985. Energy analysts believe that by 1993 costs will have risen another 600%.

Figure 11-1 Passive solar houses capture sunlight's energy in interior walls and floors, and radiate it into rooms at night. Over the lifetime of the owner, passive solar energy can save tens of thousands of dollars in heating bills.

A $210 bill for one month of home heating will come to $1470 a month, equaling or exceeding many home mortgages. Should these predictions come true, many families that have purchased cheaply made homes heated with natural gas or electricity will find themselves facing hard times. Some experts go as far as to predict that the middle class may split into solar and nonsolar homeowners, one group coping with the high cost of living and the other buckling under the pressures of high bills.

The rise in energy costs is inevitable. Deregulation, rising demand, and declining supplies of nonrenewable fuels, especially oil, ensure a future of escalating costs. Few people will be immune to the rising costs. Making matters worse, many experts predict that after 2000 or 2010 the global demand for oil will outstrip supply. The cost of gasoline and other oil byproducts will soar as a result. Along with them the cost of food, clothing, and shelter will begin to climb, creating global inflation and economic stagnation as industrial economies falter.

This chapter examines many aspects of energy. It explores our dependence on oil and other fossil fuels, the impacts of energy use, and how long conventional fossil fuels will last. Finally, taking a long-range look, it suggests ways to build the foundation of a wise energy strategy.

The Fossil Fuel Connection: Discovering Our Energy Dependence

Spilling up from deep wells or scooped up by the truck-load in surface mines, energy in its many forms is the lifeblood of modern industrial society. At the same time, it is our Achilles heel. Cut the supply off for even a brief moment, and pandemonium would ensue. Industry would come to a standstill. Millions would be out of work. Agriculture and mining would halt, with cataclysmic effects. Automobiles would vanish from city streets.

Important as it is, energy was taken for granted for many years, and used wastefully. The prevailing mood was that there would always be more and it would always be cheap. The days of energy nonchalance came to an abrupt halt as a result of the 1973 oil embargo imposed by the Organization of Petroleum Exporting Countries, or OPEC, and a second embargo by Iran in 1979. OPEC nations used the 1970s to wield enormous economic power. Crude oil prices shot up from $3 a barrel to $34. Previously poor nations like Kenya rejoiced over their newfound wealth generated from oil. But in Europe and the United States the news was bleak. In step with this shocking price increase, the costs of consumer goods and farm products, produced and distributed with the aid of petroleum, shot upward. Inflation began a long climb that crippled the American and world economies; many countries have not recovered. In the United States long lines formed at gas stations. People became used to colder houses. All in all the 1970s were a rude awakening for a frontier society nurtured on the idea of unending resources. (For more on the frontier ethic see Chapter 19).

But good often comes from disaster. The oil shortages of the 1970s were no exception. The OPEC tactics, while devastating to world economies, heightened awareness of the industrial world's dependency on foreign oil. Many cut back on energy waste, improved efficiency wherever possible, and found new sources.

The most significant outcome of the 1970s was drastic cutback in energy use. Conservation came to the rescue, helping ailing economies gain a foothold. Conservation soon created an excess of oil. Consumers had turned off the spigots, but producers had left the oil wells running. Temporary gluts stabilized prices of consumer goods, and industry was able to recover. Gradually, the economy began to pick up.

Stimulated by the still relatively high price of oil, many non-OPEC nations (Britain, for example) increased exploration and oil production. OPEC's share of the world oil market fell. In 1977 OPEC nations supplied two-thirds of

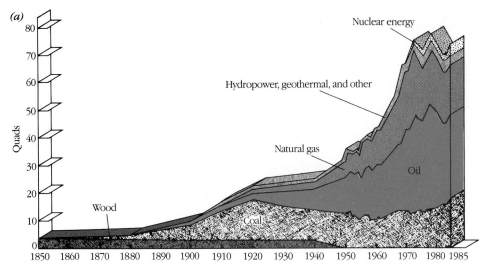

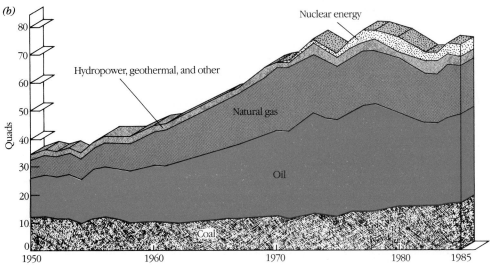

Figure 11-2 (*a*) Energy consumption in the United States by fuel type from 1850 to 1982. (*b*) Energy consumption from 1950 to present.

the world's oil. By 1985 their share had dropped to one-third. To combat the loss in market share, OPEC announced in December 1985 that it would cut prices to undercut its competitors. For the consumer, in the near term, this was good news. By April 1986 crude oil prices had dropped by half.

Lowered energy prices, although good for the economy, may have stifled energy conservation and certainly have crippled the development of renewable sources, such as wind power and solar energy (Chapter 12). Max Neiman, a political science professor at the University of California, Riverside, found that few local governments showed any sustained interest in the energy conservation programs they had drafted in the late 1970s. A potentially dangerous result of the lack of concern for energy conservation and alternative sources, says Christopher Flavin, a senior researcher at the Worldwatch Institute, is that the stage is now being set for an even stronger OPEC in the 1990s. With 56% of the world's oil, OPEC nations will

be in position to control prices once again as the non-OPEC nations deplete their reserves. In other words, cheap energy today may mean a heavy dependence on OPEC oil in the future, with the potential for another energy crisis in the 1990s.

These major global dramas played out in the international economy distract the public from the underlying problem of modern industrial society: oil, in many ways the lifeblood of such societies, is disappearing fast. The present oil "gluts" are only temporary—in many ways, the calm before the storm.

Energy Use—Then and Now

The history of energy use in the United States has been one of shifting dependency, as shown in Figure 11-2. This pattern may well continue in the future as today's energy sources run out and as new ones are developed.

Figure 11-3 Breakdown of energy consumption in the United States.

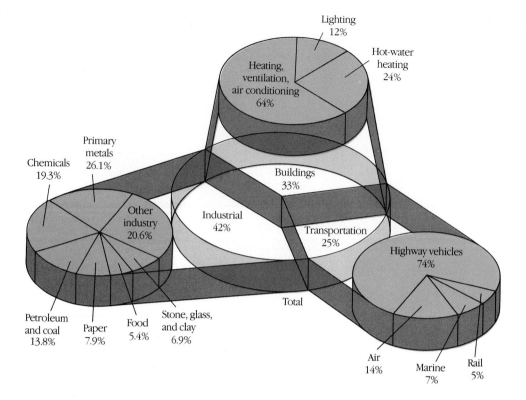

One hundred years ago Americans had few choices for energy. Wood was the chief source. Today, our options are many—coal, oil, natural gas, hydropower, geothermal energy, solar power, nuclear power, and wind. American energy options began to expand in the late 1800s when factories shifted to coal as wood supplies were depleted. But many people found coal to be a dirty, bulky fuel, expensive to mine and transport. When oil and natural gas were made available in the early 1900s, therefore, coal use began to fall. These new fuels were much easier and cheaper to transport and had the additional advantage of burning more cleanly.

Today, despite a far greater number of energy options, the United States depends primarily on three fuels: oil, natural gas, and coal. In 1986 oil accounted for 43% of total U.S. energy consumption. Natural gas provided 26%, and coal, 22%. Hydroelectric, solar, geothermal, and nuclear power supplied the remaining 9%. Although it does not show up in the energy calculations, conservation provides us with a great deal of energy, too.

Figure 11-3 breaks down U.S. energy consumption. The center pie chart shows where energy is used. Industry tops the list, using 42% of all U.S. energy. Homes and commercial buildings are second, and transportation is third.

The United States is a major consumer in the international energy market. With only 6% of the world's population, the United States consumes about 30% of its energy. For many years the nation's energy appetite grew rapidly. Between 1965 and 1971, for example, energy con-

sumption grew at 4.8% per year. After the oil embargoes of the '70s energy consumption took a dramatic downturn. Between 1979 and 1983, in fact, total annual energy consumption dropped by 10%. Higher prices, a poor economy, improved energy efficiency, and conservation all contributed to the decline. With falling prices and a revitalized economy since then, however, energy consumption has climbed steadily upwards.

The United States needs energy, and needs it badly. But each day thousands of tons of fuel are wasted. In fact, over half the energy consumed in the United States is wasted. The second law of thermodynamics states that energy is "degraded" when it changes form, as discussed in Chapter 3, so some waste is inevitable. But the amount of energy wasted in the United States far exceeds the inevitable loss. Given the nation's dependency on energy, the high cost, and the rapid decline in global resources, continued waste may become a detriment to Americans' future well-being. As Bruce Hannon put it, "A country that runs on energy cannot afford to waste it." No better advice was ever given to an industrial society. (Chapter 12 discusses ways in which energy waste can be cut.)

Impacts of Energy Production and Consumption

Energy does not come cheaply. In addition to the economic costs, which were discussed above, society pays a huge price for damage to the health of its people and its

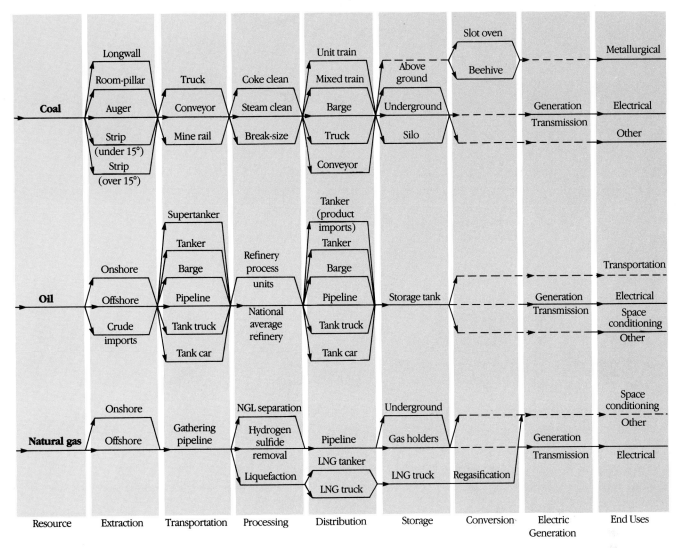

Figure 11-4 Energy systems, or energy fuel cycles.

environment. Lung disease, acid rain, thermal pollution, and battered landscapes are but a few of the many costs we have paid, and will continue to pay, for energy use. In the words of the economists, pollution and its impacts are **external costs**, because they are born by society and not by the manufacturers directly responsible for them (Chapter 20). Making external costs known, reducing them whenever possible, and finding fair ways to pay for them are the main goals of the environmental movement, and the subject of much of this book.

For many people energy comes from the electric outlet or the gas station pump. Few people know much about the oil wells or coal mines from which our energy comes or the impacts they create. This section looks at some of the effects of the energy production–consumption cycle. This chain of events, called an **energy fuel cycle**, or **energy system**, is composed of many stages, as illustrated in Figure 11-4. The major phases are exploration, extraction, processing, distribution, and end use. The most not-

able environmental impacts occur at the extraction and end-use phases.

When you turn up your thermostat in the winter, you trigger (indirectly) a series of events that you are barely aware of. If you live in the East, for instance, miles away from your home miners are drilling into the hills searching for seams of coal. Because of new regulations on exploration in hilly terrain, their activities do little damage today, but years ago bulldozers were used to strip away surface soils to explore for coal. The excavated soil was simply pushed over the side of the exploratory cut, creating ugly scars, landslides, and severe erosion problems.

Other workers descend into mines where they will remove coal that has been exposed by deep tunnels. Coal mines are notorious for explosions and cave-ins, which make underground coal mining the most hazardous of the major occupations in the United States. Since 1900 more than 100,000 Americans have been killed in underground coal mines, and 1 million have been permanently

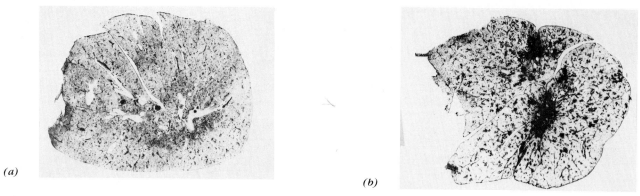

(a)

(b)

Figure 11-5 (*a*) A cross section of a normal lung. (*b*) A cross section of a lung from a retired coal miner with black lung.

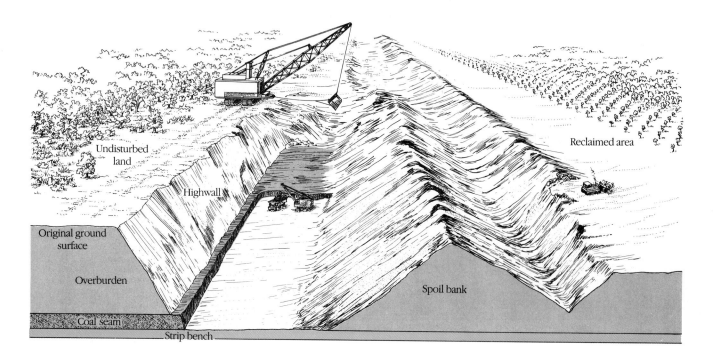

Undisturbed land

Highwall

Reclaimed area

Original ground surface

Overburden

Spoil bank

Coal seam

Strip bench

Figure 11-6 A strip mine (above). Dragline removes the overburden to expose the coal seam. Aerial view of a strip mine (left). If land is not carefully reclaimed, it could be permanently ruined.

Figure 11-7 Contour strip mining is common in the hilly terrain of eastern U.S. coal fields. Until recently, overburden was dumped on the downslope, creating enormous erosion problems.

disabled. Thanks to stricter safety regulations deaths have dropped substantially in the last 50 years. Underground coal mines also cause **black lung**, or **pneumoconiosis**, a progressive, debilitating disease caused by breathing coal dust and other particles (Figure 11-5). Victims have difficulty getting enough oxygen because the tiny air sacs (alveoli) in the lungs break down. Exercise becomes difficult, and death is slow and painful. Despite safety improvements one-third of all underground coal mines still have conditions conducive to black lung, a problem that costs taxpayers over $1 billion a year in federal worker disability benefits.

Collapsing mines not only kill workers but also cause subsidence, a sinking of the surface. Cracks form on the surface, ruining good farmland. In some cases streams vanish in the cracks. Over 800,000 hectares (2 million acres) of land has already subsided in the United States from underground coal mining. For every hectare of coal mined in central Appalachia, over 5 hectares (12.5 acres) of surface becomes vulnerable to subsidence.

In the West coal is largely mined in **strip mines** (Figure 11-6). In surface mining operations the topsoil is first removed by scrapers and is set aside for later reapplication. Next, the **overburden**, the rock and dirt overlying the coal seam, is dynamited and removed by huge shovels, called **draglines**, to expose the coal seam. The coal is removed and hauled away, and then another parallel strip is cut. The overburden from the new cut is placed in the

previous one, as illustrated in Figure 11-6. The overburden is then regraded to the approximate original contour, and the topsoil is replaced. Seeds are sown, increasing the likelihood that the area will revegetate.

Strip mines create eyesores, destroy wildlife habitat and grazing land, and may increase erosion. Destroying the natural vegetation and stockpiling overburden in spoil piles in the hilly terrain of Kentucky, for instance, have been shown to increase erosion from .4 metric tons per hectare to 2.4 to 145 metric tons per hectare (Figure 11-7). Proper reclamation can restore wildlife habitat and grazing land and eliminate the eyesores, but unless reclamation is carried out immediately after mining, erosion can become a major problem.

Surface mines can also disrupt and pollute groundwater supplies in the West, because many aquifers are located near or in coal seams. In Decker, Montana, extraction of coal from an aquifer seam resulted in a drop in the water table of 3 meters (10 feet) or more within a 3-kilometer (2-mile) radius of the mine. Residents who depended on the aquifer were forced to find new water supplies.

The dirt roads that transport the workers to the mines create enormous problems in hilly eastern regions if they have not been properly built. During heavy rains, for instance, sediment from the roadways washes into nearby streams, killing fish and other aquatic organisms. Sediment also fills streams, reducing their water-carrying

Novel Approaches to Energy Production

Rising energy prices have inspired many people to come up with their own solutions to creating energy.

- In Miami, the Florida Power & Light Company burns confiscated bales of marijuana, courtesy of the U.S. Customs Department, for power. The marijuana provides enough energy to produce electricity for one of its plants.

- "There's a future in sludge" says James E. Alleman, Associate Professor of Civil Engineering at Purdue University. Alleman says that sludge, the solid material left over after sewage treatment, can replace 30% of the clay needed to make bricks. Sludge has also been tested in other products, including fences and telephone poles. It is cheap, easy to come by, and helps reduce outside energy use because it releases heat as it burns.

- In Midlothian, Virginia, Stephen Harris found a way to turn paper waste into an inexpensive fuel source for a magazine printing plant. He devised a system to shred and burn the plant's excess paper, producing enough steam and heat to generate power for both machinery and lighting. He says the system should pay for itself in about ten years.

- At the Knouse Foods Co-op in Peach Glen, Pennsylvania, a food-processing plant is partially run on the sticky, fibrous pulp left over from fruits after juicing. The pulp, which has long created a problem in landfills because of its slow decomposition, is now dried and then burned, generating 60% of the plant's energy needs. The steam is also used to pasteurize apple juice. Company spokesmen report that their new system actually nets a profit of $474 per day.

- A thermal blanket helps prevent ice from melting in an indoor skating rink in Johnstown, Pennsylvania. When the rink is not being used, the blanket covers the ice, saving 54% on electric bills and 24% on heating bills. This is quite a bit when a typical electric bill for such a rink usually runs up to $12,000 per month.

- The Prudential Insurance Company uses an "ice pond" to help cut air con-

ditioning costs by about $12,000 a year. Theodore Taylor, the inventor, created the .2-hectare (half-acre) pond by using a snow-making machine. The mountain of ice was then covered with a thermal blanket. As the ice slowly melted throughout the summer, the cold water was pumped into the building air ducts to help cool circulating air.

- Bill Schultz of Grants Pass, Oregon, used rabbit power for 18 months to heat his greenhouse. Because a bunny's average temperature is 40° C (102.6° F), about 400 rabbits were able to match the heat produced by one commercial greenhouse heater—180,000 BTUs per hour. When it was 0° C (32° F) outside, it was 13°C (56° F) inside the greenhouse. Schultz saved about $25 a day in heating costs thanks to his rabbits. Adding to his profits, he sold $300 to $400 worth of rabbits each week to food outlets. His experiment ended when the stores were finally inundated with rabbit fryers.

Source: Adapted from *International Wildlife*, 1983, by Phyllis Lehmann.

---

capacity. When rain falls, water spills over the streams' banks, flooding farms and communities.

Many abandoned coal mines in the East leak sulfuric acid into streams. **Acid mine drainage**, as it is called, consists of sulfuric acid formed from water, air, and sulfides (iron pyrite) in the mine. Acid mine drainage kills plants and animals and inhibits bacterial decay of organic matter in water, thus allowing large quantities of organic matter to build up in streams. The sulfuric acid also leaches toxic elements such as aluminum, copper, zinc, and magnesium from the soil and carries them to streams.

Acid can render water unfit for drinking and lakes unsuitable for swimming. Municipal and industrial water must be chemically neutralized before use. Acid also corrodes iron and steel pumps, bridges, locks, barges, and ships, causing damage estimated in the millions of dollars each year.

U.S. mines, most of them abandoned, produce about 2.7 million metric tons of acid a year. Acid mine drainage pollutes over 11,000 kilometers (7000 miles) of U.S. streams, 90% of which are in Appalachia (Figure 11-8). Further increases in coal production could increase acid mine drainage, although awareness of the problem has brought about many efforts to reduce it. In any case, cleaning up the abandoned mines could take decades and billions of dollars.

Underground mines produce enormous quantities of wastes, which are transported to the surface and dumped around the mouth of the mine. These wastes, called **mine tailings**, often wash into streams during heavy rains. The sediment, laden with heavy metals, acids, and other pollutants, taints nearby streams. Coal-cleaning plants, which are designed to crush the coal and wash away impurities, produce enormous quantities of waste. These wastes are

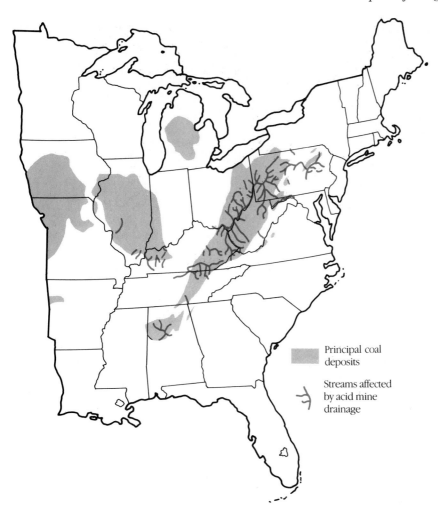

Figure 11-8 Streams affected by acid mine drainage in the United States.

Principal coal deposits

Streams affected by acid mine drainage

often stored in holding ponds that sometimes leak and pollute nearby streams.

Railroad workers load the coal and ship it off to power plants, where it will be transported by conveyer into the furnaces. Diesel trains pollute the air with a black cloud of particulates and other potentially harmful pollutants, such as sulfur dioxide.

About two-thirds of U.S. coal is burned to generate electricity. The remainder is burned in various industrial processes to create heat or to produce steel and other metals. Numerous environmental pollutants are produced during coal combustion. The most notable are waste heat (Chapter 16), particulates, sulfur oxides, nitrogen oxides, and oxides of carbon (carbon monoxide and carbon dioxide). The formation and effects of air pollutants are discussed in Chapter 15.

A 1000-megawatt coal-fired power plant, which produces electricity for about 1 million people, burns about 2.7 million metric tons of coal each year. In the process it produces about 5 million metric tons of carbon dioxide, about 18,000 metric tons of nitrogen oxides, 11,000 to

110,000 metric tons of sulfur oxides, and 1500 to 30,000 metric tons of particulates.

Coal combustion produces millions of tons of potentially harmful chemical substances in the United States and abroad, causing billions of dollars in damage to fish, lakes, buildings, and human health. Pollution control devices aimed at reducing atmospheric contamination create enormous quantities of solid waste, which is now being disposed of in landfills. For example, a fine dust known as fly ash is formed during combustion. Fly ash comes from the mineral matter that makes up 10% to 30% of the weight of uncleaned coal. It is carried up the smokestack with the escaping gases and, if it is captured by pollution control devices, becomes a solid waste. Sulfur dioxide gas is also emitted from the stack but can be removed by **smokestack scrubbers** (described in Chapter 15). Scrubbers produce a toxic sludge, containing fly ash and sulfur compounds, that must be disposed of. Some mineral matter that is too heavy to form fly ash remains at the bottom of the coal-burning furnace as bottom ash. It, too, must be disposed of. The wastes from coal-burning

Table 11-1 Major Environmental Impacts of Fossil Fuels

Fuel	Extraction	Transportation	End Uses
Coal	Destruction of wildlife habitat, soil erosion from roadways and mine sites, sedimentation, aquifer depletion and pollution, acid mine drainage, subsidence, black lung disease, accidental death	Air pollution and noise from diesel trains	Air pollution from power plants and factories—especially acid pollutants and carbon dioxide, thermal pollution of waterways
Oil	Offshore leaks and blowouts causing water pollution and damage to fish, shellfish, birds, and beaches; subsidence near wells	Oil spills from ships or pipelines	Air pollution similar to that from coal
Natural gas	Subsidence and explosions	Explosions, land disturbance from pipelines	Fewer air pollutants than coal and oil, but nitrogen oxides and carbon dioxide

furnaces and their pollution control devices are generally buried in the ground, but toxic substances from these sites may leak into groundwater supplies, polluting them.

A 1000-megawatt power plant may produce 180,000 to 680,000 metric tons of solid waste each year, including fly ash, bottom ash, and sludge from scrubbers. By 1990 U.S. coal-fired power plants may be producing 110 million metric tons of solid waste per year.

A simple flick of the switch by millions of consumers indirectly kills fish, buries streams in sediment, increases flooding, destroys wildlife habitat, and fills the sky with hazardous pollutants. By understanding the hidden consequences of energy consumption, we can acknowledge that all of us are to blame for the long list of environmental problems discussed in this text. Knowing that the problems arise from our actions may stimulate us to take steps to reduce our contribution—say, by cutting back on waste. Knowing is not enough. Action is required.

Figure 11-4 showed that our three main fuels (oil, coal, and natural gas) have similar cycles. Table 11-1 lists some of the major impacts of energy production and consumption. More specifics are given in Part 4, on pollution.

Energy Trends: Supplies and Demands

Since 1860 energy use has grown worldwide at a rate of 5% a year, except for brief respites in the Great Depres-

sion years 1930–1935 and in the recent worldwide economic recession of the early 1980s. In 1980 global consumption had risen to 250 quadrillion British thermal units (BTUs), or 250 quads. The United States used one-third of that energy. Assuming a growth rate in energy use of 4% to 5% a year, world energy consumption could be 550 to 600 quads by 2000, over twice what it was in 1980. Will there be enough fossil fuel energy to meet these demands?

Answering this question is not easy, primarily because the amount of fossil fuel within the earth's crust is difficult to determine. Experts disagree on the amount of fuel remaining. Few people know what will happen to energy consumption.

With these considerations in mind, the next three sections examine the supply-and-demand picture for our three dominant fossil fuels, oil, natural gas, and coal. Rough estimates of fossil fuel supplies are compared with global consumption to give estimates of the lifespan of these important fuels.

Oil: The End Is Near

Most experts agree that when the last drop of crude oil has been burned, the world's oil fields will have yielded about 2000 billion barrels of oil. This figure is called the **ultimate production**. To date, 500 billion barrels have been produced and consumed globally. Of the remaining 1500 billion barrels, approximately 500 billion are **proven**

Coping with the Next Oil Cutoff

James T. Bruce

The author is majority counsel of the U.S. Senate Committee on Energy and Natural Resources.

More than a decade after the question was first posed, there is still remarkably little consensus on an answer: what course of action should the U.S. government pursue if a major portion of the world's oil supply is again cut off? The world has a dangerous vulnerability to an oil supply disruption, and this threat is likely to persist for decades. More than half of the world's estimated proved reserves of crude oil lie in countries bordering the politically unstable Persian Gulf.

Nearly all observers agree that extensive government regulation in the market is a hazardous policy, as illustrated in the last two oil cutoffs, in 1973 and 1979. The dynamics of the market are too complicated for governmental regulations to anticipate or control precisely. But everyone, including free-market advocates, agrees that there will be intense political pressure from the public for heavy government involvement, especially if the crisis becomes a matter of life or death—in the figurative sense for businesses and in the literal sense for the poor. I believe that, as in any other crisis involving public health and welfare, selected government intervention to mitigate or prevent tragedy is a governmental obligation.

The chief federal program designed to cope with an oil shortage is the Strategic Petroleum Reserve (SPR). The SPR stored over 375 million barrels in salt caverns in Louisiana and Texas at the end of 1983. If there is any unanimity of opinion on emergency preparedness it is on the need for a large SPR, but there is debate over when and to whom this oil ought to be sold.

There are several reasons why government intervention in the market in a severe oil shortage will be unavoidable. First,

even if the federal government refuses to address the crisis, the state and local governments are certain to intervene, probably creating a web of conflicting laws that could make the situation worse. As of April 15, 1982, 41 states had provided their governors with statutory powers to intervene in an energy supply emergency. In the same year, however, President Ronald Reagan pointed out that the courts would strike down any local laws regarding petroleum regulations that were unconstitutional.

Second, the United States is a signatory to the International Energy Agreement (IEA), in which it pledges to share its oil with 20 other nations in the free world and achieve a specified amount of reduction in U.S. consumption of oil in a severe energy supply disruption. A test exercise in the summer of 1983 simulated what would happen if Persian Gulf oil shipments were halted. In this test the Reagan administration attempted to fulfill its IEA obligations by sharing oil with its allies and reducing U.S. consumption of oil by relying exclusively on voluntary cooperation between oil companies and high oil prices to curb petroleum demand. The result was a failure. Consequently, not only do U.S. allies now question the sincerity of the U.S. commitment to the IEA, but it appears doubtful whether the country can credibly affirm those commitments without intervening in the domestic market.

Third, Department of Energy officials acknowledge that in a dire oil shortage some form of federal aid for the poor is probably inevitable. Unless this financial assistance is planned in advance of the shortage, it may come too late, encouraging Congress to respond with price controls.

Fourth, the oil market in a severe oil crisis is not a "free market," even in the absence of government controls. When oil companies don't have sufficient product to meet their contractual obligations, they shun new customers and allocate what they have, offering each distributor (based on historical purchases) a pro rata share of what is available. This is a contractual if not a legal obligation. Thus, in a severe oil shortage an allocation system run by the oil companies will be imposed across the country. Additionally, in a severe disruption prices may not rise to keep demand in balance with supply. There is ample evidence from past oil shortages that some large oil companies actually underpriced their products—particularly in frigid areas—probably for fear of provoking governmental reaction. The result is that in a severe petroleum disruption the "free market" will involve a multitude of allocation systems and lag times in moving petroleum products to customers dependent on the oil suppliers hardest hit by the shortage. Amid the suspicions that inevitably arise in a severe energy supply disruption, the public may perceive little advantage in the "free market" that evolves early in the short-

◀ *Viewpoint (continued)*

age as compared with a market subject to government control.

For the reasons cited above, a noninterventionist policy will probably be unworkable in the next major oil crisis. The real issue is whether the government will seek intervention in the market and contain the powerful political pressures that will arise or will instead adopt a laissez-faire approach that will be inevitably overwhelmed by these political forces and replaced by congressionally imposed federal regulatory programs, hastily fashioned in the heat of the crisis. The tragedy is this: without new legislation and new preparedness initiatives, the only option is the latter.

reserves—that is, are known to exist. The remaining 1000 billion barrels are undiscovered—that is, are thought to exist.

On the surface it appears as if the world is blessed with an abundance of crude oil. This illusion quickly shatters when we compute how quickly that oil may be used up by the energy-hungry world we live in. At the current rate of consumption the 500 billion barrels of proven reserves would last only about 25 years; the remaining 1000 billion barrels, if indeed they exist, would last about 50 years.

Seventy-five years of oil—that's the good news. Now for the bad news: Any increase in the rate of oil consumption would drastically cut the lifespan of oil. With much of the Third World struggling to industrialize and the developed world still increasing in population and industrial output, an increase in oil consumption is very likely. The startling conclusion is that even a modest increase in energy use could cut the 75-year supply of oil in half.

Making matters even worse, long before the last drop is burned, signs of failure will be evident. You can understand this by studying Figure 11-9. These graphs show that petroleum production in the United States and the world is expected to follow a bell-shaped curve. Annual oil production rises to a peak and then begins to fall as reserves are depleted. As the proven reserves decline, oil companies are forced to work harder and harder to maintain production. But continued high demand will inevitably outstrip supplies, resulting in worldwide shortages and exorbitant oil prices. If alternative energy sources are not available, industry will suffer. Countries that have not developed other energy options will experience economic turmoil: inflation, economic stagnation, and widespread unemployment.

Global oil production is expected to peak sometime around 2000 or 2010. U.S. oil production peaked in 1975. At that time half of the domestic supplies had been extracted and consumed. Despite greatly increased efforts the United States produced only 8.8 million barrels of oil per day in 1984, compared with 11 million in 1973. As a measure of how hard it is getting to find oil, in 1973

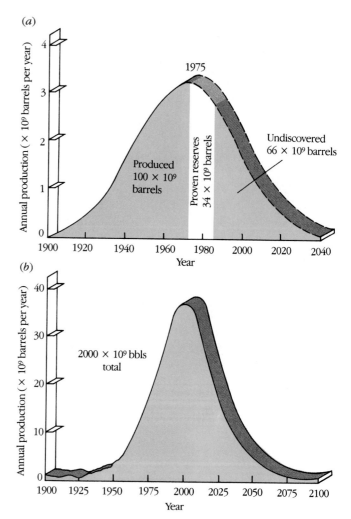

Figure 11-9 Petroleum production curves for the United States (*a*) and the world (*b*).

nearly 10,000 oil wells were producing more barrels of oil per day than 40,000 wells in 1984.

Fortunately, trend need not be destiny. Restraint, through conservation, and our ingenuity can rescue the world from the impending disaster. To prevent widespread economic turmoil, however, we must act soon. If we learn nothing else from the bell-shaped curves in Figure 11-9 we should learn that to maintain our standard of living we must find something to replace oil, which powers our transportation system, heats our homes, and provides the raw materials for plastics and other synthetic materials, such as nylon. The replacements must come soon. Guidelines for wise energy choices are presented later in this chapter. Some energy options are discussed in Chapter 12.

Natural Gas: A Better Outlook

The outlook for natural gas is considerably brighter than the outlook for oil, although experts debate the size of our ultimate production. Estimates range from 5,000 to 12,000 trillion cubic feet. Taking 10,000 trillion cubic feet as the most reasonable estimate, let's examine the global outlook. About 2000 trillion cubic feet of natural gas has already been produced and consumed, leaving 8000. Of this, 2000 is proven reserve (we know it exists), and 6000 is yet to be discovered.

How long will the global supply of natural gas last? At the current rate of usage (50 trillion cubic feet per year), proven global reserves would last about 40 years. The as-yet-undiscovered reserves would last about 120 more years. As with oil, increased consumption could cut the lifespan of natural gas considerably, perhaps by as much as half. At least for the time being it appears that global supplies are adequate. In the United States, however, the picture is dimmer. The total known reserves of natural gas are about 200 trillion cubic feet. This is expected to last slightly less than 40 years. Since domestic gas production has already peaked and continues to drop, prices are likely to shoot upward. The rise in costs suggests a need for cheaper options and, especially, a need for more conservation.

Coal: The Brightest but the Dirtiest?

Coal is the world's most abundant nonrenewable fossil fuel. World proven reserves (estimated to be 786 billion tons) will last 200 years at the current rate of consumption. **Total resources** (all the coal in the ground) are estimated at 12,600 billion metric tons; half are believed to be recoverable. (Some energy analysts think that this estimate exaggerates the reserves by five or six times.) The recoverable reserves (an estimated 6300 billion tons) would last 1700 years. Growth rates of 4% to 5% would greatly reduce the lifespan of coal, but the large surplus suggests that coal could be with us for many years to come. Coal will probably play a large role in the near term, for it can also be used to make liquid fuels to power our transportation systems and can be converted into a synthetic natural gas for home heating. (See Chapter 12 for a discussion of synthetic fuels from coal.)

The United States has about 30% of the world's coal proven reserves, or about 225 billion metric tons that can be recovered. This could last the country 100 to 200 years even at increased rates of consumption. It is believed that at least 360 billion additional metric tons of coal can be recovered in the United States, giving Americans a supply of coal that could last several hundred years.

Unfortunately, coal is not a clean-burning fuel. In fact, with the exception of oil shale, coal is the dirtiest fossil fuel known. When burned, as we have seen, it produces solid waste (bottom ash) that is buried in landfills. Particulates (fly ash) can escape up the smokestacks. Harmful gases are released into the air; some of them are converted into dangerous acids in the atmosphere. New and cleaner ways to burn coal are being developed, but progress has been slow. New technologies to burn coal and pollution control devices may help lessen the environmental damage, although some problems such as carbon dioxide pollution are inescapable. (Chapter 15 and Chapter Supplement 15-1 discuss the pollution problems associated with coal in more detail.)

Our Energy Future

The twin oil embargoes of the 1970s spurred many energy-dependent countries into action. Most cut back on consumption and sought to become energy independent by increasing their domestic fuel production. But the crisis also began a colossal debate on energy—particularly, on which sources should form the foundation of our future.

Hard Paths and Soft Paths

Participants in this debate often line up in two camps. On one hand are the advocates of large, centralized sources such as the coal and nuclear power plants in operation today (Figure 11-10). Amory Lovins, an energy consultant and author, coined the term **hard path** to describe this option. The hard path relies primarily on nonrenewable energy resources, at least to meet near-term needs. Advocates of this path generally believe in the **technological fix**, arguing that new technologies or improvements in existing technologies are the answer to our energy problems. Hard-path strategies generally involve extensive distribution networks to transport energy from sources to the end users and have many advantages, discussed in A. David Rossin's essay in Chapter 12. The alternate option is the **soft path**. Its advocates support conservation and renewable energy sources—active and passive solar heating, solar photovoltaics (which produce electricity from sunlight), wind, biomass, and hydropower. The soft path calls on both nontechnological solutions, such as indi-

Figure 11-10 Coal-fired power plants like this one produce electricity for millions of Americans. But even with pollution control devices, they emit large amounts of pollutants, such as carbon monoxide and nitrogen dioxide. Solid wastes are also generated from these enormous plants.

vidual actions to save energy, and technological solutions, such as solar panels and wind-powered electric generators. Advocates of this path generally promote decentralized energy, controlled by the consumers rather than the large corporations. They see their path as a way of ensuring a sustainable future in a world of finite fossil fuel supplies. Additional advantages are outlined in Amory and L. Hunter Lovins's essay in Chapter 12.

The debate between hard-path and soft-path advocates has had the important side effect of showing us the impressive number of energy options from which we can choose. At the same time, however, the sheer number of options and our lack of experience with them creates a paralysis of sorts. Poised between two proverbial roads, each offering benefits and risks, few of our governments have clear insights into which options are worth pursuing. The remainder of this chapter presents six guidelines that can help nations and individuals choose the energy future that makes the most sense in the long run.

Guidelines for Wise Decisions

Ensuring Positive Net Energy Production The first rule of energy production is, quite simply, that the energy we get out of an energy resource must not be exceeded by the energy we invest in its exploration, extraction, transportation, and so on. In other words, energy input should not exceed energy output. This is sound energy policy as well as economic policy.

The energy we acquire from energy resources, such as coal, wind, and oil shale, minus the energy that is invested in producing the fuel is called the **net energy**. Net energy may be positive, meaning we get more energy out of the system that we put in, or it may be negative, meaning that we put in more energy than we get out. The higher the net energy yield, obviously, the better the energy source.

One way of improving net energy efficiency is to reduce transportation. Transporting energy in any form is expensive and also requires energy. The longer the distance, the more energy it takes to supply end users, and the greater the cost. Energy sources close to the end user, such as local power plants or even solar panels on individual homes and commercial buildings, can often be the most economical strategy for supplying energy where it is needed. Indeed, as you will see in the next chapter, Third World nations are now tapping solar energy and wind energy to supply rural villages many kilometers from centralized power plants.

The idea of net energy, however elementary, is frequently overlooked by advocates on both sides of the debate. Chapter 12 looks critically at net energy yield when considering our energy options.

Energy Matching You wouldn't cut butter with a chain saw. Nor would you try to melt steel with sunlight. But for all intents and purposes that's just what people have been doing for years. We have mismatched energy sources with needs—by heating homes with electricity, for instance. Wise energy use requires a careful matching of energy sources with needs. As you well know, energy comes in a variety of forms. Each of these forms has a

Table 11-2 Energy Quality of Different Forms of Energy

Quality of Energy	Form of Energy
Very high	Electricity, nuclear fission, nuclear fusion*
High	Natural gas, synthetic natural gas (from coal gasification), gasoline, petroleum, liquified natural gas, coal, synthetic oil (from coal liquefaction), sunlight
Moderate	Geothermal, hydropower, biomass (wood, crop residues, manure, burnable municipal refuse), oil shale, tar sands

*Workable nuclear fusion reactors do not yet exist. Even if they would technically be operable by the end of the first quarter of the twenty-first century, they will probably remain economically unfeasible.

different **energy quality**, a measure of the amount of available work you can get from it (Table 11-2). Oil and natural gas, for instance, are highly concentrated and are said to be high-quality energy resources. When burned, they produce large amounts of heat. Sunlight is a lower-quality form. Streaming through the south-facing windows of a house, it produces a lower-level heat, more appropriate for home heating.

Using energy wisely means employing low-quality energy sources for tasks that call for it and high-quality energy for appropriate tasks. This approach reduces waste, conserves energy, and saves money. Energy matching should be applied to the planning of future needs, although many countries forget to do it. The rule is: determine what your energy needs will be, and then find sources that match those needs. If a community will need energy for home heating, don't build electric power plants, which are an inefficient source of home heat. Instead, develop energy conservation, passive solar energy, and other low-quality energy sources that match the end needs more precisely.

Converting Energy Efficiently The third rule of wise energy use is to convert energy into work as efficiently as possible. **Conversion efficiency** is often called **first-law energy efficiency**. The first law of thermodynamics states that energy is neither created nor destroyed but merely transformed from one form to another (see Chapter 3). Thus, when natural gas is burned, it is converted into light and heat. To measure the conversion efficiency, simply divide the total amount of work you get out of a system by the total energy input. Multiplying this result by 100 converts it into a percentage. For example, suppose we burned 10 BTUs of natural gas to make a motor work and got 2 BTUs of actual work out of this fuel. The conversion efficiency would be 20%. As a practical example,

conventional incandescent light bulbs have a conversion efficiency of about 5%. In other words only 5% of the electricity it takes to run the bulb is converted into light, and the rest is converted into heat. Fluorescent light bulbs, on the other hand, are about 22% efficient.

First-law energy efficiencies can be determined for all of our machines. By increasing their efficiency, we can cut energy use and reduce environmental impacts.

Another way of looking at efficiency is through the second law of thermodynamics. The second law tells us that when energy is converted from one form to another, it is degraded; a certain amount of heat loss is inevitable (Chapter 3). First-law efficiency calculations do not take this law into account. To determine energy efficiency taking into account the unavoidable loss, we can make a **second-law efficiency calculation**. To do this, divide the minimum amount of work needed to perform a task by the actual amount used. This is a more precise measurement of energy efficiency. Reconsider the example given above. Here 10 BTUs are used to get 2 BTUs of work. Because of the second law, however, some energy is lost as heat; that inescapable. Let's say that in this system we lose 5 BTUs. That means that from the remaining 5 BTUs we get only 2 BTUs of work. The second-law efficiency is only 40% by this reasoning when, in theory, the motor could have a second-law efficiency of 100%.

Reducing Pollution and Ensuring Safety In many respects the opposing camps agree on the fourth rule of wise energy use: to produce energy safely and cleanly. Proponents of nuclear power, for instance, argue that this source of electricity is much cleaner than coal-fired power plants, which spew out a variety of harmful gases. They also note that uranium mining has caused fewer deaths than underground coal mining. Soft-path proponents support clean, low-risk energy resources but think that nuclear energy doesn't fit the bill. Accurately determining the risk, then, becomes a major challenge (see Chapter 14).

Ensuring Abundance and Renewability A careful look at the energy debate shows that hard- and soft-path advocates also often agree on the fifth rule of wise energy use: a desirable resource is one that is abundant and, ultimately, renewable. Developing renewable, long-term resources maximizes economic returns on money invested in research, development, and commercialization.

At the heart of the soft-path advocacy is a belief that renewable energy resources are the wave of the future. Hard-path advocates see fusion energy, which uses abundant hydrogen from the ocean, as the answer (Chapter 12).

Interestingly, the basis of energy production in the two pathways is the same. The sun and fusion reactors both produce energy from the fusion of atomic nuclei. The difference lies in the fact that hard-path advocates want to make their own miniature suns here on earth and try to contain the enormous amounts of heat and radiation given off. Solar advocates prefer to let the sun contain the fusion reactions and to capture the energy that beams down to earth.

Abandoning the Old

A positive net energy balance (the bigger the better), energy matching, converting energy efficiently, reducing pollution, and achieving inexhaustibility are the principles of an intelligent energy policy. The choice of our future energy resources rests on a fair comparison of our options. Our choices should be made with these criteria in mind.

To create an energy system that is economically and environmentally sound is an enormously complicated task, made more difficult by current controversies. We must often abandon old allegiances and base our decisions solely on what is economically sensible, environmentally benign, and socially acceptable. Our goal is to design an energy system that makes sense given the world's limited resources and the need for a clean environment. Anything short of this is failure.

The trouble with our times is that the future is not what it used to be.

PAUL VALÉRY

Summary

The rising cost of energy is bound to become a major economic problem in the coming decades both in the United States and abroad. Energy is, in many ways, the lifeblood of modern industrial society. At the same time, it is our Achilles heel. Cut off the supply, even for a brief moment, and pandemonium would ensue.

Important as it is, energy was taken for granted for many years. The days of energy nonchalance came to an abrupt halt in the 1970s as a result of two oil embargoes. Although devastating to the economies of many nations, the embargoes heightened awareness of our energy dependency. Many nations took steps to conserve energy. Because of cutbacks and increased production by non-OPEC nations, the world seems to be awash in oil. The present oil "glut" is only temporary, however, and diverts public attention from an important problem: oil is fast on the decline.

The history of energy use has been one of shifting dependency, a trend likely to continue as conventional energy resources run out. Today, the United States depends primarily on three nonrenewable sources: oil, natural gas, and coal. The United States is the leading energy consumer in the world. With only 6% of the population, it uses about 30% of the world's energy. At least half of the energy Americans consume is wasted.

Energy does not come cheaply. In addition to the economic costs, society pays a price in the form of the destruction of health and the environment, effects that differ with each energy source. Because these costs are not part of production expenses, they are called **external costs**. Understanding the external costs requires us to understand **energy systems**, the long chains of events that span from energy exploration to extraction to consumption and, finally, to disposal.

One of the most perplexing problems facing society is whether there will be enough energy to go around in the future. A careful look at world oil supply and demand shows that the end is near for petroleum. Conservation and substitutes for this precious liquid fuel are badly needed. The prospects for natural gas are better, and the prospects for coal are much better. Unfortunately, coal is the dirtiest of the three.

Energy shortages stimulated a continuing debate on which energy resources should form the foundation of our future. Participants in this debate often line up in two camps. **Hard-path** advocates support large, centralized energy sources such as coal and nuclear power plants. **Soft-path** advocates support conservation and decentralized, renewable resources. This debate has exposed the impressive number of energy possibilities. The sheer number of options and our lack of experience with many of them, however, has created paralysis.

To develop a sensible energy future requires us to consider some basic guidelines: ensuring a positive net energy yield, matching energy quality with end use, improving the efficiency of conversion, using sources that do minimal environmental damage, and developing inexhaustible sources. These guidelines can help us achieve a sustainable energy system that minimally disrupts the environment.

Discussion Questions

1. What is energy? Describe the first and second laws of thermodynamics.
2. What were the results of the oil embargoes in the 1970s? How did they affect your life?
3. Debate the statement "There is enough oil to go around for at least 70 more years."
4. Describe the term *energy system*. List all of the steps you can think of needed to produce gasoline from oil, starting with exploration, and discuss some of the impacts on the environment associated with each step.
5. Debate the statement "Coal is our energy savior. We must come to rely very heavily on it to achieve a stable future."
6. Describe the differences between hard energy paths and soft energy paths.
7. On what points do hard- and soft-path advocates agree?

8. You are studying future energy demands for your state. List and discuss the factors that affect how much energy you'll be using in the year 2000.

Suggested Readings

Atwood, G. (1975). The Strip-Mining of Western Coal. *Scientific American* 233 (6): 23–29. Good background paper on energy impacts.

Branson, B. A. (1976). Ecological Impact of Strip Mining. In *The Ecology of Man: An Ecosystem Approach*, ed. R. L. Smith. New York: Harper and Row. Good overview of impacts.

Chandler, W. U. (1985). *Energy Productivity: Key to Environmental Protection and Economic Progress.* Worldwatch Paper 63. Washington, D.C.: Worldwatch Institute. Excellent look at energy costs and the role of conservation in stretching energy reserves.

Council on Environmental Quality. (1980). *The Global 2000 Report to the President.* New York: Penguin. Superb analysis of energy demands and supply.

Council on Environmental Quality. (1981). *Environmental Trends.* Washington, D.C.: U.S. Government Printing Office. Well-illustrated book on energy and other environmental issues.

Dorf, R. C. (1982). *The Energy Answer: 1982–2000.* Andover, Mass.: Brick House. A concise, readable book.

Flavin, C. (1985). *World Oil: Coping with the Dangers of Success.* Worldwatch Paper 66. Washington, D.C.: Worldwatch Institute. A candid look at oil supplies.

Gates, D. M. (1985). *Energy and Ecology.* Sunerland, Mass.: Sinauer. Excellent coverage of energy.

Hayes, E. T. (1979). Energy Resources Available to the United States, 1985 to 2000. *Science* 203 (4377): 233–239. Detailed review.

Ridgeway, J. (1982). *Powering Civilization.* New York: Pantheon. A collection of essays on energy.

12

Future Energy: Making the Best Choices

I cannot say whether things will get better if we change; what I can say is they must change if they are to get better.

G. C. Lichtenberg

You will probably live to see the end of conventional oil. Your children may see the end of conventional natural gas. Over time, coal, possibly nuclear energy, and a variety of renewable energy resources could dominate the energy market.

The shift in energy dependency has already begun. France and the Soviet Union have opted to produce electricity with nuclear energy on a large scale. Brazil has chosen ethanol produced from sugar cane to power its fleet of trucks and cars. As world oil reserves decline and population and demand increase, more and more countries will make the shift away from oil to a variety of renewable and nonrenewable energy resources. To avoid major economic turmoil, experts believe, we must start developing replacement fuels immediately. But which of the many energy options should we turn to?

Answering this question requires an objective look at all possible sources—their supplies and, especially, their environmental impacts. This chapter broadly outlines the world's energy needs, establishing a "shopping list" to help us plan our energy future intelligently. It looks at the immediate-, intermediate-, and long-range needs and then discusses the most important energy options, their benefits, and their environmental consequences. Finally, it suggests ways to achieve a sustainable system that will satisfy the energy demands of future generations.

Establishing a Shopping List

You should probably never go grocery shopping when you are famished; you will inevitably come back with trunkload of goodies that you didn't really need and a bill that rivals the national debt. To avoid such calamities, you probably prepare a shopping list so that you buy only what you need.

In many ways the United States and other major countries have been shopping hungrily for new energy without a shopping list. The exorbitant cost of this activity is now coming back to haunt us. Nowhere are the signs more evident than in the nuclear power industry. Spurred by projects of enormous electrical demand and the two oil crises in the 1970s, American utilities went on a rampage of sorts, planning and building nuclear power plants at a frenetic pace. But companies quickly found out that the demand projections were grossly inflated, and in the last decade American utilities have canceled plans to build over 100 nuclear reactors.

Canceling plans to build power plants is one thing, but more devastating is the abandonment of nuclear power plants already under construction. For example, the Washington Public Power Supply System (nicknamed WooPPS!) canceled plans to build several nuclear power plants in the state and halted construction on another (Figure 12-1). Grossly exaggerating its energy demands has cost the system plenty. For instance, WPPS defaulted on $2.25 billion worth of bonds, money lent to finance the plant that would have been paid back with interest from earnings from the generation of electricity. Washington is not alone. An Indiana company scrapped a plant that was 97% complete and had cost it $2.5 billion, enough money to make you and 2499 friends millionaires.

Clearly, it is time to reassess our energy demands and establish some priorities—to draw up a shopping list for the near term and long term. Chapter 11 discussed the future of oil, natural gas, and coal, our key energy resources today. Several important trends were observed: (1) oil supplies are fast on the decline and in need of a substitute; (2) globally, natural gas supplies are adequate for the near term (the next 50 years), but domestic shortages and rising prices suggest the need for a replacement; and (3) coal is our most abundant fossil fuel, with supplies that could last hundreds of years. Conservation, discussed later, can stretch our supplies of oil and other nonrenewable resources. It is the cheapest and quickest source of energy. Tapping the largely untapped conservation potential, many experts believe, must be our first order of business. Why throw another log on the fire when an extra blanket will do? Conserving energy should be our top priority, but even so, new energy resources will need

Figure 12-1 Washington's Public Power Supply System's abandoned nuclear power plant.

to be developed. Thus, our energy shopping list might look like this:

Short-term goal (within 20 years):
  Item 1   Improve the energy efficiency of all machines, homes, appliances, buildings, factories, and so on.
  Item 2   Find a replacement for oil (primarily used to make transportation fuel and plastics). Oil shale, oil from coal, hydrogen, and biofuels (ethanol) are possible replacements.

Intermediate-term goal (within 50 years):
  Item 3   Find a replacement for natural gas (which is primarily used for heating and industrial processes). Passive solar, synthetic gas from coal, and biofuels are possible replacements.

Long-term goal (within 100 to 200 years):
  Item 4   Find a replacement for coal (which is primarily used to generate electricity). Solar voltaics, breeder reactors, fusion reactors, and hydropower are possible substitutes.

Figure 12-2   (*a*) In a fission reaction a uranium-235 nucleus struck by a neutron is split into two smaller nuclei. Neutrons and enormous amounts of energy are also released. (*b*) A chain reaction is brought on by placing fissile uranium-235 in a nuclear reactor. Neutrons liberated during the fission of one nucleus stimulate fission in neighboring nuclei, which in turn release more neutrons. Thus, the chain reaction can be sustained.

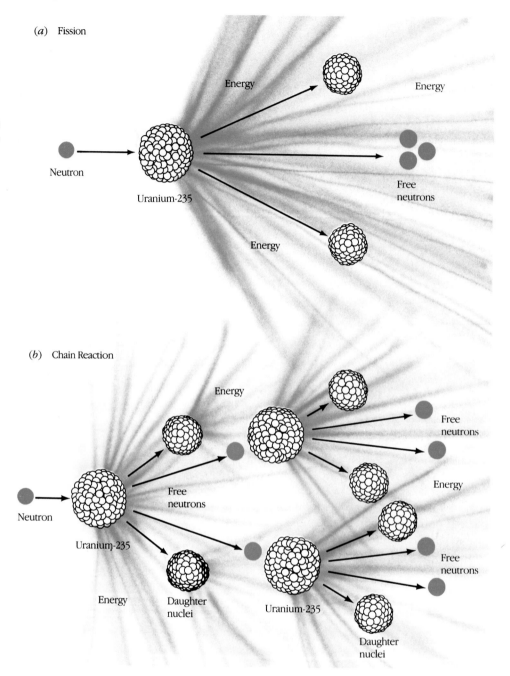

(*a*)   Fission

(*b*)   Chain Reaction

Nonrenewable Energy Resources

This section discusses future energy sources that are non-renewable—that is, ones we can exploit only once and generally for a limited time, although that time may be considerable in the case of coal. Nonetheless, they may serve as important bridges to the sustainable energy system that must be in place a century from now. Oil is not covered here because of its limited potential.

Nuclear Fission

The nuclear reactors in use today in the United States and most of the rest of the developed world are fueled by naturally occurring uranium-235. This is a form of uranium (an "isotope") whose nuclei split, or **fission**, easily when they're struck by neutrons, giving off enormous amounts of energy (Figure 12-2). In fact, 1 kilogram (2.2 pounds) of this material, completely fissioned, could yield as much energy as 2000 metric tons of coal!

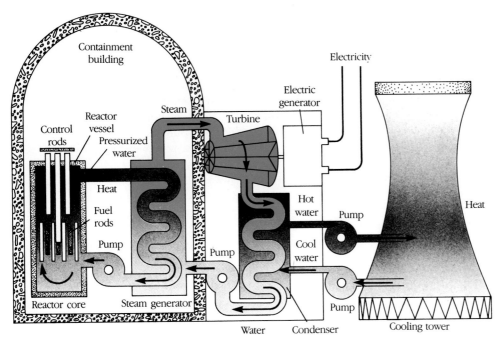

Figure 12-3 In a nuclear power plant, nuclear fission reactions in the reactor core heat up water to generate steam. The steam runs a turbine that generates electricity as in conventional power plants. Note that the water surrounding the reactor core circulates in a closed system, through which it heats up water in the steam generator. This double water heating system is used to prevent the possible escape of radioactivity in the steam.

Fission reactors basically provide an environment in which uranium-235 nuclei can be bombarded with neutrons. Uranium-235 (U-235) is housed in **fuel rods** within the **reactor core** (Figure 12-3). The nuclei of U-235 naturally emit neutrons. These bombard other nuclei and cause them to split. Heat produced during fission is transferred to water that bathes the reactor core. As shown in Figure 12-3, the heated water, which circulates in a closed vessel, heats up water in another closed system. This water is converted to steam which drives a turbine, generating electricity. Most nuclear plants are cooled by water and are called **light water reactors** (LWRs). Other reactors use coolants such as liquid sodium but operate on the same principle.

The process of fission in a light water reactor is begun by neutrons given off by U-235 in the fuel rods. When one of these neutrons strikes another U-235 nucleus, it may cause it to undergo fission, producing two smaller nuclei, called **daughter nuclei**, or **fission fragments** (Figure 12-2). Over 400 different fission fragments can form during uranium fission; many of them are radioactive. (Radioactivity is described in Chapter Supplement 12-1). When a U-235 nucleus fissions, it releases additional neutrons, which may strike other nuclei in the fuel rods and initiate a **chain reaction**. However, the chain reaction is controlled to regulate energy releases and prevent the reaction from getting out of control. Runaway chain reactions could produce enough heat to melt the reactor core in a **core meltdown**. An atomic explosion is unlikely because the fuel is not sufficiently concentrated.

The fission reaction is kept in check by water and the control rods. Bathing the core and carrying off energy, water absorbs some of the neutrons, reducing the rate of fission. The **control rods**, made of neutron-absorbing materials, are inserted between the fuel rods. Raising or lowering the control rods regulates the rate of the fission reaction. When the control rods are completely lowered, the reactor is shut off.

The entire assemblage of fuel and control rods, bathed in coolant, is housed in a 20-centimeter-thick (8-inch-thick) steel container, called the **reactor vessel**. The reactor vessel is surrounded by a huge shield, and the entire unit is contained in a 1.2-meter-thick (4-foot-thick) cement shell, the **reactor containment building**.

Nuclear fuels, like fossil fuels, pass through a complex chain, from extraction to waste disposal. At each stage radioactive materials can escape, either by accident or during normal operation, creating environmental and health impacts. A full assessment of the entire energy system is necessary to evaluate the risk of nuclear power. Before doing so, let us look at the benefits of this source of energy.

Nuclear Power: Pros and Cons When nuclear power was first developed, proponents bragged that its energy would be so cheap that it wouldn't pay to meter houses. That dream has failed to materialize. In the United States nuclear power costs about 10 to 12 cents per kilowatt-hour, about twice the cost of coal. Building a nuclear power plant is two to six times more expensive than an equivalent coal-fired power plant. Nevertheless, nuclear power has become an important source of energy, providing approximately 60,000 megawatts of electricity, enough for 60 million people. It fits well into an electrical grid system that provides electricity to large numbers of people. Perhaps the most convincing argument for using nuclear power, as opposed to coal and oil, is that it produces very little air pollution. Studies show that the release of radioactive materials into the atmosphere from nuclear power plants is insignificant under normal operating conditions. In fact, one study found that coal-fired power plants released more radioactivity. Moreover, nuclear plants do not produce toxic gases such as sulfur dioxide and nitrogen dioxide, which are converted into acids in the air. Carried to the earth in rain, snow, and on particulates, these acids can cause considerable damage to the environment. (For more on acid precipitation see Chapter Supplement 15-1.) Another advantage of nuclear power is that it requires less strip mining than coal because the fuel is a much more concentrated form of energy. Reductions in mining mean less land disturbance and fewer impacts on groundwater, wildlife habitat, and so on. (See Chapter 11 for a description of some of the impacts of strip-mining coal.) The cost of transporting nuclear fuels is lower than that for an equivalent amount of coal. By using more nuclear power in the future we would also free coal for making synthetic liquid and gaseous fuels, which can be used to power our transportation system and homes, respectively. (Synthetic fuels are discussed later in this chapter.)

Despite its many advantages nuclear power has some substantial drawbacks, worthy of careful consideration. The most important are (1) waste disposal, (2) possible contamination of the environment with long-lasting radioactive materials, (3) thermal pollution from power plants, (4) health effects of low-level radiation, (5) limited supplies of uranium ore, (6) low social acceptability, (7) high construction costs, (8) a lack of support from insurance companies and the financial community, (9) questionable reactor safety, (10) vulnerability to sabotage, (11) the proliferation of nuclear weaponry from high-level reactor wastes, and (12) questions about what to do with nuclear plants after their useful life of 20 to 25 years. This section examines reactor safety, waste disposal, social acceptability and cost, and the proliferation of nuclear weapons, four of the major areas of concern.

Reactor Safety Uncertainties regarding safety add to the list of problems. A 1975 study on reactor safety, called the Rasmussen Report for its principal author, Norman Rasmussen of the Massachusetts Institute of Technology, showed that the probability of a major accident at a nuclear power plant was not more than one in 10,000 reactor-years. (A reactor-year is a nuclear reactor operating for one year; for example, 10 reactors operating for 20 years are 200 reactor-years.)

If 5000 reactors were operating worldwide, as some advocates propose for the year 2050, we could expect a major core meltdown every other year! *Each accident* might cause between 825 and 13,000 immediate deaths, depending on the location of the plant. In addition, 7500 to 180,000 cancer deaths would follow in the years after the accident. Radiation sickness would afflict 12,000 to 198,000 people, and 5,000 to 170,000 genetic defects would occur in infants. Property damage could range from $2.8 billion to $28 billion.

In 1986, 374 nuclear reactors were operating throughout the world, and 157 were on order. If the Rasmussen report is correct, when all 531 reactors are functional, we can expect a major meltdown every 19 years.

The Rasmussen study was heavily criticized for failing to include such possibilities as sabotage and human error. The report was discredited later by the Nuclear Regulatory Commission, which argued that it had underestimated the real risk.

Perhaps the weakest point in the Rasmussen Report is the failure to consider the role of human error. Many experts believe that an accident at a nuclear power plant at Three Mile Island, Pennsylvania, in March 1979 was worsened by operator confusion. A small problem subsequently turned into a disaster. Many people argue that misjudgment and performance errors among personnel could negate technological improvements designed to make plants safer. Human errors and oversight can also occur during construction.

Critics are also concerned with unforeseen technical difficulties. A hydrogen bubble at the Three Mile Island plant, for example, took the experts by surprise. Fortunately, the utility was able to release the pressure before a catastrophe occurred. Critics wonder what would happen if the utility had been unsuccessful.

Numerous backup systems in nuclear power plants are designed to prevent a core meltdown and the release of radiation. The accident at the Three Mile Island, near Harrisburg Pennsylvania, showed that plants were not invulnerable. The April 1986 accident at Chernobyl in the Soviet Union reinforced deep concerns about the dangers of nuclear energy and awakened the world to the widespread environmental contamination that can result from a meltdown of a reactor without proper containment (see Essay 12-1).

At Three Mile Island a malfunctioning valve in the cooling system triggered a series of events that led to the worst commercial reactor accident in U.S. history. Radioactive steam poured into the containment building. Pipes in the system burst, releasing more radioactive water, which spilled onto the floors of two buildings. Some radiation escaped into the atmosphere, and some was dumped into the Susquehanna River. The accident then took a turn for the worse. Hydrogen gas began to build up inside the reactor vessel, threatening to expose the core and cause a complete meltdown. The gas bubble was slowly eliminated, but thousands of area residents

The Nuclear Disaster at Chernobyl

On the morning of April 29, 1986, Swedish technicians at the Forsmark Nuclear Power Plant, 100 kilometers (60 miles) north of Stockholm, detected abnormally high levels of radiation at their plant. Fearing a leak, they began a frantic search of the nuclear facility but found nothing out of the ordinary. All systems were operating normally. Then officials quickly began to test plant workers. To their surprise they found unexpectedly high levels of radiation on workers' street clothes, indicating an outside source. Tests on the soil and vegetation around the plant showed levels five times greater than background. The conclusion was inescapable: the radiation was coming from outside the plant. But from where?

In short order the clues began to accumulate, as similar reports poured in from Denmark, Norway, Finland, and elsewhere in Europe. A cursory study of the wind patterns suggested to the Swedes that the radiation had arisen in the Soviet Union. Swedish officials quickly pressed Moscow for an explanation, but their demands were ignored or met with denials until 9:00 that evening, 12 hours after the first radiation detectors went off in Sweden. The Soviet television announcement was a four-line, ambiguous statement: "An accident has taken place at the Chernobyl power station, and one of the reactors was damaged. Measures are being taken to eliminate the consequences of the accident. Those affected by it are being given assistance. A government commission has been set up."

The world press, by now, had picked up the story and begun to piece together the facts despite the extreme Soviet secrecy. Early reports from diplomats within the Soviet Union suggested that upwards of 2000 people had died in an explosion at the Chernobyl nuclear reactor 36 hours before the official Soviet announcement. The Soviets flatly denied reports of widespread death and destruction and downplayed the severity of the accident. They did admit in the days following the accident that 2 workers had

died from unspecified causes and that several hundred had been hospitalized; around 40 were in serious condition.

Investigators of the accident at Chernobyl reported the cause of the meltdown in a hefty report released in August 1986 by the Soviet government. It appears that plant operators were testing the plant's turbines to examine how they might be used in an emergency. To approximate an emergency, however, they decided to deactivate several safety systems, in violation of the strict nuclear power plant regulations. During the test, the cooling water flowing through the reactor core decreased rapidly. If the safety systems had

Essay 12-1 (continued)

still been on, the reactor would have shut off automatically, but in this case the flow of coolant kept decreasing.

Without sufficient coolant the 200 tons of uranium housed in the reactor's fuel rods quickly heated up. The reactor temperature soared as high as 2800° C (5000° F), twice the temperature required to melt steel. An enormous steam explosion blew the roof off the building. Flames from 1700 tons of burning graphite, a neutron-absorbing agent in the core, shot 30 meters (100 feet) into the air. While Soviet fire fighters risked their lives to contain the disaster by spraying water down on the reactor core from the roofs of nearby buildings, the uranium fuel melted, giving off a host of highly radioactive isotopes. These were swept upward by the intense heat and eventually circulated globally.

Combating the fire at Chernobyl proved to be a major challenge. On the advice of Swedish and West German nuclear experts Soviet helicopters began to drop sand, lead, and boron on the molten mass of graphite and uranium, which experts feared could burn a hole into the ground beneath the crippled reactor. Later, officials announced that the core had melted down but had not melted through the thick cement slab below. They also announced plans to tunnel under the burning core and install a cooling system to help carry off heat. In addition, cement slabs would be poured on all sides of the molten uranium fuel to keep the radioactive glob from contaminating groundwater. The plant, the Soviet government announced, would be entombed in concrete until radiation levels reached manageable levels, which could take several hundred years. To prevent radioactive soil particles deposited near the plant from being blown away, officials announced, they would spray the soil with a special liquid plastic that would harden on contact.

The Chernobyl accident is a tragedy of epic proportion to the Soviet people, made worse by their government's slow response. Thirty-six hours after the government admitted that an accident had occurred, officials began to bus 49,000 res-

idents who lived near the power plant to distant communities; 1100 buses formed a caravan taking locals within a 10-kilometer (6-mile) radius away from the nuclear industry's most tragic and costly accident. Subsequent caravans trucked off citizens who lived within a 30-kilometer radius. Eventually, Soviet officials announced, 84,000 people were relocated. Many of the victims will never be able to return to their homes. For them, 10,000 homes will be built in other regions and $284 will be provided as compensation, about one month's pay for an average worker.

Besides losing their homes, tens of thousands of Soviets may have been exposed to high levels of radiation. Estimates of human exposure near Chernobyl indicate that whole-body radiation for persons in the immediate area of the plant probably ranged from 20 to 100 rems (see Chapter Supplement 12-1). Exposures to 200 to 400 rems are known to kill half the exposed victims within 30 days; survivors suffer an increased incidence of cancer and are more likely to give birth to defective children. Exposures below 100 rems cause nausea and vomiting and also increase the likelihood of cancer. Although little information is available from the Soviet Union regarding exposure levels, it is likely that tens of thousands of people living near Chernobyl may have been seriously irradiated. Even a 20-rem exposure would increase one's chances of getting cancer.

In an effort to save the lives of people exposed to high levels of radiation, the Soviets accepted an offer from Dr. Robert Gale, a physician at the University of California, Los Angeles, and several colleagues to perform bone marrow transplants. This difficult and risky procedure is the only hope that some victims have to overcome the immediate health effects of the disaster. Bone marrow is especially sensitive to radiation; irradiation wipes out cells involved in immune protection against bacteria and viruses. Replacing irradiated bone marrow with genetically matching marrow from healthy people increases the likelihood of surviving high-

level irradiation. Health physicists are quick to point out, however, that even if these patients do survive, they must contend with a high risk of cancer and birth defects.

Within four months of the accident the Chernobyl death toll stood at 31. According to Dr. Gale, an estimated 100,000 who were in the direct path of the radiation cloud will have to be monitored for the rest of their lives for the delayed effects of radiation. They may not be alone.

One hundred thirty kilometers (eighty miles) south of Chernobyl lies Kiev, the third largest city in the Soviet Union, with a population of 2.4 million. Early reports indicated that Kiev had been unaffected by the accident, since prevailing winds had swept the radioactive cloud north and west. But the winds shifted, sending radioactivity over the city. Residents were told to wash frequently and to keep their windows closed. Water trucks washed down city streets, and residents were warned not to eat lettuce. Soviet officials also closed schools down two weeks earlier than normal so that Kiev's 250,000 students could be evacuated. Confirming that Kiev had also been pelted with radiation, U.S. technicians found that 14 American tourists who had visited the city two days after the accident had absorbed 1.5 rems, or about the equivalent of 50 chest X rays. Residents may have received significantly higher doses. A 5-rem exposure would cause an additional 14 cases of cancer per 100,000 people, or about 335 additional cases of cancer in the total population.

Besides exposing large numbers of people to potentially harmful radiation, the Chernobyl accident threatened crops, farmland, and livestock in the Ukraine, the Soviet Union's "breadbasket." By some estimates, up to 150 square kilometers (60 square miles) of land may be so contaminated that it cannot be farmed for decades, unless the Soviets remove the contaminated topsoil. Agriculture outside of the Soviet Union may suffer from the ill effects of radiation. Soon after the accident, for example, Italian officials turned back 32 freight cars loaded with

Essay 12-1 (continued)

cattle, sheep, and horses from neighboring Austria and Poland because of abnormally high levels of radiation.

Experts could also not help wondering whether the remaining reactors at Chernobyl would remain in operation. If radiation levels in and around the plant were dangerously high, the hundreds of workers needed to keep the plant going would be jeopardizing their lives. Should the plant, which had four reactors, close down, the supply of electricity in the western Soviet Union would fall.

For people outside the Soviet Union, radiation levels were generally thought to be too low to cause untoward health effects. Even though levels in West Germany were 10 times higher than normal, most health experts predicted that the

overall impact would be hardly noticeable. Even in Polish towns near the Ukraine, where levels were 500 times greater than background levels, the overall exposure was believed to have been a few hundred millirems. Even lower levels reached Canada and the United States.

Experts were quick to point out, however, that even though whole-body radiation exposures were generally low, some radionuclides enter the body and persist in tissues for many years, locally irradiating cells and greatly increasing the risk of mutations and cancer. Iodine-131 is concentrated in the thyroid gland in the neck and may produce tumors. Barium-140 collects in bones, and cesium-137 collects in muscles.

To critics of nuclear power, Chernobyl was a painful reminder of the hazards of nuclear energy and the economic costs of pursuing this controversial option. It showed the potential for widespread health effects and the difficulties encountered in mass evacuations. It stands as a symbol of the Faustian bargain we have made with the atom to power modern society. Supporters of nuclear energy say that the accident was an anomaly. Adequate shielding would have minimized the widespread contamination. But what of the costs? Can nations throughout the world afford accidents like the one at Three Mile Island, even if they can be contained, which cost a billion dollars or more to clean up?

had to be evacuated. Photographs of the core showed that a partial meltdown had occurred.

The accident at Three Mile Island had many long-term effects. It cost the utility (and its customers) many millions of dollars to replace the electricity the plant would have generated. Even more money (over $1 billion) was needed for the cleanup. By 1986 officials had not decided what to do with the radioactive water and sludge in the containment building. Bacteria proliferated in the contaminated water and might pose a significant health hazard.

The accident at Three Mile Island severely damaged the prospects of the nuclear power industry in the United States. However, nuclear advocates applauded the manner in which the accident had been handled and pointed to their success in preventing a major catastrophe as proof of the safety of nuclear reactors. Utility authorities said the accident might cause a few cancers. John Gofman and Arthur Tamplin, radiation health experts, contended that the exposure to low-level radiation that residents received for 100 hours or longer would cause at least 300, and possibly as many as 900, fatal cases of cancer or leukemia. (For more on the health effects of low-level radiation, see Chapter Supplement 12-1.)

Clouding the issue of reactor safety is the possibility of terrorism. In 1975 two French reactors were bombed. Nuclear power plants could become targets of similar attacks. Damage to the cooling system could result in a meltdown, with radiation leakage. Most plants are easily

accessible and hence vulnerable to attack. Protection from ground and air assaults may be impossible. Even though security has been improved at many plants, the threat of well-planned terrorist actions cannot be ignored.

All told, the question of reactor safety remains open. Continued development of nuclear power in the United States and abroad will give us a chance to find answers, but the cost of this experiment, many critics say, could be astronomical.

Waste Disposal One of the most notable sources of contamination from the nuclear energy system is the uranium mill, where ore is crushed and the uranium is extracted to make nuclear fuel (the **enrichment** process). In the United States **mill tailings** were indiscriminately dumped near mills and along rivers until the late 1970s (Figure 12-4).Some were even used for fill in construction of homes and buildings. In Grand Junction, Colorado, for example, tailings were spread over land before 4000 homes were built. Residents in these homes are exposed to radiation equivalent to ten chest X rays per week. The leukemia rate in Grand Junction is twice that of the rest of Colorado. Workers are now busy removing the sandy radioactive waste.

In the United States approximately 125 million metric tons of tailings have been haphazardly discarded on or near mill sites. Some of this waste has been buried and then covered with topsoil and vegetation. Nearly 11 million tons were dumped along the banks of the Colorado

Figure 12-4 Radioactive mill tailings from a uranium processing plant in Grants, New Mexico. Wastes like these have been dumped throughout the American West, sometimes along river banks where they can enter waterways.

River and its tributaries. Stricter regulations should help prevent a recurrence of this problem.

Nuclear power plants produce an assortment of high- to low-level wastes. In the United States over 3 million cubic meters (4 million cubic yards) of low-level radioactive wastes from reactors and other facilities (hospitals, laboratories) have been buried in shallow excavations. Low-level wastes are hazardous for a relatively short time, usually no more than 300 years. In contrast, high-level wastes can be dangerous for *tens of thousands of years*. The common way of measuring the lifespan of a radioactive substance is by its **half-life**, the time it takes for half of the material to decay. The half-life of plutonium-239 (Pu-239), a highly radioactive waste product of nuclear reactors, is 24,000 years. It generally takes about eight half-lives for a material to be reduced to .1% of its original mass, at which point it is often considered safe. For Pu-239, this is about 200,000 years!

Because high-level waste disposal is such a tricky polit-ical issue, few U.S. politicians have been willing to tackle it. Only recently has Congress passed a law that calls on the Department of Energy to find a suitable site to build a disposal facility for high-level waste. (See Chapter 18 for a discussion of this law.) Meanwhile, high-level wastes are building up at nuclear power plants throughout the United States. In some locations wastes have begun to leak. At Richland, Washington, where fissile ores are enriched for atomic bombs, high-level wastes have been stored in large steel tanks since the plant opened in World War II. During its first 25 years of operation the plant produced 260 million liters (70 million gallons) of highly radioactive liquid waste. Gradually, the tanks deteriorated. Between 1958 and 1973 an estimated 2 million liters of waste leaked out of 15 tanks into the soil and, possibly, the groundwater. Approximately 150 million liters of waste is still in storage tanks that could leak. Clearly, something needs to be done about these wastes and the 12,600 metric tons of waste currently held at nuclear power plants. (For more on radioactive waste and what's being done about it, see Chapter 18.)

Low- and medium-level wastes are a problem because of their sheer volume and potential for contaminating the environment. For many years these wastes have been improperly disposed of. In some cases they were deposited in steel drums that were stored underground. The drums can leak radioactive materials into groundwater and surface waters. Because of such problems half of the low-level waste sites in the United States have been closed.

Until the early 1960s low- and medium-level radioactive wastes were often mixed with concrete, poured into barrels, and dumped at sea off the coast. Thousands of barrels of waste were dumped in Massachusetts Bay near Boston; some were dumped in the harbor itself. Approximately 47,000 barrels of radioactive wastes were dumped 48 kilometers (30 miles) off the coast of San Francisco, near the Farallon Islands, and numerous barrels were dumped in the ocean near New York City. Although this acitivity has been banned in U.S. waters since 1970, it still occurs in the Irish Sea. England annually dumps large quantities of radioactive wastes there without even placing them in barrels.

Social Acceptability and Cost Two of the most important factors controlling the future of nuclear energy are its social acceptability and its cost. The two are tightly linked.

The construction of a nuclear reactor costs $2 billion to $8 billion, compared with $500 million to $1 billion for an equivalent coal-fired power plant. Costs are high because of strict building standards, expensive labor, construction delays, and special materials needed to ensure that plants will operate safely. Because of the high cost

Figure 12-5 A nuclear explosion unleashes enormous destructive power. The bomb that destroyed Hiroshima killed 130,000 people.

and risk of damage, U.S. banks are refusing to lend utilities the money needed to finance construction. Repair costs are many times higher than those for conventional coal-fired plants. For example, saltwater corrosion of the cooling system in a reactor owned by the Florida Power and Light Company cost over $100 million to repair. The utility paid $800,000 a day to make up for the lost electricity. A similar problem in a coal-fired power plant would have cost a fraction of this amount.

A lack of public support, exorbitant costs, and a rash of canceled plants in recent years have crippled the atomic power industry. Increasingly, critics argue that nuclear power may be costing us millions of dollars unnecessarily. France, which gets 50% of its electricity from nuclear plants, is thought to be paying 35% to 60% more for that electricity than it would have for electricity from coal.

What makes nuclear power so expensive and threatens to make it so costly in the future, besides high construction and maintenance costs, are poor performance, accidents, decommissioning costs, and, now, loan defaults. Colorado's only nuclear reactor generated its first electricity in 1976. In its ten-year lifetime, the plant has been shut down nearly five years because of various mechanical problems. The long "down time" means that utility customers pay higher-than-expected electric bills. Accidents and routine maintenance cost utilities dearly and raise the costs of nuclear power, as we saw at Three Mile Island.

Now that some nuclear power plants are reaching the end of their lifetime, a new and very costly problem faces utilities—decommissioning. Experts estimate that it may cost utilities $500 million to $1 billion to decommission a 1000-megawatt plant. This cost will inevitably add to electric bills. Finally, the rash of cancellations puts a huge burden on the U.S. economy. Even though utilities halt construction of nuclear plants, they must still pay back the billions of dollars they have borrowed. Customers inevitably foot most of the bill. Bondholders, who sometimes finance municipal projects, can also be left in financial ruins, as was the case when the Washington Public Power Supply System defaulted on $2.25 billion in bonds. Because of the default electric rates have increased dramatically. The region is now saddled with a debt that may climb to $8 billion or $9 billion with interest. Utilities have assumed the financial responsibility for three of the canceled reactors. The cost will be passed on to the customers. Bondholders have been stuck with the rest.

Proliferation of Nuclear Weapons At least 21 countries have the materials and the technical competence to build nuclear bombs (Figure 12-5). Many of these countries are politically unstable or are in volatile regions where war could easily erupt. Six countries—the United States, China, the Soviet Union, Britain, France, and India—have already test-fired nuclear weapons. The plutonium used in these bombs comes from special reactors

Figure 12-6 Nuclear reactions in a breeder reactor. Neutrons produced during fission strike nonfissionable "fertile" materials such as uranium-238. U-238 is then converted into fissionable plutonium-239, which can be used in the reactor as fuel.

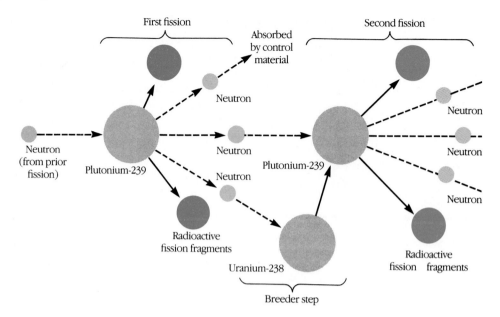

designed to make it and from conventional nuclear reactors. Critics of nuclear power argue that the spread of nuclear power throughout the world will make fissionable materials more widely available.

Nuclear fuels could be stolen by terrorist groups. According to the energy analyst Denis Hayes, with careful planning an armed group could steal plutonium from any number of nuclear facilities. "No wizardry is required to build an atom bomb that would fit comfortably in the trunk of an automobile," he writes. Strategically planted, a terrorist bomb could prove disastrous.

Breeder Reactors   The world's supply of the uranium-235 used in light water reactors will last about 100 years at the current use rate. Increases in nuclear-generated electricity, however, could greatly reduce the lifespan of uranium reserves. To counter the decline in fuel supply, the breeder reactor has been proposed. The **breeder reactor** is similar in many respects to the light water reactor described earlier. However, it performs an additional function: it makes the fissionable material plutonium-239 from uranium-238, an abundant isotope of the element uranium. In the breeder reactor fast-moving neutrons from the reactor core strike the nonfissionable U-238 placed around the core and convert it into Pu-239 (Figure 12-6). The neutrons come from small amounts of Pu-239 located in the fuel rods of the breeder reactor. Theoretically, for every 100 atoms of Pu-239 consumed in fission reactions, 130 atoms of Pu-239 are produced—hence, the name "breeder."

The attraction of breeder reactors is that they would be fueled by U-238 found in the wastes of uranium processing plants or in spent fuel from fission reactors. In

the United States the estimated supply would last 1000 years or more. In addition to providing a long-lasting supply of electrical energy, breeder reactors could reduce the need for mining, processing, and milling uranium ore. Fuel prices might remain stable because of the abundance of uranium-238. Breeder reactors also do not create chemical air pollution (if we ignore problems from mining and milling).

Breeder reactors have been under intensive development in the United States for over 30 years. The most popular design is the **liquid metal fast breeder reactor**, which uses liquid sodium (instead of water) as a coolant. Heat produced by nuclear fission in the reactor core is transferred to the liquid sodium coolant, which in turn transfers this heat to water. The water is then converted to steam and used to generate electricity.

This breeder reactor, on the surface, sounds like the answer to our electrical energy needs. It has numerous problems, however, some so great that they may make the technology impractical. The most significant problem is that it takes about 30 years for the reactor to break even—that is, to produce as much Pu-239 as it consumes, although scientists are now attempting to shorten this period. Clearly, the fate of breeder reactors hinges on a drastically shortened pay-back period. The second major problem is the cost: $4 billion to $8 billion. In addition, many of the problems of light water reactors are applicable to the breeder reactor.

Another problem would be the large quantities of plutonium located at breeder reactors. Plutonium is long-lived and extremely toxic if inhaled. The liquid sodium coolant can also be dangerous. It reacts violently with water and burns spontaneously when exposed to air.

Leaks in the coolant system could trigger a catastrophic accident at a breeder reactor. Should the core melt down, experts warn, a small nuclear explosion equivalent to several hundred tons of TNT might occur. Rupturing the containment building, the explosion would send a cloud of radioactive gas into the surrounding area.

In 1983 the U.S. Congress canceled further funding on an experimental breeder reactor, the Clinch River project in Tennessee. Having spent nearly $2 billion for planning, Congress decided that further investments were not wise. The prospects of the breeder reactor will be more thoroughly assessed once France begins to report on its commercial breeder reactor, the "Superphenix," which began to operate in 1986.

Nuclear Fusion

The sun, a solar furnace powered by a special type of nuclear reaction called fusion, has been the inspiration of humankind for millennia. **Nuclear fusion**, taking place in the sun and other stars, results when four hydrogen nuclei fuse to form a helium nucleus, a slightly larger nucleus (see Chapter 2). Fusing four nuclei, however, requires extremely high temperatures to overcome the mutual electrostatic repulsion of the positively charged nuclei. When hydrogen nuclei fuse, they emit large quantities of energy in the form of high-energy radiation. Several fusion reactions are of interest today. The fusion of two deuterium nuclei (a hydrogen nucleus with one neutron) and of deuterium and tritium (a hydrogen nucleus with two neutrons) are popular in experimental reactors (Figure 12-7).

Controlled fusion, if it proves successful, offers several advantages. The most important is the abundance of fuel. Deuterium, for example, is found in water, plentiful in the earth's oceans. Tritium does not exist naturally and must be made from lithium, but lithium supplies will not constrain energy production. The energy analyst John Holdren estimates that at current rates of energy consumption in the United States fusion would meet energy needs for up to 10 million years!

Unfortunately, fusion also has some drawbacks, which may forever make it unattainable commercially. The first of these is that fusion reactions take place at temperatures measured in the hundreds of millions of degrees celsius. The main obstacle, then, is finding a way to contain such an extremely hot reaction. No known alloy can withstand these temperatures; in fact, metals would vaporize. To contain fusion reactions scientists have devised two possible reactors, which suspend tiny amounts of fuel in air within a metal reactor vessel. The most popular technique now used in experimental fusion reactors is called **magnetic confinement** (Figure 12-8). The superheated fuel

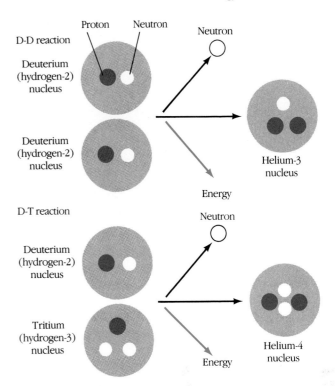

Figure 12-7 Two potentially useful fusion reactions.

forms a hot plasma—a hot gas of nuclei and electrons—that is suspended in an electromagnetic field set up by magnets inside a reactor vessel. Small-scale experimental reactors of this type have been developed and operated in the United States, Europe, the Soviet Union, and Japan. Despite 35 years of research, however, researchers have failed to reach the break-even point—that is, where they get as much energy out of the system as they put into it. Achieving this point would be just the first step in a long, costly climb to commercialization. To be economical, fusion reactors must generate energy efficiently.

In the proposed designs, heat released from the fusion reaction would be drawn off by a liquid lithium blanket. The heat would be used to boil water and create steam for electric generation. The lithium blanket would also capture neutrons, creating tritium, which would be extracted and then used as fuel.

Scientists estimate that a prototype fusion reactor could be running by the year 2000, but commercial-scale plants would not be possible until 2020 or 2030 at the earliest. Experts believe that a prototype 10-megawatt fusion reactor (enough electricity for about 10,000 people) would cost about $10 billion. The cost of a commercial fusion reactor cannot be accurately assessed at this time, but it could cost three to five times more than a comparable breeder reactor, or about $12 billion to $20 billion.

Figure 12-8 One type of fusion reactor. The fusion reactions occur suspended in an electromagnetic field.

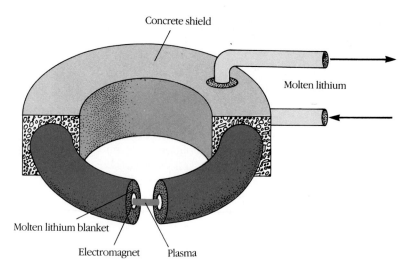

Concrete shield

Molten lithium

Molten lithium blanket

Electromagnet   Plasma

The deuterium–tritium fusion reactor is the most feasible type of fusion reactor, but tritium is radioactive and is difficult to contain. Because of the high temperatures in fusion reactors tritium can penetrate metals and escape into the environment. There are other problems. Fusion reactors would produce enormous amounts of waste heat (see Chapter 16). Fusion reactions would also emit highly energetic neutrons, which would strike the vessel walls and weaken the metal, necessitating replacement every two to ten years. Metal fatigue could lead to the rupture of the vessel and the release of tritium and molten lithium, which burns spontaneously when it contacts air. A leak might destroy the reaction vessel and the containment facilities. Neutrons emitted from the fusion reaction would also convert metals in the reactor into radioactive materials. Periodic maintenance and repair of reactor vessels would be a health hazard to workers, and radioactive components removed from the reactor would have to be disposed of properly.

Coal

Coal is the most abundant fossil fuel, one not likely to be depleted soon. As we saw in Chapter 11, world coal supplies could last hundreds of years, and the United States has about one-third of world reserves. Coal's abundance is its chief advantage. In the United States coal is widely used to generate electricity for millions of homes and businesses. Some businesses also burn coal directly to generate heat and steam. The abundant supply ensures its continued use. Like nuclear energy, coal fits nicely into the electrical grid system, and it currently costs 5 to 7 cents per kilowatt-hour (about half the cost of nuclear energy). Energy conservation and cogeneration, dis-

cussed later, are the only energy sources presently cheaper than coal. Coal-fired power plants are an established and low-risk technology, and they are inexpensive to build (compared with nuclear power plants), giving coal an edge over nuclear power. Additionally, synthetic natural gas and oil can be made from coal, providing fuel for transportation and buildings. For countries with abundant supplies coal is clearly an economical fuel to burn.

On the other hand, coal is a dirty and environmentally costly fuel. At virtually every step in the coal energy system significant impacts may occur—air pollution, black lung, subsidence, and erosion are just a few. (Table 11-1 summarized many of those problems; see also Chapter 15 and Chapter Supplement 15-1.) Surely, the impacts of the coal production–consumption cycle can be lessened through tougher laws and enforcement of existing laws. In addition, technological developments could help us burn coal more efficiently and more cleanly (see Chapter 15).

Although the price of coal-generated electricity is bound to increase as tighter controls are placed on smokestacks, coal will undoubtedly serve as a major source of energy in the coming years. Our challenge is to control the many impacts or, if the cost of control becomes too high, to switch to cleaner, cheaper forms of energy production.

Natural Gas

Natural gas is a mixture of low-molecular-weight hydrocarbons, but the main one is methane. It is burned in homes, factories, and electric utilities and is often described as an ideal fuel because it contains few contaminants and burns cleanly. Like oil it is easy to transport, but only within countries where it is transported from one location to the next through pipelines. It has a high net energy yield, too.

Natural gas is extracted from wells as deep as 10 kilometers (6 miles). On land, drilling rigs generally have minimal impact unless they are located in wilderness areas, where roads and noise from heavy machinery and construction camps can disturb wildlife. However, natural gas extraction can cause subsidence, a sinking of the earth, within a considerable radius of wells. One notable example occurred in the Los Angeles–Long Beach Harbor area. Extensive oil and gas extraction beginning in 1928 has caused severe subsidence. Over well sites the ground has dropped 9 meters (30 feet). Natural gas is generally safe to transport in the gaseous form in pipelines. To transport it across oceans, however, it must be liquified. In the liquid form natural gas is unstable and highly flammable. A ship containing liquified natural gas would burn intensely.

Natural gas supplies, as described in the last chapter, are uncertain. The best estimates indicate that enough natural gas exists throughout the globe for 40 to 160 years of consumption at current rates. Like oil it, too, will be replaced in the coming years.

Synthetic Fuels

The world is running out of oil, essential for transportation, heating, and chemical production. Three nonrenewable substitutes are available: oil shale, tar sands, and coal. Each of these can be converted into liquid and gaseous fuels, known as **synthetic fuels**, or **synfuels**.

Oil Shale   Oil shale is a sedimentary rock that contains an organic material known as **kerogen**. Kerogen is driven from the rock by heating. In a liquid state this thick, oily substance is called **shale oil**. Like crude oil it can be refined and purified to make gasoline and other by-products.

Oil shale is also found in large quantity. Deposits lie under much of the continental United States, with the richest ones in Colorado, Utah, and Wyoming. Large deposits are also found in Canada, the Soviet Union, and China. The U.S. Geological Survey estimates that shale deposits in the country contain more than 2 trillion barrels of oil, although not all of it would be recoverable.

The chief advantages of oil shale are its versatility and its large supply. Oil shale technology is not fully developed, however, and costs currently make it uneconomical to produce. The high cost of production stems from shale's poor net energy efficiency: about one-third of a barrel of oil (or an energy equivalent) is needed to mine, extract, and purify a barrel of shale oil. Net energy analysis

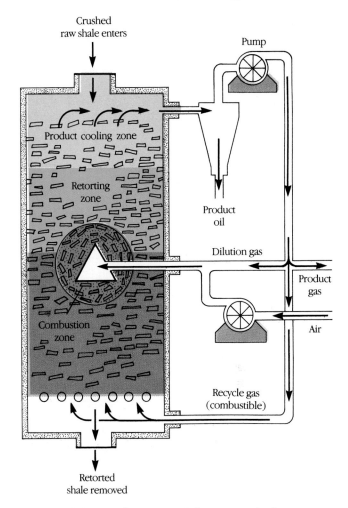

Figure 12-9   A surface retort used to extract the kerogen from oil shale. Raw shale is introduced at the top of the retort vessel. Retorted shale is removed at the bottom after being burned. Oil is driven off as a vapor in the hot gas at the top of the retort.

shows that shale oil production creates only about one-eighth as much energy as conventional crude oil production for the same energy investment.

Oil shale brings with it some environmental costs, as well. Shale that is strip-mined, as coal is, disturbs large tracts of land, increasing erosion and reducing wildlife habitat. Mined shale is next crushed and heated, a process called **surface retorting** (Figure 12-9). Surface retorting also produces enormous amounts of solid waste, called **spent shale**. A small operation producing 50,000 barrels per day would generate about 19 million metric tons of spent shale each year. Since the shale expands by about 12% on heating, not all of it could be disposed of in mines. Dumped elsewhere, the spent shale may be leached by water, producing an assortment of pollutants that could contaminate underground and surface waters.

Oil shale retorts require large quantities of water, too, but oil shale is typically found in arid country. Retorts would also produce significant amounts of air pollutants unless carefully controlled.

To bypass the solid waste problem, oil shale companies have experimented with a process called ***in situ* retorting**. Shale deposits are fractured by explosives. A fire is started underground and forced through the shale. The heat drives off the remaining oil, which is collected and then pumped above ground.

In situ retorts eliminate many impacts caused by surface mining but have not worked well, for several reasons. One of the chief problems is keeping the fire burning. Operators have found that groundwater often seeps into the retorts and extinguishes the fires. Operators have also found it difficult to fracture the shale evenly, which is necessary for uniform combustion. In addition, *in situ* retorts produce more sulfur emissions than surface retorts, raising the cost of extracting shale oil.

A 1980 study by the U.S. Office of Technology Assessment found that by 1990 the oil shale industry could produce only about 1% of the nation's projected oil needs. Huge government investments would be needed to help the industry, however. In 1985 the federal government withdrew virtually all of its support from the industry because of the poor economics.

Tar Sands Tar sands are sand deposits impregnated with a petroleumlike substance called **bitumen**. Found throughout the world, tar sands are another source of liquid fuels. Tar sands can be strip-mined and then treated in a variety of ways to extract the bitumen. Hot-water processing is the only method used commercially. *In situ* methods similar to those used in oil shale extraction are also being tested.

The largest deposits of tar sand are in Alberta, Canada, in Venezuela, and in the Soviet Union. In the United States six states have commercially attractive deposits.

Tar sands are plagued with many of the problems that face oil shale. They are expensive to mine. The sand sticks to machinery, gums up moving parts, and eats away at tires and conveyor belts. Tar sand expands by 30% after processing, and, as with oil shale, its production requires large amounts of water, which is badly polluted with oil in the process. Safe disposal is difficult and costly.

Perhaps the most significant barrier to tar-sand development is poor economics. Like oil from oil shale, synthetic crude oil from tar sands has a poor energy efficiency: at least .6 of a barrel of energy are consumed per barrel produced. Making matters worse, world reserves of tar sand oil are insignificant compared with world oil demands.

Coal Gasification and Liquefaction The abundance of coal in the United States and abroad has stirred interest in **coal gasification** and **liquefaction**. In both technologies coal is reacted with hydrogen to form synfuels. Coal gasification produces combustible gases. Coal liquefaction produces an oily substance that can be refined as crude oil can.

Unfortunately, coal gasification produces numerous air pollutants and requires large quantities of water. Many critics argue that gasification is a dirty alternative compared with natural gas and renewable energy options. Reducing pollution could make gasification too costly to be practical. The cost of synthetic natural gas is high enough without expensive pollution control equipment. For example, building a plant may cost $1.3 billion to $2 billion. An additional, and serious, problem is the low net energy production. Synthetic gas produced from surface mines is about 1.5 times more expensive than natural gas, and synthetic gas from coal taken from underground mines is 3.5 times more expensive.

Coal liquefaction is similar in principle to coal gasification. There are four major ways of making a synthetic oil from coal, but each involves the same general process—adding hydrogen to the coal. The oil produced by liquefaction must be purified to remove ash and coal particles.

Coal liquefaction could provide us with liquid fuels, but it would be costly. It produces air and water pollutants and requires large amounts of energy. Like coal gasification, it might be preempted by other energy sources that are cheaper and cleaner.

Renewable Energy Resources

Imagine a world powered by the sun, the winds, and other renewable forms of energy. Two hundred years from now, maybe sooner, our descendants may well live in such a world. Houses would be heated by the sun. Windmills and photovoltaics would provide electricity. Liquid fuels would come from crops. This vision of a soft-path energy future will be examined in this section.

Solar Energy

Oil, natural gas, oil shale, coal—all have limits. The sun, in contrast, is expected to last for several billion years. Even though only two-billionths of the sun's energy strikes the earth, it still adds up to an impressive total. An area the size of Connecticut, for instance, annually receives as much solar energy as Americans use in a year in all of their homes, factories, and vehicles. Despite the enormous influx in energy from the sun, solar energy provides only a fraction of U.S. energy needs. Contrary to popular misconception, this poor showing is not because solar is limited to a few areas. In fact, significant sources of solar radiation are available across the nation.

Figure 12-10 Schematic representation of a passive solar house.

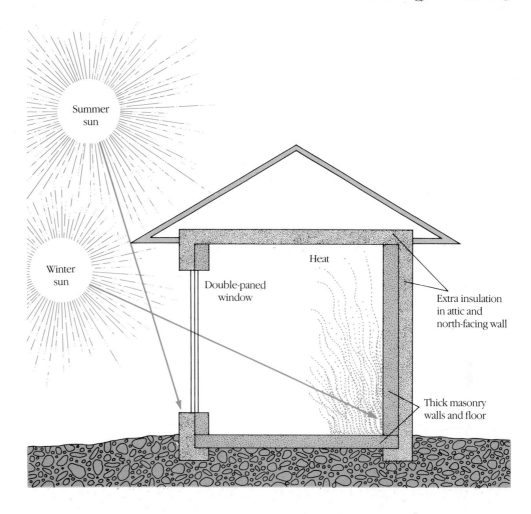

Summer sun

Winter sun

Double-paned window

Heat

Extra insulation in attic and north-facing wall

Thick masonry walls and floor

Pros and Cons of Solar Energy The most notable advantage of solar energy is that the fuel is free. All we pay for are devices to capture and store it. Solar energy is a nondepletable energy resource available as long as the sun survives. It is a clean form of energy, although construction of solar units creates pollution and solid wastes, as does any manufacturing process. Over their lifetime solar systems produce much more energy than is needed to make them. Years of pollution-free operation offset the pollution created by production. Most solar systems can be integrated with building designs and therefore do not take up valuable land.

Solar energy offers the advantage of great flexibility. Current systems provide energy for remote weather-sensing stations, single-family dwellings, and commercial operations. Solar energy can be collected to meet the low-temperature heat demands of homes or the intermediate- or high-temperature demands of factories. Some systems provide electricity to power radios, lights, and space satellites.

No major technical breakthroughs are required before we can use many existing solar systems, such as active solar water heating and passive solar space heating. Some improvements in design and costs could enhance the economic appeal of others, such as active solar space heating and cooling and solar voltaics.

Because rising prices of natural gas and oil will take a larger and larger chunk out of family and corporate budgets in the near future, those who invest in solar now could well enjoy an advantage over those who continue using costly fossil fuels. Over a lifetime solar energy can save a homeowner in cold climates $50,000 to $80,000 at current energy prices. As fossil fuel prices rise, solar homes may be the only affordable homes of the future.

The major limitation of solar energy is that the source is intermittent: it goes away at night and is blocked on cloudy days. Consequently, solar energy must be collected and stored, but current storage technologies are limited. As a result, many solar users must have a backup system to provide heat during cloudy periods. Some forms of solar energy are currently uneconomical (for example, solar cells used to generate electricity).

There are three major types of direct solar energy systems: passive, active, and photovoltaics. Understanding each one can help us assess the potential of this largely untapped energy source.

Passive Solar Heating Passive solar heating is the simplest and most cost-effective solar system available. Often described as a system with only one moving part, the sun, it is designed to capture solar energy within a building (Figure 12-10). Sunlight streams through south-facing windows and heats interior walls and floors of brick, tiles, or cement. The heat stored in these structures radiates into the rooms, heating the air day and night. On cloudy days superinsulated homes are kept warm by heat that continues to radiate from heat-absorbent materials and by backup systems.

Passive solar design requires good insulation, internal heat storage (thermal mass), south-facing windows, and, usually, shutters or heavy curtains to block the outflow of heat at night. Overhangs block out the summer sun (Figure 12-10). Passive solar, unlike other forms of direct solar energy, may be difficult to install in existing homes without major modifications (Figure 12-11). Because of the problems of such retrofitting, passive solar is best suited for new homes.

Well-designed passive systems can provide 100% of a home's space heating. One passive solar home in Canada, built by the Mechanical Engineering Department of the University of Saskatchewan, had an annual fuel bill of $40, compared with $1400 for an average American home. The house was so airtight and well insulated that heat from sunlight, room lights, appliances, and occupants provided enough energy to keep it warm. The cost of this house is little more than that of a tract home. As a rule of thumb solar houses today cost about 10% more than houses of similar size. Rising energy costs, however, could easily offset the high price.

Thousands of American homeowners have selected another solar option—the **earth-sheltered** house, built partly or entirely underground to take advantage of the insulative properties of soil. Properly designed earth-sheltered homes are well lighted, dry, and comfortable. They require less external maintenance. Partial sheltering—say, along the back of the house only—saves energy and renders the house virtually indistinguishable from a conventional solar home.

Active Solar Active heating and cooling systems rely on solar collectors, generally mounted on rooftops. Most collectors are insulated boxes with a double layer of glass on one side (Figure 12-12). These are called **flat plate collectors**. The inside of the box is painted black. Sunlight is absorbed by the black material and converted into heat. The heat is carried away by water (or some other fluid) flowing through pipes in the collector or by air blown in by a fan. The heated water or air is then carried to some storage medium, usually water, in a superinsulated storage tank. After transferring its heat to the storage medium, the water or air is returned to the collectors.

In many parts of the country active solar water and space heating are competitive with electric heating. As natural gas prices rise, active solar is likely to become a cheaper option.

Photovoltaics Photovoltaics, or **solar cells**, provide

Figure 12-12 An active solar heating system. The flat plate collectors shown here circulate a fluid that picks up heat captured by the black interior.

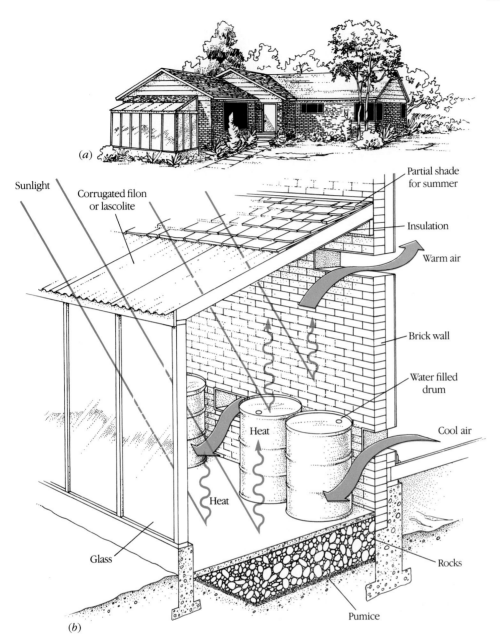

(a)

(b)

a way of generating electricity from sunlight. Solar cells consist of thin wafers of silicon or other materials. These materials emit electrons when sunlight strikes them; the electrons then flow out of the wafer, forming an electrical current (Figure 12-13).

Electricity from solar voltaics currently costs much more (five to ten times more) than electricity from conventional sources, but costs have fallen quickly in the last two decades. Experts predict that improvements in production could make photovoltaics competitive with electricity from coal and nuclear power plants by 1990 or so (Table 12-1). Governmental support of the industry could help it become competitive much sooner.

Photovoltaics may have their first significant market in the less developed nations. Many of these nations lack fossil fuel resources and can't afford to import them, or they can't afford to build centralized fossil-fuel-burning plants. In addition, the needs of these countries are generally small and are concentrated regionally.

Wind

About 2% of the sun's energy striking the earth is converted into wind. Winds form in two major ways. First,

>< *Point/Counterpoint*

Hard Paths versus Soft Paths—Opposing Views

The Best Energy Buys

Amory B. Lovins and L. Hunter Lovins

Amory Lovins is a consulting physicist; his wife and colleague, Hunter, is a lawyer, sociologist, and political scientist. They have worked as a team on energy policy in over 15 countries, are policy advisors to Friends of the Earth; and are principals of the nonprofit Rocky Mountain Institute, which explores the links between energy, water, agriculture, security, and economics.

Raw kilowatt-hours, lumps of coal, and barrels of sticky black goo are more messy than useful. Energy is only a means of providing services: comfort, light, mobility, the ability to make steel or bake bread. We don't necessarily want or need more energy of any kind at any price; we just want the amount, type, and source of energy that will do each desired task at least cost.

In the United States about 58% of all delivered energy is needed as heat; 34%, as liquid fuels for vehicles; and 8%, as electricity (for motors, lights, electronics, smelters). Electricity is a premium form of energy. It is able to do difficult kinds of work but is extremely expensive—far too costly to provide economical heat or mobility. Yet over the next 20 years utilities want to build another trillion dollars' worth of plants—causing spiraling rates, bankrupt utilities, and unaffordable energy.

What's the alternative? First, we ought to use energy just as efficiently as is worthwhile. We're starting to do this. Making a dollar of gross national product (GNP) takes a quarter less energy now than it did ten years ago. Since 1979 the United States has gotten more than a hundred times as much new energy from savings (conservation and improving efficiency) as from all the new oil and gas wells, power plants, and coal mines opened in the same period. Yet it's worth saving even more. With our current technology we could double the energy efficiency of industrial motors or jet aircraft, triple that of steel mills, quadruple that of household appliances, quintuple that of cars, and improve that of buildings by tenfold to a hundredfold. Such increased "energy productivity" gives us the same services as now just as conveniently and reliably but at less cost to ourselves and the earth.

Electricity, being expensive, is especially worth saving. We are writing this under a new kind of light bulb that gives better light than the old kind, last ten times as long, uses a quarter as much electricity, and repays its $20 cost in a year or two. Better motors and drive trains in factories could save more electricity than all nuclear plants produce. The best refrigerator we can make uses 1/27th as much electricity as the one in use today. If Americans used all the best technologies now on the market, they could be using less than a quarter as much electricity as they use now. And they could be paying, for each kilowatt-hour saved, less than it would cost just to run a nuclear plant to generate that kilowatt-hour. Thus, even if a new nuclear plant cost nothing to build, was perfectly safe, and didn't produce radioactive wastes or bomb materials, it would still save the country money to write it off, never run it, and buy efficiency instead.

Indeed, neither new fossil-fueled nor nuclear power plants would be necessary or economically feasible if we used electricity efficiently. Existing and small hydroelectric plants plus a bit of wind power (or, optionally, solar cells or industrial cogeneration—the use of waste hot water to generate electricity or for heat) would be enough. A government study showed that even if by the year 2000 the United States' GNP had increased by 66%, by buying the cheapest energy options Americans would use a quarter less energy and electricity than now and nearly 50% less nonrenewable fuel. The net saving: several trillion dollars and about a million jobs.

After efficiency, the next best energy buys are, as a Harvard Business School study found, the appropriate renewable sources. Such "soft technologies" include passive and active solar heating, passive cooling, high-temperature solar heat for industry, converting farm and forestry wastes to liquid fuel for efficient vehicles, present and small hydroelectric power, and wind power. Solar cells, too, will soon be generally cost-effective and join the list. Soft technologies tend to be smaller than huge power plants, so they can provide the cheapest energy where it's needed. Small isn't necessarily beautiful, but it usually saves money by matching the relatively small scale of most energy uses.

Careful studies in 15 countries show that the best soft technologies now available are cheaper than new power plants and could meet essentially all our long-term global energy needs.

Already, efficiency and renewables are sweeping the market, not because we say they should but because millions of people are choosing them as the best buys. The United States since 1979:

- has gotten more new energy from renewable sources than from any or all of the nonrenewables

- has ordered more new electric generating capacity from small hydroelectric plants and wind power than from coal or nuclear plants or both

- is now getting about twice as much delivered energy from wood as from nuclear power, which had a 30-year head start and direct subsidies officially calculated at over $40 billion.

Wood burning, solar heat, and the like aren't always done well. People need much better information and quality control to choose and use the cheapest, most effective opportunities. But it is faster to build many small, simple technologies that anybody can use than a few huge, complex projects that take ten years and cost billions of dollars each. And that's what

Americans are doing, to the tune of $15 billion worth in 1980 alone.

Every time you buy weather stripping instead of electricity—because you can get comfort cheaper that way—you're part of the transition. And your part matters. The United States could eliminate oil imports in the 1980s, before a power plant ordered now can provide any energy whatever and at a tenth of its cost, just by making buildings and cars more efficient. Conversely, each dollar spent on reactors can't be spent on faster, cheaper ways to save oil, and hence it delays energy independence. Power plants also provide fewer jobs per dollar than any other investment. Thus, every big plant built loses the economy, directly and indirectly, about 4000 net jobs, by starving all other sectors for capital.

In the United States 64% of the capital charge for new reactors is subsidized via taxes. The taxpayer also picks up much of the tab for nuclear fuel, decommissioning the worn-out plants, developing and regulating them, exporting them, coping with their hazards, and trying to fend off the nuclear bombs they spread. Despite the enormous government intervention, nuclear power is dying of an incurable attack of market forces throughout the world's market economies (and is in deep trouble even in the centrally planned economies, notably, France and the Soviet Union). Wall Street won't pay for more reactors; over a hundred have been canceled; and most of the industry's best people have already left.

Fortunately, the same best energy buys that are vital to a healthy economy are also keys to national security. Centralized, complex, computer-controlled nuclear plants are sitting ducks for terrorists, accidents, or natural disasters. In contrast, a more efficient, diverse, dispersed, renewable energy system could be resilient. Major failures of energy supply simply couldn't happen. Hooking together decentralized electrical sources via the existing power grid, so that they could back one another just as giant power stations do now, would actually make electrical supplies more reliable, move supplies nearer users, and reduce dependence on fragile transmission lines.

People and communities are starting to solve their own energy problems. They've discovered that the problem isn't where to get 70 quadrillion BTUs a year but how to seal the cracks around their windows. People are finding more to trust in local weatherization programs, community greenhouses, and municipal solar utilities. The energy transition is happening from the bottom up, not from the top down: Washington will be the last to know.

It's not for "the experts" to choose whether you need caulk or electricity. Pick your own best buys. The energy future is your choice.

If Energy Sources Are Thrown Away

A. David Rossin

The author is director of the Nuclear Safety Analysis Center of the Electric Power Research Institute in Palo Alto, California. He spent 16 years studying nuclear power safety at Argonne National Laboratory.

Society continually makes choices among energy alternatives. It often counts on these choices to function effectively for 20, 30, or even 40 years or more and makes large commitments of resources to them. Once commitments are made, the cost of changing them is large, and in fact it may be so large that society is unable to try alternative energy methods. As examples, consider the 50-cycle electric system in Japan's southern half and the 60-cycle system in the northern. The two force large extra costs and inconveniences on everyone, but the cost of converting either half at this time is so great that the Japanese can't do it. Or take Chicago. Its combined storm and sanitary sewer system is out of date, inefficient, and dangerous when heavy storms hit, but it is too costly to rebuild it differently.

Electric utility companies are expected to supply reliable power to all segments of society. Naturally, they prefer to build large plants that will operate for a long time. Of course, an isolated farm may get by with cylinders of propane gas for heat and windmills for electricity until a power line is built to reach it, offering a new choice. But the important thing to society at large is that choices be available and that they be rational, economically affordable, and environmentally acceptable, freeing the citizens from constant worry about the availability (and, if possible, the cost) of energy. (One need look back no further than the 1960s in the United States for an example of such an era.)

Some energy activists propose an alternative called the "soft path." By contrast, the "hard path" entails building coal and nuclear power plants linked to the electric transmission grid. The hard path is characterized by large, expensive facilities requiring much engineering to design, build, and operate. In the early days, soft-path advocates called for a stop to the building of new nuclear and coal-burning power plants and the phasing out of existing ones. Later, the theme changed. Soft-path proponents said existing electric plants could survive, and a few new coal plants would be tolerated. (Why? There was a dilemma about tidal, ocean-thermal, and large solar plants: they fit the "renewable" definition but needed the grid anyway.) The soft-path promoters had begun to recognize the obvious: the dispersed, individual, and small-is-beautiful energy sources could exist only for the very hardy and the wealthy elite. Even more important, to make any meaningful contribution to our energy supply problem, these alternative energy sources needed to be complementary to a strong electrical infrastructure.

In other words, there really is no such thing as the soft path. Ironically, it turns out to be only a strategy for closing off alternatives and eliminating some that might be preferable—the right tools for the right tasks. In fact, rather than being the cheapest, alternatives such as solar, wind, and small hydroelectric power are expensive, capital-intensive, and require money up front. These alternatives would force the consumer to pay higher electric bills or require subsidies in the form of taxes to meet their costs. (Contrary to popular belief, nuclear power plants are not subsidized. The government does support research, and thus far the greatest return to the taxpayer per energy research dollar has come from nuclear power.) Shamefully, delays have made most new nuclear power plants horribly expensive. Yet some approach half the cost of solar power.

Electric power systems with big power plants are actually efficient, resilient, and decentralized. But there must be enough power plants to generate all the electricity needed at any given time, especially at the time of peak demand. Except for a few special storage facilities (called pumped hydro dams) all electricity is generated at the instant it is used. Our well-planned systems utilize the most economical mix of plants to meet demand. Interestingly, if solar electric plants are built, they will be natural partners with nuclear plants. Solar electricity is only generated during the day, but that is when the load peaks.

The transmission and distribution systems provide diverse pathways for electricity to reach all but the most isolated neighborhoods. In the event of storms (or even sabotage) trained crews are dispatched to repair the damage. Outages occur, but repairs are made within hours, at most, days. On the other hand, imagine finding enough plumbers and electricians to put a community of individualized energy sources back into operation after a severe storm!

There is public concern about nuclear power. Even with the Three Mile Island accident the industry's public safety record is perfect—no other energy source can approach it. For a source that produces more than one-eighth of all the electricity in the country (more than gas or hydro), this is very important. There is no shortage of information available on nuclear safety. Every plant licensing requires extensive public hearings with full public documentation.

Safety risks are a serious matter and need to be understood. But part of the perspective needed involves understanding the risks of not having enough energy. Some are obvious: jobs, production, health care, living standards, schools, and recreation. But failure to prepare because alternatives are closed off or because there is not enough money to build anything means frightening risks for society.

We need not look far to find examples. Many nations have not been able to develop their own natural or human resources, because their electric generating base is too small. Some that were only recently building up their industry were dependent on oil imports. When prices quadrupled, devel-

opment ground to a halt. Inflation depleted those nations' money, and none was left to build alternative energy sources.

Ohio faced a chronic gas shortage in the 1970s. During a severe winter industries were forced to shut down. Businesses canceled plans for expansion in Ohio and moved elsewhere. The jobs went with them. New homes were not built in Cleveland for three years because the gas company could not guarantee supplies. Builders and laborers were out of work. The problem arose because stringent state regulation had prevented the gas companies from building the pipelines and tanks to support growth in the region. No soft-path alternatives could help.

In a number of nations today new factories or commercial establishments cannot be built without an energy permit from the government. This gives the government complete control over the economy; it can make or break business. There is a real risk of a society's falling into this mode.

The risks from energy shortages are real indeed. Prudent investment in long-term energy supply capacity may be vital in reducing international tensions. The threat of war over the Middle East continues, and oil remains the critical commodity.

In a democracy good energy policy depends on the public's willingness to accept long-term investment in energy supply—even in technologies given unattractive names such as the "hard path."

---

because sunlight falls unevenly on the earth and its atmosphere, some areas are heated more than others. The warm air rises, and cooler air flows in from adjacent areas. The earth's most important circulation pattern develops as warm air near the equator rises, drawing cooler polar air toward the tropics. The earth's rotation then causes air to circulate clockwise in the Northern Hemisphere and counterclockwise south of the equator. The second major wind-flow pattern results from the unequal heating of land and water. Air over the oceans is not heated as much as air over the land. Therefore, cool oceanic air often flows landward to replace warm, rising air.

The potential of wind energy is enormous. Tapping the globe's windiest spots could provide 13 times the electricity now produced worldwide. The Worldwatch Institute estimates that wind energy could provide 20% to 30% of the electricity needed by many countries with

extensive development. Today, however, wind-generated electricity accounts for only a tiny portion of the world's enormous energy needs.

Wind can be tapped to generate electricity and heat, pump water, or do mechanical work (grinding grain, for example). Wind developers generally see two possibilities: large wind farms and backyard models that supply individual needs. Small-scale generators are easier to mass-produce than large systems. They have small blades that are less subject to the stress that adds to the cost of building larger units (Figure 12-14). Small generators produce more electricity in light winds and, therefore, operate more efficiently. Small wind generators can be located close to the end user. A breakdown jeopardizes only the individual, whereas breakdowns in large-scale operations can affect a whole community or city. On the negative side small generators create a greater aesthetic

Figure 12-13 (*a*) Photovoltaic cells made of silicon (and other materials). When sunlight strikes the silicon atoms, it causes electrons to be ejected. Electrons can flow out of the photovoltaic cell through electrical wires, where they can do useful work. Electron vacancies are filled as electrons complete the circuit. (*b*) Array of solar voltaic cells. These cells are being used to power a railroad switching station in Alaska.

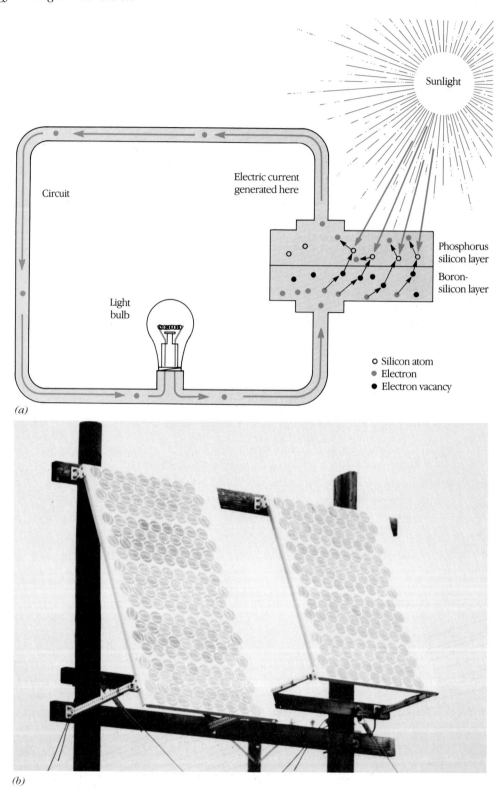

Sunlight

Circuit

Electric current generated here

Phosphorus silicon layer

Boron-silicon layer

Light bulb

○ Silicon atom
● Electron
● Electron vacancy

(a)

(b)

impact than large units on carefully selected wind farms. Individual units require a fairly substantial investment ($5,000 to $20,000), and many homeowners may not have enough knowledge of local wind resources to make intelligent decisions about the feasibility of a proposed system.

Wind energy offers many of the advantages of direct solar energy: It is clean and renewable, uses only a small amount of land, and is safe to operate. Moreover, wind

Figure 12-14 Windmill generators near Livermore, California.

technologies do not preclude other land uses; wind farms, for example, can be grazed and planted. The technology is well developed, and the fuel is free. Among solar-related electrical generating options, wind is the closest to being ready for widespread adoption. The technology is fairly well developed. The costs of wind-generated electricity are rapidly dropping, but they are currently greater than those of coal, hydroelectric power, and nuclear energy (Table 12-1). According to some energy experts, mass-producing wind generators could bring the prices down further, and by 1990 wind-generated electricity could be one of the cheapest sources available. Wind energy requires few materials. Finally, like solar voltaics, wind may become a source of energy in many developing nations.

There are, of course, disadvantages to wind systems. The wind does not blow all of the time, so backup systems and storage are needed. Storage technologies seem to be one of the major weaknesses of the wind energy system. Second, many states haven't extensively surveyed their winds, making it difficult for businesses and homeowners to decide whether wind energy would be practical. Third is the visual impact. Individual windmills and wind farms can be eyesores. Fourth, large wind generators may be noisy and may impair television reception, although fiberglass blades reduce interference by half. Some generators may also impair the microwave communications used by telephone companies.

Table 12-1 Estimated Cost of Electricity in U.S. in 1983 and 1990

Source	1983 (Cents per Kilowatt-Hour)[1]	1990 (Cents per Kilowatt-Hour)[1]
Cogeneration	4–6	4–6
Coal	5–7	7–9
Small hydropower	8–10	10–12
Biomass	8–15	7–10
Nuclear	10–12	14–16
Wind power	12–20	6–10
Photovoltaics	50–100	10–12

[1]Costs expressed in 1982 dollars.
Source: Worldwatch Institute

Biomass

Biomass is the organic matter contained in plants. It is produced by photosynthesis and is, therefore, a form of solar energy. Biomass supplies about 19% of the world's energy. In the United States and other developed countries it supplies a smaller portion of the energy needs—only about 3%.

Table 12-2 Estimate of Available Biomass in the U.S.

Type	Total Resources (Million Tons)	Total Energy Potential (Quads)	Recoverable Energy (Quads)
Crop residues	340	5.1	1.0–4.6[1]
Forestry residues	300	4.5	0.9–4.0
Urban refuse	135	1.2	0.3–1.1
Manure	45	0.7	0.1–0.6
Total	820	11.5	2.3–10.3

[1]Recoverable energy probably lies in the middle to lower part of the range given here.
Source: Kendall, H.W., and Nadis, S.J. (1980), *Energy Strategies: Toward a Solar Future*, Cambridge, Mass.: Ballinger, p. 170.

Useful biomass includes wood, wood residues left over from the timber industry, crop residues, manure, urban waste, industrial wastes, and municipal sewage. Some of these can be burned directly, and others are converted to methane and ethanol. The simplest way of getting energy from biomass is to burn it, but it may make more sense to convert it to gaseous and liquid fuels and raw materials for the chemical industry to replace declining oil and natural gas supplies.

The U.S. Office of Technology Assessment recently projected that biomass could supply 15% to 18% of the nation's energy needs by 2000 with aggressive research and development, government sponsorship, tax breaks, and other incentives. Crop and forestry residues, urban refuse, and manure could produce 3% to 14% of U.S. energy demands (Table 12-2). Fuel farms (discussed in Chapter 7) could add additional energy. One of the most important contributions from biomass would be ethanol, a liquid fuel that can be burned in vehicles. Wood burned in factories and homes can provide large amounts of energy. Burnable municipal trash could likewise help produce heat, electricity, and steam, supplementing coal and other fossil fuels.

By using wastes and converting cropland to fuel farms, we could make biomass a significant, renewable energy resource in the future. Biomass can help us reduce our dependence on nonrenewable energy resources, and it offers many other advantages. The most notable advantages are its high net energy efficiency, when it is collected and burned close to the source of production, and its wide range of applications. Biomass does not pollute the atmosphere with carbon dioxide, long implicated in the greenhouse effect (Chapter 15), as long as the plant matter burned equals the plant matter produced each year. Burning some forms of biomass, such as urban refuse, reduces the need for land disposal, as discussed in Chapter Supplement 18-1.

Biomass has some drawbacks, too. Improper manage-

ment of fuel farms and forests that produce biomass could lead to soil erosion, sedimentation, destruction of reservoirs, and flooding. Chapters 7, 9, and 10 point out some of the impacts of improper land management. Removing crop and forestry residues may reduce soil nutrient replenishment. Increasing reliance on fuel farms and forests could increase competition for their products, raising the prices of food, wood, and wood products. Biomass can create large amounts of air pollution—for example, smoke from wood stoves. Finally, transportation costs for biomass are higher than traditional fossil fuels, because biomass has a lower energy content.

Fuel farms growing sugar cane, corn, and grain to produce alcohol could help fill the need for an alternative to oil. Certain nonfood crops could also be grown to produce liquid fuel. For example, a desert shrub (*Euphorbia lathyris*) found in Mexico and the southwestern United States produces an oily substance that could be refined to make liquid fuel. In arid climates the shrub could yield 16 barrels of oil per hectare on a sustainable basis. The copaiba tree of the Amazon yields a substance that can be substituted for diesel fuel without processing. Sunflower oil can also be used in place of diesel. Farmers could convert 10% of their cropland to sunflowers to produce all the diesel fuel needed to run their machinery. Eventually, the entire transportation system could be powered by renewable fuels.

Hydroelectric Power

Humankind has tapped the power of flowing rivers and streams for thousands of years. The hydrologic cycle is driven by sunlight, making hydropower yet another form of indirect solar energy. Falling water, propelled by gravity and replenished by rainfall, offers many advantages. It is renewable, creates no air pollution or thermal pollution, and is relatively inexpensive. Furthermore, the technology is well developed.

Figure 12-15 This view of Mono Dam in California shows how the reservoir was filling with silt. In succeeding years the dam filled completely and gradually was reclaimed by the surrounding forest.

On the opposite side of the coin are numerous problems. Sediment fills in reservoirs, giving them a typical lifespan of 50 to 100 years (although large projects may last 200 to 300 years). Thus, even though hydroelectric power is renewable, the dams and reservoirs needed to capture this energy have a limited lifetime (Figure 12-15). Once a good site is destroyed by sediment, it is gone forever. Dams and reservoirs create many additional problems, which were discussed in detail in Chapter 10, on water resources.

Brazil, Nepal, China, and many African and South American countries have a large untapped hydroelectric potential. In South America, for instance, hydroelectric generating potential is estimated at 600,000 megawatts. By comparison, the United States, the world's leader in hydroelectric production, has a present capacity of about 70,000 megawatts and an additional capacity of about 160,000 megawatts.

Estimates of hydroelectric potential can be deceiving, because they include all possible sites. Such estimates do not take into account whether dams would be economical or technically possible. For example, half of the U.S. potential is in Alaska, far from places that need power. The potential for additional large projects in the United States is small, because the most favorable sites have already been developed. In addition, the high cost of constructing large dams and reservoirs has increased the cost of hydroelectric energy by 3 to 20 times since the early 1970s.

For the United States the most sensible strategy may be to increase the capacity of existing hydroelectric facilities and install turbines on the over 50,000 dams already built for flood control, recreation, and water supply. In appropriate locations small dams could provide energy needed by farms, small businesses, and small communities. But all projects must be weighed against impacts on wildlife habitat, stream quality, estuarine destruction, and other adverse environmental effects.

In the developing nations small-scale hydroelectric generation may fit in well with the demand. In China over 90,000 small hydroelectric generators account for about one-third of the country's electrical output.

Geothermal Energy

The earth harbors an enormous amount of heat, or **geothermal energy**, which comes from the decay of naturally occurring radioactive materials in the earth's crust and from magma, molten rock beneath the earth's surface. Geothermal energy is constantly regenerated, but because the rate of renewal is slow, overexploitation could deplete this resource regionally.

Geothermal resources fall into three major categories. The map in Figure 12-16 locates zones where the two most practical forms of geothermal energy can be tapped.

Hydrothermal convection zones are places where magma penetrates into the earth's crust and heats rock containing large amounts of groundwater (Figure 12-16). The heat drives the groundwater to the earth's surface through fissures, where it may emerge as steam (geyser), or as a liquid (hot spring).

Geopressurized zones are aquifers that are trapped by

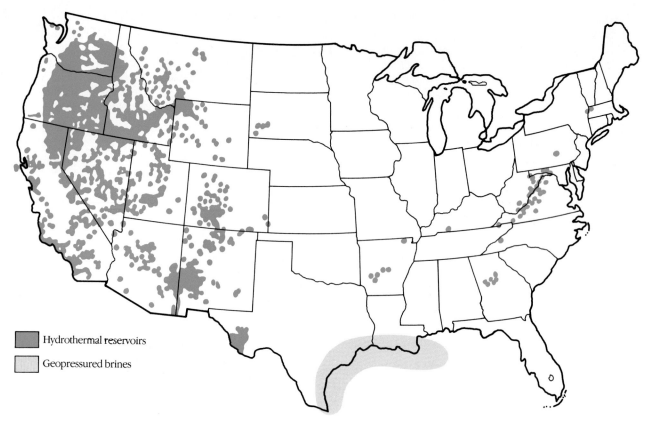

Figure 12-16   Geothermal resources in the United States.

Hydrothermal reservoirs

Geopressured brines

impermeable rock strata and heated by underlying magma. This superheated, pressurized water can be tapped by deep wells. Some geopressurized zones also contain methane gas.

Hot-rock zones, the most widespread but most expensive geothermal resource, are regions where bedrock is heated by magma. To reap the vast amounts of heat, wells are drilled, and the bedrock is fractured with explosives. Water is pumped into the fractured bedrock, heated, and then pumped out.

Geothermal energy is heavily concentrated in a so-called ring of fire encircling the Pacific Ocean and in the great mountain belts stretching from the Alps to China. Within these areas hydrothermal convection zones are the easiest and least expensive to tap. Hot water or steam from them can heat homes, factories, and greenhouses. In Iceland, for example, 65% of the homes are heated this way. Iceland's geothermally heated greenhouses produce nearly all of its vegetables, and the Soviet Union and Hungary also heat many of their greenhouses in this way. Steam can be used to run turbines to produce electricity. The Philippines hopes to make geothermal energy its second-ranking source of electricity soon. Although still in the early stages of development, geothermal elec-

tric production is growing quickly in the United States, Italy, New Zealand, and Japan. By 2000, some experts believe, the United States could produce 27,000 megawatts of electricity from geothermal energy, enough for 27 million people, about one-tenth of the population.

Hydrothermal convection systems have several drawbacks. The steam and hot water they produce are often laden with minerals, salts, toxic metals, and hydrogen sulfide gas. Many of these chemicals corrode pipes and metal. Steam systems may emit an ear-shattering hiss and release large amounts of heat into the air. Pollution control devices are necessary to cut down on air and water pollutants. Engineers have also proposed building closed systems that pump the steam or hot water out and then inject it back into the ground to be reheated. Finally, because heat cannot be transported long distances, industries might have to be built at the source of energy.

Hydrogen Fuel

Hydrogen could help replace oil and natural gas. Hydrogen gas is produced by heating or passing electricity through water in the presence of a **catalyst**, a chemical that facilitates the breakdown of water into oxygen and hydrogen without being changed. When hydrogen burns, it produces water and energy. Thus it is a renewable fuel with an essentially limitless supply. Hydrogen burns cleanly, too, producing nitrogen dioxide and water vapor. What makes it so appealing is that it does not add carbon dioxide to the air. Hydrogen is also easy to transport and has a wide range of uses, such as automobiles, gas ranges, and furnaces.

Unfortunately, it takes considerable energy to produce hydrogen fuel. This low net energy yield could make it an expensive form of energy. Hydroelectric power, wind, solar power, and other renewable energy resources, however, could be used to generate the electricity needed to make hydrogen. They are "free" energy sources and have unlimited supplies. Proponents argue that when power demand is low, renewables could generate electricity to make hydrogen economical. Still, the prospects for hydrogen are questionable today because of its low net energy yield. An efficient technology aimed at breaking down water by sunlight may not be available until the year 2000 or later.

Conservation

Conservation must be at the heart of all energy strategies. Nations that rely on energy cannot afford to waste it. Conserving energy offers numerous advantages: First, it can significantly reduce the cost of producing goods, giving industries an economic advantage in the marketplace, reducing inflation, and saving consumers millions of dollars. Second, it helps us stretch our fossil fuel supplies and thus gives us more time to find substitutes. Third, energy conservation can reduce environmental pollution, land destruction, and waste disposal.

The economic savings from energy conservation can be enormous. For example, improving the efficiency of machines and appliances—that is, reducing their energy demand—costs about 1 to 2 cents per kilowatt-hour of energy saved. In contrast, coal-fired power plants produce electricity for 5 to 7 cents per kilowatt-hour. Nuclear power plants, on average, produce it for 10 to 12 cents per kilowatt-hour.

Slightly more expensive than reducing the energy demand (improving efficiency) of machines and appliances is a process called **cogeneration**, in which waste heat from one industrial process is captured and used for other purposes, usually electrical production. Cogeneration is an emerging source of energy. In the United States it now produces 15,000 megawatts of energy each year. Two hundred more projects, which will generate an additional 6,000 megawatts of electricity, are soon to be completed. For years, most American industries produced their own steam using natural gas or oil. They purchased electricity from local utilities. The overall effi-

ciency of this scheme was between 50% and 70%. Cogeneration, however, boosts the efficiency to 80% to 90%. The cost of electricity from cogeneration is 4 to 6 cents per kilowatt-hour. Some experts believe that the United States could generate 100,000 to 200,000 megawatts of electricity through cogeneration, or about one-third of its total electrical demand.

Conservation does not mean "freezing in the dark," as some would have us believe. For factory owners it means installing equipment that captures waste heat to generate inexpensive electricity. Ultimately, it translates into enormous savings. It may mean redesigning manufacturing processes to cut waste energy, so that goods like steel or aluminum can be produced with considerably less energy and at a fraction of the cost. It can mean more profit or economic survival in the international market. For the homeowner, it may mean adding insulation to reduce heat loss, resulting in significant savings on utility bills, money that can be spent on summer vacations. It means installing storm windows that cut drafts and make rooms more comfortable. Both insulation and storm windows are small investments that are paid back in short periods. For the commuter, conservation may mean driving within the speed limit, keeping the car tuned, driving an energy-conserving car, or using mass transit whenever possible. Certainly, personal efforts require a little sacrifice, but in the end they can save us hundreds of dollars a year and can fill us with pride for doing something about the condition of the world's resources and its environment.

The United States has made great strides in energy conservation, but its conservation potential has hardly begun to be tapped. Enormous opportunities exist in buildings, industry, and transportation. Several auto manufacturers, for example, now have test models that get 98 miles per gallon, whereas the average new car rolling off the assembly line in the United States gets only 26, the lowest average in the developed world. By increasing the average mileage to 40 or 50 miles a gallon, we could double the lifespan of our oil supplies. Similar gains could be made in home heating and industrial processes.

Waste only speeds up the depletion of valuable energy supplies. It is time to change our ways. Each of us can make small changes in life-style, cutting back a little waste here or there. Collectively, our actions can add up to enormous savings. For some suggestions to save energy, see Table 12-3.

Building a Sustainable Energy System

Many observers see coal and nuclear power as the mainstays of the American energy diet in the year 2000. But others see a solar energy transition in the making. They believe that solar energy in its many forms could supply

Table 12-3   Energy Conservation Suggestions

1. Water Heating
   Turn down thermostat on water heater.
   Use less hot water (dishwashing, laundry, showers).
   Install flow reducers on faucets.
   Coordinate and concentrate time hot water is used.
   Do full loads of laundry, and use cooler water.
   Hang clothes outside to dry.
   Periodically drain 3 to 4 gallons from water heater.
   Repair leaky faucets.

2. Space Heating
   Lower thermostat setting.
   Insulate ceilings and walls.
   Install storm window, curtains, or window quilts.
   Caulk cracks and use weatherstripping.
   Use fans to distribute heat.
   Dress more warmly.
   Heat only used areas.
   Humidify the air.
   Install an electronic ignition system in furnace.
   Replace or clean air filters in furnace.
   Have furnace adjusted periodically.

3. Cooling and Air Conditioning
   Increase thermostat setting.
   Use fans.
   Cook at night or outside.
   Dehumidify air.
   Close drapes during the day.
   Open windows at night.

4. Cooking
   Cover pots, and cook one-pot meals.
   Turn off the pilot lights on stove.
   Don't overcook, and don't open oven unnecessarily.
   Double up pots (use one as a lid for the other).
   Boil less water (only the amount you need).
   Use energy-efficient appliances (crock pots).

5. Lighting
   Cut the wattage of bulbs.
   Turn off lights when not in use.
   Use fluorescent bulbs wherever possible.
   Use natural lighting whenever possible.

6. Transportation
   Car-pool, walk, ride a bike, or take the bus to work.
   Use your car only when necessary.
   Group your trips with the car.
   Keep car tuned and tire pressure at recommended level.
   Buy energy-efficient cars.
   Recycle gas guzzlers.
   On long trips take the train or bus (not a jet).

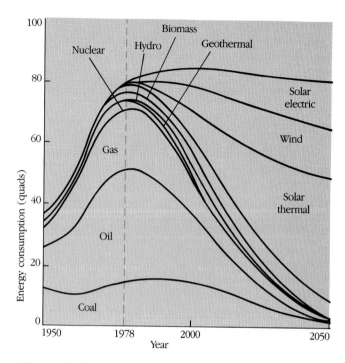

Figure 12-17   One projection of possible energy resources in the United States. These figures are based on full commitment to renewable resources.

the bulk of U.S. energy demands, along with conservation (Figure 12-17).

A renewable energy system will bring many changes. One major shift is that energy production will become a more personal matter. Conservation, photovoltaics, active solar heating, passive solar heating, and windmills will be built, replacing huge centralized nuclear- and coal-powered electric plants. Placing energy sources closer to the consumer could be a good thing; knowing where our energy comes from may help us respect its importance and use it more efficiently.

But how will renewable energy supplant the nonrenewables that currently power U.S. society? Where will the fuel come from to power the transportation system? Increasing efficiency is the first and perhaps most important source. Cars that routinely get 50 to 80 miles per gallon could double or triple the existing oil supply. Mass transit, many times more efficient than the automobile, would further stretch energy supplies (Chapter 22). To power automobiles, trucks, and buses, ethanol would be used. Hydrogen might be a supplement, but its economic prospects are not very bright. Electricity generated from inexpensive photovoltaics could power cars, trains, and buses.

Low- to intermediate-temperature thermal energy in the sustainable society would come from solar energy. Solar sources could be used for home space heating, water heating, and many industrial processes. Electricity would come from solar voltaics and windmills. Table 12-4 gives a further breakdown of energy demand by sector, showing us what kind of energy is needed and how it would be used.

A wise energy future is economically, ecologically, and

Table 12-4 Meeting Energy Needs of a Solar-Powered Society

Demand Sector	Sources	Application	Percentage of Total Energy Use
Residential and Commercial	Passive and active solar systems, district heating systems	Space heating, water heating, air conditioning	20–25
	Active solar heating with concentrating solar collectors		
	Solar thermal, thermochemical, or electrolytic generation	Cooking and drying	~5
	Biomass		
	Photovoltaic, wind, solar, thermal, total energy systems	Lighting, appliances, refrigeration	~10
			Subtotal ~35
Industrial	Active solar heating with flat plate collectors, and tracking solar concentrators	Industrial and agricultural process heat and steam	~7.5
	Tracking, concentrating solar collector systems	Industrial process heat and steam	~17.5
	Solar thermal, thermochemical, or electrolytic generation		
	Solar thermal, photovoltaic, cogeneration, wind systems	Cogeneration, electric, drive, electrolytic, and electrochemical processes	~10
	Biomass residues and wastes	Supply carbon sources to chemical industries	~5
			Subtotal ~40
Transportation	Photovoltaic, wind, solar thermal	Electric vehicles, electric rail	10–20
	Solar thermal, thermochemical, or electrolytic generation	Aircraft fuel, land and water vehicles	
	Biomass residues and wastes	Long-distance land and water vehicles	5–15
			Subtotal ~25
			100

Source: Kendall, H. W., and Nadis, S. J. (1980), *Energy Strategies: Toward a Solar Future*, Cambridge, Mass.: Ballinger. p. 262.

socially acceptable. Today's decisions about energy should take into account future generations. Perhaps one of our greatest challenges is building a system that works well for us now and will provide the foundation of a system with which our offspring, and theirs in turn, can live and prosper.

A smooth transition to a solar-powered economy, beginning now, could ensure that future generations will not have to spend their lives cleaning up a polluted planet littered with nuclear waste dumps and scarred by surface mines. Decisive actions now could mean that they won't have to struggle in the face of shortages to do what many experts believe we should have been doing all along—tapping the generous supply of clean, renewable energy that the earth and sun offer free of charge.

There are many ways of going forward, but only one way of standing still.

FRANKLIN D. ROOSEVELT

Summary

The world is fast depleting oil and natural gas, two mainstays of its voracious energy appetite. But there are many untapped sources of energy. Developing an energy strategy requires us to look at all sources.

Some of the nonrenewable energy sources may have a place in the immediate future. Nuclear reactors are fueled by uranium-235, whose nuclei split when they are struck by neutrons. This process, **fission**, releases an enormous amount of energy. Nuclear fuels pass through a complex cycle from mining to waste disposal; at each stage of the cycle radioactive materials can escape, either by accident or through normal operations.

Nuclear power offers many advantages over coal and oil. Its light water reactors produce very little air pollution. Less land is disturbed by mining. The cost of transporting nuclear fuels is lower than for an equivalent number of BTUs of coal. Using nuclear fuels to generate electricity also frees coal for the production of synthetic oil and gas.

The major problems with nuclear power are disposal of radioactive wastes, contamination of the environment, thermal pollution, health impacts from radiation, limited supplies of uranium ore, low social acceptability, high construction costs, questionable reactor safety, lack of experience with the technology, vulnerability to sabotage, proliferation of nuclear weaponry from high-level wastes, and loss of individual freedom as security is tightened to protect citizens from sabotage and theft of nuclear materials.

Supporters of nuclear power have proposed the **breeder reactor** to get around the problem of limited fuel supply. Besides producing electricity, the breeder reactor makes fissionable plutonium-239 from the abundant uranium-238. Breeder reactors could use U-238 from waste piles, spent fuel rods, and uranium ore, providing electricity for several hundred years. **Liquid metal fast breeder reactors**, the technology of choice today, have many problems. The rate of conversion of U-238 to plutonium-239 is quite slow, requiring about 30 years for fuel production to equal consumption. A liquid metal fast breeder reactor could cost \$4 billion or more. The presence of large quantities of fissionable materials packed in the core could lead to meltdowns or very-low-magnitude nuclear explosions in case of accidents. In addition, all the problems of light water reactors are applicable.

Another proposed energy system is **fusion power**. Fusion is the uniting of two or more small nuclei to form a larger one, a process accompanied by the release of energy. After three decades of research fusion is still a long way from being commercially available. But optimism prevails, for the forms of hydrogen needed to fuel the fusion reactor are abundant and could provide energy for millions of years.

Fusion reactions occur at extremely high temperatures. Safely containing such reactions is a major challenge. The cost of a commercial fusion reactor could reach \$12 billion to \$20 billion, many times more than that of conventional fission reactors, which currently face financial difficulties. The emission of highly energetic neutrons from the fusion reaction would weaken metals and necessitate replacement every five years. Metal fatigue might lead to repture of the vessel and the release of radioactive materials or highly reactive lithium.

Coal could be a major source of energy for years to come, but unless it can be burned more cleanly, the environmental cost of continued use may become astronomical. Natural gas supplies are greater than oil reserves, but they, too, will be depleted within the next century. Rising prices and the eventual decline suggest the need to find a replacement. Substitutes for oil and natural gas could come from oil shale, tar sand, and coal, which can be converted into liquid and gaseous fuels, known as **synfuels**.

Oil shale contains an organic material known as **kerogen**. Kerogen can be extracted by heating. Widespread development of this resource would require mining of extensive regions and large energy inputs, and it would result in numerous air pollutants and the production of large quantities of solid waste that would have to be disposed of safely to prevent groundwater and surface water contamination. Currently, the costs of shale oil compared with those of crude oil impede the development of this industry.

Tar sands are sand deposits impregnated with a petroleumlike substance called **bitumen**. Found throughout the world, tar sands can be mined and treated with heat or chemical solvents to remove the bitumen. Only a small proportion of the bitumen can be recovered, however, and global supplies are insignificant compared with energy demand. A low net energy yield also plagues this industry.

Coal can be converted to gaseous and liquid fuels. **Coal gasification** produces large quantities of air pollution and solid waste. Natural gas produced in such operations is expensive because of the low net energy yield. Surface mining destroys vegetation and habitat. **Coal liquefaction** is similar in principle, and it has many of the same problems.

Solar energy is abundant, but it provides only a fraction of our energy needs. **Passive solar** systems are the simplest and most cost-effective. Buildings are designed to capture sunlight energy and store it within **thermal mass**, walls and floors; the stored heat is gradually released into the structure. **Active solar** systems rely on collectors that absorb sunlight and convert it into heat, which is then transferred to water or air flowing through them. Pumps generally move water or air to a storage unit, where heat can be drawn off as needed. **Photovoltaics** are made of silicon or other materials that emit electrons when struck by sunlight, thus producing electricity.

Solar systems provide many advantages over conventional power sources. The fuel is free, nondepletable, and clean. When operating, systems produce no pollution and pay back the energy invested in their production. The major limitations are that the source is intermittent, making it necessary to store energy overnight or on cloudy days.

Winds can be tapped to generate energy. Wind energy offers many of the advantages and disadvantages of solar energy.

Biomass, a form of indirect solar energy, has some potential. Forest and crop wastes and fuel farms could be used to supply large amounts of energy. Useful biomass includes wood, wood residues, crop wastes, industrial wastes, manure, and urban waste. The simplest way of getting energy from biomass is to burn it, but many believe that a more sensible strategy would be to convert it to gaseous and liquid fuels and chemicals needed by the chemical industry.

Hydroelectric power, another indirect form of solar energy, is renewable, creates no air pollution, and is relatively inexpensive. Sediment fills in reservoirs, however, giving them an average lifespan of 50 to 100 years. The potential for hydroelectric power is limited in the developed countries, because the best sites have already been developed or are located far from population centers where the energy is needed. In the developing nations sites capable of producing large amounts of energy are available, but high construction costs may impair their development.

The earth harbors a great deal of energy from the decay of naturally occurring radioactive materials in the crust and from **magma**, molten rock. The most useful geothermal resource is the **hydrothermal convection zone**, where magma penetrates into the crust and heats rock formations containing large amounts of groundwater. The heat pressurizes the groundwater and drives it to the surface through fissures. Currently these zones are exploited for space heating and electricity. Such systems produce steam and hot water laden with toxic minerals,

salts, metals, and hydrogen sulfide. Noise pollution is also a problem.

Hydrogen fuel is produced by heating or passing electricity through water in the presence of a catalyst. Water breaks down into hydrogen and oxygen. Hydrogen is a clean-burning fuel that could replace gaseous and liquid fuels. It is easy to transport but is explosive. Electricity needed to make hydrogen could be generated from solar energy, wind energy, or hydroelectric facilities. The prospects for hydrogen are questionable today because of its negative energy yield.

Conservation is one of the key untapped energy resources for tomorrow. By reducing energy waste in home, factories, and transportation, we could inexpensively unleash an enormous supply of energy. The largest gain can be had when new homes and offices are built with passive and active solar and heavy insulation.

Energy experts have shown that we can substitute renewable energy resources such as solar energy for nonrenewables such as oil, natural gas, coal, and nuclear power without drastically changing society. A smooth transition can be made into a sustainable future, but it will require an immediate investment in renewable energy resources by governments and individuals.

Discussion Questions

1. Describe how a light water fission reactor works. What is the fuel, and how is the chain reaction controlled?
2. What are the advantages and disadvantages of nuclear power?
3. What is a breeder reactor? How is it similar to a conventional fission reactor? How is it different? Discuss the advantages and disadvantages of the breeder reactor.
4. What is nuclear fusion? Discuss the advantages and disadvantages of fusion energy.
5. What is oil shale? Discuss the benefits and risks of oil shale development.
6. Discuss the potential of tar sands in meeting our future energy demands.
7. Define coal gasification and liquefaction.
8. Discuss the advantages and disadvantages of solar energy.
9. Describe the difference between passive and active solar systems. What features are needed in a home to make passive solar energy work well?
10. What are photovoltaic cells? In your opinion, should we develop photovoltaic cells in preference to nuclear energy? Why or why not?
11. Wind energy is close to being competitive with conventional electricity. Should we develop this energy resource in preference to nuclear power, coal, or shale? Why or why not?
12. What is biomass? How can useful energy be gained from it?
13. How is geothermal energy formed? How can it be tapped? Describe the benefits and risks of geothermal energy.

14. Debate the statement "Hydroelectric power is an immensely untapped resource in the United States and could provide an enormous amount of energy."

15. What are the major problems facing hydrogen power? How could these be solved?

16. Debate the statement "Conservation is our best and cheapest energy resource."

17. Discuss ways in which you could conserve more energy at home, at work, and in transit. Draw up a reasonable energy conservation plan for you and your family.

18. Make a list of criteria (cost, pollution, and so on) to judge energy resources, and list them in decreasing importance. Which energy technologies discussed in this chapter would be most suitable, according to your criteria?

Suggested Readings

Nonrenewable Energy Systems

Environmental Protection Agency. (1980). *Environmental Perspective on the Emerging Oil Shale Industry.* EPA-600/2-80-205a. Washington, D.C.: Author. Superb overview of the environmental impacts of oil shale development.

Flavin, C. (1985). *World Oil: Coping with the Dangers of Success.* Worldwatch Paper 66. Washington, D.C.: Worldwatch Institute. Detailed study.

Flavin, C. (1987). *Reassessing Nuclear Power: the Fallout from Chernobyl.* Worldwatch Paper 75. Washington, D.C.: Worldwatch Institute. Important look at nuclear power and its future.

Gofman, J. W., and Tamplin, A. R. (1979). *Poisoned Power: The Case against Nuclear Power Plants before and after Three Mile Island.* Emmaus, Pa.: Rodale Press. Well-written analysis.

Hohenemser, C., Deicher, M., Ernst, A., Hofsass, H., Linder, G., and Recknagel. (1986). Chernobyl: An Early Report. *Environment* 28 (5): 6–13, 30–43. Comprehensive preliminary report on the accident.

Jungk, R. (1979). *The New Tyranny.* New York: Warner Books. An important, well-written book.

Kaku M., and Trainer, J., eds. (1982). *Nuclear Power: Both Sides.* New York: Norton. Excellent, balanced coverage.

Manning, R. (1985). The Future of Nuclear Power. *Environment* 27 (4): 12–17, 31–37. Excellent overview of the industry view of changes needed to revive nuclear power in the United States.

Weaver, K. F. (1979). The Promise and Peril of Nuclear Energy. *National Geographic* 155 (4): 459–493. Graphically illustrated study of nuclear power for the layperson.

White, I. L., and Spath, J. P. (1984). How Are States Setting Their Sites? *Environment* 26 (8): 16–20, 36–42. Good summary of what states are doing to handle low-level radioactive waste.

Renewable Energy Systems

Brown, L. R. (1981). *Building a Sustainable Society.* New York: Norton. General, optimistic survey of sustainable energy technologies.

Bungay, H. R. (1983). Commercializing Biomass Conversion. *Environ. Sci. and Technol.* 17 (1): 24A–31A. Technical overview of biomass conversion.

Chandler, W. U. (1985). *Energy Productivity: Key to Environmental Protection and Economic Progress.* Worldwatch Paper 63. Washington, D.C.: Worldwatch Institute. Detailed study of energy conservation.

Deudney, D., and Flavin, C. (1983). *Renewable Energy: The Power to Choose.* New York: Norton. Fact-filled, highly readable book.

Elridge, F. R. (1980). *Wind Machines.* New York: Van Nostrand Reinhold. Excellent overview.

Flavin, C. (1981). A Renaissance for Wind Power. *Environment* 23 (8): 31–41. Interesting look at wind energy.

Flavin, C. (1983). Photovoltaics: International Competition for the Sun. *Environment* 25 (3): 7–11, 39–43. Good survey of economics and history of solar voltaics.

Flavin, C. (1984). *Electricity's Future: The Shift to Efficiency and Small-Scale Power.* Worldwatch Paper 61. Washington, D.C.: Worldwatch Institute.

Flavin, C., and Pollock, C. (1985). Harnessing Renewable Energy. In *The State of the World,* ed. Linda Starke. New York: Norton. Superb overview of the potential of renewable energy.

Group, L. (1978). *Solar Houses: 48 Energy-Saving Designs.* New York: Pantheon. Filled with interesting information on solar houses.

Hempel, L. C. (1982). The Original Blueprint for a Solar America. *Environment* 24 (2): 25–32. Excellent look at some highlights in solar history.

Kakela, P., Chilson, G., and Patric, W. (1985). Low-Head Hydropower for Local Use. *Environment* 27 (1): 31–38. Realistic look at the potential of small dams for generating electricity.

Kendall, H. W., and Nadis, S. J., eds. (1980). *Energy Strategies: Toward a Solar Future.* Cambridge, Mass.: Ballinger. Detailed survey of energy sources and their prospects for the future. Superb!

Pollock, C. (1986). *Decommissioning: Nuclear Power's Missing Link.* Worldwatch Paper 69. Washington, D.C.: Worldwatch Institute. Authoritative coverage of the costs involved.

Tucker, J. B. (1982). Biogas Systems in India: Is the Technology Appropriate? *Environment* 24 (8): 12–20, 39. Excellent study.

Radiation Pollution

Chapter 12 discussed nuclear energy, but this is only one potential source of radiation exposure. This supplement describes radiation—its sources and its effects.

As we saw in Chapter 2, the **atom** is composed of a **nucleus** and an **electron cloud**. The nucleus contains **protons** and **neutrons** and constitutes 99.9% of the mass of an atom. The much lighter **electrons** orbit in a cloud around the positively charged nucleus.

Atoms of a given element, say, carbon or uranium, all have the same number of protons in their nuclei. But they may contain slightly different numbers of neutrons. For example, uranium atoms all contain 92 protons. Some uranium atoms may have 146 neutrons, however, and others have 143. These alternate forms are called **isotopes**. To distinguish them scientists add up the protons and neutrons and tack the sum of these two onto the name of the element. The form of uranium containing 146 neutrons is called uranium-238 (92 protons + 146 neutrons = 238). The form containing 143 neutrons is called uranium-235.

Excess neutrons in some isotopes sometimes make them unstable. To reach a more stable state, they emit radiation. Unstable, radioactive nuclei are called **radionuclides**. They occur naturally or can be produced by various physical means. For the most part the naturally occurring radionuclides are isotopes of heavy elements, from lead (82 protons in the nucleus) to uranium (92 protons in the nucleus). There are three major types of naturally occurring radioactive emissions: alpha particles, beta particles, and gamma rays. X rays, which are also considered in this chapter, are artificially produced as described below.

Alpha particles consist of two protons and two neutrons, the same as a helium nucleus. They are positively charged. Alpha particles have the largest mass of all forms of radiation. In air they travel only a few centimeters. They can be stopped by a thick sheet of paper, so it is easy to shield people from them. In the body, alpha particles can travel only about 30 micrometers (about the width of three cells) in tissues. They cannot penetrate skin and are therefore often erroneously assumed to pose little harm to humans. But if alpha emitters enter body tissues, say,

through inhalation, they can do serious, irreparable damage to nearby cells and their chromosomes.

Beta particles are negatively charged particles that are emitted from nuclei. They are equivalent to electrons found in the electron cloud, except that they contain more energy. Beta particles arise when neutrons in the nucleus are converted into protons, a process that helps stabilize radionuclides. A small amount of mass and energy is lost; this is the energetic beta particle that is ejected out of the nucleus.

The beta particle is much lighter than the alpha particle and can travel much farther. It can penetrate a 1-millimeter lead plate and can travel up to 8 meters (27 feet) in air but only 1 centimeter in tissue. Beta particles from some radionuclides have enough energy to penetrate one's clothing and skin but generally do not reach underlying tissues. They can, however, damage the skin and eyes (causing skin cancer and cataracts).

Gamma rays are a high-energy form of radiation with no mass and no charge, much like visible light but with much more energy. Gamma rays are emitted by nuclei to achieve a lower-energy, more stable state. They are often emitted after a nucleus has ejected an alpha or beta particle, because the loss of these particles does not always allow the nucleus to reach its most stable state. Some gamma rays can travel hundreds of meters in the air and can easily penetrate the body. Some can penetrate walls of cement and plaster or a few centimeters of lead.

Unlike the three previously discussed forms, the **X ray** does not originate from naturally occurring unstable nuclei. Rather, X rays are produced in X-ray machines when a high voltage is applied between a source of electrons and a tungsten collecting terminal in a vacuum tube (Figure S12-1). When the electrons are ejected, they strike the collecting terminal. Colliding with tungsten atoms, they are rapidly brought to rest. The energy they carried in is released in the form of X rays, which behave like gamma rays but have considerably less energy. They cannot penetrate lead.

All the forms of radiation described above are called **ionizing radiation**, because they possess enough energy to rip electrons away from atoms, leaving charged ions. Ions are the primary cause of damage in tissues.

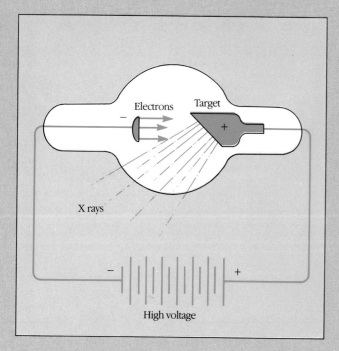

Figure S12-1   An X-ray machine.

Table S12-1 Estimated Radiation Exposure in the U.S.	
Source	Average Exposure (mrem/year)[1]
Natural	
Soil and rock	40
Cosmic radiation	28–44
Internal exposure	18–24
Total	80–100
Anthropogenic	
Medical	74
Nuclear-weapons fallout	4
Nuclear energy	.05–5
TV (1 hour/day)	5
Watch (luminous dial)	1–4
Air travel	4
Total	80–100
Total	160–200

[1]These values are averages published in several different studies.

How Is Radiation Measured?

Radioactive elements lose mass over time because of the emissions from their nuclei. Each radionuclide gives off radiation at its own rate, called the **radioactive decay rate** and measured in disintegrations per second. For example, 1 gram of radium decays at a rate of 37 billion disintegrations per second! The rate of radioactive decay determines the **half-life** of a radionuclide—that is, the time it takes for half of a given mass of a given radionuclide to decay into more stable isotopes.

Radiation exposure in humans is expressed in several different ways. One of the most widely used measures is the rad. **Rad** is the **radiation absorbed dose**, or, simply, the amount of energy that is released in tissue (or some other medium) when it's irradiated. One rad is equal to 100 ergs (a unit of energy) deposited in 1 gram of tissue.

As radiation travels through tissue, it loses its energy. The rate of energy loss is called the **linear energy transfer**, or LET. Put another way, LET is the amount of energy lost per unit of distance the radiation travels. Because of their mass, alpha particles travel only short distances through tissue and, therefore, lose their energy rapidly. They are said to have a high LET. The energy is transferred to the tissues. X rays, gamma rays, and beta particles travel farther through tissues and lose their energy more slowly; they have low LETs. Consequently, 10 rads of energy from beta particles would do less damage than 10 rads from an alpha particle, because the energy from an alpha particle is lost in a shorter distance.

The term **rem** takes into account the linear energy transfer and thus indirectly indicates the damage that a given amount of radiation will cause in tissue. For X rays, gamma rays, and beta particles 1 rem is essentially equivalent to 1 rad, but for alpha particles, because of their high LET, 1 rad is equivalent to 10 to 20 rems.

As a point of reference, a medical X ray may be equivalent to about .1 to 1 rem, depending on the type. The safety standard for workers in the United States is 5 rems per year. Background radiation is measured in thousandths of rems, or millirems (mrems).

Sources of Radiation

Radiation comes from two sources: natural and anthropogenic. Both contribute to our daily radiation exposure.

Natural Sources

Radiation is all around us. It is in rocks, in the air we breathe, and in the water we drink. Even the sun and distant stars bombard us with radiation. As shown in Table S12-1, these natural sources provide about half of our exposure. The average exposure from all naturally occurring sources of radiation is about 80 to 100 millirems per year. In some areas such as Denver and Salt Lake City, because of altitude and high background levels, the average exposure may be as high as 200 millirems per year.

Anthropogenic Sources

Anthropogenic radiation sources are many: (1) medical therapy (X-ray treatment for cancer) and diagnosis (X rays for bone fractures), (2) detonation of nuclear weapons in testing and the Second World War, (3) nuclear energy, (4) television sets, (5) luminous dials on watches, and (6) air travel.

Anthropogenic sources are responsible, on the average, for about half of the total annual dose to the general public (Table S12-1). Medical diagnosis and treatment constitute about 80% of the anthropogenic exposure. Medical X rays are the largest medical source, with the U.S. average being about 72 to 80 millirems. However, averages cover up the fact that some individuals receive large doses of radiation from X rays each year and others receive none.

Effects of Radiation

How Does Radiation Affect Cells?

All forms of radiation ionize and excite biologically important molecules in tissues. Positively charged alpha particles, for example, draw electrons away from atoms in body tissues. Negatively charged beta particles in tissues may repel electrons of various atoms, causing them to be expelled from their atoms. They, too, produce positively charged ions. Gamma rays and X rays, on the other hand, are uncharged, but they possess lots of energy, which may be transferred to electrons as they pass through tissue. This energy excites the electrons and may cause their expulsion from the atoms, forming ions. Alternatively, the energy imparted to the electrons may make chemical bonds in molecules unstable and more easily broken. (Recall from Chapter 2 that all molecules are made up of atoms.)

Ionization of atoms in water and other molecules in tissues is responsible for much of the damage caused by radiation. Water molecules become positively charged when electrons are ripped from their atoms, as shown in Figure S12-2. Electrons that are freed from water molecules may combine with uncharged water molecules, forming negatively charged water molecules. Both positively and negatively charged water molecules rapidly break up into highly reactive fragments called **free radicals** (Figure S12-2).

Free radicals react almost instantaneously with biologically important molecules. When they react with oxygen, for example, hydrogen peroxide is formed. This powerful oxidizing agent damages or destroys proteins and other molecules, causing cell death. If it is extensive enough, cellular destruction can kill the organism. In some instances damage may be quickly repaired by the cells without any long-term effect; in other cases the damage may not be expressed until years after the exposure, in the form of mutations and cancer (Chapter 14).

Health Effects of Radiation

The effects of radiation on human health depend on many factors, such as the amount of radiation, the length of exposure, the type of radiation, the half-life of the radionuclide, the health and age of the individual, the part of the body exposed, and whether the exposure is internal or external.

Numerous studies of radiation have revealed some interesting generalizations: (1) Fetuses are more sensitive to radiation than children, who are, in turn, more sensitive than adults. (2) Cells

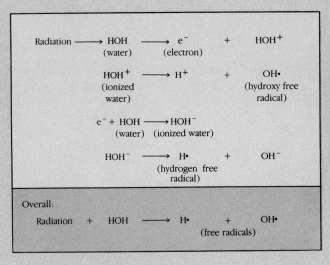

Figure S12-2 Ionization of atoms in water molecules.

undergoing rapid division appear to be more sensitive to radiation than those that are not. This is especially true in regard to cancer induction. Thus, lymphoid tissues (bone marrow, lymph nodes, and circulating lymphocytes) are the most sensitive of all the body's cells. Epithelial cells—those that line the inside and outside of body organs such as the intestines—also undergo frequent cellular division and are highly sensitive to radiation. In sharp contrast, nerve and muscle cells, which do not divide, have a very low sensitivity and rarely become cancerous. (3) Most, if not all, forms of cancer can be increased by ionizing radiation.

Health experts divide radiation exposure into two categories. Exposures over 5 to 10 rems per year are considered high-level. Below this, the exposure is low-level.

Impacts of High-Level Radiation The most important information on high-level radiation comes from studies of the survivors of the two atomic bombs dropped on Japan at the end of World War II (Figure S12-3). Studies of these and other groups have led to several important findings. First, the lethal dose for one-half the people within 60 days is about 300 rads. Second, a dose of 650 rads kills all people within a few hours to a few days. Third, sublethal doses, or doses that do not result in immediate death, range from 50 to 250 rads. Victims suffer from **radiation sickness**. The first symptoms, which develop immediately, are nausea and vomiting; 2 to 14 days later, diarrhea, hair loss, sore throat, reduction in blood platelets (needed for clotting), hemorrhaging, and bone-marrow damage occur. Fourth, sublethal radiation has many serious delayed effects, including cancer, leukemia, cataracts, sterility, and decreased lifespan. Fifth, sublethal radiation also has profound effects on reproduction, increasing miscarriages, stillbirths, and early infant deaths.

High-level radiation exposure is rare today. We could anticipate such exposures only in workers at badly damaged nuclear power plants or munitions factories or in nearby residents. Nuclear war, even on a limited scale, would also expose large segments of the human population to dangerously high levels

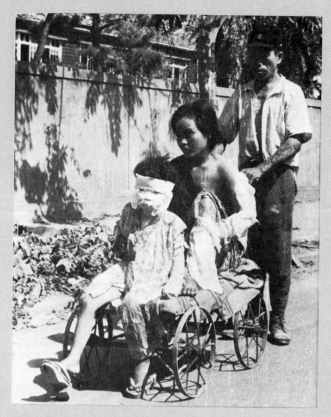

Figure S12-3 Hiroshima survivors.

of radiation (Chapter Supplement 4-1). Accidents during the transporting of nuclear fuels and high-level wastes might also result in dangerously high exposures.

Impacts of Low-Level Radiation The effects of high-level radiation are well established, but as is the case with low-level exposure to any toxic agent, health effects are harder to discern with low-level radiation. A growing body of evidence shows that low-level radiation increases the likelihood of developing cancer (Figure S12-4). For example, studies of individuals who years earlier were treated with radiation for acne, spinal disorders, and even syphilis show elevated levels of cancer and leukemia. In addition, children whose necks have been irradiated by medical X rays have an elevated rate of thyroid cancer. Lung cancer rates are elevated in uranium and fluorspar (calcium fluoride) miners, both of whom are exposed to radon gas. Factory workers who painted watch dials with radium early in this century developed bone cancer and a serious disease of the bone marrow called aplastic anemia. Several studies show that the rates of leukemia, tumors of the lymphatic system, brain tumors, and other cancer are 50% higher in infants whose mothers have been exposed to ordinary diagnostic X rays (2 to 3 rads). One study showed that a 1-rem exposure to fetuses causes an 80% increase in mortality from childhood cancer. According to some estimates, low-level radiation from testing of nuclear weapons in the 1950s and 1960s caused 400,000 deaths in children because of cancer. Studies of workers at a plant in Hanford, Washington, the U.S. government's source of radioactive materials for nuclear weapons, showed that the death rate from

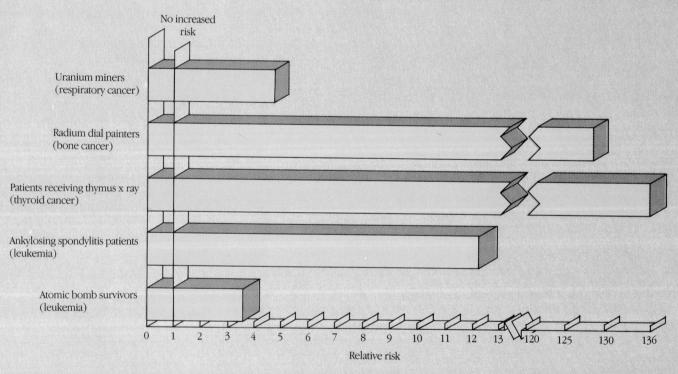

Figure S12-4 Relative risk of cancer in people exposed to various kinds of radiation. The relative risk tells us the probability of contracting cancer. In other words, a uranium miner is four times more likely to develop respiratory-tract cancer than someone who is not a miner. Atomic bomb survivors, in general, are 3.5 times more likely to develop leukemia than non-irradiated people.

cancer was 7% higher than expected and that workers who died of cancer had received on the average only about 2 rems per year, well below the supposed safe level of 5 rems a year.

Low-level radiation is probably much more harmful than many scientists estimated a decade ago. The noted radiation biologist Dr. Irwin Bross, for example, estimates that low-level exposure is about ten times more harmful than previously calculated. He and others have called for major revisions of the maximum allowable doses for workers.

But is there a threshold level below which no damage occurs? No one can say for certain. Some health officials believe that no level is safe, because the effects of continued low-level exposure are cumulative.

According to two radiation experts, John Gofman and Arthur Tamplin, exposure to the current public health standard set for anthropogenic sources—.17 rad per year—will result in a 30-year exposure of 5 rads. This would cause 14 additional cases of cancer each year for every 100,000 people exposed, or about 14,000 additional cancer cases per year in adults over 30 and at least 2000 cases of cancer in individuals under 30 years of age. Studies by the National Academy of Sciences and the National Research Council suggest that a .17-rad exposure to anthropogenic radiation will probably increase the rate of cancer by 2% and the incidence of serious genetic diseases by about 1 birth in every 2000. Thus, some experts suggest lowering the health standard to 0.017 rad per year.

Some geneticists warn, however, that genetic disorders caused by radiation may be passed from generation to generation and may increase in incidence with subsequent generations. For example, if the incidence of genetic disorders and birth defects with a genetic basis were 1 in 2000 in the first generation, it would be 5 in 2000 in their offspring. A major consideration, then, is what impact radiation exposure today will have on subsequent generations. Are current policies and radiation standards posing a danger to future generations?

Low-level effects are small and hard to detect. The long latent period between exposure and disease makes it difficult for researchers to link the cause and the effects. Thus, studies such as those cited above have stirred a considerable amount of controversy. Although the results and conclusions of individual low-level radiation studies are debatable, on the whole they seem to consistently point to one conclusion: a substantial risk is created by subjecting people to low-level radiation. The question becomes what level of risk is acceptable. At what point do the benefits of X rays, nuclear power, and other uses outweigh the risks?

Bioconcentration and Biological Magnification Table S12-2 lists some radionuclides emitted from nuclear weapons and nuclear power plants. Some of these radionuclides are absorbed by humans and organisms and may become concentrated in particular tissues.

For example, iodine-131 is released from nuclear power plants, both during normal operations and in accidents. Fallout on the ground may be incorporated in grass eaten by dairy cows. It is then selectively taken up (bioconcentrated) by the human thyroid gland, where it irradiates cells and may produce tumors. Milk contaminated with I-131 is especially harmful to children.

Strontium-90 is released during atomic bomb blasts. It may

Table S12-2 Radionuclides from Nuclear Weapons and Reactors

Nuclear Weapons	Nuclear Reactors
Strontium-89	Tritium (Hydrogen-3)
Strontium-90	Cobalt-58
Zirconium-95	Cobalt-60
Rubidium-193	Krypton-95
Rubidium-106	Strontium-85
Iodine-131	Strontium-90
Cesium-137	Iodine-130
Cerium-141	Iodine-131
Cerium-144	Xenon-131
	Xenon-133
	Cesium-134
	Cesium-137
	Barium-140

also be released from reactors in small amounts under normal operating conditions but in large quantities in accidents. Strontium-90 is readily absorbed by plants and may also be passed to humans through cow's milk. It seeks out bone, where it is deposited like calcium. With a half-life of 28 years, it irradiates the bone and can cause leukemia and bone cancer.

Accumulation of radionuclides within tissues has important implications for human health, as seemingly low levels may become dangerously high in localized regions. Some radionuclides may be biologically magnified in the higher trophic levels of food chains.

Minimizing the Risk

Radiation can be reduced in several ways. Since X rays are the most significant anthropogenic source of exposure, prudence dictates a cautious use of them. High-dose exposures especially warrant thorough discussion with the doctor.

Important ways to reduce X-ray exposure include (1) asking the physician if previous X rays or diagnostic procedures you've had would provide the same information; (2) reducing X-ray exposure in children; (3) informing physicians and dentists that you are pregnant (don't wait to be asked); (4) if you are pregnant, avoiding all X rays of the pelvis, abdomen, and lower back unless they're absolutely necessary; (5) avoiding mobile X-ray unit, because they tend to give higher-than-necessary doses; (6) if you are a woman under the age of 50 and have no family history of breast cancer, avoid routine mammographs; (7) questioning the necessity of preemployment X rays; (8) if you must be X-rayed, requesting that a full-time radiologist do it; (9) asking if the X-ray machine and facilities have been inspected and set to minimize excess exposure; (10) requesting that a lead apron be placed over your chest and lap for dental X rays and that a thyroid shield be placed around your neck; (11) cooperating with the X-ray technologist (do not breathe or move during the X ray); and (12) making sure the operator exposes only those parts of the body that are necessary.

Radiation exposure from medical diagnosis and treatment is by far the easiest to control on an individual level. Controls on exposures from nuclear weapons testing, possible nuclear war, and possible catastrophic accidents at nuclear power plants may seem out of the average citizen's hands. Nevertheless, individual citizens can have a significant cumulative impact on nuclear policies by educating themselves and others, voting responsibly, becoming involved in political organizations, and writing letters to Congresspersons. For an opinion on the influence of such letter writing and for some suggestions on how to write letters on political issues, see the Viewpoint "The Right to Write" in Chapter 21.

Suggested Readings

Gofman, J. W. (1981). *Radiation and Human Health*. San Francisco: Sierra Club Books. Comprehensive survey of the effects of low-level radiation and health.

Gofman, J. W., and Tamplin, A. R. (1970). Low Dose Radiation and Cancer. In *Global Ecology: Readings toward a Rational Strategy for Man*, ed. J. P. Holdren and P. R. Ehrlich. New York: Harcourt Brace Jovanovich. Excellent article.

Hobbs, C. H., and McClellan, R. O. (1980). Radiation and Radioactive Materials. In *Toxicology: The Basic Science of Poisons* (2nd ed.), ed. J. Doull, C. D. Klaassen, and M. O. Amdur. New York: Macmillan. Excellent review.

Johnson, C. J., Tidball, R. R. and Severson, R. C. (1976). Plutonium Hazard in Respirable Dust on the Surface of Soil. *Science* 193: 488–490. Interesting case study.

Laws, P. W., and Public Citizen Health Research Group. (1983). *The X-Ray Information Book*. New York: Farrar, Straus, and Giroux. General coverage of X rays, their effects, and ways to minimize exposure.

Mancuso, T. F., Stewart, A., and Kneade, G. (1977). Radiation Exposures of Hanford Workers Dying from Cancer and Other Causes. *Health Physics* 33: 369–385. Excellent study.

Solon, L. R., and Sidel, V. W. (1979). Health Implications of Nuclear Power Production. *Annals of Internal Medicine* 90 (3): 424–426. Good review.

The Earth and Its Mineral Resources

Conservation is humanity caring for the future.

NANCY NEWHALL

Gazing out on a vast expanse of land—the prairies of Oklahoma or Texas, for instance—the earth seems stable and permanent. But churning deep within its interior is molten rock that spews out in frightening displays, burying villages and farmland, leveling trees, and killing wildlife. Huge land masses fold and twist as they crash together. Others move like pieces of a jigsaw puzzle as if possessed by a fiery devil in the earth's interior.

Evidence of the earth's restlessness is all around us in earthquakes, volcanoes, and mountain ranges. Nowhere is this more apparent than in California. Consider, for instance, that in 1.5 million years Los Angeles will lie where San Francisco is. My publisher, now just south of San Francisco, will be well on its way to Canada. (Bundle up, gang.)

What's happening is that a narrow strip of land, bounded on the east by the San Andreas fault and on the west by the Pacific Ocean, is inching its way northward. It is part of a huge plate in the earth's crust encompassing nearly the entire Pacific Ocean. On its slow northward creep it is taking along its tiny strip of exposed land—and millions of unsuspecting passengers. The rumbling and earth-shattering quakes that now plague the West Coast give evidence of the Pacific plate grinding against the American plate, which includes North and South America (Figure 13-1).

The Earth and Its Riches

To understand this process and to understand the important resources we gather from the earth's restless crust,

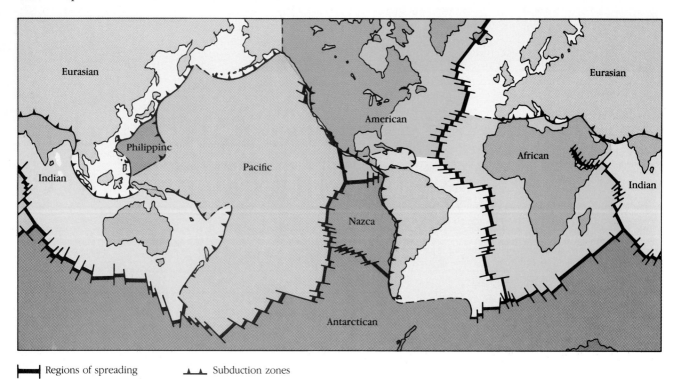

├─┤ Regions of spreading   ▲▲ Subduction zones

Figure 13-1   The earth's crust is broken into thin moving plates on the surface. Parallel lines indicate regions of spreading. Lines with solid triangles indicate subduction zones where one plate slides under another. Arrows indicate movement of the plates.

let us turn back to the time the earth began to form. Five billion years ago the earth began to cool; the surface of this molten mass gradually transformed into a thick rocky crust (Chapter 2). As the earth cooled, water vapor in the atmosphere condensed and rained down, forming oceans, lakes, and rivers. Today 29% of the earth's surface is land, and 71% is water. Beneath the crust is the mantle, and beneath that, the core.

A Rocky Beginning

In the beginning, the earth's crust was solid rock. Over time, this rock was subject to many altering forces. Soil formed from particles that had been eroded from the rock by rain, and later, plants evolved to take advantage of the solid earth. New types of rock formed from the once-molten mass. Mountain ranges lifted up. Despite these dramatic changes, the earth's crust contained the same inorganic compounds, called **minerals**, that had been there since its fiery beginning. These minerals are made of elements (Chapter 2). The most abundant elements in the earth's crust are oxygen, aluminum, iron,

and magnesium. Others, like gold and platinum, are extremely rare.

Rocks are solid aggregates of minerals. Several types of minerals are usually found in any one type of rock. Rocks fall into three major classes: (1) **Igneous rocks**, such as basalt and granite, are those formed when molten minerals cool. (2) **Sedimentary rocks**, such as shale and sandstone, are formed from particles eroded from other types of rock. (3) **Metamorphic rocks**, such as schist, are formed when igneous or sedimentary rocks are transformed by heat and pressure during mountain-building processes.

Igneous rocks are the major source of nonfuel minerals that modern industrial nations need. Certain geological processes have concentrated minerals in igneous rocks. A concentrated deposit of minerals that can be mined and refined economically is called an **ore**. The exploitation of these ores has transformed our world. Ores are valuable sources of important metals, such as chromium, which hardens steel; silver, used in photographic films; and iron, which holds up bridges and skyscrapers. Most ores are mined and then treated to extract important metals, such as aluminum and zinc.

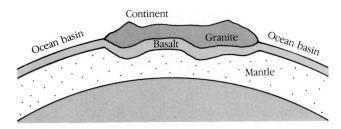

Figure 13-2 The earth's crust consists of two layers: the continental (granite) and subcontinental (basalt).

The Movements of Continents

Unknown to many, the earth's crust is continuously being recycled. As parts of it are gobbled up and turned into molten rock, new rock is formed elsewhere. Geologists call this process the **rock cycle**. To understand it we must take a closer look at the earth's surface.

The earth's mineral crust consists of two layers: the outer **continental layer**, made mostly of granite, and the inner **subcontinental layer**, made mostly of a black rock called basalt. The continental layer is found only where land masses have formed. The subcontinental layer, lying beneath it, extends along ocean bottoms (Figure 13-2). As we saw in Figure 13-1, the crust is broken into a number of plates, called **tectonic plates**. Some are oceanic, having little or no exposed continent riding on them. They consist mainly of a huge slab of basalt. Other tectonic plates consist of both land masses and ocean floor. Both the continental and the subcontinental layers are present in these plates.

If we could travel back in time 200 million years, we would find the continents lying close together (Figure 13-3). But the migrating tectonic plates pulled them apart, shuffling them about like so many pieces of a puzzle. This process is called **continental drift**. It continues today but at such a slow pace that it is undetectable to ordinary observation.

Geologists are not sure why plates move. Many think that the underlying mantle consists of a semisolid, plasticlike molten rock that rises along one end of the plate and sinks along the other. This movement carries a plate along. As shown in Figure 13-4, two adjoining plates pull apart at midoceanic ridges. Some of the rock pours out into the crack and solidifies. This formation of new crust under the ocean is called **sea-floor spreading**. Underlying molten rock sweeps the plate along. At the other end the plate crashes against an adjacent plate and is pushed under it. This process is called **subduction**. The continental and subcontinental layers are thrust into the mantle and melted, thus becoming part of the slow-flowing molten rock that sustains the cycle. The Nazca plate (see Figure 13-1) clearly shows the relationships. The eastern border of this plate is a subduction zone. Here it is pushed

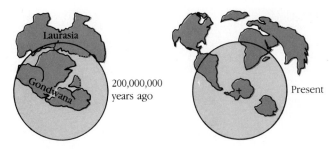

Figure 13-3 View of the earth 200 million years ago and today. The movements of the tectonic plates cause the continents to move over the earth's surface.

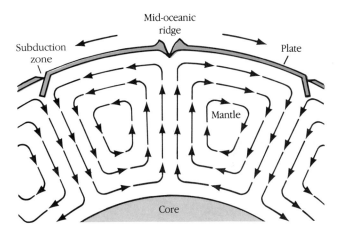

Figure 13-4 Movement of molten rock in the mantle (arrows) propels the tectonic plates.

under the American plate. The western border is a region of sea-floor spreading.

The rock cycle shows that rocks of the earth's crust are reformed and implies that mineral resources must be renewable. However, new mineral deposits are formed primarily along the midoceanic ridges, inaccessible to humankind. We must make do with the finite ore deposits within our reach.

Mineral Resources and Society

More than 100 nonfuel minerals are traded in the world market. These materials, worth billions of dollars to the world economy, are vital to modern industry and agriculture. The major minerals used in the United States are shown in Table 13-1. Several dozen are so important that if any one of them was suddenly no longer available at a reasonable price, industry and agriculture would be brought to a standstill.

Table 13-1 Major Metals and Mineral Consumption in the U.S.[1]

Metal/Mineral	1978	1982	1986[4]
Aluminum	6,045,000	4,740,000	5,290,000
Antimony	40,536	33,200	33,261[5]
Chromium	590,000	330,000	476,000
Cobalt	10,182	5,500	7,500
Copper	2,553,100	1,980,000	1,953,000
Gold	5,100,000 troy ounces[2]	3,800,000 troy ounces	3,300,000 troy ounces
Iron ore	115,000,000	54,000,000	50,000,000
Lead	1,477,300	1,171,500	999,000
Magnesium	131,000	114,000	120,000
Manganese	1,363,000	700,000	665,000
Mercury	76,547 flasks[3]	50,700 flasks	44,582 flasks[6]
Molybdenum	33,862	16,500	19,500
Nickel	273,000	174,000	184,000
Platinum	2,635,000 troy ounces	2,200,000 troy ounces	3,671,000 troy ounces
Silver	148,000,000 troy ounces	144,000,000 troy ounces	168,000,000 troy ounces
Tin	76,904	50,600	55,000
Vanadium	8,164	6,500	5,700[7]
Zinc	1,230,900	891,000	919,000

[1]Measured in short tons (2000 pounds) unless indicated otherwise.
[2]1 troy ounce = 31.1 grams.
[3]1 flask = 76 pounds.
[4]Estimates published in 1987 based on the first 9 months of consumption.
[5]1984 consumption. 1985 and 1986 consumption withheld to avoid disclosing company proprietary information.
[6]1985 consumption. 1986 withheld.
[7]1984 consumption. 1985 and 1986 consumption withheld to avoid disclosing company proprietary information.
Source: U.S. Bureau of Mines.

Who Consumes the World's Minerals?

The developed countries are the major consumers of minerals. With one-fourth of the world's population, they consume at least three-fourths of its mineral resources. These resources come from domestic mines and from many distant developing countries. The United States, with only about 6% of the world's population, consumes about 20% of its minerals.

The developing nations use the remaining mineral resources. Latin America, Africa, and Asia have nearly three-fourths of the world's people but use only 7% of the aluminum, 9% of the copper, and 12% of the iron ore. Continued slow economic growth will probably not change these figures much by the year 2000, although there are notable exceptions, such as South Korea and Taiwan, which are quickly becoming industrialized.

Growing Interdependence and Global Tensions

As shown in Figure 13-5, the United States, Japan, and Europe depend heavily on mineral imports. This dependency, growing rapidly in recent years, results from the depletion of high-grade ore deposits in most developed

countries and lower mineral costs in developing nations, primarily because of cheaper labor. Because of the shift to foreign producers and because of domestic conservation and recycling, the American mining industry has suffered drastic declines in recent years. Between 1980 and 1983, for instance, mining revenues declined by 30%. Employment in American mines dropped by 18% between 1981 and 1986—a decline equivalent to 600,000 jobs. Employment is expected to fall further in the next few years.

The vast majority of the United States' mineral resources come from fairly reliable sources, countries that are politically stable. What frightens some U.S. analysts is that some crucial minerals, such as chromium and platinum, come from unreliable sources (Figure 13-6). To protect against embargoes or sudden cutoffs resulting from political upheaval in mineral-exporting nations, the United States stockpiles a three-year supply of strategic minerals. If these supplies would run out before imports resumed, however, the economic foundation of the Western world would crumble.

Many poor, mineral-exporting nations complain about the low prices they receive for their exported raw minerals. They also feel cheated by the Western world, which buys minerals cheaply and converts them into products

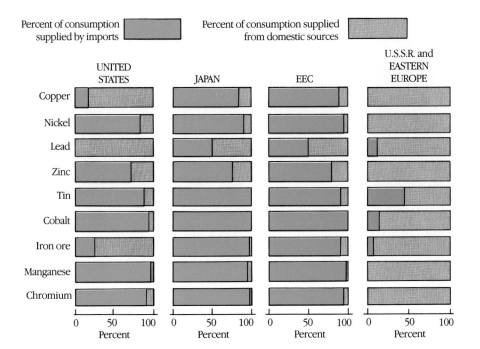

Percent of consumption supplied by imports

Percent of consumption supplied from domestic sources

Figure 13-5 Reliance of the United States, Japan, the European Economic Community, and the Eastern bloc on foreign and domestic mineral supplies.

that reap them trillions of dollars a year. Making matters worse, many mineral-exporting nations have borrowed heavily from the West. Interest payments amount to billions of dollars. They have little hope of repaying the debt without a renewed source of income. The developing world is a pot boiling with anger toward the Western world. Things are bound to change.

Following the lead of the OPEC nations, mineral-exporting countries may unite to form OPEC-style cartels to raise the price of mineral exports. Since over half of the copper and nearly all of the tin and aluminum reserves are in developing nations, cartels could form around these commodities. Developed countries would be forced to pay higher prices for imported minerals. Worldwide inflation could follow, crippling industry and sending millions of workers home.

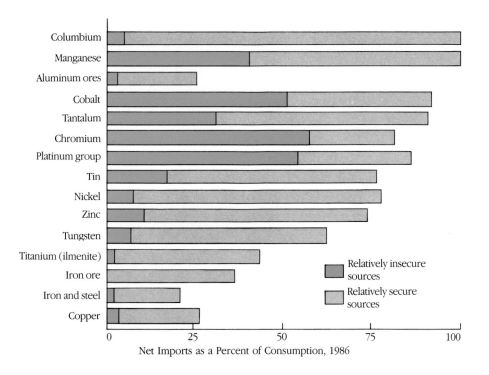

Net Imports as a Percent of Consumption, 1986

Relatively insecure sources

Relatively secure sources

Figure 13-6 U.S. imports of some major minerals as a percentage of total consumption. The complete bar shows the total imports as a percentage of U.S. consumption; the colored part of the bar indicates the percentage of the minerals consumed which comes from insecure sources. The difference between the total and the colored bar represents the imports from secure sources as a percentage of total consumption.

Will There Be Enough?

This chapter concerns itself primarily with matters of supply, answering the critical question "Will there be enough?" Finding an answer to this question is no easy task. We will look at the question in both the short term and the long term.

In the short run strategic supplies can help us weather sudden embargoes. That problem seems well taken care of. In the long run, however, the outlook is mixed. Some mineral supplies are adequate for many years to come, even at an increased rate of use. But other important minerals, for which no known substitutes exist, are fast on the decline. Gold, mercury, and silver are examples of such minerals. Something must be done, and done quickly, to bridge the gap.

Remember also the effect of exponential growth. Should mineral consumption increase rapidly, minerals thought to be in abundance would quickly become depleted. A resource with a billion-year lifespan would last only 580 years at a 3% growth rate.

Meeting Future Needs

Future demand can be met by at least four strategies: expanding reserves, finding substitutes, recycling, and conserving. This section looks critically at each of these options.

Can We Expand Our Reserves?

In the short term we have many opportunities to expand reserves. In the long term, however, some insurmountable barriers lie in wait. This section looks at the factors that can help us expand reserves as well as factors that limit the long-term potential of this strategy.

The Price, Supply, and Demand Triangle The **law of supply and demand** has been the centerpiece of Western economic thinking for years. This law essentially says that when demand outstrips supply, prices rise. Rising prices stimulate production, which in turn increases supply.

Economists use this law to support their belief that we can continually expand the supply of minerals. Their logic follows this path: First, rising mineral prices will make it economical for companies to mine deposits of minerals that were previously uneconomic to extract. Rising prices will also stimulate exploration. Companies will find new reserves, which can be mined as needed. This line of reasoning works well in the short term, but in the long run it falls apart. It is conceivable that as supplies dwindle, the price of a mineral would rise so high that people would simply stop buying it. In other words, when a mineral supply falls below a certain point, mining becomes too costly. For all intents and purposes the mineral is depleted. What all this means is that rising prices will expand our supplies, but only up to a point. Beyond that other measures must come into play.

Technology to the Rescue Technological advances could be one of those factors. Over the years technological improvements in the mining and processing of ore have increased our reserves of numerous minerals. Figure 13-7 shows the expansion of reserves in recent times.

Scientists and engineers are working on techniques to improve mining efficiency, allowing companies to exploit low-grade ore economically. One group of biologists, for example, recently found that certain algae bind gold ions; it is believed that they could help extract gold from mine wastes or even natural waters.

Technological advances are badly needed to increase mining efficiency. But technology is cost-driven. When mineral supplies fall below a certain point, costs could conceivably become too great for consumers to bear. Mining would be curtailed.

The Downside Just as higher prices can stimulate production and new technologies can expand our reserves, a handful of factors can have the opposite effect. Rising energy and labor costs, for example, tend to cut our reserves. When these costs rise faster than the cost of minerals, reserves that were once economically attractive may become uneconomical to mine.

Exploration, mining, and production are influenced by interest rates. High interest rates on capital needed for exploration and mining may slow these activities. Some economists predict that competition for capital will escalate in coming years, driving up interest rates and slowing the expansion of our reserves.

Reserves expand and contract in response to many factors. Therefore, it is not safe to assume that a reserve base listed for any one year is all the mineral we have at our disposal. As prices rise or as technologies improve, reserves can expand. But increased fuel prices, labor costs, higher interest rates, and depletion of resources can have the opposite effect.

In the long run, it is important to recall, all mineral resources are finite. This fundamental reality cannot be ignored. The long-term prospects for minerals are bleak. Realizing this, some scientists and science fiction writers have begun to promote asteroid mining. A critical evaluation of the energy, money, and technology these programs would require makes many experts skeptical. Obtaining minerals from outer space is probably a pipe dream, too costly to pursue.

Rising Energy Costs: A Key Factor Mineral resources will eventually be **economically depleted**—that

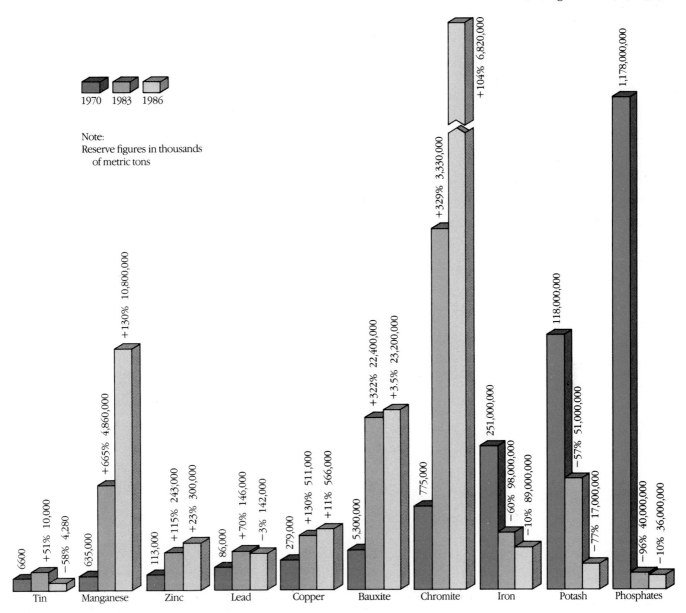

Figure 13-7 Changes in world reserves of selected minerals and metals between 1970 and 1986.

is, mined until they can no longer be produced at a profit. Energy prices will play a big role in determining when mining a particular mineral becomes uneconomical and stops. As lower- and lower-grade ores are mined, the amount of energy required for mining and refining is fairly constant up to a certain point, beyond which it increases dramatically (Figure 13-8). At this point these resources become uneconomical to mine; their costs exceed what the market will bear. For all intents and purposes they are depleted.

According to the U.S. Department of the Interior, the costs of minerals will remain constant until the year 2000. After 2000, though, they are expected to increase 5% a year, the same rate at which energy costs are predicted to increase. Rising energy prices combined with declining ore deposits could very well bring an end to some of our import mineral resources within 30 to 40 years. Runaway inflation could grip the world economy unless something is done.

Environmental Costs A final problem that dims the prospects of long-term expansion of mineral reserves is environmental costs. Mining lower-grade ores will produce increasing environmental damage: larger surface mines will be needed to produce the same amount of ore, more material will be transported to smelters for

Figure 13-8 Energy investment for recovery of minerals related to the concentration of ore.

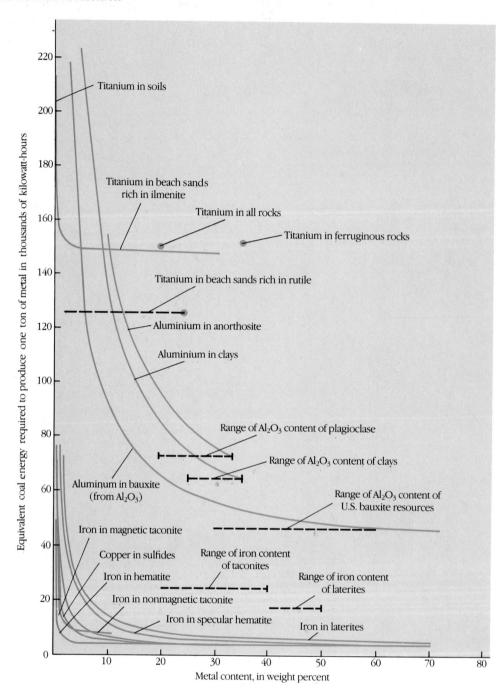

processing, more waste will be produced at the mines and smelters, and more air and water pollution will result. As a result, environmental protection costs will escalate, adding to the cost of production and ushering in the economic depletion of some minerals.

Minerals from the Sea   The ocean is a vast resource of minerals, many of which are dissolved in the water itself. However, the concentrations of most dissolved minerals are generally too low to be of economic importance.

More important are mineral deposits on the seafloor. Most noteworthy of these minerals are small lumps called **manganese nodules**, which lie along deep ocean bottoms (Figure 13-9). Abundant in the Pacific Ocean, manganese nodules contain several vital minerals, notably manganese (24%) and iron (14%), with smaller amounts of copper (1%) and cobalt (0.25%).

Several mining companies have explored the possibility of dredging the seabed to mine these odd mineral deposits. The environmental impacts of this action are

Figure 13-9 Manganese nodules on the ocean's floor.

largely unknown. Preliminary studies show that seafloor mining may be technically feasible and may be profitable. The biggest impediment is a legal one. No international agreements spell out who owns the deep seabed. Western countries have the wealth to exploit the resource. Developing nations, contending that the seabed belongs to all nations, believe they should receive a portion of the proceeds.

At a United Nations Conference on the Law of the Sea the developing countries proposed an international tax on seabed minerals, which could provide millions of dollars a year for agricultural and economic development. A comprehensive Law of the Sea Treaty, worked out with U.S. negotiators during the Carter administration, would have included this plan, but so far it has not been ratified by the U.S. Senate, largely because of opposition from U.S. mining interests.

Many people believe that seabed taxation to benefit the developing nations is fair. Others see it as an unfair way of cutting into profits. As a result of the growing conflict, progress toward mining the seabed has come to a halt.

Can We Find Substitutes?

The substitution of one resource for another that has become economically depleted has been a useful strategy for industrialized nations. Shortages of cotton, wool, and natural rubber, for example, have been eased by synthetic materials derived from oil. Synthetic fibers have found their way into American clothes. Synthetic rubber has replaced most natural rubber from trees. Substitution will unquestionably play an important role in the future, too. But is substitution a crutch we can lean on forever?

Critics argue that substitutions have created unreasonable faith among the public in the ability of scientists to come up with new resources to replace those that are being depleted. They also note that many substitutes have limits themselves. Plastics have replaced many metals, for example, but the oil from which plastics are made is a limited resource.

Substitutions will play an important role in the future, but they are not a cure-all for pending mineral shortages. Some resources may have no substitutes at all. For instance, it may be impossible to find substitutes for the manganese used in desulfurizing steel, the nickel and chromium used in stainless steel, the tin in solder, the helium used in low-temperature refrigeration, the tungsten used in high-speed tools, or the silver used in photographic papers and films.

Finding substitutes has become a race against time. Since we have rounded the bend of the exponential curve of demand, the time of economic depletion is fast approaching, perhaps more quickly than substitutes can be found. A wise strategy would be to identify those resources that are nearest to economic depletion and then promote widespread conservation and recycling. Research to find substitutes should begin immediately or be stepped up.

Can Recycling Stretch Our Supplies?

Recycling of materials can alleviate future resource shortages, greatly reduce energy demand, cut pollution, and reduce water use. Instead of being discarded in dumps, valuable minerals can be returned to factories, melted down, and reshaped. Some of the environmental benefits are shown in Table 13-2. In the United States and many

Table 13-2 Environmental Benefits of Recycling in the United States

	Paper	Aluminum	Iron and Steel
Current level of recycling	27%	32%	35%
Reduction in energy use	30–35%	90–95%	60–70%
Reduction in air pollution	95%	95%	30%

Antarctica: Protecting the Last Frontier

New lands have always meant riches to explorers. Precious metals and gems were the rewards for those who reckoned with sometimes-dangerous and uncharted territories far from their homelands. When a French explorer with an unpronounceable name (Yves-Joseph de Kerguelen-Tremarec) first saw the new continent in the southernmost reaches of the Indian Ocean in the 1700s, his mind raced wildly with thoughts of hidden wealth, among them timber, rubies, and diamonds.

Two hundred years later this vast expanse of land, now called Antarctica, has offered up virtually none of the promised mineral riches.

Making up one-tenth of the earth's surface, Antarctica might be considered an attractive land holding—were not most of it covered with a sheet of ice a mile thick. Despite the formidable cold, fierce winds, and long winter darkness, this remote wilderness and the frigid but nutrient-rich waters around it support a varied biological community. Penguins, seals, whales, sea birds, algae, krill, and fish—all uniquely adapted to the severe weather—thrive there, offering scientists an unparalleled opportunity to study life at the extremes of habitability.

The promise of riches brought humanity to the frozen tip of the world where a summer day of $-38°$ C ($-35°$ F) is considered warm and where temperatures as low as $-89°$ C ($-127°$ F) have been recorded. But the wealth reaped from this land so far has been in the form of knowledge. Fighting frequent storms with winds commonly reaching 320 kilometers per hour (200 miles per hour), scientists have sought to unravel the mysteries of Antarctic life. And they hope that knowledge about ocean currents and Antarctic weather will help them better understand global weather. The officials who send them, while interested in advancing science, still look on Antarctica, much as the first explorers did, with hopes that important mineral resources and oil might be locked beneath the ice.

The first real impetus for Antarctic mineral exploration came after the perilous climb in oil prices in the 1970s, when developed nations became aware of their dependence on foreign sources. A number of promising reports from the U.S. Geological Survey speculated that huge oil reserves lay beneath Antarctica's continental shelf. But evidence of oil, many experts say, is sketchy. Similar studies of the Atlantic coast of the United States, for instance, have indicated that oil might lie beneath the continental shelf, but so far virtually no oil has been discovered there.

Sizable mineral deposits may also lie beneath the ice and snow of Antarctica. This conclusion is based on geological evidence showing that this huge continent was once a part of an ancient supercontinent called Gondwanaland (Figure 13-3). Part of Antarctica may have abutted South Africa, which is rich in minerals. And traces of minerals have been located in the Pensacola Mountains, which rise out of the ice of this frozen land, giving some even more hope that rich mineral deposits are awaiting them.

Like the early rumors of gold in the American West, these discoveries have stirred the tempo of life in Antarctica. Developed and developing nations have begun to line up for their share of the envisioned wealth. Conflict is now arising over ownership of minerals and oil, should they be found. For many years, however, peace has prevailed among the scientists studying the region. Scientists work amicably with others from different countries, often sharing information while their home governments are exchanging harsh words—or even fighting each other as Argentina and Great Britain did in the Falklands War of 1982. Antarctica's cooperative governance was established by the 1959 Antarctic Treaty System, which had two objectives: to maintain the continent for peaceful uses by prohibiting all military activities, weapons tests, and nuclear explosions; and to promote freedom for scientific research.

Between 1908 and 1943 Great Britain, France, Norway, Australia, New Zealand, Chile, and Argentina had claimed 85% of Antarctica. The United States and the Soviet Union, which had done its share of South Pole exploration and research, did not establish specific claims. Finding it preferable to retain an interest in all of the continent, the superpowers refused to acknowledge the territorial claims of the others, making for a sticky international situation.

But the treaty settled the debate in 1959. Perhaps the single most important provision of the treaty is Article 4, in which the seven claimant nations set aside all territorial claims so that signatories of the treaty (now numbering 16) could carry out research. International cooperation in science became the basis for restraining political tensions and potential conflict. Should minerals and oil be discovered, however, the seven original claimant countries could once again lay claim to their territories.

To the shock of world leaders, who have long wrangled with the notion of world peace, scientific cooperation became the whole basis for a new political order. But the hints of Antarctic minerals and oil now threaten to destabilize the climate, pitting one nation against another. The confrontation arises between the haves—the seven claimant nations—and the have-nots—those who signed the treaty and have participated in Antarctic research and management but have no legal claim on the land or resources. The have-nots also include a growing number of Third World nations, which have done no research in Antarctica but would like a share in any potential wealth. Added to the growing fray are several international organizations, such as Greenpeace International and the International Union for the Conservation of Nature and Natural Resources. Their interest, of course, is to protect the environment from exploration

Essay 13-1

and extraction and from adverse impacts resulting from the growing tourism trade, as well.

This concern for environmental protection is well founded. Offshore oil rigs, for instance, would operate in some of the roughest seas in the world. Huge icebergs could rip apart platforms and drilling rigs. Ice flows could trap and crush ships. Mining would require huge amounts of energy just to melt the mile-thick icecap. Mining is made more problematic by physical constraints. Overland transport of ore, for example, would be difficult because of fierce winds and cold temperatures. Ice extending 1000 miles from land would make it difficult and costly to transport ores to awaiting ships.

Environmentalists are also concerned about the potential impacts of resource development on the rich marine ecosystem. Oil spills, they assert, could be carried ashore and wipe out huge breeding colonies of penguins, birds, and seals. Slicks might also kill algae, which are responsible for replenishing 20% of the region's oxygen. Caught under the ice and in the chilly waters, oil could persist 100 times longer than in warmer waters.

Finally, cleaning up an oil spill would be impaired by the short "warm" season. And, if a well blew out, winter might set in before workers could plug it up, thus allowing oil to collect under the ice for up to nine months, with potentially devastating effects.

Mineral extraction would require enormous amounts of energy, create pollution, damage the ice pack, and severely disrupt the exposed land, with its notoriously short growing season. A footprint scar takes a decade to heal. Pollution from mining operations would also disrupt scientific research on air pollution. Most damaging to wildlife, however, would be the use of ice-free coastal areas for processing and shipping ores to faraway countries.

Some experts believe that dreams of minerals and oil are just that. Only enormous oil fields could ever be economical. Mineral extraction is even more economically preposterous, they say. But others are quick to point out that political factors could set aside all economic logic as well as the numerous ecological constraints to development. For example, if world supplies of strategic minerals were threatened

by political instabilities, they argue, world leaders might overlook the environmental and economic barriers to mineral extraction.

The Antarctic presents an unparalleled global challenge. Owned by no one but potentially benefiting many, it is a harsh and fragile land where damage to the rich marine ecosystem could easily be irreparable. For years Antarctica has stood as a symbol of world peace and cooperation, but with the hint of its mineral and oil riches reaching the outside world, that unique and harmonious relationship has begun to deteriorate. The challenge, many say, is to balance the costs and benefits of resource exploitation. When the costs to wildlife and the economic costs of extracting resources in the world's harshest environment are stacked against the benefits, the whole idea of development may seem preposterous.

The true test of a sustainable society is to separate what is technologically possible from what is ecologically unsound. In doing so we reach a new level of cultural development that may ensure our long-term survival.

---

other countries, however, recycling efforts have fallen short of their full potential except for a few instances such as the automobile. Approximately 90% of all American cars are recycled. The recycling of aluminum, steel, and many other metals could be doubled.

Economic Factors That Influence Recycling If recycling is such a good idea, why don't we do more of it? The reasons are complex. First, industrial societies grew up with abundant resources. They saw little need for recycling. Factories were set up to handle virgin material. The entire production–consumption system was fashioned without recycling. Redesigning this system has only recently begun. Second, tax breaks have been enacted for mining companies, giving them an unfair advantage over recyclers by making virgin ore cheaper than recycling. Third, the shipping rates for virgin materials in the United States are lower than those for most scrap metals because of a quirk in federal regulations. Fourth, the labor and energy costs of recovering scrap from trash are often high, making recycling less profit-

able. Fifth, many products contain a mixture of materials, making them more difficult to recycle.

Many advocates of recycling argue that it will become more profitable as the high-grade ores are depleted. Changes in transportation rates, subsidies for recycling to put it on even ground with the use of virgin materials, and widespread citizen cooperation in separating recyclables from nonrecyclables could greatly help (Figure 13-10). Eliminating the diverse mixture of materials in products would also be helpful.

Many major U.S. cities are facing a crisis in waste management—too much garbage and not enough land in which to bury it. As a result, some cities have invested millions of dollars in their recycling programs to reduce trash disposal. In 1985, for instance, Philadelphia topped out its last landfill. The next closest dump is a 335-kilometer (210-mile) round trip. Because of this, the city plans to recycle 600 tons of trash per day by 1990. Twenty neighborhood recycling stations will handle much of the waste.

The story is much the same in other American cities,

Figure 13-10 Recycling of aluminum is catching on in the United States. New automated recycling machines like this one in a grocery store parking lot encourage people to exchange their aluminum cans for cash. Ten states now have bottle and can bills to promote recycling.

including New York, Chicago, Minneapolis, and Berkeley, California. Shrinking land has forced city officials to look for alternatives; recycling is coming out on top. By recycling and other resource conservation measures, Berkeley hopes to cut its trash by 40%. In 1984 Minneapolis launched a pilot curbside recycling service to cut trash. Encouraged by the participation, city officials have begun a more ambitious citywide program. New York City, which has only one landfill left, launched an extensive recycling program in the spring of 1986 with hopes of cutting its solid municipal waste by 15% by 1990. For more on recycling see Chapter Supplement 18-1, on solid waste.

Our Personal Role Many people simply refuse to recycle newspapers, aluminum cans, scrap steel and iron, beverage cans, and glass bottles. Many think it is silly and a waste of their time. This lack of personal commitment is translated into a lack of public interest, which is then communicated to the government.

State Recycling Programs In 1972 the Oregon Legislature passed a law that requires individuals to pay a deposit on beverage containers. The deposit is refunded when the container is returned to the store. Vermont, Michigan, Maine, Connecticut, Iowa, Massachusetts, and New York have followed suit. Deposit laws help reduce litter, greatly increase recycling, and reduce energy consumption by manufacturers of cans and bottles (see Table

13-2). In Oregon over 90% of all cans and bottles are returned. Nationwide beverage-container recycling could save the equivalent of 70,000 to 140,000 barrels of oil per day. Deposit laws also reduce solid waste by about 6%, assuming 100% return.

Opponents of deposit laws argue that solid waste reduction would be minimal and that mandatory recycling would cost jobs, raise the price of beverages, decrease retail sales, and reduce tax revenues. However, a study by the Maryland Governor's Council of Economic Advisors predicted that a law that eliminated throwaway bottles and cans in Maryland would create 1500 jobs (at pickup and recycling plants), add to personal income in the state, and provide $1.5 million in extra income-tax revenue to state and local governments. In addition, the law would save local governments $7 million by reducing litter pickup.

Proponents of recycling believe that a uniform national law is needed. If Texas and a few other major states enacted "bottle bills," the momentum created could bring about a national program in short order, some analysts predict. The 1983 bottle bill in New York state and the 1986 bill in California should increase the national momentum.

A study commissioned by New York to assess its beverage-container law after the first year of operation reported that the law had been a great success. Bottle trash was cut by 70%, and landfill space required to dispose of New York's trash was reduced between 5% and 8%. Besides cutting waste and the demand for waste disposal sites, the new law created 3,900 jobs in the recycling industry. The price of beverages remained fairly stable. Three out of four New Yorkers were in favor of the bill, especially because it cut litter along roads and highways.

Recycling: Only a Partial Answer Recycling helps increase the time a mineral or metal remains in use, or its **residence time**. It also helps us save an enormous amount of energy. For example, manufacturing an aluminum can from recycled aluminum uses only 5% of the energy required to make it from aluminum ore (bauxite). Recycling, however, will not permit our current exponential growth in mineral use to continue indefinitely. Why is this so?

First, during the production–consumption cycle some minerals and metals enter into long-term uses—for example, aluminum used for wiring or bronze for statuary. Also, some materials are lost through processing inefficiencies, are lost accidentally, or are thrown away on purpose. Because of these reasons it is impossible to recycle 100% of a given material. A more practical goal would be 60% to 80%. Thus, recycling can slow down the depletion of a mineral resource but cannot stop it. In theory, recycling can double our mineral resource base, but continually rising demand and inevitable losses will eventually deplete that reserve.

Can Conservation Stretch Our Supplies?

The author Nancy Newhall once observed that "conservation is humanity caring for the future." Conservation is often the cheapest and easiest strategy for stretching our mineral resources. In the long run our consumption of mineral resources will inevitably fall as prices rise. Prudence dictates strategies that delay the economic depletion of minerals. This book takes the position that conservation must begin with individuals like yourself and spread through society to the highest levels, where it will be reflected in national policies. Combined with recycling, conservation measures can greatly extend the lifetime of many valuable mineral resources. As shown in Figure 13-11, continued exponential growth—the track we have been on until recently—is the fastest route to depletion; recycling will slow down, but not stop, this depletion. Recycling and conservation measures combined will give us more time to develop new mining technologies and find substitutes.

Some Suggested Personal Actions   Tolstoy wrote that "everyone thinks of changing the world, but no one thinks of changing himself." Personal actions go a long way toward increasing our mineral supplies, and they can save you money. Recycling and conservation are two such actions. Careful buying can also reduce waste. By purchasing food in recyclable containers or renewable wrappers (paper), for example, you and millions like you can curb the depletion of various minerals and oil, from which plastics are made.

When you buy soft drinks and other beverages, choose returnable bottles (although they are increasingly hard to find) in preference to recyclable aluminum cans, and aluminum cans above steel cans. Returnable bottles can be reused with a minor expenditure for transportation and washing; recyclable ones have to be transported, melted down, and then reformed, requiring more energy.

As for transportation, any measure that saves energy also saves valuable minerals. Buy smaller cars, and use mass transit so your family can get by with only one car. Build smaller homes. Buy solar homes.

When buying something, look for quality; a well-made product, by outlasting its inexpensive imitations, will be well worth the extra labor and material that was put into it. In the long run high-quality materials save resources.

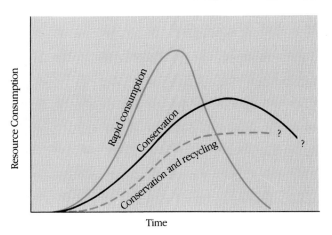

Figure 13-11   Three possible scenarios on a hypothetical time scale. Which one will we take?

Write letters supporting durable products, and complain to manufacturers whose junk falls apart on you soon after you get it home. Remember that consumers are to economics what voters are to elections.

You can also help by supporting various legal solutions—for example, recycling programs on a local, state, or national level. Recycling bins in neighborhoods should be encouraged: volunteer groups can pick up the materials regularly and sell them for profit. (The city might even assist by providing trucks.) Waste recovery systems at local dumps might also be helpful in conserving recyclable materials. Palo Alto, California, for example, gives city residents a free dump pass if they bring recyclable materials to the recycling center just outside the dump gates.

Recent polls show that three-fourths of all Americans questioned favor increased recycling. However, only 10% of U.S. waste is recycled. "Between saying and doing," the author F. W. Robertson wrote, "is a great distance." Blessed with cheap energy resources and abundant food sources, the United States has become the most wasteful country in the world. Used to the no-deposit, no-return appeal of modern products, the nation is unnecessarily throwing away its future. Clearly, Americans are robbing their descendants of their future. Conservation is not a roadblock to progress. For a society that has always viewed uncontrolled, ever-escalating production and consumption as evidence of prosperity, conservation is a sign of progress.

Tomorrow's growth depends on the use we make of today's materials and experiences.

ELMER WHEELER

Summary

Five billion years ago the molten earth began to cool, forming a crust of rock. This rock was subject to many altering forces. Soil formed from particles eroded by rainfall. New types of rock formed in the earth's crust.

The crust contains inorganic compounds called minerals. There are usually several types of mineral in any one type of rock. Concentrated deposits of minerals that are economical to mine and process are called **ores**.

The earth's crust participates in an enormous rock cycle, in which new rock is continuously formed while parts of the crust are melted. The crust is broken into huge **tectonic plates**, which move about over millions of years, a process called **continental drift**. The tectonic plates pull apart at midoceanic ridges. Molten rock flows up into the gap, creating new crust. In other parts of the plate the crust is thrust under adjoining plates and is melted.

Minerals are worth billions of dollars in the world market. Some are so important that industry and agriculture in developed nations would come to a standstill if they suddenly became unavailable. The developed countries are the major consumers of minerals. With one-fourth of the world's population, they consume three-fourths of its minerals. Most of these nations import large quantities from developing nations.

Developing nations have become increasingly unhappy with the low prices they receive for their raw minerals. Some analysts fear that they will form cartels to control prices. This would result in an upward trend in the cost of metals, with serious consequences for the economies of industrial nations.

One of the key issues regarding minerals is whether there will be enough to meet future needs. In the short term, strategic supplies will help us weather any sudden drops in supply. In the long term, however, some important minerals are being used up.

Some economists believe that rising prices will stimulate exploration and new technologies, which will increase our reserve of nonfuel minerals. They also argue that substitutes for economically depleted mineral resources will be made available through advances in science and technology. As mineral resources of lower and lower concentration are exploited, however, energy investments in mining and processing will become higher and higher. After 2000 or 2010 the real cost of minerals may begin to rise by 5% a year, making many minerals uneconomical to mine and process. Competition for capital may raise interest rates, which also makes it economically unprofitable to mine and process lower-grade ores. Mining low-grade ores increases environmental damage as well.

Minerals from the sea may help expand our reserves, but economic, environmental, and legal questions have yet to be worked out. One of the most promising resources is **manganese nodules**, which are found on the seabed. They primarily contain manganese and iron.

Substitution of one resource for another that has become economically depleted has been a useful strategy in the past, but it will be of limited value in the future. Substitutes for scarce minerals may have limits themselves. Some minerals have no adequate substitutes. Finally, in some cases economic depletion may occur before substitutes can be developed.

Recycling can alleviate future resource shortages, cut energy demand, reduce environmental pollution, and create jobs, but it is not a panacea. Many materials are put into permanent use. For short-term goods, such as cans and bottles, recycling recovers 60% to 80% of total production. In short, recycling can slow down the depletion but cannot stop it.

Conservation is a highly favored approach. Combined with recycling, it can greatly extend the lifetime of many valuable minerals and give us more time to find substitutes and develop new mining strategies.

Discussion Questions

1. Describe the earth's crust using the following terms: *continental* and *subcontinental layers, midoceanic ridges, sea-floor spreading, subduction zones, tectonic plates,* and *continental drift.*

2. Define nonrenewable and renewable mineral resources, and give examples of each. How are they different?

3. Why is it difficult to determine the level of future mineral demand? How would you go about calculating the demand for minerals in the year 2000?

4. Debate the statement "Economic forces will ensure us a continual supply of mineral resources. As prices rise, we'll find new resources, develop new technologies, and find substitutes for minerals currently used."

5. What are reserves? Explain how mineral reserves can expand.

6. The trend over the past few decades has been increasing mineral reserves. Why has this occurred? Will it continue? Why or why not?

7. Outline a plan to meet the future mineral needs of our society. Describe your plan. What are its most important components?

8. Draw a graph of the energy required to mine an ore as the grade decreases. What are the long-term implications?

9. Debate the statement "There is no need to worry about running out of minerals; we will find substitutes for them."

10. List the advantages of recycling and resource conservation.

11. Make a list of ways in which you can cut down your resource consumption by 20%.

Suggested Readings

Barry, P. (1985). Cities Rush to Recycle. *Sierra* 70 (6): 32–35. How American cities are responding to shrinking land sites for waste disposal.

Chandler, W. U. (1984). Recycling Materials. In *State of the World,* ed. Linda Starke. Washington, D.C.: Worldwatch Institute. Superb review.

Council on Environmental Quality. (1980). *The Global 2000 Report to the President.* New York: Penguin. Chapter 12 provides an excellent survey of nonfuel mineral resources.

U.S. Bureau of Mines. (1983). *The Domestic Supply of Critical Minerals.* Washington, D.C.: U.S. Government Printing Office. Full of useful information.

U.S. Bureau of Mines. (1984). *Mineral Commodity Summaries, 1984.* Washington, D.C.: U.S. Government Printing Office. Excellent source of information on minerals published every year.

U.S. Bureau of Mines. (1985). *Mineral Facts and Problems* (1985 ed.). Washington, D.C.: U.S. Government Printing Office. Superb reference published every five years.

IV

POLLUTION

14

Toxic Substances: Principles and Practicalities

Life is a perpetual instruction in cause and effect.

RALPH WALDO EMERSON

Shortly after midnight on December 3, 1984, a 35-meter-high (100-foot) cloud of methyl isocyanate gas escaped from the Union Carbide Corporation's chemical plant in Bhopal, India. Within minutes, chaos erupted. Frightened residents—coughing, screaming, defecating uncontrollably—ran helter-skelter through city streets to escape. Few people knew what was going on. Fewer still knew what to do.

When the toxic cloud and panic had disappeared, 2,500 people lay dead. All told, 200,000 people had been injured (Figure 14-1). Of these, 17,000 have been permanently disabled, largely with lung ailments. Several thousand dead and decaying animals littered the streets.

What makes the Bhopal accident more tragic is that any number of simple steps could have prevented it or lessened its severity. Had citizens been advised to breathe through wet towels, for example, many victims would be alive today. Had one of the backup systems in the plant operated, the accident could have been prevented altogether.

What caused the actual leak that sent toxic fumes into the air? Late on December 2, 450 to 900 liters (120 to 240 gallons) of water were pumped into storage tanks containing liquid methyl isocyanate, a chemical used to produce Sevin, a commonly used pesticide. The water triggered a series of runaway chemical reactions that increased temperature and pressure within the tanks. Unable to withstand the pressure, the tank's seal broke, sending 22,500 kilograms (50,000 pounds) of the chemical into the air. Four backup systems, for one reason or

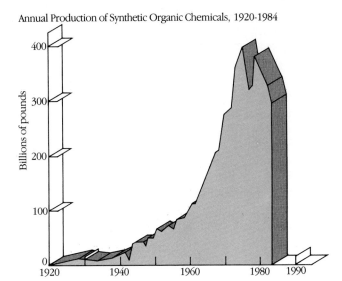

Annual Production of Synthetic Organic Chemicals, 1920-1984

Figure 14-2 Growth in the production of synthetic organic chemicals in the United States.

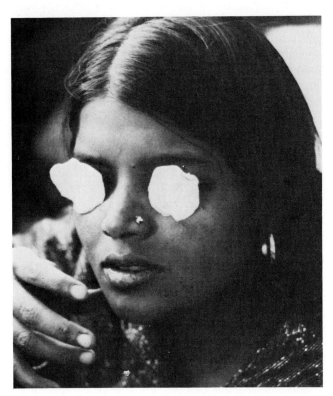

Figure 14-1 Indian woman being treated for exposure to deadly MIC that escaped from Union Carbide's Bhopal, India facility. The emission caused widespread sickness and death.

another, were out of order or failed to work. The one that did work proved inadequate.

Many factors contributed to the accident at Bhopal: (1) Union Carbide's decision to store large quantities of methyl isocyanate—a practice shunned by the chemical industry—was undoubtedly one of them. (2) A cooling system that could have thwarted the buildup of pressure was not working. (3) The transfer of the chemical to backup tanks was manually controlled but should have been automatically controlled. (4) An effective emergency plan was lacking. (5) The facility was too close to a major population center. In more ways than one the tragedy of Bhopal is rooted in overpopulation—too many people, creating a need for pesticides to increase food production; too many people, pushing residences into the meager buffer zone surrounding the plant.

Focusing world attention on the risk of toxic chemicals, Bhopal remains a stark symbol of one of the possible consequences of the marriage between modern society and the chemical industry. This chapter looks at toxic substances—their effects and their control. It concludes with an assessment of the risks and benefits of life in a world dependent on technology and the products of the chemical industry.

Principles of Toxicology

Sixty thousand chemical substances are sold commercially in the United States. By various estimates, 8,600 food additives, 3,400 cosmetic ingredients, and at least 35,000 pesticides are in use. Chemical production and use have skyrocketed since World War II (Figure 14-2). Of the commercially important chemicals, however, only a small number—perhaps 2%—are known to be harmful. Still, this small percentage amounts to hundreds of potentially dangerous chemicals, hazardous mainly to workers but also to the general public, as the Bhopal tragedy makes clear. According to an EPA survey, more than 6,900 accidents involving toxic wastes occurred in the United States between 1980 and 1985. The human cost in comparison with Bhopal was small—138 people killed and 4,717 injured. A large percentage of the victims were workers.

Perhaps the biggest problem with toxic substances is our lack of knowledge about their effects. The National Academy of Sciences noted that fewer than 10% of U.S. agricultural chemicals and 5% of food additives have been fully tested to assess chronic health effects. Testing potentially harmful substances is a costly and time-consuming task, made more difficult by the 700 to 1000 new chemicals entering the marketplace each year.

Biological Effects of Toxins

Toxic substances, or **toxins**, are chemicals that adversely affect living organisms. **Toxicology** is the study of these effects. Our concern in this chapter is primarily with the effects on humans.

Average citizens are exposed to toxic substances at home, at work, or while moving about outdoors. In many cases they have little control over exposure. Polluted air from nearby power plants or highways exposes them to dozens of potentially harmful substances. In some cases, however, we intentionally expose ourselves to harmful substances, such as smoke from cigarettes.

Chemical substances exert a wide range of effects, depending on the amount we receive. This amount, in turn, is determined by the concentration (or dose) of the toxin and the duration of the exposure—known as the two D's (dose and duration). Some effects may be subtle, such as a slight cough or headache caused by air pollution. Others can be pronounced, such as the violent convulsions brought on by exposure to certain insecticides. **Toxicologists**, the scientists who study toxins, classify effects as acute or chronic.

Acute Effects Acute effects are those symptoms that appear right after exposure. In Bhopal, for example, many people complained of chest pains and severe eye irritation. Many children died soon after being exposed. Acute effects often disappear shortly after the exposure ends and are generally caused by fairly high concentrations of chemicals during short-term (acute) exposures.

Chronic Effects Chronic effects are delayed, but long-lasting, responses to toxic agents. They may occur months to years after exposure and usually persist for years, as in the case of emphysema caused by cigarette smoke or pollution. Chronic effects are generally the result of low-level exposure over long periods (chronic exposures). It is important to note, though, that short-term exposures may also have delayed effects. In Bhopal, for example, methyl isocyanate may have caused a host of long-term effects, symptoms such as paralysis that appeared weeks after the exposure.

Chemicals can affect virtually every cell in the body. Their hidden effects, such as cancer, mutations, birth defects, and reproductive impairment, pose the most serious challenge to society.

Cancer Cancer annually kills 400,000 people in the United States. **Cancer** is an uncontrolled proliferation of cells that forms a mass, or **primary tumor**. Cells may break off from the tumor and travel in the blood and other body fluids. The spread of cancerous cells is called **metastasis**. In distant sites the cancerous cells may form **secondary tumors**.

Every cancer starts when a single cell goes haywire, a process that occurs most often in tissues undergoing rapid cellular division—for example, the bone marrow, lungs, lining of the intestines, ovaries, testes, and skin. Nondividing cells, such as nerve cells and muscle cells, rarely become cancerous.

Despite years of intensive research scientists remain uncertain about the causes of some types of cancer. Many cancers, they know, begin after **mutations**, or changes in the genetic material, DNA. Ninety percent of all chemicals known to cause cancer also cause mutations in bacterial test systems. The causative agents include viruses, a variety of chemical substances, and physical agents such as X rays and ultraviolet light.

Although the chromosomes of cancer cells are typically abnormal in structure or in number, a number of **carcinogens** (agents that cause cancer)—such as asbestos, certain plastics, and certain hormones—apparently do not directly alter the DNA or cause mutations. Other mechanisms must be involved.

In the 1970s many experts believed that about 90% of all cancers were caused by environmental pollutants and other agents such as X rays, ultraviolet light, and viruses. The public was shocked at this revelation. However, more careful research has shown that only 20% to 40% of all cancers are caused by workplace and environmental pollutants. The rest presumably arise from smoking, dietary factors, and natural causes. In the 1970s it seemed as if cancer was sweeping the United States. Many people began to believe that cancer rates were rising rapidly. As shown in Figure 14-3, however, most cancer rates have remained fairly constant for 50 years, except for lung cancer, which has risen dramatically in both men and women, testicular cancer, which has also risen, and stomach cancer, which has fallen.

By one of the most commonly cited estimates, made by two Oxford University scientists, 8000 Americans die each year of cancer caused by environmental factors, such as air pollution. Another 8000 cancer deaths are attributed to food additives and industrial products, such as pesticides used around the house; 16,000 deaths result each year from occupational exposure to harmful substances. The researchers note, by comparison, that tobacco causes at least 120,000 cancer deaths each year.

Mutations Agents that cause mutations are called **mutagens**. In general, three types of genetic alteration are seen: (1) changes in the DNA itself, (2) alterations of the chromosomal structure that are visible by microscope (deletion or rearrangement of parts of the chromosome), and (3) missing or extra chromosomes. For our purposes the term *mutation* encompasses all three.

Mutations can be caused by chemical substances, such as caffeine, or physical agents, such as ultraviolet light and other high-energy radiation (Chapter Supplement 12-1). In humans, mutations can occur in normal body cells, or **somatic cells**, such as skin and bone. Such mutations occur quite frequently but are usually repaired by cellular enzymes. If a mutation is not repaired, it may lead to cancer.

The reproductive cells, or **germ cells**, in the male and

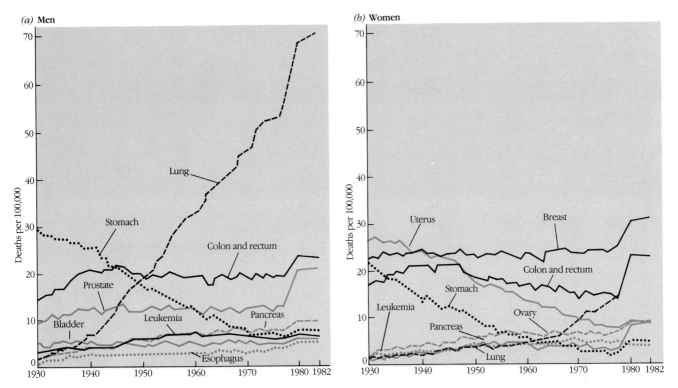

(a) Men

(b) Women

Figure 14-3 Cancer rates in men and women in the United States. Most cancer rates have stabilized except for lung cancer, which is rising, stomach cancer, which has fallen, and testicular cancer, which has risen (but is not shown on the graph).

female gonads are also susceptible to mutagens. Unrepaired germ-cell mutations may be passed on to offspring. If a genetically damaged ovum, for example, is fertilized by a normal sperm, the mutation is passed on to every cell in the offspring. The defective gene may prove lethal, or it may manifest itself as a birth defect or a metabolic disease. However, some germ-cell mutations may not evidence themselves in the first generation but may be expressed in the second and third generations. This delayed effect makes it difficult for scientists to pinpoint the causes of various diseases.

Genetic mutations are present in about 2 of every 100 newborns. The causes of mutations in humans are not well understood. Abnormal chromosome numbers, responsible for some diseases such as Down's syndrome, are related to maternal age (Figure 14-4). Broken and rearranged chromosomes are also related to maternal age. As women enter their 30s, their chances of having a baby with an abnormal number of chromosomes increases; after age 40 the chances skyrocket. Geneticists believe that the older a woman is, the greater the chance that she has been exposed to mutagens, hence the greater the likelihood that her child will have a mutation.

Other diseases, associated with actual structural defects in the DNA molecule itself, seem to increase in incidence

as the father gets older but are not related to the mother's age (Figure 14-5). These defects may be caused by mutagens and may result in birth defects, cancer, and other diseases.

Birth Defects Seven percent of children born in the United States have a birth defect—a physical (structural), biochemical, or functional abnormality. The most obvious defects are the physical abnormalities such as cleft palate, lack of limbs, or spina bifida. According to many scientists, the incidence of birth defects is greater than 7% (perhaps as high as 10% to 12%), because many minor defects escape detection at birth. For example, mental retardation and certain enzyme deficiencies are commonly missed by physicians.

Agents that cause birth defects are called **teratogens**; the study of birth defects is **teratology** (from *teratos,* Greek for "monster"). In humans, teratogenic agents may be drugs, physical agents such as radiation, or biological agents such as the rubella (German measles) virus (Table 14-1). No one knows for sure what percentage of birth defects is caused by chemicals in the environment.

Embryonic development can be divided into three parts: (1) a period of early development right after fertilization, (2) a period when the organs are developing

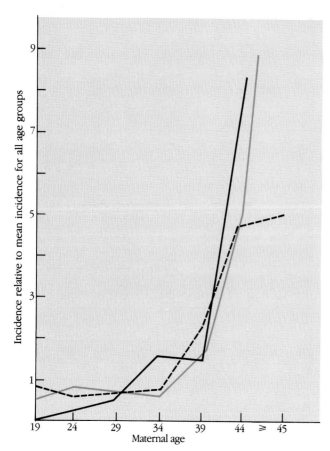

Figure 14-4 The incidence of several chromosomal abnormalities in newborns, involving the wrong number of chromosomes, is related to the mother's age. All abnormalities are trisomies of various chromosomes, resulting when chromosomes fail to separate during development of the ovum. When fertilization occurs, the offspring has an extra chromosome for certain chromosome pairs. (Incidence of abnormalities is given relative to their mean incidence for all ages. Mean incidences were calculated and assigned a value of one to allow comparison of three abnormalities in one group.)

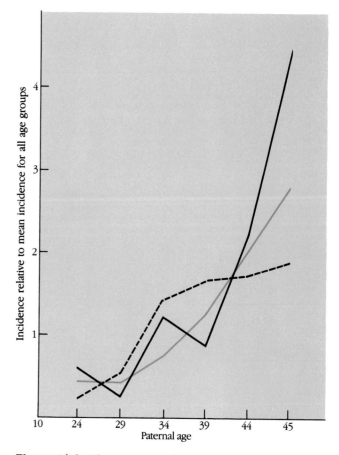

Figure 14-5 The incidence of several cartilage and bone diseases in newborns, caused by DNA damage, is related to the father's age. (Incidence is given relative to mean incidence of diseases for all age groups.)

Table 14-1 Some Known and Suspected Teratogens in Humans	
Known Agents	**Possible or Suspected Agents**
Progesterone	Aspirin
Thalidomide	Certain antibiotics
Rubella	Insulin
(German measles)	Antitubercular drugs
Alcohol	Antihistamines
Irradiation	Barbiturates
	Iron
	Tobacco
	Antacids
	Excess vitamins A and D
	Certain antitumor drugs
	Certain insecticides
	Certain fungicides
	Certain herbicides
	Dioxin
	Cortisone
	Lead

(*organogenesis*), a (3) a period during which the organs have formed and the fetus mainly increases in size. Teratogenic agents have a pronounced effect on development during organogenesis (Figure 14-6). The organs are most sensitive early in their development; as time passes, they become less and less sensitive.

The effect of a teratogenic agent is related both to the time of exposure and the type of chemical. Certain chemicals affect only certain organs; for example, methyl mercury damages the developing brains of embryos. Other chemicals, such as ethyl alcohol, can affect several systems; for instance, children born to alcoholic mothers exhibit numerous defects, including growth failure, facial disfigurement, heart defects, and skeletal defects.

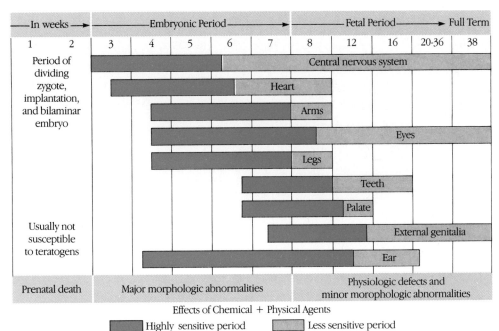

Figure 14-6 Schematic representation of human development, showing when some organ systems develop. Sensitive periods are early in development. Exposure to teratogens during these times will almost certainly cause birth defects.

Reproductive Toxicity Reproduction is a complex process, involving many steps. An ovum and sperm must be formed and successfully united. The zygote, the product of this union, must divide by mitosis and become implanted in the wall of the uterus, where it acquires nutrients from the mother's blood. Tissues develop from the ball of cells, and then organs develop from these tissues. Meanwhile, the mother is undergoing metabolic and hormonal changes. At the end of the developmental period birth takes place, requiring hormones that contract the uterus and expand the cervix (the opening between the vagina and uterus). Next, the breasts begin to produce milk, a hormonally regulated process called lactation. Chemical and physical agents may interrupt any of these complex processes, interfering with reproduction. The field of study that examines the effects of physical and chemical agents on reproduction is called **reproductive toxicology**.

The effects of drugs and environmental chemicals on reproduction have become a major health concern in recent years. Studies have shown that male factory workers temporarily become sterile when exposed on the job to DBCP (1,2-dibromo-3-chloropropane). Men who routinely handle various organic solvents often have abnormal sperm, unusually low sperm counts, and varying levels of infertility. A wide number of chemicals such as diethylstilbestrol (DES), borax, cadmium, methyl mercury, and many cancer drugs are toxic to the reproductive systems of males and females.

Some examples will help illustrate the effect of chemical toxins on reproduction. Two researchers from Laval University in Quebec examined the records of 386 children who had died of cancer before the age of 5. Their study showed that many of these children's fathers had been working at the time the children were conceived in occupations that exposed them to high levels of hydrocarbons. Some were painters exposed to paint thinners, and some were mechanics exposed to car exhaust. This study suggests that hydrocarbons had entered the bloodstream, traveled to the testes and there damaged the germ cells. The resulting genetic defect (mutation) was passed to the offspring.

Another example occurred when pregnant women were given the synthetic estrogen DES in the 1950s and 1960s. DES was administered to women who either had a history of miscarriages or had begun to bleed during pregnancy. Bleeding is an early symptom of miscarriage, and DES was given in hopes of preventing it. (It is now known that DES cannot prevent miscarriage.) Years later, uterine and cervical cancers began to appear in the daughters of DES-treated women. Research is uncovering reproductive damage in their sons, too. (For more on reproductive toxicology see Essay 14-1.)

How Do Toxins Work?

Toxic substances exert their effects at the cellular level in three major ways: First, they can affect **enzymes**, the cellular proteins that regulate many important chemical reactions. A disturbance of enzymatic activity can seriously alter the functioning of an organ or tissue. As examples, mercury and arsenic both bind to certain enzymes,

Figure 14-7 Dose-response graph for two chemicals (*a* and *b*) with differing toxicities. The LD_{50} is the amount of chemical that kills one-half of the experimental animals within a given time. The higher the LD_{50} value, the less toxic the chemical is.

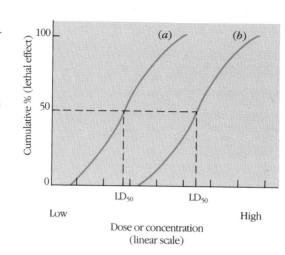

APPROXIMATE ACUTE LD_{50}s OF A
VARIETY OF CHEMICAL AGENTS IN RATS

AGENT	LD_{50} (mg/kg)
Ferrous sulfate	1,500
Morphine sulfate	900
Phenobarbital sodium	150
DDT	100
Picrotoxin	5
Strychnine sulfate	2
Nicotine	1
d-Tubocurarine	0.5
Hemicholinium-3	0.2
Tetrodotoxin	0.10
Botulinus toxin	0.00001

blocking their activity. Second, some toxins can bind directly to cells or molecules within the cell, thereby upsetting the chemical balance within the body. Carbon monoxide, for example, binds to hemoglobin in the blood; this interferes with the transport of oxygen and can lead to death if levels are high enough (see Chapter 20). Third, some toxins can cause the release of other naturally occurring substances that have an adverse effect. Carbon tetrachloride, for example, stimulates certain nerve cells to release large quantities of epinephrine (adrenaline), believed to cause liver damage.

Factors Affecting the Toxicity of Chemicals

Predicting the harmful effects of chemicals is no easy task. Age, sex, health, and a variety of other factors contribute to the final outcome. Consider this case: a family of six was living near a Canadian lead and zinc smelter that released large quantities of lead. Each member was exposed to high levels of lead. Because of age and health differences, however, the symptoms were quite varied. For example, the father and a 4-year-old boy suffered from colic and pancreatitis. The mother developed a neural disorder. Two other children experienced convulsions, and the last developed diabetes.

Three of the most important factors influencing the effects of a given chemical are the dose, the duration of exposure, and the biological reactivity of the chemical in question.

Dose and Duration In general, the higher the dose and the longer the exposure, the greater the effect. To demonstrate the effect of dose, toxicologists expose laboratory animals to varying doses and determine the response. The resulting graph is called a **dose–response curve** (Figure 14-7). The dose that kills half of the test

animals is called the LD_{50}, or the lethal dose for 50% of the test animals. By comparing LD_{50} values, scientists can judge the relative toxicity of two chemicals. For example, a chemical with an LD_{50} of 200 milligrams per kilogram of body weight is half as toxic as one with an LD_{50} of 100 milligrams. In other words, the lower the LD_{50}, the more toxic a chemical is.

Biological Activity The toxicity of a chemical is a function of its biological activity—that is, how it reacts with enzymes or other cellular components. The more reactive it is, the more effect it has. Inert substances—those that do not chemically react with cellular components—generally are not toxic, although there are notable exceptions such as asbestos.

Age Young, growing organisms are generally more susceptible to toxic chemicals than are mature adults. For example, two common air pollutants, ozone and sulfur dioxide, affect young laboratory animals two to three times more severely than they affect adults. Among humans, infants and children are more susceptible to lead and mercury poisoning than adults, because their nervous systems are still developing.

Health Status Poor nutrition, stress, bad eating habits, heart and lung disease, and smoking all contribute to poor health and make individuals more susceptible to certain toxins. Genetic factors may also determine one's response to certain toxic substances. Some individuals are genetically prone to heart disease, lung cancer, and other disorders brought on by environmental factors.

Synergy and Antagonism The presence of two or more toxic substances can alter the expected response. Different chemical substances can act together to produce

The Third Stage of Environmentalism

Frederic D. Krupp

The author is the executive director of the Environmental Defense Fund.

I believe the late 1980s will see U.S. conservationists embrace a major shift in tactics as we enter a newly constructive third stage in environmentalism's evolution.

The first stage of the conservation movement, represented by President Theodore Roosevelt and the early Sierra Club and National Audubon Society, was a reaction to decades of truly rapacious exploitation of natural resources, especially in the West. The early focus was on stemming the direct loss of wildlife and forest lands.

A key change occurred in the 1960s as people began to realize that they, too, were becoming victims of environmental abuses, that careless contamination of water, land, and air had sown seeds of destruction in the food chains of both wildlife and humans.

The environmental movement's response in this second phase was to work to halt abusive pollution, just as the early conservationists had tried to end the overexploitation of resources. The Environmental Defense Fund (EDF) was born in the forefront on the second phase, almost 20 years ago, in a victorious effort to stop the use of DDT, which threatened the osprey, bald eagle, and other species with extinction and had established an alarming presence in mother's milk.

The EDF's original vision—to present the evidence of environmental science in a court of law—proved to be an effective strategy to halt and even reverse environmental damage. Lawsuits, lobbying, peaceful protests and other direct efforts became the common expressions of environmental concern in this period.

Most environmental organizations still emphasize this form of reaction, but a new age of environmentalism may be dawning. The "New Environmentalists" say we cannot be effective solely by opposing environmental abuses. We must go the extra mile by finding alternatives to answer the legitimate needs that underlie ill-advised projects like destructive dams. Otherwise we are treating only the symptoms of problems that will surface again and again. When we answer the underlying needs, we perform a lasting cure.

If conservationists worry about the impact of a dam, for example, they had better address the water-supply or power-supply problem the dam was proposed to solve. They must concern themselves with the *science and economics* of environmental protection. Jobs, the rights of stockholders, and the needs of agriculture, industry, and consumers for adequate water and power—all of these issues must become part of the new environmental agenda.

For us to move beyond reactive opposition, to become a *positive* movement *for* better alternatives, means facing a difficult challenge. Our organizations will need to keep and recruit the best minds from every discipline, thinkers who can envision and persuasively lead the nation toward environmentally sound economic growth.

The EDF's experience in California utility regulation is one of several case studies in this New Environmentalism. In the late 1970s one of the country's largest utilities, Pacific Gas & Electric Company, had plans to build coal and nuclear power plants worth $20 billion. Forces on both sides were strong, and deeply entrenched. Then an EDF team—a lawyer, an economist, and a computer analyst—developed an unprecedented package of alternative energy sources and conservation investments and ultimately convinced PG&E to adopt the plan. Why? Because it not only met the same electrical needs but also meant lower prices for consumers, higher returns to PG&E stockholders, and a healthier financial future for the company itself.

The EDF's plan not only blocked construction of the polluting plants, it literally made the plants unnecessary and made obsolete an entire "bigger-is-better" mindset among electric power planners.

In the 1970s society badly needed the new institutions like environmental action groups and public-interest law firms that were created to meet the problems of that era. Today the need is for these institutions to become well equipped to envision solutions and to assemble new coalitions—even coalitions of former enemies—to bring about answers to environmental problems. But the third stage of environmentalism is in no sense a move toward compromise, a search for the in-between position. We will still need skillful advocacy—even in court—against narrow institutional vision or vested interest in the status quo. We must, however, become true advocates of a new course of action, not mere opponents of the old.

The EDF is the first environmental group to begin to fill this exciting new environmental niche, but even without its push in this new direction, the shift would have been inevitable. What the American public wants—some might say paradoxically—is both to expand our economic well-being and to preserve our natural resources and public health. It is up to us as environmentalists to prove this is no paradox and find the innovative ways to do both.

a **synergistic response**—that is, a response stronger than the simple sum of the two responses. One of the most familiar examples of toxic **synergism** is the combination of barbiturate tranquilizers and alcohol; although neither taken alone in small amounts is dangerous, the combination can be deadly. Pollutants can also synergize. For instance, sulfur dioxide gas and particulates (minute airborne particles) inhaled together can reduce air flow through the lung's tiny passages; the combined response is much greater than the sum of the individual responses.

Chemicals can also negate each other's effects, a phenomenon called **antagonism**. In these cases, a harmful effect is reduced by certain combinations of potentially toxic chemicals. When mice are exposed to nitrous oxide gas, for example, mortality is substantially reduced when particulates are also present. Scientists are uncertain of the reasons for this phenomenon.

Bioconcentration and Biological Magnification

Two factors not mentioned in the previous discussion that profoundly influence toxicity are bioconcentration and biological magnification. **Bioconcentration** is the accumulation of certain chemicals within the body. For example, the human thyroid gland bioconcentrates iodide. The level of iodide in the thyroid is thousands of times higher than that in the blood. Scallops, marine bivalve mollusks that feed on material suspended in water, selectively take up certain elements from seawater, such as zinc, copper, cadmium, and chromium. The level of cadmium in scallops, for example, is 2.3 million times that of seawater.

When harmful chemicals become concentrated in organisms, trouble may begin. For example, certain persistent (nonbiodegradable) organic molecules, such as the pesticide DDT, concentrate in body fat. Bioconcentration opens the door for a phenomenon called **biological magnification**, the buildup of chemicals in organisms in a food chain. As shown in Figure 14-8, DDT in water is taken up by zooplankton, single-celled organisms in the water. Small fish ingest DDT when they feed on zooplankton. Higher-level organisms also accumulate this substance. Tissue concentrations become higher at higher levels of the food chain. Biological magnification occurs because DDT is a fat-soluble chemical that takes up a rather permanent residence in body fat. The more fish an osprey eats, the higher its DDT levels become. The concentration of DDT may be several million times greater in fish-eating birds than it is in the water (Figure 14-8). For humans, the magnification that occurs in our food chain may be as much as 75,000 to 150,000.

Biological magnification exposes organisms high on the food chain to potentially dangerous levels of many

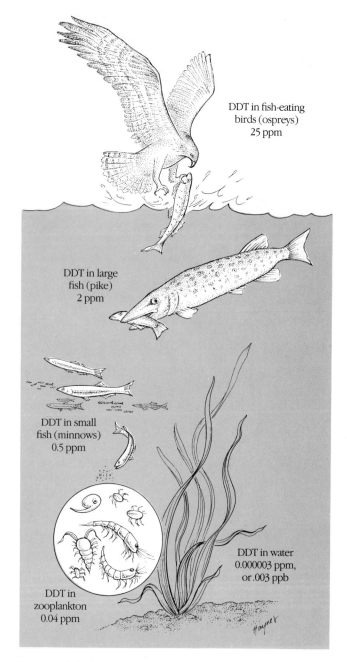

Figure 14-8 The biological magnification of DDT increases at higher levels in a food chain.

chemicals. Synthetic chemicals like DDT, some lead and mercury compounds, and even some radioactive substances are all biomagnified.

The Roots of Controversy

Human society has progressed considerably in the last 200 years. Its understanding of toxic chemicals, however, is still barely out of the Dark Ages. The reasons for this

◄ *Viewpoint*

Are We Losing the War against Cancer?

John C. Bailar, III, and Elaine M. Smith

John Bailar is a biostatistician at Harvard University's School of Public Health. Elaine Smith is a biostatistician at the University of Iowa Medical Center. This Viewpoint is adapted from an article published in the New England Journal of Medicine, *May 1986.*

Between 1950 and 1982 both private- and government-sponsored cancer research grew at a tremendous rate. Toward the end of that period substantial efforts were made to apprise physicians, patients, and the general public of the research that had gone on in the previous three decades. But what progress have we made in the fight against cancer? Have our efforts to find treatments for this disease been successful?

In 1962 cancer was the recorded cause of death for 278,562 Americans. In 1982, just 20 years later, 433,795 Americans died of cancer, an increase of 56%. But this increase is somewhat deceptive. During that period the U.S. population was growing. The relative proportion of people in older age categories also increased. When these two factors are considered, the real growth in the cancer rate turns out to be 8.7%.

But mortality data do not tell the whole story. We might ask not how many Americans die of cancer but how many contract the disease? From 1973 to 1981 the crude incidence rate, adjusted for rising age, increased by 8.5%. The conclusion: cancer is on the rise.

But have we made inroads in other areas, such as treatment? To look at the overall effectiveness of new cancer treatments, we might focus on long-term survival rates. Our data show that survival rates for patients with all forms of cancer rose by 4.2% between 1973 and 1978. However, the survival rates for all other forms of disease during that period rose by 5.1%.

Our data show that cancer mortality rates have increased slowly but steadily over several decades. There is no evidence of a recent downward trend. There has been, in our view, little progress in treating most cancer as reflected in the survival rate data. In this sense, we are losing the war against cancer. Substantial increases in our understanding of the nature and properties of cancer have not led to a corresponding reduction in the incidence or mortality of this disease.

The National Cancer Institute recently announced a nationwide goal of reducing cancer mortality by 50% by the year 2000. It is unlikely, in our view, that it will achieve this goal.

These comments about a lack of progress are in no way an argument against the earliest possible diagnosis and the best possible treatment of cancer. The problem, as we see it, is the lack of any substantial recent improvements in treating the most common forms of cancer.

The main conclusion we draw is that 35 years of intense effort focused largely on improving treatment is a qualified failure. The results have not been what they were intended or expected to be. But we think that there could be much current value in an objective review of the reasons for this failure. Why were hopes so high? What went wrong? Can future efforts be built on more realistic expectations? And why is cancer the only major cause of death for which age-adjusted mortality rates are still increasing?

On the basis of past medical experience with infectious and other nonmalignant diseases, however, we suspect that the most promising route to cut cancer rates is prevention. Reducing smoking, indoor air pollution, and workplace exposure and other efforts could pay huge dividends in the long run. History suggests that savings in both lives and dollars would be great.

are many. One of the most important is that it is neither practical nor ethical to test toxic chemicals on human beings. As a result, toxicologists must rely on tests on rats, mice, rabbits, and other laboratory animals. The results of experiments on laboratory animals cannot always be extrapolated to humans. As a friend once reminded me, "Contrary to popular belief, the human is not a large rat." Lab animals frequently react differently to chemicals than humans do; they may be able to break them down better, or they may not be able to break them down as well. Physiological differences between humans and lab animals make it difficult to predict if a chemical harmful to an animal will be injurious to us.

Our ignorance of toxic effects also stems from the fact that humans are frequently exposed to many potentially harmful chemicals and may be exposed over long periods. For practical reasons most toxicity tests are performed on one substance at a time. Because of synergy and antagonism, extrapolating the results from single-chemical tests to the real world can be misleading.

Another problem is that most tests of toxicity, especially those for mutations and cancer, are performed at high exposure levels rarely if ever experienced by the average citizen or even by most workers. The fact that a large dose of a chemical induces cancer in a lab animal does not necessarily mean that the chemical will cause cancer

(a) No Threshold

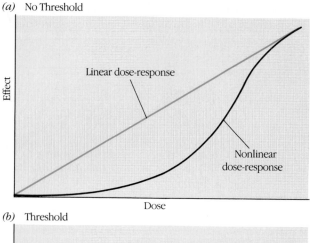

(b) Threshold

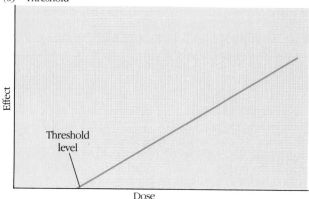

Figure 14-9 *(a)* A hypothetical dose–response curve indicating the absence of a threshold level, a level below which no effect occurs. *(b)* A hypothetical dose–response curve showing a threshold level.

in the typically low doses to which humans are exposed.

If scientists can't make accurate extrapolations from high doses to low doses, why do they perform their experiments that way? Researchers use such high doses to speed up their experiments. The time required to develop a noticeable cancer is quite long. Human cancers may develop 5 to 30 years after exposure. As a general rule the entire process from exposure to manifestation takes about one-eighth of the lifespan of an animal. Thus, anything that speeds up the process, such as a high dose, helps cut costs. To test for low-level effects, scientists would need very large numbers of experimental animals to generate statistically valid results. High-dose studies, therefore, reduce the number of lab animals needed and can cut time and costs—a significant factor, since cancer studies can cost $500,000 to $1 million per chemical.

One of the greatest controversies in toxicology involves the **threshold level**—that is, the level below which no effects occur. The incidence of cancers in lab animals is a function of dose: the higher the dose, the greater the

incidence of cancer. The same relationship is known to be true in some human cancers; for instance, the incidence of lung cancer clearly increases with the number of cigarettes smoked. Some workers assume that if a chemical is harmful at high levels, it will also be harmful at the lowest levels. Others argue that there is a dose level—the threshold level—below which no harmful effect occurs (Figure 14-9); in other words, extremely low levels of certain chemicals are completely safe. It appears that a threshold may exist for some chemicals but not for others, such as asbestos.

Controlling Toxic Substances

The United States produces over 136 million metric tons (300 billion pounds) of synthetic chemicals and creates over 36 million metric tons of toxic wastes each year. The need to control toxic substances has grown dramatically, and many laws have been passed to regulate them (Table 14-2).

In 1976 the U.S. Congress passed the **Toxic Substances Control Act**. It is designed to screen new chemicals and ban or limit the use of those that present an unreasonable health risk.

The act has three major parts: (1) premanufacture notification, requiring all chemical companies to tell the EPA of new substances they want to introduce into the market; (2) requirements for testing new or existing chemicals that are believed to present a risk to the public and the environment; and (3) stipulations for the control of several existing hazardous chemicals.

Under the first part of the act, companies are required to notify the EPA 90 days before they import or manufacture a chemical substance not currently in commercial use. The EPA then has 90 days to decide whether the chemical can be introduced and whether any restrictions are necessary to minimize its risk.

Scientists at the EPA review existing toxicity data on the chemical and information provided by the manufacturer. However, most new substances have not been tested for toxicity, carcinogenicity, and other adverse effects, and manufacturers generally do little toxicity research because of its cost. Thus, the EPA must rely on toxicity data from chemicals with a similar structure. In many cases new chemicals belong to classes of compounds that have been adequately tested, so EPA officials can make decisions based on this information.

If the new chemical is believed to pose little risk, it is approved. If it might be hazardous, however, the agency asks the manufacturer to test its toxicity and report back.

Second, the Toxic Substances Control Act requires the EPA to take a look at chemicals that were in use before its passage. Those deemed risky are required to undergo toxicity testing.

Table 14-2 Federal Laws and Agencies Regulating Toxic Chemicals

Statute	Year Enacted	Responsible Agency	Sources Covered
Toxic Substances Control Act	1976	EPA	All new chemicals (other than food additives, drugs, pesticides, alcohol, tobacco); existing chemical hazards not covered by other laws
Clean Air Act	1970, amended 1977	EPA	Hazardous air pollutants
Federal Water Pollution Control Act	1972, amended 1977, 1978	EPA	Toxic water pollutants
Safe Drinking Water Act	1974, amended 1977	EPA	Drinking water contaminants
Federal Insecticide, Fungicide, and Rodenticide Act	1948, amended 1972, 1973	EPA	Pesticides
Act of July 22, 1954 (codified as § 346(a) of the Food, Drug and Cosmetic Act)	1954, amended 1972	EPA	Tolerances for pesticide residues in food
Resource Conservation and Recovery Act	1976	EPA	Hazardous wastes
Marine Protection, Research and Sanctuaries Act	1972	EPA	Ocean dumping
Food, Drug and Cosmetic Act	1938	FDA	Basic coverage of food, drugs, and cosmetics
Food additives amendment	1958	FDA	Food additives
Color additive amendments	1960	FDA	Color additives
New drug amendments	1962	FDA	Drugs
New animal drug amendments	1968	FDA	Animal drugs and feed additives
Medical device amendments	1976	FDA	Medical devices
Wholesome Meat Act	1967	USDA	Food, feed, and color additives; pesticide residues in meat, poultry
Wholesome Poultry Products Act	1968		
Occupational Safety and Health Act	1970	OSHA	Work-place toxic chemicals
Federal Hazardous Substances Act	1966	CPSC	Household products
Consumer Product Safety Act	1972	CPSC	Dangerous consumer products
Poison Prevention Packaging Act	1970	CPSC	Packaging of dangerous children's products
Lead Based Paint Poison Prevention Act	1973, amended 1976	CPSC	Use of lead paint in federally assisted housing
Hazardous Materials Transportation Act	1970	DOT (Materials Transportation Bureau)	Transportation of toxic substances generally
Federal Railroad Safety Act	1970	DOT (Federal Railroad Administration)	Railroad safety
Ports and Waterways Safety Act	1972	DOT (Coast Guard)	Shipment of toxic materials by water
Dangerous Cargo Act	1952		

CPSC = Consumer Product Safety Commission
DOT = U.S. Department of Transportation
EPA = U.S. Environmental Protection Agency
FDA = Food and Drug Administration
OSHA = Occupational Safety and Health Administration
USDA = U.S. Department of Agriculture

Source: Council on Environmental Quality

Environmental Science in the News: A Sperm Crisis?

Back in the 1970s, when scientists found that the American male's sperm count seemed to have declined over the preceding 50 years, no one took the "crisis" seriously. Then, in September 1979, Professor Ralph Dougherty, a chemist at Florida State University, announced the findings of a study of 132 healthy male college students. He found surprisingly low sperm counts—only 20 million per milliliter of semen, compared with an expected value of 60 million to 100 million per milliliter—and high levels of four toxic chemicals, DDT, polychlorinated biphenyls (PCBs), pentachlorophenol, and hexachlorobenzene. The findings caused considerable alarm in some quarters.

U.S. health officials attacked Dougherty's findings. Some critics contended that the low sperm counts he had recorded were probably the result of improved counting techniques, which over the years have given science a better (and lower) estimate of the sperm content in semen. But the 70% to 80% drop he had observed was much too large to be attributed to changes in technique alone.

Other health officials argued that his findings were erroneous because his population of students had probably been exposed to high levels of toxins. Dougherty argued that the students' level of exposure was more likely to have been below average, for Florida is a relatively unpolluted part of the country. In addition, students are not exposed to workplace pollutants, one of the most common sources of high exposure.

For now, the jury is still out. Whether the United States and the rest of the developed world are facing an epidemic of low sperm counts brought on by toxins in the environment remains to be seen. Not surprisingly, though, physicians now recognize that sperm counts below 20 million per milliliter contribute to infertility among American couples to a much

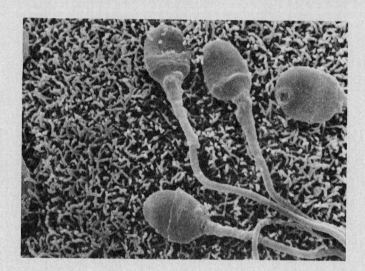

greater extent than they once thought. In the 1960s the prevalent thinking attributed 90% of infertility problems to women. The current estimate is that 40% to 50% of all infertility is the result of problems among males, mostly low sperm counts. Have physicians simply recognized a fundamental flaw in their thinking, or is a new biological trend under way? Many experts on male fertility think the latter.

The testes are sensitive to a wide range of toxins. Testicular cancer has doubled since 1950 in white Americans and has tripled in blacks. Today, it is one of the most common cancers in men between the ages of 15 and 34. A century ago it was practically unheard of in men under 50. Medical researchers want to know why.

The increased cancer and decreased

sperm counts may be explained by the proliferation of industrial chemicals, pesticides, food additives, and water pollutants. "There has been an explosion of spermatotoxins in the environment," says Dr. Bruce Rappaport, former director of an infertility clinic in San Francisco. "The problem is environmental pollution." According to the Council on Environmental Quality, at least 20 common industrial chemicals are believed to be reproductive toxins. The list includes lead, radiation, X rays, dioxin, some pesticides, and many others. Even tobacco and marijuana smoke reduce sperm count, as well as ten common antibiotics. Tagamet, a drug used to treat stress that is now the most-prescribed drug in the United States, reduces sperm count by over 40%. All told, at least 40 drugs in common use depress sperm production. Thousands of other drugs and environmental pollutants have not been tested.

Potentially new problems could arise from toxins found in groundwater, which is widely contaminated by a variety of substances (Chapter 16). With their knowledge of the effects of low-level toxins on reproduction growing, experts warn of the need for careful controls on hazardous waste facilities, to prevent environmental contamination; better regulation of workplace pollution; tighter controls on all sources of ambient air and water pollution; and careful regulation of pesticides and other chemicals.

Michael Castelman, a medical writer, has summed it up best: "Even when banned or restricted, [reproductive toxins] tend to persist in the environment. As they work their way up the food chain, their concentrations tend to increase. Thus it is that humans, who occupy the highest position in the food chain, are finding that perch an increasingly precarious one."

Source: Adapted from Michael Castleman (1985), "Toxics and Male Infertility," *Sierra* 70 (2): 49–52.

Finally, through the act Congress also took specific actions against certain chemicals it believed were hazardous. The most radical controls were placed on polychlorinated biphenyls (PCBs), an insulating fluid used in electrical transformers. Because of PCBs' stability in the environment (persistence and resistance to biodegradation), the widespread contamination they had already caused, their ability to bioconcentrate, and their known toxicity to laboratory animals, Congress in May 1979 banned their manufacture and distribution except in a few limited uses.

Determining the Risks

Ralph Waldo Emerson once wrote, "As soon as there is life there is danger." Every day of our lives we face many dangers—some obvious, some hidden. The study of the daily risks of modern technological societies has become an important policymaking tool. This section looks at risk and how it is assessed.

Risks and Hazards: Overlapping Boundaries

Two types of hazard are broadly defined by risk assessors: anthropogenic and natural. **Anthropogenic hazards** are those created by human beings. **Natural hazards** include events such as tornadoes, hurricanes, floods, droughts, volcanoes, and landslides. Natural hazards often have a human component. For instance, the damage from floods is, in large part, the result of our living along floodplains, channelizing streambeds, or changing the vegetative cover (Chapter 10). Similarly, earthquake damage can be greatly magnified by overpopulation and bad building practices (Figure 14-10). Hazards befalling human society

Figure 14-10 The devastating 1985 earthquake in Mexico City—a deadly combination of human overpopulation and a restless earth.

exact an enormous price: human lives, human health, economic ruin, social disruption, mental illness, environmental destruction, and animal and plant extinction. Measuring the damage is never easy.

Citizens of the developed world have become increas-

The Dangers of Asbestos

Asbestos is the generic name for several naturally occurring silicate mineral fibers. It is useful because of its resistance to heat, friction, and acid; its flexibility; and its great tensile strength. Over 3 million metric tons of asbestos is used worldwide each year for thousands of different commercial applications.

Two-thirds of all asbestos produced is added to cement, giving it a better resistance to weather. Asbestos also insulates steel girders in buildings and serves as heat insulation in factories, schools, and other buildings. In addition, it can be found in brake pads, brake linings, hair driers, patching plaster, and a multitude of other products.

Asbestos is dangerous because its fibers are easily dislodged. Floating in the air, these fine particles may be inhaled into the lungs, where they are neither broken down nor expelled but remain for life. Three disorders may result: pulmonary (lung) fibrosis, lung cancer, and mesothelioma.

Pulmonary fibrosis, or **asbestosis**, is a buildup of scar tissue in the lungs that may occur in people who inhale asbestos on the job or in buildings with exposed asbestos insulation. The disease takes 10 to 20 years to develop after the first exposure.

Exposures to asbestos at low levels, even for short periods, can cause lung cancer. The death rate from lung cancer in asbestos insulation workers in the United States is four times the expected rate. The incidence of lung cancer in asbestos workers who smoke is 92 times greater than in asbestos workers who don't smoke, providing a striking example of synergism.

Asbestos is the only known cause of **mesothelioma**, a cancer that develops in the lining of the lungs (the pleura). Highly malignant, this cancer spreads rapidly and kills victims within a year from the time of diagnosis.

An estimated 8 million to 11 million American workers have been exposed to asbestos since World War II. Studies show that over a third had lung cancer, mesothelioma, or gastrointestinal cancer. The expected death rate in the population for these diseases is roughly 8 percent.

The use of asbestos in the United States for insulation, fireproofing, and decorative purposes was banned in 1978. In 1979 the EPA began to assist states and local school districts in identifying and removing hazardous asbestos crumbling from pipes and ceilings. Since that time, Johns Manville, a major supplier of asbestos products, has been inundated with personal damage suits amounting to over $2 billion. In 1983 the corporation filed for bankruptcy and reorganization under federal law.

In 1986 the EPA proposed a ban on all remaining asbestos products, completely phasing them out by 1996. To protect workers in the meantime, the Occupational Safety and Health Administration toughened its rules.

ingly aware of the hazards to which they are exposed. This increase in awareness of risk results from several factors. First, television and other advanced communication systems bring news of the hazards to our homes from all over the world. Second, our increased material wealth has given us more free time to consider the hazards around us. In poor societies, for example, people tend to ignore risks in the workplace because of their need to make a living wage. Third, we are more aware of hazards today because we are exposed to more hazards. As technology and population grow, more and more dangers are created.

Risk Assessment

Since the mid-1970s a new and rather imprecise science, called **risk assessment**, has been developed to help us understand and quantify risks posed by technology, our life-styles, and our personal habits (smoking, drinking, and diet).

Risk assessment involves two interlocked steps: hazard identification and estimation of risk. **Hazard identification** is both the recognition of dangers that exist today and the complicated art of predicting future dangers. **Estimation of risk** generally involves two processes (Figure 14-11). The first is determining the **probability** that an event will occur. This process answers the question "How likely is the event?" The second stage is determining the **severity** of an event, answering the question "How much damage is caused?" Determining probability and severity is complicated and fraught with uncertainty.

The next step, determining the overall level of risk, is often a difficult one. To understand how difficult it is to assess risk, consider nuclear power. The probability of a nuclear core meltdown is thought to be small. (Nuclear power advocates tell us that the probability is one chance in 10,000 years of reactor operation. See Chapter 12 for more information on nuclear power plant accidents.) Even though the probability of a meltdown may be small,

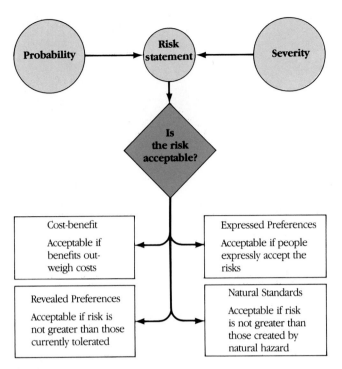

Figure 14-11 Determining the acceptability of a risk. Cost-benefit analysis is the most common method of determining risk acceptability, but three other methods can also be used, as shown here.

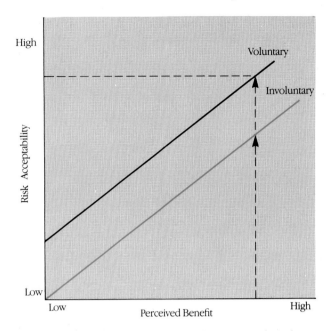

Figure 14-12 Risk becomes acceptable, in general, as the perceived benefit rises. Voluntary risks, that is, ones people agree to, are generally more acceptable than risks imposed without consent.

the consequences of such an event would be severe. Thousands of lives might be lost, and billions of dollars in property damage would result. Thus, the probability and severity factors indicate distinctly different levels of risk. Assigning a risk value to nuclear power is nearly impossible because of the disparity between probability and severity. A combined scale is now being developed to help scientists solve this problem.

Risk Management: Decisions about Risk Acceptability

Risk assessment is ultimately designed to help society manage its hazardous environment. No matter what we do—whether it is screwing in a light bulb or flying cross-country in a jet—we put ourselves (and possibly our environment) at risk. Nothing is safe, or "entirely free from harm." The science of risk assessment recognizes that human life is haunted by hazards. Rather than talking in terms of safety, which is absolute, the risk assessor speaks in terms of risk, which is relative. Activities that we commonly consider safe are better seen as low-risk functions. "Unsafe" activities are better labeled as "high-risk functions."

Knowing the relative risk of a technology is one thing.

Knowing the acceptability of that risk, what price society will pay for certain activities, is quite another story. **Risk acceptability** is one of the trickiest issues facing modern society. Why? Because we are fickle. What appears "safe" one day becomes suspect the next after a widely publicized accident. Irrational fears crop up and frighten us away from relatively low-risk activities.

The acceptability of risks is also determined by **perceived benefit**—how much benefit people think they will get from something. In general, the higher the perceived benefit, the greater the risk acceptability (Figure 14-12). As an example, the risks of a new steel mill might be overlooked by a community with high unemployment. Automobile travel provides the most telling example of the way in which perceived benefits affect our decisions. The risk of dying in an automobile accident in the United States is 1 in 5000 in any given year. (Incidentally, the risk of a fatal accident is greatly increased on Friday and Saturday evenings.) Over your lifetime, the risk of dying in a car accident is far higher if you don't wear seat belts, about 2 in 100, than if you do, 1 in 100. Meanwhile, substances believed to be far less hazardous are banned from public use primarily because their benefit is not so highly valued or because a ban is involuntarily imposed on us.

Perceived harm, the damage people think will occur, also heavily influences our views of risk acceptability. In

Figure 14-13 Asarco parents at a town meeting in Tacoma, Washington. The sign reads, "Don't risk our children."

general, the more harmful a technology or its by-product is perceived to be, the less acceptable it is to society. Efforts to find a burial ground for high-level nuclear wastes clearly illustrate this point (Chapter 18). Over two-thirds of Americans recently polled favor nuclear power, but few of them want a waste repository in their state—an inconsistent by entirely human reaction based on perceived harm.

Decisions, Decisions   Decisions on modern sources of risk—technologies, personal habits, and pollution—are becoming more and more commonplace as environmental scientists uncover harmful effects. Nowhere was this more evident than in Tacoma, Washington, south of Seattle. A copper-smelting plant owned by Asarco Incorporated annually contributed $20 million to $30 million to the local economy. Unfortunately, it daily spewed out 765 kilograms (1700 pounds) of arsenic into the air, 23% of the total arsenic emissions in the United States. Arsenic, which has been linked with both lung and skin cancers and neurological disorders, was found in alarmingly high quantities in the blood of smelter workers and their children at a nearby school. In 1983 health officials estimated that residents nearest the smelter had a lifetime cancer risk of 9 in 100. Even after applying the best available control technology, health experts predicted that the cancer risk would be about 2 in 100, still an unacceptable health risk. The company argued that reducing arsenic emissions would force it to close the factory, costing the community millions of dollars in tax revenue and income for its 1300 employees.

In this landmark case the EPA went to the people of Tacoma to explain the situation (Figure 14-13). William Ruckelshaus, then head of the agency, proposed that the residents be brought into risk–benefit analysis. This action angered many environmentalists, who accused the agency of asking residents to make a choice between clean air and jobs. The EPA held extensive hearings in Tacoma to outline the risks. The company hired a public relations firm to outline the benefits of the smelter. By the end of the hearings dozens of residents were wearing buttons that expressed their sentiment. The buttons said, quite simply, "Both." During the public clamor over the Tacoma smelter Asarco decided to close the plant because of the declining metals market, which made operations uneconomical.

Nonetheless, the Tacoma experiment points out the trade-offs that many countries must make in which environmental risk is weighed against economic risk and employment. Clearly, the choices are not easy. Uncertainty about the health effects of arsenic levels also made the situation more confusing.

Several ways of making decisions about risk acceptability were shown in Figure 14-11. Each is riddled with problems. The most common decision-making tool is the **cost–benefit technique**, the method left to the people of Tacoma. While popular, this technique of weighing costs against benefits has serious weaknesses. For example, the benefits are generally easily measured: financial gain, business opportunities, jobs, and other tangible items. Many of the costs are less tangible. External costs, discussed in Chapter 20, are among the most difficult to

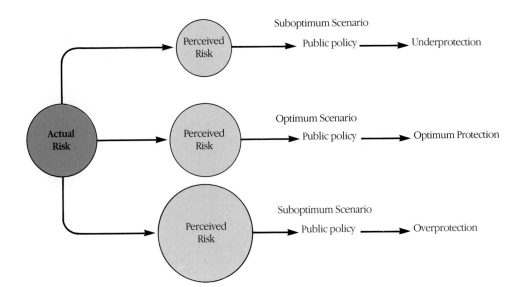

Figure 14-14 Matching the actual risk and the risk that a society perceives is essential to the formulation of good public policy. But perceived risk and actual risk do not always match, as shown.

quantify. Human health, environmental damage, and lost species come with no price tags attached. Cost–benefit analysis then suffers because many important costs are poorly documented, spread out, and unquantifiable, whereas the benefits are often clear and quantifiable.

Recent efforts by economists to assign a dollar value to environmental and health costs may help make decisions of cost and benefit more useful. In addition, the efforts of ecologists and environmental scientists to measure the impacts of technologies and their by-products on wildlife, the environment, recreation, health, and society in general may also help.

Actual versus Perceived Risk The main purpose of risk assessment is to help us create cost-effective laws and regulations to protect human health, the environment, and other living organisms. Ideally, good lawmaking requires that the **actual risk**, or the amount of risk a hazard really poses, be equal to the risk perceived by the public. When actual and perceived risk are equal, public policy can be formulated to yield cost-effective protection (Figure 14-14).

When the perceived risk is much larger than the actual risk, costly **overprotection** may occur. For example, laws and federal regulations regulating air pollution in the United States are believed by many, especially those in industry, to be too strict. These people argue that the damage caused by air pollution (actual risk) is less than the public thinks (perceived risk). Therefore, they assert that the cost of air-pollution control far outweighs the savings in damage to human health and the environment. Others argue that the perceived risk of air pollution is far smaller than the actual risk and that current policies do not adequately protect the public. In their eyes **under-protection** places a burden on society, affecting people's health, welfare, economics, and environmental quality.

Only through arduous efforts to identify and quantify risk accurately can we match perceived and actual risks.

The Final Standard: Ethics

Ultimately, our environmental decisions are based on our **ethics**—that is, the values we hold, or, simply, what we view as right and wrong. Values that affect our decisions come from our parents, relatives, friends, enemies, teachers, religious leaders, and politicians. These values shift over the years—sometimes subtly, sometimes dramatically—changing as we become older and as our priorities shift. Although our ethics are often never explicitly stated, they play an important role in our lives. They determine how we vote, what friends we associate with, how we treat one another, how we carry on business affairs, and, finally, how we act with regard to the environment.

Prioritizing Values Values play an important part in decisions of risk acceptability. Benefits and costs will be incurred in virtually all of our decisions, and we must always weigh them against each other. This balancing of costs and benefits requires us to prioritize our values. If a coal mine were to be placed outside of your community, for instance, clear advantages might be realized—more jobs and a stronger economy. However, certain costs such as air and water pollution might be incurred. The decision to open the mine would be influenced by the priority of values.

Prioritizing values requires us to ask what we value the most. What is more important to us in environmental decision making? Economics? Health? Wildlife? A new reservoir will bring much-needed water to an area, thus allowing it to grow and prosper, but will destroy valuable wildlife habitat and recreation areas. How do we choose? Do we save recreation areas and wildlife habitat and find

Figure 14-15 Various people's spatial and temporal interests are indicated by points on this graph. Most individuals tend toward the lower end of the scales, being concerned primarily with self and the present.

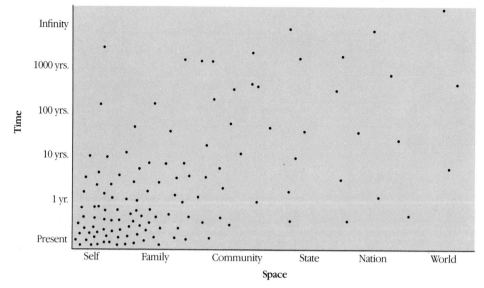

other solutions to the water shortage, or do we dam the river, destroying the wildlife and the recreation area?

Space–Time Values   Further insight into values comes from looking at **space–time values**. These are simply the concerns we have for other people and other living organisms in time (the present and the future) and space (you, your family, community, state, nation, and world).

As shown in the scatter diagram in Figure 14-15, individual interest can be identified by a single point that denotes one's space and time concerns. Most people's interest lies toward the lower end of the scales, tending toward self-interest and immediate concerns. Some people call this selfishness, but it can also be considered a natural biological tendency to be concerned with the self. Among animals, awareness of the needs of others is a feature only of social creatures like monkeys and lions; however, concern for the uppermost end of the space–time graph is a distinguishing feature of the human animal. The unique human ability to ponder the consequences of actions is indeed fortunate. It is fortunate because humans have reached a position of unprecedented power as molders of the world's environment. Our power to change the world to our liking has never been greater; nor has our power to destroy ever attained such heights.

Sound decision-making in a sustainable society requires that we know where our priorities lie on the scatter diagram. Three important space–time questions require answers: (1) Is our decision based primarily on self-inter-

est? In other words, are we looking at the issue solely in terms of how we might benefit or be harmed? (2) Is our decision based primarily on concern for others who are alive now who might benefit or be harmed? And how far does our concern go? Are we concerned with the well-being of stockholders or citizens of the community, state, nation, or world? (In some cases, local actions can have global impact.) (3) Finally, is our decision based on the good of future generations? Will our decisions today benefit or harm those who follow us?

Building the Future   Incidents like the chemical accident at Bhopal, India, point out the Faustian bargain modern society has struck with manufacturing. The Toxic Substances Control Act and risk assessment are attempts to make that bargain with the devil as cost-free as possible.

In a general sense, society is in the business of protecting itself and ensuring an adequate future for generations to come. What we do with hazardous materials, in many ways, lays the foundation for the future. If we are reckless with them, future generations will pay the price. If we exploit them cautiously, our offspring will probably be better off. Ethics helps bridge the gap between the present and the future. As our concerns expand along the time–space continuum, we can begin to take a different look at our actions.

Slowly, modern society is learning what the American Indians have known for centuries. Unborn generations have a claim on the land, air, and water equal to our own. The need for a new, broader ethic that protects the future can no longer be ignored.

Chance fights ever on the side of the prudent.

EURIPIDES

Summary

Citizens of developed countries depend on a vast number of chemical substances, some of which may be harmful to human health and the environment. Toxic substances, or **toxins**, are those chemicals that cause any of a wide number of adverse effects in organisms. **Toxicology** is the study of these effects. Humans are exposed to toxins at home, at work, and while moving about in the environment. **Acute effects** are manifest immediately after exposure, are often short-lived, and are generally caused by high levels of exposure. **Chronic effects** are delayed, long-lasting, and generally the result of low-level exposure. Toxic effects include cancer, mutations, birth defects, and reproductive impairment.

Cancer, an uncontrolled proliferation of cells, is often caused by an alteration of the genetic material, although other mechanisms may be involved. The incidence of cancer has leveled off since 1950 in most cases except for lung cancer, testicular cancer, and stomach cancer. Recent evidence shows that 20% to 40% of all cancers are caused by environmental workplace pollutants.

Mutations, or structural changes in the genetic material of cells, are caused by chemical and physical agents called **mutagens**. Mutations occur in humans at a fairly rapid rate but are usually repaired. If not repaired, they may lead to cancer. If they occur in **germ cells**, they may be passed on to offspring, leading to birth defects, stillbirth, spontaneous abortion, or cancer.

Birth defects, structural and functional ailments, are observed in 7% of all newborn American children. The study of birth defects is called **teratology**. Agents that cause them are called **teratogens**. In humans, there are few known teratogens, although many substances are suspected.

Reproductive toxicity is the study of the toxic effects of chemical and physical agents during the reproductive cycle. Numerous chemical agents impair human reproduction.

Toxins exert their effects at the cellular level by blocking enzyme activity, by binding to cells or molecules within cells, and by causing the release of naturally occurring substances in amounts harmful to organisms. Numerous factors affect toxic agents, making it difficult to predict the effects. Some of these include dose, age, health status, synergy, and antagonism. **Synergy** occurs when different substances act together to produce a response that is stronger than expected. **Antagonism** occurs when substances negate the effects of each other.

Toxicity is also profoundly influenced by **bioconcentration**, the ability of an organism to selectively accumulate certain chemicals within its body in certain tissues. **Biological magnification**, the buildup of chemicals within food chains, also affects toxicity. Biological magnification occurs with chemicals that can be concentrated in certain tissues (such as fat) and are resistant to chemical breakdown.

The **Toxic Substances Control Act** was passed by the U.S. Congress in 1976. It requires premanufacture notification to the EPA of all new chemicals to be produced or imported, calls for EPA-mandated testing of new and existing chemicals thought to be harmful, and establishes specific controls on several existing chemicals.

Risk assessment is the science dedicated to understanding risk. Risk assessors first identify actual and potential hazards and then determine the **probability** (likelihood) and **severity** of the hazard. Once these are determined, a statement regarding risk can be made. It is then up to **risk managers**, usually our public officials, to determine how best to deal with the risk.

To regulate hazards better, risk managers must determine the **acceptability of risk**. Risk acceptability is determined by many factors, the most important being the **perceived benefit** (the benefit people think they will gain) and the **perceived harm** (the harm they expect to suffer).

Risk assessment is ultimately designed to manage risks in the most cost-effective manner. To do so, the **perceived risk** (the amount of risk people think is posed) must be equal or very close to the **actual risk**. The actual risk may be difficult to determine, especially in the case of new technologies with which society has had little experience.

Ethics is a code of what is right and wrong. All decision making entails ethical considerations, but ethics are often not clearly understood by individuals. Thus, it is helpful to prioritize our values to help us think about our decisions. Space and time are two important components of ethics. Most people tend to be concerned with the immediate future and self-interests. The interests of future generations, therefore, are often neglected.

Decision making requires a better understanding of the **space–time values**. Through education, more people can be made aware of the needs of future generations and the effects that current actions have on them. A value system that seeks to optimize the future by acting now is critically needed to build a sustainable society.

Discussion Questions

1. Define the terms *toxin, carcinogen, teratogen,* and *mutagen.*

2. Compare and contrast *acute toxicity* and *chronic toxicity* in terms of time to onset of symptoms, persistence of the effect, level of the toxic agent, and duration of exposure.

3. What is cancer? Discuss how it may form.

4. List some of the possible consequences of somatic and germ-cell mutations in humans.

5. What is teratology? Do teratogenic chemicals always create birth defects when given during pregnancy? Why or why not?

6. Make a list of factors that influence the toxicity of a chemical in a given individual.

7. Define the terms *synergism* and *antagonism.*

8. Define the terms *bioconcentration* and *biological magnification.* What factors can be used to predict whether a chemical will be biologically magnified?

9. Why is our knowledge of the effects of toxic chemicals on humans so limited?

10. Describe the major provisions of the Toxic Substances Control Act.

11. What are the two major types of risk? Give examples.

12. Describe the major steps in determining the level of risk posed by technology.

13. What factors determine whether a risk is acceptable to a population?

14. Many more people die in Montana and Wyoming from falls while hiking than are killed by grizzly bears. Why, then, are people so concerned about being killed by a bear when their chances of being killed in a fall are much greater?

15. What are space–time values? In general, where does your concern lie in space and time?

16. Discuss some ways to encourage people to think about the future when making decisions in government and their everyday lives.

Suggested Readings

Bowonder, B., Kasperson, J. X., and Kasperson, R. E. (1985). Avoiding Future Bhopals. *Environment* 27 (7): 6–13, 31–37. Superb study of the Bhopal tragedy and ways to avert future accidents.

Doull, J., Klaassen, C. D., and Amdur, M. O. (1980). *Toxicology: The Basic Science of Poisons* (2nd ed.). New York: Macmillan. Superb reference.

Goldbaum, E. (1987). Can Cell Cultures Predict Toxicity? *Industrial Chemist* January: 34–37. Interesting look at an alternative way to test toxicity.

Loomis, T. A. (1974). *Essentials of Toxicology* (2nd ed.). Philadelphia: Lea and Febiger. Good overview of toxicology.

Mausner, J. S., and Kramer, S. (1985). *Epidemiology: An Introductory Text*. Philadelphia: Saunders. Excellent reference.

Waldbott, G. L. (1978). *Health Effects of Environmental Pollutants* (2nd ed.). St. Louis: C. V. Mosby. Good coverage of toxic effects of pollutants.

Willgoose, C. E. (1979). *Environmental Health: Commitment for Survival*. Philadelphia: Saunders. Good introductory text.

Risk

Center for Ethics and Social Policy (1977). *Ethics for a Crowded World*. Berkeley, Calif.: Graduate Theological Union. A concise, readable book that raises ethical consciousness regarding environmental issues.

Chiras, D. (1982). Risk and Risk Assessment in Environmental Education. *Amer. Biol. Teacher* 44 (4): 460–465. A more technical presentation of risk and risk assessment.

Fischhoff, B., Slovic, P., and Lichtensten, S. (1979). Weighing the Risks. *Environment* 21 (4): 17. An excellent article on risk assessment.

Harriss, R. C., Hohenemsen, C., and Kates, R. W. (1978). Our Hazardous Environment. *Environment* 20 (7): 6. Excellent article on risk.

Kates, R. W. (1978). *Risk Assessment of Environmental Hazard*. New York: Wiley. A good source on risk, but fairly technical.

Lowrance, W. W. (1976). *Of Acceptable Risk: Science and the Determination of Safety*. Los Altos, Calif.: Kaufmann. A fine book on risk that covers many important issues.

McKean, K. (1985). Decisions, Decisions. *Discover* 6 (6): 22–31. An interesting look at the psychology of risk assessment.

Opians, G. H. (1986). The Place of Science in Environmental Problem Solving. *Environment* 28 (9): 12–17, 38–41. Important look at the role of science in assessing risk.

Peterson, C. (1985). How Much Risk Is Too Much? *Sierra* 70 (3): 62–64. A lively but critical look at risk assessment.

Global Lead Pollution

Lead is one of the most useful metals in modern industrial societies. Used by humankind for over 3000 years, lead is found in ceramic glazes, batteries, fishing sinkers, solder, and pipe. In gasoline, lead enhances combustion and helps reduce engine knocking.

Lead has long been known as a highly toxic poison. It affects many organs and enters the body in many ways. It has a special affinity for bone and brain tissue. High-level exposure in certain factory workers has caused neurological symptoms: fatigue, headache, muscular tremor, clumsiness, and loss of memory. If exposure is discontinued, patients may slowly recover, but residual damage—such as epilepsy, idiocy, and hydrocephalus (fluid accumulation in the brain)—often results. Continued high exposure may lead to convulsions, coma, and death. Some scientists believe that lead drinking vessels and lead pipes in water systems may have caused a decline in birth rates and increased psychosis in ancient Rome's ruling class, contributing to the fall of the Roman Empire.

Today, because of better controls on lead in the workplace and in commercial products, acute poisonings are rare. Nonetheless, many people throughout the world are regularly exposed to low levels of lead with serious consequences.

Sources of Lead

Lead contaminates our food, water, air, and soils. No one is free from this potentially toxic metal. Figure S14-1 shows the major sources of lead among the general public. For most of us, food tops the list. Some of the lead in food comes from lead-arsenate pesticides or from automobiles, power plants, and smelters. Deposited in the soil, it is taken up by food crops. About half the lead in the human diet comes from the solder in cans.

Until recently, most of the concern for lead exposure has centered on atmospheric lead. In a recent study the EPA estimated that 88% of the lead in the air we breathe comes from automobiles, except around lead smelters and steel factories, both of which release large quantities of this harmful metal into the atmosphere.

Lead is a discriminator. Its victims are primarily children and, among them, mostly children of poor black families (Figure S14-2). Lead is a poison of the poor. Even today children living in old, neglected buildings often ingest flakes of lead-based paint, which was applied before a ban was enacted in the 1940s. Children may also eat dirt contaminated with lead from passing vehicles, or may inhale lead in the atmosphere near highways. In 1986 a major study by the EPA revealed that lead levels in drinking water in many cities exceeded federal standards, potentially threatening the health of millions of Americans. Lead is believed to come from solder in pipes and from lead pipes used in older homes.

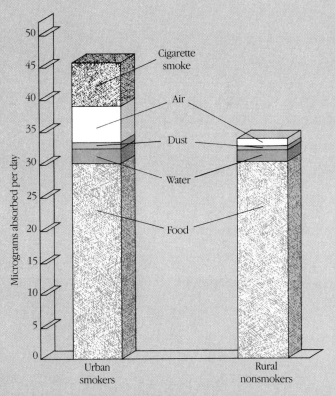

Figure S14-1 Source of lead absorption in humans. The major source of lead is food—from lead arsenate pesticides, air pollution deposited on the soil, and food containers.

Effects of High-Level Exposure

High-level lead exposure can cause a number of neurological disorders, including fatigue, headache, muscular tremor, lack of appetite, clumsiness, and loss of memory. These symptoms are a result of damage caused by inorganic lead in the brain and spinal cord (the central nervous system). If the damage is severe enough, death results. Organic lead (alkyl lead in gasoline, for example) causes a host of psychological disorders, including hallucinations, delusions, and excitement, and may lead to delirium and death.

Lead exposure can also affect the nerves that arise from the brain and spinal cord (the peripheral nervous system). The most common symptom in individuals exposed to high levels of lead is weakness of the extensor muscles, which cause the joints to open. On a cellular level, lead destroys the insulation (myelin sheath) of nerve cells. This may be responsible for the reduction in nerve-impulse speed commonly seen in patients who have been exposed to high levels of lead.

Lead also damages the kidneys, causing a disturbance in the mechanisms that help us conserve valuable nutrients (such as glucose and amino acids) that might otherwise be lost in the urine. Prolonged, high-level exposure causes a progressive buildup of connective tissue in the kidney and degeneration of the glomeruli, the filtering mechanism that separates wastes from the blood stream.

Lead has a profound effect on reproduction, in laboratory animals and humans alike. Numerous reports show that the rate of spontaneous abortion is much higher in couples either of whom has been exposed to high levels of lead in the workplace. Recent studies show decreased fertility and damaged sperm in male workers with high to medium levels of lead in their blood. According to one study, exposure of a pregnant woman to high levels of lead in household drinking water nearly doubles the risk of her having a retarded child.

Effects of Low-Level Lead Exposure

The toxic effects of large doses of lead have long been known, but only recently have we begun to understand what effects low-level exposure may have in human populations.

About 8% to 10% of the lead ingested by adults is absorbed by the intestines, but children have a much higher absorption rate—perhaps as high as 40%. In addition, children are more sensitive to the effects of lead than adults. The developing brain seems to be the most sensitive organ. The toxicity of lead is increased in malnourished and iron-deficient children, who often come from poor urban families.

A number of studies have looked at the effects of lead levels on mental functions. Herbert Needleman and his colleagues performed a study of over 3000 children in the first and second grades in two towns near Boston. Children with high lead levels in their bodies (but still below toxic levels) had significantly lower IQ scores than those with low levels. Attention span and classroom behavior were also significantly impaired. Several other studies showed that lead levels in the blood of greater than 40 micrograms per 100 milliliters diminish intelligence and mental capacity in children under 6 years of age. A recent study in England showed that at an early age even marginally elevated levels of lead may have lasting adverse effects on intelligence and behavior.

Lead contaminates livestock and wildlife as well as humans. Studies in Illinois, for example, show that lead levels in urban songbirds were significantly higher than those in their rural counterparts, although concentrations in urban birds did not approach toxic levels. A similar study of mice and voles showed that rodents living near major highways had significantly higher levels of lead than those living near less frequently used roads, but the elevated levels were apparently not toxic. Possible long-term effects on reproduction were believed to be minimal.

No one is free from lead exposure today, not even the residents of rural, nonindustrialized countries. Sergio Piomelli and his colleagues estimate that blood levels in humans before lead pollution became prevalent were about 100 times lower than the normal range found today in Americans. Clearly, the highest exposures occur in the citizens of technological societies, whose air is polluted by automobiles, power plants, and smelters and whose food is contaminated by lead solder and atmospheric fallout. However, even residents of Nepal have levels 10 times higher than those estimated to be present before the widespread use of lead.

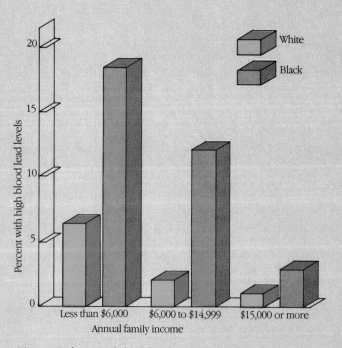

Figure S14-2 High lead levels in U.S. children from 6 months to 5 years old, according to their parents' income and race (1976–1980).

Controls on Lead

Alarmed by the mounting evidence regarding the effects of lead in children, the EPA in 1973 began a progressive restriction of

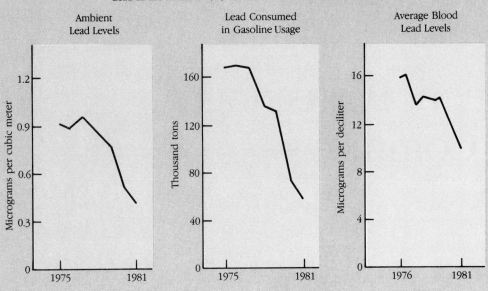

Lead in the Ambient Air, Gasoline and Blood Has Declined

Ambient Lead Levels

Lead Consumed in Gasoline Usage

Average Blood Lead Levels

Figure S14-3 Reductions in lead in gasoline have resulted in marked decreases in lead in the air and blood of Americans.

Source: *National Air Quality and Emissions Trends Report, 1982*, USEPA

the lead content of gasoline (Figure S14-3). Between 1974 and 1980 lead consumed in gasoline dropped by 62%, and ambient lead levels decreased by 54%. According to a study released in 1983, blood levels in over 27,000 Americans living in 64 areas have dropped from an average of 14.6 micrograms per 100 milliliters in February, 1976 to 9.4 micrograms in February, 1980.

Studies that found a strong statistical link between lead levels in blood and high blood pressure spurred the EPA to impose a 90% reduction in the lead in gasoline by the end of 1985. The agency believed that a 90% reduction could prevent 1.8 million cases of high blood pressure among middle-aged white men. Its estimates also indicated that such a cut might prevent as many as 5000 heart attacks and more than 1000 strokes among white males each year. Health benefits could be higher for blacks, who are routinely exposed to higher levels and have higher rates of hypertension. The EPA is also seriously considering a nationwide ban on all leaded gas.

While the United States has aggressively gone after lead in gasoline, most European nations have done little in this area, and it appears that regulations may be a long way off. There are several reasons. First, even though many nations favor the conversion to unleaded gasoline, a uniform policy is necessary, because Europeans make frequent border crossings. Cars that burn unleaded fuels cannot burn leaded fuels without destroying their catalytic converter (see Chapter 15). France and Italy are strongly opposed to unleaded fuels, largely for economic reasons. It would cost about 2 cents per gallon more to burn it and about $150 to $400 per car more to manufacture cars equipped with catalytic converters. Not until a European consensus can be reached will unleaded fuels be introduced there. Great Britain and West Germany, however, have at least begun to take positive steps to get the lead out of their gasoline and air.

Cities in Third World nations are even further behind. The lead content of their gasoline is, on the average, twice that of the developed countries. Malnutrition and high lead levels in the air will almost certainly have serious effects on their children.

As noted above, food is the major source of lead in the United States. The lead concentration in the average American diet is 100 times that of our prehistoric ancestors. In 1979 the Food and Drug Administration issued an advance notice of allowable lead levels in food, aimed at reducing the intake of lead from lead-soldered cans by one-half over a five-year period. These measures should go a long way toward reducing lead levels in the American diet. In 1986 Congress also banned the use of lead solder in pipes. The EPA was expected to reduce by 60% the allowable lead in drinking water, a move that would save the nation nearly $1 billion in health bills.

Suggested Readings

Doull, J., Klaassen, C. D., and Amdur, M. O. (1980). *Toxicology: The Basic Science of Poisons*. New York: Macmillan. Good, technical resource.

Leyden, J. (1985). Nobody Wins with Lead. *National Wildlife* 23 (1): 46–48. Clearly written overview of the lead controversy.

Needleman, H. L., and Landrigan, P. J. (1981). The Health Effects of Low-Level Exposure to Lead. Annual Review. *Public Health* 2: 277–298. A critical look at the effects of lead in children.

Singhal, R., and Thomas, J. A. (1980). *Lead Toxicity*. Baltimore: Urban and Schwarzenberg. Excellent technical review.

15

Air Pollution: Protecting a Global Commons

Not life, but a good life, is to be chiefly valued.

SOCRATES

Springtime. That glorious time of year when birds return from their wintering grounds in colorful breeding plumage, full of song. Trees explode in foliage. Forests turn green overnight. Flowers poke through the earth's crusty skin, bending in warm sunshine. Spring rejoices in new promises—unless, of course, you make the water your home.

Along the pristine Tovdal River basin in southern Norway, far from urban centers, spring has arrived. The year is 1975. With each day the sun climbs higher above the horizon. Squirrels, chattering high on tree branches, shake off a chill that has been with them over the long, gray winter months.

In the river the ice cracks with the rising heat, and huge chunks drop into the frigid waters. The snow becomes mushy. A small trickle percolates through the crystalline lattice, dripping to the ground. From here, tiny rivulets flow to the nearby river. As the days get longer, rivulets of melted snow swell. The Tovdal River rises in its banks. But something is awry. Fish dart fitfully along the bottom. Respiration becomes labored. Frantically, they flit from sunken log to rock. But there is no shelter from the invisible stranglehold. Within days the fish become listless, then die, turning belly up and floating to the sea.

What has happened to the fish of the Tovdal River? Toxic air pollutants deposited in the now-melting snow have suddenly flooded the river. The two most harmful are sulfuric acid and nitric acid. Besides being toxic, these acids leach harmful substances like aluminum from the soil and carry them to receiving streams. Aluminum irritates the gills and causes mucus to build up on them, eventually suffocating the fish.

The story of the Tovdal River is a tale of modern destruction brought on by air pollutants from an expanding industrial society. This chapter discusses air pollution, providing the principles needed to understand it. Four chapter supplements follow, giving details on some of the most important air pollution issues facing us today.

Air: The Endangered Global Commons

Air is a mixture of gases, including nitrogen (79%), oxygen (20%), carbon dioxide (.03%), and several inert gases—argon (almost 1%), helium, xenon, neon, and krypton. Water vapor exists in varying amounts.

Air is a finite resource capable of cleansing itself of many, but not all, pollutants. Satellite pictures show how huge air masses sweep across the earth's surface, picking up moisture and pollutants in one region and depositing them kilometers away.

Transparent, powerful, nurturing, air is a global resource. It is owned by no one. Many share in its use, but no one has sole responsibility for protecting it. This makes it easy to pollute and difficult to protect. As the example of the Tovdal River basin clearly shows, even those who do not pollute it suffer from the disregard of others.

The Trees Are Responsible

Ronald Reagan has argued that acidic pollutants, like those that caused the death of Tovdal River fish, come largely from natural sources, such as volcanoes. A former mayor of Denver contended that the city's summertime air pollution was, in his view, caused by pine trees. The message of both politicians is "Don't worry about air pollution. The biggest source is natural events—volcanoes, dust storms, forest fires and the like" (Table 15-1). Unfortunately, both men were telling only half the truth.

In sheer quantity, natural pollutants often outweigh the products of human activities, the so-called **anthropogenic pollutants**. Despite this prevalence of natural pollutants, however, the anthropogenic variety represents the most significant long-term threat to the biosphere. The reason is that natural pollutants come from widely dispersed sources or infrequent events. Therefore, they generally do not raise the ambient pollutant concentration very much. In contrast, power plants, automobiles, and factories release large quantities in a restricted area, so their contribution to local pollution levels is often quite significant.

Air Pollutants and Their Sources

Take a deep breath. If you live in a city, the chances are you have just inhaled tiny amounts of dozens of different

Table 15-1 Natural Air Pollutants

Source	Pollutants
Volcanoes	Sulfur oxides, particulates
Forest fires	Carbon monoxide, carbon dioxide, nitrogen oxides, particulates
Wind storms	Dust
Plants (live)	Hydrocarbons, pollen
Plants (decaying)	Methane, hydrogen sulfide
Soil	Viruses, dust
Sea	Salt particulates

air pollutants, most in concentrations too small (we think) to be harmful. This chapter concerns itself primarily with six major pollutants: carbon monoxide, sulfur oxides, nitrogen oxides, particulates, hydrocarbons, and photochemical oxidants. Lead, an important air pollutant, was discussed in the Chapter Supplement 14-1; radiation was examined in Supplement 12-1; noise pollution is explored in Supplement 15-4.

In 1970 over 600 million metric tons of air pollutants entered the atmosphere from anthropogenic sources worldwide. The United States produced about 200 million metric tons, or a little under 1 metric ton of air pollution for every man, woman, and child. Thanks to energy conservation and better pollution control, by 1980 world production had dropped to 488 million metric tons. The U.S. share had fallen by 20% (to about 160 million metric tons).

The six major air pollutants listed above come from five principal sources: transportation (55%), power plants (17%), industry (15%), agricultural fires (7%), and the incineration of solid wastes (4%) (Figure 15-1). Air pollutants are released from vaporization (or evaporation), attrition (or friction), and combustion. **Combustion** is by far the major producer.

Coal, oil, natural gas, and their refined products, such as gasoline, are organic fuels. They come from either plant or animal remains buried by sediments millions of years ago. For this reason they are called fossil fuels. Fossil fuels consist primarily of carbon and hydrogen atoms linked by covalent bonds. When this organic matter is ignited, an interesting thing happens. The initial source of heat, say, a match, breaks some of the covalent bonds. This releases energy in two forms: light and heat. Heat released in this process breaks other bonds, permitting the burning to occur until the fuel runs out. Oxygen reacts with carbon and hydrogen. Complete combustion, which rarely occurs, produces carbon dioxide (CO_2) and water (H_2O). Incomplete combustion produces carbon mon-

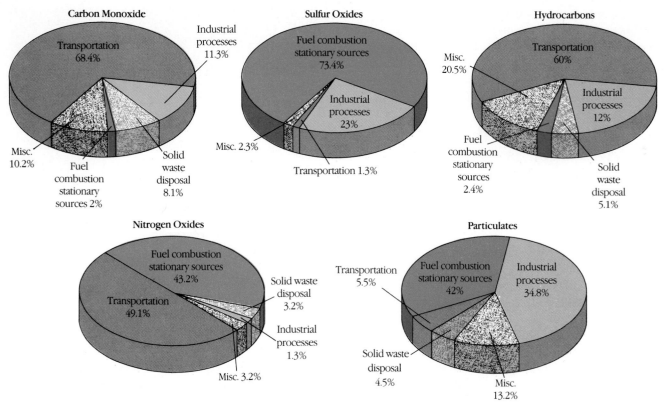

Figure 15-1   Source of the five regulated air pollutants in the United States.

oxide (CO) gas and unburned hydrocarbons (Figure 15-2).

Most fuels contain some mineral contaminants. These unburnable contaminants may be carried off by hot combustion gases, escaping into the air as particulates. Other contaminants, such as sulfur, actually react with oxygen at high combustion temperatures, forming sulfur oxide gases, notably sulfur dioxide (SO_2) and sulfur trioxide (SO_3) (Figure 15-2). In the absence of pollution control devices these gases escape with the other smokestack gases.

Combustion must take place in air, for air provides a source of oxygen. But air also contains nitrogen. During combustion, nitrogen (N_2) reacts with oxygen to form nitric oxide (NO). NO is quickly converted to nitrogen dioxide (NO_2), a brownish-orange gas seen in many modern cities.

Primary and Secondary Pollutants

The atmosphere is, in many ways, a chemist's nightmare, for it contains hundreds of air pollutants from natural and anthropogenic sources. These pollutants, called **primary pollutants**, often react with one another or with water vapor. A whole new set of pollutants, called **sec-**

ondary pollutants, is made in this way. Technically, secondary pollutants are chemical substances produced from the chemical reaction of natural or anthropogenic pollutants, reactions powered by energy from the sun. These new pollutants may be more harmful than the chemicals that gave rise to them. For example, sulfur dioxide gas is released from a variety of sources such as coal-fired power plants and oil shale retorts. In the atmosphere, SO_2 reacts with oxygen and water to produce sulfuric acid (H_2SO_4), a toxic pollutant with far-reaching effects (Chapter Supplement 15-2).

The Effects of Climate and Topography on Air Pollution

Brown-Air and Gray-Air Cities

If you are like most Americans you live in a city. That city generally falls into one of two categories, based on the climate and the type of air pollution. Older, industrial cities like Nashville, New York, Philadelphia, St. Louis, and Pittsburgh belong to a group of **gray-air cities** (Figure 15-3a); newer, relatively nonindustrialized cities such as

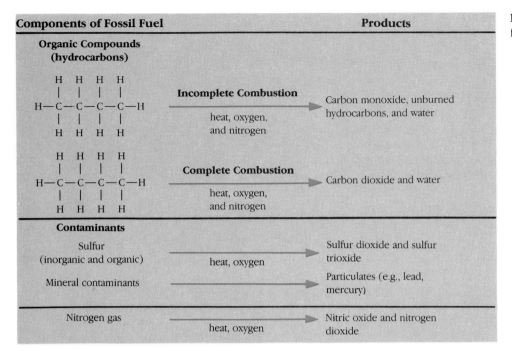

Components of Fossil Fuel		Products
Organic Compounds (hydrocarbons)		
H—C—C—C—H (with H atoms)	**Incomplete Combustion** — heat, oxygen, and nitrogen	Carbon monoxide, unburned hydrocarbons, and water
H—C—C—C—H (with H atoms)	**Complete Combustion** — heat, oxygen, and nitrogen	Carbon dioxide and water
Contaminants		
Sulfur (inorganic and organic)	heat, oxygen	Sulfur dioxide and sulfur trioxide
Mineral contaminants		Particulates (e.g., lead, mercury)
Nitrogen gas	heat, oxygen	Nitric oxide and nitrogen dioxide

Figure 15-2 Products of fossil fuel combustion.

Denver, Los Angeles, and Albuquerque belong to the group of **brown-air cities** (Figure 15-3b).

Gray-air cities like New York are generally located in cold, moist climates. The major pollutants are sulfur oxides and particulates. These pollutants combine with atmospheric moisture to form the grayish haze called **smog**, a term coined in 1905 to describe the mixture of smoke and fog that plagued industrial England. The gray-air cities depend greatly on coal and oil and are usually heavily industrialized. The air in these cities is especially bad during cold, wet winters, when the demand for home heating oil and electricity is heavy and atmospheric moisture content is high.

Brown-air cities are typically located in warm, dry, and sunny climates and are generally newer cities with few polluting industries. The major sources of pollution in

(a)

(b)

Figure 15-3 Two types of air pollution. (*a*) Gray-air smog in Detroit. (*b*) Brown-air smog in Los Angeles.

these cities are the automobile and the electric power plant; the primary pollutants are carbon monoxide, hydrocarbons, and nitrogen oxides.

In brown-air cities atmospheric hydrocarbons and nitrogen oxides from automobiles and power plants react in the presence of sunlight. A number of secondary pollutants such as ozone, formaldehyde, and PAN (peroxyacylnitrate) are formed in this witch's brew. The reactions are called **photochemical reactions** because they involve both sunlight and chemical pollutants. The resulting brownish-orange shroud of air pollution is called **photochemical smog**. Ozone (O_3) is the major photochemical oxidant; a highly reactive chemical, it erodes rubber, irritates the respiratory system, and causes severe damage to trees.

In brown-air cities early morning traffic provides the ingredients for photochemical smog, which reaches the highest levels in the early afternoon (Figure 15-4). Since the air laden with photochemical smog often drifts out of the city, the suburbs and surrounding rural areas may have higher levels of photochemical smog than the city itself. Major pollution episodes in brown-air cities usually occur during the summer months, when the sun is most intense.

Today, the distinction between gray- and brown-air cities is rapidly disappearing. Most cities have brown air in the summer (when sunlight and automobile pollutants are prevalent) and gray air in the winter (when pollution from wood stoves and oil burners and the moist, wet air conspire to darken the skies).

Factors Affecting Air Pollution Levels

Wind and Rain Pollution is something of an enigma to many people. One day is clear. The next finds the skies filled with ugly crud. Numerous factors contribute to this puzzle. For example, wind sweeps dirty air out of cities. Rain washes pollutants from the sky. But contrary to many people's views, these natural events only transfer the pollution to some other location, a little like sweeping dust under a carpet. Airborne pollutants can travel hundreds, perhaps thousands, of kilometers to other cities or unpolluted wilderness. The acidic pollutants responsible for the massive fish kills in the Tovdal River basin were blown into Scandinavia from industrial England and Europe (Chapter Supplement 15-2).

Mountains and Hills Salt Lake City stretches out below a giant mountain range, covered with snow much of the year. Granite peaks and jagged cliffs make this one of the most scenic American cities—that is, when the mountains are visible through the hazy air pollution. Residents of Salt Lake City would tell you that mountain ranges and hills can be an asset to a city, but they can also be a curse. They often block the flow of winds and

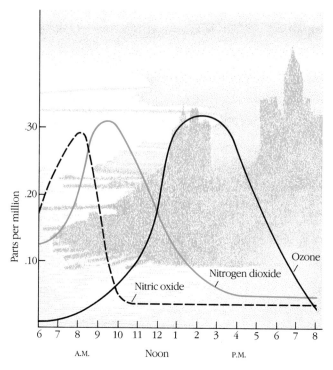

Figure 15-4 Nitrogen oxides and hydrocarbons (not shown here) react to form ozone and other photochemical oxidants. Because sunlight and time are required for the reactions to occur, maximum ozone concentration occurs in the early afternoon. Hydrocarbon levels would follow the same pattern as nitric oxide levels.

trap pollutants for days on end. Other factors contribute to pollution buildup, or pollution episodes.

Temperature Inversions Suppose you could ride a hot-air balloon into the sky on a normal day. You would find that warm ground air rises and expands. As it expands, it cools. Pollution rises with the warm ground air. Because of this, the atmosphere is gently stirred, and ground-level pollution is reduced (Figure 15-5a). Atmospheric mixing is brought about by sunlight. Striking the earth, sunlight heats the rock and soil. This heat is transferred to the air immediately above the ground. The warm air then rises, mixing with cooler air.

On your flight into the wild blue yonder you would find that the temperature dropped steadily as the balloon rose. Under certain atmospheric conditions, however, you would find a different temperature profile with tremendous implications for air pollution levels (Figure 15-5b). For example, on some winter days you would find that the air temperature dropped as you rose, but only to a certain point. After that the temperature would begin to increase. This inverted temperature profile is called a **temperature inversion**. Temperature inversions create warm-air lids over cooler air (Figure 15-5b). Because the

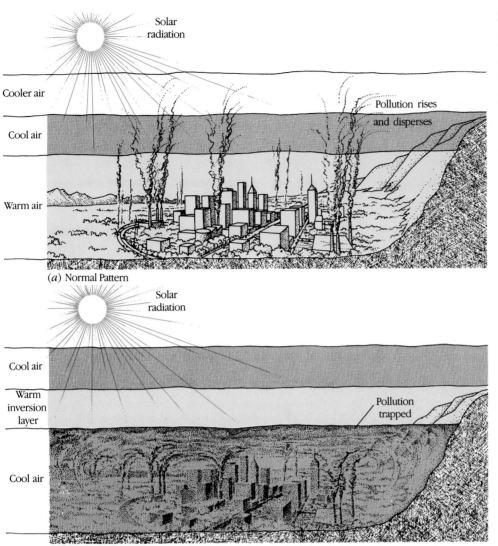

(a) Normal Pattern

(b) Thermal Inversion

Figure 15-5 (*a*) During normal conditions, air temperature decreases with altitude; thus, pollutants ascend and mix with atmospheric gases. (*b*) In a temperature inversion, however, warm air forms a "lid" over cooler air, thus trapping air pollution.

cool ground air does not rise, pollutants become trapped in the lower layer of air, often reaching dangerous levels.

Temperature inversions fall into two categories. A **subsidence inversion** occurs when high-pressure air mass stalls and forces a layer of warm air down over a region. These inversions may extend over many thousands of square kilometers (Figure 15-6). A **radiation inversion**, on the other hand, is usually local and short-lived. It is a phenomenon many of us witness on cold winter days. Radiation inversions begin to form a few hours before the sun sets. As the day ends, the air near the ground cools faster than the air above it. Thus warm air lies over the cooler ground air. The cool ground air cannot rise. Pollutants accumulate. The inversion usually breaks up in the morning when the sun strikes the earth, beginning the vertical mixing. Radiation inversions are common in mountainous regions, especially in the winter when the

sun is obstructed by the mountains and therefore unable to warm the ground enough to stimulate vertical mixing.

Effects of Air Pollution

According to a recent government report, 51,000 Americans died prematurely in 1980 because of air pollution. By the year 2000 an estimated 57,000 people each year will be dying unnecessarily from it. Air pollution causes $12 billion to $16 billion worth of damage to crops, buildings, forests, and health in the United States, damage people are often unaware of. Many other costs cannot be calculated: the loss of scenic view, the destruction of a favorite fishing spot, the erosion of an important statue. This section looks at the external costs of pollution, outlining a small fraction of the damage.

Figure 15-6 This large subsidence inversion occured in August 1969.

Health Effects

Acute Health Effects   Considerable evidence has accumulated to show that air pollution affects us on a day-to-day basis (Table 15-2). In 1966, for example, a study of 950 residents of New York City showed that when levels of sulfur dioxide rose, a large proportion of the subjects became ill. The incidence of colds, coughs, rhinitis (nose irritation), and other symptoms increased fivefold almost overnight. When the air cleared, the acute effects disappeared.

Many other acute effects come about from exposure to air pollution. Visitors to Los Angeles often complain of burning or itching eyes and irritated throats caused by photochemical smog. Commuters in heavy traffic are familiar with the headaches caused by carbon monoxide from automobile fumes. These acute effects, however, are generally ignored or simply seen as part of the price we pay for city living.

Chronic Health Effects   Long-term exposure to air pollution may result in a number of diseases, including bronchitis, emphysema, and lung cancer.

One out of every five American men between the ages of 40 and 60 has **chronic bronchitis**, a persistent inflam-

mation of the bronchial tubes, which carry air into the lungs. Symptoms include a persistent cough, mucus buildup, and difficulty breathing. Cigarette smoking is a major cause of this disease, but urban air pollution is also a contributing factor. Sulfur dioxide, nitrogen dioxide, and ozone are believed to be the major causative agents.

Emphysema, another chronic effect, kills more people than lung cancer and tuberculosis combined. Emphysema is the fastest growing cause of death in the United States. Over 1.5 million Americans suffer from this incurable disease. As they become older, the small air sacs, or **alveoli**, in the lungs break down. This reduces the surface area for the exchange of oxygen with the blood. Breathing becomes more and more labored. Victims suffer shortness of breath when exercising even lightly.

Emphysema is caused by cigarette smoking and may be caused by urban air pollution as well. One study, for instance, showed that the incidence of emphysema was higher in relatively polluted St. Louis than in relatively unpolluted Winnipeg (Figure 15-7). Studies in Great Britain showed that mail carriers who worked in polluted urban areas had a substantially higher death rate from emphysema than those who worked in unpolluted rural areas. Ozone, nitrogen dioxide, and sulfur oxides are the chemical agents believed responsible for this disease.

A number of studies have shown that lung cancer rates are higher among urban residents than among rural residents (even after the influence of cigarette smoking has been ruled out). However, since other factors (such as occupation) common to urban residents and not to rural residents may be the cause of lung cancer in these studies, the link with urban pollution is still in question.

High-Risk Populations   Not all individuals are affected equally by air pollution. Particularly susceptible are the old and infirm, especially people with lung and heart disorders. Carbon monoxide is especially dangerous to people with heart disease, because it binds strongly to hemoglobin, the oxygen-carrying protein in red blood corpuscles. This binding reduces the oxygen-carrying capacity of the blood. For sufficient oxygen to be delivered to the body's cells, the heart must pump more blood during a given period. This puts a strain on the heart and may trigger heart attacks in individuals with weakened hearts.

Medical researchers recently announced that the health risk from air pollution is six times greater for children than for adults. Children are more susceptible than healthy adults because they are more active and therefore breathe more. As a result, they may be exposed to more pollution. In addition, children typically suffer from colds and nasal congestion and thus tend to breathe more through their mouths. Air bypasses the normal filtering mechanism of the nose, so more pollutants enter the lungs.

Table 15-2 Major Air Pollutants—Their Sources and Health Effects

Pollutant	Major Anthropogenic Sources	Health Effects
Carbon monoxide	Transportation Industry	Acute exposure: headache, dizziness, decreased physical performance, death
		Chronic exposure: stress on cardiovascular system, decreased tolerance to exercise, heart attack
Sulfur oxides	Stationary combustion sources, industry	Acute exposure: inflammation of respiratory tract, aggravation of asthma
		Chronic exposure: emphysema, bronchitis
Nitrogen oxides	Transportation, stationary combustion sources	Acute exposure: lung irritation
		Chronic exposure: bronchitis
Particulates	Stationary combustion sources, industry	Irritation of respiratory system, cancer
Hydrocarbons	Transportation	Unknown
Photochemical oxidants	Transportation, stationary combustion sources (indirectly through hydrocarbons and nitrogen oxides)	Acute exposure: respiratory irritation, eye irritation
		Chronic exposure: emphysema

Effects on Other Organisms

Fluoride and arsenic poisonings have occurred in cattle grazing downwind from metal smelters. Acids produced from power plants, smelters, industrial boilers, and automobiles have been shown to be extremely harmful to

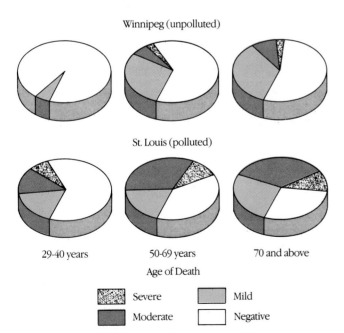

Figure 15-7 Incidence of emphysema in St. Louis and Winnipeg. Note the increased incidence of emphysema in all three age groups in the more polluted urban environment of St Louis.

wildlife, especially fish (see Chapter Supplement 15-2). Reports from Scandinavia, West Germany, and the United States suggest that forest productivity may be reduced significantly by acid precipitation. In southern California millions of ponderosa pines have been damaged by air pollution (mostly ozone) from Los Angeles.

Ozone, sulfur dioxide and sulfuric acid are the pollutants most hazardous to plants. Farms in southern California and on the East Coast report significant damage to important vegetable crops. City gardeners also report damage to flowers and ornamental plants. Air pollutants damage plants directly, causing spotting of leaves. Recent studies show that air pollutants may also make some plant species more desirable to leaf-eating insects. According to botanists from Cornell University, air pollution and other stresses cause plants to produce a chemical called glutathione, which protects leaves from pollution but also attracts insects that normally have no interest in these plant species.

Effects on Materials

Air pollutants may severely damage metals, building materials (stone and concrete), paint, textiles, plastics, rubber, leather, paper, clothing, and ceramics (Table 15-3). The two most corrosive, and therefore harmful, pollutants are sulfur dioxide and sulfuric acid.

The damage to human materials is both costly and tragic, for many of the structures attacked by air pollutants are irreplaceable works of art. The stone in the Parthenon in Athens, for instance, has deteriorated more in the last 50 years than in the previous 2000 years because of air

Table 15-3 Damage to Materials from Air Pollution

Material	Damage	Principal Pollutants
Metals	Corrosion or tarnishing of surfaces; loss of strength	Sulfur dioxide, hydrogen sulfide, particulates
Stone and concrete	Discoloration, erosion of surfaces, leaching	Sulfur dioxide, particulates
Paint	Discoloration, reduced gloss, pitting	Sulfur dioxide, hydrogen sulfide, particulates, ozone
Rubber	Weakening, cracking	Ozone, other photochemical oxidants
Leather	Weakening, deterioration of surface	Sulfur dioxide
Paper	Embrittlement	Sulfur dioxide
Textiles	Soiling, fading, deterioration of fabric	Sulfur dioxide, ozone, particulates, nitrogen dioxide
Ceramics	Altered surface appearance	Hydrogen fluoride, particulates

pollution. The Statue of Liberty, which was recently restored, had been pitted by sulfuric and nitric acids. The Taj Mahal in India, like many other buildings in the world, is being defaced by air pollution from local power plants.

Sulfuric and nitric acids cause cosmetic damage to metals and reduce their strength. In the Netherlands bells that had been ringing true for three or four centuries have, in recent years, gone out of tune because of air pollution. Acidic pollutants have eaten away at them, lowering their pitch and rendering once familiar tunes indecipherable. Particulates blown in the wind erode the surfaces of stone, doing significant damage; hydrogen sulfide gases tarnish silver and blacken leaded house paints. Ozone cracks rubber windshield wipers, tires, and other rubber products, necessitating costly antioxidant additives.

The economic damage caused by air pollution is immense. Society pays for cleaning sooty buildings, repainting pitted houses and automobiles, and replacing damaged rubber products and clothing. The economic damage to statuary and other works of art cannot be calculated.

Effects on Climate

Scientists have long known that air pollution can affect local weather. For example, smoke from factories can substantially increase rainfall in areas downwind. In recent years, however, scientists have debated the effects of air pollution on global climate. Before examining the issue, let us first look at the global energy balance, the basis for all climate.

Global Energy Balance Each day the earth is warmed by the sun. Sunlight strikes the earth and heats the surface; this heat is then slowly radiated back into the atmosphere. Eventually this heat, or **infrared radiation**,

escapes the earth's atmosphere and returns to space. Thus, an energy balance is set up: energy input is balanced by energy output.

This balance may be altered by air pollutants, notably CO_2. Naturally occurring CO_2 allows sunlight to pass through the atmosphere and heat the earth, but absorbs infrared radiation escaping from the earth's surface and radiates it back to earth. This process helps maintain the earth's temperature. Any increase in the concentration of CO_2 would slow down the escape of heat.

Upsetting the Balance: The Greenhouse Effect
Visitors from another galaxy circle our planet. Directions from an ancient transmission helped them make the long voyage. But upon arriving they find a barren, hot desert. Instruments on board indicate that life once existed on this planet, but there is nothing to show of it now. Only heat and parched land.

Scientists on board speculate that runaway carbon dioxide levels turned the earth into a planet much like Venus. A nearby planet, Venus may have met a similar fate at some early point in its history, which accounts for its daily temperature averaging well over 450° C (842° F).

Of course, all of this is speculation, but it points to a trend about which scientists have wondered for decades, the **greenhouse effect**—a rise in global temperature brought on by increasing atmospheric CO_2.

The thermometer in the little greenhouse that heats much of my house in winter reads 38° to 49° C (100° to 120° F) on a sunny winter day even when the outside temperature is well below freezing. Imagine what the global temperature would be if we were to encompass the earth in a sphere of glass. In many ways we may be doing just that, for CO_2 acts like the glass in a global greenhouse, slowing down the escape of infrared radiation from the earth's surface.

Between 1870 and 1985 global concentrations of CO_2

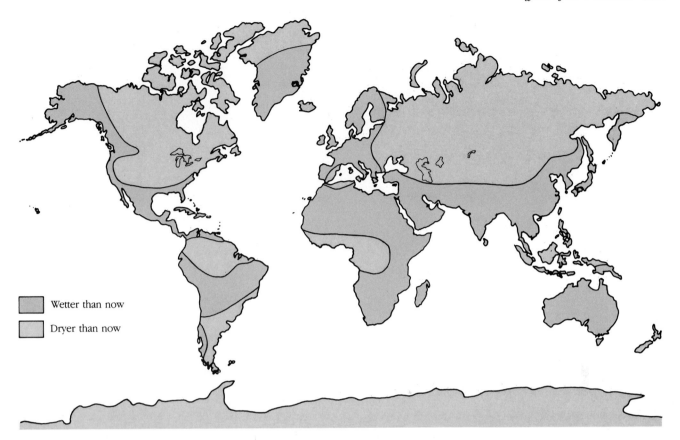

Figure 15-8 Possible future changes in climate resulting from the greenhouse effect. This map is based on climatic conditions thought to have existed 4500 to 8000 years ago, when the average temperature was highest.

increased 19% (from 290 to 345 parts per million). This rise is attributed to increasing global consumption of fossil fuels. Many scientists believe that global CO_2 levels could double in the next four decades, increasing the average daily temperature by about 2° to 5° C (3.5° to 9° F). At first glance this increase seems insignificant. However, such a change could drastically alter global climate (Figure 15-8). Much of the United States and Canada would be drier than normal. If this happened, many midwestern agricultural states, now barely able to support rainfed agriculture, would suffer crippling declines in farming. The United States and Canada, now major food exporters, could become food-importing nations.

To trace the potential effects of rising carbon dioxide levels, let us start with the polar ice packs and the glaciers (Figure 15-9). A global warming trend would slowly melt all ice. Melting of the land-based Antarctic ice pack and glaciers, scientists believe, would raise the sea level 60 to 90 meters (200 to 300 feet), flooding about 20% of the world's land area. Half the U.S. population lives within an hour's drive of the ocean. Many of their homes, cities, and places of work would eventually become inundated by salt water. Most, if not all, of Florida would be under water. Coastal cities such as New York and Los Angeles

would cease to exist. Farmland, already suffering because of lower rainfall, would shrink as the U.S. population moved inland.

Don't flee for high ground yet. Melting would probably be a gradual process, taking 1000 years or more. But once the changes were set in motion, a dangerous positive feedback would occur. First, as the amount of ice and snow gradually declined, more and more land mass would be exposed. Less light would be reflected, because land masses absorb sunlight. A decrease in the reflective surface would increase global temperature, further accelerating the CO_2-caused rise in water levels. Another vicious cycle would begin as the oceans heated up. The oceans are a major reservoir for CO_2, storing 60 times more CO_2 than the atmosphere. An increase in ocean temperature would decrease its ability to dissolve and store CO_2.

Fossil fuel combustion, a major source of atmospheric CO_2, will continue to rise as industrial production increases and as new countries enter the industrial age. Forests, which incorporate CO_2 in plant matter during photosynthesis, will continue to fall, especially in the tropics. Burning of trees adds CO_2 to the atmosphere. Stripping them away to make room for agriculture, highways,

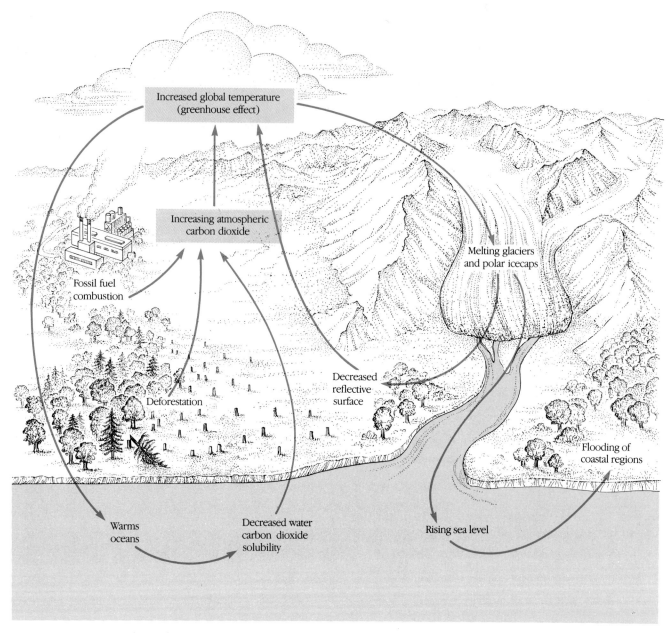

Figure 15-9 Possible elements of a global temperature increase.

and new cities destroys the CO_2 storehouses. The overall effect of reducing forest cover is not known, but many scientists suspect that it will also raise atmospheric CO_2.

Scientists recently discovered that a variety of gases, found in increasing concentrations in the atmosphere, reradiate infrared radiation to earth more effectively than CO_2. Most of these gases are from human sources, although a few like methane come from natural sources. Adding just one molecule of freon gas is equivalent to 10,000 molecules of carbon dioxide. Freons are discussed in Chapter Supplement 15-1.

Effects of Particulates on Climate It is not very often that one problem solves another. But with global climate, this may be happening. Let me explain. Many poorly understood factors determine global climate. One such factor is particulate levels. Particulates from factories, power plants, automobiles, agriculture, and many natural sources such as volcanoes alter the climate in several different ways (Figure 15-10). In some cases they may cause cooling; in others, heating. As mentioned above, even precipitation patterns may be changed by particulates.

White particulates tend to reflect sunlight like a white top on an automobile. Dark particulates, on the other hand, tend to absorb sunlight and radiate the heat to the earth. Particulates may also alter weather by making clouds. As discussed in Chapter 10, particulates act as condensation nuclei for cloud formation. The average daily cloud cover for the globe is approximately 31%; a 5% increase in cloudiness, some say, could trigger another glacial age.

Greenhouse Effects or a New Ice Age? Are we bringing on a new ice age, or a major global warming trend? Overall, global temperature has increased slightly (.4° C) over the last 100 years. Two of the hottest years in the past century have occurred in the 1980s. Global warming trends, however, may be offset by an increase in cloudiness. Scientists estimate that a 10% increase in CO_2 could offset a 1% increase in cloudiness; unfortunately, no one knows what the net effect of increasing particulates and CO_2 will be. Not knowing has produced a policy of inaction, a wait-and-see attitude that may have serious repercussions in the next 1000 years.

Air Pollution Control

Air pollution can be controlled at three interlocking levels—legal, technological, and personal. This section examines some of the major strategies we have used to control this pervasive problem and some still untapped solutions.

Cleaner Air through Better Laws

Society's laws are like the earth's creatures; evolving to fit the present better. This is true with clean-air legislation, now in its third decade of existence in the United States. Early clean-air laws were fairly weak and ineffective, but they laid the foundation for some of the most progressive environmental legislation in the world.

Today, the federal **Clean Air Act** (and its amendments) provides a wide range of protection through various measures. The first major advances came with a sweeping set of amendments to the act in 1970. They resulted in (1) emissions standards for automobiles, (2) emissions standards for new industries, and (3) air-quality standards applied to urban areas and aimed at protecting human health and the environment.

The 1970 amendments successfully reduced air pollution from automobiles and industry. They stimulated many states to pass their own air pollution laws, but they also created some major problems. For instance, in regions that exceeded ambient air-quality standards, the law prohibited new factories or the expansion of existing

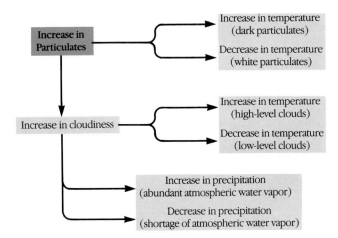

Figure 15-10 The effects of particulates on global temperature depend on their color and their altitude, as well as on the amount of moisture in the atmosphere.

facilities. The business community objected, arguing that this stipulation prevented business expansion. In addition, some of the wording of the 1970 amendments was vague and required clarification. Of special interest were provisions dealing with the deterioration of air quality in areas that were already meeting federal standards.

Because of these and other problems the Clean Air Act was once again amended in 1977. To deal with the limits on industrial growth in areas that were exceeding the ambient air-quality standards, or **nonattainment areas**, lawmakers presented a creative policy. It allowed factories to expand and new ones to be built in nonattainment areas only if three provisions were met: (1) new sources must achieve the lowest possible emission rates, (2) other sources of pollution under the same ownership or control in that state must comply with emissions-control provisions, and (3) newcomers must ask existing companies to reduce their pollution emissions, thus allowing the newcomers a portion of the air resource. The last provision, the **emissions offset policy**, proved quite successful. Combined with the stipulations described above it allows industrial expansion while ensuring a net decrease in pollution. In most cases the newcomers pay the cost of air-pollution control devices.

How to protect air quality in areas that were already meeting standards sparked considerable debate in Congress. Environmentalists felt that the ambient air-quality standards, in effect, gave industries a license to foul clean air, letting them pollute up to permitted levels. The 1977 amendments set forth rules for the **prevention of significant deterioration** of air quality in clean-air areas. These rules apply only to sulfur oxides and particulates, the pollutants viewed by Congress as the two most deserving of immediate action. Many air pollution experts disagree.

◼ *Point/Counterpoint*

Smoking in Public Places—Whose Rights?

An Attack on Personal Freedom

Anne Browder

The author is assistant to the president of the Tobacco Institute, a trade association. Its member companies make cigarettes and other tobacco products.

Tobacco has meant many things to many people. But if it had another name, it would be "controversy," for as long as we've known about tobacco, controversy has surrounded its use. The boundaries of the controversy seem to keep widening. Today they go far beyond just the effect on the smoker or the occasional bother to the nonsmoker. We are involved in civil rights, human rights, life-styles. We are involved in the controversy of individual rights versus government regulations. We are involved in environmental, occupational, and national health policies. In the largest sense, we are involved in the fundamental questions of American life and the role of government in relation to it.

Those adults who choose to smoke as part of their heritage of free choice deserve defense. Efforts to make social outcasts of smokers reveal one of the sorrier sides of those who condemn those who do not share their convictions. They are seeking to affect smoking behavior by inconvenience and compulsion.

We believe business in general, and the tobacco business in particular, has a right and a necessity to be heard. For where free enterprise does not respond, its very existence is jeopardized. It is in recognition of this reality that the Tobacco Institute represents tobacco companies on the basis of this three-point platform:

1. The question of smoking and health is still open.

2. Tobacco smoke has not been shown to cause disease in nonsmokers.

3. The freedom of choice of our industry's customers must be preserved.

The Tobacco Institute neither encourages smoking nor discourages quitting. We regard tobacco use as an adult custom—not for children—to be decided on by mature minds.

The 1964 Report of the Surgeon General's Advisory Committee, which was a review of selected population and other studies involving smoking and health, linked smoking with several diseases. The report focused on a statistical association between smoking and increases of such maladies as lung cancer, heart disease, and emphysema. However, its authors conceded that "statistical methods cannot establish proof of a causal relationship in an association."

Although the Surgeon General's Advisory Committee reached a judgment that smoking causes certain diseases, it was just that—the committee's judgment. Other scientists did not—and do not—agree. They say the theories have not been established. Dr. Milton Rosenblatt, a former professor at New York Medical College, testified at a congressional hearing that "the smoking–lung cancer theory is fraught with inconsistencies both statistical and biological."

When that first report was given to the press, per capita cigarette consumption for those 18 years of age and over was 4194. Ten years later it was 4141, hardly any different. Since antismoking activists were unsuccessful in reducing cigarette consumption, the focus of their attention switched from the smoker to the environmental smoke issue and efforts to control the behavior of smokers. Their strategy clearly was, and has been, to make smoking socially unacceptable. They attempt to turn public opinion by telling nonsmokers that their health is endangered by tobacco smoke.

In 1983 Dr. Ragnar Rylander organized a second international symposium on environmental tobacco smoke at the University of Geneva. The medical and scientific experts gathered at that symposium concluded that many frequently heard claims concerning exposure levels and adverse health effects are unfounded and unrealistic.

No one says tobacco smoke can't be annoying or bothersome at times and under certain circumstances. In a closed, crowded, or confined room or a poorly ventilated area, smokers as well as nonsmokers are likely to be aggravated. But tobacco smoke, with its high visibility, has become an easy target for people anxious to solve our nation's health problems. Leaders of drives seeking to prohibit smoking in public places have used emotional propaganda and scare tactics in their effort to make smoking socially unacceptable.

The constituents found in environmental tobacco smoke—particularly carbon monoxide, particulates, and nicotine—are often mentioned as having a significant impact on the quality of indoor air. Quite often those studies that report high levels of these pollutants have been performed under extreme test conditions. However, scientific evidence appears to indicate that under realistic conditions environmental tobacco smoke does not have a significant effect on indoor air quality.

In fact, research shows that the main sources of carbon monoxide in the indoor environment include infiltration from traffic, industry, cooking, and heating. Evidence regarding the minimal impact of tobacco smoke on the indoor environment has recently been published.

The issue of "rights" is one that has been argued throughout the history of our court system. As it pertains to cigarette smoking, the issue is equally as prevalent. Several years ago, a federal judge dismissed a complaint that asked a ban on smoking in the New Orleans Superdome. The plaintiffs contended that several of their constitutional rights were being violated. Judge Jack Gordon's decision held that permission to smoke in the Superdome "adequately preserves the delicate balance of individual rights without yielding to the temptation to intervene in purely private affairs." Judge Gordon decided that the "Constitution does not provide judicial remedies for every social and economic ill." He held that to prohibit smoking would create a "legal avenue. . . through which an individual could attempt to regulate social habits of his neighbor."

In September 1983 the Tenth U.S. Circuit Court of Appeals in Denver dismissed a lawsuit by an Oklahoma Department of Human Services employee who contended that the state of Oklahoma had violated his constitutional rights by not prohibiting smoking in his office. The court rejected his plea, saying he had failed to prove he was being deprived of a federally protected right by the lack of a no-smoking area.

Judge William Pryor of Washington, D.C., ruled in another case that "common law does not impose upon an employer the duty or burden to conform his work place to the particular needs or sensitivities of an individual employee."

Some antismokers argue that smoking on the job leads to loss of productivity. But smoking bans impose unnecessary costs on many businesses, adversely affect employee morale and may possibly lead to a loss in productivity and profits themselves. It must be pointed out, however, that productivity can be reduced by many things—gossiping, personal phone calls, frequent coffee breaks. Perhaps those concerned with productivity will want to regulate these, too.

Some have also asserted that absenteeism is a characteristic of smoking employees. But that, however, is a multifactorial problem faced by many employers, with reasons including family and personal problems, alcohol and drug abuse, boredom, lack of commitment, and low pay.

Some antismokers urge that employers shouldn't hire smokers. They advocate a situation no different from that which exists when women, blacks, and others are systematically excluded for reasons unrelated to job performance.

Several communities today are considering legislation similar to that enacted in 1983 in San Francisco. It leaves veto power to nonsmokers, whose preference—no smoking at all—becomes the rule if a mutually acceptable policy can't be established in the work place.

The *San Francisco Examiner* said of this ban, "This ordinance, affecting office workers but failing to include many other businesses, would introduce unnecessary conflict and expense into the work place for benefits that are vague indeed. The law would barge in where voluntary adjustments should be allowed to work . . . and are working in a great many places."

In a society where individual freedom of action is a basic right and productivity a major concern, laws that make smoking illegal in most enclosed places are ill-advised. Once the principle of legislating behavior becomes established, where does it stop?

Most people would prefer to work out social annoyances for themselves by using a little common sense rather than by official fiat. Common sense tells us not to raise our voice in a restaurant or a busy office. It tells us not to bathe in heavy perfume. Common sense tells us that cooperation and mutual understanding—respect for the preferences and sensitivities of others—are the simplest and least intrusive means by which smokers and nonsmokers continue to get along.

There is no attempt to deny the government an opportunity to advise the American public. Everyone is familiar with the health warning message appearing on the side of every pack of cigarettes, as well as every cigarette ad in this country. How many inherent freedoms can these same people recite from the Bill of Rights? The issue becomes whether any government should attempt to force or coerce a people to follow its edict regarding personal life-styles and freedom of choice.

Abe Lincoln really summed it all up when he said, "In all that an individual can do as well for himself, the government ought not interfere."

><| *Point/Counterpoint (continued)*

Let's Clear the Air

Clara L. Gouin

The author is the founder of GASP (Group Against Smokers' Pollution), an organization dedicated to promoting the rights of nonsmokers, which began in 1971 and now has chapters across the United States.

Everyone has the right to breathe clean air, but some people choose not to do so, and others have no choice. Smokers maintain that they have the right to choose to smoke. They say it's their business, their health and their decision. But they fail to realize that by making this choice they are often depriving someone else of the choice of breathing clean air. It would be fine if a person's tobacco smoke were contained in a plastic bubble, but smoke knows no bounds. Any nonsmoker who happens to be in the vicinity of the smoker becomes an involuntary smoker himself. He has no choice. Why should the only choice be the smoker's?

Laws and regulations to limit smoking in public places are helping to give everyone a choice. Smokers may still choose to smoke in designated smoking areas, and nonsmokers may choose to breathe clean air. Only where there are alternatives can there be choices.

But public places are not the only spaces that smokers and nonsmokers must share—the workplace brings them together and presents a special set of problems. Nonsmokers are often trapped for eight hours a day, every day, in a smoke-filled atmosphere without any escape. Although it may impair their work performance, lower their productivity and decrease their job satisfaction, they must accept smoke as a condition of their employment. Studies show that a nonsmoker in this situation can inhale as much tobacco smoke as if he smoked several cigarettes a day!

The air pollution level in some work places has been measured at 10 to 100 times higher than the allowable limits set for outside air. Some nonsmokers work every day in conditions that would warrant designation as an air pollution emergency zone. And in these days of energy conservation, most workplaces have been sealed tighter to reduce energy loss, causing less fresh air to circulate. Further energy cutbacks often result in less ventilation.

The chemicals swirling around in tobacco smoke are every bit as dangerous, and more so, than the substances found in air pollution alerts. Many are known irritants, some are carcinogens, and others are biologically toxic. Yet nonsmokers are expected to passively accept this chemist's nightmare of ingredients into their lungs.

It should not be surprising that inhaling smoke causes health problems for nonsmokers. Most severely affected are people who have medical conditions such as asthma, bronchitis, or heart disease. Others at risk are pregnant women and persons with allergies. At least 10% of the population can be considered smoke-sensitive. But even otherwise healthy nonsmokers are affected, whether they have visible symptoms or not. A 1980 study published in the *New England Journal of Medicine* concluded that chronic exposure to smoke in the work environment significantly reduces small airways function in the lungs. This condition often precedes such crippling diseases as emphysema. To argue that smoke is merely an annoyance misses the point and ignores documented medical findings.

Tobacco smoke has been defined not only medically but also legally as an occupational health hazard. In a precedent-setting case in 1975, Donna Shimp, an employee of Bell Telephone Company in New Jersey, sued for her right to work in a smoke-free environment and won. The presiding judge, Philip A. Gruccio of the New Jersey Superior Court, declared: "The right of an individual to risk his or her own health does not include the right to jeopardize the health of those who must remain around him or her in order to properly perform the duties of their jobs." Since that time other nonsmokers have been successfully challenging smoky conditions on the job, and employers have begun to realize that reducing workplace smoking is better for business.

Thirty percent of U.S. businesses limit smoking on the job to some extent (including tobacco companies that prohibit smoking in factory areas where cigarettes are manufactured, as a fire-preventive measure). Many employers have found that the workplace becomes more pleasant, production improves, and there is less absenteeism. The bottom line is that reducing smoking on the job saves money.

Not only do the nonsmokers and employers benefit, but so do the smokers. Surveys show that most smokers would rather quit than smoke but find it difficult to do in an atmosphere that is supportive of smoking. Where smoking regulations are in effect, it is often easier to smoke less or to give it up entirely.

The result can be a healthier work force with fewer workers becoming prematurely disabled by chronic respiratory diseases.

But what of the addicted smokers who need to have that cigarette? Don't they have any rights? Our society prides itself on considering the rights of the minority, and in this case, smokers are clearly in the minority, representing slightly more than one-fourth of the population (and their proportion continues to shrink). Certainly there can be concessions made to smokers such as special areas for smoking, private offices, or smoking breaks away from meetings. But smoking should always be superseded by the right to breathe clean air whenever the two conflict.

For too long the prevalent attitude about smoking has been that it is a socially acceptable, even desirable activity. We need to question this premise and look at smoking for what it really is—a socially unacceptable practice that pollutes the indoor air and causes health problems for everyone around.

Years ago, another undesirable practice was very much in evidence—the custom of spitting in public. At the turn of the century, spittoons were as common as ashtrays are today. And spitters were as adamant about their right to spit as smok-ers are now about their right to smoke! In 1905, Governor Pennypacker of Pennsylvania declared: "Spitting is a gentleman's constitutional right. To forbid it is an infringement of liberty."

However, spitting spread disease, and concerned citizens set out to protect the public health by passing laws and making spitting unpopular. One of these social reformers was an attorney named Sam Scoville, who wrote in 1909 what is as applicable to smoking today as it was to spitting then:

"The object of law is the protection of the public. The great majority of our public have not yet learned to use their own rights so as not to injure the rights of their neighbors. Every man has, for example, the inalienable right to spit on his own domain. In fact, the right of expectoration seems to be as constitutional in America, judging from appearances, as the right to life, liberty, and the pursuit of happiness. If, however, by exercising this right a citizen spreads disease and death, or encourages others to do so, he should be impelled to forgo this American birthright."

If history repeats itself, perhaps one day the ashtray will be as obsolete as the spittoon.

The 1977 amendments strengthened the enforcement power of the EPA. In previous years when the EPA wanted to stop a polluter, it had to initiate a criminal lawsuit; violators would often engage in a legal battle, since court costs were often lower than the cost of installing pollution control devices. Thanks to the 1977 amendments, the EPA can now initiate civil lawsuits, which do not require the heavy burden of proof needed for criminal convictions.

More important, the EPA was allowed to levy noncompliance penalties without going to court. These penalties are assessed on the ground that violators have an unfair business advantage over competitors that comply with the law. Penalties equal to the estimated cost of pollution control devices eliminate the cost incentive of polluting. (For more on enforcement of environmental laws see Essay 18-1; "Getting Tough on Polluters".)

The Clean Air Act is working, there can be no question about it (Figure 15-11). Public support for clean air is as strong today as it was 10 to 20 years ago. Between 1970 and 1982 particulate emissions in the United States dropped by more than half. During the same period emissions of sulfur oxide gases, hydrocarbons, and carbon monoxide all fell (Figure 15-11). The only major air pollutant to increase was nitrogen oxide, which rose by 12%.

Efforts to clean up the air in the United States continue today, despite deep economic cuts in environmental programs. The most recent advance came in 1986, when the EPA announced that it was drawing up regulations requiring all wood-burning stoves to have pollution-reducing devices such as catalytic converters, which convert unburned hydrocarbons into water and carbon dioxide and also convert carbon monoxide into carbon dioxide.

As successful as it has been, the Clean Air Act still has its critics. Environmentalists, in particular, argue that the law needs to be broadened to include ways to cut back on acid precipitation (Chapter Supplement 15-2).

Cleaner Air through Technology

Legal solutions, in many cases, require technological solutions—new ways to cut down on pollutants. Two general approaches are generally pursued: (1) the removal of harmful substances from emissions gases and (2) the conversion of harmful pollutants in emissions gases into harmless substances. The first strategy is the most common for stationary combustion sources.

Stationary Sources In electric power plants, for example, **filters** separate particulate matter from the stack gases (Figure 15-12a). Smoke passes through a series of cloth bags; the bags filter out particulates. Filters often remove well over 99% of the particulates, but they do not remove gases.

Figure 15-11 Because of tighter pollution controls and increased efficiency, emission of many pollutants has decreased. Nitrogen oxide levels have climbed because of a lack of U.S. technology to eliminate the gas from combustion sources.

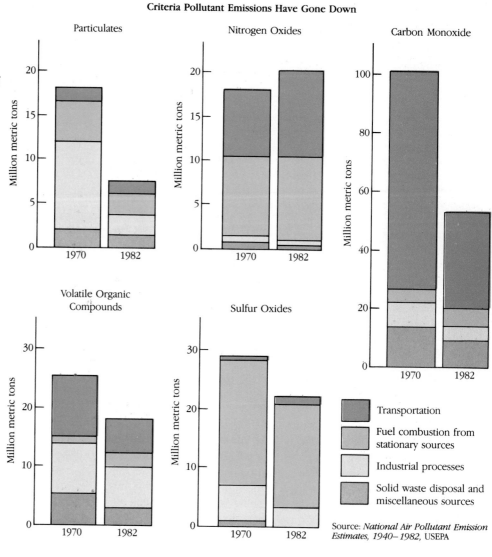

Criteria Pollutant Emissions Have Gone Down

Source: *National Air Pollutant Emission Estimates, 1940–1982*, USEPA

Cylones are also used to remove particulates, generally in smaller operations (Figure 15-12b). In the cyclone, particulate-laden air is passed through a metal cylinder. The particulates strike the walls and fall to the bottom of the cyclone, where they can be removed. Cyclones remove 50% to 90% of the large particulates but few of the small and medium-sized ones. Like filters, cyclones have no effect on gaseous pollutants.

Electrostatic precipitators, also used to remove particulates, are about 99% efficient; many of the major coal-burning facilities in the United States have installed them (Figure 15-12c). In electrostatic precipitators, particulates first pass through an electric field, which charges the particles. The charged particles then attach to the wall of the device, which is oppositely charged. The current is periodically turned off, allowing the particulates to fall to the bottom.

The **scrubber**, unlike the other methods, removes both particulates and gases such as sulfur dioxide (Figure 15-12d). In scrubbers, pollutant-laden air is passed through a fine mist of water and lime, which traps particulates (well over 99%) and sulfur oxide gases (approximately 80% to 95%).

Removing air pollution from stack gases helps clean up the air, but it creates a problem that many people forget to consider: hazardous wastes (see Chapter 18). Particulates from pollution control devices, for instance, contain harmful trace elements and other inorganic substances. Scrubbers produce a toxic sludge rich in sulfur compounds and mineral matter. Improper disposal can create serious pollution problems elsewhere.

Mobile Sources Reducing pollution from mobile sources can also be achieved by changes in engine design that reduce emissions. However, most new engine designs do not reduce emissions of carbon monoxide,

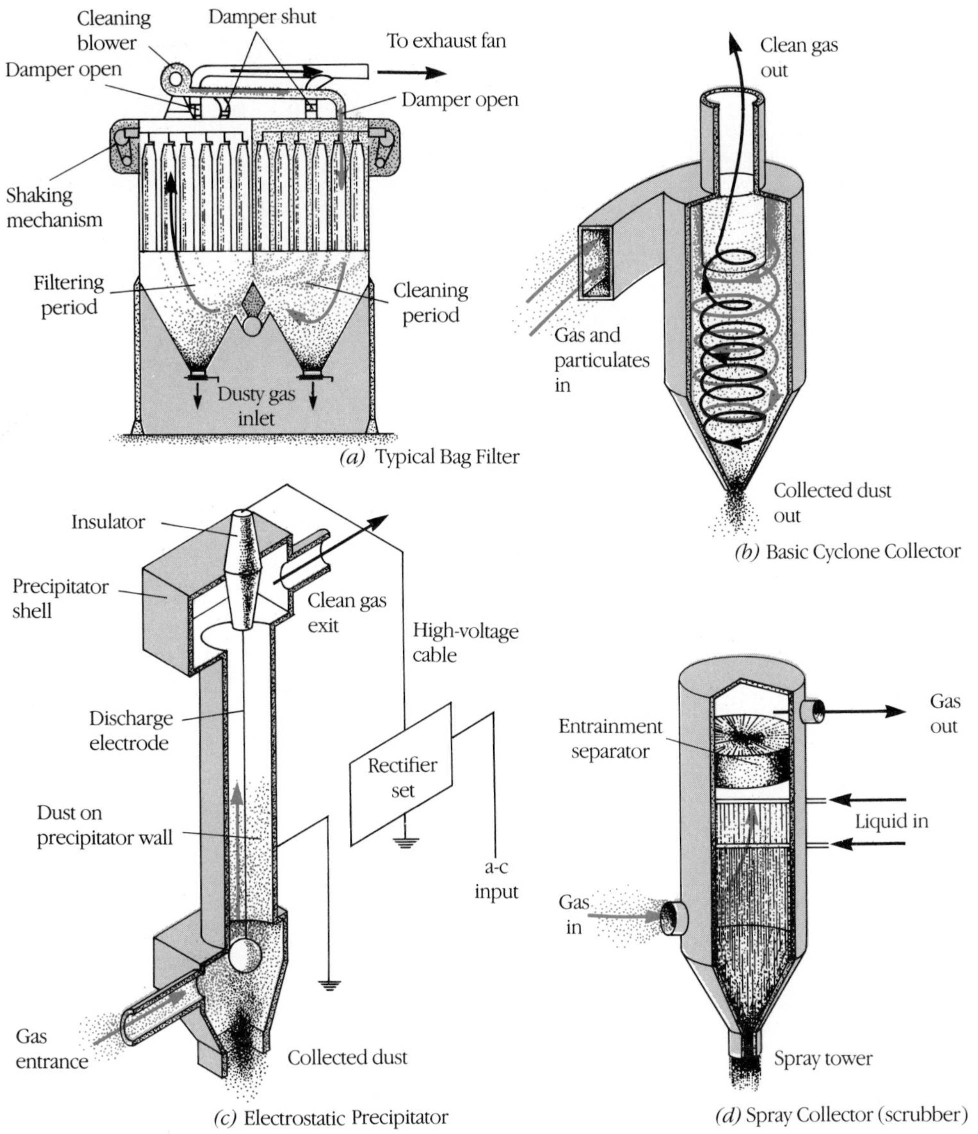

Figure 15-12 Four pollution control devices used for stationary combustion sources.

(a) Typical Bag Filter

(b) Basic Cyclone Collector

(c) Electrostatic Precipitator

(d) Spray Collector (scrubber)

nitrogen oxides, and hydrocarbons to acceptable levels. This makes it necessary to pass the exhaust gases through **catalytic converters**. Attached to the exhaust system, these devices convert carbon monoxide and hydrocarbons into water and carbon dioxide.

Cars with catalytic converters can meet emissions standards if they are kept well tuned. The use of leaded gasoline in these vehicles destroys the catalytic surface, often resulting in emissions that greatly exceed standards. Recent statistics show that one of every ten American vehicles equipped with a catalytic converter is run on leaded gasoline.

In the United States conventional catalytic converters do not remove nitrogen oxides, leaving this pollutant largely uncontrolled. American auto manufacturers contend that an affordable converter to do this job cannot

be developed. But Volvo, the Swedish automobile manufacturer, introduced a catalytic converter in 1977 that lowered nitrogen oxide emissions to well below current U.S. automobile standards.

New Ways to Burn Coal China has a bountiful supply of coal. Already heavily used for home heating and cooking, China's coal is burned in inefficient stoves with low smokestacks. As a result, much of the smoke escapes at street level, making winter air quality in northern Chinese cities among the worst in the world. More efficient stoves, a relatively simple technological advance, could help the Chinese clean up their air.

Recent technological developments on a larger scale may help all nations use coal more efficiently and reduce air pollution in the process. One of these is **magneto-**

Figure 15-13 Magnetohydrodynamics. Coal is mixed with an ion-producing "seed" substance, such as potassium, and burned. A hot ionized gas is given off and shot through a magnetic field. The movement of the ionized gas through the magnetic field creates the electrical current. Air or water is also heated and used to run an electrical generator.

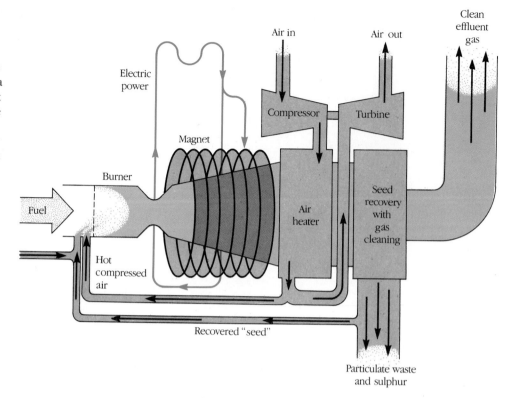

hydrodynamics (MHD) (Figure 15-13). Coal is first crushed and mixed with potassium carbonate or cesium, substances that are easily ionized (stripped of electrons). The mixture, burned at extremely high temperatures, produces a hot ionized gas—a **plasma**—containing electrons. The plasma is passed through a nozzle into a magnetic field, generating an electrical current. The heat of the gas creates steam, which powers a turbine.

MHD is about 60% efficient, compared with the 30% to 40% efficiency of a conventional coal-burning power plant. MHD systems remove 95% of the sulfur contaminants in coal, have lower nitrogen oxide emissions, and produce fewer particulates than conventional coal plants, but they release more fine particulates.

Coal may also be burned in **fluidized bed combustion** (FBC), a developing technology that is more efficient and cleaner than conventional coal-fired burners. In FBC finely powdered coal is mixed with sand and limestone and then fed into the boiler. Hot air, fed from underneath, suspends the mixture while it burns, thus increasing the efficiency of combustion. The limestone reacts with sulfur, forming calcium sulfate and reducing sulfur oxide emissions. Lower combustion temperatures in FBC reduce nitrogen oxide formation.

In 1985, under strong pressure from environmentalists, the U.S. Congress approved $400 million for research on clean coal-burning technologies. Advocates hope that this money will stimulate the development of ways to cut down on harmful pollutants, especially those contributing to acid precipitation.

Cleaner Air through Conservation: A Framework for Personal Actions

Conservation can also help reduce air pollution. Recycling, increasing efficiency, and reducing demand are part of the conservation strategy. Through individual, corporate, and government conservation, energy demand can be substantially lowered. When energy demand falls, so does air pollution. Any segment of society, any activity big or small, can benefit from conservation.

The conservation strategy applies to every aspect of our lives. Each unnecessary product we buy, each bottle or can we toss out, and each gallon of gas we waste contribute to global pollution. This book promotes individual responsibility as an effective means of cutting down on resource demand and pollution. Individual actions, added together, can help us extend the lifetime of limited resources and can protect the global commons.

Cost of Air Pollution Control

Air pollution control costs money, but in many cases it can prove profitable. Today many companies are finding that pollution control can actually be financially rewarding; for instance, the Long Island Lighting Company recovers vanadium from particulates collected at its power plants; in 1976, when the company began its program, it sold 362 tons of vanadium—about 9% of the total U.S. vanadium production—for $1.2 million. The Chemical Division of the Sherwin-Williams Company installed pollution control systems at a Chicago plant, saving that

Number of cigarettes
consumed annually per capita

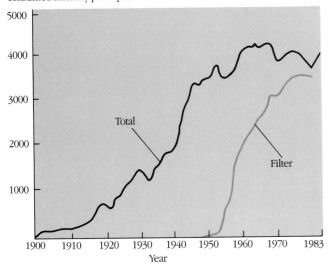

Figure 15-14 Per capita consumption of cigarettes by those over 18 in the U.S., 1900–1983. Note that per capita consumption includes nonsmokers in the adult popualtion. Per capita cigarette consumption for smokers over 18 is actually more than 500 packs per year.

company $60,000 a year.

The EPA estimates that an annual expenditure of $5 billion in the United States would eliminate or sharply decrease most air pollution damage, saving between $7 billion and $9 billion a year from this investment, improving the quality of life, bettering people's health, improving visibility, reducing damage to buildings and statues, and protecting wildlife. Chapters 19 and 20 explain why society is often reluctant to invest in pollution control even though it could save billions of dollars.

Smoking: Personal Pollution

About 56 million Americans smoke, or one of every three people over 18. The average smoker consumes nearly 190 packs per year, or 3800 cigarettes (Figure 15-14). Even though smoking is declining in the United States, it is still a major health and environmental issue. One thousand people die each day in the United States from lung cancer, emphysema, heart disease, and other ailments caused by smoking, making cigarettes the leading single cause of fatal disease in the country.

Globally, cigarette smoking is increasing at a rate of 2.1% per year, according to William Chandler of the Worldwatch Institute. Over 1 billion people smoke a total of 1 trillion cigarettes a year. The worldwide cost is enormous. Nearly 2.5 million people die each year from one of the many diseases caused by tobacco consumption. This is almost 5% of the deaths.

The direct economic cost of smoking is enormous. In

the United States smoking-related health bills come to a whopping $12 billion to $35 billion a year. Lost income and work due to death and illness caused by smoking cost $27 billion to $61 billion per year. Overall, every pack of cigarettes sold costs the United States and its people $1.27 to $3.17 in health bills and lost income.

Preventing illness and unnecessary suffering has been a common theme of humankind for decades. It is one of the key reasons that air- and water-pollution control schemes are actively pursued by many nations throughout the world. However, far greater improvements in public health would result from a complete ban on smoking than from the billions we spend to clean the air and water. Unfortunately, it's not so simple as that. Tobacco is big business. Annual U.S. sales total $30 billion. Hundreds of thousands of jobs are involved. But growing evidence points out how dangerous smoking is to nonsmokers. This and the accumulated knowledge on health effects to the smoker recently led to a campaign by the American Medical Association aimed at making the United States a smoke-free society by first banning all tobacco advertisements.

Few can deny that the image of smoking has changed drastically from the days of John Wayne and Humphrey Bogart (who both died of cancers that may well have been caused by smoking). The first U.S. Surgeon General's report on smoking, issued in 1964, identified smoking as a health hazard and stirred Congress to pass the **Federal Cigarette Labeling and Advertising Act** in 1965, which required manufacturers to print a warning label on cigarette packs. In 1970 the working was strengthened to: "Warning: The Surgeon General has determined that cigarette smoking is dangerous to your health." As a result of the act, cigarette ads were taken off the air. In 1983 the Senate Labor and Human Resources Committee pushed for new, more explicit labeling for cigarettes. In 1984 Congress passed legislation calling for four new health labels describing the effects of smoking.

Effects of Smoking on Health

Tobacco smoke contains high concentrations of hundreds of harmful chemicals, including nitrogen oxides, sulfur dioxide, carbon monoxide, particulates, lead, tar, resins, nicotine, benzopyrene, cadmium, polonium-210, and nickel. Dozens of chemical components of cigarette smoke are carcinogenic (such as benzopyrene, nitrosamines, nickel, cadmium, and polonium-210).

Lung Cancer Lung cancer is the most prevalent U.S. form of cancer, and it has increased dramatically since 1950 (Figure 15-15). One of every four Americans dying of cancer each year has lung cancer, and 85% of these cases are caused by smoking. Smoking-related lung cancer kills 94,000 men and women each year in the United

Figure 15-15 Lung cancer in white males and females (*a*) and nonwhite males and females (*b*) by age group and period. Note the increase in recent times, especially in males.

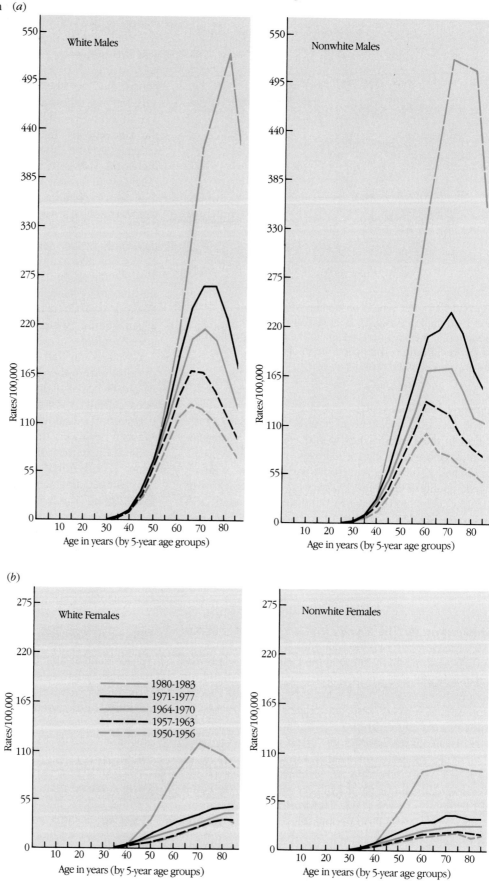

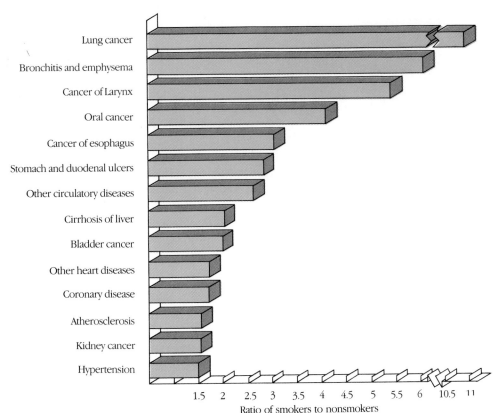

Figure 15-16 Increased ratio of smoker deaths from 14 disorders. A smoker is 10.8 times as likely to die of lung cancer as a nonsmoker—108 smokers will die of lung cancer for every 10 nonsmokers in the general population.

States, almost twice as many people as auto accidents.

The correlation between smoking and lung cancer was first made over 50 years ago. Since then, more than 40 studies on humans have supported this finding. They show, in general, that smokers are 10.8 times more likely to die from lung cancer than nonsmokers (Figure 15-16). Heavy smokers (more than 20 cigarettes a day) are 15 to 25 times more likely to die from lung cancer than nonsmokers.

A diagnosis of lung cancer is almost always a death sentence, for only 10 people out of 100 are alive five years after being found to have this dreadful disease; most die within the first year despite treatment, because cancerous cells from the lung spread rapidly to the brain and lymphatic system. Smokers who quit gradually decrease their chances of getting lung cancer, but even 15 years after quitting they are twice as likely to contract lung cancer as nonsmokers.

Other Cancers   Lung cancer is not the only problem facing smokers. Cancer of the larynx, oral cavity, and esophagus have also been linked to cigarette smoking (Figure 15-16). Pipe and cigar smokers have about the same risk of contracting these cancers as cigarette smokers. Cigarette smoking may also contribute to cancer of the urinary bladder, stomach, pancreas, and kidney, but the risk of developing these cancers is only slightly greater

in smokers than in nonsmokers.

Effects on Fetuses and Infants   Physicians frown on smoking during pregnancy for several reasons. First, babies of women who smoke are, on the average, shorter and approximately 200 grams (about 8 ounces) lighter than babies born to nonsmokers. Smoking also slightly increases the risk of spontaneous abortion, fetal death, and early infant death (Table 15-4). The more a woman smokes, the greater the probability of these effects. Up to 14% of all premature births in the United States may be caused by maternal smoking. Some physicians maintain that smoking during pregnancy may impair the physical growth, mental development, and behavior of children up to 11 years after birth.

Chronic Obstructive Lung and Cardiovascular Disease   Smoking is a major cause of **chronic obstructive lung diseases**, which are characterized by restricted air flow. The two major diseases of this type are bronchitis (irritation of the bronchi) and emphysema (enlargement of the alveoli in the lung). However, patients usually have symptoms of both diseases.

Smoking greatly increases the likelihood that an individual will die from a chronic obstructive lung disease. For example, in a 20-year study of British physicians the

Table 15-4 Smoking and Pregnancy

Problem	Incidence among Nonsmokers	Incidence among Smokers	Unit of Measure
Spontaneous abortion	7.2	9.4	Per 100 pregnancies
Stillbirth	1.3	1.54	Per 100 births
Premature birth	33.0	65.0	Per 100 births
Early infant death	12.1	16.1	
Up to age 25[1]			Per 1000 live births
25–34[1]	12.6	13.2	
35 and over[1]	23.0	41.7	

[1]Maternal age

death rate was 3 per 100,000 for nonsmokers but 38 to 88 per 100,000 for smokers, depending on daily tobacco consumption.

Smokers also suffer more frequent colds and respiratory infections. They miss more days of work than nonsmokers and have symptoms of cough and sputum production more frequently than nonsmokers. Several studies have also shown that smoking increases the incidence of atherosclerosis (hardening of the arteries) and heart attacks (myocardial infarction).

Breaking the Habit

Smoking is addictive and enjoyable to many people. Giving it up is no easy matter. To some, smoking may be a mild tranquilizer or a mild stimulant, depending on the amount of smoke inhaled and other factors. Smoking is also threaded in the social fabric, and may be seen as a sign of maturity or sophistication in some circles. To many smokers the real but distant risks of health are outweighed by personal gains in social acceptance. Smokers often express a distrust in official statistics. There are always 85-year-olds who have smoked three packs a day for 50 years to support their belief that smoking isn't harmful.

The benefits of giving up smoking probably exceed the pleasures. Carbon monoxide levels in the blood drop within a day; symptoms of cough, mucus production, and shortness of breath disappear in a few weeks; the incidence of stillbirth and perinatal death drops to normal in women who stop smoking by the fourth month of pregnancy; deterioration of lung function slows down; death rates from heart attack, bronchitis, and emphysema are lowered, and the risk of developing cancer of the lungs, larynx, or oral cavity declines (Table 15-5). Already, the drop in male smokers in the United States has resulted in a noticeable decrease in myocardial infarction.

Voluntary and Involuntary Smokers

In enclosed areas tobacco smoke may increase the particulate and carbon monoxide concentrations well beyond the levels considered safe for public health (see Chapter Supplement 15-3). Nonsmokers are involuntarily exposed to what many believe are dangerous levels of harmful pollutants. For this reason critics frequently assert that there is no such thing as a smoker or a nonsmoker—only voluntary (active) smokers and involuntary (passive) smokers.

Research in Greece, Japan, and the United States found that nonsmoking wives of smokers had a significantly higher risk of lung cancer than nonsmoking wives of

Table 15-5 Lung Cancer Risks of Smokers and Ex-Smokers

Study	Years since Smoking Stopped	Increased Risk as Compared with Nonsmokers
British physicians	1–4	16 times more likely
	5–9	6
	10–14	5
	Over 15	2
	Current smoker	14
Americans	1–4	18.8 times more likely
	5–9	7.7
	10–14	4.7
	15–19	4.8
	Over 20	2.1
	Current smoker	11.3

Essay 15-1

MPTP Pollution and Parkinson's Disease

In 1983 Dr. J. W. Langston made a bizarre discovery. Several young men and women were admitted to his hospital in a catatoniclike stupor. Completely immobile, the patients were unable to feed themselves, to move their limbs, or to talk.

Several months of intensive detective work showed that the hopelessly "frozen" patients were drug addicts who had happened on a laboratory-synthesized heroin, one of many of the new "designer drugs." This particular batch had been improperly made in the basement of the supplier's home and was contaminated with a chemical substance called MPTP, a pyridine compound.

Researchers have since discovered that MPTP attacks the substantia nigra, a portion of the midbrain involved in muscle movement. The substantia nigra is the region that gradually deteriorates in victims of the debilitating malady known as Parkinson's disease, which usually develops late in life. Parkinson's victims suffer from tremor and partial or complete paralysis.

Individuals exposed to MPTP, even tiny amounts, develop symptoms of Parkinson's disease within a few days of exposure. Some scientists believe MPTP accelerates the naturally occurring nerve cell degeneration in the substantia nigra.

What is disturbing about this discovery is that MPTP is strikingly similar to a number of common industrial chemicals and widely used pesticides. It most closely resembles the herbicide paraquat. This has led some researchers to believe that Parkinson's disease may actually be caused by environmental pollution from industry and from agricultural pesticides.

Opponents of this view argue that, at the cellular level, Parkinson's disease is not that similar to paraquat toxicity. A number of studies have failed to show a link between industrialization and Parkinson's disease. Other studies have shown no increase in the disease in the United States since the 1940s, at which time pollution levels began climbing. Thus, at a 1985 meeting held at the National Institutes of Health, researchers largely agreed that the disease is not produced by environmental contamination.

No sooner had these researchers left their meeting than André Barbeau and his colleagues at the Research Institute of Montreal announced the startling results of a study on the incidence of Parkinson's disease in Quebec province. The researchers showed, quite to the surprise of the academic community, a remarkable correlation between the use of pesticides and the incidence of the disease. The statistical correlation was so high as to be irrefutable.

The researchers stressed, however, that herbicides are just one of many neurotoxins capable of destroying the nerve cells of the substantia nigra and causing this disease. They noted that a large number of industrial pyridines were also suspect. Many of these chemicals come from the chemical industry.

Further evidence supporting an environmental cause of Parkinson's disease, according to Barbeau and his colleagues, is that the malady was nonexistent before the Industrial Revolution. The incidence of the disease increased sharply through the 1800s and reached a plateau in the early decades of the 1900s, for unknown reasons. However, Barbeau warns that the rising use of paraquat and other chemically similar substances could cause a rise in Parkinson's disease in years to come.

Clearly, the jury is still out. At this time Barbeau's work stands pretty much alone in showing a link between MPTP and Parkinson's disease. Further research is needed to determine if the link does indeed exist and what we can do about it.

Source: Adapted from Lewin, R. (1985), "Parkinson's Disease: An Environmental Cause?" *Science*, July 19, pp. 257–258.

nonsmokers. The risk increased as the number of cigarettes their husbands smoked increased. Nonsmokers exposed for 20 years or more have the same incidence of lung cancer as smokers of 11 cigarettes per day. Ten studies have shown the link between passive smoking and cancer and respiratory disease. A recent study indicated that passive smoking causes more cancer deaths than all regulated ambient air pollutants combined. About 5000 passive smokers die yearly, or about one-third of the cases of lung cancer not attributed to smoking.

High carbon monoxide levels in smoke-filled rooms may impair one's attentiveness and other mental functions and cause chest pain in individuals with heart disease. The incidence of upper respiratory disease is two times higher in children whose parents smoke than in children of nonsmoking parents. Their illnesses also last longer.

Smoking is restricted in 36 states, and it is increasingly viewed as a public transgression rather than a personal freedom. In June 1983 the city of San Francisco passed an ordinance requiring that all private employers provide reasonable accommodations for smokers and nonsmokers. Failure to comply can cost a company $500 per day in fines. In California alone at least 20 communities have restricted smoking in recent years. Many cities across the nation have taken similar steps.

Smokeless Tobacco

Many Americans have kicked the smoking habit by replacing it with another slightly less harmful, but still dangerous, one—chewing tobacco or snuff. Smokeless-tobacco sales continue to grow today while the rest of the market is holding steady. This growth is attributed, in part, to advertising, which implies that these alternatives offer a safe option to cigarettes, an assertion that science has shown to be false.

The most serious threat is cancer of the oral cavity, particularly the cheek and gums. One study found that people who chewed tobacco for 50 years or more were nearly 50 times more likely to contract cancer of the oral cavity than nonchewers. Although oral cancer is not so lethal as lung cancer, it does spread rapidly to other areas and therefore has a high mortality rate. Because of its known effects, health groups are currently working to ban advertising and require manufacturers to carry warning labels on all ads and packages.

The Outlook for Tobacco

The long-term prognosis for a smoking ban is probably not good. With annual sales of $30 billion, the cigarette manufacturers can hardly be expected to voluntarily close their doors. Nor can we expect the federal government, even though it has banned comparatively minor health hazards such as saccharin, to put a stop to smoking. The government is caught in a bind. Each year it buys up surplus tobacco to support the industry. At the same time, it publishes lengthy reports on the hazards of tobacco, spends millions to learn more about this well-known health hazard, bans ads from television, and requires manufacturers to print health warnings on cigarette packages. This inconsistency bodes poorly for the AMA's smoker-free society.

Cigarette manufacturers have remained aggressive and innovative in the increasingly antismoking climate, changing to meet the times and appealing to women, blacks, and young people. Low-tar cigarettes were introduced in recent years with great success, but new research suggests that the low-tar varieties may be as harmful as the ones they've replaced, because smokers inhale deeper and longer and end up with the same dose of harmful substances.

Without a doubt, a complete ban on smoking would be the most cost-effective way of improving health in the United States, but opposition would be stiff. It would come from addicted smokers, half a million farmers, and 2 million workers in 23 states (especially North Carolina and Kentucky) who make a living from tobacco.

The power of man has grown in every sphere, except over himself.

WINSTON CHURCHILL

Summary

Air pollutants come from a variety of **natural** and **anthropogenic** sources. Anthropogenic pollutants—the products of human activities—represent the most significant threat to the environment and its inhabitants. The six major pollutants are carbon monoxide, sulfur oxides, nitrogen oxides, hydrocarbons, particulates, and photochemical oxidants. The major sources are transportation, power plants, and industry.

Cities fall into two categories. **Brown-air cities** are new and relatively nonindustrialized and are found in sunny, dry climates. Their major pollutants are carbon monoxide, ozone, and nitrogen oxides. In these cities hydrocarbons and nitrogen oxides react in the presence of sunlight to form secondary pollutants, major components of **photochemical smog**. **Gray-air cities** are older, industrialized cities, often in colder climates. The major pollutants are particulates and sulfates; they combine with moisture to form **smog**.

Numerous factors such as wind, precipitation, topography, and temperature inversions affect regional air pollution. A **temperature inversion** occurs either when a high-pressure air mass stagnates over a region and forces a layer of warm air down (**subsidence inversion**) or when ground air cools faster than the air above it (**radiation inversion**). Both inversions result in the buildup of air pollution.

Air pollution affects human health in many ways. Short-term pollution episodes have numerous acute effects, including discomfort, burning eyes and throat, colds, coughs, heart attacks, and death (in extreme cases). Particularly susceptible are children and patients with heart and lung disease. Chronic effects are also possible. **Bronchitis**, a persistent inflammation of the bronchi, is characterized by a persistent cough, mucus buildup, and difficulty breathing. Cigarette smoking and air pollution are two major causes of this condition. **Emphysema**, the progressive breakdown of the air sacs in the lungs, is also caused by air pollution and smoking. Some studies have linked air pollution with cancer, but on the whole the evidence is contradictory.

Domestic animals are affected by many air pollutants, but the most noticeable impacts of air pollution are on materials, such as rubber, stone, and paint. Ozone, sulfur dioxide, and sulfuric acid are the most damaging. Crops and forests are also damaged by air pollutants, particularly ozone, sulfuric acid, and sulfates, although the exact magnitude of the effect is unknown.

The most potentially hazardous effects are those on climate. Carbon dioxide released from the combustion of fossil fuels acts as a reflector of infrared radiation. Thus, heat that normally escapes into space is reradiated to the earth's surface, warming the atmosphere. This so-called **greenhouse effect** may gradually change global climate, melting glaciers and Antarctic ice, raising the sea level, and disrupting agriculture. Particulates also affect climate, but the effect is not clear cut.

Air pollution is controlled at three interlocking levels—legal, technological, and personal. In the United States the most powerful tool is the Clean Air Act, its amendments, and its resultant regulations, which collectively provide for emissions standards for automobiles, national ambient air-quality standards for major pollutants, emissions standards for new stationary pollution sources, ways to prevent deterioration of pristine and less polluted air, and stronger EPA enforcement.

Reductions in pollution can also be brought about by energy conservation and by using alternative energy sources such as solar energy and wind energy. Harmful pollutants can be removed from smokestacks by cyclones, filters, electrostatic precipitators, and scrubbers, but each of these produces solid wastes that must be safely disposed of.

Air pollution control costs money, but many companies are finding that it makes good business sense to reduce pollution by recovering waste products. The EPA estimates that an annual expenditure of $5 billion would save $7 billion to $9 billion annually in reduced damage to crops, forests, buildings, and health.

After several decades the evidence overwhelmingly shows that smoking is hazardous to health. Smoking causes 85 percent of the lung cancers in the United States and is associated with a number of other illnesses. Tobacco smoke contains high concentrations of hundreds of harmful chemicals such as sulfur dioxide, benzopyrene, and lead. Dozens of these substances are carcinogenic.

The conflict over smoking in public places is growing more intense today, because recent evidence indicates that nonsmokers are placed in jeopardy by breathing tobacco smoke. It is highly doubtful that we will see an end to smoking, although continuing public pressure will undoubtedly curtail it in public places.

Discussion Questions

1. Why do anthropogenic air pollutants generally have more impact than natural pollutants?

2. What are the six major air pollutants? What are the five major air pollution sources?

3. Toward what specific pollutants should most of our control efforts be directed? Why? Give specific examples of damage caused by these pollutants.

4. Describe the pollutants produced by burning fossil fuels. How is each product formed? Why is coal a "dirtier" fuel than gasoline?

5. Define the terms *primary* and *secondary pollutant*.

6. In what ways are brown-air and gray-air cities different? What are the major air pollutants in each city? Why does the distinction break down?

7. What is photochemical smog? How is it formed? Why are suburban levels of photochemical smog often higher than urban levels?

8. Describe some factors that affect air pollution levels in your community.

9. What is a temperature inversion?

10. What are the acute health effects of (1) carbon monoxide, (2) sulfur oxides and particulates, and (3) photochemical oxidants?

11. What are the chronic health effects of air pollution? Which pollutants are thought to be the cause of these effects?

12. Of all the impacts of air pollution, which are of the most concern to you? How have your education, home life, and religious beliefs affected your answer to this question?

13. Describe how pollutants may affect the global energy balance.

14. Make a complete list of your ideas for controlling air pollution in your city or town, and rank them according to their effectiveness and their feasibility. Which ones are practical?

15. Discuss the air pollution control legislation enacted by the U.S. Congress, highlighting important features of the acts and amendments.

16. Discuss the control of air pollution from stationary pollution sources. In what general ways can pollution be reduced? Give specific examples of how you can help reduce air pollution.

17. How does smoking differ from other sources of pollution?

18. How prevalent is smoking in the United States? Discuss the health effects of smoking. How does smoking affect pregnancy?

19. Debate the statement "Smokers have a right to smoke wherever they want."

20. Define the terms *voluntary* and *involuntary smoker*. Are the levels of risk for passive, or involuntary, smokers the same as those for active, or voluntary, smokers?

21. You are appointed the U.S. surgeon general. What would you do about smoking? Would you ban it in public places and at work? Would you push for the government to cease its support for the tobacco industry?

Suggested Readings

Clarke, R. (1984). Atmospheric Pollution. In *Ecology 2000*, ed. E. Hillary. New York: Beaufort Books. Good overview of important air pollution problems.

Carnow, B. W., and Meier, P. (1973). Air Pollution and Pulmonary Cancer. *Arch. Environ. Health* 27: 207–218. Valuable review.

Hardin, G. (1985). *Filters against Folly.* New York: Viking. See Chapter 14 for an interesting discussion of the greenhouse effect and the political difficulties in solving it.

Henderson, B. E., Gordon, R. J., Menck, H., SooHoo, J., Martin, S. P., and Pike, M. C. (1975). Lung Cancer and Air Pollution in Southcentral Los Angeles County. *Am. Jour. Epidem.* 101 (6): 477–488. Excellent study of air pollution and cancer.

Hileman, B. (1982). Crop Losses from Air Pollutants. *Environ. Sci. and Tech.* 15 (9): 495A–499A. General overview.

Hileman, B. (1982). The Greenhouse Effect. *Environ. Sci. and Tech.* 16 (2): 90A–93A. Update on this important issue.

Kane, D. N. (1976). Bad Air for Children. *Environment* 18 (9): 26–34. An important article on an overlooked problem.

Kellog, W. W., Schware, R., and Friedman, E. (1980). The Earth's Climate. *The Futurist* 14 (5): 50–55. Excellent overview.

Maranto, G. (1986). Are We Close to the Road's End? *Discover* January: 28–38. Excellent review of current information on the greenhouse effect.

McCarroll, J. R., Cassell, E. J., Ingram, W. T., and Wolter, D. (1966). Health and the Urban Environment: Health Profiles Versus Environmental Pollutants. *Am. Jour. Public Health* 56 (2): 66–275. Eye-opening study.

Myers, N. (1984). Will the Climate Change? In *Ecology 2000,* ed. E. Hillary. New York: Beaufort Books. An excellent look at the important question of climate change.

Organization for Economic Cooperation and Development. (1985) *Environmental Data.* Paris: Author. See Chapter 1 for up-to-date statistics on air pollution in the developed countries.

Organization for Economic Cooperation and Development. (1985). *The State of the Environment 1985.* Paris: Author. See Chapter 1, on air pollution in the developed countries.

Postel, S. (1986). *Altering the Earth's Chemistry.* Worldwatch Paper 71. Washington, D.C.: Worldwatch Institute. Detailed study of air pollution's effect.

Smoking

Chandler, W. U. (1986). Banishing Tobacco. *The Futurist* 20 (3): 9–15. Fact-filled treatise on the harmful effects of smoking.

Hales, D. R., and Williams, B. K. (1986). *An Invitation to Health: Your Personal Responsibility.* Menlo Park, Calif.: Benjamin/Cummings. Excellent overview of smoking and health hazards of air pollution.

U.S. Surgeon General. (1979). *Smoking and Health.* U.S. Department of Health and Human Services, Public Health Service, Office on Smoking and Health. Washington, D.C.: U.S. Government Printing Office.

U.S. Surgeon General. (1981). *The Health Consequences of Smoking.* U.S. Department of Health and Human Services; Public Health Service, Office on Smoking and Health. Washington, D.C.: U.S. Government Printing Office.

Stratospheric Ozone Depletion

Encircling the earth is a thin, protective layer of ozone gas (O_3), which screens out 99% of the sun's harmful ultraviolet light. The **ozone layer** occupies the outer two-thirds of the stratosphere, 20 to 50 kilometers (12 to 30 miles) above the earth's surface (Figure S15-1). The screening effect of the ozone layer protects all organisms from damage caused by ultraviolet light, which is known to be mutagenic and carcinogenic.

When ultraviolet light strikes ozone molecules, it causes them to split apart (Figure S15-2). The products, however, quickly reunite, reforming ozone and giving off heat. Thus, the ozone layer is a renewable layer that converts harmful ultraviolet light into heat.

Life on earth depends on this screening mechanism; without it, life would not exist. If the ozone layer suddenly disappeared, animals would be seriously burned and would develop cancer and lethal mutations, and plants would perish.

Activities That May Deplete the Ozone Layer

Many experts believe that some human activities are destroying the ozone layer. Three major activities have been singled out: (1) the use of spray cans and refrigerants that contain freon gas, (2) high-flying supersonic jets, and (3) the detonation of nuclear weapons.

Freons

In 1951 freon spray-can propellants hit the market in the United States. Freons, described in Table S15-1, are also known as **fluorocarbons** or **chlorofluoromethanes**. Two freons were commonly used: (1) freon-11, a propellant now banned in several countries, including the United States, and (2) freon-12, still used in refrigerators, air conditioners, and freezers.

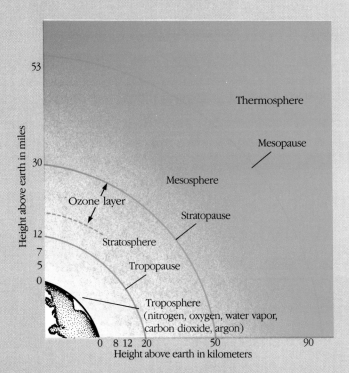

Figure S15-1 The earth's atmosphere is divided into layers. Ninety-five percent of the oxygen is found in the troposphere. The ozone layer occupies the outer two-thirds of the stratosphere.

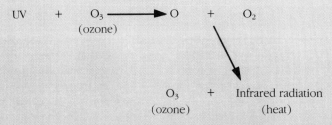

Figure S15-2 Screening effect of ozone in the stratosphere. The ozone molecule is split by ultraviolet (UV) light, but the reaction is reversible. When ozone reforms, infrared radiation or heat is given off.

Table S15-1 Commonly Used Freons

Generic Name	Use	Chemical Name	Chemical Formula
Freon-11	Spray-can propellant	Trichloromonofluoromethane	$\begin{array}{c} Cl \\ | \\ Cl-C-Cl \\ | \\ F \end{array}$
Freon-12	Coolant in refrigerators, freezers, and air conditioners	Dichlorodifluoromethane	$\begin{array}{c} Cl \\ | \\ F-C-Cl \\ | \\ F \end{array}$

(*a*) Photodissociation of Freon 12

$$\begin{array}{c} Cl \\ | \\ F-C-Cl \\ | \\ F \end{array} \xrightarrow{UV} \begin{array}{c} \\ F-C-Cl \\ | \\ F \end{array} \quad + \quad Cl$$

(*b*) Ozone Depletion

$$\underset{\substack{\text{(Chlorine free} \\ \text{radical)}}}{Cl} \quad + \quad \underset{\text{(ozone)}}{O_3} \longrightarrow ClO \quad + \quad O_2$$

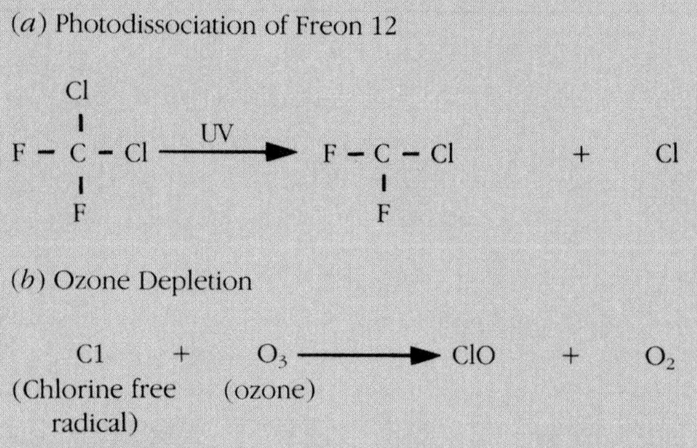

Figure S15-3 (*a*) The freons, or fluorocarbons, are dissociated by ultraviolet light in the stratosphere. This produces a highly reactive chlorine free radical. (*b*) The free radical can react with ozone in the ozone layer, thus reducing the ozone concentration and eliminating the ultraviolet screen.

Until the early 1970s chemists listed freons as inert (unreactive) chemicals. Their release into the atmosphere was therefore of little concern. Conventional wisdom held that freon gases simply diffused into the upper layers of the atmosphere, where they were broken down by sunlight, without harm.

In the early 1970s, however, two U.S. scientists reported that the breakdown products of freons could react with stratospheric ozone (Figure S15-3). They hypothesized that these products could eventually deplete the protective ozone layer. Shortly after their announcement, three other research teams reported similar findings, showing that a single chlorine free radical (a highly reactive chlorine atom produced when freons are broken down) could react with as many as 100,000 molecules of ozone (Figure S15-4). By many estimates, this process would eventually deplete the ozone layer.

High-Altitude Jets and Nuclear Explosions

The ozone layer may be vulnerable to other human activities, as well. For instance, scientists believe that aircraft such as the supersonic transport (SST) flying in the stratosphere may also destroy ozone through the release of nitric oxide produced by jet engines. The nitric oxide gas reacts with ozone to form nitrogen dioxide and oxygen (Figure S15-5).

In 1971 the U.S. Congress killed plans to help finance the construction of 300 to 400 SSTs; however, the British–French Concorde is in use today on a limited scale. Because the Concorde flies lower and burns less fuel than the proposed U.S. SST, it has less impact on the ozone layer. Ordinary commercial jets also produce nitric oxide. They help deplete the ozone layer but to a smaller degree.

The detonation of nuclear weapons in the atmosphere also produces nitric oxide. The active period of atmospheric testing of nuclear weapons in the 1940s and 1950s caused a moderate and short-lived decrease in ozone, suggesting that nuclear war could cause a dangerous reduction (see Chapter Supplement 4-1).

$$\text{(}a\text{)} \quad \underset{\text{(Chlorine oxide)}}{ClO} \quad + \quad \underset{\substack{\text{(oxygen free} \\ \text{radical)}}}{O} \longrightarrow \underset{\substack{\text{(chlorine free} \\ \text{radical)}}}{Cl} \quad + \quad \underset{\substack{\text{(molecular} \\ \text{oxygen)}}}{O_2}$$

$$\text{(}b\text{)} \quad ClO \quad + \quad O_3 \longrightarrow ClO_2 \quad + \quad O_2$$

Figure S15-4 (*a*) A single molecule of freon gas can eliminate many thousands of molecules of ozone, because the chlorine free radical is regenerated. (*b*) Chlorine oxide (formed when the chloride free radical reacts with ozone) can also react with ozone.

$$\text{Supersonic Transport Jet} \longrightarrow \underset{\text{(nitric oxide)}}{NO} + \underset{\text{(ozone)}}{O_3} \longrightarrow \underset{\text{(nitrogen dioxide)}}{NO_2} + \underset{\text{(oxygen)}}{O_2}$$

Figure S15-5 Supersonic and subsonic jets produce nitric oxide, which can react with ozone and reduce the ozone layer.

Other Sources of Destruction

Nitrogen fertilizer that farmers apply to their fields may be converted into nitric oxide gas. It could gradually diffuse into the stratosphere, there reacting with ozone molecules. Although the use of fertilizers has risen dramatically in the last decade, no one knows what harm they may cause in the long run.

Other chemical pollutants such as methyl chloride and carbon tetrachloride may also diffuse into the ozone layer and eliminate ozone molecules. Natural pollutants such as nitrogen oxides from volcanoes and chloride ions from sea salt may also destroy the ozone layer, although these processes are presumably in balance with natural ozone replenishment.

Extent and Effect of Depletion

The chemists F. Sherwood Rowland and Mario Molina first warned, in 1974, that chlorofluorocarbons could destroy the ozone layer. Their early projections indicated that these substances would eventually destroy 20% to 30% of the layer. In the years since their first reports scientists have steadily decreased their estimates of depletion. By 1984 many scientists believed that it would be only 2% to 4% by sometime in the next century. Ozone became a "dead" issue for a while. However, a recent study by the EPA projects a 60% decline in stratospheric levels by 2050 if the production of chlorofluorocarbons continues to grow by 4.5% a year. Even a 2.5% increase would deplete the ozone layer 26% by 2075.

These projections come in the wake of startling news from satellites taking atmospheric ozone measurements over Antarctica. These studies show a mysterious thinning in the ozone layer over Antarctica, which appears to be getting worse each year. Other studies show that ozone levels have steadily declined by a constant .15% per year from 1970 to 1981. More recent satellite studies show a decline of .5% per year. Moreover, satellite measurements of chlorofluorocarbons in the stratosphere show that levels have more than doubled in the last ten years.

Ozone depletion will increase the amount of ultraviolet light striking the earth. In reasonable amounts, ultraviolet light tans light skin and stimulates vitamin D production in the skin. However, excess ultraviolet exposure causes serious burns and may induce skin cancer. It would also be lethal to bacteria and plants.

Medical researchers believe that a 1% depletion of the ozone layer would lead to a 2% increase in skin cancer. Given a 16% decrease in ozone by 2000, skin cancer would rise by 32%, resulting in 100,000 to 300,000 more diagnosed cases each year. Assuming a 4% mortality rate, about 4,000 to 12,000 additional deaths would occur each year in the United States alone.

Studies of skin cancer show that light-skinned people are much more sensitive to ultraviolet light than more heavily pigmented individuals. In addition, some chemicals commonly found in drugs, soaps, cosmetics, and detergents may sensitize the skin to ultraviolet light. Thus, exposure to sunlight may increase the incidence of skin cancers.

Plants are also affected by excess ultraviolet light. Intense ultraviolet light is usually lethal to plants; smaller, nonfatal doses damage leaves, inhibit photosynthesis, cause mutations, or stunt growth.

Preventing Ozone Depletion

Considerable scientific debate has been stimulated by the projections discussed above. Some nations, including the United States, Sweden, Finland, Norway, and Canada, have already cut back on chlorofluorocarbon emissions. A ban on freon spray-can propellants in the United States, which produces 40% of the world's fluorocarbons, went into effect in 1978. However, freon-12, used as a refrigerant and coolant and also in the production of plastic foam, was not affected by the ban. A recent study showed that voluntary cutbacks in freon use are working. Emissions in 1984 were 21% lower than those in 1974.

Unilateral actions of the sort taken by the United States, Canada, and the Scandinavian countries may be offset by increasing freon use throughout the world. Therefore, in 1985 the United Nations Environment Program negotiated an agreement with 50 nations calling for international cooperation in studying stratospheric ozone depletion. Some chemists suggested using CF-22, a less harmful freon, for air conditioners and other similar uses. The United States and other countries that have banned freons have urged the rest of Europe, Japan, and the Soviet Union to cut back all nonessential uses of freon.

Although they initially met with opposition, the efforts by the United Nations Environment Program and countries such as the United States have begun to pay off internationally. In 1987, the Environment Program sponsored new negotiations on the issue among 31 countries, aimed at actual reduction of global fluorocarbon production. In a tentative accord, the nations agreed to freeze production of at least two fluorocarbons at 1986 levels, starting in 1990. By 1992, that production would be cut by 20 percent. An additional 30 percent cut has been proposed in the agreement, but without an exact timetable or a firm commitment to achieve such a reduction. Although the details of the agreement are still to be worked out, the shown resolve of the participating countries to tackle the ozone problem is very encouraging.

The problem with ozone depletion is that it is potentially life-threatening but filled with uncertainty. Scientists do not know how much stratospheric ozone will be depleted in coming decades. This uncertainty has slowed down steps that may be needed to protect future generations from harmful ultraviolet radiation.

Worldwide cooperation is essential if we are to deal with this potentially disastrous problem. Some scientists warn that further delays only lead us perilously close to disaster. By the time we are able to detect decreases in the ozone concentration, it may be too late, because millions of tons of freons already in the atmosphere are working their way toward the ozone layer.

Acid Deposition: Roadblock to Progress or Environmental Hazard?

In the 1960s a forest ranger named Bill Marleau built the cabin of his boyhood dreams on Woods Lake in the western part of New York's Adirondack Mountains. Isolated in a dense forest of birch, hemlock, and maple, the lake offered Marleau excellent fishing and an unequaled opportunity for solitude. Ten years after Marleau finished his cabin, however, something bizarre happened: Woods Lake, once a murky green suspension of microscopic algae and zooplankton, teeming with trout, began to turn clear. As the lake went through a mysterious transformation, the trout stopped biting and soon disappeared altogether. Then the lily pads began to turn brown and die; soon afterward, the bullfrogs, otters, and loons disappeared, too.

What had happened to Woods Lake? What had destroyed the web of life at this small, isolated lake, far from any sources of pollution? Scientists from the New York Department of Environmental Conservation say that Woods Lake is "critically acidified." As a result, virtually all forms of life in and around it have perished or moved elsewhere. The lake became acidified from acids and acid precursors deposited from the skies in several forms.

Acid deposition—acid rain and snow and acidic precursors that are deposited in other ways—is becoming widespread, as are lakes like Marleau's. Woods Lake is only one of 237 lakes and ponds in the western Adirondacks turned acidic and hazardous to virtually all forms of life by acid deposition. In eastern Canada 100 lakes have met a similar fate. In Scandinavia the death count is 10,000. Across the globe thousands of lakes now lie in wait; according to researchers, their turn is coming unless something is done, and quickly.

Widely publicized as one of the most serious environmental threats facing us today, acid deposition is a phenomenon of great environmental and economic importance. It is also, as one person in the coal industry has said, at "the core of the next battle between the coal industry and the environmentalists." Focusing on this battle, Ann Hughey reiterated a popular industry view in *Forbes* magazine when she called acid precipitation "the latest roadblock in a long series that always seems to keep coal from becoming the energy savior." The EPA's Stephen Gage prefers to call it "one of the most significant environmental problems of the coming decade."

Evidence is mounting to show that acid deposition turns lakes acidic, kills fish and other aquatic organisms, damages crops, destroys forests, alters soil fertility, and destroys sandstone and marble structures. Moreover, scientists are finding that acid precipitation is more widespread than once thought and is taking a larger toll on our environment and pocketbooks than originally imagined. Recent reports indicate that it poses a universal threat, affecting the developed countries as well as many Third World nations. Earthscan, an international environmental group, reports that acid deposition is already damaging soils, crops, and buildings in much of the Third World. Rapidly growing urban centers with their poorly regulated industry and traffic congestion are largely the culprits. Ironically, tough pollution laws in developed countries have given multinational corporations incentives to set up operations in Third World nations, whose pollution laws are, if existent, certainly much weaker.

What Is Acid Deposition?

Acid deposition refers to the deposition of all forms of acids from the sky. To understand this phenomenon more clearly requires a look at acids—how they form in the atmosphere and how they are deposited.

Acidity is related to the amount of free hydrogen ions (H^+) in solution. The degree of acidity is measured on the pH (potential hydrogen) scale, which ranges from 0 to 14 (Figure S15-1). Substances that are acidic, such as vinegar and lemon juice, have low pH values—that is, less than 7. Basic (alkaline) substances, such as baking soda and lime, have high pH values on the scale—greater than 7. Neutral substances, such as pure water, have a pH of 7. A change of 1 pH unit represents a tenfold change in the level of acidity; thus, rain with a pH of 4 is 10 times more acidic than rain with a pH of 5, 100 times more acidic than rain with a pH of 6, and 1000 times more acidic than rain with a pH of 7.

In an unpolluted environment rainwater is slightly acidic, having a pH of approximately 5.7; the normal acidity of rainwater is created as atmospheric CO_2 is dissolved in water in clouds, mist, or fog and is converted into a mild acid, carbonic acid. **Acid precipitation** is rain and snow with a lower pH—below 5.7.

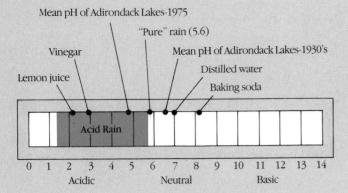

Mean pH of Adirondack Lakes-1975

"Pure" rain (5.6)

Vinegar

Mean pH of Adirondack Lakes-1930's

Distilled water

Lemon juice

Baking soda

Acid Rain

| 0 | 1 | 2 | 3 | 4 | 5 | 6 | 7 | 8 | 9 | 10 | 11 | 12 | 13 | 14 |

Acidic   Neutral   Basic

Figure S15-1   A pH scale to indicate acid-base level.

Wet Deposition

Acid rain and snow are formed when two pollutant gases, the sulfur and nitrogen oxides, combine with water. Sulfur oxides form sulfuric acid; nitrogen oxide gases react with water to form nitric acid. Both are powerful acids. They may accumulate in clouds and fall from the sky in rain and snow. This process is called **wet deposition**. Even coastal fogs may contain droplets of acid that, when deposited on buildings or plants, can cause noticeable damage. Recent studies suggest that the evaporation of recently deposited cloud water from forest canopies may result in acid concentrations on leaf surfaces that are higher than those found in the cloud droplets themselves.

Dry Deposition

Sulfur and nitrogen oxide gases also form sulfate and nitrate particulates. These may settle out of the atmosphere like fine dust particles. This process is called **dry deposition**. Settling onto surfaces, these particulates can combine with water to form acids. Sulfur and nitrogen oxide gases may also be adsorbed onto the surfaces of plants or solid surfaces, where they, too, combine with water to form acids. This is another type of dry deposition.

Where Do Acids Come From?

Acid precursors come from both natural and anthropogenic sources. The natural sources of sulfur oxides include volcanoes, forest fires, and bacterial decay. Anthropogenic sources of this pollutant are of major concern, however, because they are often concentrated in urban and industrialized regions, causing local levels to be quite high. About 70% of all anthropogenic sufur dioxide comes from electric power plants, most of which burn coal.

Like the sulfur oxides, the nitrogen oxides arise from a wide variety of sources. The most important anthropogenic sources are electric power plants and motor vehicles. (Figure S15-2).

American factories, cars, and power plants currently produce approximately 22 million metric tons of sulfur dioxide and about 19 million metric tons of nitrogen oxides a year. The EPA estimates that annual sulfur dioxide emissions may increase to

Total Human-caused Nitrogen Oxide Emissions in the U.S. in 1977

Stationary sources
(50% electricity generation)
56%

Mobile sources
44%

Figure S15-2   Anthropogenic sources of nitrogen oxides.

around 26 million metric tons by 2000 and that annual nitrogen oxide emissions will increase to 25 million metric tons.

The Transport of Acid Precursors

It is not uncommon for rains in the northeastern United States to have pH values of 4 to 4.21; values similar to these have been reported consistently for 25 years. The acidic substances in the rain of this region often originate many hundreds of kilometers away.

Acid precursors and acids can remain airborne for two to five days and may travel hundreds, perhaps even thousands, of kilometers before being deposited. Scientists have found that the acid rain and snow in southern Norway and Sweden comes from England and industrialized Europe. In the United States acid precipitation falling in the Northeast originates in the industrialized Midwest, primarily the Upper Mississippi and Ohio River valleys. Indiana and Ohio are the two major producers. Moving eastward, the mass of pollutants tends to converge on New York state and New England, where recent studies show

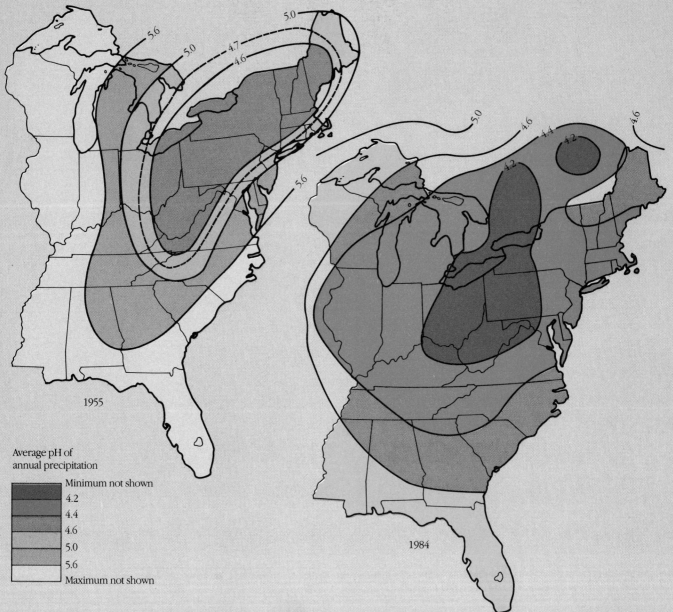

Average pH of
annual precipitation

Minimum not shown

4.2

4.4

4.6

5.0

5.6

Maximum not shown

Figure S15-3 Acid precipitation in the eastern United States, 1955 and 1984. Note the worsening of acid rain and the wider area experiencing it.

that over half of the lakes are in jeopardy because of low acid-neutralizing capacities.

Acid deposition is widespread. Montana, Florida, Colorado, New Jersey, California, Canada, the Amazon Basin, and the Netherlands, to name a few, have all documented acid precipitation in regions downwind of polluted areas.

The level of precipitation acidity at these locations can be quite high. In the White Mountains of New Hampshire, between 1964 and 1974, the average annual pH was about 4 to 4.21, nearly 100 times more acidic than normal precipitation. During that decade the level of acid increased 36%. In Europe rain and snow samples frequently have pH values between 3 and 5; in Scandinavia rain with a pH as low as 2.8 has been recorded. Rainfall samples collected in Pasadena, California, in 1976 and

1977 had an average pH of 3.9. One of the lowest pH measurements was made in Kane, Pennsylvania, where a rainfall sample with a pH of 2.7 was recorded—rain as acidic as vinegar. The grand prize for acidic rainfall, however, goes to Wheeling, West Virginia, where a rainfall sample had a pH of 2—stronger than lemon juice. More recent studies of acid fog downwind from Los Angeles basin, however, show fog water with pH levels as low as 1.69.

In well-studied areas such as southern Norway and Sweden and the northeastern United States, two ominous trends have been observed. The first is that acid precipitation is falling over a wider area than it was 10 to 20 years ago; the second is that the areas over which the strongest acids are falling are expanding (Figure S15-3).

Frequency Distribution of pH in Adirondack Lakes

Figure S15-4 The pH level in Adirondack lakes.

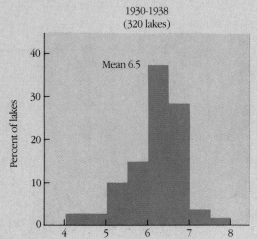

1930-1938
(320 lakes)

Mean 6.5

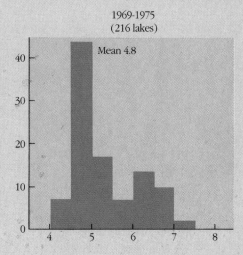

1969-1975
(216 lakes)

Mean 4.8

Impacts of Acid Precipitation

Acidification of Lakes

Throughout the world, lakes and rivers and their fish are dying at an alarming rate. In the 1930s, for example, scientists surveyed lakes in the western part of the Adirondacks. Sampling the pH of 320 lakes, they found that most were fairly normal, with pHs ranging from 6 to 7.5. In 1975 a survey of 216 lakes in the same area showed that a large number had pH values below 5, a level at which most aquatic life perishes (Figure S15-4). Of the acid-

ified lakes, 82% were devoid of fish life. Currently, at least 237 lakes and ponds in the western Adirondacks have passed the critical mark. Hundreds of other lakes are fast approaching this point. In Maine, the acidity of nearly 1400 lakes has increased nearly 10 times in the last 40 years. A recent study of the upper Midwest showed that 121,000 hectares (300,000 acres) of lakes are highly vulnerable to acids because of low buffering capacity.

Recent studies have shown that acid deposition occurs widely over the northern and central portions of Florida, with precipitation ten times more acidic than normal (Figure S15-5). Furthermore, in lakes like Lake Brooklyn, the pH of which decreased from 5.5 in 1957–1960 to 4.9 in 1977–1979, are in

Figure S15-5 Rainfall pH values in Florida.

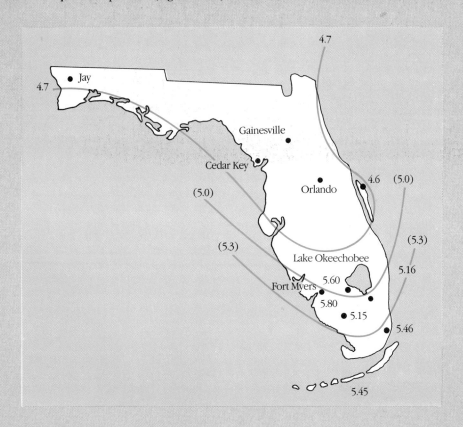

serious danger because of their inability to neutralize the acids falling from the sky. Rapidly growing Florida is demanding more electricity. Six coal-fired power plants are operating in the state; 15 were planned for the region by 1987.

In the mountains of southern Scandinavia the story is being repeated but on a much larger scale. Acidification of surface waters has occurred at a rapid rate for 30 to 40 years. In the Tovdal River basin in southern Norway, 48 of 266 lakes were found to be acidified and without fish in 1950. By 1975, 175 lakes were devoid of fish. In Sweden approximately 20,000 lakes are without or soon to be without fish. Salmon runs in Norway have been entirely eliminated because of the impact of acid precipitation on egg development. As a result, inland commercial fishing has ended in some areas.

In Canada the prospects for lakes and rivers are dimming. Nine of Nova Scotia's famous salmon-fishing rivers have already lost their fish populations because of acidity. Eleven more are teetering on the brink of destruction. In southern Ontario and Quebec acid precipitation has destroyed at least 100 lakes. By 2000, scientists predict, nearly half of Quebec's 48,000 lakes will have been destroyed. Because much of the acid reaching these lakes is believed to come from the United States, Canada has exerted considerable pressure on the U.S. government to reduce air pollution. Its plea has fallen on deaf ears.

Parks and Wilderness Areas

Parks and wilderness areas in the United States are endangered by acid precipitation, because many lie downwind from major industrial centers and have thin soils and waters low in **buffers**, chemical substances that allow aquatic systems to resist changes in pH. When H^+ levels increase, buffers combine with the free ions and eliminate them from the solution. When levels fall, they release them, thus maintaining a constant pH.

Preliminary data suggest that acid precipitation in the great Smoky Mountains National Park has already put stress on existing trout populations in the poorly buffered lakes. Also of particular concern is the Quetico-Superior lake country of Canada and northern Minnesota. There are three major parks in this area: Quetico Provincial Park in Canada and Voyageurs National Park and the Boundary Waters Canoe Area Wilderness in the United States. A recent EPA report stated that one-quarter to one-third of the lakes in the two U.S. parks have so little buffering capacity that fish and other life forms are in danger. In the first comprehensive study of parks in the U.S. West, scientists found that Yosemite, Sequoia, Mount Ranier, North Cascades, and Rocky Mountain national parks were already affected by acid precipitation. A number of others were not affected but could be if western acid precipitation continues to increase.

Effects on Aquatic Ecosystems

Many species of fish (brown trout and lake trout) die when the pH drops below 4.5 to 5 (Figure S15-6), although some species such as yellow perch and lake trout are slightly more resistant.

Acidity is only part of the reason fish die in acidified lakes. Scientists have found that when a lake's pH falls below the critical level, the concentration of toxic trace elements increases. Acidic rainwater or snowmelt dissolves elements like aluminum, mercury, and lead, which are naturally found in the soil and

rocks. The acidic waters carry the metals to streams and lakes. Dr. Carl Schofield has shown that aluminum irritates the gills of brook trout, causing a buildup of mucus and, ultimately, death by asphyxiation (Figure S15-7).

Springtime Snowmelt: An Acid Bath   Spring creates a special threat to fish and other aquatic organisms. Melting snow releases its acid in a sudden torrent, quickly elevating the acidity of lakes and streams. This surge of acids coincides with the sensitive reproductive period for many species of fish. What happens is that acids accumulate in the snow over the winter. When the snow begins to melt, the surface melts first. This water drains through the unmelted snowpack and leaches out the majority of the acids. The first 30% of the meltwater contains virtually all of the acid and typically has a pH of 3 to 3.5, which is toxic to eggs, fry, and adult fish as well.

Widening the Circle of Destruction   Fish are only one of the many organisms affected by acid precipitation. Professor Erik Nyholm of Sweden's University of Lund has found that songbirds living near acid-contaminated lakes lay eggs with softer shells than birds feeding around unaffected lakes. He also found elevated levels of aluminum in the bones of the birds that lived near acidic lakes, and he hypothesized that the aluminum had come from ingestion of aquatic insects living in acidified waters. The aluminum interferes with normal calcium deposition, resulting in defective (soft) eggshells and, ultimately, fewer offspring.

In 1987, the Izaak Walton League of America, a private environmental protection group, reported preliminary evidence that acid precipitation has contributed to a steep decline in the population of black ducks on the East Coast. The number of black ducks sighted has decreased by 60% in the last three decades. Although other factors have accounted for part of this decline, it appears that acidified lakes and wetlands produce considerably fewer black ducklings than regular breeding grounds. It is believed that acidic food (insects, weeds, and algae, for example) may cause significantly higher mortality rates among young ducks raised in an acidified environment. Baby black ducks in acidic areas also grow up to 60% more slowly than ducks raised in non-acidic wetlands.

Professor F. Harvey Pough of Cornell studies fertilized spotted salamander eggs in his laboratory and found that exposure to water with a pH of 5 prevented normal embryonic development and resulted in gross deformities that were usually fatal. The mortality of fertilized eggs was 60% at pH 6 but only 1% at pH 7.

Spotted salamanders breed in "temporary ponds" created by melted snow. These ponds are likely to be highly acidic in regions where acid precipitation is prevalent; as a result, the fate of the spotted salamander is bleak. The spotted salamander is as important as birds and small mammals in the food chain. "A drastic change in its population," Pough says, "would be likely to have repercussions throughout the entire ecosystem."

Some Human Consequences

In addition to damaging aquatic ecosystems, acids also damage crops, forests, buildings, and statues. Current estimates hold the economic costs of acid precipitation to be around $5 billion a year in the United States.

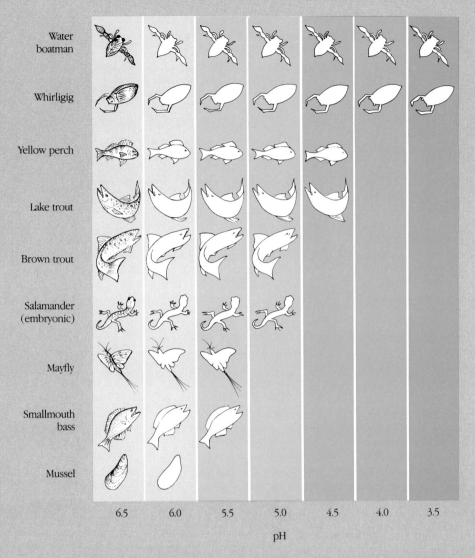

Figure S15-6 The sensitivity of fish and other aquatic organisms to acid levels varies. The figure indicates the lowest pH (highest acidity) at which the organisms can survive. The yellow perch, for example, can withstand a pH of 4.5, while a mussel cannot live at pH levels lower than 6.0.

Water boatman

Whirligig

Yellow perch

Lake trout

Brown trout

Salamander (embryonic)

Mayfly

Smallmouth bass

Mussel

6.5   6.0   5.5   5.0   4.5   4.0   3.5

pH

A report by the Ohio state government contends that if some-thing is not done quickly to control acid precipitation, 2500 lakes a year will die in Ontario, Quebec, and New England throughout the remainder of the century. Many of the areas most susceptible to acid precipitation depend economically on recreation. In Ontario alone approximately 2000 fishing lodges contribute $150 million a year to the economy. A spokesperson for the Ontario Ministry of the Environment says that even at the current rate of acid precipitation, "there could be a $64-million loss and serious survival problems for 600 lodges over the next 20 years."

The same ominous future seems probable for parts of the

Figure S15-7 These fish were confined to a cage in a stream affected by acid rain. They died of asphyxiation.

United States. In New York state the destruction of lakes and the subsequent decrease in sport fishing is expected to cause a loss of about $1 million annually.

Forest Damage   Numerous studies show that acid precipitation damages forests and may cause significant decreases in productivity. Acid precipitation causes foliar damage to birch and pines, impairs seed germination of spruce seeds, erodes protective waxes from oak leaves, and leaches nutrients from plant leaves. In Czechoslovakia researchers estimate that 300,000 acres of forest has been destroyed by pollution, mostly acid precipitation. In West Germany, 500,000 hectares (1.25 million acres) of forest is dying. Even the famous Black Forest is now severely damaged by acidic pollutants from industry and, especially, the automobile. In Vermont's Green Mountains half the red spruce, a high-elevation tree, have died from acid precipitation and acid fog. Lower-elevation sugar maples are also on the decline. With each passing day the stakes get higher. Nowhere is the impact felt more than in Canada, where the forestry industry contributes about 15% of the gross domestic product.

Swiss scientists believe that damage to trees may increase the likelihood of avalanches, because trees help retain snow on steep mountainsides. In the next few years 10% of the "barrier forests" may be lost, endangering the safety of mountain residents, skiers, and highway travelers.

Crop Damage   Concern for agriculture has also been raised by numerous researchers, but the results of many studies are inconclusive. Some researchers have reported that simulated acid precipitation decreases crop productivity, but other scientists have found increases, and still others, no effect. Acid precipitation with a pH less than 3.0 damages leaves on bean plants. Laboratory studies of tobacco plants show that simulated acid precipitation leaches calcium from leaves. Furthermore, timothy grass treated with simulated acid rain with pHs ranging from 2.2 to 3.7 died after extended exposure.

Acid precipitation is particularly harmful to buds; therefore, acids falling on plants in the spring might impair growth. In addition, acid precipitation appears to inhibit the dark reactions of photosynthesis, a series of chemical reactions in which plants produce carbohydrates and other important chemicals.

Acids may also damage plants by altering the soil. For example, acid rain may leach important elements from the soil, resulting in lower yield and reduced agricultural output. Acidification of soils may also impair soil bacteria and fungi that play an important role in nutrient cycling and nitrogen fixation, both essential to normal plant growth. Recent evidence shows that acids dissolve aluminum from the soil; aluminum damages cells in the water-transporting tubules of trees, essentially closing off water transport. Trees die from thirst.

In some areas sulfur and nitrogen from acid rain may enhance soil fertility. However, direct damage to growing plants and damage to the soil could easily offset the fertilizing effect.

Acid-Sensitive Areas   Acidification of lakes and streams occurs quite predictably in areas with a common geological denominator: thin soils with low acid-neutralizing capacities. Acid-sensitive areas in the United States, shown in Figure S15-8, include many mountainous regions. Ironically, the major pro-

ducers, Indiana and Ohio, are the least vulnerable. Their thick topsoils contain abundant buffers.

Damage to Materials   Acid precipitation also corrodes manmade structures and has taken its toll on some of special importance, such as the Statue of Liberty, the Canadian Parliament Building in Ottawa, Egypt's temples of Karnak, and the Caryatids of the Acropolis—not just architectural works but works of art, priceless treasures. John Roberts, Canada's former environmental minister, estimates that erosion of buildings in North America may be costing $2 billion to $3 billion a year. Acid rain may also damage house paint and etch the surface of automobiles and trucks. A recent U.S. report claims that acid precipitation causes an estimated $5 billion in damage to buildings in 17 northeastern and midwestern states. The price tag includes the cost of repairing mortar, galvanized steel, and stone structures as well as the cost of repainting. It does not include damage to automobile paint, roofing materials, and concrete, potentially adding billions of dollars to the cost.

Solving a Growing Problem

U.S. Drags Its Feet

The first significant U.S. governmental action against acid precipitation came in 1979 when Congress passed the **Acid Precipitation Act** to identify the sources and evaluate the effects of acid deposition. Congress promised to take steps to limit or eliminate sources of acid deposition. But so far little has been done.

There are 140 air pollution monitors in the United States and Canada collecting data to determine levels of acid deposition. But little has been done to correct the problem, largely because of President Reagan's insistence that more research is needed before actions should be taken. Critics of Reagan's wait-and-see policy include many of his top science advisors.

In 1981 the prestigious and usually cautious National Academy of Sciences recommended a 50% cut in emissions of sulfur, as well as sharp cuts in nitrogen emissions. Continued emissions at present levels, the committee noted, represent a threat to human health and to the biosphere. Many other scientists and environmentalists agree with the academy. Strong support for control is gathering behind three strategies: (1) installation of scrubbers on all existing coal-fired power plants, (2) combustion of low-sulfur coal in all utilities, (3) combustion of coal that has been cleaned to remove sulfur. Individual conservation efforts, when taken together, could add up to significant cuts in sulfur emissions.

In 1982 Senator George Mitchell of Maine introduced a bill with the support of the National Clean Air Coalition calling for a 50% reduction in sulfur oxide emissions in 31 eastern states. Despite the fact that this would increase electric bills by an average of only 1.9%, the bill did not make it through Congress.

One of the few bits of encouraging news in the United States comes from New York state. In 1984 the legislature passed a bill calling for a 30% reduction in sulfur emissions by 1991. In that same year, nine European nations and Canada signed a

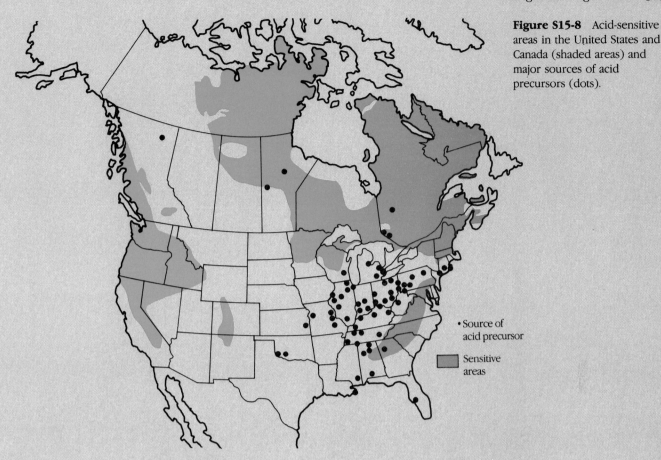

Figure S15-8 Acid-sensitive areas in the United States and Canada (shaded areas) and major sources of acid precursors (dots).

• Source of acid precursor

Sensitive areas

agreement to reduce sulfur emissions by 30% over a ten-year period. In 1985 a federal judge ruled that the EPA must order midwestern states to cut sulfur dioxide emissions that cause acid precipitation in Canada, in keeping with a provision of the Clear Air Act (Chapter 15). Minnesota also recently passed legislation to curb the growing problem.

Many countries, impatient with the slow cuts in acid pollutants, have looked toward another strategy: attacking the symptoms directly. For example, in 1977 the Swedish government embarked on an expensive program to neutralize acidic lakes by applying lime. By 1986, 3000 lakes had been neutralized, at a cost of $25 million. Water quality improved, and fish populations were saved. Sweden also undertook an ambitious stream-liming program in an effort to save inland salmon and other fish. In 1982 it built a liming plant on the banks of the Fyllea River and in the next two years added 2250 metric tons of lime to the waters, at a cost of $2.2 million. Critics argue that liming is an intermediate solution at best, a little like cardiopulmonary resuscitation administered to a heart attack victim. In Canada liming costs $120 per hectare ($50 per acre), so that treating a single lake can cost between $4,000 and $40,000. In five years, however, treated lakes turn acidic again. And if treatment is not begun early, lakes may never reestablish the complex food web.

Pursuing another approach, Cornell's Carl Schofield is developing a strain of acid-resistant brook trout. Despite its imme-

diate logic, this approach is doomed to fail. Even if a strain of trout that could survive at pH 4.8 were developed, what would happen when the pH dropped to 4.5? And what about the trout's food supply?

Prospects for the Future

The United States is one of the few industrialized nations that has not taken steps to curb acid precipitation. Between 1979 and 1995, the U.S. power industry projects, 350 new coal-burning power plants will go on line. The EPA predicts that sulfur dioxide emissions could increase from current levels of 22 million metric tons to about 26 million metric tons per year by 2000; nitrogen oxide emissions may increase from current levels of 19 million metric tons to 25 million metric tons by 2000.

Without decisive action, many experts believe, hundreds, perhaps thousands, of lakes will be destroyed in the next two decades. A 50% reduction in sulfur emissions would go a long way toward reducing acid precipitation in the East. In the West, restrictions on automobile use would help curb the nitrogen oxide emissions responsible for much of the acid precipitation. Energy conservation, solar energy, and wind energy could also become valuable allies in this battle.

Suggested Readings

Beamish, R. J. (1976). Acidification of Lakes in Canada from Acid Precipitation and the Resulting Effects on Fishes. *Water, Air and Soil Pollution* 6: 501–514. Technical report on toxic effects of acid rain on fish.

Crocker, T. D., and Regens, J. L. (1985). Acid Deposition Control. A Benefit–Cost Analysis: Its Prospects and Limits. *Environ. Sci. and Technol.* 19 (2): 112–116. Good look at cost–benefit analysis.

Environment Canada (1982). *Downwind: The Story of Acid Rain.* Ottawa: Minister of Supply and Services. Good overview.

Greenberg, D. S. (1985). Fast Cars and Sick Trees. *International Wildlife* 15 (4): 22–24. A short, well-written article on the connection between automobile pollution and the destruction of Germany's forests.

Havas, M., Hutchinson, T. C., and Likens, G. E. (1984). Red Herrings in Acid Rain Research. *Environ. Sci. and Technol.* 18 (6): 176A–186A. Excellent rebuttal of false claims made by opponents of acid-precipitation controls.

Johnson, A. H. (1986). Acid Deposition: Trends, Relationships, and Effects. *Environment* 28 (4): 6–11, 34–43. Comprehensive summary of the National Academy of Sciences report. Well worth reading.

Kahan, A. M. (1986). *Acid Rain: Reign of Controversy.* Golden, Colo.: Fulcrum. Balanced view of acid deposition.

LaBastille, A. (1981). Acid Rain: How Great a Menace? *National Geographic* 160 (5): 652–681. Vividly illustrated and well written.

Luoma, J. R. (1980). Troubled Skies, Troubled Waters. *Audubon* 82 (6): 88–111. Exquisitely written.

Luoma, J. R. (1984). *Troubled Skies, Troubled Waters: The Story of Acid Rain.* New York: Penguin. The best of the books on acid precipitation.

Postel, S. (1984). *Air Pollution, Acid Rain, and the Future of Forests.* Worldwatch Paper 58. Washington, D.C.: Worldwatch Institute. Detailed analysis of air pollution and forests.

Rhodes, S. L., and Middleton, P. (1983). The Complex Challenge of Controlling Acid Rain. *Environment* 25 (4): 6–9, 31–38. Good review of the politics of acid-rain control based on a lack of knowledge on the known effects.

Scheiman, D. A. (1986). Facing Facts. *The Amicus Journal* 7 (4): 4–9. Superb overview of the latest findings on acid deposition.

Sholle, S. R. (1983). Update: Acid Deposition and the Materials Damage Question. *Environment* 25 (8): 25–32. Fairly detailed account of material damage from air pollution.

U.S. Senate Committee on Environment and Public Works. (1981). *Hearings on Acid Rain.* October 29, 1981. Serial No. 97-H30. Washington, D.C.: U.S. Printing Office. Up-to-date testimony by scientists doing research on acid rain. Excellent.

U.S. Senate Committee on Environment and Public Works. (1982). *Acid Rain: A Technical Inquiry.* May 25 and 26, 1982. Serial No. 97-H53. Washington, D.C.: U.S. Government Printing Office. Excellent.

Wentworth, M. (1986). What's Wrong with Liming? *Outdoor America* 51 (1): 12–14. Wonderful survey of ameliorative attempts to offset the effects of acid precipitation.

Wetstone, G. S., and Foster, S. A. (1983). Acid Precipitation: What Is It Doing to Our Forests? *Environment* 25 (4): 10–12, 38–40. Good review.

Indoor Air Pollution

Recent studies show that many Americans are exposed to high levels of toxic substances. Radioactive materials, formaldehyde, particulates, and dozens of other toxins in remarkably high levels enter our bodies through inhalation and skin absorption. Where they come from may be a startling surprise.

Dozens of studies show that American homes are the source of these potentially harmful substances. A new rug, a new couch, a stove, or new paneling may all be emitting toxic chemicals into the air we breathe. In a recent report the EPA said that toxic substances from the home and office are much more likely to cause cancer than ambient air pollutants, for two reasons. First, indoor levels are often much higher than outdoor levels, in some cases up to 100 times higher. Even in pristine rural areas, indoor air can be more polluted than outside air next door to a chemical plant. Second, most people spend the bulk of their lives indoors. In 1986 the EPA scientist announced that indoor air pollution may be causing several hundred U.S. cancer deaths a year. The two chemicals believed responsible for most of the deaths are benzene, from cigarette smoke, and chloroform, a water contaminant given off during hot showers.

Indoor air pollutants come from a variety of sources. Some of the most important are wood and kerosene stoves, natural gas appliances, tobacco smoke, plywood, paneling, furniture, and rugs. Even making homes energy efficient, if not done correctly, can increase the danger.

Products of Combustion

Cigarettes, pipes, cigars, gas stoves and ovens, gas space heaters, water heaters, kerosene stoves, and wood stoves are the major combustive sources of indoor air pollution. Water heaters and furnaces are generally vented outside, so gaseous pollutants do not build up inside. But gas stoves and kerosene space heaters are not vented. Thus, as the fuel burns, carbon monoxide and nitrogen dioxide enter the room air.

As shown in Figure S15-1, carbon monoxide (CO) levels in the kitchen can increase from a few parts per million to over 40 parts per million when four burners are in operation for half an hour or so. CO levels increase appreciably in neigh-

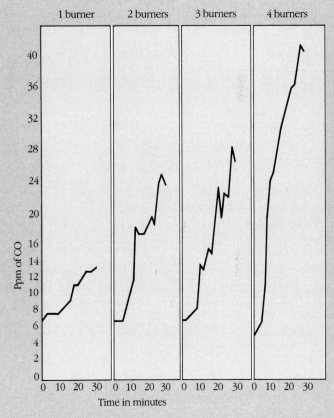

Figure S15-1 Carbon monoxide levels in a kitchen with one to four gas burners on.

boring rooms, too. Nitrogen dioxide levels often follow the same pattern. (For a summary of the health effects see Table 15-2.)

Concentrations of indoor air pollutants fall after combustion sources are turned off, of course, but it may take several hours before normal levels are reached in conventional, poorly sealed homes (Figure S15-2). In well-sealed, energy-efficient homes

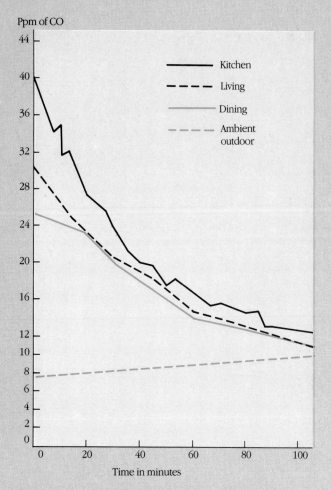

Figure S15-2 Drop in carbon monoxide level in the kitchen, dining room, and living room after the stove is turned off.

that haven't made allowances for ventilation, it could take much longer. If several lengthy meals are cooked during a day, exposure to these pollutants can be quite high.

Researchers have found that in certain homes the nitrogen oxide and carbon monoxide levels can exceed the limits set to protect human health. What the long-term implications are, no one knows.

Sulfur dioxide is not generally a problem in homes unless kerosene stoves are used. New kerosene space heaters introduced in the late 1970s, for example, can release significant amounts of carbon monoxide, nitrogen dioxide, and sulfur dioxide if they are improperly functioning. For example, if the wick is damaged or covered with soot or if there is water in the fuel, pollution levels may become intolerable, creating headaches, coughing, and irritation of the throat.

Particulates are generally not found in homes unless smokers are present. One study showed that the average particulate level was 40 micrograms per cubic meter in a home without smokers. Smokers raised particulate levels in some cases to 700 micro-

grams, over ten times greater than the level allowed by air-quality standards.

Carbon monoxide binds to blood hemoglobin and reduces the oxygen-carrying capacity of the blood, an effect especially harmful to individuals with heart and lung diseases. Sulfur oxides and nitrogen oxides are lung irritants and are responsible for emphysema and chronic bronchitis. In the long term they may also cause lung cancer. Cigarette smoke contains a number of carcinogens.

To reduce the buildup of these toxic chemicals, all combustion sources should be properly vented. With gas stoves, the overhead fans should be used. Kerosene stoves should probably be avoided altogether, especially in small rooms. Cigarette smoking should be prohibited.

Some scientists have suggested that gas stoves should be eliminated from homes and replaced with electric stoves, even though electric cooking is an inefficient way of using this energy source. Passive solar heating can help reduce gas space heating. In tightly sealed, energy-efficient homes, air-exchange systems should be installed (Figure S15-3). These periodically replace room air with outside air; heat exchangers transfer heat to the incoming air, so little heat is lost to the outside.

One scientist working for the National Aeronautics and Space Administration found that certain plants help reduce indoor air pollution. Spider plants appear to be the best at gobbling up pollution. One plant per room is sufficient to prevent the buildup of nitrogen oxide.

Formaldehyde

Formaldehyde is a familiar preservative for biological specimens. It is also a common indoor air pollutant. About 3.2 million metric tons of formaldehyde is used in the United States each year. Because it is in so many consumer products, formaldehyde has become a chemical that few of us can escape. It is found in the adhesive in plywood, particle board, and wood paneling, and it leaks into houses and trailer homes, often in high concentrations. It is hard to avoid these days. Foam insulation (urea-formaldehyde foam that is injected into walls) contains it, as do permanent-press clothes, paper products, carpets, toothpaste, shampoos, waxed paper, grocery bags, and some medicines, to which it is added to kill bacteria, fungi, and viruses.

The levels of formaldehyde in homes insulated with foam are four times higher than those in homes with other types of insulation. Furniture containing formaldehyde in the wood and fabric has been shown to increase the levels in a previously unfurnished house by three times.

People with the greatest risk are those living in trailers or in homes with newly installed foam insulation, particle board, plywood, or paneling (Table S15-1). The better sealed a home or trailer is, the higher the levels of formaldehyde. In conventionally built homes with their abundance of cracks and poor insulation, air exchange between the inside and the outside occurs roughly once every hour. In airtight homes the turnover is much slower, perhaps once every five hours. The tighter the home, the greater the concentration of formaldehyde unless special precautions are taken to avoid products containing this harmful substance.

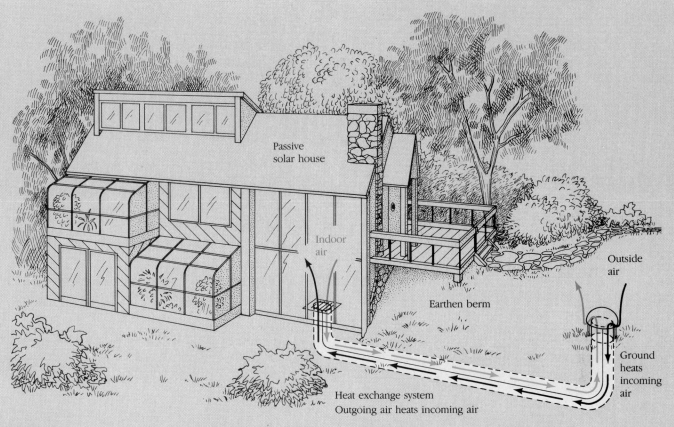

Figure S15-3 Air-exchange mechanism in a tightly sealed, energy-efficient house can prevent the buildup of toxic substances and greatly cut down on heat loss and energy use.

Formaldehyde irritates the eyes, nose, and throat, but sensitivity among people varies. Some are sensitive to levels of 1.5 to 3 parts per million, but others who have been exposed to formaldehyde for long periods become sensitized and respond to levels as low as .05 parts per million.

Formaldehyde causes nasal cancer in rats and possibly mice at high levels. Given to monkeys at levels to which humans are typically exposed at work and at home, formaldehyde causes cellular changes believed to be the early stages of cancer within the linings of the respiratory tracts. It has also been shown to cause mutations in bacteria and many other organisms; many mutagens are also carcinogens. So far evidence linking formaldehyde to cancer in humans is sketchy. One epidemiological study showed a possible link between formaldehyde exposure and skin cancer.

The U.S. Consumer Product Safety Commission banned urea-formaldehyde insulation on February 22, 1981, but removed the ban in 1983. So far the EPA, which could regulate formaldehyde under the Toxic Substances Control Act, has refused to take action, despite recommendations from independent health scientists as well as scientists in the agency itself.

The EPA's refusal to regulate formaldehyde reflects a new attitude. In previous regulatory decisions the fact that a chemical had caused cancer in any laboratory animal was enough to warrant controls. Under the Reagan administration, though, the EPA took a more conservative approach, maintaining that without conclusive proof from statistical studies on humans exposed to formaldehyde, regulations were unwarranted.

Many critics believe that this approach could weaken protection of human health. Norton Nelson, a highly regarded health scientist, contends: "Epidemiological studies must be regarded as a crude and insensitive tool. Only the most violent and intense carcinogens are likely to be detected by epidemiological techniques." Many critics, satisfied with imposing bans based on

	Average Level of Formaldehyde (Parts per Million)
Table S15-1 Formaldehyde in Mobile Homes and Houses Insulated with Urea-Formaldehyde Foam (UFF)	
Type	
Homes without UFF	0.03
Homes with UFF	0.12
Mobile homes with UFF	0.38
Background[1]	0.01

[1]The background level is the normal atmospheric concentration of formaldehyde.

positive results in animal carcinogenicity studies, argue that the EPA should ban the use of formaldehyde in plywood, particle board, paneling, and textiles.

Radioactive Pollutants

A more difficult indoor air pollutant to control is the naturally occurring radioactive gas radon. A daughter product of radium, radon is found in rocks and soils. It enters homes through cracks in the foundation or from the soil in homes without foundations. In some cases stone, brick, and cement contain small quantities of radium that emit radon into homes and other buildings.

Indoor concentrations of radon may be several times the natural, or background, level. Homes built on tailings from uranium mines have levels two to five times higher than normal background, as do the more energy-efficient, airtight homes without proper ventilation. In 1986 the EPA estimated that 4 million U.S. homes had radon levels that posed a danger to human health.

Inhaled, radon gas may emit radiation in the lungs that can cause mutations and lung cancer. Of greater concern, however, are the radioactive decay products of radon, particles like radioactive lead that can become lodged in the lung, providing long-term internal exposure to radiation. These decay products may also adhere to airborn particles that can be breathed into the lungs and also become lodged. The EPA estimates that radon gas in U.S. homes may account for one out of every ten deaths from lung cancer. Bernard Cohen, a health physicist from the University of Pittsburgh, notes that radon in houses may be causing more deaths than all other types of radiation exposure—natural and anthropogenic—combined.

Radon is more difficult to control than other indoor pollutants because it occurs naturally. However, careful selection of building materials and seals on basement walls can help reduce radon levels. More frequent air exchange may also be helpful.

Chloroform and Trichloroethylene

In recent years two toxic and highly volatile chemicals, chloroform and trichloroethylene, have been identified in many municipal drinking-water supplies. These substances come primarily from groundwater polluted by industry and by hazardous waste dumps. Julian Andelman of the University of Pittsburgh estimates that drinking of water tainted with these chemical contaminants causes an estimated 200 to 1000 cancer deaths each year. However, Andelman believes that toxic vapors given off from showers and baths could be more dangerous than poisoned drinking water. His work, for example, shows that a hot shower gives off half of the dissolved chloroform and 80% of the TCE, exposing the bather as well as other family members. Dishwashing and laundry water may also increase the indoor concentrations of these substances.

Controlling Indoor Air Pollutants

Indoor air pollution is a relatively new problem. No U.S. laws directly address it. Legal experts argue that the **Clean Air Act** could be applied. The EPA, which enforces the act, has used it only once to regulate an indoor air pollutant, asbestos.

One way to address indoor air pollutants would be to develop indoor air standards, but the technical and legal problems in enforcing indoor standards would undoubtedly be enormous.

A provision of the Clean Air Act that could be applied to indoor air pollutants authorizes the EPA to draw up emissions standards for hazardous air pollutants. The EPA could develop formaldehyde emissions standards for plywood, particle board, paneling, and other household products.

A second approach might be to use the **Toxic Substances Control Act** (Chapter 14). It gives the EPA broad authority to control the production, distribution, and disposal of potentially hazardous chemicals. Bans on plywood, carpets, furniture, and other products containing formaldehyde could be applied. To date, the EPA Toxic Substance Office has been too burdened with other duties to take such actions. Outright bans would seem less desirable than emissions controls.

A final potential weapon is the **Consumer Product Safety Act**. It gives the Consumer Product Safety Commission the authority to regulate consumer products deemed hazardous to the public. Products that generate indoor air pollution could certainly qualify. The commission can, by law, develop safety standards for various products. Standards for stoves, for example, could indicate the permissible emissions of carbon monoxide, and standards for plywood, textiles, and furniture could set acceptable formaldehyde emissions. The commission can also require manufacturers to warn the public of potential dangers associated with the use of their products.

Indoor air pollution is an emerging problem that has only recently been brought to the attention of the American public. More work is needed to find out how indoor air affects our health. Creative solutions are needed to reduce exposure to the health. Creative solutions are needed to reduce exposure to the potentially harmful substances found in the air in homes.

Suggested Readings

Hileman, B. (1982). Formaldehyde. *Environ. Sci. and Technol.* 16 (10): 543A–547A. Superb overview.

Hileman, B. (1984). Formaldehyde: Assessing the Risk. *Environ. Sci. and Technol.* 18(7): 216A–221A. Good analysis.

Kirsch, L. S. (1983). Behind Closed Doors: I. The Problem of Indoor Pollutants. *Environment* 25 (2): 16–20, 37–42. Good survey.

Kirsch, L. S. (1983). Behind Closed Doors: II. Indoor Air Pollution and Government Policy. *Environment* 25 (3): 26–39. In-depth study of laws that might apply to the control of indoor air pollution.

Lipske, M. (1987). How Safe Is the Air Inside Your Home? *Natural Wildlife* 25 (5): 34–39. Excellent reference.

Spengler, J. D., and Soczek, M. L. (1984). Evidence for Improved Ambient Air Quality and the Need for Personal Exposure Research. *Environ. Sci. and Technol.* 18 (9): 268A–280A.

Sterling, T. D., and Sterling, E. (1979). Carbon Monoxide Levels in Kitchens and Homes with Gas Cookers. *Jour. Amer. Pollution Control Assoc.* 29 (3): 238–241.

U.S. House Committee on Science and Technology. (1985). *Radon and Indoor Air Pollution*. Hearing before the Subcommittee on Natural Resources, Agriculture Research, and Environment. Ninety-Ninth Congress. October 10, 1985.

Vietmeyer, N. (1985). Plants That Eat Pollution. *National Wildlife* 25(5): 10–11. A look at plants thought to lower pollution.

Noise Pollution

Noise is rapidly becoming one of the most widespread environmental pollutants. Few of us can escape it: even when we are enjoying a backcountry camping trip, the silence is broken by the roar of jets, chain saws, and off-road vehicles. Especially noisy are the cities and factories where many of us live and work. (Figure S15-1). To understand noise pollution and its effects, let us first take a look at sound.

Figure S15-1 A new freeway or an airport can drastically change the stress and comfort levels in neighborhoods. Some people do not have the resources to move.

What Is Sound?

Sound is transmitted through the air as a series of waves. For a simple example, take the bass speaker element of a loudspeaker. When the music is loud, the speaker can be seen to vibrate, and a hand placed in front of it can feel the air move. If we could slow down the speaker cone to observe what was happening, we'd see that as it moves outward, it compresses the air molecules in front of it. As the speaker cone returns inward, the air it just compressed expands in both directions, much as a coiled spring would expand when released. This expansion compresses neighboring air molecules slightly farther away. These have the same effect that the outward-pushing speaker cone had (Figure S15-2). Thus, waves of expansion and compression are set up, transmitting the sound. Air molecules do not travel with the sound but only oscillate back and forth in the direction the sound is traveling. Sound is a train of high-pressure regions following one another through the air at about 340 meters per second (760 miles per hour).

Sound can be described in terms of its loudness and its pitch, or frequency. Loudness is measured in **decibels** (dB). The decibel scale (Table S15-1) encompasses a wide range of volume. The lowest sound the human ear can detect is set at 0 dB; this is the threshold of hearing. In the decibel scale a tenfold

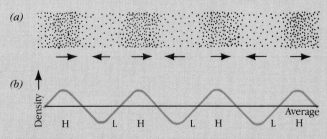

Figure S15-2 Sound waves are created by air molecules moving back and forth (arrows), causing regions of higher pressure (H) and of lower pressure (L). If we could see sound waves they would look like the drawing in (a), but they can be described mathematically by the curve in (b).

Table S15-1 A Decibel Scale

Sound Intensity Factor	Sound Level, dB	Sound Sources	Perceived Loudness	Effects — Damage to Hearing	Community Reaction to Outdoor Noise
1,000,000,000,000,000,000	180—	• Rocket engine			
100,000,000,000,000,000	170—				
10,000,000,000,000,000	160—				
1,000,000,000,000,000	150—	• Jet plane at takeoff	Painful	Traumatic injury	
100,000,000,000,000	140—			Injurious range; irreversible damage	
10,000,000,000,000	130—	• Maximum recorded rock music			
1,000,000,000,000	120—	• Thunderclap • Textile loom • Auto horn, 1 meter away	Uncomfortably loud		
100,000,000,000	110—	• Riveter • Jet flying over at 300 meters			
10,000,000,000	100—	• Newspaper press		Danger zone; progressive loss of hearing	
1,000,000,000	90—	• Motorcycle, 8 meters away • Food blender			Vigorous action
100,000,000	80—	• Diesel truck, 80 km/hr, at 15 meters away • Garbage disposal	Very loud	Damage begins after long exposure	
10,000,000	70—	• Vacuum cleaner • Ordinary conversation	Moderately loud		Threats
1,000,000	60—	• Air conditioning unit, 6 meters • Light traffic noise, 30 meters			Widespread complaints
100,000	50—	• Average living room			Occasional complaints
10,000	40—	• Bedroom	Quiet		No action
1000	30—	• Library			
		• Soft whisper			
100	20—	• Broadcasting studio	Very quiet		
10	10—	• Rustling leaf	Barely audible		
1	0—	• Threshold of hearing			

Source: Turk et.al. (1978). *Environmental Science.* Philadelphia: Saunders, p. 523.

increase in sound intensity is represented by a 10-dB increase on the scale. That is, a 10-dB sound is 10 times louder than a 0-dB sound; a 20-dB sound is 10 times louder than a 10-dB sound and 100 times louder than a 0-dB sound.

Pitch, or frequency, is a measure of how high or how low a sound is. Bass notes played by a tuba have a low pitch, and a violin's treble notes have a high pitch. Pitch is measured in cycles (that is, waves) per second. This is the number of compression waves passing a given point each second. The higher the pitch, the larger the number of cycles per second. Cycles per second are commonly called hertz (Hz), after the German physicist Heinrich Rudolf Hertz.

The human ear is sensitive to sounds in the range of 20 to 20,000 hertz. Sounds below 20 hertz are not detected by the human ear and are described as **infrasonic**. Sounds above the audible range are called **ultrasonic**.

What Is Noise?

Ambrose Bierce wrote that "noise is a stench in the ear, and the chief product of civilization." To the scientist, **noise** is any unwanted, unpleasant sound. Beyond that, it is hard to say with any certainty what a group of people would consider noise. The rumble of construction machinery at a building site might be pleasing to the owner of the new building but insufferable to the doctor whose office is next door.

What any individual considers noise depends on his or her background, mood, occupation, location, and hearing ability. But the time of day, the duration and volume of a sound, and other factors also contribute to our judgment. A sound may be pleasant when it is soft but noisy when it is loud, or it may be acceptable when you generate it but obnoxious when someone else does. People generally agree that the louder a sound is,

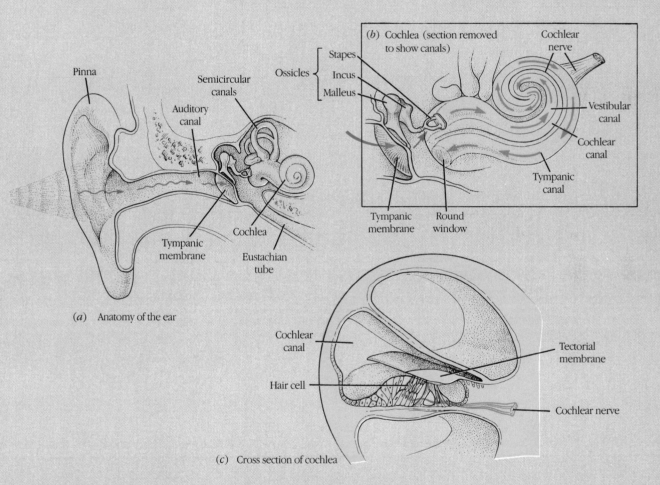

Figure S15-3 Anatomy of the ear. (*a*) Sound waves enter the auditory canal, causing the tympanic membrane (eardrum) to vibrate. The vibrations are transferred to the cochlea by the ossicles, three small bones. (*b*) Vibrations travel in the fluid of the cochlea and cause the tectorial membrane to vibrate. (*c*) Nerve impulses are generated and sent to the brain. Thus, sound waves are first converted to the vibrations of the eardrum, and then converted to fluid compression waves in the cochlea. These waves stimulate the hair cells. The brain translates these fluid waves into sound.

the more annoying it becomes and the more likely people are to describe it as noise.

Sources of noise fall into four categories: transportation, industrial, household, and military. As the world becomes more dependent on technology, noise pollution will grow worse. Of greatest concern are noises from off-road vehicles, construction, air traffic, home appliances, and surface transportation.

Impacts of Noise

Noise affects us in many ways. It damages hearing, disrupts our sleep, and is an annoyance in our everyday lives. It interferes with conversation, concentration, relaxation, and leisure.

Hearing Loss

Our hearing declines with aging and exposure to noise. Natural hearing loss results from degeneration of the hair cells, sensory cells in the ear that translate sound into nerve impulses (Figure S15-3). This natural decline is presumably brought about by infections in the inner ear and natural aging of the sound receptors.

Men generally suffer a greater loss of hearing with age than women. This difference probably results from factors other than sex, such as firing guns or exposure to noise at work. Therefore, what appears to be a natural decline may in fact be brought about by factors under our own control.

Many sounds from a variety of sources impinge upon our ears. Some of these, if loud and persistent enough, can cause premature degeneration of the hair cells. Experts believe that 1 in every 10 to 20 people suffers some hearing loss from anthropogenic noise.

We have all been exposed to noise so loud that we experienced a momentary decrease in our ability to hear. This is called a **temporary threshold shift**. A loud concert, a party with a loud stereo and lots of noisy friends, a drive in the car with the windows open, noisy machinery, or gunfire can all deafen us for a little while.

A permanent loss of hearing, or a **permanent threshold shift**, occurs after continued exposure to loud noise. Recent studies suggest that continuous, long-term exposure to noise levels as low as 55 dB can permanently damage hearing. Noise of this level is common in many factories and jobs, especially in construction and mining. Even city traffic noise can damage the hearing of people exposed on a regular basis. It should be no surprise, then, that a 20-year-old New York City resident hears as well as a 70-year-old tribesman from Africa's grasslands.

As a general rule, the higher the sound level, the less time it takes to induce a permanent threshold shift. In addition, intermittent noise is generally less hazardous than continuous noise. Different frequencies produce differing amounts of damage. The lower frequencies, for example, do less damage than the higher-pitched sounds at the same loudness.

Explosions (130 dB) and other extremely loud noises can cause instantaneous damage to the hair cells, resulting in deafness. Noise levels over 150 dB can severely damage the hair cells, rupture the eardrum, and displace the tiny bones in the ear, the **ossicles**, which convey sound waves from the eardrum to the hair cells.

According to many sources, occupational noise is slowly deafening millions of Americans. Large numbers of Americans work at jobs where the noise levels are over 80 dB. Military personnel are victims of noise from tanks, jets, helicopters, artillery, and rifles. Studies show that about half of the soldiers who complete combat training suffer so much hearing loss that they no longer meet the enlistment requirements for combat units. Bars, nightclubs, discotheques, and traffic noise (especially diesel trucks and buses) are other important contributors to the deafening of America.

The importance of good hearing cannot be emphasized enough. In children it is important for learning language. The loss of hearing impairs our ability to understand what's being

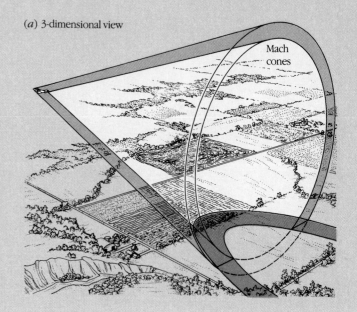

(*a*) 3-dimensional view

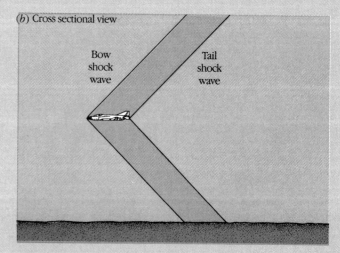

(*b*) Cross sectional view

Figure S15-4   The sonic boom is created when a jet travels faster than the speed of sound. A high-compression wave trails the jet much like the wave of a speeding power boat, but this conical wave of compression sounds like an explosion.

said. Communication with family, friends, and coworkers can be severely impaired, causing increased tension not only because the sufferer can't understand what's being said but also because deafened individuals may talk annoyingly loudly.

Because speech comprehension is so crucial, techniques have been devised to measure social impairment caused by hearing loss. The **social adequacy index** takes into account effects of hearing loss in pitch and loudness. Studies show that there can be a fairly large intensity loss without loss of social adequacy. However, a loss of frequencies—for example, the inability to hear sounds of 4000 hertz—greatly impairs social functioning. A classic study compared social adequacy in weavers, who had been exposed to a 100-dB work environment, with that in a control group of people not exposed to loud noises. Nearly three-fourths of the weavers said they had difficulties at public meetings, compared with 5% of the control group. Eighty percent of the weavers experienced difficulty talking to strangers, compared with 16% of the controls. Sixty-four percent of the weavers had difficulty understanding phone conversations, compared with 5% of the controls.

Effects of Noise on Sleep

Noise affects sleep in many ways: (1) it may prevent us from falling asleep as soon as desired, (2) it may keep us from sleeping at all, (3) it may wake us during the night, and (4) it may alter the quality of sleep, leaving us irritable.

Effects of Sonic Booms

When jet aircraft travel faster than the speed of sound, they create a sonic boom. A sonic boom is a cone-shaped wave that trails behind the jet, as shown in Figure S15-4. Residents in the flight paths of supersonic military jets and the supersonic transports operated by France, England, and the Soviet Union com-

Table S15-2 Strategies to Control Noise Pollution

Design and Planning

Minimize air turbulence created by vehicles.
Minimize vibration from vehicles, machines, and home appliances.
Build railroads and highways away from densely populated areas.
Build better-insulated subways, railroad cars, trucks, and buses.
Eliminate noisy two-stroke motorcycle engines.
Install better mufflers on motorized vehicles and equipment.
Build airports away from high-density population centers.
Restrict growth in the vicinity of existing airports.
Require low-noise home appliances, tools, and office equipment.
Pass laws to eliminate or block noise.
Control traffic flow to eliminate stop-and-start driving.

Barriers and Sound Absorbers

Build embankments along noisy streets.
Use smooth road surfaces.
Build level streets to cut down on engine noise generated on steep inclines.
Plant dense rows of trees along highways and around sources of noise.
Construct artificial noise barriers along streets and around factories.
Install better insulation in houses.
Use double- and triple-paned windows.
Add sound-absorbent materials in factories, offices, and homes.
Provide earplugs for ground personnel at airports and workers in factories and construction.

Personal Solutions

Use fewer power tools and appliances.
Time activities to minimize disturbance of others.
Use mass transit.
Refuse to buy noisy vehicles, tools, office equipment, and appliances.
Maintain vehicles to eliminate noise.
Wear ear guards when engaged in noisy activities.
Work with employer to reduce noise.

plain about interrupted sleep, rest, conversation, and radio and television reception caused by sonic booms. Studies in the United States and England show that most people are startled by sonic booms, even if they live in an area where they are common. Because there is no warning of its coming, the sonic boom invariably catches people off guard.

Sonic booms do minor damage to buildings, monuments, and other structures in a state of poor repair. Very little is known about their effects on animals.

Sonic booms are likely to become more frequent occurrences as the world's military capability expands and as population centers grow. Careful siting of military bases and regulation of population growth around bases and in flightpaths could help reduce exposure to sonic booms. Commercial supersonic transport jets designed to carry passengers and cargo have not been successful in this age of declining fossil fuel supplies, so our major exposure will continue to be from military aircraft.

Controlling Noise

Noise pollution has received little attention compared with other forms of air pollution. One reason is that hearing loss is generally progressive: victims are unaware of the gradual loss in auditory acuity. Workers who are exposed to loud noises eventually become accustomed to them, partly because their hearing declines.

Noise control can be carried out on many different levels. (Table S15-2). Changing the design of machinery and other products can cut turbulence and vibration. Better urban planning can isolate people from noisy railroads, highways, factories, and airports. Legal controls on noise emissions can also be helpful. Many countries have regulations to control noise from motorized vehicles, including Japan, Norway, the Netherlands, Sweden, Switzerland, the United Kingdom, Denmark, France, Italy, and Canada. In the United States the **Noise Control Act** (1972) authorized the EPA to establish maximum permissible noise levels for motor vehicles and other sources. Individual cities and towns have passed noise ordinances.

Noise in U.S. workplaces is controlled by the Occupational Safety and Health Administration. The workplace standard is 90 dB for an eight-hour exposure, a level many authorities believe is too high. The agency can issue abatement orders for noise violations. They require the employer to first tackle the problem through engineering and design changes in the equipment. Should these prove infeasible, ear guards must be worn by workers, or workers must be moved regularly from noisy jobs to quieter jobs to reduce their overall exposure. Personal protective equipment is a less desirable solution, because it is uncomfortable to wear and also blocks out important sounds or signals necessary for worker safety.

In May 1977 the EPA released its first comprehensive national plan for reducing noise and preventing hearing loss. It called for a reduction of the average daily exposure to no more than 65 dB in the short term and 55 dB in the long term; product labeling; cooperation from states and local agencies; federal policies to encourage noise buffer zones around transportation facilities; and the use of quieter equipment on federal construction projects. To date, however, noise control has been pushed to the back burner in favor of seemingly more pressing environmental problems like hazardous wastes.

Suggested Readings

Berland, T. (1970). *The Fight for Quiet*. Englewood Cliffs, N.J.: Prentice-Hall. Good, general introduction.

Bugliarello, G., Alexandre, A., Barnes, J., and Wakstein, C. (1976). *The Impact of Noise: A Socio-Technological Introduction*. New York: Pergamon Press. Detailed analysis.

Kryter, K. D. (1984). *Physiological, Psychological, and Social Effects of Noise*. Washington, D.C.: NASA Scientific and Technical Information. Comprehensive report on noise and its effects with an extensive list of references.

Milne, A. (1979). *Noise Pollution: Impact and Countermeasures*. New York: David and Charles. Well worth reading.

Water Pollution: Protecting Another Global Commons

It's a crime to catch a fish in some lakes, and a miracle in others.

EVAN ESAR

"If there is magic in this planet, it is in water," wrote Loren Eiseley. Covering 70% of the earth's surface and making up two-thirds or more of the weight of living organisms, water is indispensable to life. Despite its crucial role in our lives water is one of the most badly abused resources. Chapters 7 and 10 described how overexploitation of groundwater and surface water creates regional shortages that disrupt agriculture and society. Pollution of estuaries was discussed in Supplement 10-1. This chapter covers water pollutants: where they come from; how they affect living organisms; and, finally, legal, technological, and personal measures to reduce them.

Water and Water Pollution

Water pollution is any physical or chemical change in water that may adversely affect organisms. It is global in scope, but the types of pollution vary according to a country's level of development. In the poorer nations water pollution is predominantly caused by human and animal wastes, pathogenic organisms from this waste, and sediment from unsound farming and timbering practices. The rich nations also suffer from these problems, but with their more extravagant life-styles and widespread industry they create an additional assortment of potentially hazardous pollutants: heat, toxic metals, acids, pesticides, and organic chemicals.

Like air pollutants, water pollutants come from numerous natural and anthropogenic sources. Because water

(a)   *(b)*

Figure 16-1   Water pollution. (*a*) This boat dumping waste into the Cuyahoga River in Cleveland is an example of a *point source*. (*b*) Runoff from a feedlot is a *nonpoint source*.

respects no boundaries, pollutants produced in one country often end up in another's drinking or bathing water. The thoughtless dumping of wastes in rivers, unfortunate accidents, and uncontrolled growth without controls on pollution can have dire consequences for important commercial fisheries. For years the Mediterranean Sea has been viewed as an unlimited dump for domestic and industrial wastes. Extensive negotiations finally brought forth a regionwide plan that slows the increase in pollution.

Movement of pollutants from lakes and rivers to oceans is only half the problem. In recent years scientists have revealed **cross-media contamination**—that is, the movement of a pollutant from one medium to another, such as from air or land to water. Pesticides sprayed on crops can waft on the winds to nearby lakes and, from there, flow to the oceans. Toxic organics dumped in evaporating ponds ascend with the warm spring breezes, only to rain down on land and lakes. Hazardous wastes buried in the ground leak into aquifers, whose waters replenish streams. A joint committee of the U.S. National Research Council and the Royal Society of Canada announced in 1986 that levels of DDT and PCBs in the water of the Great Lakes had declined only slightly since 1978 despite tight controls on industrial emissions in both countries.

Controlling industrial releases has been quite successful in reducing emissions, they noted; however, significant levels of these and other toxic chemicals persist in the lakes because of contaminated groundwater and atmospheric pollution (see Case Study 16-1).

Controlling water pollution requires us to make special efforts to reduce or eliminate cross-media contamination. Reducing air pollution and the dumping of toxic wastes is necessary (see Chapter 18, on hazardous waste controls).

Point and Nonpoint Sources

When we ponder the sources of water pollution, we generally think of factories, power plants, and sewage treatment plants that pour tons of sometimes toxic chemicals into sewers and lakes and rivers (Figure 16-1a). These **point sources**, so named because they are in discrete locations, are relatively easy to control. But they are only half the problem. The other half is sources we rarely think about, the **nonpoint sources**—less discrete sites like farms, forests, lawns, and urban streets (Figure 16-1b). Rainwater carries oil, from driveways and streets, and pesticides and fertilizers, from urban lawns, into storm sewers and then into streams (Table 16-1). Nonpoint

Table 16-1 Major Nonpoint Pollution Sources in the U.S.

Activity	Explanation
Silviculture	Growing and harvesting trees for lumber and paper production can produce large quantities of sediment.
Agriculture	Disruption of natural vegetation leads to increased erosion; pesticide and fertilizer use, coupled with poor land management, can pollute neighboring surface water and groundwater.
Mining	Leaching from mine wastes and drainage from mines themselves can pollute surface and groundwater with metals and acids; disruption of natural vegetation accelerates sediment erosion.
Construction	Road and building construction disrupts vegetation and increases sediment erosion.
Salt use and groundwater overuse	Salt from roads and storage piles can pollute groundwater and surface water; saltwater intrusion from groundwater overdraft pollutes ground and surface water.
Drilling and waste disposal	Injection wells for waste disposal, septic tanks, hazardous waste dumps, and landfills for municipal garbage can contaminate groundwater.
Hydrological modification	Dam construction and diversion of water both can pollute surface waters.
Urban runoff	Pesticides, herbicides, and fertilizers applied to lawns and residues from roads can be washed into surface waters by rain.

sources release half the pollutants that end up in our waters. Some of the substances include dust, sediment, pesticides, asbestos, fertilizers, heavy metals, salts, oil, grease, litter, and even air pollutants washed out of the sky by rain. Because the sources are many and spread out, control has proved difficult.

Some Features of Surface Waters

This chapter is concerned primarily with pollution of surface water. Therefore, it is important to examine some features of surface waters that affect pollution. Information on groundwater can be found in Chapters 7 and 10.

Freshwater ecosystems fall into two categories. **Standing systems**, such as lakes and ponds, are usually more susceptible to pollution, because water is replaced at a slow rate. A complete replacement of a lake's water may take 10 to 100 years or more; thus, pollutants can build up to hazardous levels. **Flowing systems** include rivers and streams. Because water flows more quickly in them, they tend to purge their pollutants. However, this purging effect is useless if the supply of pollutants is constant or is spread evenly along its banks, as is common along many rivers.

As shown in Figure 16-2, lakes may consist of three zones: (1) the **littoral zone**, the shallow waters along the shore where rooted vegetation (such as cattails and arrowheads) can grow; (2) the **limnetic zone**, the open water that sunlight penetrates and where phytoplankton such as algae live; and (3) the **profundal**, or deep, zone, into which sunlight does not penetrate. The fish population in the profundal zone is denser in shallow lakes than in deep lakes.

In the warmer months lakes can also be divided into three temperature zones (Figure 16-3). The upper, warm water is called the **epilimnion**; the deeper, cold water forms the **hypolimnion**; and the transition between the two is called the **thermocline**, or **metalimnion**.

In temperate regions lakes go through an important mixing process twice a year, which allows upper and lower waters to be exchanged. In the fall the air temperature begins to drop, and the surface waters begin to cool. When the surface water reaches 4° C (39° F), it becomes cooler and heavier than the water below. The denser surface water sinks to the bottom. The thermal stratification disappears during this **fall overturn**. Winds help churn the waters.

In spring the lake turns over again. Water expands when it freezes, which is why ice floats. As ice melts it warms from 0° C; when the meltwater is at 4° C, it becomes denser than the slightly warmer water below and then sinks to the bottom, causing the **spring overturn**. Winds may again participate by churning the waters. The sea-

Figure 16-2 The three ecological zones of a lake. Note the difference between shallow entropic lakes, which tend to have high levels of plant nutrients, and deep oligotrophic lakes, which support fewer fish because they lack nutrients that stimulate plant growth.

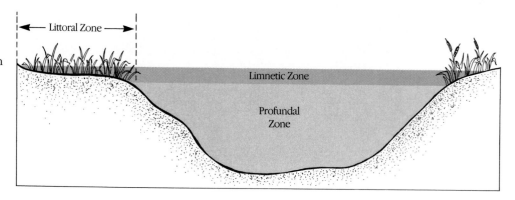

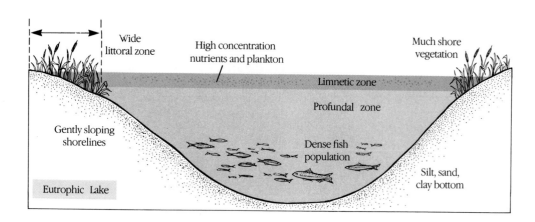

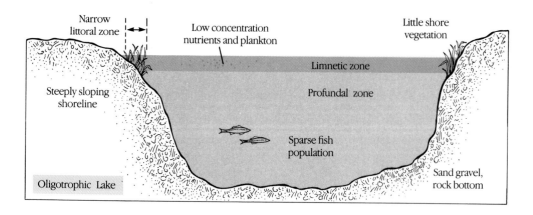

sonal turnover of lakes is important because it helps circulate oxygen from surface waters to deeper waters in the fall, which allows organisms to survive in the profundal zone. It also carries important nutrients from the lower levels of a lake to its upper levels, where they can be used by plants and algae.

With these few basics in mind, let's look more closely at water pollution.

Types of Water Pollution

Nutrient Pollution and Eutrophication

Rivers, streams, and lakes contain many organic and inorganic nutrients needed by the plants and animals that live in them. In higher-than-normal concentrations they become pollutants.

Figure 16-3 The three thermal zones of a lake.

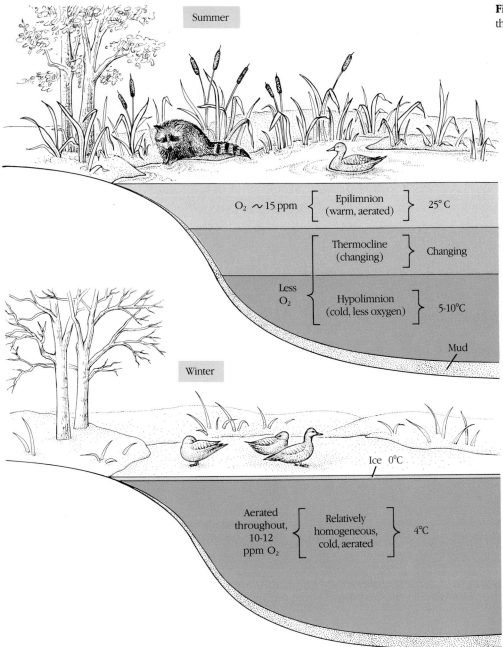

Summer

O₂ ~ 15 ppm

$O_2 \sim 15$ ppm $\left\{\begin{array}{c}\text{Epilimnion}\\(\text{warm, aerated})\end{array}\right\}$ 25° C

$\left\{\begin{array}{c}\text{Thermocline}\\(\text{changing})\end{array}\right\}$ Changing

Less O₂ $\left\{\begin{array}{c}\text{Hypolimnion}\\(\text{cold, less oxygen})\end{array}\right\}$ 5-10°C

Mud

Winter

Ice 0°C

Aerated throughout, 10-12 ppm O₂ $\left\{\begin{array}{c}\text{Relatively}\\\text{homogeneous,}\\\text{cold, aerated}\end{array}\right\}$ 4°C

Organic Nutrients Feedlots, sewage treatment plants, and some industries such as paper mills and meat-packing plants may release large quantities of organic pollutants. These substances stimulate bacterial growth. Bacteria, in turn, consume the organics, helping to purify the waters. But there's a catch. During the degradation of organic pollutants, bacteria consume dissolved oxygen (Figure 16-4). As oxygen levels drop, fish and other aquatic organisms perish. When oxygen levels become very low, **anaerobic** (non-oxygen-requiring) bacteria take over, breaking

down what's left but producing foul-smelling and toxic gases (methane and hydrogen sulfide) in the process. Oxygen depletion in rivers and streams occurs more readily in the hot summer months, because stream flow is generally lower and organic pollutant concentrations are higher. In addition, increased water temperatures speed up bacterial decay.

As the organic matter is depleted, oxygen levels return to normal. When numerous sources of organic pollutants are found along the course of a river, recovery may be

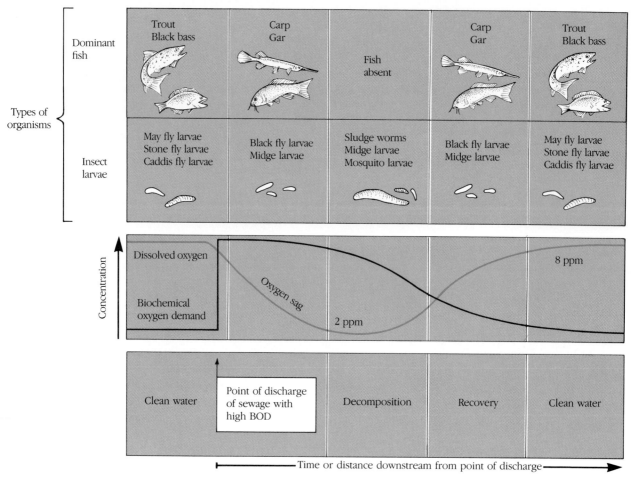

Figure 16-4 The oxygen sag curve. Oxygen levels and biochemical oxygen demand are shown below a point source of organic nutrients.

impossible. Dissolved oxygen levels are replenished by oxygen from the air and from photosynthesis in aquatic plants, but oxygen replacement is generally quite slow unless the water is turbulent. Lakes recover from organic pollutants, but usually much more slowly than rivers.

The organic nutrient concentration in streams is measured by determining the rate at which oxygen is depleted from a test sample. Polluted water is saturated with oxygen and kept in a closed bottle for five days; during this period bacteria degrade the organic matter and consume the oxygen. The amount of oxygen remaining after five days gives a measurement of the organic matter present; the more polluted a sample, the less oxygen left. This standard measurement is called the **biochemical oxygen demand**, or **BOD**.

Inorganic Plant Nutrients Whereas organic nutrients nourish bacteria, certain inorganic nutrients stimulate the growth of aquatic plants. These plant foods

include nitrogen, phosphorus, iron, sulfur, sodium, and potassium.

Nitrogen, in the form of ammonia and nitrates, and phosphorus, in the form of phosphates, are often limiting factors for populations of algae and other plants. Consequently, if levels become high, plant growth can go wild, choking lakes and rivers with thick mats of algae or dense growths of aquatic plants. In freshwater lakes and reservoirs phosphate is usually the limiting nutrient for plant growth; marine waters are usually nitrate-limited.

Excessive plant growth impairs fishing, swimming, navigation, and recreational boating. In the fall most of these plants die and are degraded by aerobic bacteria, which can deplete dissolved oxygen, killing aquatic organisms. As oxygen levels drop, anaerobic bacteria resume the breakdown and produce noxious products. Thus, inorganic nutrients ultimately create many of the same problems that organic nutrients do.

Inorganic fertilizer from croplands is the major an-

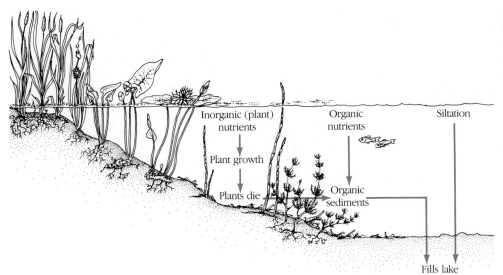

Figure 16-5 Contributions of inorganic and organic nutrients and sediment to succession of a lake into swampland and finally dry land.

thropogenic source of plant nutrients in fresh waters. When highly soluble fertilizers are used in excess, as much as 25% may be washed into streams and lakes by the rain. More careful use could greatly reduce this problem.

Laundry detergents are the second most important anthropogenic source of inorganic nutrient pollution in this country. Many detergents contain synthetic phosphates, called tripolyphosphates (TPPs). These chemicals cling to dirt particles and grease, keeping them in suspension until the wash water is flushed out of the washing machine. Unfortunately, the phosphates stimulate the growth of aquatic algae, causing sudden spurts in growth called **blooms**.

Nearly 60% of the U.S. population lives in soft-water regions where soap-based cleansing agents work as well as detergents. In the hard-water regions, harmless substitutes for TPPs can be used. For example, lime soap-dispersing agents have been used in bar soaps for years and could easily be used for laundry detergents.

Eutrophication and Natural Succession Lakes naturally pick up nutrients from surface runoff and rainfall. The amount becomes excessive and lakes suffer when watersheds are disturbed by farming or timber cutting. Major pollutant sources such as sewage treatment plants can also disturb the chemical balance in lakes.

The natural accumulation of nutrients in lakes is called **natural eutrophication**. Nutrient accumulation and natural erosion can, given sufficient time, transform lakes into swampland and then into dry land, a process called natural succession (discussed in Chapter 3). In this process inorganic nutrients stimulate plant growth; plants eventually die and contribute organic sediment to the lake's bottom (Figure 16-5). This sediment combines with silt from erosion and may gradually fill in a lake.

Accelerated erosion, caused by human activities, and **cultural eutrophication**, resulting from inorganic nutrients released from farms, feedlots, and sewage treatment plants speed up the process. Good, productive lakes become choked with vegetation that rots in the fall, depleting oxygen and giving off an offensive odor. The fate of lakes overfed with nutrients from sewage treatment plants and farms, however, is not as dim as we once believed; if nutrient inflow is greatly reduced or stopped, a lake may make a comeback. For example, Lake Washington near Seattle became a foul-smelling, eutrophic eyesore after decades during which millions of gallons of sewage was dumped into its waters. In 1968 local communities began to divert their wastes to Puget Sound, an arm of the sea with a greater capacity to assimilate the wastes. Lake Washington began a slow recovery.

Of course, the diversion of sewage to Puget Sound has had some negative consequences for that body of water. Although the open Sound can cleanse itself more easily than the lake, certain toxins in the waste may be having a harmful effect on marine life in the Sound. The effects are especially noticeable in areas where industries have discharged their wastes for decades. Discussion continues on ways to alleviate the harm done by sewage and industrial discharges in the Sound.

Eutrophication is the most widespread problem in U.S. lakes. Today, seven out of eight lakes are experiencing accelerated eutrophication. Nearly all receive wastes from industry and municipalities, but even if these sources were eliminated, only half of the lakes would improve because of continued pollution from nonpoint sources.

Infectious Agents

Water may be polluted by pathogenic (disease-causing) bacteria, viruses, and protozoans. Waterborne infectious

The Great Lakes: Alive but Not Well

The Great Lakes are among North America's most important natural resources. Carved by ancient glaciers, these five mammoth lakes hold one-fifth of the world's standing fresh water. Approximately 50 million people live within their drainage basin. The interconnected lakes flow slowly toward the St. Lawrence River and, beyond that, the ocean. Like so many of the continent's waters, they have suffered years of abuse from pollution and poor land management. Especially hard hit were the lower lakes, Ontario and Erie.

Cultural Stress: The Death of a Lake?

The story of Lake Erie serves as a reminder of the immense impact of human civilization and a lesson on ways to prevent future deterioration of the world's water bodies.

Lake Erie was once surrounded by dense forest land. Streams ran clean and free of sediment. Today, however, more than 13 million people live in the lake's watershed. The dense woodlands that once protected the soil were cut down to make room for farms, homes, industries, and roadways. As a result, large quantities of topsoil were washed into the rivers and the lake, clogging navigable channels and destroying spawning areas essential to the lake's once-rich fish life. In the early 1900s many of the swamps along the lake's shore were drained, and hundreds of small dams were constructed to provide power to mills, thus blocking the upstream migration of fish such as the walleye and sturgeon.

Before the widespread settlement of Lake Erie's shores, the water was clear most of the year. By the 1960s, however, the pristine waters had become polluted by organic and inorganic nutrients. Raw sewage floated on the water's surface, and algal blooms were common. Dissolved oxygen levels frequently dropped to dangerously low levels, especially in the profundal zone that occupies the large central basin of the lake. Blue-green algae proliferated in the warm summer months in the shallow western end of the lake, creating a foul-smelling, murky, green water. Lead, zinc, nickel, mercury, and other toxins from industry polluted harbors and built up in nearshore sediments. In 1970 and 1971 mercury levels in fish taken from Lake Erie often exceeded safe levels set by the U.S. Food and Drug Administration. Reductions in mercury discharges in 1975 brought about a sharp drop in mercury in fish, but violations of health standards continue to be reported.

In Colonial days numerous fish species inhabited the lake and its tributaries. Largemouth and smallmouth bass, muskellunge, northern pike, and channel catfish were common in the tributaries of Lake Erie. Lake herring, blue pike, lake whitefish, lake sturgeon, and others made the open waters their

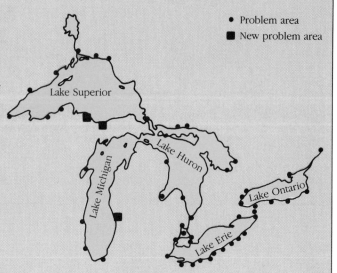

Water-quality problems in the Great Lakes.

home. By the 1940s, however, blue pike and native lake trout had vanished. Sturgeon, lake herring, whitefish, and muskellunge managed to hold on in reduced numbers.

Lake Erie suffered from severe cultural stress caused by overfishing, introduction of alien species, pollution, and destruction of shorelines and spawning grounds. Algal blooms, beach closings, thick deposits of sludge, oxygen depletion, taste and odor problems, and contaminated fish were the legacy of years of disregard and mismanagement.

By the late 1950s large areas of Lake Erie's central basin were anoxic (without oxygen) for weeks on end during the summer. Until the late 1970s anoxia spread cancerously. The lake was pronounced dead; many ecologists feared that the other lakes would follow suit.

The Joint Cleanup Program—Not Enough

In 1972, alarmed by the condition of Lake Erie and other lakes, the United States and Canada agreed to restrict pollutant discharge into the Great Lakes. The Great Lakes Water Quality Agreement, updated in 1978, called for controls of point and nonpoint pollution sources. It demanded that release into the lakes of "any or all persistent toxic substances" be "virtually eliminated." With widespread cooperation from industrial and

Case Study 16-1

municipal polluters, the lakes, among them Lake Erie, began to show signs of recovery. Lake Erie is the shallowest and fastest-flowing of the Great Lakes, which helped it to make a quick recovery from years of insult. Today the lake is teeming with fish. Gone are the raw sewage discharges that once discolored the waters. Controls on phosphorus have eliminated the massive algal blooms. The other lakes followed suit.

Despite these efforts about 50 areas still fail to meet the standards set out in the U.S.-Canadian accord (see figure). In 1986, a Buffalo-based environmental group, Great Lakes United, held hearings involving hundreds of residents, environmental activists, government officials, and water pollution experts. Their collective testimony, published in 1987, showed that while visible, smelly pollutants such as sewage have been significantly reduced, many toxic substances not visible to the naked eye continue to pour into the Lakes. For instance, PCBs and pesticides still persist at unacceptable levels. Officials administering the 1978 Agreement conceded that the U.S. and Canadian governments had not fully lived up to the terms of the Agreement.

Studies of toxic residues in fish and wildlife reaffirm that the lakes' pollution problems are far from solved. The basin acts as a huge sink for the 50 million people who live and work nearby. Toxins enter the lakes from factories and sewage treatment plants; nonpoint pollution, including farmland and urban runoff; toxic fallout, i.e. pollutants deposited from the atmosphere; and, finally, resuspension of substances contained in the bottom sediments caused, in part, when harbors and river mouths are dredged.

One of the most significant avenues is atmospheric deposition. Trace metals, pesticides, phosphorus, nitric acid, nitrates, sulfates, sulfuric acid, and organic compounds are all deposited from the air. Available data show that 60% to 90% of all PCBs entering Lakes Superior and Michigan come from the atmosphere. An estimated 14,000 metric tons of aluminum is deposited in Lake Superior from the atmosphere, and nearly 29,000 metric tons annually falls from the skies into Lake Michigan. The atmosphere is also a major source of phosphorus, providing an estimated 59% of the total input to Lake Superior.

The 1987 report released by Great Lakes United charged that the United States was not adhering to the provisions of the Clean Air Act that require control of airborne toxic pollutants. Without such controls, it will be impossible to achieve the Agreement's stated goal of no toxic discharges into the Great Lakes. Canada has come under similar criticisms.

What does all this mean? For one, commercial fishing, which was once an economic mainstay in the Great Lakes, continues to be banned in all of the lakes except for Lake Superior. Even there, the commercial fishermen operate under continual uncertainty, never knowing when their catch will exceed safe limits and be declared unsafe by the Food and Drug Administration. Second, introduced salmon and lake trout survive in the lakes, but the salmon population must be restocked each year because the fish do not reproduce successfully. Restocking costs millions of dollars a year. Third, continued pollution has forced some states to issue warnings advising women who are pregnant, lactating, or of childbearing age not to eat certain fish caught in the lakes. Parents are also advised to keep children away from lake-caught fish. This warning came after a first scientific study on chronic low-level exposure, which showed that infants of women who had eaten PCB-contaminated fish two to three times a month were smaller, more sluggish, and had weaker reflexes than infants of women who had not eaten contaminated fish. Acceptable levels for most of the 800 pollutants found in the lakes simply have not been established, primarily because of a lack of information on health effects.

On first glance the Great Lakes appear to have been brought back to life. Gone are the smelly sewage sludge and thick tangles of algae from days past. In their place, however, is a host of toxins that make the fish inedible, leaving the lake a sick patient in need of renewed efforts to cut back on nonpoint pollution and atmospheric deposition. Reducing these problems is complicated. Seven states, two provinces, numerous tribal councils, and two nations share an interest in managing the waters of the Great Lakes. The result is often conflict that holds up the important steps needed to bring the Great Lakes back to a full, productive, and healthy life.

---

diseases are a problem of immense proportions in the less developed nations of Africa, Asia, and Latin America. They were once the major water pollutants of now developed nations before sewage treatment plants and disinfection of drinking water became commonplace.

The major sources of infectious agents are (1) untreated or improperly treated sewage; (2) animal wastes in fields and feedlots beside waterways; (3) meat-packing and tanning plants that release untreated animal wastes into water; and (4) some wildlife species, which transmit

waterborne diseases. The major infectious diseases include viral hepatitis, polio (viral), typhoid fever (bacterial), amoebic dysentery (protozoan), cholera (bacterial, schistosomiasis (parasitic worm), and salmonellosis (bacterial). These diseases are especially harmful to the young, old, and already ill.

Measuring the level of each pathogenic organism would be costly and time-consuming. By measuring levels of a naturally occurring intestinal bacterium, the *coliform bacterium*, water-quality personnel can determine how much fecal contamination has occurred. The higher the coliform count, the more likely the water is to contain some pathogenic agent from fecal contamination. About one-third of our rivers now violate standards for coliform bacteria.

Toxic Organic Water Pollutants

About 10,000 synthetic organic compounds are in use today. Many of these find their way into our water, creating what may be our most important water pollution problem.

The reasons for concern over these pollutants are several: (1) Many toxic organic compounds are nonbiodegradable or are degraded slowly, so they persist in the ecosystem. (2) Some are magnified in the food web (Chapter 14). (3) Some may cause cancer in humans; others are converted into carcinogens when they react with the chlorine used to disinfect water. (4) Some kill fish and other aquatic organisms. (5) Some are nuisances, giving water and fish an offensive taste or odor.

Unfortunately, our knowledge of the effects of synthetic organics, which are often found in low concentrations, is rudimentary. Reports of diseases traceable to a single chemical are few; but many experts worry that cancer and genetic damage may result from long-term exposure.

Toxic Inorganic Water Pollutants

Inorganic water pollutants encompass a wide range of chemicals, including metals, acids, and salts. Most states report that toxic metals, such as mercury and lead, are a major water pollution problem. Metals come from industrial discharge, urban runoff, mining, sewage effluents, air pollution fallout, and some natural sources. Recent surveys of U.S. drinking water show contamination from pipes and groundwater supplies.

Mercury   One of the more common and potentially most harmful toxic metals is mercury. In the 1950s mercury was thought to be an innocuous water pollutant, although it was known to have been hazardous to miners and to nineteenth-century hat makers, who frequently developed tremors, or "hatter's shakes," and lost hair and teeth.

In the 1950s an outbreak of mercury poisonings in Japan raised awareness of the hazard. Residents who ate seafood from Minamata Bay, which was contaminated with methyl mercury, developed numbness of the limbs, lips, and tongue. Muscle control was lost. Deafness, blurring of vision, clumsiness, apathy, and mental derangement also occurred. Of 52 reported cases, 17 people died and 23 were permanently disabled.

Mercury is a by-product of manufacturing the plastic vinyl chloride. It is also emitted in aqueous wastes of the chemical industry and incinerators, power plants, laboratories, and even hospitals. Worldwide, about 10,000 metric tons of mercury is released into the air and water each year. In 1980 over two-thirds of water samples in the United States exceeded the national standard for safe drinking water.

In streams and lakes inorganic mercury is converted by bacteria into two organic forms. One of these, dimethyl mercury, evaporates quickly from the water. But the other, methyl mercury, remains in the bottom sediments and is slowly released into the water, where it enters organisms in the food chain and is biologically magnified.

Nitrates and Nitrites   Nitrates and nitrites are common inorganic pollutants of water. **Nitrates** come from septic tanks, barnyards, heavily fertilized crops, and sewage treatment plants; they are converted to toxic **nitrites** in the intestines of humans.

Nitrites combine with the hemoglobin in red blood corpuscles and form methemoglobin, which has a reduced oxygen-carrying capacity. Nitrites can be fatal to infants. Over 2000 cases of infant nitrite poisoning, about 160 of which resulted in death, have been reported in Europe and North America in the last 40 years. Most poisonings occurred in rural areas, where drinking water is contaminated by septic tanks and farmyards.

Salts   Sodium chloride and calcium chloride are used on winter roads to melt snow. Melting snow carries these salts into streams and groundwater. Salts kill sensitive plants, such as the sugar maple. In surface waters they may kill salt-intolerant organisms, allowing salt-tolerant species to thrive. However, the fluctuations in the flow of salt lead to varying concentrations, so that neither salt-tolerant species that thrive in high salt concentrations nor salt-intolerant organisms can survive.

Chlorine   Chlorine is a highly reactive inorganic chemical commonly used (1) to kill bacteria in drinking water, (2) to destroy potentially harmful organisms in treated wastewater released from sewage treatment plants into streams, and (3) to kill algae, bacteria, fungi, and other organisms that grow inside and clog the pipes of the cooling systems of power plants. Chlorine and some of the products it forms in water are highly toxic to fish and other organisms.

Chlorine reacts with organic compounds to form chlorinated organics. These chemicals may show up in drinking water downstream from sewage treatment plants and other sources. Many of them are known carcinogens and teratogens. However, medical studies indicate that the rates of certain cancers (liver, intestinal tract) are only slightly elevated in populations consuming water contaminated by these compounds.

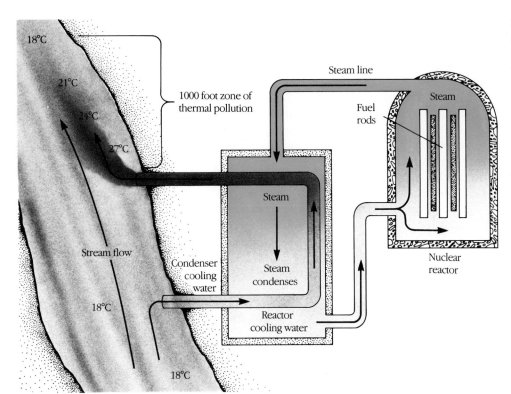

Figure 16-6 The cooling system of an electric power plant and its effects on surface waters and organisms.

Labels on figure: 18°C, 21°C, 24°C, 27°C, 1000 foot zone of thermal pollution, Steam line, Steam, Fuel rods, Steam, Steam condenses, Stream flow, Condenser cooling water, 18°C, Reactor cooling water, Nuclear reactor, 18°C, 18°C

Sediment

Sediment, the leading water pollutant in the United States in terms of volume, is a by-product of timber cutting (Chapter 9), agriculture, (Chapter 7), mining (Chapters 11–13), and construction of roads and buildings. Agriculture increases erosion rates four to eight times above normal. Poor construction and mining may increase the rate of erosion by 10 to 200 times. Sediment destroys spawning and feeding grounds for fish, reduces fish and shellfish populations, smothers eggs and fry, fills in lakes and streams, and decreases light penetration, which destroys aquatic plants.

The deposition of sediment in lakes speeds up natural succession. The filling in of streambeds, or **streambed aggradation**, results in a gradual widening of the channel, and as streams become wider, they become shallower. Water temperature may rise, lowering the amount of dissolved oxygen and making streams more vulnerable to organic pollutants that deplete oxygen. Streambed aggradation also makes streams more susceptible to flooding. Sediment can fill shipping channels, which must then be dredged. Hydroelectric equipment may be worn out by sediments. Finally, some pollutants—such as pesticides, nitrates, phosphates from agricultural fertilizers, and pathogenic organisms—bind to sediment. This extends their lifetime and impacts.

Sediment pollution can be checked, and even eliminated, by good land management (described in Chapters 7 and 9).

Thermal Pollution

Rapid or even gradual changes in water temperature can disrupt aquatic ecosystems. Industries frequently bring about such change by using water to cool various industrial processes. The U.S. electric power industry is a major contributor (Figure 16-6). It uses about 75% of all cooling water in the United States, or about 9 billion liters (2.4 billion gallons) per day. Steel mills, oil refineries, and paper mills also use large amounts of water for cooling.

Small amounts of heat have no serious effect on the aquatic ecosystem; but large quantities can kill heat-intolerant plants and animals outright, disrupting the web of life dependent on the aquatic food chain. Elimination of heat-intolerant species may allow heat-tolerant species to take over. These are usually less desirable species.

Thermal pollution lowers the dissolved oxygen content of water, at the same time increasing the metabolic rate of aquatic organisms. Since metabolism requires oxygen, some species may be eliminated entirely if the water temperature rises 10° C (18° F). At the Savannah River nuclear power plant the number of rooted plant species and turtles was at least 75% lower in ponds receiving hot water than in ponds at normal temperature. The number of fish species was reduced by one-third.

Sharp changes in water temperature cause **thermal shock**, a sudden death of fish and other organisms that cannot escape. Thermal shock is frequently experienced when power plants begin operation or when they temporarily shut down for repair. The latter can devastate heat-tolerant species that inhabit artificially warmed waters. Aquatic life cannot adapt to sudden, unpredictable temperature changes.

Fish spawn and migrate in response to changes in water temperature, so heated water may interfere with these processes. Water temperature influences survival and early development of aquatic organisms. For instance, trout eggs may not hatch if water is too warm. Thermal pollution can also increase the susceptibility of aquatic organisms to parasites, certain toxins, and pathogens.

Thermal pollution can be controlled by constructing ponds for collecting and cooling water before its release into nearby lakes and streams. Cooling towers are another way to dissipate heat (see Figure 10-12).

Groundwater Pollution

Aquifers supply drinking water for 117 million Americans. That water, scientists are now reporting, is increasingly threatened by pollution. In fact, many pollutants are present at much higher concentrations in groundwater than they are in most contaminated surface supplies. And many contaminants are tasteless and odorless at concentrations thought to threaten human health.

About 4500 billion liters (1185 billion gallons) of contaminated water seeps into the ground in the United States every day from septic tanks, cesspools, oil wells, landfills, agriculture, and ponds holding hazardous wastes. Unfortunately, very little is known about the extent of groundwater contamination. Some experts believe that groundwater pollution is a minor problem. They estimate that 1% to 2% of U.S. groundwater is polluted. However, an EPA study completed in 1981 showed groundwater contamination in 28% of 954 cities with populations over 10,000. By more recent estimates, at least 8000 private, public, and industrial wells are contaminated.

Thousands of chemicals, many of them potentially harmful to health, turn up in water samples from polluted wells. The most common chemical pollutants are chlorides, nitrates, heavy metals, and various toxic organics like pesticides and degreasing agents. The low-molecular-weight organic compounds are particularly worrisome, since many of them are carcinogenic. Concern among medical experts is great because some fear that there is no threshold level for these compounds—that is, there is no level free from risk of cancer or other problems. Others fear that many chemicals may act synergistically, turning a potentially difficult problem into a health nightmare (Chapter 14). Beverly Paigen, a researcher in Oakland, California, who is renowned for her studies at Love Canal, in Niagara Falls, New York, recently released a summary of health studies of Americans exposed to groundwater pollutants. The most common problems include miscarriage, low birth weight, birth defects, and premature infant death. Adults and children suffer skin rashes, eye irritation, and a whole host of neurological problems, including dizziness, headaches, seizures, and fainting spells. In a now widely publicized case in San Jose, California, pollutants from a leaky underground storage tank owned by the Fairchild Camera and Instrument Company are thought to have doubled the rate of miscarriage in pregnant women and tripled the rate of heart defects in newborns. In Woburn, Massachusetts, contaminated groundwater is blamed for a doubling in the childhood leukemia rate.

Many people think of groundwater as fast-flowing underground rivers. Nothing could be further from the truth. Groundwater typically moves from 5 centimeters (2 inches) to 64 centimeters (2 feet) a day. Since groundwater moves so slowly, it may take years for water polluted in one location to appear in another. Additionally, once an aquifer is contaminated, it may take several hundred years for it to cleanse itself.

Detecting groundwater pollution is expensive and time-consuming. Numerous test wells must be drilled to sample water and determine the rate and direction of flow. Despite intensive drilling health officials can easily miss a tiny stream of pollutants that flows through one portion of a large aquifer. For example, liquids that do not readily mix with water may travel along the top or bottom of the aquifer in thin layers, which are difficult to detect.

Groundwater supplies one-fourth of the annual water demand in the United States, and use has been growing at a rate of about 5.6% per year. Preventing groundwater pollution is generally the cheapest way to protect this vital resource. Cutting down the production of hazardous wastes would be an important first step. Improvements in the ways we dispose of wastes would also help. Ways to achieve this goal are discussed in Chapter 18.

To reclaim polluted aquifers it may be necessary to pump contaminated water to the surface, purify it, and then return it to the aquifer (Figure 16-7). In June 1983 the Aerojet Corporation of Sacramento, California, began withdrawing 6.4 million liters (1.7 million gallons) of water a day from aquifers it had contaminated with several toxic chemicals. Projects like this invariably cost millions of dollars more than prevention, but they are needed to save important groundwater supplies.

Ocean Pollution

"When we go down to the low-tide line," Rachel Carson wrote, "we enter a world that is as old as the earth itself—the primeval meeting place of the elements of earth and water, a place of compromise and conflict and eternal

Figure 16-7 Air Stripper at a site in Massachusetts (like the one in Elkhart, Indiana) removes dissolved volatile organic compounds from water. Although the removal rate depends on the contaminant, most Air Strippers remove 98% of the contaminants.

change." Today the compromise, conflict, and eternal change have taken on a new meaning as humankind forges out into the oceans in search of food, fuel, and minerals. But even the Kansas farmer and Minnesota factory have an impact on this vast body, containing more than 1.3 billion cubic kilometers of water, for inland pollutants slowly make their way to the ocean.

The hazards of pollution in the biologically rich coastal zones were discussed in Chapter 10. This section deals with two problems: oil and plastic pollution.

Oil in the Seas

About 3.2 million metric tons of oil enters the world's seas every year. About half of the oil that contaminates the ocean comes from natural seepage from offshore deposits. One-fifth comes from well blowouts, breaks in pipelines, and tanker spills (Figure 16-8). The rest, quite surprisingly, comes from oil disposed of inland and carried to the ocean in rivers.

Leakage from offshore wells occurs during the transfer of oil to shore and also during normal operations. Contamination from this source has not captured the public attention, even though its effect on marine life and birds can be quite significant. What captures the headlines are the large spills—well blowouts or wrecked tankers that spill out tons of black, viscous oil. From 1973 to 1984 there were 125,000 spills of various sizes in U.S. waters, an average of 10,400 incidents per year.

Figure 16-8 The anatomy of an oil spill from an improperly drilled hole.

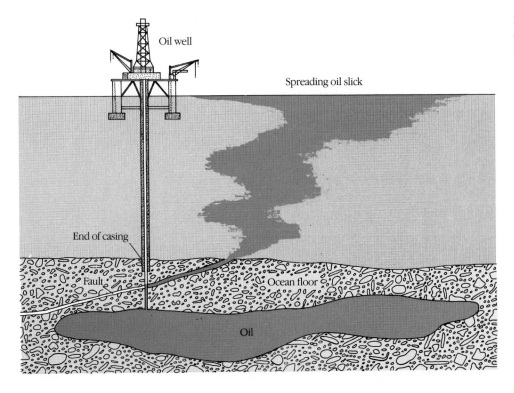

Figure 16-9 This bird is beyond the help of volunteers, who, after a 1981 oil spill in San Francisco, attempted to save the oil-covered animals.

The harmful effects of oil spills are many. Oil kills plants and animals in the estuarine zone. Especially hard hit are the barnacles, mussels, crabs, and rock weed (a type of algae). After a major spill it may take two to ten years for aquatic life to recover. Oil settles on beaches and kills organisms that live there. It also settles to the ocean floor and kills benthic (bottom-dwelling) organisms such as crabs. Those that survive may accumulate oil in their tissue, making them inedible. Oil poisons algae and may disrupt major food chains and decrease the yield of edible fish. It also coats birds, impairing flight or reducing the insulative property of feathers, thus making the birds more vulnerable to the cold (Figure 16-9).

About 25% of the crude oil in a spill is volatile and evaporates within three months. Other compounds, relatively nonvolatile but lighter than water, float on the surface, where they are broken down by bacteria over the next few months. Nearly 60% of the oil spill is destroyed in this way. The remaining 15% consists of heavier compounds that stick together and sink to the bottom in huge globs. In cold polar waters oil decomposes very slowly. In some cases it may become incorporated in sea ice and be released for years afterward.

The amount of damage caused by oil pollution depends partly on the direction in which it is carried by the wind and ocean currents. If slicks reach land, they damage beaches and shorelines, recreational areas, and marine organisms. Oil may be driven over portions of the continental shelf, a highly productive marine zone, and there it can poison clams, scallops, flounder, haddock, and other important food species. Oil driven out to sea has

fewer environmental consequences, because there is little life in the deep ocean.

Oil pollution of the oceans poses less of a threat to the overall marine environment than was once feared, a National Research Council committee has concluded. However, oil can have serious local effects, the group noted. And these can persist for decades. But overall, the marine environment has not suffered irrevocable damage from oil. The committee was quick to point out that marine scientists have only limited knowledge about the potential damage of oil in tropical and arctic regions, where much of the current oil development is occurring.

Thanks to public outcry and stricter controls, the number of oil spills began to fall after 1980 and has remained relatively stable in recent years. Tougher governmental standards for new oil tankers went into effect in 1979. New safety standards for older tankers were phased in between 1981 and 1985. Dual radar systems, backup steering controls, collision avoidance aids, and improved inspection and certification were instrumental in reducing spills. Under the new regulations crude oil must be cleaned to eliminate sludge buildup in tanks. This sludge was once rinsed out at sea. New regulations also require tankers to have separate ballast tanks. These tanks are filled with salt water to help ships keep their balance when returning after discharging their cargo. In older ships emptied oil tanks were filled with water for ballast. When the ship arrived at port, the oil-contaminated water was dumped into the sea. The serious effects of oil washing and segregated ballast must not be underestimated. About 1.3 million metric tons of oil was released each year during tank purging and ballast tank discharge, or over six times the amount released by tanker spills.

Although the number of oil spills has decreased, the quantity of oil released fluctuates wildly. In 1984, for example, approximately twice as much oil was released as in 1983 in about the same number of spills. Much room for improvement remains.

Plastic Pollution

A young seal swims playfully in the coastal waters of San Diego Bay. Floating in its watery domain is a piece of a plastic fishing net that has drifted with the currents for months. The seal swims around and around curiously, checking out its new plaything, and then plunges through an opening in the net only to be entrapped.

At first the net is just a mild nuisance, but as the seal grows, the filament begins to tighten around its neck. Eventually, it cuts into the seal's skin, leaving an open ring of raw flesh exposed to bacteria. Unless it is helped, the seal will perish along with an estimated 100,000 other sea mammals each year that tangle with the 160,000 metric tons of plastics discarded into the ocean annually by

American fishermen and sailors. Tens of thousands of tons may also come from private boats and factories.

According to some estimates, a million seabirds die each year from plastics. No one knows the number of fish that perish from this growing problem, caused by the careless discarding of nylon fishing nets, plastic bags, six-pack yokes, plastic straps, and a myriad of other objects made from nonbiodegradable plastic.

Plastic nets entangle fish, birds, and sea mammals. They may strangle, starve to death, or drown their victims. Plastic bags, looking like jellyfish, are eaten by sea turtles. One scientist pulled enough plastic out of a leatherback turtle's stomach to make a ball several feet in diameter. Starvation generally results, because the animal's stomach is packed with undigestible plastic that cannot pass through its digestive tract. Birds and fish gobble plastic beads resembling the tiny crustaceans that are a normal part of the food chain. They may become poisoned and die. Discarded plastic eating utensils, when swallowed, may cut into an animal's stomach lining, causing it to bleed to death.

Scientists throughout the world have recently begun to study the impact of plastic on ocean life. With the first round of results already in, they are calling for stiff measures to stop sailors from discarding plastic overboard. Biodegradable plastic containers have been strongly advised, as have educational programs to increase public awareness of the problem. Mandatory recycling of plastics would certainly help. So would tighter controls on the outflows of factories that produce plastics.

Already, growing awareness has created a groundswell of activity. The Oregon Fish and Wildlife Department has organized annual beach cleanups to remove plastic. In 1985 they netted 22 metric tons of plastic garbage. Italy recently placed a ban on all nonbiodegradable plastics, which becomes effective in 1991. Oregon and Alaska have passed laws requiring that all six-pack yokes be biodegradable.

Despite these steps millions of fish, birds, and sea mammals will perish in coming years. Without stricter controls, biodegradable plastic, and widespread public cooperation, rising use of plastic will bring the unnecessary death of innumerable sea creatures.

Water Pollution Control

Legal Controls

Most efforts to reduce water pollution in the United States and abroad have been aimed at point sources. Building sewage treatment plants to handle municipal wastes and reducing waste discharges by industry have been the key strategies of the U.S. **Clean Water Act** (Table 16-2). Since 1981, 10,000 sewage treatment plants have been con-

---

Table 16-2   Major Provisions of the U.S. Clean Water Act

Planning

The states receive planning grants from the EPA to review their water pollution problems and to determine ways to solve them by reducing or eliminating point and nonpoint water pollutants.

Standards development

The states adopt water quality standards for their streams. These standards define a use for each stream and prescribe the water quality needed to achieve that use.

Effluent standards

The EPA develops limits on how much pollution may be released by industries and municipalities. These limits are developed at the national level based on engineering and economic judgments. The EPA or the states are required to make the discharge limits for individual plants more stringent if necessary to meet the state water quality standards.

Grants and loans

The EPA provides financial assistance to state water programs for the construction of sewage treatment plants, permit applications, water quality monitoring, and enforcement. Federal grants for treatment facilities will be phased out by 1990.

Dredge and fill program

The EPA develops environmental guidelines to protect wetlands from dredge and fill activities. These guidelines are used to assess whether permits should be issued.

Permits and enforcement

All industries and municipal dischargers receive permits from either the EPA or the states. The EPA and the states regularly inspect these dischargers to determine whether they are in compliance with the permit and take appropriate enforcement actions if necessary.

Source: U.S. Environmental Protection Agency.

---

structed (Figure 16-10). In 1987, a program of Federal assistance to the states for construction of these plants was reauthorized in an amendment to the Clean Water Act, providing a total of $9.6 billion in grants through 1990. From 1991 until 1994, states will be able to get loans only for treatment facility construction. After 1994, all Federal loans for this purpose will stop.

Unfortunately, in many cases nonpoint pollution from expanding cities offsets the gains of sewage treatment plants. Thus, water quality has not improved or has improved only slightly in many areas experiencing rapid growth. Many experts argue that tighter controls are

Figure 16-10 A vast sewage treatment plant in Des Moines, Iowa.

needed to clean up the nation's waters. The 1987 amendment to the Clean Water Act addressed this necessity. Under a major provision of the amendment, states are required within 18 months to identify the problem areas and nonpoint sources in question. The states must also draft a management program, outlining the ways in which they will implement needed controls on nonpoint sources. On the basis of the reports and programs, the EPA will distribute $400 million over four years to the states' programs. Critics point out that this amount of funding will hardly put a dent in nonpoint pollution. Some local governments have already taken the initiative, however, through zoning ordinances to reduce agricultural and urban runoff. Local soil conservation districts identify trouble spots and work with farmers. Much work is needed in the years ahead.

New laws at all levels of government can help reduce pollution. Laws requiring terracing of steep roadbanks, revegetation of denuded land, use of mulches to hold soil in place while grasses are growing on newly constructed highways and housing sites, sediment ponds to collect runoff before it can reach streams, and porous pavements that soak up rainwater could help.

Some experts believe that a groundwater pollution control act is needed, although various provisions of the hazardous waste laws already address much of the problem (Chapter 18). In recent years the EPA has begun to establish standards for acceptable levels of 22 groundwater contaminants. In 1984 it issued a formal groundwater protection plan that, among many things, establishes an Office of Groundwater Protection. It also describes how the EPA will provide technical assistance in analyzing problems and advice needed by states to

establish water-protection programs. The states are expected to play the chief role in groundwater protection, a point with which many critics take issue, mainly because states often lack funds, experience, and expertise. By EPA estimates 32 states have already adopted their own groundwater standards. Some have taken preventive measures by mapping out aquifers and banning industrial development over them.

In 1986 Congress toughened the U.S. drinking water law by adding regulations that protect groundwater. Congress also recently passed legislation that requires the EPA to set standards of drinking water quality for 85 additional chemical substances, including pesticides and various industrial chemicals. The new law requires drinking water suppliers to test for these chemicals and maintain the drinking water standards. It also requires them to monitor drinking water supplies for other substances that might pose a threat to human health.

Control Technologies

The first sewage treatment plant in the United States was built in Memphis, Tennessee, in 1880; today, there are over 13,000 of them (Figure 16-10). Sewage entering a treatment plant contains pollutants from homes, hospitals, schools, and industries. It contains human wastes, paper, soap, detergent, dirt, cloth, food residues, microorganisms, and a variety of household chemicals. In some cases water from storm drainage systems is mixed with municipal wastes to save the cost of building separate systems for each, which can be exorbitant. Combined systems generally work well, but during storms inflow may exceed plant capacity. Consequently, some untreated storm runoff

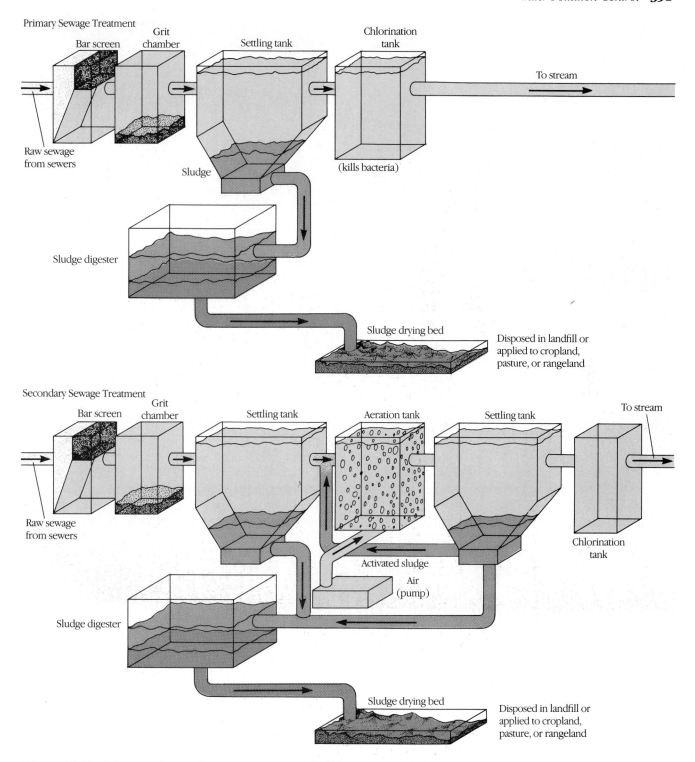

Figure 16-11 Primary and secondary sewage treatment facilities.

and sewage passes directly into waterways, raising the coliform count in downstream waters and rendering them unfit for swimming.

Sewage treatment can take place in three stages: primary, secondary, and tertiary. **Primary treatment** physi-

cally removes large objects by first passing the sewage through a series of grates and screens. Sand, dirt, and other solids settle out in grit chambers (Figure 16-11a). The solid organic matter, or sludge, settles out in a settling tank.

Figure 16-12 Trickling filter. A detritus food chain consisting of bacteria and other microorganisms in the rock or bark bed of the system consumes organic matter, nitrates, and phosphates in the liquid sewage.

Table 16-3 Removal of Pollutants by Sewage Treatment Plants

	Percentage Removed by Treatment	
Substance	Primary	Primary and Secondary
Solids	60%	90%
Organic wastes	30	90
Phosphorus		30
Nitrate		50
Salts		5
Radioisotopes		0
Pesticides		0

Secondary Treatment The secondary stage destroys biodegradable organic matter through biological decay (Figure 16-11b). Sludge from primary treatment enters a large tank, where bacteria and other organisms decompose the agitated waste. Another common way is to pass the liquid sludge through a **trickling filter** (Figure 16-12). Here, long pipes rotate slowly over a bed of stones (and sometimes bark), dripping wastes on an artificial detritus food chain consisting of bacteria, protozoa, fungi, snails, worms, and insects. The bacteria and fungi consume the organics and, in turn, are consumed by protozoans. Snails and insects feed on the protozoans. Some inorganic nutrients are also removed. This step is followed by a secondary settling basin or clarifier to remove residual organic matter.

In most municipalities liquid remaining after secondary treatment is chlorinated to kill potentially pathogenic bacteria and protozoans and is then released into receiving streams, lakes, or bays. The efficiency of primary and secondary treatment is shown in Table 16-3.

Tertiary Treatment Many methods exist for removing the chemicals that remain after secondary treatment. Most of these **tertiary treatments** are costly and therefore are rarely used unless water is being released into bodies of water that require a high level of purity. Fortunately, some cheaper options are gaining recognition. For example, effluents can be transferred to holding ponds after secondary treatment. Algae and water hyacinths growing in the water consume the remaining nitrates and phos-

phates. Certain aquatic plants such as duckweed absorb dissolved organic materials directly from the water.

Aquatic plants grown in sewage ponds can be harvested and converted into food for humans or livestock. In Burma, Laos, and Thailand duckweed has been consumed by farmers for years. The protein yield of a duckweed pond is six times greater than that of an equivalent field of soybeans. One of the problems with this approach, however, is that water hyacinths and duckweeds also absorb toxic metals from the water. Therefore, consumption by humans and livestock must be carefully monitored.

Another suggestion is the age-old process of **land disposal**. In ancient times land disposal of human sewage was commonplace; it is still practiced in many developing nations, such as China and India. As the populations of developing countries grew and became more urbanized, this natural method of recycling wastes was gradually eliminated. Land disposal, discussed in Chapter 10 as a means of recharging groundwater, uses the surface vegetation, soil, and soil microorganisms as a natural filter for many potentially harmful chemicals. Sewage can be piped to pastures, fields, and forests (Figure 16-13). Organic matter in the effluent enriches the soil and improves its ability to retain water. Nitrates and phosphates are taken up by plants. The water supports plant growth and helps recharge aquifers. Crops nourished by effluents from treated sewage show a remarkable increase in yield.

Land disposal of sludge from sewage treatment plants has some problems. First, treated sewage may contain harmful bacteria, protozoans, and viruses that could adhere to plants consumed by humans or livestock or become airborne after the effluent dries. To get around this problem the Swiss and West Germans heat their sludge to destroy such organisms before applying it to pastures and cropland. Alternatively, sewage sludge can be decayed in compost piles before application. The heat

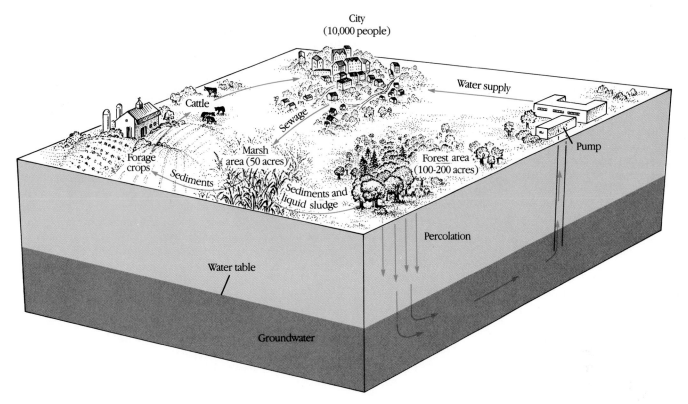

Figure 16-13 Land disposal of sewage helps fertilize farmlands and forests, reduce surface water pollution, and replenish groundwater supplies.

given off during composing kills virtually all of the viruses, bacteria, and parasite eggs.

The second problem is that toxic metals found in some sewage may accumulate in soils and be taken up by plants and livestock. Metal-contaminated sewage usually comes from industries. By removing metals from their waste stream, an option called pretreatment, industries can eliminate the problem. Third, transporting sludge to fields increases the cost of sewage treatment, limiting some of the incentive to use this method. Experts are quick to point out, however, that land disposal is ten times cheaper than building and operating a tertiary treatment plant.

Scientists at the University of Maryland recently developed an unusual way to put sludge to good use. By combining it with clay and slate they formed odorless "biobricks," which look like ordinary bricks. Washington's Suburban Sanitary Commission recently put the idea to the test by building a 750-square-meter (8,300-square-foot) maintenance building in Maryland with 20,000 biobricks. If successful, biobricks could help reduce land distur-

bance from mining materials for brick making and could help cut sewage disposal costs and environmental contamination.

Personal Solutions

Personal efforts can improve our waterways. Limiting family size and reducing the consumption of unnecessary goods can help cut down on water pollutants. Reducing the use of goods eliminates hazardous waste that sometimes seeps into our waterways. Another effective way to cut your personal contribution is to install a composting toilet. The composted wastes can be added safely to gardens, eliminating the need for synthetic fertilizer. When you become a homeowner, restrict your use of synthetic fertilizers, insecticides, herbicides, bleaches, detergents, disinfectants, and other household chemicals. Select low-phosphate or no-phosphate detergents for washing your clothes. You may also contact local and federal officials in support of further cleanup efforts.

It is astonishing with how little wisdom mankind can be governed, when that little wisdom is its own.

W. R. INGE

Summary

Water pollutants come from **nonpoint** and **point** sources. The effects on aquatic systems depend, in large part, on whether polluted waters are standing or flowing. Standing systems (lakes and ponds) are generally more susceptible because of slow turnover.

The major water pollutants are organic nutrients, infectious agents, toxic organics, toxic inorganics, sediment, and heat. **Organic nutrients** come from feedlots, municipal sewage treatment plants, and industry. They serve as foodstuffs for aerobic bacteria and cause proliferation of natural populations of aquatic bacteria. Bacterial decomposition of these materials results in a drop in dissolved oxygen, with dire effects on other oxygen-requiring organisms.

Two **inorganic plant nutrients**, nitrogen and phosphorus, are also major anthropogenic pollutants. Inorganic fertilizer and laundry detergents are the leading sources in the United States. Both cause excessive plant growth and clogging of navigable waterways. Bacterial decay of plants in the fall results in a drop in dissolved oxygen, which may suffocate fish and other organisms.

Water may contain pathogenic bacteria, viruses, protozoans, and parasites. Waterborne infectious diseases are a problem in developing nations. Untreated or improperly treated sewage, animal wastes, meat-packing wastes, and some wild species are the major sources. While uncommon in the United States and other developed countries, infectious agents are not altogether absent.

Toxic organic pollutants include a large number of chemicals, many of which are nonbiodegradable or only slowly degraded, biologically magnified, and carcinogenic in humans.

Toxic inorganic pollutants include a wide range of chemicals such as metals and salts from an array of sources. Most states report that toxic metals, such as mercury and lead, are major pollutants. Mercury can be converted into methyl and dimethyl mercury by aerobic bacteria. These forms are more toxic than inorganic mercury. Methyl mercury is biologically magnified in the food chain.

Nitrates and nitrites are common inorganic water pollutants coming from septic tanks, barnyards, heavily fertilized crops, and sewage treatment plants. They are converted to nitrites in the intestines of humans. In the blood they combine with hemoglobin, reducing its oxygen-carrying capacity. At high levels they may be fatal to children under 3.

Salts used on roadways to melt snow and ice enter streams and lakes and can upset the ecological balance. Salt-sensitive trees along salted roads may also be killed as the salt water percolates down to the roots. Chlorine is used to kill bacteria in drinking water and treated sewage and to kill organisms that might clog pipes used to cool water in power plants and industry. Chlorine and chlorine by-products can severely affect aquatic organisms.

Sediment, the leading water pollutant in the United States, is a by-product of timber cutting, agriculture, ranching, mining, and construction of roads and buildings. Sediment destroys spawning and feeding grounds for fish, reduces fish and shellfish populations, destroys deep pools used for resting, smothers eggs and fry, fills in lakes and streams, and decreases light penetration, which may kill aquatic plants.

Thermal pollution refers to the heating or cooling of water, both of which drastically alter biota in a body of water. Large quantities of heat can kill heat-sensitive organisms and harm organisms dependent on the aquatic ecosystem. Heat lowers the dissolved oxygen levels but increases the metabolic rate of organisms. Sudden changes in temperature bring about rapid death by **thermal shock**. Temperature changes can also interfere with migrations, spawning, and early development.

The concentration of many pollutants in groundwater is often higher than that in most contaminated surface water supplies. Many of these chemicals are tasteless and odorless at concentrations believed to pose a threat to human health. The major groundwater pollutants are chlorides, nitrates, heavy metals, and organics. Since groundwater usually moves slowly through an aquifer, it may take years for pollution to show up in nearby locations. Additionally, once an aquifer is contaminated, the pollutants may remain for centuries.

Oil pollution is another major problem. About half of the oil that contaminates the ocean comes from human sources—oil-well blowouts, tanker spills, and inland disposal of oil. Oil harms many organisms, especially if a spill occurs near an estuarine zone. After a spill it may take two to ten years for aquatic life to recover. Thanks to public outcry and stricter controls, the number of oil spills has decreased sharply.

Most control efforts in the United States and abroad have sought to reduce point-source pollution. Sewage treatment plants and limitations on factory discharges have been key strategies of the U.S. **Clean Water Act**. Sewage treatment can take place in three stages. **Primary treatment** removes large objects by passing the sewage through a series of grates and screens. Solid organic matter, or sludge, settles out in a primary settling tank. **Secondary treatment** removes biodegradable organic material and some inorganic substances. Sludge may be decomposed by bacteria in large aerated tanks or may be passed through a trickling filter, where it is dripped over a bed of rocks or bark housing a detritus food chain. In most municipalities liquid remaining after secondary treatment is chlorinated to kill potentially pathogenic organisms and released into receiving streams. Many methods exist for **tertiary treatment**, the final cleanup stage, but most are expensive and therefore rarely used. Fortunately, there are some cheaper options, such as algae and water hyacinth ponds and land disposal.

Progress in cleaning up U.S. waters has been slow. Continued population growth, industrial growth, and agricultural expansion have negated many gains. Nonpoint sources often offset gains at point sources, making it imperative that further controls be directed at them.

Discussion Questions

1. List the major types of water pollutants found in developing and developed nations.

2. Define the terms *point source* and *nonpoint source*. Give some examples of each, and explain why nonpoint sources of water pollution are often more difficult to control than point sources.

3. What are the three major ecological zones of a lake. Describe each one.

4. Explain why a lake "turns over" in the spring and fall and how this natural turnover benefits aquatic organisms.

5. Describe where organic nutrients come from, what effects they have on aquatic ecosystems, and how they can be controlled.

6. What are the inorganic plant nutrients, and how do they affect the aquatic environment?

7. Define the term *eutrophication*. Describe how inorganic and organic nutrients accelerate natural succession of a lake.

8. What are the major sources of infectious agents in polluted water? How can they be controlled?

9. What dangers do synthetic organic water pollutants pose?

10. What are some of the major inorganic water pollutants? How do they affect the aquatic environment and human populations?

11. Why is chlorine used in the treatment of human sewage and drinking water? What dangers does its use pose? How would you determine if the risks of chlorine use outweigh the benefits?

12. What are the major sources of sediment, and how can they be controlled? What are the costs and benefits of sediment control?

13. Describe ways to eliminate or reduce thermal pollution.

14. If you were going to survey your state for groundwater pollution, how would you go about locating sources and taking samples of groundwater?

15. What are the major sources of groundwater pollution? What factors determine whether a toxic waste disposal site or some other source will pollute groundwater? How can groundwater pollution be reduced or eliminated? What can you do?

16. Discuss the sources of oil in the ocean and ways to reduce oil contamination.

17. Even though thousands of new wastewater treatment plants have been constructed in the United States, water quality in many areas has not improved. Why?

18. Describe primary and secondary wastewater treatment. What happens at each stage, and what pollutants are removed?

19. Debate the pros and cons of land disposal of wastewater.

Suggested Readings

Belton, T., Roundy, R., and Weinstein, N. (1986). Urban Fisherman: Managing the Risk of Toxic Exposure. *Environment* 28 (9): 18–20, 30–37. Detailed look at ways to communicate the risk to the public.

Bowker, M. (1986). Caught in a Plastic Trap. *International Wildlife* 16 (3): 22–23. Excellent discussion of the impacts on wildlife of plastics discarded in the ocean.

Burmaster, D. E. (1982). The New Pollution: Groundwater Contamination. *Environment* 24 (2): 6–13, 33–36. Good overview.

Clarke, R. (1984). What's Happening to Our Water? In *Ecology 2000*, ed. E. Hillary. New York: Beaufort Books. Good overview of water pollution.

Gibbons, J. W., and Sharitz, R. R. (1974). Thermal Alterations of Aquatic Ecosystems. *American Scientist* 62: 660–670. Good review.

Hileman, B. (1982). The Chlorination Question. *Environ. Sci. and Technol.* 16 (1): 15A–18A. Excellent overview.

Hileman, B. (1984). Water Quality Uncertainties. *Environ. Sci. and Technol.* 18 (4): 124A–126A. Wonderful overview.

Hillman, W. S., and Culley, D. D. (1978). The Uses of Duckweed. *American Scientist* 66: 442–451. Excellent look at an alternative biotechnology.

Peskin, H. M. (1986). Cropland Sources of Water Pollution. *Environment* 28 (4): 30–34, 44. Important article on nonpoint water pollution control.

Pye, V. I., and Patrick, R. (1983). Ground Water Contamination in the United States. *Science* 221 (Aug. 19): 713–718. Excellent overview of groundwater.

Robertson, G. P. (1986). Nitrogen: Regional Contributions to the Global Cycle. *Environment* 28 (10): 16–20, 29. Detailed report on nitrogen pollution.

Weber, M., Bierce, R., Atkins, N., McManus, R. E., Roet, E., and Yolen, N. (1985). *The 1985 Citizen's Guide to the Ocean.* Washington, D.C.: Potomac Publishing. Wonderful overview of the major environmental issues pertaining to the ocean.

Wolman, A. (1977). Public Health Aspects of Land Utilization of Wastewater Effluents and Sludges. *Journal Water Pollution Control Federation* November: 2211–2218. Interesting article.

17

Pesticides: A Double-Edged Sword

What we do for ourselves dies with us. What we do for others and the world remains and is immortal.

ALBERT PINE

"What is a weed?" Ralph Waldo Emerson asked. "A plant whose virtues have not yet been discovered." Most farmers would scoff at such a remark. To them, weeds—and other pests—are an impediment to efficient farming. They hold down production and cut into profits. To them, pests are pests.

Each year weeds, insects, bacteria, fungi, viruses, birds, rodents, mammals, and other pests consume or destroy an estimated 48% of the world's food production. The highest rate of destruction is in the tropics and subtropics, where as many as three crops are grown each year on the same field. Pest destruction is high even in the developed nations despite elaborate control strategies costing several billion dollars a year. In the United States, for instance, preharvest losses are estimated to be about 34%, and postharvest losses amount to 9% of what is left (Figure 17-1). Together, about two-fifths of annual production is lost to various pests, or about $9 billion worth of food for humans and livestock. Pest control costs approximately $2.5 billion a year.

Similar losses are reported in other developed countries. For example, wheat production in Saskatchewan has been reduced in some years by three-fourths as a result of wireworm infestation. In a world where 17% to 40% of the people are hungry, such losses are tragic. Reducing losses through pest control represents an enormous opportunity to increase world food supplies.

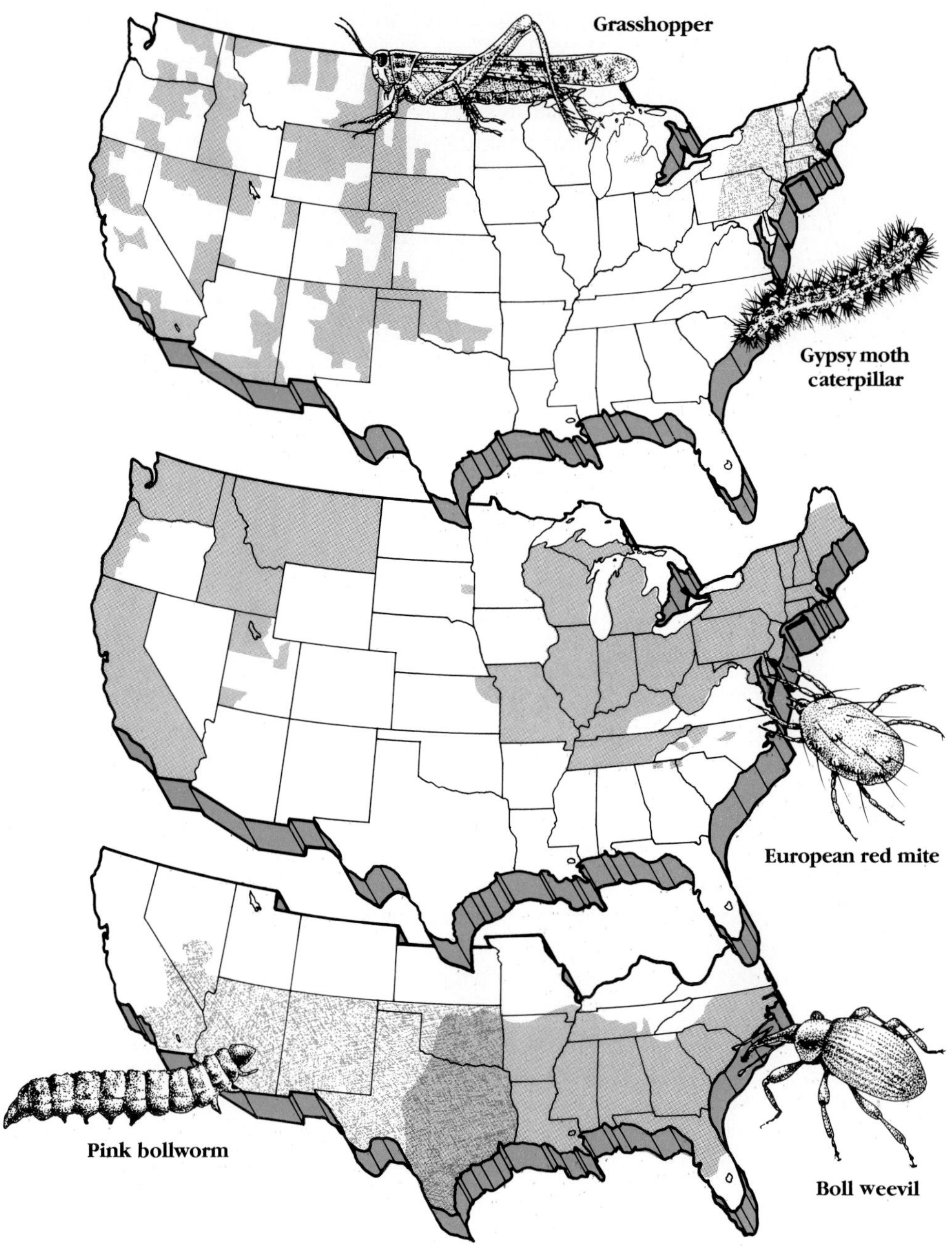

Grasshopper

Gypsy moth caterpillar

European red mite

Pink bollworm

Boll weevil

Figure 17-1 Pest damage in the United States.

A Historical Overview

Pest control measures have been used throughout the centuries. In China over 3000 years ago, for example, farmers controlled locusts by burning infested fields. In the ancient Middle East, open ditches were used to trap immature locusts. Arsenic poisons were used as pesticides in A.D. 900, and in 1182 Chinese citizens were required to collect and kill locusts in an effort to control an outbreak. Techniques similar to these have been in use since the beginning of agriculture in many other parts of the world.

Development of Chemical Pesticides

In recent years chemical pesticides (biocides) have come to form the cornerstone of pest management. **Pesticides** are chemicals used to kill troublesome pests, including weeds, rodents, and insects. Early pesticides, known as **first-generation pesticides**, were simple preparations made of ashes, sulfur, arsenic compounds, ground tobacco, or hydrogen cyanide. Today few of these remain in use, because they are toxic or relatively ineffective.

In 1939 the Swiss chemist Paul Müller introduced a new synthetic organic insecticide called DDT (*d*ichloro-*d*iphenyl*t*richloroethane). This was the first in a long line

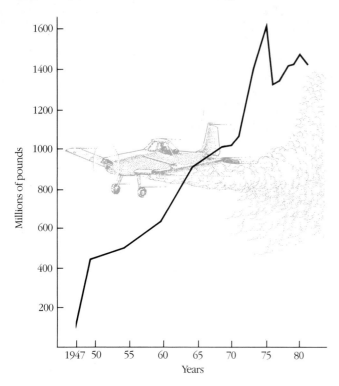

Figure 17-2 Increasing pesticide production in the United States.

of **second-generation pesticides**, synthetic organic compounds that kill a variety of pests. For the 25 years following its development DDT was viewed by many as the savior of humankind. It quickly removed insects and increased crop yield. Being relatively inexpensive to produce, it spread to all corners of the world. In 1944 Müller was awarded a Nobel Prize.

Over the years thousands of new chemicals have been synthesized and tested. Today 1500 different substances are used in over 33,000 commercial herbicides, insecticides, fungicides, miticides, and rodenticides, with one goal in mind: to reduce pests to tolerable levels (Figure 17-2). Some pesticides, like DDT, are **broad-spectrum** biocides, which attack a wide variety of organisms; others are **narrow-spectrum** pesticides, used in controlling one or a few particular pests.

Chemical pesticides fall into three chemical families: chlorinated hydrocarbons (organochlorines), organic phosphates, and carbamates. The **chlorinated hydrocarbons** are a high-risk group including DDT, aldrin, kepone, dieldrin, chlordane, heptachlor, endrin, mirex, toxaphene, and lindane. All of these have been banned or drastically restricted or are being considered for such actions because of their ability to cause cancer, birth defects, neurological disorders, and damage to wildlife and the environment. Generally, the chlorinated hydrocarbons are extremely resistant to breakdown, persist in

the environment, are passed up the food chain, and remain for long periods in body fat.

The second group, the **organic phosphates**, consists of chemicals such as malathion and parathion. These break down more rapidly than chlorinated hydrocarbons and thus are less likely to pass through the food chain. However, most are highly toxic. Humans exposed to even low levels may suffer from drowsiness, confusion, cramps, diarrhea, vomiting, headaches, and breathing difficulty. Higher levels cause severe convulsions, paralysis, tremors, coma, and death.

The third group, the **carbamates**, are widely used today as insecticides, herbicides, and fungicides. One of the most common is carbaryl (commonly known as Sevin). As a group the carbamates are less persistent than the organic phosphates, remaining a few days to two weeks after application. But like the organochlorines and organophosphates, they are nerve poisons that have been shown to cause birth defects and genetic damage.

Approximately 2.3 million metric tons of chemical pesticides are used annually throughout the world, approximately 34% in North America, about 45% in Europe, and the remaining 21% primarily in developing countries. About one-fifth of all pesticides are applied to U.S. crops each year. Of these pesticides 35% are insecticides for insect control, 51% are herbicides for weed control, and the rest are mostly fungicides used to reduce fungal growth. According to the University of Illinois entomologist Robert Metcalf, author of a standard college textbook on pest management, farmers apply more than twice the pesticide they need. Adding to the unnecessary environmental contamination are a cadre of misinformed homeowners who apply about one-third of all U.S. chemical pesticides on gardens, lawns, and trees in higher amounts per acre than farmers do.

Pesticides constitute only about 3% of the commonly used commercial chemicals in the United States each year. Nonetheless, because they are released into the environment in large quantities and have the potential to alter ecosystem balance and threaten human health, their use has created widespread and often heated controversy.

Exploration, Exploitation, and Reflection

Pesticide use has progressed through three developmental stages: (1) exploratory, (2) exploitive, and (3) reflective. These periods illustrate a common progression of human behavior and attitude that follows the introduction of many chemicals and technologies.

Exploration During the exploratory stage, starting in the 1940s, DDT and other new pesticides were applied to a variety of crops, with astonishing results. DDT was even used to delouse soldiers and civilians in World War II.

Figure 17-3 Pesticide resistance. A tobacco budworm crawls through deadly DDT unaffected.

DDT and other new chemical preparations proved to be fast and efficient in controlling insects, weeds, and other pests. In India, for example, before the use of DDT in the 1950s to control malaria-carrying mosquitoes, there were over 100 million cases of malaria a year. By 1961 the annual incidence had been reduced to 50,000. Pesticides also allowed farmers to respond quickly to outbreaks, often avoiding economic disaster. Second-generation pesticides were cheap and relatively easy to apply, and their use resulted in substantial financial gains as yields increased. Some insecticides, such as DDT and dieldrin, persisted long after application, giving extended protection.

Exploitation The successes of the explorative phase led to the **exploitive phase**, during which pesticide production and use expanded considerably. Researchers developed many new pesticides. Steps were taken to protect farm workers from exposure and consumers from toxic residues remaining on vegetables and grains.

In the rush to expand pesticide use, however, many problems arose. First, many pesticides, especially broad-spectrum chemicals, often killed predatory and parasitic insects that help control pests and potential pests. Thus, insects that had not been pests suddenly increased in number, creating a need for additional pesticides. Agronomists call this population explosion of new pests an **upset**.

A classic example of such an upset has taken place in California. Spider mites, once only a minor crop pest, have become a major pest because pesticides killed off many of their natural enemies, which were more sensitive to the sprays. Today the mites cause twice as much damage as any other insect pest in California and cost farmers

(in damage and control) five times what they cost 15 years ago. Two of modern farming's most costly pests, the cotton bollworm and corn-root worm, were minor problems 50 years ago before widespread pesticide use wiped out their natural predators.

Pesticides also destroy beneficial insects, such as honeybees, which play an important role in pollination. Honeybees pollinate crops that provide one-third of our food, crops annually worth over $1 billion. Apple orchards are particularly hard hit. Over 400,000 bee colonies are destroyed or severely damaged in the United States each year by pesticides.

Second, because of genetic diversity (see Chapter 2), a small portion of any insect population (roughly 5%) is genetically resistant to the pesticides and is not killed by a normal application (Figure 17-3). Therefore, even though pesticides initially reduce pests to a level at which they do little damage, the surviving resistant insects reproduce and eventually form a new population that can be killed only by large doses or new pesticides.

Genetic resistance to DDT was first reported in 1947 by Italian researchers. Today, according to some estimates, over 400 insect pests are resistant to DDT and other insecticides. Twenty of the worst pests are now resistant to all types of insecticide, according to Metcalf, the entomologist. This unexpected development called for new strategies. The first was to increase the amount of pesticide. When DDT and other insecticides were introduced in Central America, cotton fields were sprayed eight times each growing season; today, 30 to 40 applications are necessary. The second strategy was the development of new pesticides. However, scientists found that it was expensive to create pesticides and that the insects developed genetic resistance to these new chemicals.

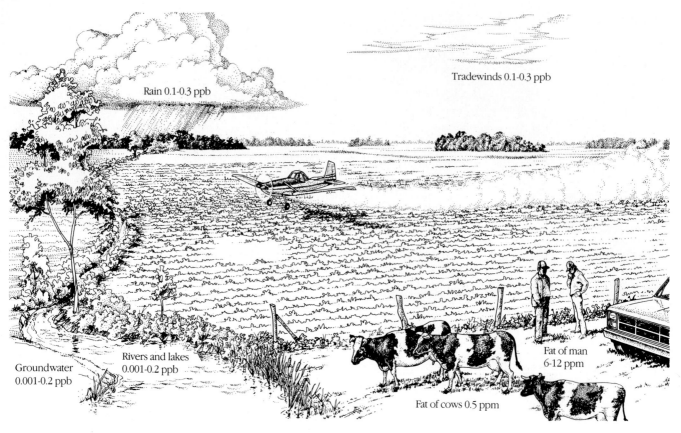

Rain 0.1-0.3 ppb

Tradewinds 0.1-0.3 ppb

Fat of man
6-12 ppm

Rivers and lakes
0.001-0.2 ppb

Groundwater
0.001-0.2 ppb

Fat of cows 0.5 ppm

Figure 17-4 Pesticide sprayed from planes contaminates the ecosystem because much of the pesticide drifts away. Various avenues for the dispersal of pesticides are shown. Average values for DDT concentrations are indicated in parts per million and billion.

Even weeds and plant diseases can develop a resistance to pesticides, although not so quickly as insects.

The third problem was that many of the second-generation pesticides proved to be hazardous environmental contaminants. These synthetic pesticides persist in the ecosystem because microconsumers (bacteria) lack the enzymes to degrade them. Increased spraying resulted in widespread contamination of the ecosystem (Figure 17-4). Trout in upstate New York showed elevated levels of DDT and its chief breakdown product, DDE (dichlorodiphenyldichloroethylene), because of spraying in nearby forests. These toxins did not affect the adults but reduced survival among newly hatched fry. Insect- and worm-eating birds also perished in areas where aerial spraying of insecticide had occurred. As a result of widespread pesticide use, populations of many birds plummeted.

The manufacturers of pesticides argued that the chemicals were found in only minute concentrations in the environment and could not be the cause of declining populations of fish and wildlife. But numerous experi-

mental studies showed that certain persistent pesticides—even when present in small amounts in the environment—could drastically affect the reproduction and survival rate of birds and other animals.

One of the most important findings was that although DDT and DDE levels in aquatic ecosystems were quite low, concentrations were higher in producers and still higher in consumers, a phenomenon called biomagnification (Chapter 14). Fish-eating birds, the consumers at the top trophic level, had the highest concentrations of DDT and DDE. Although these levels were not lethal to adults, they impaired reproduction. Birds that feed on fish and other birds, such as peregrine falcons, brown pelicans, cormorants, bald eagles, gulls, and ospreys, DDE and DDT reduced the deposition of calcium in eggshells. Of the two, biologists discovered that DDE posed the greater physiological threat to birds and was persistent in the environment. Reduced eggshell calcium levels create a thinner, more fragile shell that cracks easily during incubation. As a result of widespread DDT contamination many predatory populations were nearly wiped out. (For

Figure 17-5 Crop duster spraying potato fields. One-half to three-fourths of the pesticide never reaches the ground and is carried off by wind.

a more detailed discussion see Chapter 8.) In one study of bald eagle reproduction James Grier, a zoologist at North Dakota State University, showed that the number of young per nest in northwestern Ontario declined by about 70% between 1966 and 1974.

Other work soon showed the presence of DDT in fish, beef, and other foods. DDT also appeared in the fatty tissues of seals and Eskimos in the Arctic, far from its point of use, indicating that it was traveling in the atmosphere to remote parts of the globe, being washed from the sky by rain, and passing through the food chain. DDT has also been detected in human breast milk, a discovery that caused considerable alarm, although the long-term effects of low levels on humans remain unknown.

Farm and chemical workers suffered from direct exposure to pesticides on the job as well, indicating widespread misuse. Workers pick up pesticide on their clothing and skin through accidents, negligence, or prematurely entering sprayed fields. Symptoms of poisoning include insomnia, loss of sex drive, reduced powers of concentration, irritability, nervous disorders, and, in severe cases, death. At least 100,000 U.S. workers are seriously poisoned each year, but many experts believe that this figure grossly underestimates the number of serious poisonings. Surveys in California, for instance, show that three-fourths of all serious poisonings go unreported. Each year 200 to 1000 people die from pesticide poisoning in the United States. Worldwide, there are at least 500,000 pesticide poisonings annually, according to some experts. These result in at least 5000 immediate deaths and numerous chronic and fatal illnesses.

Although farm and chemical workers are the groups most heavily exposed to pesticides, residents of rural and even suburban areas are often exposed to high levels if they live near agricultural lands. Families living near fields sprayed with herbicides and pesticides outside Scottsdale, Arizona, for example, suffered from persistent headaches, cramps, skin rashes, dizziness, high blood pressure, chest pains, persistent coughs, internal bleeding, and leukemia. People living near sprayed fields are so heavily exposed because one-half to three-fourths of the sprayed material never reaches the ground but is carried away by light winds (Figure 17-5). Health officials are worried the most by possible long-term problems from exposure.

In their zeal to control mosquitoes, many cities in the U.S. South have routinely sprayed insecticides in neighborhoods and nearby breeding areas. In Florida various mosquito control agencies argue that controlling the insect is vital to real estate interests and tourism, because it minimizes the risk of encephalitis, a disease carried by mosquitoes. The price citizens pay to have trucks spewing out mists of pesticides while they sleep is unknown. Florida wildlife officials, however, think that pesticide use is largely responsible for a 70% decline in the population of snook, a popular sport fish. Adding to the problem, city officials use a variety of pesticides in city parks, and lawn-care companies and individuals douse lawns and trees with a variety of toxic substances, often incorrectly and without warning neighbors.

Consumers may also become the victims of pesticide poisonings. In the summer of 1985, for instance, 1400 people on the West Coast were stricken with nausea, diarrhea, vomiting, and blurred vision after eating watermelons that had been sprayed with the pesticide aldicarb. The EPA permits aldicarb for use on cotton and food crops that are cooked before consumption, such as beans and

◀ *Viewpoint*

The Myth of the "Banned" Pesticides

Lewis Regenstein

The author wrote America the Poisoned, *published by Acropolis Books. He is vice president of the Fund for Animals and is past president of the Monitor Consortium, a coalition of 35 national environmental and animal protection groups. He is also the author of* The Politics of Extinction: The Story of the World's Endangered Wildlife *(Macmillan, 1975).*

As of 1977 there were 33,000 to 35,000 registered pesticide products on the market, using 1500 active ingredients combined with 2000 other possibly toxic substances. Over 100 of the pesticides in general use today are thought to cause cancer. The EPA estimates that about one-third of the active ingredients used in pesticides are toxic and that one-fourth are carcinogenic.

Since its beginning the EPA has effectively banned the domestic use of only about a dozen of these by canceling their registration. (In addition, an unknown number of pesticides have either not been granted registration or been withdrawn voluntarily by the manufacturer.)

One often comes across erroneous references to certain highly toxic pesticides, such as DDT, as having been "banned." Ronald Reagan has even complained that "the world is experiencing a resurgence of deadly diseases spread by insects because pesticides like DDT have been prematurely outlawed." The sad fact, however, is that after many years of efforts by scientists, conservationists, and some government officials, very few restrictions have been placed on pesticides. Despite the overwhelming evidence that many pesticides cause cancer and are extremely damaging to humans and the environment, almost none of these chemicals has ever been "banned" by the government in the true sense of that word. In the very few cases where pesticides have been the subject of suspen-

sions, cancellation proceedings, or court actions, the results have usually been restrictions or bans placed on some or most uses while other applications are allowed to continue.

Even in the handful of cases where all domestic use has been prohibited (such as with kepone), manufacture for export can still be (and often is) legally undertaken. When production for export continues, it inevitably results in exposure of workers and the public through pollution, dumping of wastes, and other accidental and intentional releases of the substance, as well as through foodstuffs imported from foreign countries to which the chemical is exported.

The way the EPA has carried out its policy on "banning" toxic pesticides is contradictory and nonsensical. In numerous instances the agency has proclaimed a chemical hazardous to humans and the environment and prohibited major uses of the compound. At the same time, it has allowed other uses to continue as before, often depending on label instructions to ensure adherence to the prohibitions. Several cancer-causing chemicals that have been restricted but not banned are aldrin, dieldrin, chlordane, heptachlor, DDT, 2,4,5-T, mirex, and DBCP. In these and other instances, the EPA action has often been presented to the public by the news media as another pesticide "ban."

In canceling the registrations for major uses of these most obviously dangerous pesticides, the EPA in many cases allowed them to be slowly phased out or permitted the sale and distribution of existing stocks. This made it possible for large quantities to continue to be sold and used long after they were "banned" and even for users to stockpile them for future use.

The implications of this EPA policy should be obvious. It is impossible to know what use will be made of these products. Indeed, EPA end-use restrictions are considered a joke within the agricultural community, and many farmers use certain chemicals as they always have, regardless of whether such applications have been banned.

Moreover, there is no way to determine how and where such carefully restricted and regulated chemicals are being disposed of. Common sense would dictate that if a chemical is so dangerous that it has been declared a threat to humans and the environment, it should simply be banned—its manufacture, sale, transport, use, or possession prohibited.

Pesticides that have been restricted are listed in the EPA publication "Suspended and Cancelled Pesticides," which gives the conditions, if any, under which these substances may be used. The rules and regulations outlined in this largely incomprehensible document are so complex and unfathomable that their only real use and value are to lawyers and bureaucrats interested in the byzantine world of federal regulations. It is difficult to believe that farmers and agricultural workers, particularly illiterate or Spanish-speaking migrants, could understand the meaning of these rules or the labels on pesticides.

◀ *Viewpoint*

For example, 2,4,5-T cannot be used in "ponds" or on "food crops intended for human consumption" but can be applied to rice, a food crop grown in pond-like areas. It cannot be sprayed on pastureland, where cattle graze, but can be used on rangeland, where livestock also forage. The regulations for endrin prohibit spraying within certain distances from lakes, ponds, and streams, varying from 15 to 200 meters (50 feet to one-eighth of a mile), depending on the crop being sprayed. The instructions allow spraying closer to ponds that are owned by the user but warn against its causing fish kills. The document also gives detailed instructions on what to do if fish kills do occur and how to dispose of the fish (burial), and requires the posting of a "No Fishing" sign for half a year or a year after the kill has occurred.

Under "aerial application," the regulations warn, "Do not operate nozzle liquid pressure over 40 psi or with any fan nozzle smaller than 0.4 gpm or fan angle greater than 65 degrees such as type 6504. Do not use any can type nozzles smaller than 0.4 gpm nor whirl plate smaller than #46 such as type D-4-46."

Ground application instructions are equally bizarre. But in the final analysis these details don't really matter. What happens in real life is that a migrant worker is given a container of endrin and told to spray it on the crops, and that's that.

Label requirements for other potentially toxic chemicals, even when clearly written, are equally useless. For example,

the brochure requires that metaldehyde, used to kill slugs and snails, "must have the following statement on the front panel of the product label: 'This pesticide may be fatal to children and dogs or other pets if eaten. Keep children and pets out of treated areas.'" But such a warning in no way prevents this extremely toxic chemical from being widely used throughout the nation in precisely the way the label cautions against. U.S. government agencies, including those oriented toward the environment, pay little attention to the labels. In recent years the National Park Service used metaldehyde on the White House lawn and the public grounds around and between the White House and the Capitol. In 1977, 40 kilograms (88 pounds) was used just in the President's Park, an area adjacent to the White House. Such use in these areas not only potentially endangers the president and his family but also countless thousands of tourists who flock to the Ellipse, the Mall, and other areas around the White House.

The EPA's labeling and restricted-use policies, unintelligible and contradictory as they may seem, do serve several purposes. They keep the public reassured that it is being protected from "banned" and "restricted" pesticides while allowing chemical and agribusiness interests to carry on business as usual with many of these products. It is, in fact, an ideal arrangement: it keeps the bureaucrats, the politicians, and industry happy, even if the public gets poisoned in the process.

---

potatoes. This incident points out how difficult it is for government officials to regulate the way farmers use pesticides.

Herbicides have also drawn a considerable amount of attention in recent years. Their uses in times of peace and war are discussed later in this chapter.

In addition to the ecological and health concerns discussed above, many experts have begun to question the efficacy of pesticide use. Despite the increased application of chemical pesticides, annual losses due to pests have continued to climb. In the first 30 years after the introduction of second-generation insecticides, use increased tenfold, and insect damage doubled.

Reflection As a result of growing concern over the biological and ecological effects of pesticides and growing skepticism regarding their effectiveness, industrial societies have entered the reflective stage, a period of caution. Gone are the days of unbridled enthusiasm for pesticide use.

Caution regarding pesticide use has grown enormously since the publication of the late Rachel Carson's book *Silent Spring*, which pointed out many of the real and

potential impacts of pesticide use. Our understanding of pesticide impacts continues to grow, casting further doubt on conventional pest-control practices. Quite recently researchers found that herbicides penetrate the soil up to ten times deeper than laboratory tests had indicated. Such findings explain why groundwater is often polluted with herbicides. Researchers are finding that bans on pesticides have benefited wildlife. The endangered bald eagle appears to be on the upswing. Recent studies show that DDE and DDT levels have dropped in wild populations and that normal reproductive rates have returned. Researchers caution, however, that domestic pesticide bans are only part of the answer. Continued use of pesticides outside of the United States poisons migratory species, such as songbirds. Much of the produce imported into the United States has recently been found to be contaminated with pesticides. One-fourth of the fruit and vegetables sold in the country come from foreign soil. Global bans of harmful pesticides are needed to protect the biosphere.

Pesticides are indispensable for agriculture and will remain in use, despite their many drawbacks. However, many experts believe that pesticides will play a much smaller role in agriculture in years to come as other, less harmful, controls are developed and integrated into pest management strategies. For example, the red spider mite can be kept under control in apple orchards by insecticides applied early in the season, well before the mite's natural predators emerge. Throughout the rest of the season farmers hold back on pesticide, letting the natural predators do their work. Using a similar approach on cotton, researchers at Texas A&M have cut pesticide use by 70% while maintaining normal crop production.

Integrated Pest Management

Integrated pest management calls for the combined use of four basic means of pest control: environmental, genetic, chemical, and cultural. Together, these can form an effective, long-lasting, and environmentally sound way of controlling pest damage.

Environmental Controls

Environmental control methods are designed to alter the biotic and abiotic environment, making it inhospitable to the pest. Because they generally rely on knowledge more than technology, these practices are especially suitable for poor nations. Still, they can be equally effective if used properly in modern agricultural societies.

Increasing Crop Diversity   In Chapter 7 we saw that monocultures generally promote the proliferation of insects and disease organisms. Crop diversity, on the other hand, reduces the amount of food available to any one pest and helps prevent such rapid population growth. Two basic techniques increase crop diversity: heteroculture and crop rotation.

The planting of several crops side by side is called **heteroculture**. It works because it provides environmental resistance so the biotic potential of pests cannot be reached. Pest populations are often much smaller in heterocultures than in monocultures. For example, intercropping corn and peanuts can reduce corn borers by as much as 80%. Part of the reason for this success may be that peanuts harbor predatory insects that feed on the corn borer.

Crop rotation increases soil fertility and can help reduce erosion, as discussed in Chapter Supplement 7-1, but it also helps hold down pest populations. For instance, wireworms feed on potatoes but not alfalfa. Therefore, if potatoes and alfalfa are alternated from year to year, food becomes a limiting factor that holds the wireworm population in check.

Altering the Time of Planting   Some plants naturally escape insect pests by sprouting early or late in the grow-

ing season. A good example of this adaptation is the wild radish, which sprouts early in the season before the emergence of the troublesome cabbage maggot fly.

Agriculturalists can use their knowledge of an insect's life cycle to their advantage by coordinating plantings with the expected date of hatching. Delayed planting of wheat, for example, helps protect this crop against the destructive Hessian fly. In general, if a pest emerges early in the spring, planting can be delayed to avoid that pest. Without food the pest will perish. If the pest emerges late in the growing season, an early planting may prove effective.

Altering Plant and Soil Nutrients   The levels of certain nutrients in soil and plants can also affect pest population size. Thus, by regulating soil nutrients a farmer may be able to control pests.

Nitrogen is one of the important nutrients that insects and parasites derive from plants. Too much or too little of this key element can alter the population size of various pests. For example, grain aphids reproduce better on grain high in nitrogen. Other insects, such as the greenhouse thrip and mites, do poorly on high-nitrogen spinach and tomatoes, respectively. Therefore, knowledge of pest nutrient requirements, soil nutrient levels, and plant nutrient levels can be helpful in controlling pests. Plants rich or poor in nitrogen can be selected to control pests as long as the level of nitrogen is adequate for human consumption.

Controlling Adjacent Crops and Weeds   Adjacent crops and weeds may provide food and habitat for pests, especially insects. In some cases plants adjacent to valuable food crops harbor viruses that can infest pest species and later be transmitted to crops. Thus, elimination of adjacent crops and weeds can prove helpful in the control of insects and other pests.

Sometimes adjacent low-value crops (trap crops) attract pests away from more valuable crops. Alfalfa is a good example. When planted adjacent to cotton, it lures the harmful lygus bug and thus prevents serious damage to the cotton.

Introducing Predators, Parasites, and Disease Organisms   In nature thousands of potential insect pests never become real pests because of natural controls exerted by predators, diseases, and parasites (that is, biotic components of environmental resistance). Farmers can capitalize on this knowledge through **biological control** or **food chain control** to manage weeds, insects, rodents, and other pests.

There are over 250 examples of partial or complete control of pests through predators and parasites. For example, the prickly pear cactus was introduced in Australia from its native Mexico. By 1925 over 24 million hectares (60 million acres) of land had been badly infested; half of this land was abandoned because of the thick carpet of cactus. Farmers introduced a cactus-eating insect to Australia to eradicate the pest, and seven years later much of the land had been cleared and could once again be used.

The predatory lady beetle was introduced into California, from Australia in the 1880s to control an insect that destroyed citrus trees. Parasitic insects from Iran, Iraq, and Pakistan have been introduced to control the olive scale, an insect that once threatened the state's olive trees. Both lady beetles and the predatory insects now exert complete control on their prey, keeping their populations at manageable levels without the use of pesticides.

Entomologists in the United States are currently experimenting with a new method of controlling mosquitoes using *Toxorbynchites rutilis* (Big Tox, for short), a large, nonbiting mosquito whose larvae feed on the larvae of other mosquitoes. Bred in captivity, this predatory mosquito will be released in infested regions to control biting mosquitoes.

Insect pests can also be controlled by birds, a natural control organism whose potential has been overlooked. Brown thrashers can eat over 6000 insects in one day. A swallow consumes 1000 leafhoppers in 12 hours, and a pair of flickers can snack on 500 ants and go away hungry. In China thousands of ducklings are driven through rice fields; in some places they reduce the populations of insects by 60% to 75%, allowing farmers to reduce insecticide use considerably.

Bacteria and other microorganisms can be brought to bear on pests. One common example is the bacterium *Bacillus thuringiensis* (BT), used to control many leaf-eating caterpillars. Cultivated in the lab and sold commercially, it can be applied as a powder or mixed with water and then sprayed on plants. Caterpillars that eat it become sick and die.

BT is used by organic gardeners with considerable success. It has been sprayed in China to control pine caterpillars and cabbage army worms. In California it has been used for more than 20 years to control various troublesome caterpillars, and it is currently applied in the northeastern United States to help control gypsy moths, which devastate forests (Figure 17-6). BT has also been employed in the battle against mosquitoes. Although BT is more expensive than chemicals, it has reduced overall insecticide use in California from 270,000 kilograms (600,000 pounds) in 1970 to about 23,000 kilograms (50,000 pounds) in 1983.

Viruses and fungi may be used similarly. In Australia, after years of fruitless efforts to control rabbits, scientists introduced a pathogenic *myxoma* virus, which eliminated almost all of the rabbits within one year. Cabbage loopers can be controlled with .5 gram of an experimentally produced virus applied to a hectare of cropland. Other

Figure 17-6 Gypsy moths kill large sections of trees by eating leaves near their hatching site. Efforts are now underway to control the moth using biological control techniques, such as the bacterium BT.

viruses are being used to control pests such as the pink bollworm, which damages cotton, and the gypsy moth. U.S. scientists are now testing a fungus *(Tolypocladium cylindrosporum)* to manage mosquitoes. Special traps are set out to attract adult females. Females enter the traps and are contaminated with spores, but they are allowed to escape, thus carrying the fungal spores back into the environment, where they infect eggs and larvae.

These biological control agents must be developed with caution to ensure that they are not harmful to humans, livestock, and other members of the ecosystem. Pest control agents must not become pests themselves.

Organisms can develop genetic resistance to biological controls; in Australia, for example, rabbits are developing a resistance to *myxoma* virus. Researchers in Kansas also recently found that larvae that eat stored grain (Indian meal moth larvae) develop genetic resistance to BT. In such cases new controls could be introduced, but in some instances biological control agents themselves may undergo genetic changes that offset the newly acquired resistance of the pest. This process is called **co-evolution**.

Genetic Controls

We will consider two major genetic control strategies, the sterile male technique and the breeding of genetically resistant plants and animals. Both are important components of integrated pest management.

Sterile Male Technique The **sterile male technique** has been effective against several species of insect pests, including the screwworm fly in Mexico and the United States, the Mediterranean fruit fly in Capri, the melon fly on the island of Rota, near Guam, and the Oriental fruit fly in Guam.

In this technique males of the pest species are raised

Figure 17-7 The USDA prevents buildup of screwworms by rearing and releasing sterile male flies.

in captivity and sterilized by irradiation or special chemicals. Then they are released in large numbers in infested areas, where they mate with wild females. Since many insect species mate only once, eggs produced by such a union are infertile. If the population of sterilized males greatly exceeds that of the wild males, most of the matings will be with sterile males. Populations can be brought under control swiftly.

In the United States screwworms have been controlled by this method, saving millions of dollars each year (Figure 17-7). The screwworm fly lays eggs in open wounds of cattle and other warm-blooded animals. The eggs hatch within a few hours, and the larvae feed off blood and tissue fluid. This keeps the wound open, allowing a bacterial infection to set in, which eventually kills the host.

In 1976 there were over 29,000 cases of screwworm infestation in the United States. Because of inclement weather and an extensive release of sterile males, costing $6 million, the following year there were only 457 reported cases. The screwworm has practically been eliminated from the southeastern United States, but it still remains in the Southwest, where new flies migrate in from Mexico. With continued cooperation between Mexico and the United States, though, the future of the screwworm as a major pest may be a short one. Even if the fly is never eradicated, controlling it provides substantial economic benefits at a relatively low cost. The program is saving the cattle industry about $120 million annually.

Sterile males have been introduced in other instances with much less success. For example, California imported sterilized Mediterranean fruit flies (medflies) from Hawaii in efforts to control this pest in 1980 and 1981. The medfly lays its eggs in 235 different fruits, nuts, and vegetables;

its larvae develop in the ripening fruits and eventually destroy them. Agricultural interests argued that if the medfly proliferated, it would cause $2.6 billion in damage per year in California alone.

At first the state tried a combined approach, using sterile males and baited traps laced with malathion to avoid widespread aerial spraying, which, scientists had argued, would cause undue health risk. Combined programs had worked well in two areas in the state in 1975 and 1980. In the 1980–1981 incident, however, poorly funded control efforts were inadequate, and fertile medflies kept appearing both inside and outside of areas believed to be infested. Farmers became nervous, and the U.S. Department of Agriculture threatened to quarantine all California produce, forcing the governor to order a massive aerial spraying program that eradicated the medfly. Follow-up studies showed that the spraying, although successful in controlling the medfly, had also reduced the populations of many predatory and parasitic insects that control populations of other insect pests. Researchers found, for instance, that aphids and whitefly populations in home gardens had increased dramatically because of the loss of natural controls. Insects that destroy olive trees increased substantially in sprayed agricultural regions, for similar reasons.

The sterile male technique has also proved unsuccessful at mosquito control. Scientists believe that the chief reason for these failures is the lower sexual activity of sterilized males compared with wild males. Other reasons may include an inadequate number of sterile males, ignorance of the insect pest's breeding cycle, and the inmigration of additional pests. Some researchers also suggest that through natural selection a new race of screwworm flies may evolve that recognizes and avoids sterile males.

Despite these problems the sterile male technique is an important tool in pest control. It is species-specific, can be used with environmental controls, and can be effective in eliminating pests in low-density infestations.

Developing Resistant Crops and Animals Genetically resistant plants and animals can be developed through genetic engineering and artificial selection. Genetic engineering may be especially useful in this regard, because it allows for a much more rapid development of new strains than artificial selection.

In a recent example of artificial selection, scientists have found that certain oils in the skin of oranges, grapefruits, and lemons are highly toxic to the eggs and larvae of the Caribbean fruit fly, which lays its eggs in the skin of these fruits. The flies' larvae destroy the fruit, but scientists may now be able to selectively breed citrus to increase the amount of toxic oils in their peels.

Cornell University scientists are developing a new type of potato plant whose leaves, stems, and sprouts are covered with tiny, sticky hairs, which trap insects and immobilize their legs and mouth parts. Field tests show that this plant can reduce green peach aphids by half. The new variety was developed by crossing cultivated potatoes with a wild species, with sticky hairs, which grows as a weed in Bolivia.

Other genetic research has led to Hessian fly–resistant wheat and leafhopper-resistant soybeans, alfalfa, cotton, and potatoes. Work on chemical factors that attract insects to plants may help scientists selectively remove them to make plants unappealing.

Robert Kaufman of the Monsanto Company recently announced another promising weapon in the fight against pests. Kaufman and his colleagues have isolated the gene that gives BT its pesticidal action. The scientists have transferred that gene to another bacterium, *Pseudomonas fluorescens*, that lives on the roots of corn and several other plants. The transplanted gene renders the host bacterium lethal to insects and other organisms, such as the black cutworm, that feed on the roots of important commercial plants. Simply by planting seeds that have been pretreated with *P. fluorescens* bearing the toxic gene, farmers can provide long-term protection without the dangers of pesticides.

Kaufman hopes that more insecticidal genes can be added to *P. fluorescens* in the years to come, giving corn a wider range of protection, reducing chemical pesticide use and in the process protecting wildlife from the harmful toxic pesticides that have been the mainstay of agriculture for decades.

Root-zone protection is not the only strategy that geneticists are developing. Numerous bacteria colonize aboveground plant parts; fitted with insecticidal genes from BT and other naturally occurring biological agents, these bacteria could create a protective barrier to ward off dozens of insect pests.

Genetic resistance is a necessary element of effective pest management. The major problem is the time, money, and labor involved in producing resistant varieties. Furthermore, genetic resistance can be overcome when pests adapt. In this case, scientists must be ready with new varieties.

Chemical Controls

Second-Generation Pesticides
Although many environmentalists support banning pesticides, this view is impracticable for political and economic reasons. Second-generation pesticides will remain a part of our pest control strategy. However, several principles should guide their use: (1) they should be applied sparingly; (2) they should be applied at the most effective time to reduce the number of applications; (3) they should destroy as few natural predators, nonpest species, and biological control agents as possible; (4) they should not be applied

Figure 17-8 Pheromone trap, containing a sticky substance to immobilize male gypsy moths in search of mates.

near drinking water supplies; (5) they should be carefully tested for toxic effects; (6) persistent pesticides and pesticides that bioaccumulate should be avoided; (7) exposure to workers should be as low as possible; and (8) pesticides should be used to reduce populations to low levels, and environmental, genetic, and cultural control measures should then be used to keep populations low.

Chemical pesticides will continue to play an important role in pest management. Today, however, several new chemical agents have been developed, such as pheromones, hormones, and natural chemical repellants. These are **third-generation pesticides**.

Pheromones
Pheromones are externally released chemicals produced by insects and other animals. One well-known group of pheromones is the **sex attractants**, which are emitted by female insects to attract males at the time of breeding. Effective in extraordinarily small concentrations, pheromones draw males to females, an evolutionary adaptation that ensures a high rate of reproductive success.

Many sex attractants are now synthesized in the laboratory and are commercially available for pest control. They are used in three ways. First, **pheromone traps** can be used to lure males. Traps may contain a pesticide-laden bait or a sticky substance that immobilizes insects (Figure 17-8). Second, pheromones can be sprayed

Figure 17-9 The insect life cycle.

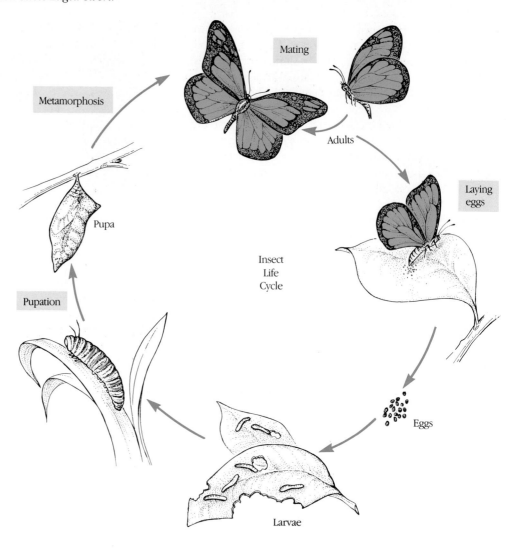

Mating

Metamorphosis

Adults

Laying eggs

Pupa

Insect Life Cycle

Pupation

Eggs

Larvae

widely at breeding time. This is known as the **confusion technique**, as the males are drawn by the pheromone from all directions and may never find a partner. One modification of this technique involves the release of wood chips treated with sex attractants. Males are drawn to the wood chips and may attempt to breed with them. Third, pheromone traps can be used to pinpoint the time when insect eggs hatch. Males emerging at this time are attracted to the traps, allowing farmers to apply their pesticides at the opportune time. This technique helps reduce the amounts of pesticide applied. Pheromones can also be used to lure beneficial insects from fields so that pesticide sprays can be applied.

Pheromone traps of various sorts have been used to control at least 25 insect species. Early work on clearwing moths, cotton bollworms, and other species has been quite successful. Pheromones offer many advantages: they can be used with other methods, they are nontoxic and biodegradable, they can be used at low concentrations, they are highly species-specific, and they are not expected

to present any environmental hazards. The major disadvantage is the high cost of developing new pheromones.

Insect Hormones The life cycle of many insects is shown in Figure 17-9. Insects pass through the larval and pupal stages before reaching adulthood. The entire life cycle is regulated by two hormones, **juvenile hormone** and **molting hormone**. **Hormones** are chemical substances that are produced by specific cells in the body and travel through the bloodstream to distant sites, where they exert some effect. Altering the levels of juvenile and molting hormones disrupts an insect's life cycle, resulting in death. For example, larvae treated with juvenile hormone are prevented from maturing and eventually die. If given molting hormone, they will enter the pupal stage too early and die. Experiments are under way to assess the effectiveness of spraying crops with insect hormones.

Insect hormones offer many of the same advantages that pheromones offer, including biodegradability, lack of toxicity, and low persistence in the environment. Like pheromones, however, they have a high cost and long production time. In addition, insect hormones act rather slowly, sometimes taking a week or two to eliminate a pest, by which time extensive damage may have been done. Insect hormones are not as species-specific as pheromones and therefore may affect natural predators and other nonpest species. The timing of application is also critical, for hormones are effective only at certain times in an insect's life cycle.

Natural Chemical Pesticides Natives of the South American tropics have used the seeds and leaves of the neem tree for many years to control pests. Researchers have found that this tree produces chemicals that kill or repel a variety of insects. This extract may become useful in the control of larvae that feed on vegetables and ornamental crops.

Egyptian researchers noticed that flies ignored a species of brown algae left out on a counter to dry. Curious, they extracted a mixture of chemicals from the algae and found that they, too, repel a variety of insects that attack cotton and rice.

Natural chemicals like these may prove useful in years to come. Like other third-generation pesticides, they are biodegradable and nonpersistent.

Cultural Controls

Cultural control refers to many other simple techniques to control pest populations. These methods include cultivation to control weeds, noisemakers to frighten birds, lights that draw insects to electrocution devices, manual removal of insects from crops (especially suitable for smaller gardens), destruction of insect breeding grounds, improved forecasting of insect emergence, quarantines to regulate the spread of pests, and water and fertilizer management to ensure optimum crop health and resistance to pests.

Economics, Risk, and Pest Control

The central goal of pest control is to reduce pest populations to levels that do not cause economic damage. The cost of pest control, including internal and external costs, should not exceed the economic benefits of increased yield (Chapter 14). To be certain that benefits do not outstrip the actual economic, environmental, and health costs, thorough and fair studies must be made comparing each of the pest control strategies.

Today, most of the money for pest control research goes for conventional chemical methods. Many critics agree that we must be willing to spend money today on newer strategies, such as natural predators, that can be part of a long-term, sustainable pest management strategy.

Though costs may be high initially, over the long term they may become insignificant.

Society might also rethink some of its demands for unblemished fruits and vegetables. Pesticide use just to prevent harmless blemishes is probably a waste of energy, time, and money. A few more spots on our oranges could mean a few more birds overhead, cleaner waterways, improved health for workers and the general public, and cheaper oranges.

As for poor nations, pest management programs can (1) make use of people to destroy bugs and weeds by hand; (2) employ environmentally sound measures, such as crop rotation, heteroculture, timed plantings, natural predators, and genetically resistant plants and animals; and (3) minimize the use of first- and second-generation pesticides. Developed nations must keep companies from exporting pesticides that have been banned at home. (For more on banned chemicals see the Viewpoint in this chapter.) The rich can also help the poor develop a sustainable pest management program through technical and financial assistance.

Herbicides in Peace and War

Herbicides are a form of pesticide used to control weeds. Before World War II few herbicides were used in the United States. Today, however, the herbicide industry is large and prosperous, with sales over $1.3 billion a year.

In the United States herbicides account for over 50% of the chemical pesticides applied each year. Although there are over 180 types of synthetic herbicides on the market, the leading ones are atrazine and alachlor, which collectively account for half of the total sales. In addition, butylate and 2,4-D (2,4-Dichlorophenoxyacetic acid) are used in large quantities.

Despite the number of herbicides in use, two particular chemicals have received most of the attention; these are 2,4-D and 2,4,5-T, nonpersistent synthetic organic compounds similar in function to plant hormones, called **auxins**. When sprayed on plants, 2,4-D and 2,4,5-T increase the metabolic rate of cells so much that plants cannot keep up with increased nutrient demands and literally "grow to death."

Peacetime Uses: Pros and Cons

In peacetime 2,4-D and 2,4,5-T have been sprayed on brush and plants along roadways, power lines, and pipelines and have been used to control poison ivy and ragweed, to eliminate unwanted trees in commercial tree farms and in national forests, to control aquatic weeds, and to rid rangelands of brush and poisonous plants. Overall, three-fourths of these chemicals are used for weed control on farms.

The benefits of herbicides such as these are many:

1. They decrease the amount of mechanical cultivation needed to control weeds and thus reduce fossil fuel consumption and soil erosion.

2. They reduce human labor and thus cut costs.

3. They reduce losses to weeds when soils are too wet to cultivate, because spraying of crops can be done by plane.

4. They help farmers reduce water usage, since water escapes more rapidly from ground tilled to control weeds.

However beneficial their use may be, herbicides have many drawbacks:

1. Some weeds that are not normally pests are resistant to herbicides and tend to proliferate after spraying. Elimination of the new pest may require the use of an additional herbicide.

2. Weeds can become resistant to herbicides. Many agronomists believe that the problem of plant resistance has been underestimated.

3. Herbicide use may increase the need for insecticides. When herbicides are used, farmers often reduce tillage; weeds killed by herbicides remain on the ground and provide food and habitat for insect pests. In addition, herbicides that are used to control weeds around the periphery of fields may destroy the habitat of predatory insects. Herbicides may also decrease the farmer's incentive to rotate crops, an effective way of reducing insect pests.

4. Herbicides may make some crops more susceptible to disease. For example, some herbicides reduce the waxy coating on plants, change their metabolic rates and retard or stimulate plant growth; all of these may make plants more susceptible to disease.

5. There is great concern that some herbicides are toxic and may cause birth defects, cancer, and other illnesses.

Critics argue that **integrated weed management** could reduce the use of herbicides. Such management would employ special equipment such as wick applicators that apply herbicide only on weeds between rows. Wick applicators use much less herbicide than aerial spraying and create less environmental contamination. The reasonable use of herbicides could be complemented by mechanical cultivation, proper spacing of rows for healthy crops, biological weed controls, and crop rotation.

Controversy over Wartime Use of 2,4-D and 2,4,5-T

Herbicides were used extensively in the Vietnam War as defoliants to prevent guerrilla ambushes along roads and waterways, to deter the movement of soldiers through demilitarized zones and across the border of Laos, to destroy crops, which might be eaten by the enemy, and to clear areas around camps. Three herbicide preparations were sprayed from planes, helicopters, boats, trucks, and portable units from 1962 to 1970: Agent Orange (58%), Agent White (31%), and Agent Blue (11%).

Ecological Effects of Agent Orange The most effective and most controversial of the herbicides was Agent Orange, a 50-50 mixture of 2,4-D and 2,4,5-T. During the war over 42 million kilograms (93 million pounds) of Agent Orange was sprayed on the swamps and forests of Vietnam, resulting in the decimation of 1.8 million hectares (4.5 million acres) of countryside and at least 190,000 hectares (470,000 acres) of farmland. Over half of the mangrove vegetation of South Vietnam (1930 square kilometers, or 744 square miles) and about 5% of the hardwood forests were destroyed. The forests alone represent about $500 million worth of wood, a supply that would last the country 30 years.

The prospect for these forests seems dim, especially since hardy weeds such as cogon grass and bamboo have invaded the deforested zones. Ecologists fear that these species may greatly delay recovery or prevent it altogether. The U.S. National Academy of Sciences estimates that defoliated mangroves may take 100 years to recover, because the destruction was so great that few seed sources remain.

Defoliants and numerous insecticides sprayed to control mosquitoes created an unprecedented ecological disaster in Vietnam, resulting in the death of numerous fish and animals. In one survey of a heavily sprayed forest, which was visited years after the war ended, the Harvard University biologist Peter Ashton found 24 species of birds and 5 species of mammals, compared with 145 and 170 bird species and 30 and 55 mammal species in two nearby forests that had not been sprayed. The total impact of such actions will never be known.

Health Effects of Agent Orange Agent Orange may have been the cause of serious medical problems that developed in soldiers and villagers throughout Vietnam. In 1969 the first indication of such health effects came from Saigon newspapers, which reported an increase in miscarriages and birth defects in babies born in local hospitals. Critics argued that such reports were merely a propaganda campaign aimed at the United States. But Agent Orange sprayed in Vietnam was contaminated with dioxin, a chemical that causes birth defects and cancer in mice and rats. Dioxin, discussed in more detail in Chapter 18, is believed to be 100,000 times more potent than the tranquilizer thalidomide, which has caused many birth defects in the United States (for a discussion of birth defects see Chapter 14).

U.S. and Australian soldiers fighting in herbicide-defoliated areas drank water and bathed in bomb craters believed to have been contaminated by Agent Orange, ate sweet potatoes and other vegetables from contaminated fields, and in some instances were doused with herbicides while in the field. Often unable to wash or change their clothes after such frequent exposures, soldiers developed severe headaches, nausea, diarrhea, internal bleeding, chloracne (a severe skin rash similar to acne), and depression.

In 1970, as a result of the public outcry in the United States over reported birth defects and miscarriages in the Vietnamese population, the government banned the use of Agent Orange in Vietnam. In addition the secretaries of Health, Education and Welfare and Agriculture suspended the use of 2,4,5-T in U.S. lakes and ponds, where it was used to control aquatic plants; on ditch banks, where it was used to control weeds; around homes and recreation sites; and on all crops except rice. Shortly after the suspension, the use of 2,4-D and 2,4,5-T was stepped up in U.S. forests, supposedly to increase the growth of commercial evergreens by reducing competition from hardwood trees. To this day the use of 2,4-D is virtually unrestricted. Studies have shown that 2,4,5-T probably does not cause birth defects itself. This has led some people to suggest that the herbicide be reauthorized if dioxin contamination can be eliminated. However, other studies indicate that 2,4,5-T causes an increase in hydrogen peroxide in cells, which, in turn, alters the DNA and may lead to cancer.

Starting in the late 1970s Vietnam veterans who had returned from the war began to suffer an unusual number of medical disorders. Once-healthy men experienced bouts of dizziness, nausea, insomnia, and diarrhea. Many men developed chloracne over large parts of their bodies, some developed blurred vision, and others suffered from fits of uncontrollable rage and depression. A high proportion of the men have fathered fetuses that were born dead or aborted prior to term and infants with multiple birth defects. Experts estimate that over 2000 defective babies will be born to Vietnam veterans. Other veterans have developed cancers such as lymphoma, leukemia, and testicular cancer, a rare disease normally found only in 6 of 100,000 young men. (Similar symptoms have been observed in people living near forested areas in Oregon and northern California that are sprayed with herbicide to eliminate deciduous trees and brush.)

The Australian government sponsored a study on health effects of 2,4-D and 2,4,5-T that were contaminated with dioxin at levels at least 20 to 50 times lower than the Agent Orange used in Vietnam. This survey showed no adverse effects. In addition, health statistics from a poorly run survey of an industrial accident in Italy where dioxin was released also showed no effect. Based on these studies, both of which had numerous faults, the U.S. Veterans Administration argued that veterans' claims were unfounded. However, a study of pilots and crews responsible for spraying Agent Orange is now under way in the United States to determine whether defoliants were the cause of the symptoms manifested in many veterans. This study will not be completed until the 1990s. The Veterans Administration has also begun a long-term health study of veterans.

Over 1200 disability claims have been filed with the Veterans Administration by U.S. soldiers, arguing that Agent Orange caused a host of disabilities. For many years the agency and chemical manufacturers denied any connection between defects and Agent Orange and dismissed the symptoms as the results of stress, or "post-Vietnam syndrome."

In spite of the lack of comprehensive medical study of Vietnam veterans, mounting evidence from the United States and abroad strongly supports a cause-and-effect relationship between Agent Orange and much of the illness described above. In 1986 a University of Kansas researcher, Shelia Hoar, and her colleagues found that farmers exposed to 2,4-D for 20 days or more a year were six times more likely to develop one type of cancer (non-Hodgkin's lymphoma) than the general public. Workers who mixed and applied the chemicals were eight times more likely to develop this cancer. Results from studies of workers at herbicide factories in Sweden; experiments with monkeys, rats, and mice; dioxin analyses of fatty tissues in Vietnam veterans; liver function tests in veterans; and studies of birth defects among offspring of Vietnamese soldiers all support the veterans' claims that Agent Orange produced the broad spectrum of symptoms described above.

Perhaps the most compelling evidence came from a study carried out by Vietnamese doctors. They examined the rate of birth defects in the offspring of 40,000 Vietnamese couples. The researchers found that women whose husbands had fought in South Vietnam, where Agent Orange was sprayed, were 3.5 times more likely to miscarry or give birth to defective children than women whose husbands had remained in the North during the war. American scientists who have studied the results, although expressing caution, find the study convincing. Even more recent evidence has implicated dioxin as the cause of soft-tissue sarcomas (cancers); veterans exposed to dioxin had a rate of soft-tissue sarcomas seven times higher than expected. Such findings have shifted the Veterans Administration's position on Agent Orange. In May 1984 manufacturers and Vietnam veterans reached an out-of-court settlement that established a $180-million fund for veterans and their families who claim injury from Agent Orange.

Treatment of Vietnam veterans suffering from chronic (long-term) debilitation may soon be possible with a drug called cholestyramine. Used to purge individuals poisoned with the insecticide kepone, this drug may prove successful in flushing dioxin from the fatty tissues of veterans where it is stored. Such a cure, if possible, could reverse the slow and painful deterioration that as many as 40,000 men are now experiencing. Whether it will prevent birth defects in yet unborn children remains to be seen.

Our doubts are traitors and make us lose the good we oft might win by fearing to attempt.

SHAKESPEARE

Summary

Each year, insects, weeds, bacteria, fungi, viruses, parasites, birds, rodents, and mammals consume or destroy an estimated 48% of the world's food crop. Reducing losses through pest control represents an enormous opportunity to increase world food supplies.

In recent years chemical pesticides have come to form the cornerstone of pest management. **Pesticides** are chemicals used to kill troublesome pests. The **first-generation pesticides** were simple preparations made of ashes, sulfur, and other chemicals. **Second-generation pesticides** are synthetic organic compounds like DDT. Some are **broad-spectrum** chemicals able to kill a wide variety of organisms. Others are **narrow-spectrum** pesticides used to control one or a few pests.

Second-generation pesticides fall into three classes: (1) chlorinated hydrocarbons, a high-risk group that is largely banned today; (2) organic phosphates, less risky, but still quite toxic; and (3) carbamates, widely used today because they tend to break down quickly and do not bioconcentrate as the other groups do.

Pesticide use has helped control pests but not without many problems. For example, some broad-spectrum pesticides kill predatory and parasitic insects that help control pests and potential pests. Pesticides also destroy beneficial insects such as honeybees. Perhaps the most striking problem is genetic resistance among pest populations, which has been met with increasing doses and new chemical preparations, resulting in considerable environmental pollution. DDT proved especially harmful to predatory bird populations, because it impaired eggshell deposition. Increasingly, evidence grew that many pesticides had a harmful effect on people, especially workers carelessly exposed on farms.

The problems with pesticide use have led many to suggest the need for an **integrated pest management** strategy that relies on environmental, genetic, chemical, and cultural controls.

Environmental controls are designed to alter a pest's immediate environment, making it lethal or inhospitable. Some options include increasing crop diversity, varying the time of planting, altering plant and soil nutrients, controlling adjacent crops and weeds, and introducing predators, parasites, and disease organisms. **Genetic controls** are alterations in the genetic composition of pests, crops, and livestock. In the sterile male technique, for example, captive-raised males of the pest species are sterilized and then released into fields, where they greatly outnumber wild, fertile males. This technique ensures a high percentage of infertile matings. Genetic resistance can be bred into plants and livestock or introduced through genetic engineering. A new arsenal of naturally occurring chemicals may also play a big role in pest control. For example, **sex attractant pheromones**, chemicals released by females to attract males, have been synthetically produced and marketed. Synthetic sex attractants can be used to draw males into traps laced with poison or sticky materials. Insect hormones that control vital life processes can also be applied to crops, throwing off the normal developmental cycle and killing the pests. Naturally occurring pesticides may also provide a partial answer to low-risk pest control.

The central goal of pest control is to reduce pest populations to levels that do not cause economic damage. Logic dictates that the cost of pest control should not exceed the economic benefits. External costs must be factored into the cost equation.

Herbicides are a type of pesticide used to control weeds. Despite the large number of herbicides in use today, 2,4-D and 2,4,5-T have received the most attention. They are nonpersistent synthetic organic compounds that, when sprayed on plants, increase the metabolic rate in cells so much that plants "grow to death."

Herbicides reduce the mechanical cultivation needed to control weeds, cut energy demand, and cut costs, but also have some drawbacks. For instance, some weeds that are normally no trouble are resistant to herbicides and grow wildly after others are killed. Some weeds also develop resistance to herbicides, requiring farmers to apply more or different varieties. Herbicides may also increase the need for insecticides and may make some crops more susceptible to disease.

Integrated weed management could reduce the use of herbicides and their adverse effects. Special wick applicators could be used to apply herbicide only on the weeds between rows. Proper spacing of rows for healthier crops, biological weed control, and crop rotation could all be used, too.

Herbicides were used extensively in the Vietnam War as defoliants to prevent guerrilla ambushes along roads and waterways and to deter the movement of enemy soldiers. The most effective, and most controversial, was Agent Orange, a 50-50 mixture of 2,4-D and 2,4,5-T. Sprayed on nearly 2 million hectares of countryside and farmland, Agent Orange created an unprecedented ecological disaster. It may also have been responsible for a number of medical problems in civilians and soldiers, because it was found to be contaminated with dioxin, a chemical that causes birth defects and cancer in mice and rats. Mounting evidence from the United States and abroad supports the view that Agent Orange and dioxin are responsible for illness, birth defects, and cancer in U.S. veterans. In 1970, the U.S. government banned its further use in Vietnam. The use of the herbicides in Agent Orange has continued virtually unchecked in the United States.

Discussion Questions

1. List and discuss reasons why pest damage is high in developed nations despite elaborate pest control strategies.
2. Describe some of the problems encountered with the use of pesticides. How can they be avoided?
3. Why do DDT and other chlorinated hydrocarbons persist in the environment?
4. What is integrated pest management? What advantages does it offer over current management techniques?
5. Why do crop rotation and increasing crop diversity cut back on pests?
6. Describe some of the biological control methods. Give examples.
7. Describe why the sterile male technique works.
8. Discuss some ways in which genetic engineering is being used to help cut down on pest damage.
9. Outline how you would go about determining the costs and benefits of modern pest control techniques.
10. What is Agent Orange, why was it used in Vietnam, and why were some soldiers exposed to high levels of it?
11. List and describe the pros and cons of herbicide use.

Suggested Readings

Barrons, K. C. (1981). *Are Pesticides Really Necessary?* Chicago: Regnery. A balanced view of pesticides.

Boraiko, A. A., and Ward, F. (1980). The Pesticide Dilemma. *National Geographic* 157 (2): 145–183. A general account of pesticides and pest management.

Bosch, R. van der. (1978). *The Pesticide Conspiracy*. New York: Doubleday. A study of the influence of pesticide manufacturers on integrated pest management.

Carson, R. (1962). *Silent Spring*. Boston: Houghton Mifflin. The book that raised worldwide alarm over the use of pesticides.

Clark, D. R., and Krynitsky, A. J. (1983). DDT: Recent Contamination in New Mexico and Arizona? *Environment* 25 (5): 27–32. Information on continued use of banned DDT.

Davis, D. E. (1979). Herbicides in Peace and War. *BioScience* 29 (2): 84–94. An early account of the controversy over Agent Orange.

Dreistadt, S. H., and Dahlsten, D. L. (1986). California's Medfly Campaign: Lessons from the Field. *Environment* 28 (6): 18–20, 40–44. Sober look at pest control.

Galston, A. W. (1979). Herbicides: A Mixed Blessing. *BioScience* 29 (2): 85–90. An interesting view of herbicides and their effects on humans and other organisms.

Goldberg, E. D. (1986). TBT: An Environmental Dilemma. *Environment* 28 (8): 17–20, 42–44. Worthwhile article.

Heckman, C. W. (1982). Pesticide effects on aquatic habitats. *Environ. Sci. and Technol.* 16 (1): 1982: 48A–57A. Detailed analysis on the effects of pesticides on aquatic systems.

Hileman, B. (1982). Herbicides in Agriculture. *Eniron. Sci. and Technol.* 16 (12): 645A–650A. A thoughtful analysis of the benefits and costs of herbicides.

Josephson, J. (1983). Pesticides of the Future. *Eniron. Sci. and Technol.* 17 (10): 464A–468A. Overview of chemical pesticides.

McEwen, F. L. (1978). Food Production—The Challenge for Pesticides. *BioScience* 28 (12): 773–776. An excellent presentation on the history of pesticide use.

Metcalf, R. L., and Kelman, A. (1981). Integrated Pest Management in China. *Environment* 23 (4): 6–13. Superb account of pesticide problems and solutions in China.

Regenstein, L. (1982). *America the Poisoned*. Washington, D.C.: Acropolis. Detailed account of pesticides and their effects.

Wilcox, F. A. (1983). *Waiting for an Army to Die: The Tragedy of Agent Orange*. New York: Vintage Books. Moving account of the herbicide's effects on Vietnam veterans.

Hazardous Wastes: Progress and Pollution

There is nothing more frightful than ignorance in action.

GOETHE

Shenandoah Stables was a large and successful quarter-horse ranch in Moscow Hills, Missouri, northwest of St. Louis. But in the last week of May 1971 a routine procedure triggered a disastrous chain of events. To control dust, the owners had hired a man to spread 3800 liters (1000 gallons) of waste automobile oil on the arena. Shortly after the oil had been applied, one of the owners noticed strong chemical odors in the air in the barn and on the grounds. A day later she discovered dozens of dead sparrows on the floor of the barn. Then the dogs and cats at the ranch began to lose their fur and to dehydrate. By mid-June 11 cats and five dogs had died, each with the same symptoms.

Of 85 horses routinely exercised in the arena, 43 died within a year. Autopsies revealed that their internal organs were swollen and bloody. In 1971, 41 horses on the ranch had been bred; most pregnancies ended in spontaneous abortion. Of those born alive, all but one died within a few months.

Soon afterward, both of the owner's daughters, who lived at the stables, became ill, complaining of severe headaches; one developed sores on her hands. The other began bleeding internally and was hospitalized. The owner herself suffered chest pains, headaches, and diarrhea.

What caused the poisonings and deaths? Tests on the oil applied to the arena showed dioxin, PCBs, and other highly toxic contaminants. Investigators found that the oil had been sold to a company that was supposed to remove

(a)

(b)

Figure 18-1   (*a*) In May 1984, workers from the Neville Chemical Plant in Santa Fe Springs, California, began covering soil believed to be contaminated with highly toxic chemical wastes. The covering prevented the toxic soil from blowing from the site. Company officials were recently found guilty of illegally disposing of hazardous wastes. (*b*) Pollution Abatement Services chemical dump at Oswego, N.Y. The dump is now inactive and awaiting cleanup.

the contaminants before reuse. Instead, the company spread the oil on at least four sites in Missouri, leaving behind "a trail of sickness and death," in the words of the state assistant attorney general.

The tragedy at Shenandoah Stables is representative of a much larger problem: illegal and irresponsible hazardous waste disposal that continues even today (Figure 18-1). What we can do to clean up the mess and what we can do to prevent further disasters are the topics of this chapter.

Hazardous Wastes: Coming to Terms with the Problem

Love Canal: The Awakening

Hazardous wastes are waste products of industry that if not disposed of properly or destroyed pose a threat to the environment. The problem of hazardous waste caught

the attention of the American public in the 1970s when toxic chemicals began to ooze out of a dump known as Love Canal, in New York near Niagara Falls. The incident has forever changed the way Americans view hazardous wastes.

The story of Love Canal began in the 1880s when William T. Love began digging a canal that would run from the Niagara River just above Niagara Falls to a point on the river below the falls. For one reason or another, the canal was never completed. Only a small remnant of the canal remained in the early 1900s. In 1942 the Hooker Chemical Company signed an agreement with the canal's new owner, the Niagara Power and Development Corporation, to dump wastes there. In 1946 Hooker bought the site, and from 1947 to 1952 it dumped over 20,000 metric tons of highly toxic and carcinogenic wastes, including the deadly poisonous dioxin.

In 1952 the story took an ironic twist. In that year the city of Niagara Falls began condemnation proceedings on the property that would allow it to use the land for an elementary school and residential community. With no

(a)

(b)

Figure 18-2 (*a*) House is bulldozed in the Love Canal area of Niagara Falls, N.Y.
(*b*) A young but concerned resident.

other choice, Hooker sold the land for $1 in exchange for a release from any future liability. Hooker insists that it warned against any construction on the dump site itself, but it allegedly never disclosed the real danger of building on the abandoned dump. Before turning the land over to the city, Hooker sealed the dump with a clay cap and topsoil, once thought sufficient to protect hazardous waste dumps.

Troubles began in January 1954, however, when workers removed the clay cap during the construction of the school. In the late 1950s rusting and leaking barrels of toxic waste began to surface. Children playing near them suffered chemical burns; some became ill and died. Hooker asserts that it warned the school board not to allow children to play in chemically contaminated areas, but it apparently made no effort to warn local residents of the potential problems.

The problem continued for years. Chemical fumes took the bark off trees and wiped out grass and garden vegetables. Smelly pools of toxins welled up on the surface. In the early 1970s after a period of heavy rainfall, the water table rose, and basements in homes near the dump began to flood with a thick, black sludge of toxic chemicals. The chemical smells in homes around the dump site became intolerable.

Tests in 1978 on water, air, and soil in the area detected 82 different chemical contaminants, a dozen of which were known or suspected carcinogens. The State Health Department found in 1978 that nearly one of every three pregnant women in the area had miscarried, a rate much higher than expected. Birth defects were observed in 5 of 24 children. Another study, released in 1979 by Dr. Beverly Paigen of the Roswell Cancer Institute, showed that over half of the children born between 1974 and 1978 to families living in areas where groundwater was leaching toxic chemicals from the dump had birth defects. In this study the overall incidence of birth defects in the Love Canal area was one in five, compared with a normal rate of less than one in ten (Chapter 14). The miscarriage rate was 25 in 100, compared with 8 in 100 women moving into the area. Asthma was four times as prevalent in wet areas as dry areas in the region; the incidence of urinary and convulsive disorders was almost three times higher than expected. The incidence of nasal and sinus infections, respiratory diseases, rashes, and headaches was also elevated.

As a result of public outcry the school was soon closed. The state fenced off the canal and evacuated several hundred families (Figure 18-2). President Carter declared the dump a disaster area. In May 1980 a new study revealed high levels of genetic damage among residents living near the canal. An additional 780 families were evacuated from outlying areas.

As of early 1981 Love Canal had cost the state of New York about $35 million and the federal government $7 million for cleanup, research, and relocation of residents. Lawsuits amounting to over $3 million have been filed against the city of Niagara Falls.

A 1980 study by the EPA showed that chemical contamination was pretty much limited to the canal area (the

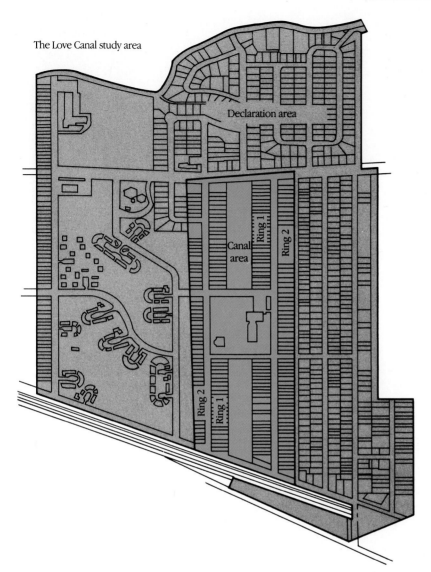

The Love Canal study area

Declaration area

Canal area

Ring 1

Ring 2

Ring 2

Ring 1

Figure 18-3 Love Canal. Area within the colored rectangle was closed off, and citizens were evacuated. Citizens were also evacuated from the declaration area, but tests have shown that hazardous wastes have not migrated into this area.

actual dump), an area immediately south of it, and two rows of houses on either side of the canal (Figure 18-3). The last group of residents to be evacuated, the report said, were probably moved out unnecessarily. The EPA study also showed that the dump had contaminated shallow groundwater, but not the deeper aquifers. The EPA concluded that further migration of toxic chemicals was highly unlikely.

The Dimensions of a Toxic Nightmare

Love Canal began the frenetic search for hazardous waste dumps and illegal waste-disposal practices that is still going on. Many people, previously unable to explain bizarre diseases in their family, soon found the answer in nearby waste dumps or factories that leaked hazardous wastes into groundwater, nearby streams, or the air.

In the years following the Love Canal incident the American public has been barraged by a list of startling statistics showing that what appeared to be an isolated incident was in fact just the tip of the iceberg. The EPA, for instance, estimated that there were 14 other sites in Niagara Falls alone that it considered an "imminent hazard." Nationwide, the EPA announced, Love Canal was one of a thousand or more sites in need of a cleanup. Today, some experts put the number of dangerous hazardous waste facilities that need to be cleaned up well over 10,000.

Making matters worse, each year factories create an estimated 54 to 72 million metric tons of waste considered hazardous by federal standards and about 200 million metric tons of hazardous waste covered by state regulations. The total is well over a ton per person. But the United States is not alone. European countries also produce millions of tons of hazardous waste each year.

Even more startling than the sheer amount of waste produced is its fate. Until quite recently 90% of the hazardous wastes in the United States ended up in abandoned

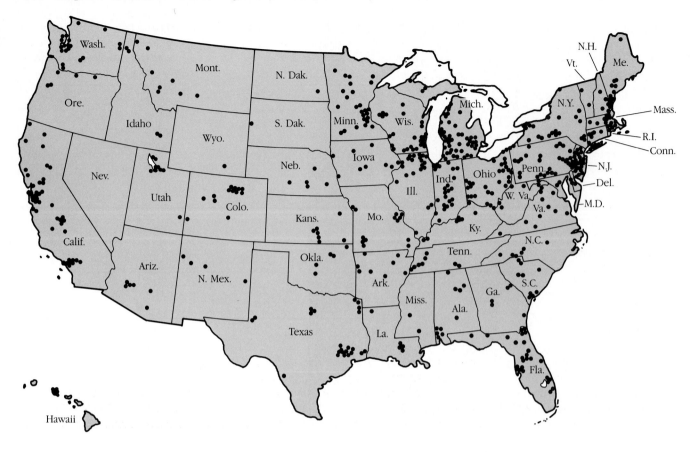

Alaska has no sites. Sites in U.S. territories not included.

Figure 18-4 Each dot represents a hazardous waste dump that poses a serious threat to health. These sites were on the 1986 priority list for cleanup, but there are thousands of other dangerous waste dumps in the U.S.

warehouses; in rivers, streams, and lakes; in leaky landfills that contaminate groundwater; in fields and forests; and along highways.

Ill-conceived and irresponsible waste disposal has left a legacy of polluted groundwater and contaminated land. The U.S. Office of Technology Assessment recently issued a report contending that it would cost $100 billion to clean up the 10,000 sites in the United States that pose a serious threat to health (Figure 18-4).

The ecologist Barry Commoner recently remarked about hazardous wastes, "We are poisoning ourselves and our posterity." In truth, improper waste disposal has left behind a long list of costly effects: (1) groundwater contamination, (2) well closures, (3) habitat destruction, (4) human disease, (5) soil contamination, (6) fish kills, (7) livestock disease, (8) sewage treatment plant damage, (9) town closures, and (10) difficult cleanups.

A decade after the United States first awakened to the hazardous waste issue, experts believe that we are in for a much longer, more difficult battle than once anticipated. Lee Thomas, head of the EPA, argued, "There are far more sites that are far more difficult to deal with than anybody ever anticipated." Despite an outpouring of national sentiment calling for cleanups, in the first five years of work only six sites had been cleaned up and, many critics contend, not very well. Delays only prolong the spread of toxic substances and human exposure.

LUST—It's Not What You Think

You feel dizzy. Your head spins. Your insides ache. You haven't been yourself for weeks. What may be ailing you is LUST—but not the usual kind. Your symptoms may be caused by the latest in a long list of hazardous chemical problems, groundwater pollution from a leaking underground storage tank, which EPA's top acronymists have dubbed LUST.

Underground tanks containing petroleum by-products, toxic chemicals, and hazardous wastes deteriorate over time, springing leaks and dripping out their toxic substances. Moisture and soil acidity are primarily responsible for the leaks. The environmentalists' and health officials' main concern is the potential effect on groundwater and human health. Even a small leak can contaminate large quantities of groundwater. For example, a leak of only 1.5 cups of hazardous liquid per hour can contaminate nearly 3.8 million liters (1 million gallons) of groundwater in a single day. Contaminated groundwater is very difficult and expensive to clean up (Chapter 16).

Many people in affected areas have switched to bottled water, only a temporary solution at best. Contaminated water used for baths and showers can also be dangerous. Benzene, a component of gasoline that can cause cancer, is absorbed through the skin when bathing. Showering generates dangerous vapors that can cause skin and eye irritation.

A report by the New York Department of Environmental Conservation suggests that at least half of the state's underground steel tanks containing petroleum products over 15 years old may now be leaking. Nationwide, 3 to 5 million underground storage tanks containing hazardous materials dot the United States.

Major oil companies have already spent millions to clean up polluted groundwater and soil. Many other companies have installed new tanks at a quicker pace to avoid further contamination, but the cost of such actions can be exorbitant. Chevron alone estimates its replacement costs at about $100 million. Unfortunately, half of U.S service stations are owned by independent dealers, who generally are not financially able to replace the leaking tanks. Many tanks that could be leaking are under schools, police stations, and private homes.

Attacking Hazardous Wastes on Two Fronts

Two hazardous waste problems face society today: (1) what to do with the enormous amounts of hazardous waste produced each year, and (2) how to deal with the leaking waste disposal sites or areas like Times Beach, Missouri, which was contaminated by road oil containing dioxin.

What to Do with Today's Waste

The Legal Approach In 1976 congressional representatives proudly announced a tough, new law—the **Resource Conservation and Recovery Act (RCRA)**—designed to cut back on illegal and improper waste dis-

posal. What are its major provisions? First, RCRA named the Environmental Protection Agency as the hazardous waste watchdog. The EPA's first role was to determine which wastes were hazardous. Second, RCRA called on the agency to establish a nationwide reporting system for all companies handling hazardous chemicals. This requirement created a trail of paperwork that would follow hazardous wastes from the moment they were generated to the moment they were disposed of—from cradle to grave. This stipulation, Congress believed, would make it difficult for waste generators to dump wastes improperly. Third, and perhaps most important, RCRA directed the EPA to set industrywide standards for packaging, shipping, and disposal of wastes. Only licensed facilities could receive wastes.

Unfortunately, RCRA's implementation has been slow. It was not until four years after Congress passed the act that the EPA came up with its first hazardous waste regulations. To the dismay of many, the regulations were full of loopholes, so much so that about 40 million metric tons of pollutants escaped control each year!

Public pressure mounted, and in 1984 Congress passed a set of tough amendments to RCRA to eliminate loopholes and ensure proper waste disposal. For example, under the original law if a company produced under 1000 kilograms (2200 pounds) of hazardous wastes per month, it could dump them in a local garbage dump if it wanted. Today any generator of waste over 100 kilograms (220 pounds) must follow the same guidelines imposed on large waste producers. In a bold move Congress's 1984 amendments declared that it was the national policy to reduce or eliminate land disposal of hazardous waste. Congress made it clear that land-disposal technologies must be considered a last resort. Preference is given to recycling, destruction, and other processes, discussed below. The newest additions to RCRA also address the problem of leaking underground storage tanks. Beginning in May 1985 all newly installed underground tanks must be protected from corrosion for the life of the tank. The lining of the tank must be compatible with stored substances. Owners and operators must have methods for detecting leaks, must take corrective action when a leak occurs, and must report such action.

Technological Answers In 1983 the prestigious National Academy of Sciences issued a lengthy report outlining, in order of desirability, many of the United States' options for handling hazardous wastes (Figure 18-5). At the top of the list are **in-plant** options, changes that can be made to reduce hazardous waste production. Changes in the way products are manufactured can drastically cut waste. In some instances wastes can be separated and purified, yielding salable or reusable chemicals. **Recycling and reuse** strategies help cut waste and may

Figure 18-5   A three-tier hierarchy of options for handling hazardous wastes. The top tier reduces the hazardous waste stream; it contains the most desirable options. The middle tier converts hazardous materials into nonhazardous or less hazardous substances. Perpetual storage, the lowest tier, is the least desirable, but often the cheapest, alternative.

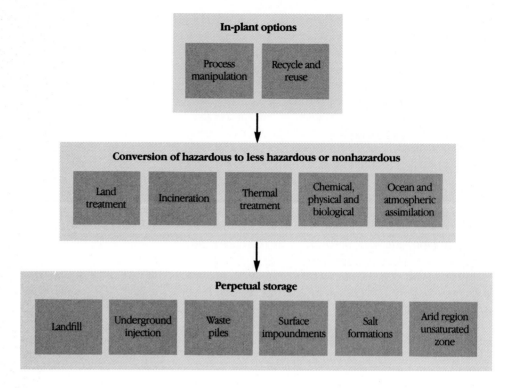

save companies millions of dollars a year in operating costs. The recycling-and-reuse option also eliminates the cost of waste disposal, cuts down on potential environmental and health damage, and saves valuable raw materials, including energy.

Not every waste product can be used, however. Therefore, some waste will always be produced. The academy recommended that these remaining wastes be destroyed or detoxified, converted to less hazardous materials. **Detoxification** can be accomplished for certain types of waste by applying them to land and mixing them with the top layer of soil, where they are broken down by chemical reactions, oxidation by sunlight, or by bacteria or other organisms in the soil. Some nondegradable wastes may be absorbed onto soil particles and held there indefinitely. Others may migrate into deeper layers. Land treatment is an inexpensive option, but great care would be necessary to avoid polluting ecosystems, poisoning cattle and other animals, and contaminating groundwater.

Destroying hazardous wastes by **incineration** is an attractive option for getting rid of organic wastes. High-temperature furnaces at stationary waste disposal sites, on ships that can burn their wastes at sea, and on mobile trailers are all workable (Figure 18-6). In each of these sites, oil or natural gas is burned, and hazardous substances are injected into the furnace or mixed with the fuel before combustion. In 1985 the EPA announced that its new mobile incinerator destroyed 99.9999% of the dioxin wastes in soil and liquids. Officials at the EPA are

optimistic that the incinerator will be useful in cleaning up dioxin wastes at sites targeted for cleanup by Congress.

Incineration can provide energy for plant operations, can efficiently eliminate toxic organic wastes such as dioxin and PCBs, and can reduce perpetual storage. However, communities often object to incinerators, fearing environmental contamination because of possible spills during transport or emissions and leaks from the plants.

Low-temperature decomposition of cyanide and toxic organics such as pesticides also offers some promise. In this technique wastes are mixed with air and maintained under high pressure while being heated to 450° to 600° C (840° to 1100° F); during the process organic compounds are broken into smaller biodegradable molecules. Valuable materials can be extracted and recycled. This process uses less energy than incineration.

Chemical, physical, and biological agents can be used to detoxify or neutralize hazardous wastes. For example, lime can neutralize sulfuric acid. Ozone can be used to break up small organic molecules, nitrogen compounds, and cyanides. Toxic wastes can be encapsulated with a plastic waterproof seal, lowering the risk of land disposal. Many bacteria can degrade or detoxify organic wastes and may prove helpful in the future. New strains capable of destroying a wide variety of organic wastes may be developed through genetic engineering.

In-plant modifications and conversion technologies that destroy or detoxify wastes cannot rid us of all of our waste. By various estimates, 25% to 40% of the waste

Figure 18-6 A mobile hazardous waste incinerator owned and operated by the EPA avoids the problem of transporting exceptionally dangerous materials.

stream will remain even after the best efforts to recycle, reuse, and destroy it.

Wastes that cannot be destroyed entirely and detoxified wastes as well must be stored. Residual waste can be dumped in **secured landfills**, excavated pits lined by synthetic liners and thick, impermeable layers of clay. To lower the risk of leakage, landfills should be placed in arid regions—neither over aquifers nor near major water supplies. Special drains must be installed to catch any liquids that leak out of the site. Groundwater and air should be monitored to detect leaks.

Growing public opposition to hazardous wastes makes it more difficult for companies to find dump sites. Observers have labeled this the NIMBY syndrome—get rid of the stuff, but *not in my* backyard. It seems that most people want the products that make waste, but no one wants the wastes dumped (or even burned) nearby.

Even though the EPA has issued tough new regulations for landfills, critics argue that landfills are only a temporary solution. No matter how well constructed they are, they will eventually leak. Landfills are one of the cheapest waste disposal practices in use today and are therefore highly favored by industry. But savings today, critics warn, are inevitably charged to future generations. In an attempt to avoid making problems for future generations, the EPA has drawn up a list of chemicals that cannot be disposed of in landfills.

Other methods of **perpetual storage** include (1) use of surface impoundments and specially built warehouses that hold wastes in ideal conditions and prevent any material from leaking into the environment, (2) deposition in geologically stable salt formations, and (3) deposition deep in the ground in arid regions where groundwater is absent.

Disposing of Radioactive Wastes High-level radioactive wastes are some of the United States' most hazardous wastes, but they have long been ignored. Even today, despite the buildup of 12,600 metric tons of spent uranium from commercial reactors and 10,000 metric tons of Department of Defense waste from weapons production, the country is without a solution. The seriousness of continued delay is underscored by three facts: many radioactive wastes have a long lifetime, some materials can concentrate in animal tissues, and radiation poses a serious threat to human health (Chapter 12).

High-level radioactive waste is not a problem that will go away, even though the American nuclear power industry faces bad times. By 1998, experts predict, 30,000 more tons of radioactive wastes will have been generated by existing commercial plants. Expanded nuclear capacity (possible in the future), continued operation of the existing facilities, and construction of nuclear weapons necessitate long-term, low-risk storage of nuclear wastes, and soon. But progress in developing storage sites has been painfully slow.

The 1982 **Nuclear Waste Policy Act** established a strict timetable for the Department of Energy to choose sites for disposal of high-level radioactive wastes. According to the act, the Department of Energy (DOE) had to select a site by 1987, and the site must be in operation by 1998. States have the right to veto sites unless overridden by

Getting Tough on Polluters

For years part of corporate America has been dumping hazardous wastes in rusty drums in empty fields, sometimes without even burying them. More resourceful companies have diverted them through hidden pipes to rivers and streams. Others have mixed them with oil that is later used to control road dust or is burned in apartment buildings and office buildings. Still others have dumped their wastes in sandy-bottomed pits, where they gradually seep into the groundwater. Some waste disposal companies rented warehouses, stored their wastes, then vanished, leaving the landlord with a warehouse full of dangerous chemicals. In one sordid affair Massachusetts officials found that truckers carrying liquid waste just drove down the turnpike at night and opened their spigots, letting toxic liquids spill out on the highways.

Thanks to tougher state and federal laws, it's getting harder for companies to dump their hazardous wastes. But the days of illegal waste disposal are far from over. According to an EPA estimate, one out of seven American companies that generates hazardous wastes may have disposed of them illegally in the past two years.

All across the nation citizens are banning together to fight illegal disposal. Their battle is being aided by state and federal officials, who when tipped off about potential violators, are staking out the companies, gathering evidence, and helping prosecutors put many of their officials behind bars. In Los Angeles, for instance, a toxic strike force now operates with investigators from the police, fire, and sanitation departments and from the Los Angeles County Health Department. One of the task force's first targets was David Peairs, who was under contract to dispose of hazardous wastes for several companies. Peairs simply diverted the liquid wastes into the sewer, reaping huge profits in the process. With police cordoning off the plant, strike force members went to work examining company records and inspecting the facilities. Peairs eventually pleaded no contest, was fined $100,000, and was sentenced to three months in jail. His sentence sent shock waves through California. It was the first time in the state's history that an individual had gone to jail for violating an environmental law.

In 1984 the Los Angeles strike force gathered evidence that led to the conviction of the president of American Caster. He received a $20,000 fine and a six-month jail sentence for ordering his employees to bury highly flammable toxic wastes away from the company grounds.

The strike force and the court are sending a message to white-collar executives who knowingly dump hazardous wastes. The message is that, if caught, they will be fined and could very well end up in jail.

Even the EPA has gotten into the act in recent years. Its agents, trained in firearms, stakeouts, and self-defense, are recruited from police departments, the FBI, and the Treasury Department. On the frontier of criminal enforcement, these agents often risk their lives "busting" hazardous waste violators.

"Disposing of hazardous wastes is more profitable than selling narcotics," notes one special agent of the EPA's Office of Criminal Enforcement. Because of these profits, violators may resort to violence, making the job dangerous and stressful.

In 1983 EPA investigators helped crack a case against the A. C. Lawrence Leather Company, in New Hampshire. The company had received $1.5 million from the EPA to help construct a project to demonstrate the feasibility of a special waste-treatment system. Instead of building the system, officials of the company pocketed the money and piped the waste into a nearby stream. The EPA got wind of the deceit. After three months of investigation, EPA agents arrested the president, vice-president, and three members of the board of directors, who were later convicted, fined, and sentenced to thousands of hours of community service, because they had no previous felony convictions.

EPA agents were deputized in 1984 as federal marshals for the first time, a move that gave them the power to enforce U.S. toxic substance laws. The biggest problem facing the EPA's 32 agents is the large number of violators. Because cases are generally complicated, no agent can handle more than two at a time. With months of investigation and trial time, agents are spread too thin. Even though states and the FBI provide assistance from time to time, the task of enforcing the hazardous waste laws is overwhelming. Compounding the lack of personnel is a severe budgetary constraint.

Critics argue that increased personnel and funding are necessary to put tighter reins on illegal hazardous disposal. Many violators must know that they stand a reasonable chance of getting caught and convicted before they will halt the dangerous and illegal waste disposal practices so rampant today.

Source: Adapted from Wexler, M. (1985), "Strike Force," *National Wildlife* 23 (4): 38–41; and Adler, B. (1985), "Risky Business," *Sierra* 70 (6): 22, 24, 25, 27.

both houses of Congress. If a veto stands, a new site must be chosen. Sites in Nevada, Washington, and Texas have been selected among many others. In 1986 the Washington site was dropped. Because of unavoidable delays the DOE selection deadline has already been pushed back to March 1991. Nevertheless, geologists from the U.S. Geological Survey warn that there isn't enough time to collect adequate hydrological data for a site that must contain high-level radioactive waste for tens of thousands of years. Despite the clamor of many critics the DOE is forging ahead and plans to open a facility by 1998.

Site selection depends in large measure on the relative safety of different methods of storage. Many authorities believe that deep geological disposal is the best option for dealing with dangerous radioactive wastes. However, little is known about the interaction between heat generated from radioactive wastes and the rock and nearby groundwater. Still, deep rock and salt formations 600 to 1200 meters (2000 to 4000 feet) below the surface in geologically stable regions are believed to be the best option for keeping wastes from entering groundwater and contaminating the environment.

Some people have suggested transporting wastes into space. Cost, energy requirements, and material requirements would be major problems. Disposal of radioactive wastes from a single 1000-megawatt nuclear plant would cost over $1 million a year. Furthermore, radioactive capsules shot into space might someday return to earth.

Others have suggested dumping radioactive wastes on uninhabited lands in the Arctic and Antarctica. Too little is known about the effects of this disposal technique for experts to assess its safety and effectiveness.

Radioactive waste can be bombarded with neutrons in special reactors to **transmute**, or convert, some of it into less harmful substances. However, existing reactors do a poor job of altering cesium-137 and strontium-90, two of the more dangerous by-products of nuclear fission.

Seabed disposal has been used in the past by the United States and European countries but is now forbidden. Still, some scientists suggest that the seabed may provide a site for radioactive wastes; the effects are difficult to predict.

A final suggestion has been to build special tanks on the ground: individual canisters would be placed in enormous 35-ton steel casks surrounded by a thick concrete covering. Canisters might also be stored in cooled and guarded warehouses.

Ironically, the United States has spent billions of dollars of private and public money on nuclear reactors but very little on research on radioactive wastes. The disposal issue is independent of the future of nuclear weapons and nuclear power; a complete ban on nuclear weapons and nuclear power would not solve the problems of accumulated waste. Therefore, wisdom dictates establishing a

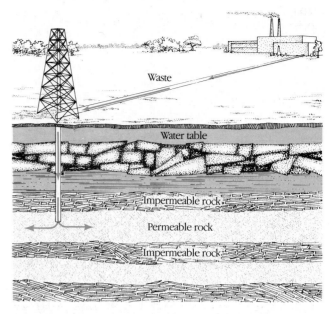

Figure 18-7 Deep well injection. Careful site analysis must be made to ensure that wastes will not migrate into groundwater, and ideally hazardous wastes must be removed from the waste water.

cost-effective and low-risk disposal method, keeping in mind the costs to future societies.

Some Obstacles Hazardous waste production has dropped steadily between 1980 and the present in the United States. This encouraging trend resulted partly because of a slump in the chemical industry but also because of in-plant efforts to reduce hazardous waste production by process modification, recycling, and reuse. Still the nation is not out of the woods. Tens of thousands of tons of waste are cranked out every day. Some companies continue to dump their wastes illegally whenever they can get away with it.

Another problem is that much of the United States' hazardous waste (85%) is highly diluted in water that is released by various industrial processes. This dilute waste stream is typically pumped into deep wells, from which hazardous substances may leak into ground water. (Figure 18-7). The sheer volume of this polluted water has made it hard to regulate. Removing the hazardous substances from the water is extremely costly, so most plant owners are unwilling to make the investment in waste water treatment. To cut down on deep-well discharges, inexpensive techniques must be developed to separate the hazardous wastes.

Ironically, one of the biggest hurdles to overcome is posed by the EPA. Despite the agency's commitment to cutting back on dumping wastes in landfills, its permits for alternative technologies are costly and difficult to obtain. Filing for a permit to burn hazardous waste, for instance, may cost a company $250,000 or more in legal fees. Furthermore, companies are caught in a catch-22 when applying for a permit. They need information on the performance of their equipment but can't get the information without a permit.

One further obstacle is a proposed tax on hazardous waste burned to generate energy. This tax, which has been considered by Congress, could destroy the economic incentive that currently makes incineration a highly profitable way to offset the high cost of energy and hazardous waste disposal.

Cleaning Up Past Mistakes

In June 1983 the 2400 residents of Times Beach, Missouri, agreed to sell nearly all of their 800 homes and 30 businesses to the federal government for $35 million. Why, you might ask, would Washington's bureaucrats want a contaminated piece of real estate in Missouri? The answer isn't that they really wanted to purchase the town, but that they had to. The roads in Times Beach, like the arena at Shenandoah Stables, had been sprayed with oil to hold down dust. The same company provided the service and the oil, which was contaminated by dioxin and other toxic wastes (Figure 18-8). Studies showed that dioxin levels in the soil were 100 to 300 times higher than levels considered to be harmful during long-term exposure. The town had to go.

Today, Times Beach is a ghost town bordered by a tall chain-link fence. Its only occupants are occasional EPA officials and scientists from a handful of companies who are there to test ways of detoxifying the soil.

The $35-million purchase price for this contaminated piece of real estate came from a special fund, called the **Superfund**. Created in 1980, the Superfund was part of an extensive piece of legislation with an equally unwieldy title, the **Comprehensive Environmental Response, Compensation and Liability Act**, CERCLA for short. Commonly called the Superfund Act, the law makes owners and operators of hazardous waste dump sites and contaminated areas, as well as their customers, responsible for cleanup costs and property damage. More than anything else, it has forced the hazardous waste community to take serious measures to prevent further contamination. As one industry representative put it, "You are liable for your waste forever."

The Superfund Act is known primarily for its $1.6-billion fund, derived mostly from taxes on oil and chemical industries and slightly from the taxpayers. The money was earmarked for two purposes: cleaning up contaminated sites and paying for damage to property.

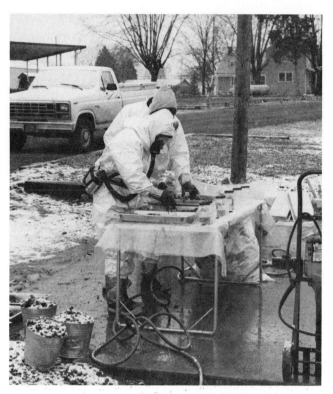

Figure 18-8 Times Beach, Missouri. Two EPA workers testing the soil for dioxin.

The Superfund Act was heralded as a breakthrough that would permit the EPA to begin cleaning up contaminated areas and leaking dump sites. Unfortunately, it didn't work out that way. One of the first problems was that it required states to pick up the tab for part of the cleanup, but only eight states had funds for this purpose. Without money, the other states were disqualified; their dump sites remained untouched.

A second problem arose from the unexpectedly high cost of cleanup. Stabilizing a leaking pond designed to hold hazardous wastes cost the EPA $500,000. A study to determine what chemicals were leaking from another site cost the agency $800,000. Five years after the fund was set up, more than $1 billion had been spent and only six sites had been cleaned up; 1800 sites remained on the EPA's cleanup list. Experts cautiously predict that full cleanup will require 50 years and at least $100 billion.

A third problem with the Superfund is that the money cannot be used to compensate victims of illegal dumping of hazardous wastes for personal injury or death. The act provides only for the cleanup of contaminated areas and compensation for damage to property. According to Senator George Mitchell of Maine, "Under the legislation it's all right to hurt people but not trees." Many people believe that a fund similar to worker's compensation is needed to provide victims with some immediate assistance.

Initial mismanagement by top EPA officials delayed serious action by the agency. Officials negotiated with owners of hazardous waste dumps to begin private cleanups, partly to eliminate the need for state money. Critics argued that the EPA let some companies off too easily, that cleanups were superficial, and that future liability was waived in some agreements, meaning that if problems developed in the future, companies would bear no responsibility. Investigations conducted in 1983 led the EPA's top leadership to resign or be fired because of the issue.

Reauthorized in October of 1986, CERCLA will provide $9 billion over a five-year period for cleanup. Thomas, the EPA's administrator, pledged that 650 of the nation's 2000 worst sites would be cleaned up by 1990. Many observers are concerned, however, that cleanup efforts will merely shift the problem from one spot to another. They note that the federal plan, in many cases, is to clean up old dumps by removing the materials and trucking them to secured landfills. Should these begin to leak in the future, as many critics believe, the problem will begin all over again.

Rectifying the improper disposal of hazardous wastes and improving waste disposal practices is as gargantuan a problem as the waste heap itself. With 60,000 generators of hazardous materials and 15,000 haulers in the United States, complicated legal and technological solutions are necessary. We are well on our way.

But what about our personal actions? Is there anything we can do individually to reduce hazardous wastes? Each of us can contribute by properly disposing of oil and other potentially toxic wastes, avoiding toxic chemicals such as pesticides and herbicides, and reducing our consumption of nonessential goods, whose production creates the problem that poisons our land and water. Together, millions of Americans using resources wisely can make significant inroads into the hazardous waste problem. Daniel Webster once wrote, "Liberty exists in proportion to wholesome restraint." A little restraint on each of our parts can go a long way toward freeing ourselves and future generations from the hazards of toxic wastes.

It is not enough for a nation to have a handful of heroes. What we need are generations of responsible people.

RICHARD D. LAMM

Summary

The problem of hazardous waste caught the attention of the American public in the 1970s when toxic chemicals began to ooze out of a dump, known as Love Canal, near Niagara Falls. That incident forever changed the way Americans view hazardous wastes. It began a frenetic search for hazardous dump sites and ways to halt illegal waste disposal practices that continues today.

Shortly after Love Canal the true proportions of the hazardous waste problem became evident. Ten thousand waste dumps need cleaning up, and millions of tons of waste are produced every year. Ill-conceived and irresponsible waste disposal has left a legacy of polluted groundwater and contaminated land. Cleanup could take 50 years and cost around $100 billion.

The latest in a long list of hazardous chemical problems stems from LUST—leaking underground storage tanks. Millions of tanks holding gasoline and other petroleum by-products and hazardous wastes of all kinds may be leaking. Health officials' main concern is the potential effect on groundwater and human health.

Two hazardous waste problems face society today: (1) what to do with the enormous amounts of waste produced each year and (2) how to deal with leaking and contaminated waste disposal sites.

In 1976 Congress passed the **Resource Conservation and Recovery Act**, aimed at cutting back on illegal and improper waste disposal. RCRA called on the EPA to determine which wastes were hazardous and how they should be handled and disposed of. A reporting network was established to trace hazardous wastes from cradle to grave. The EPA also began issuing permits for waste disposal. Unfortunately, implementation has been slow. Too many loopholes existed in the legislation, allowing much hazardous waste to escape control. New amendments closed many of the loopholes and tightened the net on hazardous wastes.

There are many technological options for controlling hazardous wastes. The first line of defense is to reduce hazardous waste production through **process manipulation, recycling,** and **reuse** of waste products. **Detoxification** and **stabilization** are the second line of attack. Detoxification can take place through land treatment, which breaks down wastes by chemical reactions, bacteria, or even sunlight. Incineration is also an attractive alternative for organic wastes. High-temperature furnaces can operate at stationary waste disposal sites, on ships, or on mobile trailers.

Hazardous wastes that cannot be broken down can be stored permanently in **secured landfills** lined by synthetic liners and thick, impermeable layers of clay. Although landfills are the cheapest option, they have many disadvantages, the most noteworthy being inevitable leaks.

Disposal of radioactive wastes creates a special problem for society. The 1982 Nuclear Waste Policy Act establishes a strict timetable for the Department of Energy to choose appropriate sites for disposal. Many experts believe that deep geological disposal is the best technical option for getting rid of most dangerous radioactive wastes. Other options include catapulting wastes into space, disposal in the Arctic and Antarctica, transmutation (bombardment with neutrons to change them into less harmful substances), seabed disposal, and special aboveground tanks and storage facilities.

To deal with leaking dumps and contaminated areas, Congress passed the **Comprehensive Environmental Response, Compensation and Liability Act** in 1980. It makes owners and operators of hazardous waste disposal sites, as well as their customers, liable for cleanup and property damage. This legislation also establishes the $1.6-billion Superfund, to be used to clean up imminent hazards. The Superfund has major drawbacks, notably, that the law requires states to pay part of the money for cleanup costs. Few states have funds for this purpose. One of the most critical weaknesses in the Superfund legislation is that it fails to address damage to human health. New legislation may help eliminate this problem by providing compensation for victims. Unfortunately, the cost of cleanup proved far greater than anticipated in the original Superfund Act. In the first five years of the program the agency had managed to clean up only six sites.

Solving the problems of hazardous waste is an enormous task that could be made easier by individual contribution. Reduced consumption, especially of unnecessary items, could but back on currently generated waste.

Discussion Questions

1. Summarize the major events occurring at Love Canal. Who was to blame for this problem? What might have been done to avoid it?

2. You are appointed to head a state agency on hazardous waste disposal. You and your staff are to make recommendations for a statewide plan to handle hazardous wastes. Draw up a plan for eliminating dumping. Which techniques would have the highest priority? How would you bring your plan into effect?

3. Discuss the major provisions of the Resource Conservation and Recovery Act (1976) and the Comprehensive Environmental Response, Compensation and Liability Act (1980), the so-called Superfund Act. What are the weaknesses of each?

4. Describe the pros and cons of the major technological controls on hazardous wastes, including process modification, recycling and reuse, conversion to nonhazardous or less hazardous materials, and perpetual disposal.

5. Debate the statement "All hazardous wastes should be recycled and reused to eliminate disposal."

6. A hazardous waste site is going to be placed in your community. What information would you want to know about the site? Would you oppose it? Why or why not?

7. List personal ways in which we can each contribute to lessening the hazardous waste problem.

8. Discuss some of the options we have for getting rid of radioactive wastes. Which ones seem the most intelligent to you? Why?

9. Debate the statement "Victims of improper hazardous waste disposal practices should be compensated by a victim compensation fund developed by taxing the producers of toxic waste."

Suggested Readings

Belliveau, M. (1983). Toxics on Tap—Poisoned Water in L.A. *CBE Environmental Review* (May/June): 8–11. Good case study.

Durso-Hughes, K., and Lewis, J. (1982). Recycling Hazardous Wastes. *Environment* 24 (2): 14–20. Excellent article.

Epstein, S. S., Brown, L. O., and Pope, C. (1982). *Hazardous Waste in America*. San Francisco: Sierra Club Books. Thorough and dramatic coverage of hazardous wastes.

Evans, R. B., and Schweitzer, G. E. (1984). Assessing Hazardous Waste Problems. *Environ. Sci. and Technol.* 18 (11): 330A–339A. Intriguing look at new techniques to locate hazardous waste dumps and trace pollutant movement.

Hileman, B. (1983). Hazardous Waste Control. *Environ. Sci. and Technol.* 17 (7): 281A–285A. Good overview.

Hinga, K. R., Heath, C. R., Anderson, D. R., and Hollister, C. D. (1982). Disposal of High-Level Radioactive Wastes by Burial in the Sea Floor. *Environ. Sci. and Technol.* 16 (1): 28A–37A. Comprehensive article.

Martin, L. (1986). The Case for Stopping Wastes at Their Source. *Environment* 28 (3): 35–37. An interesting case study.

National Materials Advisory Board (1983). *Management of Hazardous Industrial Wastes: Research and Development Needs.* Publication NMAB-398. Washington, D.C.: National Academy Press. Technical survey of hazardous waste control technology.

Plasecki, B., and Davis, G. A. (1984). A Grand Tour of Europe's Hazardous-Waste Facilities. *Technology Review* (July): 21–29. Superb account of Europe's progressive approach to waste management.

Popkin, R. (1986). Hazardous Waste Cleanup and Disaster Management. *Environment* 28 (3): 2–5. Good overview of the U.S. hazardous waste problem.

Regenstein, L. (1982). *America the Poisoned*. Washington, D.C.: Acropolis Books. Chapter 3 is a good overview of the hazardous waste problem.

Stranahan, S. Q. (1985). Putting the Heat on Polluters. *National Wildlife* 23 (5): 30–33. A look at how citizens are fighting to rid their communities of hazardous waste dumps.

Tschinkel, V. J. (1986). The Transition toward Long-Term Management. *Environment* 28 (3): 19–20, 25–31. An informative look at an important topic.

Tucker, S. P., and Carson, G. A. (1985). Deactivation of Hazardous Chemical Wastes. *Environ. Sci. and Technol.* 19 (3): 215–220. Concise but technical coverage of hazardous waste deactivation.

Wexler, M. (1985). Strike Force. *National Wildlife* 23 (4): 38–41. A look at ways in which Los Angeles is fighting corporate polluters.

Solid Wastes:
A Growing Problem

A society in which consumption has to be artificially stimulated to keep production going is a society founded on trash and waste.

DOROTHY L. SAYERS

All organisms produce wastes, but none produces so many wastes of such diverse composition as the human being. Society's wastes arise from many different activities. This section concentrates on **municipal solid wastes**—discarded materials from schools, stores, and homes handled in solid form (Figure S18-1).

Each year over 135 million metric tons of municipal solid waste is generated in the United States, about half a ton per person. A city of 1 million people produces enough solid waste each year to fill a large football stadium. Municipal solid wastes make up only about 4% of the total solid waste discarded in the United States each year. However, municipal waste is growing from 2% to 4% per year. This growth and the sheer volume of waste create major problems in cities, where land for disposal is in short supply.

Arthur C. Clarke wrote that "solid wastes are only raw materials we're too stupid to use." Currently, about 11 million metric tons of American trash is recycled, less than 10% of the total. Meanwhile, millions of tons of paper, glass, metals, tires, and plastics are dumped into the ground and buried with dirt. In many ways this heedless custom is similar to leaving good farmland unprotected from the wind and rain or dumping good oil into the ocean, for it slowly erodes our renewable and nonrenewable resource base.

Unknown to many, this thoughtless habit of consumers costs communities millions of dollars each year. The cost of trash disposal, in fact, is usually exceeded only by the cost of education and highway construction and maintenance.

Waste dumped in the ground, we are finding out, also produces water and air pollution, squanders energy, and consumes large quantities of land in and around urban centers, competing with agriculture and other interests.

Like so many other problems, municipal solid waste is the end product of many interacting factors: large populations; high per capita consumption, especially of products of marginal to low necessity; low product durability; an abundance of disposable items; a lack of recycling and reuse; a lack of personal and governmental commitment to reduce waste; widely dispersed populations where producers of recyclable and reusable items are separated from those willing to purchase these materials; and traditionally cheap energy and abundant land for disposal.

Reducing the problem requires action on three fronts (Figure S18-2). First is the **output approach**, finding better ways of dealing with trash that pours out of cities and towns throughout the United States. Second is the **throughput approach**, reducing solid waste production by reusing and recycling materials before they enter the solid waste stream. Third is the **input approach**, which attempts to reduce the amount of materials traveling through the production–consumption cycle be reducing demand, reducing overpackaging, and other techniques.

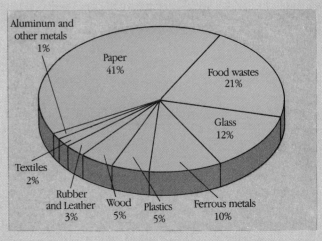

Figure S18-1 Composition of typical municipal solid waste by weight.

427

Figure S18-2 Three strategies for reducing solid waste. A combination of all three must be applied to alleviate the solid waste problem.

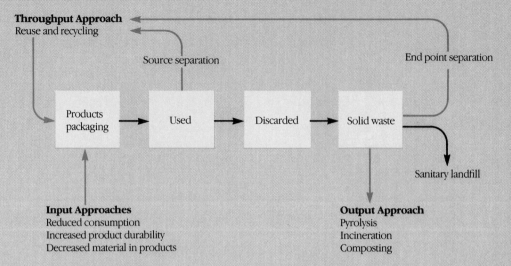

The Output Approach

The output approach takes a narrow look at solid wastes as something to be discarded as cheaply and as safely as possible. It answers two simple questions: How do we get rid of municipal wastes? And how can we reduce the volume of existing solid wastes?

From Dumps to Landfills

The garbage dump. By any other name it would smell as bad. Until the 1960s garbage dumps were prevalent features of the American landscape. But public objection to wafting odors, rat- and insect-infected midden heaps, and dark plumes of smoke that billowed out of burning dumps forced cities to look for other ways to deal with their growing trash problem. The federal government also contributed to the demise of the dump by passing the Resource Conservation and Recovery Act. It required all open dumps to be closed or upgraded by 1983.

The open dump has largely been replaced by a second cousin from a better part of town, the sanitary landfill. A **sanitary landfill** is a natural or manmade depression into which solid wastes are dumped, compressed, and daily covered with a layer of dirt. Because solid wastes are no longer burned, as they were in many open dumps, air pollution is greatly reduced. Because trash is covered each day with a layer of dirt, odors, flies, insects, rodents, and potential health problems are eliminated or sharply reduced.

Despite their immediate benefits, landfills have some notable problems. First, and most important, landfills require land. The trash from 10,000 people in a year will cover 1 acre 10 feet deep. Around many cities usable land is in short supply. Second, landfills, like dumps, require a lot of energy for excavation, filling, and hauling trash. Third, they can pollute groundwater. Fourth, they produce methane gas from the decomposition of organic materials. Methane can seep through the ground into buildings built above and around reclaimed sites, and it is explosive at relatively low concentrations. Fifth, they subside as the organic trash decays, requiring additional regrading and filling. Buildings constructed on top of reclaimed landfills may suffer

serious structural damage. Sixth, they have low social acceptability; most people don't want the noise, traffic, and blowing debris.

Fortunately, there are many solutions for reducing the energy and land requirements of landfills. Energy requirements can be cut by new methods of waste collection. For example, packer trucks now reduce waste volume by 60%; thus, fewer trucks are needed to haul garbage to landfills. Vacuum collection systems can also be used to save energy. In these systems solid waste is dumped into pipes that carry it to a central collection point. Recyclable and burnable materials can be separated here before the trash is trucked off to landfills. Recycling reduces the volume of garbage, helps cut back on energy demand, and reduces the land required to dispose of waste. Vacuum collection systems are feasible in urban areas where population density is high. Apartment complexes are extraordinarily well suited to this method of trash disposal. One such system is in operation in Sundbyberg, Sweden. Garbage is whisked away from wall chutes to a central collection facility, where the glass and metals are removed by an automated process. The burnables are incinerated, providing heat for the 1100 apartments using the system. A similar system handles 50 tons of waste per day in Disney World, Florida. Today, over 400 such systems are in operation in Europe in hospitals, apartment buildings, and housing tracts.

Water pollution problems may be reduced or eliminated by locating landfills away from streams, lakes, and wells. Test wells around the site can be used to monitor the movement of pollutants, if any, away from the site. Special drainage systems and careful landscaping can reduce the flow of water over the surface of a landfill, thus reducing the amount of water penetrating it. Impermeable clay caps and liners can reduce water infiltration and the escape of pollutants. In addition, pollutants leaking from the site can be collected by specially built drainage systems and then detoxified.

Methane gas produced in landfills can be drawn off by special pipes and sold as fuel, in many cases supplementing or replacing natural gas. Subsidence damage to buildings built on reclaimed sites can be reduced by removing organic wastes before disposal and by allowing organic decay to proceed for a number of years before construction.

Ocean Dumping

What do you think of when you think of the ocean? White beaches, gentle waves, and the sweet smell of coconut oil? For years many city officials have had a different view of the ocean—that of a limitless garbage dump for solid waste and human sewage. Until fairly recently there were at least 126 offshore dump sites in the United States: 33 in the Gulf of Mexico, 42 in the Pacific Ocean, and 51 in the Atlantic. Most of the solid waste dumped at sea was mud and sediment from dredging of harbors, estuaries, and rivers. The rest consisted of industrial wastes (acids, alkaline substances, PCBs, and arsenic compounds) and sludge left over from sewage treatment plants (Chapter 16). Even today, city garbage specialists are trying to find ways to justify dumping their trash offshore. Just think of it: offshore "islands of trash," built from discarded automobiles, demolished buildings, and other solid wastes, supporting hotels and airports. Or even artificial reefs made of discarded stone, cement slabs, and automobiles.

The concerns over ocean dumping are many. The disposal of toxic wastes might contaminate commercially valuable fish and shellfish. Biomagnification of these chemicals might harm organisms higher on the food chain, including birds and humans (Chapter 14). The long-term effects of ocean dumping are uncertain. Will ocean currents eventually wash the wastes ashore onto beaches, or will they be carried out to sea? Finally, aesthetic concerns have been raised by people like the explorer Thor Heyerdahl, who has witnessed oil and trash floating out at sea and deadened areas of the ocean that have long been the dumping sites for garbage and sludge from sewage plants.

Ocean dumping began a steady decline after the **Marine Protection, Research and Sanctuaries Act** was passed by Congress in 1972. The long-term goal of this act is to phase out all ocean dumping. Thus, in January 1977 the EPA issued regulations calling for an end by 1981 to all dumping of industrial wastes and sludge in the Atlantic Ocean, where 90% of the waste disposal was occurring. Dredged materials can continue to be dumped at sea in some locations.

Composting and Incineration

Composting and incineration are two important output strategies. **Composting** is a process in which the organic wastes are allowed to undergo aerobic bacterial decay. The resulting product, compost, is used to build soil fertility (Chapter Supplement 7-1).

Where there is an abundance of organic matter—such as at slaughterhouses and vegetable- and fruit-packing plants—composting is a good strategy. Some successful composting operations can be found in the United States, but most are in Europe—in the Netherlands, Belgium, England, and Italy—and in Israel (Figure S18-3).

Composting has a few drawbacks: (1) it requires large tracts of land and may produce odor and provide breeding sites for pests, (2) sorting out the noncompostable materials such as metals and glass is costly, (3) the demand for the organic compost is often low, and (4) sites are aesthetically unappealing.

For successful municipal composting, cities might use abandoned lots or outlying plots that could be cared for by convicts, welfare recipients, or the unemployed. Citizens could be required to sort out recyclable metals, plastics, and glass, thus eliminating the cost of separating the wastes later.

Composting can be practiced very successfully at home. Gardeners can make their own compost piles of leaves, grass clippings, and vegetable wastes from the kitchen. The product can be added to vegetable gardens and flower beds. Simply burying organic wastes in flower beds and gardens also may work well, reducing the need for artificial fertilizers.

Garbage can be burned to produce steam for heating or even generating electricity. But incinerators are costly to build and operate, on the whole costing more than landfills. The increased expense is partly due to the fact that each incinerator must be individually designed to accommodate the particular local mixture of burnable and nonburnable refuse. Operation is made more difficult because the mixture varies from season to season. To lessen this problem individual homeowners might be required to separate burnables from wet organic matter such

Material	Reuse and Recycling
Paper	Repulped and made into cardboard, paper, and a number of paper products. Incinerated to generate heat. Shredded and used as mulch or insulation.
Organic matter	Composted and added to gardens and farms to enrich the soil. Incinerated to generate heat.
Clothing and textiles	Shredded and reused for new fiber products, or burned to generate energy. Donated to charities or sold at garage sales.
Glass	Returned and refilled. Crushed and used to make new glass. Crushed and mixed with asphalt. Crushed and added to bricks and cinderblocks.
Metals	Remelted and used to manufacture new metal for containers, building, and other uses.

Table S18-1 Reuse and Recycling of Solid Wastes

Source: Modified from Nebel, B. J. (1981). *Environmental Science.* Englewood Cliffs, N.J.: Prentice-Hall, p. 297.

as grass clippings. Incinerators emit toxic pollutants, especially when plastics are burned.

Denmark burns over 60% of its solid wastes; the Netherlands and Sweden both burn about one-third of theirs. The United States, on the other hand, burns less than 1% of its solid waste.

The Throughput Approach

In addition to those output approaches (compaction, incineration, composting), which reduce waste volume and may allow us to regain a little benefit from things we normally discard, certain throughput approaches are needed. Throughput approaches—reuse and recycling—take out useful materials before they enter the waste stream (Table S18-1).

Reuse is simply the return of operable or repairable goods into the market system for someone to use. In most cities a variety of organizations will pick up usable discards or broken products, including clothes, furniture, books, and appliances. Central drop-off stations are also provided. The Salvation Army, Goodwill Industries, and Disabled American Veterans all collect items throughout the United States. So before you throw out a still-usable product, give one of these organizations a phone call.

Packaging materials, such as cardboard boxes, bottles, and grocery bags, can be reused, saving both energy and materials. Reusable beverage containers are well worth their slight extra cost; they can be sterilized, refilled, and returned to the shelf, sometimes completing the cycle as many as 50 times.

The advantages of reuse are many: (1) it saves energy, (2) it reduces the land area needed for solid waste disposal, (3) it provides jobs, (4) it provides inexpensive products for the poor

and the thrifty, (5) it reduces litter, (6) it decreases the amount of materials consumed by society, and (7) it helps reduce pollution and environmental disruption.

Recycling also helps reduce the volume of the municipal waste stream by returning materials to manufacturers, where they can be broken down and reincorporated into products. From an energy and resource standpoint recycling is not as good an option as reuse, but it is far better than throwing materials away. A variety of materials commonly discarded in municipal trash can be recycled at a huge energy savings (Table S18-1). Chapter 13 discusses recycling of metals.

Recycling is not always feasible. A steady market must always be accessible; if not, recyclers unable to sell their materials must store them until a market is opened up. Fluctuating markets for recyclables make it difficult for marginally profitable operations to survive. Extracting recyclable goods from municipal trash also adds to the cost. **Source separation**, removing recyclables before they enter the waste stream, requires widespread cooperation among residents, many of whom are unwilling to expend even the small amount of effort required.

Solutions to the recycling dilemma are badly needed as finite energy and resource supplies decline. In communities where trash is picked up two or three times a week, for example, one pickup can be devoted to recyclables at no extra cost to the community. Where trash is picked up weekly, alternate weeks can be used for recyclables.

Separating trash after collection requires little citizen cooperation. This is its chief advantage. Raw trash is simply shredded at a resource recovery center, and then blowers separate the plastics, paper, and organic matter from heavier items such as cans and bottles, and magnets separate the steel.

However beneficial resource recovery systems may be, they have some drawbacks. End-point separation is more expensive than source separation and sometimes more costly than traditional disposal in landfills. The equipment is expensive and requires maintenance and energy. Furthermore, complete separation may not be possible. The lack of complete separation decreases the value of recyclable materials.

Widespread recycling is necessary if we are to reach a sustainable society. Immediate recycling will cut energy demand, pollution, and resource depletion, with benefits to today's citizens and those yet to come. Unfortunately, the U.S. economic system fails to deal with the hidden costs of pollution (external costs). It is even more inadequate at factoring in the costs and benefits of today's actions on future generations. In a sense, economics is blind to the future even though our actions have far-reaching effects.

The EPA estimates that the United States could recycle about 25% of its urban solid waste by 1990, about twice what it does now. A goal of 60% to 80% would be far better. Increased recycling requires our personal attention. Each of us can make a commitment to recycle cans, bottles, and papers. We can gently nudge our friends to follow our lead. Tax breaks for recycling companies may prove helpful. New laws that require the return of bottles and cans on a nationwide basis would also help (Chapter 13).

Recycling is more prevalent in most of the developing countries than in the industrialized nations. The poor raid the dumps for food, clothing, and materials for shelter and also seek out discarded metals and other goods they can sell. The developed nations can help promote recycling as they assist developing nations in their efforts to raise their economic well-being. Information on the energy and material savings as well as technologies for recycling could be built into global industrialization at the start. To be credible, however, the developed nations will need to increase their own recycling efforts.

The Input Approach

Reductions in solid waste and all its attendant problems can also be achieved by an **input approach**: reducing the amount of material entering the consumption phase of the production–consumption cycle. The three ways of doing this are (1) increasing product lifespan, (2) reducing the amount of materials in goods, and (3) reducing consumption (demand for goods).

More durable items such as toys, garden tools, cars, and clothing require less frequent replacement and thus decrease overall resource use. The trouble is that, as John Ruskin noted, "There is hardly anything in the world that some man cannot make a little worse and sell a little cheaper." In the long run, however, cheaply made goods end up costing more than well-made and more expensive goods. High waste production is also an attitude problem. The attitude that "new is better" leads many consumers to purchase new goods when old ones still work.

A great deal of resource waste and solid waste production comes from packaging. Each year, for example, packaging requires 75% of the glass consumed in the United States, 40% of the paper, 14% of the aluminum, and 8% of the steel. At least 30% of the municipal solid waste is discarded packaging!

Of course, packaging is necessary, but much of it is superfluous and wasteful. The Campbell Soup Company realized this and redesigned its soup cans; today, they use 30% less material. Some beverage companies now package drinks in **aseptic containers**, boxes constructed of several thin layers of polyethylene, foil, and paper. The containers hold milk, a variety of juices, and wine and keep them fresh for several months without refrigeration. Beverages in aseptic containers cost the consumer about 10% less than those in cans. The reason is that canned drinks must be pasteurized for 45 minutes, whereas the contents of aseptic packages are sterilized out of the package for only 1 minute. This reduces energy demand and preserves flavors. Milk and juices contained in aseptics do not require refrigeration during transportation and storage, which also lowers the energy demand. Being lighter than cans also helps cut down on transportation costs.

Some manufacturers are experimenting with biodegradable packages. Most notable are plastics and food containers that dissolve in water when cooked, not only reducing solid waste but also adding nutrients to the food.

Packaging is not the only area in need of improvement. Virtually all products can be redesigned to reduce waste. Many large newspapers have gone to a more economical design that has cut the use of newsprint by 5%; what was once covered in 88 pages can now be covered in 84. Smaller cars and trucks have emerged, too.

H. W. Shaw once wrote, "Our necessities are few, but our wants are endless." It is argued that our ceaseless efforts to satisfy our wants in an age of technological marvel is a big part of the solid waste problem. By reducing our endless accumulation of questionable goods, we can help the solid waste problem as well as so many others documented in this book. Added benefits may also come from a simpler way of life.

Each of us can make a personal effort to reduce consumption by 20% with little noticeable change in life-style. There are limitless possibilities for reducing consumption; all we have to do is try them.

Suggested Readings

Chandler, W. U. (1983). *Materials Recycling: The Virtue of Necessity.* Worldwatch Paper 56. Washington, D.C.: Worldwatch Institute. Detailed study of recycling.

Goldstein, J. (1979). *Recycling: How to Reuse Wastes in Home, Industry and Society.* New York: Schocken Books. Informative and practical guide.

Iker, S. (1986). New Life from Old Junk. *National Wildlife* 24 (2): 12–17. Look at artificial reefs built from discarded junk.

Parkinson, A. (1983). Responsible Waste Management in a Shrinking World. *Environment* 25 (10): 61–67. Good overview.

Purcell, A. H. (1980). *The Waste Watchers: A Citizen's Handbook for Conserving Energy and Resources.* New York: Doubleday (Anchor). Helpful reference.

Purcell, A. H. (1981). The World's Trashiest People: Will They Clean Up Their Act or Throw Away Their Future? *The Futurist* 15 (1): 51–59. Excellent article.

White, P., and Psihoyos, L. (1983). The Fascinating World of Trash. *National Geographic* 163 (4): 424–457. An interesting and humorous look at trash.

V

ENVIRONMENT
AND SOCIETY

19

Environmental Ethics: The Foundation of a Sustainable Society

Modern man is the victim of the very instruments he values most. Every gain in power, every mastery of natural forces, every scientific addition to knowledge, has proved potentially dangerous, because it has not been accompanied by equal gains in self-understanding and self-discipline.

LEWIS MUMFORD

This book began with an outline of today's environmental crisis. Each part has explored a facet of it. Part 2 covered the population question, Part 3 surveyed resource problems, and Part 4 described the many faces of pollution. Each chapter suggested remedies for many of our problems, solutions that were technical, legal, and personal. All were aimed at developing a sustainable society.

The diverse solutions presented in earlier chapters amount to a hodgepodge without another ingredient: a set of informed values—an appropriate ethical system that serves as a foundation for the new society. This chapter outlines the old attitudes and sets forth a new set of attitudes called "sustainable ethics."

This new ethical system is already being adopted by many people in the United States and abroad. For sustainable ethics to achieve widespread acceptance will require that many more people replace long-standing beliefs that have deep roots and far-reaching effects. These ecologically out-of-date beliefs constitute the "frontier mentality" and underlie many of our environmental problems.

Table 19-1 Frontier and Sustainable Ethics Compared

Frontier Mentality	Sustainable Ethics
The earth is an unlimited bank of resources.	The earth has a limited supply of resources.
When the supply runs out, move elsewhere.	Recycling and the use of renewable resources will prevent depletion.
Life will be made better if we just continue to add to our material wealth.	Life's value is not simply the sum total of our banking accounts.
The cost of any project is determined by the cost of materials, energy, and labor. Economics is all that matters.	The cost is more than the sum of the energy, labor, and materials. External costs such as damage to health and the environment must be calculated.
Nature is to be overcome.	We must understand and cooperate with nature.
New laws and technologies will solve our environmental problems.	Individual efforts to solve the pressing problems must be combined with tough laws and new technologies.
We are above nature, somehow separated from it and superior to it.	We are a part of nature, ruled by its rules and respectful of its components. We are not superior to nature.
Waste is to be expected in all human endeavor.	Waste is intolerable; every wasted object should have a use.

The Frontier Mentality

Today's industrial world operates largely with a frontier mentality. The **frontier mentality**, or ethic, is characterized by three precepts: First, it sees the world as having an unlimited supply of resources for human use, not necessarily to be shared by all life forms; in other words, "There is always more, and it's all ours." Part of this belief is the notion that the earth has an unlimited capacity to assimilate pollution. Second, the frontier view holds that humans are apart from nature rather than a part of it. Third, it sees nature as something to conquer. Technology has become the tool by which humans subdue nature, the answer to many of the conflicts between human society and nature. See Table 19-1 for a summary of frontier ethics.

The frontier mentality has been a part of human thinking for many tens of thousands of years, perhaps all of human history. It was present in both the hunting-and-gathering and agricultural societies, but more so in the latter. The European settlers in North America, for example, cut down the forests and grew crops on the soil until the nutrients had been depleted or the soil had been eroded away by rain. Then they moved into new territory to start the cycle over again. One of the most serious aspects of the notion that there is always more is the disregard for the consequences of our actions. Why worry about soil erosion or water pollution, because there is always more soil and plenty of clean water?

The frontier mentality sees humans as separate from nature and superior to all other life forms; many societies

have continually sought to dominate nature. This view, so prevalent today, was expressed by the nineteenth-century English poet Mathew Arnold: "Nature and man can never be fast friends. Fool, if thou canst not pass her, rest her slave!" The attitude of domination has spawned a frenzy of dam building to tame rivers, highways to tame wilderness, breakwalls to hold back ocean tides, levees to hold back floods, streambed channelizations to reduce flooding, chemical pesticides to control insects, and so on. Much of this book has looked at the ecological backlashes of attempts at domination. In many instances experience has shown that cooperation with nature would have been better for humans as well as nature. Not building homes on barrier islands or in river floodplains, not grazing cattle above the carrying capacity of grasslands, and letting natural forest fires burn are three examples of cooperation that pay huge dividends in the long term (Figure 19-1).

The frontier mentality is the dominant belief structure, or paradigm, of modern society (paradigms are discussed in Chapter Supplement 1-1). So deeply imbedded is the frontier mentality that it affects not only how we view our problems but also how we go about solving them. For instance, fossil fuel shortages are "solved" by increased exploration and drilling or by developing alternatives such as oil shale and tar sands. Our single-minded dedication to the frontier mentality—for instance, the idea that there is always more—often makes us overlook the simple answers, such as conservation, or reducing our energy consumption to make supplies last longer.

The frontier mentality also influences individual goals

Figure 19-1 This Santa Cruz, California, beachside home was damaged by coastal storms in the winter of 1983. Homes placed farther from the beach were undamaged, suggesting the wisdom of playing by nature's rules.

and expectations. It is used to justify our actions. Moreover, nearly all of the social and political institutions function to maintain it. This makes it difficult to dislodge. Rediscovering that we *are* part of nature, however, could change our outlook entirely.

Roots of Our Attitudes toward Nature

Where did our attitudes toward nature come from? Most historians exploring that question have been interested primarily in the origin of the view that humans are "apart from and above nature" and "here to dominate it." But equally important are the roots of the attitude that "there is always more." Let's look at the first set of attitudes.

"Be fruitful and multiply, and replenish the earth, and subdue it; and have dominion over the fish of the sea, and over the fowl of the air, and over every living thing that moves upon the earth." This quotation from Genesis proclaims human supremacy over nature. A University of California historian, Lynn White, argues that it is the root of Western attitudes toward nature. In a widely read paper, "The Historical Roots of Our Ecologic Crisis," he writes that the Judeo-Christian ethic holds that nature has only one purpose: to serve humans. Furthermore, White argues, Christians believe it to be God's will that we exploit nature for our own purposes. Critics point out that the Hebrew word that has been translated as "dominion" connotes supremacy but along with it love, concern, and responsibility. White's reasoning, his critics contend, is not entirely accurate.

The biologist René Dubos presents an alternative viewpoint. He notes that exploitation of the natural world is a universal human trait regardless of religion. Erosion of the land, destruction of animal and plant species, excessive exploitation of natural resources, and ecological disasters are not unique to the Judeo-Christian peoples. At all times and all over the world, thoughtless interventions into nature have had disastrous consequences. Two examples were the widespread extinction of many large animals, such as the wooly mammoth and saber-toothed tiger, caused by early North American hunters and gatherers, and overgrazing and general mismanagement of the once-fertile Tigris-Euphrates region, which has led to widespread desertification.

The debate over our belief that we are above nature, outlined briefly above, illustrates a problem common to debates in general—the search for single causes when, in fact, several may be involved. Essay 19-1 discusses a simplified model aimed at getting to the real roots of environmental problems. In the debate in question, the narrow views are somewhat misleading; they present only part of the truth.

Taking a broader view, we see that environmental damage stems in part from **biological imperialism**, the tendency for every organism to convert as much of the environment as possible into itself and its offspring. Humans are no different from the rest of the biological world, except that we have technologies to achieve our goals. And we have exceeded the carrying capacity in many ways, thus wreaking considerable havoc. Other species have little ability to exceed their carrying capacity.

Dubos is correct in pointing out that humans have always damaged the environment through exploitation. Judeo-Christian teachings, however, may have reinforced this tendency. To say that these teachings are responsible for our feelings of superiority and control over nature is only a half truth; it would perhaps be more accurate to say they are a fine veneer over a deeply rooted biological trait.

Some insights from psychology shed more light on the attitude that we are apart from nature. Psychologists assert that humans create mental models that determine what reality is. These models dictate how we view the world. The psychologist Alan Watts coined the term *skin-encapsulated ego* to define the prevalent model we use: what is inside the skin is "I," and what is outside is "not I." Thus, many people operate with this view of nature as "not I." Knowing how dependent humans are on natural processes, you can see the problem with this narrow but prevalent view.

Besides supporting the notion that humans are apart from nature, a skin-encapsulated ego causes some direct damage from attempts at ego-building. According to psychologists, as we humans pass from infancy to adulthood, we develop a sense of the self, our own separate identity. Psychologists call this the **derived self**. Once the derived self becomes established, it also needs reaffirmation. New clothes, fast cars, and extravagant homes are some of the ways in which some of us build our egos, or reaffirm who we are. Reaffirmation can lead to the accumulation of materials, which depletes essential resources, causes pollution, and reduces wildlife habitat (Figure 19-2).

Having viewed some possible roots of our attitudes toward nature, let us turn to the dangerous notion that "there is always more." Tracing this viewpoint is relatively easy. For most of human history population size has been small in comparison with the earth's resource supply and capacity to assimilate wastes. We know from history that civilization has been constantly on the move in search of new resources, and it has almost always found what it wanted. In fact, there *was* always more. Now that the human population is 5 billion, however, many people have questioned this attitude. Extinction of species, depletion of natural resources, and worldwide pollution have served as reminders that the world we live in has limits.

A More Personal Look

Many modern societies operate under a frontier mentality. Many of our political leaders, who subscribe to frontierism, talk about continued economic growth and increased material wealth despite the limits to the world's resources. Many people, untrained in the environmental sciences, are caught up in their rhetoric. Why worry, if there is always more? Certainly technology will come to the rescue.

This book points out the fallacies of the frontier mentality. It shows that fossil fuels and mineral supplies are limited—there is not always more. It also shows that the renewable resources can be used up. Our study of extinction, for instance, tells us that once a species is wiped out by habitat destruction or overhunting, it is gone forever. No amount of technology will bring back the species that we are currently destroying. Surely, the attitudes passed down from some of our leaders are maladaptive; they are disadvantageous to our species to the point that they could threaten our survival. This section looks at the personal actions and attitudes of many people and points out the problems they create.

Apathy

Many people, while understanding that the earth is finite, remain apathetic about the course of modern society. Involved in their own lives, they see resource limitations and pollution as problems for which someone else must take responsibility. Apathy is effortless, noncontroversial, and cheap.

A major failing of the American democratic system is that it often doesn't teach us our responsibilities. We are

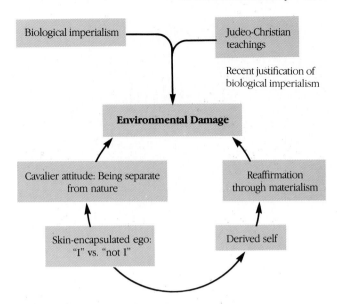

Figure 19-2 Roots of environmental damage caused by humans.

taught about our freedoms and rights but not what we must do to make the system work well for everyone. (For more on obligations, see the Viewpoint in this chapter.)

Apathy also stems from our explicit faith in technology. Many among us think that technology can offset impending resource shortages and global pollution problems. Experts, however, warn that blind optimism about technology may be the fatal flaw of modern society. As previous chapters have noted, technological solutions are only part of the answer to our problems.

The Self-Centered View

The average man and woman in the street often take a self-centered view. Their economic and noneconomic welfare governs their actions—what kinds of homes they buy, what size cars they buy, how much luxury they surround themselves with, and so on. Many of us buy what we can afford, giving little thought to the effects of consumption. Replacing the self-centered approach to life with a global environmental perspective is the main thrust of environmental education. Many people have already made an attempt to apply less self-centered principles to their personal actions.

Feelings of Insignificance

Feelings of insignificance also grip many of us. This pervasive feeling may have a powerful effect on our own lives and the world around us. In large part, feelings of insignificance create the problems we have and keep us from solving them. Let me explain this paradox. Being just one of billions of people on earth is an excuse many of us use for our wasteful ways. What difference, we ask, does it make if I drive 10 miles per hour over the speed limit and waste a little gasoline? I'm just one of 240 million Americans. I'm just

Roots of Environmental Problems

In the late 1960s and early 1970s, when environmental issues came to the forefront of attention, two noted scientists stimulated a debate over the underlying causes. Paul Ehrlich, a Stanford University biologist, argued that the root of all our pollution and resource problems was overpopulation—too many people. His argument was hotly contested by another biologist, Barry Commoner, who argued that technology was primarily to blame. Their debate engaged but misled the scientific community and the public for years. Upon closer examination it becomes clear that both scientists were wrong. The complex problems of poverty, resource depletion, pollution, wildlife extinction, and food shortages are not the result of technology or overpopulation alone but rather are caused by a variety of factors, as shown in the figure.

To illustrate the multiple etiology of environmental problems, we will use the Multiple Cause and Effect model to look at wildlife extinction, for which commercial and sport hunting and habitat destruction are often blamed. As we will see, this view—like Ehrlich's and Commoner's—gives us a simplified picture of a problem that has many hidden causes. To see why this is so, and to see how the model is used, let us examine each element of the model individually.

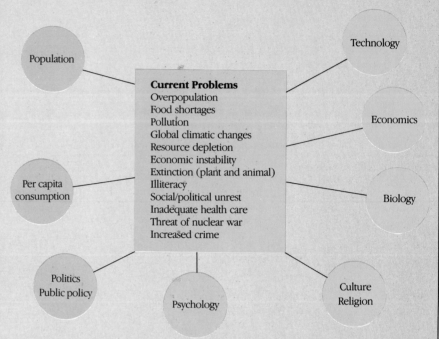

Multiple Cause and Effect model for analyzing specific environmental issues. The circled factors contribute in many ways to the problems facing the world.

Population

The human population destroys wildlife habitat in many ways. We build roads through forests once occupied by bears; we build airports and housing tracts on land that once provided food and shelter for birds and other animals; we pollute streams once the home of fish and otters; we strip-mine for coal and gravel, in the process destroying vegetation once the food of deer. These activities enhance human survival and prosperity but decrease the amount of wildlife habitat. The extent of the environmental damage depends on numerous population factors such as population size, growth rate, and geographical distribution. For example, the larger our population, the greater its impact. Likewise, the faster our population grows, the more impact we have. But population is only one of many underlying causes of extinction.

Per Capita Consumption

The amount of resources used by each member of society, per capita consumption, also plays a key role in the destruction of wildlife habitat. For example, in the United States per capita consumption of water has increased 300% in the past 80 years. Electrical energy consumption has more than doubled in the past 20 years. This rapid increase in resource consumption strains the earth's available land and water resources. It also pollutes the planet. The cars we drive pollute the air animals breathe; the oil we use to make the gasoline that powers our automobiles can, if accidentally released, pollute the ocean and rivers. Thus, how much a society consumes also plays a significant role in wildlife extinction.

Politics and Public Policy

The legal system also has an important role in wildlife extinction. Laws can affect how much habitat is destroyed, how much hunting and poaching occur, and which species will or will not be hunted. In addition, laws influence population growth, which, in turn, affects wildlife habitat. (For instance, tax laws give families deductions for each child, reducing the financial burden of rearing children, and thus may promote population growth.) Laws also affect resource acquisition and use—for example, how much coal is mined, how it is mined, and how reclamation is carried out. Before 1977 there were few legal controls on surface mining. At that time more than 1 million acres of land had been surface-mined in the United States, and about two-thirds of this land (mostly in the East) had been left barren. New laws now require the revegetation of surface-mined land and create a fund for reclaiming abandoned, unreclaimed lands. Thus, laws must also be taken into account when discussing animal extinction.

Economics

Economics is a key element in animal extinction. It plays an important role in determining how resources are acquired and used. For example, surface mining of coal is preferred to underground mining worldwide because it is much cheaper. Because surface mining is more environmentally destructive, the decision to acquire coal this way, dictated by economics, affects wildlife habitat.

Economics affects many of our daily business decisions. On the surface, there is nothing wrong with this. However, economics often fails to account for external costs—pollution, habitat destruction, and other environmental impacts that are not entered into the cost of producing goods. Air pollution from factories, cars, and power plants, for example, may cause up to $16 billion worth of damage to crops, health, forests, and buildings in the United States each year. These external costs are borne by members of the public who suffer ill health, pay a higher price for food, or pay for repairing buildings. If companies invested in pollution control devices, the external costs would be greatly reduced, but consumers would pay a higher price for energy and goods. Thus, a system of economics in which the consumer pays for the external cost would diminish environmental pollution and its threat to wildlife habitat. But because economic thinking often ignores economic externalities, it, too, is a prime causative agent in the reduction of the world's wildlife.

Psychology, Culture, and Religion

How we behave toward the environment is a function of our attitudes, as shown in this chapter. Underlying all of our behavior is a psychology that tends to put immediate needs before the long-term good of the environment and future generations. Rather than thinking about the future, we tend to be concerned with things that affect us in the short term and ways we can make the present as comfortable as possible. Although this type of thinking is shortsighted, it is very much a biological characteristic. Survival in the animal world is generally the result of animals' satisfying immediate needs by using environmental resources. Being animals ourselves, we tend to think and act with an eye to the immediate. Because our population is so large and our technologies are so well developed, however, short-term thinking leads to many problems, such as wildlife extinction.

Another crucial psychological element is the way we perceive our place in the environment. Do we see ourselves as superior to nature and at odds with the natural world? Or are we a part of nature, willing to live in harmony in accordance with important ecological laws? An attitude of being superior and somehow separated from nature predominates today. It gives many license to run roughshod over wildlife and plants, contributing to the extinction of many species.

Social, cultural, and religious factors to a large extent determine our psychological makeup. Cultural and religious attitudes in which humans are viewed as supreme and apart from nature, as we have seen, can have devastating effects on wildlife. If animals are revered for cultural or religious reasons, however, extinction from hunting and habitat destruction may be curbed.

Technology

Technology, like population, is only one of a complex of factors contributing to wildlife extinction. We typically think of technology as instruments or tools to make better use of the world's resources in meeting our needs for food, shelter, clothing, water, and so on. Technology offers us many advantages in the struggle for survival. As a result of technological developments we travel freely around the world and through space, inhabit new regions, and acquire resources from distant sites. Technology allows us to prosper in environments where survival might otherwise be impossible.

Our travels, new settlements, and resource acquisitions all contribute to the shrinking supply of wildlife habitat. This happens partly because technology enhances population growth. The more people there are, the more resources are needed and the greater the conflict over living space.

Technological advances have spelled trouble for wildlife for other reasons, too. For instance, improvements in guns used for whaling have allowed humans to severely deplete the populations of many whales. New drugs have eradicated diseases, thereby reducing infant mortality; in the process, though, they have contributed to rapid population growth. New chemical pesticides have increased agricultural productivity but have also devastated populations of birds and other animals. Therefore, although technology has been a boon to society, it has exacted a price, too.

Biology

Numerous biological features play a role in wildlife extinction, adding to the growing list of contributing factors. Some of the most important ones are adaptability, number of offspring, and sensitivity to environmental pollutants. Highly specialized species, like the California condor, are generally unable to adapt to changes brought about by human beings and are more vulnerable than less specialized animals like the coyote, which seems immune to human presence. The number of offspring a species produces also affects the resistance of the species to human pressures such as hunting, habitat alteration, and pesticide use. Sensitivity to environmental pollutants varies considerably among plants and animals, making some much more susceptible than others.

This brief example of the use of the Multiple Cause and Effect model shows that wildlife extinction, like all environmental issues, is a complex matter. This model enlarges our focus and contributes to a more organized, scientific view of the world around us. It will help us avoid the oversimplified diagnosis and treatment of contemporary problems.

Figure 19-3 (*a*) The spatial and temporal interests of individual people are indicated by points on the graph. (*b*) The exponential growth curve for population size, resource demand, and pollution is similar to the curve for the growth of a savings account that was shown in Figure 5-7. Population size, pollution, and resource demand have rounded the bend of the curve and continue to grow exponentially, as shown here.

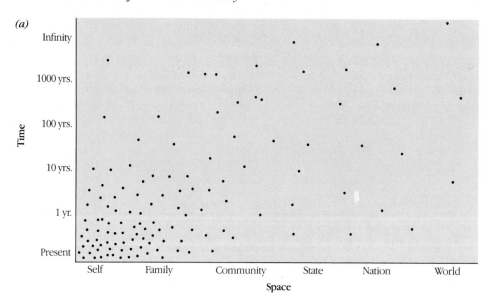

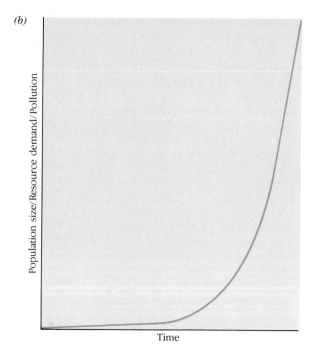

a small part of the problem, and an insignificant one at that. The trouble with this thinking is that millions of people think the same thing. Together, their actions add up to a lot of waste and pollution.

Feelings of insignificance also keep us from solving many problems. If I drive the speed limit, recycle aluminum and paper, and keep my thermostat at a reasonable temperature, what difference will it make? I'm only one of 240 million, and my contribution to the resource and pollution is insignificant, so why do it?

There you have it: feelings of insignificance create many of our problems and keep us from solving them. We need to develop an understanding that there are billions of

people and that their actions, taken together, can make or break us. Education can go a long way in this regard.

Restricted Space–Time Values Chapter 14 discussed the concerns of people related to space and time. As we saw, most people's concerns are restricted to the self, family, and community. With regard to time, most people concern themselves with the present or the near future. This restricted view, though very natural, can be a detriment to modern society in light of the rapid rate of change in population, resources, and pollution (Figure 19-3a). Resource demand, pollution, and population growth have all rounded the bend of the exponential curve (Figure 19-3b). Each doubling brings an enormous increase in the resources we use, the pollution we produce, and the people we must feed and house. Humanity's future hinges largely on how well we expand our space–time values to come to grips with the realities of exponential growth.

A Low-Synergy Society

The frontier mentality, the economic-growth orientation of modern society, and the personal attitudes described above combine to create a low-synergy society. **Synergy**, in scientific parlance, simply means "working together." Low-synergy societies are those in which the individual parts work against the benefit of the whole.

The earliest human societies were high-synergy societies. The early agriculturalists in tropical climates, for instance, practiced slash-and-burn farming that did little damage to the jungle. But back then human population size was small, and technology was simple. What damage humans caused was repaired naturally.

Today, however, synergy has been eroded. Large numbers of people, advanced technologies, and a seemingly infinite variety of pollutants have created worldwide ecological disruption. Our air, water, and land are suffering as society stretches well beyond the earth's carrying capacity.

To rebuild a high-synergy, or sustainable, society under the new conditions of human civilization will require some fundamental changes in economics and government (Chapters 20 and 21) in addition to the changes in ethics discussed here. Further alterations in housing, urban development, industry, transportation, and technology are discussed in Chapter 22.

Sustainable Ethics

The sustainable-society ethic holds that the earth has a limited supply of resources and that humans are a part of nature and not in any way superior to it.

The main concept of the sustainable ethic is that "there is not always more." As the resource chapters of this book have pointed out, the earth has a limited supply of nonrenewable resources such as metals and oil. Even renewable resources can be depleted by improper management and should be harvested only at a fixed rate (equal to the replacement rate). To develop a sustainable society we must learn that infinite growth of material consumption in a finite world is an impossibility. We must learn that ever-increasing production and consumption can only damage the life-giving environment.

These important realizations will lead to new resource-consumption strategies. The first is conservation, curtailing excessive resources use. The second strategy is reuse

and recycling of all materials. Third is the use of more renewable resources (sunlight) and fewer nonrenewable resources (coal and oil). The fourth, and most important, is the control of population growth.

Sustainable ethics also holds that humans are not apart from but rather, a part of nature. This simple message is eloquently spoken in the book *The Earth Speaks* by an Indian chief, Seattle:

You must teach your children that the ground beneath their feet is the ashes of our grandfathers. So they will respect the land, tell your children that the earth is rich with the lives of our kin. Teach your children what we have taught our children—that the earth is our mother. Whatever befalls the earth, befalls the sons of the earth. If men spit upon the ground, they spit upon themselves.

This we know. The earth does not belong to man; man belongs to the earth. This we know. All things are connected like the blood which unites one family. All things are connected. . . .

What befalls the earth befalls the sons of the earth. Man did not weave the web of life; he is merely a strand in it. Whatever he does to the web, he does to himself.

Sustainable ethics embraces a respect for the land, air, water, and all living things. It nurtures a reverence for life that would inevitably result in a curtailment of some of our activities, would diminish our view of self-importance, and would result in a decrease in the destructive, narrow (human-centered) thinking so prevalent in frontier societies. In what other ways would this view change our lives?

First, we would learn to fully examine our economic and resource decisions to see how they affect the integrity, stability, and beauty of the world. Short-term exploitive approaches would be frowned upon (Figure 19-4). Citizens would take a critical look at traditional economics, too, insisting that not everything has a price in dollars and cents. We would take a dim view of those activities that rob us of security, happiness, beauty, and health. To strive for a quality existence means controlling materialism.

Second, we would become more and more aware of the interconnection of all components of the earth and aware that our actions often have many unforeseen effects. Our growing knowledge of the global interconnection would create a more thoughtful approach to all human activities.

Third, as an outgrowth of our changes in view, we would exercise more restraint in all facets of our lives. In regard to technology and development, the ability to say "I can" would not inevitably be followed by "I will." Instead, new questions would be asked: Should we build this dam? Should we introduce this product? Should we build more nuclear weapons? Should we have another child? Instead, "I can" would be followed by two impor-

Figure 19-4 Short-term exploitive approach. An Australian hillside has been denuded by the emission of sulfuric acid from the Mount Lyell copper mine.

tant questions: "What are the environmental consequences?" and "Should I?"

The notion of restraint seems foreign now. As resources become scarce, however, restraint will become more natural and will not carry the negative connotations that it does for many people today. As the futurist John Naisbitt has written, "Change occurs when there is a confluence of both changing values and economic necessity." In essence, necessity can promote restraint.

Restraint will cause us to focus on our responsibility to the earth, future generations, and other organisms. More and more we will turn away from self-centered thinking, favoring what is good for the whole of society. Restraint is exercised because it benefits the whole of society, future generations, and the earth. Restraint will help create a high-synergy society in which the individual parts function for the good of the whole. Restraint will help us minimize our impact on nature, creating a better balance between humans and the environment.

The sustainable ethical system is a new paradigm that lays the foundation for a sustainable society. However different it may be, it does not necessarily renounce all technology, all growth, or all material goods. Instead, it advocates a thoughtful look at the long-term health of the planet and an evaluation of the consequences of technology, population growth, and materialism.

Making the Transition

As solid as entrenched belief systems seem, they do change. Colonialism and slavery, and the beliefs that sup-

ported them, for instance, have fallen by the wayside in the United States. New paradigms have replaced these outmoded systems. The same may hold true for the frontier mentality. But how can the changes be made?

Three Approaches

The shift to a sustainable society is a tall order for a society steeped in frontierism. A profound shift in attitude, many experts argue, is needed to begin the process. As people adopt a sustainable ethics, they will make the shifts in life-style. This change in values leading to a new societal order can be called the **bottom-up approach**. A **top-down** approach calls for new laws and regulations to regulate behavior. The thinking behind this approach is that forced behavioral changes will lead to belief changes. The National Enviromental Policy Act, discussed in Chapter Supplement 21-1, attempts to change beliefs by forcing developers to study their potential impacts before construction. Some people believe that disaster is necessary to bring about changes in attitude and life-style. We can call this the **crisis approach**. In reality, crisis brings about policy change (top-down) and shifts in beliefs (bottom-up). Critics argue that crises are too disruptive and that this approach must be avoided.

The bottom-up approach would cause the least hardship of the three options. However, it is probably the most difficult one. It requires some insight into our problems and their solutions and a willingness to make changes before troubles begin. Sustainability on a global scale calls for insight, commitment to change, and action among the peoples of the world.

Why We Should Feel Responsible for Future Generations

Robert Mellert

The author teaches philosophy and future studies at Brookdale Community College in Lincroft, New Jersey. He has published What Is Process Theology? *and numerous articles on process philosophy, ethics, and future studies.*

"Why should I feel obligated to future generations? We're inevitably separated by time and space. My presence here on earth now will have no influence on someone living 200 years from now."

You may have heard this opinion expressed by your friends—perhaps you even hold it yourself. But if you have ever explored a wilderness preserve, used a library, or visited a historical monument, you already have some reasons for being responsible. Much of what we value in our family, our society, and our world has been provided by our predecessors, sometimes at considerable cost and effort on their part.

In today' world we face a number of issues that will affect future generations even more profoundly than they affect us now. Exploding world populations, shrinking nonrenewable resources, and plant and animal organisms threatened with extinction all add up to one thing—an ailing environment.

These are not isolated problems. Each stems from a common perception of our relationship to the world and our future. This perception can be characterized by a description of people and things as unique, immediate, individual, and separate from everything else. Any solutions that we might use to resolve our problems would have to start by challenging this perception.

Let me propose four basic considerations that may suggest a new paradigm for understanding our relationship to the world and our future. I believe our moral responsibility to coming generations will follow directly from these.

1. Future generations will be essentially the same as we are. They may have different wants and priorities, but they will manifest the same basic needs for food, water, air, and space. In addition, they will have the same basic physical and mental capacities with which to interact with their environment. Once born, they, too, will claim a right to life and protection from life-threatening conditions, such as extreme temperatures, toxins, famine, and disease. To give them life without also providing the basic means to sustain and enhance life would be cruel. If we expect the species to continue, we are obliged to leave a hospitable environment for those still to come.

2. One is born into a given generation by historical accident. None of us chose when to be born, or to whom. Because we have no special claim to the time and place of our birth, justice would require that we have no more rights over the world and its resources than anyone else.

3. Our survival as a species is more important than our individual survival. This is confirmed in nature every day; parents, whether they be rabbits, wolves, whales, or humans, spend their energies to reproduce and care for their young before they themselves die. Many will even risk their own lives for their offspring. This is because life is not ours to keep, but to share with others.

4. Even after we die, the effects of our life continue. We will be present in the memories of others and in the habits and traditions we shared with them. Our ideas will continue to enlarge the range of options for others; and even when these memories and ideas are no longer consciously a part of the future, they will ripple onwards, actively influencing the course of future events and people. What has been can never die. We are what we have been given and what we have chosen to make of these "gifts." In short, we are the product of our ancestors— all that they died for and believed in—and we are the product of our decisions. Future generations will be the result of what we are now and how they use what we leave them.

If we accept these four simple ideas, it is easy to see why we have an obligation to future generations. Our obligation is based on the truth that we are more than unique and separate individuals, living only the immediacy of the now. We are, rather, parts of a much larger whole, one that transcends space and time.

As John Locke, the great English philosopher, once said, we owe the future "enough and as good" as we received from the past.

Some Attitudinal Changes Are Already Evident

Without a doubt, attitudes are changing. The frontier mentality of "doing more with more," prevalent for so long, is now being replaced by a new attitude, an attitude of "doing more with less." This new attitude, thrust on developed countries by the high cost of energy, dwindling resource supplies, and economic problems, is an important change, but it will not suffice to bring about a sustainable society. The principal element in the strategy of achieving "more with less" is reforming inefficient ways. According to this view, we can have our fancy cars, extravagant homes, wasteful appliances, and more, but we will do it with a little less energy and fewer resources.

To achieve a truly sustainable society, we must shift away from the "more with less" attitude. This may require a stepwise progression. The first step would be to acquire the attitude of "doing the same with less." In other words, we will maintain our standard of living but reduce our resource demands. There are signs today that some people have already adopted this attitude. The next, and perhaps most difficult, step toward a sustainable society is the development of the attitude of "doing less with less." This requires us to examine the ways we do business and run our daily lives. It means having only one small, energy-efficient car per family, using mass transit and walking; sharing tools with neighbors or renting them instead of buying a tool used only once year; digging gardens and shoveling sidewalks by hand; forgoing the latest fashion or the newest gadget designed to make life easier; taking a train home from college or for business trips; and building a small, energy-efficient solar-powered, earth-sheltered home that is warm and comfortable instead of an oversized, electric-powered home with inadequate insulation. It means breaking our wasteful habits.

Already, there are many signs that the change from "doing more with more" to "doing less with less" may be taking place. Many people have simplified their lifestyles. Some have moved to rural areas where they can grow their own food, and many are turning to nonmotorized recreation, such as cross-country skiing and canoeing.

With the changes in attitude and life-style there is room for optimism, but there is a lot more to be done. In 1986 the world's population reached 5 billion. Damage from acid precipitation is estimated to be over $5 billion a year in the United States. The last California condor was captured and taken to a zoo, where scientists are fighting to save the species. Worldwide, one vertebrate species (and subspecies) goes extinct every nine months. Clearly, any optimism we may have should be cautious optimism.

Avoiding Pitfalls

To make the transition to a sustainable society is the challenge and the opportunity of a lifetime. But to do so, we must avoid numerous pitfalls.

First, we must avoid the paralysis that comes with an attitude that we are doomed to perish by overpopulation, food shortage, war, or pollution. This paralysis will do no good. It will keep us from thinking creatively and acting with determination to make necessary changes in our own lives.

We must also avoid excessive optimism in technological solutions to our population, resource, and pollution problems. Such a view can be dangerous in the long run, for it blunts personal responsibility and action. By avoiding blind faith in technology and by carefully developing those technologies that are most useful and least harmful to the environment and human health, we can go a long way toward solving our problems. Technology is not *the* answer, but it can be a part of the answer to our problems.

We must also avoid outdated solutions—for example, building large, expensive power plants to heat our homes when insulation and solar energy will provide the warmth we need, more cheaply and with fewer impacts on the environment. The problems of today are caused by the conditions of today. New solutions to new problems are what the times call for, but we must be careful not to overlook obvious answers.

We must also avoid narrow thinking and restricted imagination. All our creativity, cooperation, and patience will be called on to achieve a sustainable society. Even though we don't know the exact form of the future society we're working for, we know the principles that will work. That gives us enough to start thinking now.

We must also avoid apathy and the attitude that someone else will solve the problem. The sustainable society comes closer to being a reality with each person's effort, no matter how small or large. We must become active and make the changes we need to achieve a less resource-intensive life-style. We must start with our immediate surroundings. Which changes we make are not as important as the choice to change.

Once we've achieved our personal goals, we might take a more active role in our communities by organizing recycling on campus or in our apartment buildings or dormitories. Working with schools or employers to reduce energy consumption is another option. Writing our congressional representatives can also help.

Remember the saying, "If you're not part of the solution, you're part of the problem." We live in an age of cooperation; we succeed as we work together. We succeed as each of us makes the small changes that eventually transform the globe.

> *A human being is part of the whole, called by us "Universe." . . . He experiences himself, his thoughts and feelings as something separated from the rest—a kind of optical delusion of his consciousness. This delusion is a kind of prison for us, restricting us to our personal desires and to affection for a few persons nearest to us. Our task must be to free ourselves from this prison by widening our circle of compassion to embrace all living creatures and the whole of nature in its beauty.*
>
> ALBERT EINSTEIN

Summary

Building a sustainable society requires a new set of beliefs—an appropriate ethical system—because our attitudes toward nature determine how we interact with the environment. Today, many people operate with a frontier mentality based on three main ideas: (1) the world has an unlimited supply of resources for human use, (2) humans are apart from nature, not a part of nature, and (3) nature is something to overcome. These attitudes toward nature stem in part from Judeo-Christian teachings and in part from biological imperialism—the tendency for all organisms to convert as much of the environment into themselves and their offspring as possible. The psychological roots of our behavior are found in the common perception of the self as "I" versus nature as "not I." As a result, we think of ourselves as apart from nature. This psychology also causes damage from the ego-building that leads many to seek material wealth.

The roots of the attitude that there is always more are easily seen. For most of human history, population size has been small in comparison with the earth's resource supplies. There always *has* been more, until recently.

The frontier mentality is the underpinning of contemporary human thought. Made aware of the limits of resources, many people simply express apathy. Resource limitations and pollution seem like problems for which someone else must take responsibility. Many people take a self-centered view of things: what they can afford determines what they buy. Feelings of insignificance also grip the average citizen. They greatly contribute to the problems we suffer and also keep us from solving them. Finally, restricted space–time values create narrow thinking that is dangerous in these times of rapid change.

The frontier mentality creates a low-synergy society whose parts work at cross purposes. A high-synergy society might be created by adopting a sustainable ethics. This system of ethics holds that the earth has a limited supply of resources and that humans are a part of nature and not superior to it. The new ethical system will help us learn to fully examine our economic and resource decisions in terms of what creates a sustainable society.

There are encouraging signs that we are shifting toward a sustainable society. Still, we are a long way from realizing this goal. To make the changes we must avoid the paralysis that comes with an attitude that humans are doomed. We must also avoid blind optimism about technology and the "good-old-days" trap, which seeks to answer today's problems with yesterday's answers. And we must avoid narrow thought and restricted imagination. We must avoid apathy and the attitude that someone else will solve the problem.

Discussion Questions

1. Describe the three major concepts of the frontier mentality. How do these attitudes affect the way humans interact with the environment?

2. How is your personal ethic similar to and how is it different from the frontier mentality?

3. Debate the statement "The frontier mentality comes from Judeo-Christian teachings that give humans dominion over the world."

4. Describe the terms *biological imperialism, skin-encapsulated ego,* and *derived self*. How are these related to environmental damage?

5. Describe the role apathy, self-centeredness, feelings of insignificance, and technological optimism play in creating environmental problems.

6. What is a low-synergy society? Give some examples.

7. Discuss the tenets of the sustainable ethics. Indicate which of these tenets coincide with your personal beliefs. Which ones don't? Why?

8. In what ways would society change if it adopted a sustainable ethics?

9. Debate the statement "We are a long way from achieving a sustainable society."

10. Which of the following attitudes best fits yours? "More with more," "more with less," "same with less," or "less with less."

11. What is the attitude of most of your friends?

Suggested Readings

Barbour, I. G. (1973). *Western Man and Environmental Ethics*. Reading, Mass.: Addison-Wesley. A collection of thought-provoking essays, including those by Lynn White (Chapters 2 and 5) and René Dubos (Chapter 11) cited in this chapter.

Brown, L. R. (1981). *Building a Sustainable Society*. New York: Norton. Highly readable discussion of the need for a sustainable society and ways to build it.

Elder, F. (1974). The New Asceticism. In *Environment and Society*, ed. R. T. Roelofs, J. N. Crowley, and D. L. Hardesty. Englewood Cliffs, N.J.: Prentice-Hall. A delightful article on sustainable ethics.

Hardin, G. (1970). To Trouble a Star: The Cost of Intervention in Nature. *Bulletin of the Atomic Scientists* January: 17–20. A well-written analysis of modern ethics.

Hardin, G. (1985). *Filters against Folly*. New York: Viking. Wonderful treatise on ethics. Important reading.

Johnson, W. (1978). *Muddling toward Frugality*. San Francisco: Sierra Club Books. An important, thoughtful book, offering a view of the transition to a more frugal society.

Leopold, A. (1966). *A Sand County Almanac*. New York: Ballantine. Wonderful collection of essays on the conservation ethic.

Milbrath, L. W. (1984). *Environmentalists: Vanguard for a New Society*. Albany: State University of New York Press. Contains an excellent attitude survey.

Naisbitt, J. (1982). *Megatrends: Ten New Directions Transforming Our Lives*. New York: Warner Books. Superb analysis of social trends.

Partridge, D. (ed.). (1980). *Responsibilities to Future Generations*. Buffalo, N.Y.: Prometheus Books. Good collection of essays on ethics.

Russell, P. (1982). *The Global Brain*. Los Angeles: Tarcher. A thoughtful book on achieving a unified society.

Schumacher, E. F. (1973). *Small Is Beautiful: Economics as if People Mattered*. New York: Harper and Row. One of the best books ever written on the subject of a sustainable society and new ethical systems necessary for survival on our finite planet.

Van Matre, S., and Weiler, B. (1983). *The Earth Speaks*. Warrenville, Ill.: The Institute for Earth Education. Superb collection of writings on nature.

20

Economics and the Environment

A penny will hide the biggest star in the Universe if you hold it close enough to your eye.

SAMUEL GRAFTON

In southern India people once made traps for monkeys by drilling small holes in coconuts, filling the shells with rice, and chaining them to the ground. The success of this trap was based on a simple principle: the hole was large enough for a monkey to insert its empty hand, but too small for it to pull a handful of rice out. Monkeys were trapped by their own refusal to let go of the rice.

Some economists believe that the same plight grips humankind: we're caught in a spiraling cycle of greed, trapped by our own refusal to let go of our growing material wealth. This chapter looks at economics, pointing out some of its major laws. It examines how the prevalent economic thinking contributes to environmental problems, and it evaluates some proposals for an economic system for a sustainable society.

Economics and the Quality of Life

Economics is a science that started two centuries ago with the publication of the Englishman Adam Smith's monumental book, *The Wealth of Nations*. Economics is the study of the production, distribution, and consumption of goods and services in a society. It concerns itself with two key variables: inputs and outputs. Inputs are things, such as labor and land, or commodities, such as minerals and wheat, that companies require to turn out their products. Outputs are the goods and services that companies produce for consumption or for further production.

Economic Systems

Economics is in many ways an applied science, for it helps society solve three fundamental problems: (1) *what* commodities it should produce and in what quantity, (2) *how* it should produce its goods, and (3) *for whom* it should produce them. Of course, there are many ways for a society to solve the three basic problems. In a **command economy** such as that of the Soviet Union, where the government dictates production and distribution goals, decisions are left to bureaucrats. In a **market economy**, where prices, supply, and demand prevail, the government usually takes a back seat to the marketplace. In such an economy, companies generally produce the goods and services that yield the highest profit—thus answering the first question, what goods and services and in what quantity? Profit dictates how goods are produced. Generally, the least costly method of production yields the greatest profit. This is the choice of prudent business people. In a market economy the question "for whom?" is determined by money. As a general rule, whoever can afford a good or service will get it.

One of the key principles of economics is the **law of scarcity**. It states that most things that people want are limited. As a result they must be rationed by price or some other means. Scarcity also applies to the inputs of an economy—labor, land, capital (money and machinery), and resources.

In a market economy price is the key tool that rations output. For instance, few of us in the United States drive Porsches because the price greatly exceeds our ability to pay for them. In a command economy governments take on the task of rationing output, although prices cannot be ruled out. For example, Porsches are not available to the masses in the Soviet Union or Poland. Even if they were, few could afford one because of the steep price and low earnings (which are government controlled).

An important fact of life in economics is that most economies are **mixed**. There are no 100% market or 100% command economies, but rather mixtures of both features. In the United States, Great Britain, and Canada—three market economies—governments play a large role in economics. They put controls on pollutants, ban chemicals and products that are harmful, regulate freight rates for raw materials, and levy taxes. At various times, the U.S. government has regulated oil and natural gas prices and airline fares.

Economics and Ecology

Economics, like environmental science, is concerned with relationships. It also employs scientific tools to discover the laws that regulate economies. The description of economic facts and relationships falls within the purview of **positive economics**, so named because it is relatively free of judgment. Positive economics is, relatively speaking, the pure science. Its questions can be answered only by facts. Economics melds with political science and sociology when it attempts to answer value-laden questions. For example, should companies pay for pollution controls? How rapidly should the economy grow? Such questions cannot be answered by empirical facts and figures. There are no right or wrong answers to them, for they are value judgments and are left to the political process, as described in the next chapter. This realm of economics is called **normative economics**. The questions it tackles create enormous disagreement among the economists, and for good reason. Here, built-in biases often muddle issues.

The Growth Issue As we saw in Chapter Supplement 1-1, bias is difficult to eliminate from science. It creeps into the interpretations of scientific findings no matter how objective the researcher is. Positive economics, like other "objective" sciences, suffers from biases, the key one being economic growth. In the 1967 edition of a popular textbook Paul Samuelson, a Nobel Prize–winning MIT economist, calls economics "the science of growth." Subsequent editions have dropped the wording, but the bias remains. In his 1984 edition, for example, Samuelson writes: "Today, the ultimate measure of economic success is a country's ability to generate a high level of and rapid growth in the output of economic goods and services. Greater output of food and clothing, cars and education, radios and concerts—what else is an economy for if not to produce an appropriate mix of these in high quantity and fidelity?" While not all economists subscribe to this view, many do, especially those in the business world or in government. To them growth has become something of a god, sacred. Economic growth is a measure of progress.

Critics call this undying dedication to economic growth "growthmania." Its roots are firmly embedded in the frontier notion that "there is always more." For many years human civilization has been caught up in it and has been willing to pay almost any price for it. Today, the dominant social view (or paradigm) that economic growth is desirable is in question. More and more Americans express skepticism over unlimited growth. More importantly, many express a strong preference for environmental protection over economic growth. In fact, a recent survey by Lester Milbrath at the State University of New York at Buffalo showed that three-fourths of the American public favored environmental protection over economic growth. Several other surveys support his findings.

Economic growth means increased consumption of goods and services. Such an increase may arise from (1) an increase in population size and (2) an increase in the amount of each of us buys—per capita consumption. Because it means greater production and, presumably,

Figure 20-1 Young agricultural students in Burkina Faso (West Africa) learn to use and maintain plows—the technology is appropriate to the region's agricultural needs and capabilities. Limited economic growth may help individuals of Third World nations eradicate hunger, improve the standard of living, and control population growth.

greater economic wealth, population growth has traditionally been viewed as an asset to society. Each new baby is seen as a new consumer.

In a world of limited resources (such as minerals and oil) and greatly exceeded carrying capacity (witnessed in global pollution and widespread extinction of plants and animals), ecologists argue that continued population growth and rising per capita consumption, particularly among the wealthy, is unwise. But what of the billions of poor people in the world who have little food, who suffer with inadequate housing and education, and who lack sufficient clean drinking water and sanitation facilities? Such a question lies in the realm of normative economics. Value-laden as it is, it can have no easy answer. Chapter 6 pointed out that most observers believe that a combination of population control and reasonable economic development are the foundations of an effective strategy to improve the welfare of these people (Figure 20-1).

Differing Perspectives on the Future Economics as an academic discipline dates back to 1776, when Smith's *The Wealth of Nations* was published. Ecology,

the formal study of living things and their interactions with the environment, comes from the latter half of the 19th century. "Growing up independently," Garrett Hardin notes, "the two subjects developed sharp differences." Nowhere is this more noticeable than in their view of the future.

For an economist the dividing line between the near term and the far term is typically five years. Political leaders, tied to upcoming elections, also often subscribe to the short-term outlook (Chapter 21). The ecologist, on the other hand, is likely to set the dividing line at a century or more. "To say that economics is near-sighted is not necessarily to condemn it," Hardin argues. "The near-sightedness is understandable. Most of the time economics is a handmaiden of business, and experience has shown that it is very difficult to predict what business will be like more than five years in the future."

In a world of rapid change, however, a five-year outlook can be dangerous. Our large population base and resource use, which grow exponentially in size, render the five-year outlook obsolete. Setting a new course for humanity almost certainly means aiming our sights much further into the future.

Economic Measures: Beyond the GNP

Economists need ways to measure economic activity. The most important measure of a nation's economy is its gross national product. The **gross national product** (GNP) is the market value of the nation's output—in other words, the cost of all goods and services that a nation produces and sells, including government purchases, in a given year. **Real GNP** is the GNP adjusted for inflation. **Per capita GNP** is the real GNP divided by the total population.

GNP is widely used to track economies. It gives a general picture of the relative wealth of nations and the living standards of their people. However, MIT's Paul Samuelson and Yale's William Nordhaus note that the "GNP is a flawed index of a nation's true economic welfare." Why is this so? The GNP includes many goods and services that make no contribution to the welfare of the people. In a sense, the GNP is blind to the quality of the air, water, and soil. As a lump sum that covers all goods and services, it fails to differentiate between good and bad expenditures. For example, the GNP includes all expenditures on homes, books, concerts, and food—deemed good because they improve the standard of living; at the same time, however, the GNP includes expenditures on cancer treatment, air pollution damage, hospitals and health services, and water pollution projects—all necessary evils brought on by pollution. Therefore, a country with filthy air and polluted water that is faced with rising cancer rates and other disorders might register a high GNP. Envious politicians looking in from the sidelines might mistake the high GNP for a sign of an enviable standard

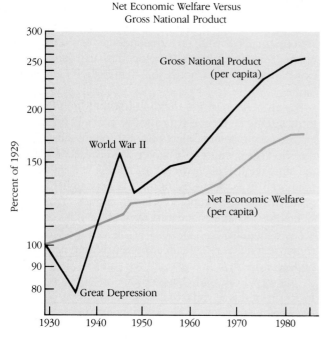

Net Economic Welfare Versus
Gross National Product

Figure 20-2 The GNP is the market value of all goods and services produced by a country. U.S. per capita GNP has risen continuously for many years. The NEW, or net economic welfare, is a measure of beneficial goods and services. It is derived by subtracting the negative aspects of the GNP which do nothing to improve the quality of life, such as damage from air pollution. The per capita NEW is lower than the GNP and rises at a slower rate, suggesting diminishing returns from economic growth.

of living while residents could decry the putrid mess they were living in.

Nordhaus and another Yale economist, James Tobin, have devised a measure that adjusts the GNP, making it a more accurate representation of the good that people receive from their nation's output. This measure, called the **net economic welfare** (NEW), subtracts the "disamenities" of an economy—the cost of pollution and other activities that do not improve the quality of life—from the GNP. It also adds the cost of certain activities, such as household services provided by husbands and wives, that are not part of the traditional GNP calculations but that improve well-being.

Figure 20-2 shows that the United States' NEW is lower than its real GNP. More important, it shows that the NEW increases at a slower rate. In other words, as the nation's output grows, the economic benefits fall behind, largely due to rising pollution. Some economists believe that this trend may be inevitable as the world becomes more congested and more dependent on fossil fuels and large-scale technologies. These produce large quantities of pol-

lution, which either escape into the air or are captured by control devices and later disposed of in landfills.

A second problem with GNP as an economic indicator is nations' dedication to GNP growth. An increasing GNP is the hallmark of a successful economy; in fact, countries are often judged by their rate of GNP growth. This criterion, however, fails to take into account the accumulated wealth of a country. A newly developed nation may have a 5% annual growth in its GNP, compared with a 2% growth rate in a developed country such as the United States. Does this mean the newly developed nation is doing better? Not really. It only means that its economy is expanding more rapidly. Most likely, it has more room to expand but its people are far less wealthy than those of the United States. Keeping in mind their accumulated wealth can help nations set aside a blind dedication to growth.

This book takes the position that, given the limits of many resources, a sustainable society based primarily on renewable resources will emerge from today's society, which is based on a mixture of renewable and nonrenewable resources. Signs of the sustainable society have already begun to appear. To assess the level of sustainability, Edwin Dolan has proposed a new measure called the **gross national cost**, or GNC. The GNC would look at the value of goods produced by an economy but would be divided into two parts: Type 1 GNC would measure the value of goods from renewable resources, and Type 2 GNC would indicate the value of goods from nonrenewable resources. As the sustainable society evolves, more and more developed countries will increase their Type 1 GNC (renewable output) relative to their Type 2 GNC (nonrenewable output).

The Law of Supply and Demand

In market economies the three essential questions—what to produce, how to produce it, and for whom—are solved by price, which is dependent on supply and demand. Figure 20-3a shows a demand curve for rice. On the vertical axis of the graph is the price (P) of rice in dollars per bushel. On the horizontal axis is the quantity (Q) demanded at each price. This graph says that a rise in price will decrease the demand. Conversely, a lowering of price will generally increase demand. P and Q are inversely related. Prices would rise if energy, land, and labor costs increased. Bad weather might cut production levels, thus also raising prices.

The supply curve for rice (Figure 20-3b) also plots the relationship between price and quantity, but this time quantity is equal to the amount of rice farmers will produce at different prices. The graph shows that the higher the price, the more rice farmers will produce; conversely, farmers produce less rice at lower prices.

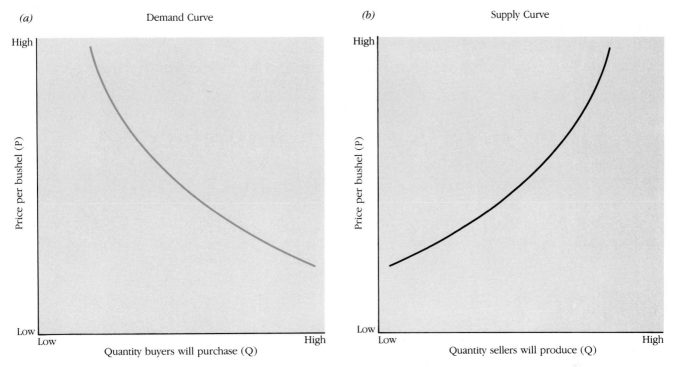

Figure 20-3 Supply and demand curves for rice. (*a*) The demand curve shows the relationship between the price (P) on the vertical axis and demand (Q) on the horizontal. This graph shows that a rise in prices will reduce the demand, and vice versa. (*b*) The supply curve shows the relationship between the price and supply, or amount produced. The higher the price, the more farmers will produce.

Supply and demand interact to establish the market price of rice. This process is illustrated in Figure 20-4a. The intersection of the supply and demand curves is the **market price equilibrium**, the point at which the forces in the marketplace are in balance. The market price equilibrium represents the price consumers are willing to pay and the quantity they will purchase. It is also the quantity farmers will produce and the price at which sellers offer their rice.

The market economy is largely driven by the interaction of supply and demand for thousands of goods and services. Supply, demand, and price are corners of the same economic triangle.

The implications of the supply and demand curves are many. Consider the effects of a decrease in supply of a given resource—say, natural gas (Figure 20-4b). If the demand for natural gas remains constant, a decline in supply will inevitably increase the cost of the fuel. Figure 20-4b shows that the supply curve shifts to the left when the supply decreases. If the demand stays the same, the price will inevitably rise as a new market price equilibrium is reached. If demand remains constant and supply increases—in other words, the supply curve shifts to the right—price will fall.

Now consider a shift in demand with a fixed supply (Figure 20-4c). A shift in the demand curve to the right represents an increase in demand. If the supply of natural gas remains the same but the demand increases, the inevitable result is an increase in price. Ultimately, rising prices usually compel producers to make more of their product or find more resources to increase supply. The net effect, at least in theory, is that rising demand ultimately increases the supply. Rising prices in the 1970s and early 1980s stimulated companies to search for natural gas, petroleum, and minerals.

The law of supply and demand operates well in most instances, aptly describing the economic behavior of most markets and the national economy of a capitalistic nation as a whole. Resource scientists, however, point out a problem with strict adherence to the law when dealing with nonrenewable resources. They point out that supply-and-demand interactions set the price for minerals and fossil fuels. But, they note that rising prices cannot expand the supply indefinitely. A point must be reached when a resource is economically depleted, or in such short supply that it cannot be economically produced (Figure 20-5).

Two monumental barriers face the frontier society: (1) accepting the limitations of the law of supply and demand—in other words, realizing that our nonrenewable

(a)

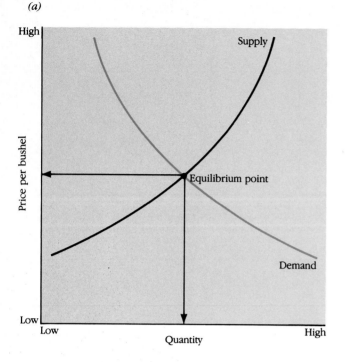

(b)

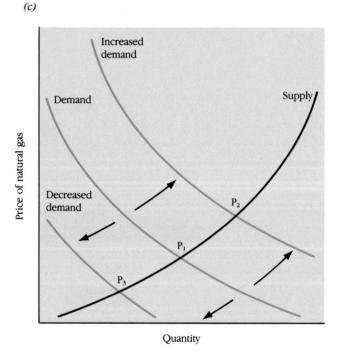

Figure 20-4 (*a*) Supply and demand interact to set the market price equilibrium. The market price represents the price consumers are willing to pay and the quantity they will purchase. It also shows what price farmers will accept and the quantity of rice they will produce at that price. Notice that price is indicated by the intersection of the supply and demand curves. (*b*) Shifts in supply raise or lower prices if demand stays the same. A decrease in supply, for instance, increases the price (P$_2$); an increase in supply drives the price down (P$_3$). Graphically, an increase in supply is shown by a shift of the supply curve to the right; a decrease is shown as a shift to the left. (*c*) Shifts in demand when supply remains constant also affect the price. For example, when demand rises, the price rises (P$_2$); when demand falls, the price falls (P$_3$).

(c)

Figure 20-5 An open pit copper mine in Arizona.

resource supply cannot expand indefinitely—and (2) accurately predicting when that end of expansion will come. The next chapter, on government, looks at the ways in which governments can affect supply and demand and help promote more responsible resource management.

Economic Behavior, Environment, and Resources

The previous section looked at the science of economics, concentrating on the GNP and the law of supply and demand. This section looks at our economic behavior—that is, the influence of economics on our actions. Two key areas are presented to introduce you to this topic—resource management and pollution control. By examining economic behavior and how it affects our decisions about natural resources and pollution, you can gain some insight into the problems of modern society and can find some new solutions to them as well.

The Economics of Resource Management

Many private decisions about natural resources are influenced by economic considerations. One of the most important of these factors is called time preference.

Time Preference Time Preference is a measure of one's willingness to postpone some current income for greater returns in the future. For example, suppose a friend offers you $100 today or $108 a year from now. If you are short on cash and need to pay for books for

school, you may take the money now. Your decision to accept the money now is based on your current needs, which in this case outweigh the benefits of waiting the year, even though you would be $8 ahead. Economists would say that your need for current income outweighs greater returns in the future.

As this example shows, your preference for immediate income is determined by your current needs. It may also be influenced by uncertainty. How certain are you that your friend will be around in a year to give you the $108 he promised? A third, and very important, factor affecting time preference is the rate of return. The higher the rate of return, the more likely you will wait for the income. For instance, if your friend had offered you $150 a year from now, it might be advisable to wait. You could borrow $100 from your parents at 10% interest and pay them back at the end of the year with the $150 your friend gave you and still have money left over.

Time preference applies equally well to the ways in which we manage many of our natural resources, such as water, farmland, and forests. Take agriculture as an example. Farmers have two basic choices when it comes to managing their land. They can choose a **depletion strategy** to acquire an immediate high rate of return for a short period. This might involve the use of multiple cropping, artificial fertilizers, herbicides, and pesticides to maximize production (Chapter 7). Soil erosion control and other techniques might be ignored. Alternatively, farmers may choose a **conservation strategy**, techniques to conserve topsoil and maintain soil fertility; these actions require immediate monetary investments. They may cost the farmers a little more in the short run and cut into their immediate profits. Over the long run, however, the conservation strategy is the more profitable.

The choice of strategy in this example depends on the time preference. Will farmers choose the cheapest route of production, which gives the highest profit in the short term? Or will they choose a more expensive route, forgoing immediate high profits in favor of much higher gains in the future. The economic needs of the farmers determine, to a large extent, their time preference. For example, a young farmer looking forward to a productive career may opt for the conservation strategy. Her immediate needs may be small. She may have no family and few debts. She can sacrifice income now for larger returns in the long run. However, an established farmer may have a family to support and excessive debt. He may, therefore, want to maximize his profits through a depletion strategy.

Farmers' willingness to give up potentially higher income from conservation may also result from uncertainty about future prices, the long-range prospects for farming, and interest rates. If the price of corn is high this year but could drop significantly in coming years, farmers may choose to make their money now. If the bottom falls out of the market in the next few years, they will have made the most of this short-term opportunity. If interest rates are likely to rise, short-term profit making may be the preferable choice. High interest rates on land and machinery that farmers purchase tend to encourage the depletion strategy.

Opportunity Cost   Another factor that greatly influences economic decisions regarding resource management is the opportunity cost. **Opportunity cost** is the cost of lost money-making opportunities. For instance, the conservation strategy requires a monetary investment. The money put into conservation could have been invested in the stock market or a new business venture, possibly yielding more profit with less work than the conservation strategy. As a result, when opportunity costs are high, farmers are likely to choose options other than conservation.

Ethics   Several noneconomic factors greatly affect our economic decisions. One of the key factors, not to be overlooked, is the ethics of the farmer. Ethics can be as powerful as—or even more power than—economic factors. A long-term view, seeking to maximize yield for future generations and ensure the survival and well-being of all life, may foster wiser management of our natural resources. Sustainable ethics, discussed in Chapter 19, contrasts sharply with the frontier mentality, which seeks to maximize personal gain with little concern for the future, in effect leaving future generations to fend for themselves.

With this brief overview of the factors that influence the way we manage our farms and forests, in mind, let us look at the topic of pollution control and the underlying economic issues.

The Economics of Pollution Control

Economics also plays an important role in how pollution is controlled. This section looks at some of the factors that influence our choices.

The free market economic system in the United States and other countries as well as the command economies of socialist and communist nations treated pollution with almost uniform disregard until the late 1960s and early 1970s. Pollution was something that issued from the smokestacks and symbolized economic progress. Where it landed no one seemed to know or care. Under such a system pollution and its impacts are considered an **economic externality**, a cost to society not paid by the manufacturer or its customers.

In many instances businesses were simply unaware of the external costs of pollution. Gradually, though, citizens throughout the world began suing polluters (if their system of government allowed it). Governments established pollution standards to protect the public as well as industry, and businesses began to curb pollution by redesigning processes and, most often, installing pollution control devices. Economic externalities came home to roost. Rather than foisting the costs onto society, companies began to control pollution. In a way, the costs were **internalized**. Preventing external costs became part of the cost of doing business.

Chapters 14–18, on pollution, described laws that have forced cost internalization. In the United States the major ones are the Clean Air Act, the Clean Water Act, the Resource Conservation and Recovery Act, and the Surface Mine Control and Reclamation Act.

More and more, governments are tightening regulations to protect the public from the tens of thousands of chemical substances and the physical agents, such as noise and radiation, we are exposed to at work and at home. But what factors determine the level of control—that is, just how much money we should spend on controlling potentially harmful substances?

Cost–Benefit Analysis and Pollution Control   As you may have guessed, economics plays a key role in determining the level of pollution control. As we saw in Chapter 14, in our study of risk assessment, the chief goal of pollution control is to achieve a maximum reduction in pollution, yielding the maximum benefit, at the lowest cost. This goal is made possible by **cost–benefit analysis**.

The cost of pollution control and the cost of the harmful effects of pollution can be plotted on a graph (Figure 20-6). Figure 20-6a shows that at high levels of pollution,

Resources Misuse

Throughout much of history, humans have been able to ignore the impact of their activities on natural resources. However, in recent years, we have been forced to recognize the error of our ways; air and water pollution, unsafe disposal of toxic wastes, the near catastrophe at Three Mile Island, depletion of precious minerals, extinction of endangered species, and more. These misuses threaten the resources needed to sustain not only our civilization, but our planet as well. Today, the earth's future lies in a combined and difficult task; not only must we correct our past mistakes, we must *understand* how and why they happened, and take steps to ensure that they don't happen again.

1 There goes the neighborhood... A wet cooling tower stands in bold contrast to a farmhouse in rural northern Ohio.

1

2 A denuded hill in Alaska has been clear-cut to remove timber for domestic and foreign markets.

3 Controlled fires burn the grassy vegetation of cleared rain forest. Some experts feel that removal of tropical rain forests will have a direct effect on climatic conditions. The release of great amounts of carbon dioxide into the atmosphere is said to contribute to the green-house effect, a phenomenon which may pro-duce an unfavorable warming trend in the earth's atmosphere.

4 Land in a tropical rain forest is cleared for farming or grazing. After removal of vegetation, the nutrient-poor soil is often washed away or baked into a brick-like consistency, rendering it useless.

5 Overgrazing turned a once-rich grassland into a lifeless desert. Without the plant-root network that once bound it, the soil is unable to retain moisture and is easily blown away.

6 An infrared aerial view of Love Canal, Niagara Falls, New York. The dump, home to dozens of chemicals including PCBs and dioxin, was sold to the city in the 1950s as a school and playground site. Healthy vegetation appears red; brown vegetation indicates contamination. The toxic wastes were spread throughout the neighborhood via underground streams; 237 families were evacuated from the area.

7 Toxic wastes are stored in steel drums, then buried or stored in toxic waste dumps like this one. The steel drums, which are supposed to separate the dangerous wastes from you and me, rust due to their corrosive contents.

8 Workers wrapped in protective clothing prepare to bury toxic wastes. About 90% of the country's toxic and chemical wastes are dumped illegally.

9 Industrial society produces massive quan-tities of refuse, some of which gets buried, burned, or recycled. The rest ends up along highways, in empty lots, or, as in this case, in someone's backyard.

10 Boats at dock on the Amazon sit immersed in a sea of floating garbage.

2

3

4

5

6

7

8

9

10

11 Waste from an iron ore processing plant colors the water of this artificial pond a bright orange. Such wastes seep into the earth, contaminating groundwater supplies.

12 Nitrogen fertilizer added to irrigation water to boost crop production in the Oro Valley, Arizona, may contaminate groundwater in this area.

13 New York City lies enshrouded in a layer of filthy air.

14 In 1977, raw sewage poured into the ocean near Miami Beach, Florida. Less than 100 yards away, sunseekers enjoy a swim.

13

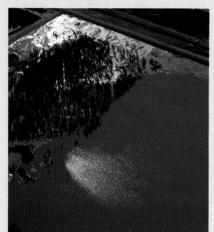

11

12

14

(a)

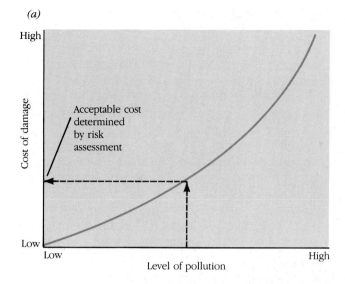

(b)

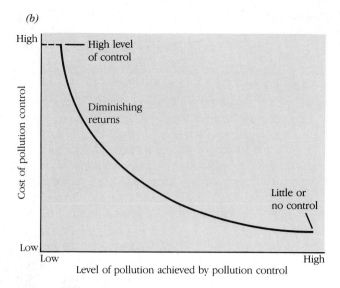

(c)

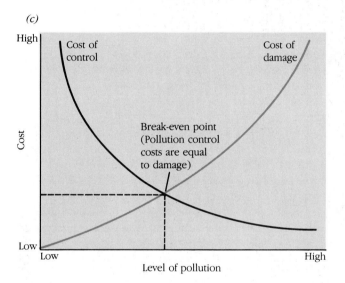

Figure 20-6 (*a*) Relationship between the pollution level and the cost of damage. The acceptable cost (risk) is also shown. (*b*) Relationship between the pollution level and the cost to achieve it, showing that small investments initially result in drastic decreases in pollution, but after a certain point the return on investment in pollution control decreases. (*c*) This graph shows the point at which pollution control costs equal damage. If society wants pollution levels lower, the costs may exceed the benefits.

the costs of the harmful effects are high. Removing pollutants decreases the cost to society. Figure 20-6b shows that the cost of pollution control is initially very cheap. A little bit of effort can remove large quantities of pollutants and cheaply. As the graph shows, however, as more and more pollutants are removed, the cost begins to rise (evidenced by the increase in the slope of the curve). Past a certain point, pollution control may become prohibitively expensive. In the initial phase, for example, removing 100 units of pollution may cost only $1. Later on, the cost of removing pollution increases rapidly— say, for example, to $1 per unit of pollution. This phenomenon is called the **law of diminishing returns**. The law states that for each dollar invested, we get a smaller return; in this case, return is measured as units of pollution removed from industrial smokestacks.

Through risk analysis scientists determine how harmful a pollutant is—the level of risk (see Chapter 14). Once the harmfulness of a pollutant is determined, decisions about the level of risk that we will accept are thrown into the political process. This level is called risk acceptability. In Figure 20-6c, risk acceptability is measured as the economic (or other) cost a society will bear, or accept. The cost of reducing pollution to that particular level can be determined on the graph. Ideally, in economics the benefits of controlling pollution should be equal to or less than the costs of control. In cases where people will accept only a small risk level, however, control costs may actually exceed the monetary benefits.

Unfortunately, determining the true costs of pollution is quite difficult, for a number of reasons. The first difficulty comes in determining the level of damage caused by pollutants. How ill do water pollutants make us? How many cases of lung cancer does air pollution cause? How many fish die from pollution each year? The second difficulty comes in assigning an economic value to lost lives, vanishing wilderness, polluted air, extinct species, or obstructed views. How much is your health worth? How much is it worth to you to have streams full of fish? Because of these problems, an accurate estimate of the cost of pollution will always seem elusive. However, estimates are necessary to ensure an equitable accounting of the costs of our modern life-styles. Such estimates help governments see the need for pollution control and tackle the important question discussed next: who should pay?

Who Should Pay for Pollution Control? Should the corporation pay to clean up the environment, in which case the costs will be passed on to the consumers of its products? This is the **consumer-pays option**. It places the obligation to pay for damage from pollutants on the users of the products. Another option, the **taxpayer-pays option**, places the responsibility on the general public, the noncorporate taxpayers. Government payments to coal miners who suffer from black lung is an example of this option. Government programs to lime lakes to neutralize acids is another.

Individuals who favor the consumer-pays option argue that the people who use the products that create pollution should bear the cost. Nonusers should not have to subsidize the costs of users. Passing the cost directly to the consumer, they add, could create more frugal buying habits. Those who support the taxpayer-pays option argue that taxpayers have allowed industry to pollute for years with impunity. Today, new standards are imposed on industry that place costly burdens on companies that have been operating under the law for long periods. Shouldn't society, which has suddenly changed the rules of the game, pay for the controls? Advocates of the taxpayer-pays option also argue that society has elected and continues to elect officials who make deals with polluters to entice them and their polluting businesses into the community. In other cases, elected officials have overlooked flagrant violations of environmental laws. If society is responsible for elected officials who permitted pollution and other forms of environmental destruction, then society must bear at least some of the cost.

As in most controversies there is validity to both arguments. In the case of old industries, taxpayers should probably bear much of the burden; but in industries that started up after the laws had been passed, pollution control costs should be borne by the corporation and consumers.

This discussion leaves the impression that pollution prevention **always** costs inordinate sums of money. Far from it. In some cases, as discussed in Chapter 18, redesigning chemical and industrial processes can sharply reduce energy use and waste. Pollution control devices in many industries can be used to capture useful products that otherwise might be dispersed into the air. Some projects can generate profits by the sale or reuse of these materials. Savings in raw materials or revenues from such sales can pay for the cost of installing and maintaining pollution control equipment and may also generate a profit.

Economic Incentives for Pollution Control Governments have many tools to control pollution. Rules and regulations described in the previous chapters are the key weapon when backed by legal recourse. (See Essay 18-1, "Getting Tough on Polluters".) In the United States and elsewhere in the world, governments have long enforced their laws by fines. More recently, prison sentences have been handed down to corporate executives of companies that violate pollution laws. In recent years, however, government officials have been exploring a variety of **economic incentives**—far gentler options to induce companies to comply with pollution laws. Billions of dollars of subsidies, for example, were provided by the Clean Water Act to assist cities and towns in improving their municipal sewage treatment plants (Chapter 16). Several additional measures are now under consideration or in use.

One incentive under consideration is the **marketable permit**, which would work this way: companies in a given region would be issued permits by the EPA to emit certain amounts of pollutants. However, a company could sell its permit to another company in the same area under certain circumstances. For example, Company A, allowed to emit 100,000 metric tons of sulfur dioxide each year, finds a way to cut its emissions to 50,000 metric tons. It can then sell its permit for 50,000 metric tons to Company B. For Company B, purchasing the permit may be cheaper than installing pollution control devices. In any event, the total emission of pollution in the region remains the same. Chapter 15 discussed the **emissions offset policy**, which is similar to the marketable permit system.

Another similar concept is the **bubble policy**, which is currently being used by the EPA. The bubble policy allows a company to increase pollution in one part of a facility if it reduces it in another, where the cost of reduction may be less.

Environmental Regulations: Do They Impede Business? Enormous federal and private expenditures on pollution control are seen by many people in the business community as an impediment. Environmental regulations and permits, business leaders argue, can delay projects. However, studies by the Conservation Foundation and other groups show that delays are often the result of uncertainty and poor planning by companies and agencies, not compliance with environmental laws. What

Case Study 20-1

Acrylonitrile: What Cost for Protection?

Acrylonitrile (AN) was one of many new chemicals that ushered in the age of plastics following World War II. Used in clothing, rugs, and numerous other home furnishings, AN and the host of other synthetic polymers created a new and prosperous industry. But in 1977 Du Pont, the maker of AN, linked it with lung and colon cancer in textile workers at its plant in Camden, South Carolina. The company and the government were forced into a precarious bind: how to balance the health of the workers with the cost of reducing their exposure to the hazardous chemical.

Acrylonitrile is big business. Its annual production and sale bring in over $1.5 billion in the United States each year. However, at least 10,000 workers are exposed to AN concentrations believed to cause cancer, and the cost of eliminating the cancer threat could run from $3.5 million to over $100 million *per life saved*.

In 1978, the Occupational Safety and Health Administration's safety standard for AN was 20 parts per million over an eight-hour workday. OSHA proposed to drop that standard to 2 ppm and considered a further reduction to .2 ppm. Economists at Du Pont, however, calculated that reductions to 2 ppm would cost millions of dollars. According to the company, reducing the level to 2 ppm would prevent seven cancer deaths among workers per year at a cost of about $3.5 million per life saved. Further reductions to .2 ppm would prevent one additional cancer death per year but would cost $126.2 million!

From a purely economic viewpoint, the investment in pollution controls makes little sense. Can we expect industry to spend billions of dollars to reduce all risks to insignificant levels? As industry officials remind us, there would be no industry if that were the case. By the same token, industry cannot be given a free license to kill people for the sake of profit.

The only principle on which there seems to be universal agreement is that a balance must be struck between the costs of doing business and the costs a business creates among the public and workers. Even this is not so easy as it may sound, however, because no universally accepted formula has been derived to balance the economic good with the health and welfare of the people.

Source: Adapted from: Behr, P. (1978); Controlling Chemical Hazards, *Environment* 20 (6): 25–29.

---

delays projects is environmental protests. These, too, could be lessened if corporations were less reluctant to invite the public or the government to participate in the early planning stages of projects. Early public involvement could reduce delays and the lawsuits that often arise when the public becomes aware of a project it finds objectionable.

Business leaders argue that environmental regulations also cut productivity. **Productivity** is the dollar value of goods per hour of paid employment. This figure has been used to show how healthy an economy is. Business people argue that environmental regulations divert workers from productive jobs (miner) to nonproductive ones (mine safety inspector). The Point/Counterpoint in this chapter shows, however, that far more jobs have been created by environmental controls than have been lost. Careful analysis shows that environmental regulations do indeed diminish the output of industry but that they are less important in decreasing output than other trends such as high energy prices, which encourage the use of labor over energy-intensive equipment, and the general shift from a manufacturing economy to a service-based economy. On balance, environmental regulations decrease productivity by an estimated 5% to 15%. This is the price for safer working conditions and a cleaner environment.

New Vistas in Economic Thought

The first section of this chapter looked at the science of economics and pointed out some differences in perspective between economics and ecology on two issues: growth and the cutoff between the short term and the long term. It also pointed out the need for a measure of economic output better than the GNP and looked at the strengths and weaknesses of the law of supply and demand. The second section discussed the economic decisions that profoundly influence resource management and pollution control. Throughout this earlier material, numerous suggestions have been made to bring economics in line with environmental realities, such as externalities and limitations to resources. But the changes discussed so far fall short of proposals by some prominent economists, who argue that a major economic transformation is necessary for the long-term survival of the human race. This section looks at these proposals, offering some options worth considering.

Sustainable Economics

Kenneth Boulding was one of the first to write about changes needed in the economies of developed countries,

Environmental Protection: Job Maker or Job Taker?

Job Blackmail and the Environment

Richard Grossman and Richard Kazis

The authors are staff members of Environmentalists for Full Employment, a policy research organization. They are the authors of the book Fear at Work: Job Blackmail, Labor and the Environment.

About 100,000 of the Americans fortunate enough to have jobs die each year from exposure to toxins at work; additionally, some 400,000 contract occupationally caused diseases. Environmental destruction from air and water pollution and diseases caused by industrial practices and waste disposal cost the United States tens of billions of dollars annually.

Yet employers and politicians keep saying that we must put up with high levels of occupational disease and extensive environmental damage. This, they say, is the price of economic growth, jobs, and the good life. The price of progress.

When workers and communities have demanded and organized for health and environmental protections along with their jobs, employers and politicians have risen to the occasion. Now that major national health and environmental laws have been in place for over a decade, we can see overwhelming evidence that protecting the public and the natural environment from industrial and government pollution is technically possible. We can also see that sound environmental policies make economic and employment sense. We don't have to be engineers or economists to understand that in a land ravaged by toxic dumps, chemical abuse, soil erosion, poisoned wells, polluted work places and choking cities, there can't be much "life" worth living.

Then what was going on when President Ronald Reagan announced that a strong Clean Air Act was a barrier to economic recovery? Why has it seemed that his appointees were doing their best to undermine health, environmental, and consumer protection laws in the name of jobs and economic growth? Why has the nuclear power industry been countering nuclear opponents over the past decade with threats of "freezing and starving in the dark"? Why did Interior Secretary James Watt sell publicly owned coal for bargain-basement prices because he "loves jobs"? Why did the *Wall Street Journal* editorialize that increased lead in the air would create "more wealth and more jobs," which "will most likely do more for ghetto children" than stringent health standards?

Call it job blackmail. Reagan, Watt, the nuclear industry, the *Wall Street Journal*—all of them have used jobs, the promise of new jobs, or the threat of unemployment in order to control decisions over investment, resource and labor use, and profit. Business and government leaders hope they can use job blackmail to keep a citizens' challenge in check, to "persuade" the public to support certain investments that are often harmful to public health and the environment.

Job blackmail is not new. Employers have long used it to fight off child labor laws, worker's compensation, Social Security, and the minimum wage. Here's an example: In 1982, the fat-melting industry of New York City threatened to shut down and throw all its employees out of work if it was forced to change production processes to eliminate the stench of slaughtered animals. When the city stood firm, however, the melters developed a closed-tank process that solved the problem, saved money, and kept workers on the job.

Now, as then, environmental protection is good for public health, good for environment, good for jobs, and good for the economy. Since 1970 many pollution trends have been reversed; air is getting cleaner, and water quality is improving. More than 100,000 new jobs have been created because of clean-air laws, and more than 200,000 have resulted from clean-water regulations.

By contrast, according to the Environmental Protection Agency, fewer than 3000 workers a year since 1971—out of a work force of more than 100 million—are even alleged to have lost their jobs because of environmental regulations. The Industrial Union Department of the AFL-CIO has concluded that "environmental regulations have not been the primary cause of even one plant shutdown."

Despite evidence that sound environmentalism is sound economics, employers, polluters, and their political supporters in government can use job blackmail effectively as long as they control where and how investments are made and how many and what kinds of jobs are created. Today, they are eyeing trillions of taxpayer dollars and vast public resources that they say they want to use to "rebuild" the nation. But don't expect extensive public discussions on (1) the values on which investment policies will be based; (2) the kinds of jobs to be created; (3) the rights of workers and the distribution of the jobs; (4) health and environmental protection; (5) how the profits will be shared; or (6) how much control communities across the nation will have over their futures. Rather, they will try to convince us that there is no way but their way, that suggested alternatives are "impractical" or "extremist." We can anticipate that they will dangle the job claims and roll out the threats of lost jobs.

The public's fight against job blackmail is a fight for control over our lives and work. This is fundamentally a struggle for an equitable share of the nation's wealth and democratic participation in decision making.

Fortunately, there is a history of successful opposition to corporate and government job blackmail. The key has been the joining of workers, communities, environmentalists, and other constituencies to challenge "business as usual." Together, such coalitions have been able to make progress toward jobs and health, jobs and environment, jobs and civil rights, jobs and worker rights, jobs and women's rights, and jobs and democratic participation in decision making.

Today, with unemployment, pollution, and environmental mismanagement all around us, people in communities across the United States must lead the struggle to integrate employment and environmental policies. There is no other option. If we are forced to choose between our jobs and our health, we'll end up with neither.

The Impact of Environmental Laws on Jobs

Catherine England

The author is a policy analyst at the Heritage Foundation. Previously, she was on the faculty of the economics department at American University in Washington, D.C. She specializes in regulatory issues.

Statutes as complex and far-reaching as the U.S. environmental laws certainly have an impact on the number of jobs generated by the economy. Since the major pieces of legislation were passed in the early 1970s, however, there has been some debate about the exact nature of that impact. Many have argued that the environmental statutes and their accompanying regulations have increased employment opportunities in the United States, and there are some econometric studies that would seem to support such a claim. There is certainly no doubt that job opportunities have increased in at least one industry over the past decade—the manufacturing of pollution control equipment.

However, there are strong reasons to believe that environmental laws, as currently written and administered, have done more than merely shift jobs from regulated sectors to control equipment industries. Rather, the current enforcement of environmental regulations has almost certainly reduced the employment-creating potential of the U.S. economy, thus costing a substantial number of jobs.

From the beginning it should be understood that the criticism here is not directed at the broad goals of the environmental statutes. There is a clear need to ensure that U.S. citizens enjoy clean air, safe water, and freedom from toxic substances and hazardous wastes. But the means used to achieve these ends have been needlessly inefficient, posing higher-than-necessary costs on society.

Let us agree that businesses, like individuals, families, or even governments, have limited financial resources. There is only so much money a company can borrow or generate through selling its product or issuing stock. Therefore, any change that increases the costs of doing business in one area requires cutbacks, however minor, somewhere else. That is not to say that a regulation may not be worth the cost, but to ensure continued economic growth, the full costs of government regulations should be understood and minimized.

In the case of environmental regulations, it is generally argued that firms cut back on investments in new plants and equipment to make the sometimes substantial expenditures needed to meet environmental requirements. But it is exactly this investment in new plants and equipment that is necessary to maintain worker productivity at a level enabling U.S. firms to remain competitive in world markets. Growing concerns about trade deficits and the relative expense of U.S. goods in international markets must, then, be laid at least partially at the door of the EPA and Congress.

The important question is, Could we meet the fundamental goals of environmental statutes at a lower cost? Yes. This response means that corporate funds could be freed to invest in new equipment, to lower costs to consumers, or for a myriad of other uses that would lead to more jobs in the country. But how?

First, the focus of environmental regulations should be changed. Currently, most EPA regulations are extremely detailed, describing the specific technology a firm must use to comply with environmental standards. This general policy has substantially reduced the potential payoff to independent research in pollution control technologies. One author has described this focus on specific technologies as "chok[ing] off the imagination and innovation of American industry." Redirecting attention to performance standards, that is, specifying acceptable behavior and leaving businesses to decide how to comply, should encourage the more rapid introduction of less expensive means of accomplishing stated goals.

Secondly, the centralized nature of decision making in the environmental area has needlessly raised compliance costs. The United States is a country marked by geographic diversity. Accordingly, the environmental impact of a particular plant in the Northeast may be very different from its impact on the desert Southwest. Not only does population density vary, but also climate, elevation, water tables, prevailing winds, and so on. It shouldn't be surprising, then, that a single national policy has satisfied almost no one.

State officials are in a much better position to recognize and react to the existing regional diversity. Furthermore, decisions made at the state level are closer to the citizens who are actually affected by changes in environmental quality. As a result, some states may with to impose standards tougher than those contained in national guidelines. State experimentation with mechanisms for setting standards and achieving compliance could result in creative ways of reaching environmental goals.

Finally, and perhaps most important for the job-creation question, current environmental laws and regulations are biased against emerging industries and new technologies. Environmental standards for new plants are much more stringent than those applied to existing sources of pollution. Yet the newer technologies employed in modern factories often cause less pollution than older ways of doing things. Despite this, federal regulators are only beginning to explore market-oriented means of encouraging economic growth while reducing pollution levels. Two promising ideas are "bubbles" and emissions trading.

To summarize, existing environmental laws and the regulations thay have spawned have cost the U.S. economy an unknown number of jobs by inhibiting the job-creating potential of American business. The costly way in which current environmental statutes are enforced has sapped the financial resources of affected firms, placed U.S. products at a cost disadvantage in world markets, and inhibited growth of new technologies and industries. Providing more flexibility through the use of plant-wide performance standards would encourage businesses to search for less expensive means of attaining environmental goals. Shifting more decision-making responsibilities to the state level would allow recognition of and response to regional diversity. Encouraging the trading of emissions rights would lead to economic growth without sacrifices in environmental quality.

The underlying aims of the environmental laws are important, but just as important is the nation's economic health. Luckily, the two goals need not be mutually exclusive.

such as the United States. In 1966 he coined the phrase "cowboy economy" to describe the present economic system, characterized by maximum flow of money, maximum production, maximum consumption, maximum resource use, and maximum profit. He suggested that the cowboy, or frontier, economy be replaced by a "spaceship economy," recognizing that the earth, much like the spaceship, is a closed system wholly dependent on a fragile life-support system. Individuals within such an economy would value recycling, conservation, the use of renewable resources, product durability, and a clean and healthy environment. Throwaways would be eliminated. Repair of broken-down goods would be encouraged to minimize the need for replacements. Waste would be intolerable. In short, people would live within the limits posed by the earth.

An economic system of this nature is also called a **sustainable economy** (Table 20-1). It can succeed only with widespread population control (Chapter 6), new environmental ethics (Chapter 19), and new political directions (Chapter 21). The spaceship economy is founded on the important concept of living comfortably and well, but perhaps not extravagantly and especially not wastefully. The key feature of the economy is a constant, rather than a continually growing, stock of physical wealth. The tradeoff is between more material wealth and a better environment with more healthful lives (Table 20-1).

The notion of a sustainable economy was not widely accepted when Boulding first proposed it in 1966 and still remains out of vogue. Today, however, more and more people recognize the inevitability of the concept. Dissatisfaction with the frontier economy stems from its widely recognized inadequacies in managing natural resources and controlling environmental pollution. Critics recognize, as some economists and many business people do not, that the production and consumption of goods and services hinge on the availability of resources. Resource availability, in turn, is governed by the finite nature of nonrenewable resources. Supporters of a sustainable economy recognize the implications of exponential growth of population, resource consumption, and pollution. They seek to avoid the catastrophe that will result from our current dedication to unlimited growth.

Table 20-1   Characteristics of a Sustainable Economy

Strives for constant GNP (growth in some areas of the economy, shrinkage in others).

Emphasizes essential goods and services.

Stresses product durability.

Avoids throwaway (disposable) products.

Reduces resource use to ensure long-term supplies.

Minimizes waste and pollution.

Relies on recycling and conservation.

Maximizes use of renewable resources.

Decentralizes certain businesses.

Uses appropriate technology.

May strive for equitable distribution of wealth.

The Steady-State Economy   Herman Daly, a professor of economics at Louisiana State University, has long argued in favor of a sustainable economic system, which he calls a **steady-state economy**. He writes, "A growth economy and a steady-state economy are as different as an airplane and a helicopter. An airplane is designed for forward motion—if it cannot keep moving it will crash." What we need is a more maneuverable, steady-state helicopter. "Throughout most of its tenure on earth," Daly points out. "humanity has existed in near steady-state conditions. Only in the past two centuries has growth become the norm." The sustainable economy is deeply rooted in history as well as sound ecological thinking.

Eventually our economic system must conform to the design principles of the ecosystem. But that does not mean that the economic future is bleak. The sustainable economy need not mean dull living and no growth. What it means is that growth will occur in some sectors, such as solar energy and conservation, while stagnation strikes others, such as oil and steel production. A sustainable economy, based largely on renewable resources, need not mean a retreat into the Dark Ages. Nonrenewable resources would remain in use, recycling through the system many times. Renewable fuels such as ethanol and perhaps even hydrogen could power our transportation system. Solar energy could heat our well-insulated homes. Solar voltaics along with wind energy might provide the electricity we need.

It may surprise you to know that the United States and many other developed nations have already reached a steady-state economy. Inflation and population growth have offset growth in the GNP for more than a decade. In fact, the economy is on a slight decline. The average American has less buying power today than he or she did fifteen years ago. Nevertheless, some industries have grown as others declined. New millionaires are made every day, and most of us remain well housed and fed.

Today's steady-state economy and that proposed by economists such as Daly are not entirely similar. One of the principal differences is the continued high level of consumption and waste, which will deplete our nonrenewable (oil and aluminum) and renewable (wood from the tropical rain forest) resources. A truly sustainable economy achieves a level of production and consumption that can be sustained forever. The key elements of a sustainable society are a dedication to population control to help us live within the carrying capacity of the earth, a reliance on renewable resources, an unflagging dedication to conservation, and an efficient system of recycling nonrenewable materials. Despite the key differences between today's steady-state economy and the one Daly proposes, we can learn from our current economic state that no growth is not a prescription for doom.

A vision of the future is one thing; a plan to get there is another (Table 20-2). How do we make the dramatic shift from the frontier system to the sustainable system of economics?

We may, of course, attain zero growth by eco-catastrophe—that is, by overshooting the earth's carrying capacity. Daly, however, argues that "the idea is to avoid that—to make a soft landing in the steady state rather than a crash landing."

Ethical Changes The most fundamental change is the ethical change. It is hard to bring about, but concerted efforts on the part of teachers, parents, and even governmental leaders could make inroads into the outdated frontier mentality. To be convinced that such changes are needed, we need to better understand the future and the dangers implicit in the frontier mentality (for more on this, see Chapter 21). Research is needed now more than ever to guide us wisely into the future.

Population Control Controlling population is necessary to achieve a sustainable economy. For some countries this may mean capping population growth; for others it may mean achieving replacement-level fertility and then decreasing the size of the population by subreplacement-level fertility. Chapter 6 discusses these goals.

Table 20-2 How to Achieve a Steady-State Economy

Education

New ethical directions can be taught in schools, with emphasis on responsibility to future generations, the value of a clean and healthy environment, preservation of wildlife and wilderness, personal growth, and peaceful coexistence.

New emphasis in economics: Bigger is not always better. More is not always desirable. Continued economic growth can be devastating.

Population Control

Population growth rate can be reduced to replacement level, and then population size can be reduced.

Resources

Nonrenewable resources can be rationed. Recycling of all cans, bottles, paper, and metals can be made mandatory. Widespread use of renewable resources, especially solar energy, can be encouraged. Energy conservation in homes, businesses, and all forms of transportation can be required.

Legislation

Legislation can be passed that promotes conservation, recycling, and use of renewable resources. Laws that promote waste and impair conservation, recycling, and renewable-resource use can be revised.

Resource Conservation Both in command economies and market economies governments can take important steps to ensure a smooth transition to a sustainable future. Although this topic is discussed at length in Chapter 21, consider some of the ways in which governments can help bring about important societal changes. One common way is through the law of the land. Laws, for example, can encourage resource conservation, recycling, waste reduction, renewable resource use, and product durability. Old laws that contradict these goals can be amended or repealed. Governments can also encourage desirable practices through tax breaks. In the United States, for instance, energy conservation and solar tax credits, no longer in effect, helped promote solar energy and conservation. The Public Utilities Regulatory Policy Act forced utilities to purchase excess electricity from individuals with windmill or other small electric generators and has helped promote renewable energy.

How the government spends its money may also affect the course of society. Significant investments in solar-energy research and biomass, for instance, may help us achieve a sustainable society earlier.

Nontraditional Proposals Beyond the traditional routes of social and economic change in capitalistic, democratic nations are some rather radical proposals, presented here to stimulate debate.

One unconventional step toward sustainability is the decentralization of some industries. Proponents of this action believe that decentralization is necessary because large-scale industries may often be less efficient than smaller industries turning out the same product. Communication failures, inflexibility, and alienation of workers create the inefficiency. Furthermore, rising energy prices will increase the cost of shipping the raw materials needed for production to distant large industries and also increase the cost of shipping goods to consumers.

A more decentralized economic system, proponents such as the late E. F. Schumacher argue, would rely on local materials to produce products for local consumption. Small decentralized industries might be appropriate for the manufacture of soap, toothpaste, and towels, but surely not for the production of ships or cars. Thus, the primary goal would be to achieve a proper mixture of large and small industry that used all resources efficiently. (For more on Schumacher's ideas on technology see Chapter 22.)

Another radical departure from the market-controlled economy of capitalistic nations is rationing. Some environmentalists believe that government rationing programs are needed to slow down or stop the depletion of nonrenewable resources. Daly suggests that nationwide and regional plans could be established to regulate the amount of oil, coal, bauxite, and other resources that could be used in a given year from domestic and foreign supplies. This would reduce excessive consumption and force recycling, conservation, and product durability. The cost of products would inevitably rise, reducing consumption of all but the most essential items and reducing pollution as well.

Depletion quotas go against the current growth ethic and the high degree of freedom that has been a part of our society from its beginning. They would be hard to establish and enforce unless an economic catastrophe or severe shortage arose. They would result in a change in life-style that is viewed as undesirable to many of the world's people. Regardless, as resource supplies run out, government rationing may become a palatable, indeed desirable, alternative to widespread resource shortage and the economic turmoil that could result.

Proponents of rationing suggest that this goal could be achieved by allocating nonmonetary units, called **natural resource units**. Under this system each individual would annually receive a given number of coupons necessary for the purchase of food, clothing, shelter, heat, and amenities. For example, an individual might receive 25,000 natural resource units each year, regardless of his or her wealth. Ten thousand would be necessary to purchase the basics—food, clothing, and energy. The additional 15,000 could be "spent" on a vacation or material

goods such as backpacking equipment, a new calculator, or a ten-speed bicycle. To buy large items, an individual would have to save coupons.

Coupons would be an adjunct to money, not a replacement for it. For instance, someone buying a car pays the $25,000 price and hands over 100,000 natural resource coupons he or she has been saving for five years. No amount of money can buy the car without the required number of resource coupons. Coupons might also be refunded when an individual returned an item for recycling. A car delivered to the recycling plant might generate enough coupons to "buy" another.

This proposal would limit resource depletion and environmental impact at some predetermined level. It says that you would be allowed a certain amount of impact on the environment, regardless of your personal wealth. Such a system, however, would be difficult to intitiate and would require honest enforcement. Planned economies in existence today have a poor record of performance, and therefore ideas such as these often meet with disapproval.

The chief advantage of rationing resources now, rather than letting the marketplace operate, is that rationing provides a mechanism by which resource supplies could be better managed. Along with recycling programs, rationing could help us stretch our supplies of important minerals, ensuring future generations an adequate supply and allowing for substitutes. The market economy, in contrast, tends to be depletive. As pointed out earlier, market economies are somewhat blind to the long-term problem of resource depletion. Proponents of this view argue that exponential growth in demand for resources suggests the need for some type of rationing, now or in the future. If mineral supplies fall short and if replacements cannot be found (Chapter 13), rationing may become a reality in traditionally capitalistic nations.

In any case, such programs are not foreign to capitalistic nations. In the United States during World War II, for instance, sugar and gasoline were rationed. The system operated well because the nation was united in a time of crisis. A severe resource shortage might provide a similar environment for the natural resource unit system, but to minimize economic and social dislocation, rationing should ideally be implemented long before the crisis develops. This would require reliable information on resource availability and demand, a coordinated governmental plan, and cooperation of the people. (See Chapter 21 for a discussion of government and planning for the future.)

The transition to a steady-state economy, already under way, will probably come because of a combination of factors: economic changes (rising prices and diminishing returns), governmental changes (stricter laws), and personal changes in attitude (Chapter 19). Some observers believe that the most probable stimulus for the drastic governmental and personal change required is a crisis—a sudden drop in oil production or mineral resources, for example. They note that we are a crisis-oriented society, often able to act only when the dangers are immediate and severe.

As we will see in the next chapter, democracies are by their very nature crisis-oriented. The urgent often displaces the important in government, eliminating the long-term solutions that are so important in times of rapid change. The crisis orientation is well recognized by governmental representatives. Through laws that protect the air, water, land, and wildlife they have sought to offer long-term protection to valuable resources, which is an essential element of a sustainable society. These laws help correct some of the important inadequacies of our economic system (especially by forcing us to internalize economic externalities).

A New Global Economic System

Obviously, a sustainable economy must be adopted on a worldwide scale if it is to be successful. Table 20-3 outlines some of the major goals that the developed and less developed nations need to achieve for a sustainable society. The primary goals of the developed nations should be to develop a sustainable ethic, reduce population growth and possibly population size, reduce material consumption and waste, cut pollution levels, promote recycling, increase self-sufficiency, and promote global peace and stability. These goals have been discussed in earlier chapters.

The less developed nations must bring their population growth under control and may eventually want to reduce population size to limit impacts and preserve their natural wealth (Chapter 6). They must develop sustainable agricultural systems and concentrate their financial resources on education, housing, and other basic needs (Chapter 7). Some economic development, discussed in Chapter 7, could be achieved using local resources and labor. It is doubtful that the world could support economic development of the scale seen in the already developed

---

Table 20-3 Goals Leading to a Sustainable Economy

Developed nations

1. Reduce population growth and population size through attrition.
2. Reduce resource consumption and waste through increased product durability, conservation, recycling, and lowered demand.
3. Increase national self-sufficiency using local resources and preferably renewable resources whenever possible.
4. Increase recyling and conservation of nonrenewable resources.
5. Protect and conserve renewable resources, such as farmland, fish, forests, grasslands, air, and water.
6. Transfer technical knowledge to developing nations.
7. Strive for global peace and stability.
8. Develop a sustainable ethical system.

Developing nations

1. Stabilize population and reduce population size through attrition.
2. Develop a sustainable agricultural system.
3. Protect and conserve renewable resources.
4. Strive to meet basic needs of people for food, shelter, clothing, and employment.
5. Promote widespread education.
6. Achieve maximum self-sufficiency.
7. Develop appropriate technologies using local resources and labor for local consumption.

---

nations. Recycling and conservation programs could be developed.

A global economic system that seeks to meet basic human needs and operate within the limits posed by the earth is a giant leap for humankind, but as Friedrich Schiller wrote, "Who dares nothing, need hope for nothing."

Civilization is a slow process of adopting the ideas of minorities.

ANONYMOUS

Summary

Economics is a science, two centuries old, that concerns itself with the production, distribution, and consumption of goods and services. It is in many ways an applied science, for it helps society solve three fundamental problems: (1) *what* commod-

ities it should produce and in what quantity, (2) *how* it should produce its goods, and (3) *for whom*. In a **command economy**, in which government dictates production and distribution goals, decisions are left to bureaucrats. In a **market economy**, where prices, supply, and demand prevail, the government usually takes a back seat to the marketplace. Most economies are mixed, having features of both although leaning in one direction or the other.

One of the key principles of economics is the **law of scarcity**, which states that most things that people want are limited. As a result, they must be rationed by price or some other means.

The description of economic facts and relationships falls within the purview of **positive economics**, so named because it is relatively free of judgment. **Normative economics** addresses questions that are value-laden, that cannot be answered by facts and figures.

Economics, like other sciences, suffers from biases, the key one being economic growth. Many economists, especially those in business and government, see economic growth as a true measure of success. Since economic growth hinges on rising population as well as increases in per capita consumption, ecologists and environmentalists often take issue with these economists. In a world of limited resources and widespread pollution, ecologists argue that continued population growth and rising per capita consumption, particularly among the wealthy, is unwise.

Economics and ecology have developed sharp differences, few as clear as their view of the future. For an economist the dividing line between the near term and the far term is typically five years. Ecologists, on the other hand, are likely to set the dividing line at a century or more.

Economists use a variety of measures to study a nation's output. The most widely used is the **gross national product**. The GNP is the value of the national output of goods and services. It gives a general picture of the relative wealth of nations and the living standards of their people. However, it fails to take into account some of the ill effects of the economy, such as damage from pollution. Economists have thus devised a new measure, the **net economic welfare**, which subtracts the negatives. The NEW in the United States is lower than the GNP and is increasing at a much slower rate.

Growth of the GNP is central to capitalistic economies, but a single-minded concern for growth fails to take into account the accumulated wealth of nations. Keeping in mind accumulated wealth can help nations set their economic priorities.

The law of supply and demand influences most economic thinking of market economies. Supply and demand interact to establish the market price of goods and services. The law of supply and demand operates well in most instances, but resource scientists point out a problem with strict adherence to the law when dealing with nonrenewable resources. They note that rising prices cannot expand the supply of nonrenewables indefinitely and that a point will be reached when a resource becomes economically depleted. One of the major barriers facing market economies is realizing that our supply of nonrenewable resources cannot expand indefinitely.

Resource management is significantly affected by economics in many ways. One of the most important economic variables that governs resource use is **time preference**, a measure of one's willingness to give up some current income for greater returns in the future. For example, farmers may choose **depletion strategies**, which favor immediate income, or **conservation strategies**, which favor long-term gains. The choice of a strategy hinges on time preference for accruing income.

Economics plays an important role in pollution control, one form of resource management. One of the chief goals of society is to achieve the maximum reduction of pollution, which yields the maximum benefit, at the lowest cost. This can be done by cost–benefit analysis, but determining the true cost of pollution, including all externalities, can be quite difficult.

Who pays the cost of pollution control is an issue of hot debate. Some argue that consumers should bear the burden, because pollution is a by-product of the goods they buy. Others argue that taxpayers should pay, because they have long allowed many industries to pollute and, now that the rules have changed, should bear some if not all of the responsibility for cleaning up the environment. In reality, there are times when consumers should pay; when new plants are being built, for example, the cost of pollution control should be incorporated into prices. In older industries now under new laws and regulations, however, the taxpayer should at least help bear the burden.

Historically, pollution control has been enforced by punitive measures, mostly fines. New economic incentives could be used to get companies to abide by environmental laws and regulations.

Conventional wisdom suggests that environmental regulations and laws delay projects, increase the cost of doing business, decrease productivity, and ultimately cost society jobs. Careful studies show that these claims are true but blown out of proportion. For instance, pollution controls have created far more jobs than they have destroyed.

Some economists suggest that a new economic system is necessary for the long-term survival of the human race. A spaceship economy, or sustainable economy, would promote recycling, conservation, use of renewable resources, product durability, and a clean and healthy environment. People would live within the limits posed by the earth. Such a system can succeed only with widespread population control and new political directions. The most fundamental change needed is an ethical shift, promoted by teachers, government officials, and parents. Government can take important steps by developing laws that encourage resource conservation, recycling, reduction in wastes, use of renewable resources, and product durability, to mention a few. Some selective decentralization of industries may be required. Some redistribution of wealth and ways to ration resource use may also be important. Overall, the shift to a sustainable society can come from a combination of economic, governmental, and personal actions.

Discussion Questions

1. Define the following terms: *command economy, market economy, law of scarcity, positive economics,* and *normative economics.*

2. Draw and describe the supply and demand curves. Describe how an increase in demand affects price. How does a decrease in supply affect price? Why do price increases generally result in an increase in supply?

3. What is the market price equilibrium?

4. What is the major weakness of the law of supply and demand?

5. Debate the statement "Economic growth has become a dangerous preoccupation of our times, so much so that we have become singularly attached to making money and blind to the quality of environment."

6. Define your own economic goals. Would you classify them as consistent with a frontier economy or a sustainable economy?

7. Debate the statement "Population growth is economically beneficial."

8. In your view, is continued economic growth possible? If so, why and for how long?

9. Describe the gross national product and its strengths and weaknesses.

10. Define the term *net economic welfare*. How does it differ from the GNP? Is it greater than the GNP or less? Does it grow as quickly or more slowly than the GNP? Is this good or bad?

11. Discuss how time preference and opportunity costs affect the ways in which people manage natural resources.

12. Define the term *economic externality* and describe why economic externalities are increasingly becoming internalized.

13. What is the economically optimal level of pollution control? Why is it impractical to consider reducing pollution from factories and other sources to zero?

14. Describe the law of diminishing returns. How does it apply to pollution control? Can you think of any other examples where the law applies?

15. There are three factories in your community. A new factory wants to move in. How could it be allowed to start operation without increasing existing levels of air pollution?

16. Describe a sustainable economy. What are its main goals? In your view, is it a practical alternative to the current economic system? What are its strengths and weaknesses?

Suggested Readings

Brown, L. R. (1983). The Changing Global Economic Context. *Environment* 25 (6): 28–34. A necessary look at deteriorating economic conditions in the world.

Brown, L. R., et al. (1987). *State of the World, 1987.* New York: Norton. See chapter 10 for a discussion of ways to achieve a sustainable economy.

Daly, H. E., ed. (1973). *Toward a Steady-State Economy.* San Francisco: Freeman. Collection of technical essays that criticize current economics and offer suggestions for changing our economic thinking.

Daly, H. (1984). Economics and Sustainability: In Defense of a Steady-State Economy. In *Deep Ecology*, ed. M. Tobias. San Diego: Avant Books. Good synopsis of Daly's thoughts on a steady-state economy.

Grant, L. (1983). The Cornucopian Fallacies: The Myth of Perpetual Growth. *The Futurist* 17 (4): 16–22. A rebuttal of the optimistic views of Julian Simon and the late Herman Kahn.

Hardin, G. (1985). *Filters against Folly.* New York: Viking. Superb reading on economics and ethics.

Kazis, R., and Grossman, R. L. (1982). Environmental Protection: Job-Taker or Job-Maker? *Environment* 24 (9): 12–20, 43–44. Excellent study of an important question.

Pope, C. (1985). An Immodest Proposal. *Sierra* 70 (5): 43–48. An important look at the role of economic incentives in promoting pollution control.

Samuelson, P. A., and Nordhaus, W. D. (1985). *Economics* (12th ed.). New York: McGraw-Hill. Chapter 1–6 provide an excellent introduction to economics.

Simon, J. (1983). Life on Earth Is Getting Better, Not Worse. *The Futurist* 17 (4): 7–14. An optimistic economic projection based on past trends that many critics doubt will continue.

Government and the Environment

The loftier the building the deeper must the foundation be laid.

Thomas à Kempis

We need a future we can believe in, one that is neither so optimistic as to be unrealistic nor so grim as to invite apathy or despair. In short, we need a future that is not only hopeful but also attainable. This book has outlined one of many possible futures—that is, a sustainable society that lives within the limits of nature. Creating such a system requires changes in people's attitudes (Chapter 19) and changes in the economic system as well (Chapter 20). Such changes may come about in many ways. Perhaps the most effective means of social and economic change is through government.

This section looks at government—the roles of government, the chief players, how decisions are made, and the governmental barriers to creating a fully sustainable society. Like the previous chapter, it discusses some relatively brazen ideas beyond the mainstream of current thinking in hopes of stimulating discussion on ways that might help us establish a sustainable society.

Government: An Overview

Chapter 20 described two basic economic systems—the market economy, in which the marketplace determines the availability and price of goods and services, and the command economy, in which the government largely assumes this task. Chapter 20 also noted that most countries have features of both command and market economies but lean significantly in one direction or the other. But what about governments? Do they correspond at all with the economic systems, and, if so, how?

Forms of Government

For the most part governments and economic systems go hand in hand. Countries with market economies are, in general, **democratic nations**—that is, governments in which officials are elected by the citizenry and which are responsive to the people's needs and desires. Representative governments operate by rules agreed on by the majority. The means of production and distribution of goods and services are, for the most part, privately held.

Countries with command economies are, as a rule, communist or socialist nations in which society owns and operates the production and distribution network. Such nations usually have a one-party system and emphasize the requirements of the state, rather than individual liberties. **Communist** nations believe that goods should be distributed equally, although in practice this is rare. **Socialism**, at least in Marxist theory, is a stage of government between capitalism and communism in which private ownership of the means of production and distribution has been eliminated.

Just as economies are mixed, so are governments. New Zealand, West Germany, and Sweden are all democratic nations but are socialistic in some regards. For instance, in all three nations the state provides health care and other services paid out of tax coffers. In China and the Soviet Union, two communist nations, private sale of products for individual profit is now allowed, although in limited quantity, and some democratic rule is allowed at the local level.

With this highly simplified overview of governments in mind, let us take a brief look at the ways governments conduct resource management and pollution control.

The Role of Government in Environmental Protection

Governments employ three major tools to regulate the economy and perform other activities, such as environmental protection: (1) taxes, (2) expenditures, and (3) regulations.

Taxes reduce private expenditure (putting a lid on consumption) and thus free money for public expenditures—rail systems, pollution control, wildlife programs, and the like. Taxes may also be used to promote or discourage certain activities. For instance, a heavy tax on gasoline in Great Britain discourages driving and promotes energy-efficient automobiles. Tax breaks, special

rules that favor some activity, can also work to the benefit of society. For example, U.S. tax credits promoted the development of solar energy.

Government expenditures—that is, the programs governments support and the goods and services they buy with tax dollars—may have a profound effect on the economy and the environment. For instance, government grants for water pollution control projects created over 200,000 jobs in the United States and helped reduce the rise in water pollution that might otherwise have occurred. Additionally, government-funded research programs in energy conservation, waste disposal, acid rain, and solar energy have yielded a wealth of new knowledge that will prove helpful in controlling pollution and better managing resources.

Regulation takes two forms. First are the laws (Chapter Supplement 21-1) that emanate from the halls of government and justice. Laws affect some activities directly, such as those statutes in the United States that make it illegal to import endangered species or those that prohibit the disposal of sludge from dredging operations into the ocean. One further example is the **Corporate Average Fuel Economy Act**, which in 1975 set gas mileage standards for automobile manufacturers in the United States, calling for a new fleet average of 27.5 miles per gallon by 1985. (In 1986 Congress rolled this standard back to 26 miles per gallon under pressure from the General Motors Corporation and the Ford Motor Company.) Some laws establish governmental agencies endowed with the power to pass legally enforceable regulations, such as air and water pollution standards or specifications for worker safety and nuclear power plants. This is the second general type of governmental regulation.

Through these three chief tools governments throughout the world have made tremendous strides in protecting the environment, managing resources, and controlling population. Many chapters in this book have pointed out the most significant advances. For a quick review of U.S. progress, see Table 14-2. It lists nearly two dozen environmental laws and amendments enacted since 1958 to regulate toxic chemicals. Similar progress has been made in most other developed nations.

But what about the developing world, where nearly 4 billion of the earth's residents now live? Many developing nations have adopted policies to control population growth, save wildlife, and reduce pollution. However, progress has been hindered in many cases by a lack of money, rapid growth of population, and governmental ineptitude, apathy, or mismanagement. In many cases hunger and poverty are so severe that environmental matters assume a lesser significance. Without population stabilization and programs to raise the standard of living and the availability of food, little progress can be expected in environmental protection.

Political Decision Making: Who Contributes?

Government isn't the only answer to our environmental problems, but it is a major determinant and has grown in power consistently for 200 years. How much should a government do to protect the environment? How much money should it spend to conserve resources or develop renewable resources?

Government Officials

In a communist government the answer comes from the officials in charge, the ruling elite. The people have little or no public input. This nonrepresentative system can be a serious detriment to environmental protection. For instance, the Soviet Union has some of the most stringent pollution standards in the world, but enforcement is virtually nonexistent. Outside pressure may be brought to bear, but the country is not noted for its responsiveness to outsiders. By and large, the communistic nations tend to be the worst environmental offenders among developed countries.

The Public

In a democratic society the voters have a much larger say in policymaking. Voters select their representatives and can influence how their elected officials vote on important legislation. Voters' letters, phone calls, and responses on surveys are direct lines of communication that allow citizens to keep in touch with their governmental representatives. Since democracies are designed to serve the public and voter preference is the guiding force, politicians are public servants. Their job is to interpret public preferences and find ways of supplying the public policies that satisfy them.

Special Interest Groups

Making policy that satisfies the public is not always as straightforward as it may sound. The **theory of public choice** tells us why. It states that politicians act in such a way as to maximize their chances of reelection. Accordingly, they must appease the general public—the voters—and the special interest groups, which frequently apply enormous pressure on elected officials to adopt policies sympathetic to their cause. As a further inducement the special interests often reward politicians with monetary support, which is badly needed to run political campaigns. To make an even larger impact, many special interests have banned together to form **political action committees**, or PACs. These are consortia that pool their individual financial resources, allowing them to make

substantial donations to political campaigns. (For more on PACs see Essay 21-1.)

Unfortunately, the desires of special interest groups and those of the general public do not always coincide. In the struggle, money often wins out. Special interest legislation may be passed that permits large benefits to accrue to a small number of people. In 1984, for instance, auto manufacturers successfully lobbied the U.S. Congress to pass import quotas on energy-efficient Japanese automobiles, which yielded the companies $300 million in profit and cost the consumer an estimated $2 billion or more.

The import quota represents a dangerous political maneuver, called the **double-C/double-P game**. Double-C/double-P stands for "commonize the costs and privatize the profits." In other words, let the taxpayer or general public pay the costs of something that will make profits for the private sector. Many U.S. water projects were built with large federal subsidies, thus providing farmers with cheap, publicly subsidized water to irrigate their crops. The taxpayer paid the bill, and the farmer benefited. Many farmers who are finding agriculture economically unsatisfying today are considering selling their water rights to cities and towns, again benefiting from the projects the taxpayer financed.

Special interest groups, both pro- and antienvironmental, use the campaign donation as a political carrot. Both groups also employ lobbyists, men and women whose job it is to make a case for their side. Well-practiced lobbyists may offset thousands of voters who feel otherwise, because they have direct access to the policymakers.

Democracy is a government of the people, by the people, and for the people, but the influence of special interest groups, especially the wealthy business PACs, may distort the process. But money does not always reign supreme in American politics. Powerful antipollution laws, auto safety standards, hazardous waste laws, and other important environmental statutes have been enacted in the last three decades despite powerful lobbying on the part of their opponents. A good measure of this success can be attributed to the efforts of environmental groups, such as the Environmental Defense Fund, the National Wildlife Federation, the Wilderness Society, the Natural Resource Defense Council, Greenpeace, the Population Institute, the Fund for Animals, the Animal Protection Institute, and hundreds of others. (For a listing of some of the major environmental groups in the United States see Appendix B.)

Environmental groups affect public policy in several ways. Some, such as Greenpeace, take an active role in the outdoors, meeting face to face with whalers, seal hunters, and polluters, endangering their own lives to protest actions they oppose (Figure 21-1). Such public displays have proved highly successful in raising awareness on various issues. Most other groups take a more passive

Figure 21-1 Greenpeace activists position themselves between Soviet whaling ships and whales to thwart the slaughter of whales.

approach to environmental awareness by publishing magazines and books that outline pressing environmental problems.

Environmental groups as a rule also publish newsletters that list important bills introduced in Congress and urge their members to write to express support or opposition. Some environmental organizations, such as the Environmental Defense Fund (EDF) and the Population Institute, research environmental problems and present their findings to governments in an effort to inform policymakers on important issues. The EDF's highly trained attorneys and scientists, for instance, have made important inroads into acid deposition, toxic wastes, and wildlife protection through their testimony. The EDF and other groups also go to court when necessary to halt dangerous activities. Environmental groups hire their own lobbyists and have also formed political action committees to pool their financial resources so they can make significant donations to pro-environmental candidates. (For a discussion of the changing role of environmental groups, see Frederic Krupp's Viewpoint, "The Third Stage of Environmentalism," in Chapter 14.)

Environmental groups can clearly offset the disproportionate influence of business, but they are usually at a disadvantage. Depending on your political leaning, this may or may not be a problem.

The failure to represent the people on all issues is not the only problem facing democratic governments. The next section looks at additional problems that make long-range solutions difficult to achieve and impair the transition to a sustainable society. The emphasis here is on the developed nations because of the disproportionate impact they have on the environment.

Some Barriers to Sustainability and Some Suggestions

From an ecologist's viewpoint government must be made responsive to the needs of future generations and the needs of other species that share this planet with us. But this is no easy task. Many barriers lie in the way.

Lack of Consensus

One of the key barriers to building a sustainable future is a lack of consensus about the future. The United States is an amalgamation of people with markedly different ideas and philosophies. Even within a single political party, opinions may vary widely on individual issues. These differences present a colossal obstacle to the long-range planning needed to achieve a sustainable society. As Herbert Prochnow once asked, "How can a government know what the people want when the people don't know?" How can we agree on a course for the future when few agree on which future is best?

Research One solution is to promote more thorough scientific study of resource depletion, the long-term effects of pollution, and the effects present generations may have on the future. A major goal of this research would be to identify the forces that affect the future and explore alternative futures. Social scientists can play a big role in this research by identifying values and studying the ways current values can be changed to achieve a sustainable society. We must also learn more about the need for long-range planning, and we must better under-

Political Action Committees: A Powerful Force

Political Action Committees, or PACs, are consortia of individuals or businesses that share a common outlook on political issues and donate their money to congressional and presidential candidates in the hope of reaping some benefits if their candidate wins office. This pooling of economic resources is growing more popular in the United States, making PACs an important political entity. In 1980 PACs donated approximately $58 million to congressional candidates. By 1982, an off-year election, the donations had grown to $86 million.

PACs have been formed among teach-ers, sympathizers with Israel, businesses concerned with govnermental environ-mental regulations, and environmentalists who want to get in on the action.

Obviously, PACs are effective because of the large sums of money that can be raised and donated. A candidate is not likely to forget a check for $100,000 from his or her "constituency." The economic influence wielded by PACs, however, has created an outcry of criticism among in-dividuals concerned that the democratic system is becoming more a government of the money, by the money, and for the money—a government that leaves the common everyday citizen in the dust while it caters to the rich.

Businesses and labor are the predom-inant organizers of PACs in the United States. In 1982 business organizations collectively donated $45.5 million, and labor gave a record $20.6 million. What are the long-term political ramifications of a PAC system of government?

Political action committees clearly con-centrate power into the hands of a few, but what can we do about them? Should we ban them or put limits on their con-tributions? Questions such as these will continue as PACs increase their power.

---

stand our obligations to future generations and other species. Support for this work could come from private and government grants.

Education   The information we gain from our intensi-fied study of the future must be made available to all citizens—to schoolchildren and adults. Long-term prob-lems of resource shortages, overpopulation, and species extinction must become more immediate concerns of everyday citizens and their elected officials.

Teachers and religious leaders can help by promot-ing a better understanding of the long-term threats posed by modern society. Environmental groups can do more to educate children on the need for environmental pro-tection, conservation, population control, renewable re-source use, and recycling (Figure 21-2).

Crisis Politics

Henry Kissinger once said that in government the "urgent often displaces the important." Immediate problems, such as strikes, emergency aid, and oil embargoes, often reduce the amount of time spent working on long-range problems. This way of operating is called **crisis politics** and is a second major barrier that hinders our building of a sustainable future. With immediate issues taking prece-dence over important long-term problems, governments may lumber along from crisis to crisis, applying tempo-rary remedies to cover up the symptoms of deeper, more complex problems. One solution is to develop govern-ments that seek a balance between proactive measures and reactive measures, as discussed below.

Proactive and Reactive Government   A govern-ment that "lives and acts for today" is by definition a **reactive government**. Its laws and regulations are some-times ill-conceived and ineffective, but they satisfy a basic need of politicians: they give the impression that some-thing is being done. Such laws are often valuable vote-getters; in the long run, though, they can further com-plicate an already serious problem, making a truly effec-tive solution harder to reach and closing down options of future generations.

Many of the laws passed by a reactive government are retrospective—that is, they attempt to regulate something that has gotten out of hand. For example, the **Superfund act** (Chapter 18) provides money to clean up thousands of existing toxic waste dumps in the United States. Ret-rospective laws are part of a "patch-it-up-and-move-to-the-next-crisis" syndrome.

The long-term outlook requires **proactive laws**, which seek to prevent potentially hazardous events from occur-ring or help build a sustainable society. One example is the **Toxic Substances Control Act**, with its provisions for

Figure 21-2 Classroom discussion on wildlife preservation.

screening new chemicals before they are introduced into the marketplace (Chapter 14). The **Resource Conservation and Recovery Act** is another example. It established a system to track hazardous substances in the United States from their production to disposal, allowing for a better accounting of the nation's wastes. Laws that promoted solar energy, conservation, recycling, and population control would be fine examples of legislation that could help today's democracies deal with environmental constraints. Ultimately, they would help bridge the gap between the largely wasteful frontier economy and the sustainable society.

Many examples of future-oriented acts by Congress exist:

1. Establishment in 1946 of the National Science Foundation to promote research.

2. Passage in 1969 of the **National Environmental Policy Act**, which requires environmental impact statements for all projects sponsored or supported by the federal government.

3. Creation in 1972 of the Office of Technology Assessment, to examine the costs and benefits of new technologies.

4. Authorization of the Congressional Research Service to create a Futures Research Group.

5. Passage in 1974 of the **Resources Planning Act** and in 1977 of the **Resources Conservation Act**, both of which required the Department of Agriculture to make periodic assessments of the supply of and demand for wildlife, farmland, water, rangeland, and recreation.

American government today is a mix of proaction and reaction, but current economic policy favors a reactive approach by letting the marketplace control resource allocation (the limitations of which were discussed in Chapter 20). One of the casualties of the market approach was long-range energy policy. In 1985, for instance, tax benefits for solar and wind energy were terminated. The economic boost both industries had received was removed, and today they have been severely crippled. The Solar Energy Research Institute's budget was also cut, further impeding the transition to a sustainable society. Federal funding for conservation was slashed by 75%. Money for population control in developing countries has also been reduced. Ironically, the government still promotes oil use through special tax incentives. Raw materials still enjoy cheaper freight costs than materials destined for recycling plants.

As we move into the last years of the 1900s and as the world population continues to grow well past the bend in the exponential growth curve, proactive government becomes more necessary than ever before, as discussed in Chapter 19. But how can we make our governments more oriented to the long term?

Long-Range Planning   Better research on the future of our resources and a better dissemination of that knowledge will make citizens more aware of the long-range problems. In representative governments that interest should result in more long-range planning.

Special commissions on the future could be appointed. In 1977 President Carter directed the Council on Environmental Quality, the State Department, and several federal agencies to study population, resources, and pollution through the end of the century. The report was to serve as a "foundation for longer-term planning." The resulting study, **The Global 2000 Report to the President**, is a gold mine of information about the future on which many decisions can be based. This work should not stop here. Estimates and projections should be periodically updated and revised as necessary. Great lessons can be learned in the coming decades from the projections. Were they too pessimistic? Were the methods of projecting resource and environmental trends faulty, and how can they be improved?

Special study sections on the future in various governmental agencies such as the Departments of Agriculture, Energy, and Interior should be better funded and better equipped to project into the future. Reports from futures

Figure 21-3 President Reagan addresses a joint session of the U.S. Congress in the Capitol Building. Does the U.S. need additional bureaucracy to deal with future issues, or can the men and women who govern our nation take on the added burden of long-range planning?

groups should be widely distributed to political leaders, teachers, and the public.

Some observers have suggested that the United States needs a Department of Long-Range Planning and Coordination, similar to one in Sweden. The department would research future issues and make recommendations to the President and Congress regarding population, pollution, and resources. Its main purpose would be to assess long-term trends and help U.S. political leaders develop a long-term strategy. It might serve as a central clearinghouse for new ideas. Those in favor of keeping the federal government from growing argue that a central interagency committee might better coordinate the future activities of all federal agencies, be less costly, and require less expansion of an already swollen bureaucracy (Figure 21-3).

One final note: Few would deny that long-range planning is badly needed. But planning is a task fraught with difficulties, which are largely due to the uncertainty of resource supplies and future demands. American utilities, for instance, planned for a regular 7% increase in electrical demand in the United States. To accommodate the expected demand they began a massive buildup of nuclear power plants, only to find in the late 1970s that there was an excess of electricity. When demand began to increase again, it climbed at a much slower 3%. The lesson we can learn from this example is that we must plan, but we must do so carefully. And we must realize that planning will be imperfect.

Limited Planning Horizons

A third barrier to sustainability is the limited planning horizon of political decision makers. There are at least two reasons for this short-sightedness. The first is that most politicians serve either two-, four-, or six-year terms. Thus, long-range planning may be difficult in political life when "long-term" implies the time until the next election. In this vein Winston Churchill noted, "The nation will find it very hard to look up to the leaders who are keeping their ears to the ground."

The second reason for limited planning horizons is budgetary constraints and inadequate cost–benefit analyses. Rupert Cutler, a former U.S. assistant secretary of agriculture for conservation, research, and education, wrote, "Compared to the problems addressed by many programs . . . natural resource issues develop more slowly and it often takes a long-term commitment to resolve them." The federal government budgets money for natural resource programs, but by law agencies must invest in projects that show a benefit-to-cost ratio greater than 1 to ensure sound expenditure of limited funds. This requirement eliminates some long-term conservation measures. The cost–benefit method of selecting projects tends to identify only easily observable, short-term benefits.

New Leaders Overcoming the barrier of limited planning horizons will require more far-sighted leaders who are willing to implement policies that have implications well past the time to their next election—policies that may not favor the immediate electorate as much as the future electorate. A broader understanding among the citizenry of the ways in which they affect the future and their obligations to future generations would help far-sighted politicians gain a foothold and pass legislation that would promote a sustainable society.

To expedite that transition, Americans can all support conservation-minded representatives who promote recycling, renewable resource use, pollution control, intelligent management of resources, protection of wildlife and plants, and population control. Citizens can write or visit their elected officials. (For some tips on writing congressional representatives see the Viewpoint in this chapter.) One effective way for citizens to make their voice heard is to join advocacy groups, such as the Environmental Defense Fund, the Population Institute, the Fund for Animals, or Greenpeace.

Election Reforms Another possible solution to limited planning horizons is longer terms of office for elected officials such as House and Senate members and even the president. A six-year nonrenewable term for the president, for example, might reduce the reelection pressure that leads to shortsighted political decisions and takes valuable time away from the office. Extended terms for House members (up to four years) would have the same effect. In both cases, longer terms would reduce the amount of time spent on the campaign trail and increase the amount of time devoted to substantive issues. Longer terms of office, of course, could have damaging effects as well.

The New Federalism: Finding the Balance

Government itself may stand in the way of building a sustainable society. Because of its size the federal government can become insensitive to local problems and can prescribe solutions that are not well suited to individual regions. You may recall from Chapter 20 that one of the proposals for building a sustainable society was selective decentralization of some industries. Society may also benefit a little from some selective governmental decentralization.

President Reagan's "new federalism" was just such an attempt. By reducing federal funding of cities and local projects, the federal government shifted more and more power to the states and local governments. This so-called "new federalism" offers several potential advantages and disadvantages. Achieving success lies in the balance: finding the optimal mix between federal and local control, especially in regard to resource and other environmental issues.

Advocates of more decentralized government see the partial shift in power to the states and local governments as a way of building a more self-reliant and responsible society, one that lives within the limits of nature. They argue that people will feel less alienated from government and more willing to participate in community decisions when more decisions are made locally.

Forced to rely on their own tax revenue and less on federal support, communities may turn to conservation and recycling to cut costs of services. In Englewood, Colorado, for instance, city fathers voted to burn methane produced at sewage treatment plants to generate electricity to run the sewage treatment plant. In other cities waste heat from power plants could be captured to heat office buildings or homes. Sewage sludge is used elsewhere to fertilize corn, which is fed to cattle or sold to local markets. Instead of building new water projects, some governments are implementing water conservation measures. Left to their own devices, local governments may find that energy conservation and nearby renewable sources, such as biomass and solar, are less expensive than coal-fired power plants.

A community that lives within the limits posed by its economic and natural resources is more easily sustainable than one that imports energy, natural resources, food, and goods from afar. Such a community provides the essential goods and services within a limited environment and is called an **essential community**.

A shift from centralized federal governments to decentralized essential communities has its disadvantages—hence the need for finding the optimal mix of governance. One of the major problems is that local governments generally lack money and may be influenced more heavily by businesses that push for relaxation of pollution laws. Decentralization, in other words, is no guarantee of wise resource use. (As you will see in the Chapter Supplement, federal rules and regulations evolved because of inadequate state and local controls.) Another problem is that local governments also rarely have the financial resources needed to sponsor feasibility studies on pollution control, recycling projects, alternative energy systems, and such.

Truly, a proper balance between local and federal power is important in developing a sustainable society. The federal government must be ready to assist communities in finding the most cost-effective and least resource-intensive approaches to providing services. Federal demonstration programs, standards for pollution control, and research are all essential for a sustainable local government to evolve, for such work could help standardize rules and regulations.

A Sustainable World Community

A sustainable system is needed in both the rich and poor nations of the world. Some world leaders are sitting back and letting things happen with the hopes that the market will steer their nations in the right direction. Their plan is not to plan. This **passive approach** could work, but more likely than not it will only create a long string of crises, many of which could cripple the world economy and create widespread environmental destruction.

An **active approach**, many argue, would be much

The Right to Write

Congressman Morris K. Udall

The author, an Arizona Democrat, is chairman of the House Interior Committee.

Surprisingly few people ever write to their United States senators or congressional representatives. Perhaps 90% of our citizens live and die without ever taking pen in hand and expressing a single opinion to the people who represent them in Congress. This reluctance to communicate results from the typical and understandable feeling that legislators have no time or inclination to read their mail, that a letter probably won't be answered or answered satisfactorily, that one letter won't make a difference anyway. Based on my own experience, and speaking for myself at least, I can state flatly that these notions are wrong.

I read every letter written to me by a constituent. A staff member may process it initially, but it will be answered, and I will insist on reading it and personally signing the reply. On several occasions, a single, thoughtful, factually persuasive letter did change my mind or cause me to initiate a review of a previous judgment. Nearly every day my faith is renewed by one or more informative and helpful letters giving me a better understanding of the thinking of my constituents.

Mail to modern-day members of Congress is more important than ever before. In the days of Clay, Calhoun, Webster, and Lincoln, members of Congress lived among their constituents for perhaps nine months of the year. Through daily contacts with constituencies of less than 50,000 people, they could feel rather completely informed about their constituents' beliefs and feelings. Today, with the staggering problems of government and increasingly long sessions in Congress, senators and representatives must not only vote on many more issues than early-day members, but rarely get to spend more than sixty days in their districts. Thus, their mailbags are their best "hot lines" to the people back home.

Here are some fundamentals:

- Address it properly: "Hon. _____, House Office Building, Washington, D.C. 20515" or "Senator _____, Senate Office Building, Washington, D.C. 20510." This may seem fundamental, but I once received a letter addressed like this: "Mr. Morris K. Udall, U.S. Senator, Capitol Building, Phoenix, Arizona . . . Dear Congressman Rhodes . . ."

- Identify the bill or issue. About 22,000 bills are introduced in each Congress: it's important to be specific. If you write about a bill, try to give the bill number or describe it by popular title ["BLM Organic Act," "Toxic Substances Bill," etc.].

- The letter should be timely. Sometimes a bill is out for committee, or has passed the House, before a helpful letter arrives.

- Concentrate on your own delegation. The representative of your district and the senators of *your* state cast your votes in the Congress and want to know your views. If you happen to be acquainted personally with a member from, say, Nebraska, he or she might answer your letter, but there is a "congressional courtesy" procedure which provides that all letters written by residents of any district to other members will simply be referred to the proper representative for reply, and vice versa.

- Be reasonably brief. Every working day the mailman leaves some 150 or more pieces of mail at my office. Tomorrow brings another batch. I recognize that many issues are complex, but your opinions and arguments stand a better chance of being read if they are stated as concisely as the subject matter will permit. It is not necessary that letters be typed—only that they be legible: the form, phraseology, and grammar are completely unimportant.

To make your letters most helpful, I would suggest the following "do's and don'ts."

First, the do's:

- Write your own views—not someone else's. A personal letter is far better than a form letter or signature on a petition. Many people will sign a petition without reading it just to avoid offending the circulator: form letters are readily recognizable—they usually arrive in batches and usually register the sentiments of the person or lobbying group preparing the form. Form letters often receive form replies. Anyway, I usually know what the major lobbying groups are saying, but I don't often know of *your* experiences and observations, or what the proposed bill will do to and for you. A sincere, well-thought-out letter from you can help fill this gap.

- Give your reasons for taking a stand. Statements such as "Vote against H.R. 100: I'm bitterly opposed" don't help much, but a letter which says, for example, "I'm a small hardware dealer, and H.R. 100 will put me out of business for the following reasons . . ." tells me a lot more. Maybe I didn't know all the effects of the bill, and your letter will help me understand what it means to an important segment of my constituency.

◄ *Viewpoint*

- Be constructive. If a bill deals with a problem you admit exists, but you believe the bill is the wrong approach, tell me what the *right* approach is.

- If you have expert knowledge, share it with your congressional representatives. Of all the letters pouring into a legislator's office every morning, perhaps one in a hundred comes from a constituent who is a real expert in that subject. The opinions expressed in the others are important, and will be heeded, but this one is a real gold mine for the conscientious member.

- Say "well done" when it's deserved. Members of Congress are human, too, and they appreciate an occasional "well done" from people who believe they have done the right thing. I know I do. But even if you think I went wrong on an issue, I would welcome a letter telling me you disagree. It may help me on another issue later.

Now some don'ts:

- Don't make threats or promises. Members of Congress usually want to do the popular thing, but this is not their *only* motivation; nearly all the members I know want most of all to do what is best for the country. Occasionally a letter will conclude by saying "If you vote for this monstrous bill, I'll do everything in my power to defeat you in the next election." A writer has the privilege of making such assertions, of course, but they rarely intimidate a conscientious member, and they may generate an adverse reaction. Members of Congress would rather know why you feel so strongly. The reasons may change their minds; the threat probably won't.

- Don't berate your representatives. You can't hope to persuade them of your position by calling them names. If you disagree with them, give reasons for your disagreement. Try to keep the dialogue open.

- Don't pretend to wield vast political influence. Write your senators or representatives as an individual, not as a self-appointed spokesperson for your neighborhood, community, or industry. Unsupported claims to political influence will only cast doubt upon the views you express.

- Don't become a constant "pen pal." I don't want to discourage letters, but quality, rather than quantity, is what counts. Write again and again if you feel like it, but don't try to instruct your representative on every issue that comes up. And don't nag if his or her votes do not match your precise thinking every time. Remember, a member of Congress has to consider all of his or her constituents and all points of view. Also, keep in mind that one of the pet peeves on Capitol Hill is the "pen pal" who weighs the mail down every few days with long tomes on every conceivable subject.

- Don't demand a commitment before the facts are in. If you have written a personal letter and stated your reasons for a particular stand, you have a right to know your representative's present thinking on the question. But writers who "demand to know how you will vote on H.R. 100" should bear certain legislative realities in mind: (1) On major bills there usually are two sides to be considered, and you may have heard only one. (2) The bill may be 100 pages long with 20 provisions in addition to the one you wrote about, and a representative may be forced to vote on the bill as a whole, weighing the good with the bad. (3) It makes little sense to adopt a firm and unyielding position before a single witness has been heard or study made of the bill in question. (4) A bill rarely becomes law in the same form as introduced; it is possible that the bill you write about you would oppose when it reached the floor.

Your senators and representatives need your help in casting votes. The "ballot box" is not far away; it's painted red, white, and blue, and it reads "U.S. Mail."

---

better. The active approach entails concerted efforts to reshape civilization. Governments and their people must be part of that movement. Some suggested changes include (1) a shift away from the growing war economies, with their enormous expenditures; (2) more sharing of knowledge between the rich and the poor, especially in areas of population, food, and energy; (3) investments in recycling, conservation, and renewable resources; and (4) strict population control policies (Table 21-1).

West Germany's Green Party: An Ecological Approach to Politics

The nations of the world may build a sustainable society in a piecemeal fashion, one country at a time. Already, signs are evident. One example is West Germany's polit-

ical party, the Greens, which won 27 seats in the national legislature in 1983. Rallying under the banner "We are neither right nor left, but in the front," the Greens are actively pushing for a sustainable society (Figure 21-4).

Largely maligned and misunderstood by the press, write the futurists Fritjof Capra and Charlene Spretnak in their book *Green Politics*, the Greens advocate measures to protect the environment, including reductions in pollution and hazardous wastes, an end to nuclear power, conservation, use of renewable resources, wise use of energy, and an end to nuclear weapons. If they get their way, West Germany will slowly be transformed into a nation of ecologically benign (nonpolluting) industries that concentrate mainly on socially necessary products. In Western Europe a dozen similar parties are now seeking office.

Table 21-1 Portrait of a Sustainable Society

Recognizes that the earth has a limited supply of nonrenewable resources such as coal, oil, natural gas, and minerals.

Operates within the limits posed by natural resource supplies by recycling, conservation, reducing its superfluous needs, and using renewable resources.

Strives for a quality life, clean air, clean water, abundant recreation opportunities for all, and intellectual achievement rather than material wealth.

Recognizes that we can never do just one thing—that all actions have hidden effects that must be determined when making cost–benefit analyses.

Cooperates with nature, rather than trying to overcome it, by using natural pest control, organic farming to replace nutrients, crop rotation, and solar and wind energy.

Stresses individual responsibility and actions to cut resource use, promote recycling, reduce pollution, and achieve a sustainable future.

Recognizes that we are a part of nature, not superior to it, and that our long-term fate is intricately linked to the health of the biosphere.

Minimizes waste through resource conservation, reduction in superfluous needs, redesigning manufacturing processes, and reusing and recycling materials.

Figure 21-4 One member of Germany's Green Party shows up at parliament in a solar-powered vehicle to demonstrate the untapped potential of clean alternative energy resources.

Despite their sometimes disruptive ways of pressing their points and the fringe elements that have adhered to them, and despite conflicts that have divided their leadership on many occasions, the Greens represent a major shift in political thinking. They take a long-term view of the future, calling for redirection of policy consistent with the sustainable ethics discussed in Chapter 19.

Conventional political wisdom holds that popular ideas are absorbed by the major political parties. They enter the mainstream of political thought and could, conceivably, become the cornerstone of important public policy. Thus, no matter whether the Greens survive or are simply absorbed into the mainstream, they may have begun a new movement in politics that could radically reshape the future of West Germany—and maybe the world.

Achieving a Global Sustainable Society

Not too long ago the world seemed unlimited, and our problems few. Today, though, the globe has begun to shrink with better transportation and communication and rapid depletion of resources. Our problems now seem as unlimited as the world once appeared. One step in solving these problems—and by no means the only one—is achieving sustainability on a global scale. But how?

As more and more countries recognize the limits of resources and the need to protect the life-giving biosphere, they will undoubtedly begin to adopt sustainable resource policies. Thus, sustainability may well evolve over time in much the same way that organisms evolve to meet changing environments.

Building a global sustainable society could be facilitated by the United Nations (Figure 21-5). Already, its population and agricultural programs have helped Third World nations in many ways. Conferences on population and its impact, for instance, have convinced virtually the entire Third World that something must be done to control rampant growth before it is too late. In 1987, the U.N. facilitated negotiations for an agreement among 31 countries to reduce the current rate of ozone depletion. Further gains could be made in solving problems of global importance, including acid rain, the greenhouse effect, marine fisheries, seabed minerals, and others. Unfortunately, conflicts of national policies have thus far kept the United Nations from realizing its potential for achieving international consensus and providing mediation on these important issues.

Global Resource Sharing: Is It a Good Idea?

Reports of millions of starving children in Sudan and elsewhere have resulted in an outpouring of aid from countries throughout the world. Global resource sharing,

Figure 21-5 The U.N. could perhaps provide a way of increasing global cooperation and a forum for promoting a sustainable society.

such as this, is seen by some individuals—many ecologists and textbook writers—as a way of benefiting those less fortunate than the citizens of wealthy countries.

On the surface, global resource sharing sounds like an excellent solution to the shortages now plaguing many countries. The ecologist Garrett Hardin takes strong exception to this view, arguing that moving wealth from the rich to the poor will create universal poverty and instability. The rich will become poorer, and the poor

will have no incentive to better their lot in life. Population growth and good resource management will be ignored if necessities are guaranteed under a world government that seeks to distribute the earth's wealth according to the Marxian principle "To each according to his need."

Hardin argues that redistribution of food and other resources creates, in effect, a "zero-sum" society in which one person's material gain is another's loss. Universal sharing of the earth's goods could lead to widespread deterioration of world resources—the air, water, and land (Chapter 9). For example, U.S. grain destined for Third World nations could contribute to the impoverishment of American soils and could contribute to sediment and nitrate pollution (Chapter 7), because farmers would probably ignore conservation measures to lower production costs.

Hardin proposes, instead, that nations share knowledge, which is a renewable resource not subject to the zero-sum principle. Sharing of knowledge would create a "plus-sum" society in which one person's gain is also another's gain. This means that knowledge shared with other countries often comes back augmented, or in a richer form. It can then be passed on and refined once again, benefiting everyone.

To be successful in the long run, both the rich and the poor nations of the world must develop sustainable systems of agriculture and industry. Chapter 20 explained how both can go about this important task of building sustainable economies. Chapter 22 will outline some specific changes for housing, transportation, technology, and urban centers.

A global sustainable society and government may seem like utopia, an unrealistic dream. As Rolf Edberg reminds us, "The utopia of one generation may be recognized as a practical necessity by the next." He adds that such goals depend on our ability to free ourselves from "ideas and emotions that once had a function in our battle for survival but have since become useless." Starving masses and the universal fear of nuclear war may be the psychological forces that set the stage for a new world society governed by sustainable principles.

The great thing in this world is not so much where we stand as in what direction we are moving.

OLIVER WENDELL HOLMES

Summary

We need a future that is optimistic, but attainable as well. Now, more than ever, we must take some decisive actions to reshape society to fit within the constraints of the biosphere.

For the most part governments and their economic systems

go hand in hand. Countries with market economies are, as a rule, democratic nations, which are ruled by elected officials responsive to the needs and desires of the people. The means of production and distribution of goods and services are, for the most part, privately held.

Countries with command economies are generally communist or socialist nations, in which the government owns the production and distribution network. Communist nations are unrepresentative and put the requirements of the state above those of individual liberty.

Governments employ three major tools to regulate the economy and other activities, such as environmental protection. They are (1) taxes, (2) expenditures, and (3) regulations. Through these tools governments throughout the world—especially in developed countries—have made tremendous strides to protect the environment, manage resources, and control population. Developing nations have been less successful because of lack of money, rapid growth of population, and governmental ineptitude, apathy, or mismanagement. In the poor nations hunger and poverty are so severe that environmental matters assume a lesser significance.

How much should a government do to protect the environment? In socialist and communist systems that answer comes from the ruling party, generally with little input from the populace. In democratic nations voters have a much larger say in policymaking. But even in representative governments the balance of power may shift away from the people because of the influence of special interest groups, especially industry. Unfortunately, the desires of business or other lobbies do not always coincide with those of the public. Nevertheless, money does not always reign supreme in politics. Powerful antipollution laws, auto safety standards, hazardous waste laws, and other important environmental legislation have been enacted in the last three decades despite powerful lobbying on the part of their opponents. A good measure of this success can be attributed to the efforts of environmental groups. They affect policy in many ways: by raising public awareness of issues, by researching issues, by lobbying, by campaign contributions, and by lawsuits.

From an ecologist's viewpoint government must be made responsive to the needs of future generations and the needs of other species that share this planet with us. Three major barriers to this goal are (1) a lack of consensus, (2) crisis politics and ignoring of long-range issues, and (3) a limited planning horizon of elected officials.

Research on the future can help solve these problems. Better educating children and adults about our obligations to future generations can also go a long way toward overcoming these barriers. Changes in government may result from fundamental shifts in our perceptions about the future. For instance, a wider acceptance of our ability and obligation to make the future habitable and healthful may produce a broader outlook among governmental representatives. The net effect would be a better balance between reactive government, which primarily concerns itself with immediate problems, and proactive government, which takes a look at long-range issues as well. All the changes outlined here can help build a sustainable society.

Revisions in the present economic system might also help us build a sustainable state. New leaders and election reforms that promote long-range planning to tackle tough issues could go a long way. More self-reliance in communities can bring resource and pollution questions to the doorstep of the average citizen.

A global sustainable society seems imperative if we are to survive in the long run. Such a society may evolve in response to rising pollution and upcoming shortages. New political par-

ties, such as Germany's Green party, or revisions of the ideology of existing parties can help bring the new sustainable ethic into practice.

Discussion Questions

1. Describe the sustainable society. What changes in our current economic and political systems would be required to make the transition to a sustainable society?

2. How do governments affect resource use and pollution? In other words, what are the major tools by which governments control economic activity and environmental protection?

3. How do citizens in democracies influence their elected officials?

4. In what ways are democracies unrepresentative? Can you give some examples?

5. How can we create a global sustainable society? Outline major goals for agriculture, energy, wildlife, population, economics, and politics.

Suggested Readings

Becker, T. (1981). Teledemocracy. *The Futurist* 15 (6): 6–9. Interesting view, worth considering.

Brown, L. R., et al. (1987). *State of the World, 1987*. New York: Norton. See Chapters 1, 10, and 11.

Burke, T. (1984). The Politics of Ecology. In *Ecology 2000: The Changing Face of Earth*, ed. E. Hillary. New York: Beaufort Books. Interesting historical look at environmental law and politics.

Ferkiss, V. (1983). The Future of the U.S. Government: Change and Continuity. *The Futurist* 17 (1): 53–57. Excellent, although possibly too conservative, assessment of future political change in the U.S.

Hardin, G. (1981). An Ecolate View of the Human Predicament. *Alternatives* 7: 241–262. Controversial and thought-provoking. As important as his classic paper, "The Tragedy of the Commons."

Hawken, P., Ogilvy, J., and Schwartz, P. (1982). *Seven Tomorrows*. New York: Bantam Books. Interesting book promoting a thoughtful consideration of our possible futures.

Klay, W. E. (1981). Nurturing Foresight in Government. *The Futurist* 15 (6): 25–28. Good overview.

Little, D. L., Dils, R. E., and Gray, J., eds. (1982). *Renewable Natural Resources. A Management Handbook for the 1980s*. Boulder, Colo.: Westview Press. Collection of thoughtful and thought-provoking essays.

Morris, D. (1983). City-States: Laboratories of the 1980s. *Environment* 25 (6): 12–20, 36–42. A lengthy treatise on changes in local government leading to a sustainable society.

Olsen, R. L. (1981). Filling the Vacuum: New Politics for a New Age. *The Futurist* 15 (6): 21–23. Insightful article.

Perry, J. S. (1986). Managing the World Environment. *Environment* 28 (1): 10–15, 37–40. Detailed look at the complex problem of global environmental management.

Rubens, J. (1983). Retooling American Democracy. *The Futurist* 17 (1): 59–64. Thought-provoking essay.

Rutter, L. (1981). Strategies for the Essential Community. *The Futurist* 15 (3): 19–28. Interesting insight into one possible future of communities consistent with the sustainable society.

A Primer on
Environmental Law

Our environmental laws are not ordinary laws, they are laws of survival.

EDMUND MUSKIE

An ancient Roman legal axiom proclaims, "The people's safety is the highest law." Today, many environmental laws embrace this principle, but it was not until the late 1960s that this idea took hold in the United States.

During the late 1960s and 1970s environmental protection became increasingly important to U.S. citizens and their congressional representatives. Numerous laws were passed during those years, so that today the United States has the world's most comprehensive and toughest set of environmental laws and regulations. The U.S. campaign has had a positive effect on the rest of the world. Many nations have patterned their environmental protection laws after U.S. statutes, benefiting from some of Americans' errors and their eagerness to make important inroads into resource and pollution issues.

National Environmental Policy Act

One of the most significant advances in environmental protection was the **National Environmental Policy Act** (1969). NEPA is a brief, rather general statute with several major goals. First, it declares a national policy calling on the federal government to "use all practicable means" to minimize environmental impact in its actions. It requires decisions regarding federally controlled or subsidized projects such as dams, highways, and airports to describe possible adverse impacts in an **environmental impact statement** (EIS). Among other things, and EIS must describe (1) what the project is; (2) the need for it; (3) its environmental impact, both in the short term and the long term; and (4) proposals to minimize the impact, including alternatives to the project. Drafts of the EIS are available for public comment and review by federal agencies at least 90 days before commencement of the project. Written comments from the pub-

lic are included and must be addressed in the final EIS, which is issued at least 30 days before undertaking the proposed action.

The EIS has been an effective way of getting businesses and governmental agencies to focus on the environmental impacts of their projects. The underlying idea is that individuals who become aware of their potential impact will act responsibly to avert it as much as possible. In this sense the EIS is a political carrot (a gentle inducement) rather than a political stick (a punishment). The EIS is a superb legal tool in a sustainable society. Available early in the planning stage, it can help decision makers determine whether they are directing their policies, programs, and plans in compliance with the national environmental goals expressed in NEPA and with other legislation.

Between 1970 and 1983 approximately 24,000 EIS's were prepared. NEPA also established the **Council on Environmental Quality** in the executive branch. The Council publishes an annual report (*Environmental Quality*) on the environment and on environmental protection efforts of the Federal government. It also develops and recommends to the president new environmental policies.

NEPA has been one of the few statutes to significantly affect federal decision making. It has led to hundreds of lawsuits, perhaps more than any other environmental statute. In addition, several states and nations throughout the world have passed laws or issued executive or administrative orders patterned after NEPA. France, Canada, Australia, New Zealand, and Sweden all require EIS's. California passed an Environmental Quality Act in 1970 that requires EIS's for all projects—private and public—that will affect the environment in a significant way.

The success of NEPA has been great, but the law is not without flaws. One of the most frequent criticisms is that the EIS's are too lengthy and deal with too many peripheral subjects. Reports are often ignored; they may show serious adverse impacts, but the project will be carried out regardless, often without ameliorative actions. A common complaint from ecologists is that reports are often based on inadequate information. Projections of environmental impact are difficult to make and often too subjective. Practically no work has been done to see if the projected impacts actually materialize; thus Americans continue to be unprepared to make sound projections about impact. EIS's

Table S21-1 Some Federal Agencies and Their Responsibilities for the Environment and Health

Agency	Responsibility
Environmental Protection Agency	Research, demonstration programs, and enforcement of most environmental laws
Occupational Safety and Health Administration	Research and enforcement of worker safety and health laws
Food and Drug Administration	Research and enforcement of laws to protect consumers from harmful foods, drugs and cosmetics
Health Services Administration	Family planning programs and community health programs
Health Resources Administration	Research, planning, and training; collection of statistics on health in the U.S.
National Institutes of Health	Study of cancer, through the National Cancer Institute, and of radiation and other environmentally related diseases, through the National Institute of Environmental Health Services
Centers for Disease Control	Epidemiological studies on disease
National Oceanic and Atmospheric Administration	Research into and monitoring of the oceans and atmosphere; ecological baseline information and models to better predict the impacts of air and water pollution

may be "doctored" by agencies or private consulting firms that write them for federal agencies to hide the real impacts. Some agencies can avoid writing EIS's by simply stating that there will be no adverse environmental impact; it is then up to others to prove the need in court. Other critics of the EIS contend that it is too costly and often leads to delays in important projects. The paperwork and time involved seem excessive.

To answer some of the complaints, the Council on Environmental Quality issued streamlined procedures for preparing EIS's in 1979. They call for (1) a maximum length of 150 pages, except for more involved projects; (2) a summary of no more than 15 pages that describes major findings and conclusions; (3) documentation and referencing of projected impacts; and (4) the use of clear, concise, and plain language.

Some environmentalists believe that NEPA should require agencies to select the most environmentally benign and cost-effective approach, both in the short term and in the long run. Currently, environmental groups can sue an agency that they believe should have filed an EIS or one that has filed an inadequate EIS, but they cannot recover attorney's fees from such suits. If they could, that would relieve the costly burden of forcing governmental agencies to heed the law; however, it might also open the door to numerous costly lawsuits, which would be a burden on the taxpayer.

Although it has its critics and still stands in need of improvement, NEPA is the cornerstone of U.S. governmental policy. Numerous federal agencies have reported important environmental benefits from it and economic savings from recently revised rules. NEPA is a landmark law of fundamental importance to a sustainable society.

Environmental Protection Agency

Another major environmental accomplishment is the establishment of the **Environmental Protection Agency** in 1970. The EPA was founded by a presidential executive order calling for a major reorganization of 15 existing federal agencies working on important environmental issues.

The EPA was directed to carry out the Federal Water Pollution Control Act and the Clean Air Act. Having grown in size, it now manages many of the environmental protection laws that issue from Congress. Current responsibilities of the EPA include research on the health and environmental impacts of a wide range of pollutants as well as the development and enforcement of health and environmental standards for pollutants outside of the workplace. The EPA is concerned with a variety of areas, including pesticides, hazardous wastes, toxic substances, water pollution, air pollution, radiation, and noise pollution. Table S21-1 lists the responsibilities of other federal agencies involved in environmental protection.

The EPA can provide incentives to state and local communities through grants for substantial portions of water pollution control projects. Grants to universities have helped expand the research capability of the agency. The EPA carries on much of its own research at four National Environmental Research Centers, located at Cincinnati, Ohio; Research Triangle Park, North Carolina; Las Vegas, Nevada; and Corvallis, Oregon.

The EPA is often caught in crossfire between opposing groups—for example, environmentalists, who seek tighter controls, and the businesses the EPA regulates, which commonly complain that regulations are too stringent and costly.

In the late 1970s widespread interest in the environment was overridden by economic hardship brought on by the oil embargoes and inflation. A powerful political movement arose in the early 1980s to dismantle or weaken the EPA. The most common argument from the business sector was that the cost of protection was too excessive and that stiff environmental protection laws were preventing a healthy economy. But Japan has tough laws, continues to fight pollution, and has done well economically. Furthermore, as Russell Peterson, former administrator of the EPA and president of the National Audubon Society, noted, "We cannot have a thriving economy without a thriving ecosystem."

The American people continue to express a strong concern for a healthy environment; they support maintaining existing laws or even strengthening them. New problems such as acid precipitation and hazardous wastes constantly crop up, demanding the attention of the EPA and other federal bureaucracies. A growing population and an expanding economy create an ever-increasing burden on the environment and on the agencies that regulate environmental issues. Thus, many argue that Americans must continue to expand their support of the EPA and other agencies involved in environmental protection.

Evolution of U.S. Environmental Law

Environmental laws and regulations have become an integral part of the complex U.S. legal system. How did this happen?

State and federal environmental laws evolved gradually over the years from scattered ordinances imposed by local governments. Interested in protecting health and environmental quality, officials of cities and towns passed local ordinances in the 19th century limiting activities of private citizens for the good of the whole. For example, municipal ordinances regulated burning of trash within city limits, to reduce air pollution.

By the end of the 1800s, however, it was clear that local control of many problems such as water pollution was inadequate in densely populated regions. Disputes arose between neighboring municipalities with different laws. Regions with strict laws were hampered in cleaning up their rivers by upstream cities with lax pollution laws. Thus, states began drafting legislation to regulate water pollution.

Soon state laws proved inadequate, too, because air and rivers flow freely across state borders. Thus, interstate conflicts over pollution replaced the conflicts between neighboring municipalities. State programs were inadequately funded and lacked the technical expertise to set pollution standards. State agencies also found themselves powerless against large corporate polluters with political influence in the courts and legislatures. Because of these problems and the growing effectiveness of special interest groups, environmental controls shifted to the federal government, gradually in the 1940s and 1950s and then more rapidly.

Initially, the federal government restricted itself to research on health and development of pollution control technologies. This approach met little opposition from state and local governments. Next, the federal government stepped in with grants to fund pollution control projects and the formation of state pollution enforcement agencies. But with increasing pressure from environmental groups and citizens, it began to take a larger role in enforcement. Today it sets ambient pollution standards and standards for emissions from factories, automobiles, and other sources and can take strict enforcement actions if needed.

The shift to federal control is based on at least two important principles of American federalism: (1) When it is important to maintain uniform standards, the federal government provides the best route. Uniform policies help minimize interstate conflicts and help create an economically fairer system for businesses. (2) The power of the federal government to tax is much stronger than a state's. To control pollution effectively requires much expensive research, which the federal government can more easily afford. Furthermore, it would be costly, time-consuming, and redundant for each state to carry out this extensive research.

The shift to the federal level has some disadvantages, however. First, the federal government may not always understand the problems within the regions it regulates as well as local officials. Another criticism is that states should have the right to do as they please with their own resources—in other words, that federal control diminishes self-determination and self-governance. But without central controls, states impinge on one another's quality of life. For example, poor watershed management in the Rocky Mountain states leading to erosion could have long-term adverse impacts on downstream users to the east and west.

One way of addressing these problems is to develop federal standards but allow the states to manage their own programs. Thus, the Clean Air Act, the Surface Mining Control and Reclamation Act, and the Resource Conservation and Recovery Act all permit the states to run their own programs as long as they are at least as stringent as the one set up by federal law. These acts also provide money to assist the states in setting up their own programs.

Principles of Environmental Law

In the United States, government's power to protect the environment is conferred by the U.S. Constitution, state constitutions, common law, federal and state statutes and local ordinances, and regulations promulgated by state and federal agencies. Statutory law and common law are the mainstays of environmental protection, and the concepts they share enter into every law and lawsuit that involves the environment.

Statutory Law

Throughout this book have appeared many examples of state and federal laws for environmental protection and resource management. These **statutory laws** generally state broad principles, such as the protection of health and environment by reducing air pollution, or the judicious use of natural resources. However, Congress and the state legislatures lack the time and expertise to determine specifically how these goals can be met. Thus, Congress assigns the setting of standards, pollution control requirements, and resource management programs to executive agencies such as the EPA. (See the discussions of the Clean Air Act in Chapter 15 and the Toxic Substance Control Act in Chapter 14.)

Common Law

Many environmental cases are tried on the basis of **common law**, a body of unwritten rules and principles derived from thousands of years of legal decisions. It is based on proper or reasonable behavior and has been replaced in many states by statutes.

Common law is a rather flexible form of law that attempts to balance competing societal interests. As an example, a company that generates noise may be brought to court by a nearby landowner who argues that the factory is a nuisance. The landowner may sue to have the action stopped through an injunction. In deciding the case, the court relies on common-law principles. It weighs the legitimate interests of the company in doing business (and thus making noise) and the interests of society, which wants its citizens employed and wants to collect taxes from the company, against the interests of the landowner, who is trying to protect the family's rest, health, and enjoyment of property.

The court may favor the plaintiff if the damage (loss of sleep, health effects, and inconvenience) is greater than the cost of preventing the risk (costs of noise abatement, loss of jobs, and loss of tax revenues). But the court may not issue an injunction causing the factory to shut down; instead, it may simply require the factory to reduce noise levels within a certain period. This way, a balance is struck between competing interests.

Cases such as this one illustrate the balance principle. But on what legal principles are cases involving common law decided? Basically, there are two—nuisance and negligence.

Nuisance   Nuisance is the most common ground for action in the field of environmental common law. A nuisance is a class of wrongs that arise from the unreasonable, unwarranted, or unlawful use of a person's own property that obstructs or injures the right of the public or another individual, producing annoyance, inconvenience, discomfort, or hurt. What this means is that one can use one's personal property or land in any way one sees fit, but only in a reasonable manner and as long as that use of the property does not cause material injury or annoyance to the public or another individual.

Generally, two types of remedy are available in a nuisance suit: compensation and injunction. **Compensation** is a monetary award for damage caused. **Injunctions** are court orders requiring the nuisance to be stopped.

Nuisances are often characterized as either public or private. Until recently the two were distinctly different concepts. A public nuisance is an activity that harms or interferes with the rights of the general public. Typically, public nuisance suits are brought to court by public officials. A private nuisance is one that affects only a few people. For example, the pollution of a well affecting only one or two families is considered a private nuisance. A public nuisance would be pollution that affects hundreds, perhaps thousands, of landowners along a river's shores. The most common environmental nuisance is noise (Chapter Supplement 15-4). Water pollutants and air pollutants such as smoke, dust, odors, and other chemicals are other major nuisances.

Historically, the distinction between private and public nuisance has hampered pollution abatement, because the courts have traditionally held that an individual's nuisance suit could be brought against a public nuisance only when the individual had suffered a unique injury, or one different from that suffered by others. An individual would be unable to sue a company for polluting a river shared by many others. Relief was possible only through a public nuisance suit brought by an official (the local health department, for instance). Public officials may be unwilling to file suit against local businesses that provide important tax dollars for the community and campaign support as well.

Increasingly, the distinction between private and public nuisance is fading; private persons can bring suit to stop a public nuisance. As a result, the private individual is gradually getting more power to stop polluters.

Several common defenses are used to fight nuisance suits. Since most nuisance suits are decided by balancing the rights and interests of the opposing parties, **good-faith efforts** of the polluter may influence the decision. For example, if a small company had installed pollution control devices and had attempted to keep them operating properly but was still creating a nuisance, the court would hold it liable but might be more lenient in damages or conditions of abatement. If, on the other hand, the company had made no attempt to eliminate pollution and had created a public or private nuisance, the court would generally be more severe.

The availability of pollution control must also be considered. If a company is using state-of-the-art pollution control and still creates a nuisance, the court may not impose damages or an injunction. In contrast, if the company has failed to keep pace with pollution control equipment, the court may order it to install such controls.

Class-action suits can be used in states that still distinguish between public and private nuisance. Class-action suits are brought by a group on behalf of many people. They emphasize the composite damage caused by a nuisance. In order for a federal class-action suit for compensation to be allowable, however, each person named in the suit must have suffered at least $10,000 in damage. If not, the suit can be dismissed. This requirement, then, provides an opportunity for a defense.

Another defense is that the plaintiff has "come to the nuisance." Coming to the nuisance occurs when an individual moves into an area where a nuisance—such as an airport, animal feedlot, or factory—already exists and then complains. An old common-law principle holds that if you voluntarily place yourself in a situation in which you suffer injury, you have no legal right to sue either for damages or an injunction. In most courts, however, even though you purchase property and know of the existence of a nuisance, you still have the right to file suit to abate it or recover for damages. This is based on another common-law principle that clean air and the enjoyment of property are rights that go along with owning the property. Thus, if population expands toward a nuisance, it may be the responsibility of the party creating the nuisance to put an end to it.

According to the environmental attorney Thomas Sullivan, "The courts are moving to strict liability for environmental nuisances, so that practically speaking, there are no good defenses. The solution is: do not create nuisances."

Negligence   A second major principle of common law is negligence. From a legal viewpoint a person is negligent if he or she acts in an unreasonable manner and if these actions cause personal or property damage. In July 1972, for example, the oil tanker *Tamano* spilled 100,000 gallons of oil in Casco Bay in Maine. The state of Maine filed suit against the federal government, contending that the damage caused to the state had resulted from negligent action on the part of the Coast Guard. According to Maine, the Coast Guard, which was in charge of cleaning up the oil, failed to do so in a timely and proper fashion. The courts held that the Coast Guard had, therefore, been negligent of its duty and that the federal government was liable for damages.

Negligence provides a basis for liability, just as nuisance does, but negligence is generally more difficult to prove. What is reasonable action in one instance may not be reasonable in another. Statutory laws and regulations help the courts determine whether behavior is reasonable. For example, regulations drawn up by the EPA specify how certain hazardous wastes should be treated. Failure to comply with those standards may be evidence of negligence.

Negligence may be shown in instances where a company fails to use common practices in the industry. For example, a company may be found negligent if it fails to transport hazardous wastes in containers like those used by other companies. Still, common practices may themselves be inadequate. Suppose that some companies transported hazardous wastes in unlined cardboard boxes; a reasonable individual would realize the inadequacy of this approach. Thus, the courts would probably find the company negligent.

In a much broader sense, the courts may decide that a company is negligent simply if it fails to do something that a reasonable person would have done. For example, negligence might be demonstrated if a company failed to test its wastes for the presence of harmful chemicals when a reasonable person would have done so. Likewise, negligence may stem from action that a reasonable person would not have taken.

In summary, negligence can result from either inaction or action that may be deemed unreasonable considering the circumstances. The concept of knowing also plays a role. Briefly, negligence can be determined on the basis of what a defendant knew or should have known about a particular risk. The standard of comparison is what a reasonable person should have known under similar circumstances. For example, a man on trial may argue that he is not negligent because he did not know that a harmful chemical was in the materials that he dumped into a municipal waste dump and that subsequently polluted nearby groundwater. His argument will be valid if a reasonable person in his position could not have known about the wastes.

The **standard of reasonableness** applies also to past mistakes. In other words, even though an operator of a hazardous waste dump did not know of the hazards it created 20 years ago, he or she may be ruled negligent for having failed to eliminate the risk when he or she learned of it or should have learned of it.

Liability for damage or harm need not be based on negligence in cases where the risk is extraordinarily large (in legal terms, an "abnormal risk"). Practically speaking, in proving liability for an activity of abnormally high risk, such as the housing of hazardous materials, one need prove only that injury or damage occurred, not that the operator was negligent or acted unreasonably.

Problems in Environmental Lawsuits

Legal actions to stop a nuisance or collect damages from a nuisance or act of negligence carry with them a burden of proof. Plaintiffs must prove that they have been harmed in some significant way and that the defendant is responsible for that harm. This is not always easy, for several reasons. First, the cause-and-effect connection between a pollutant and disease may not have been definitely established by the medical community. If doubt exists, the case is weakened. Second, diseases such as cancer may occur decades after the exposure, making it extremely difficult to prove causation. It is generally easier to link cause and effect with acute diseases. Third, it is often difficult or impossible to identify the party responsible for damage, especially in areas where there are many industries or where illegal acts, such as midnight dumping of hazardous wastes, have occurred. Any reasonable doubt about the party responsible for personal or property damage may severely cripple a lawsuit.

The **statute of limitations**, which limits the length of time within which a person can sue after a particular event, also creates problems in cases of delayed diseases. Statutes of limitations help reduce old lawsuits where evidence is unavailable or memories of potential witnesses have faded and become unreliable. In latent-disease cases, though, they create a major obstacle to individuals seeking compensation for damage in states that apply the time limitations to the onset of exposure. This essentially makes it impossible for cancer victims to file suit. Other states start the judicial clocks from the time the victim learns of the disease. This makes it a little easier to collect compensation for diseases such as cancer, black lung, and emphysema.

Out-of-court settlements present another legal problem. Such settlements have hindered environmental law. Eager to avoid a costly settlement, a company may pay victims if they agree to dismiss the company from further liability. Out-of-court settlements may also benefit plaintiffs, saving them the time, headaches, and costs of environmental litigation.

While advantageous to both parties, these settlements provide no precedents for environmental laws. In short, the fewer cases that make it to court, the fewer precedents courts have to settle cases. This lack of precedents may discourage attorneys and citizens from filing court cases. Without clear examples from the past, they may simply be unwilling to face costly, time-consuming legal battles.

Resolving Environmental Disputes Out of Court

An increasing number of disputes between environmentalists and businesses are being settled out of court by **dispute resolution**, or **mediation**. This innovative approach often employs a neutral party who mediates the discussion between opposing parties. The mediator keeps the proceedings on track, encourages rivals to work together, and tries to resolve the dispute in a way that is satisfactory to both groups.

The benefits of mediation over litigation are many. Mediation is much less costly and time-consuming. Mediation also tends to create better feelings among disputants, whereas court settlements create winners and losers and often leave bitter feelings. In addition, and perhaps most important of all, mediation may bring about a more satisfactory resolution. For instance, environmental lawsuits often hinge on specific points of law rather than substantive issues and thus may have little to do with what the plaintiff really wants. An environmental group might bring a suit over the adequacy of an EIS but, in reality, might want the government to ensure protection of a valuable species that would be affected by the project. In mediation, this will be the central issue. Mediation may therefore result in more appropriate solutions.

Mediation also tends to promote a more accurate view of problems. For instance, in lawsuits each party tends to bring up evidence that favors its goal and ignore or dismiss unfavorable information or ambiguous information that might weaken its stand. In mediation, both parties are encouraged to openly discuss the uncertainties of their positions, discovering many points of agreement and building a better understanding of opposing positions.

Mediation has its drawbacks, too. First, funding is inadequate. In the past, mediation has been financed largely by foundations. Federal, state, and local governments need to develop programs to fund mediation. Second, some groups fear they will lose their constituency if they enter into negotiations on certain issues, because they will be giving the impression that they are failing at their stated goals and compromising with the "enemy." A third drawback is a lack of faith in the outcome of mediation. Unlike court orders, resolutions drawn up in mediation are not legally enforceable. Thus, months of discussion may produce nothing but a piece of paper that polluters will ignore.

Effective mediation requires the following: (1) A truly neutral party must serve as mediator. (2) A formally agreed-upon agenda for discussion and a point of focus are also important. Resource and pollution issues should be the focus of discussion; disputes over values should not dominate the proceedings, because they cannot be solved by mediation. Although values will surely come out in the debate, they should not be the central point. (3) There must be a willingness to explore new ideas and possibilities on both sides. (4) Disputants must deal honestly with each other. (5) An adequate representation of all interested parties must also be achieved. If someone is not represented, a solution that is unsatisfactory may result. This could lead to a lawsuit. (6) Strict rules should be imposed regarding news releases. The media should not be employed as a lever by either group.

Dispute resolution is growing in the United States, but it will not replace litigation. Still, it can play a valuable role in the future. The first environmental mediations began in 1975, and as of 1983 approximately 70 disputes had been settled using this approach. Eight states have organizations that offer mediation services, and a growing number of private organizations have been formed to provide professional mediators with experience and knowledge in environmental issues. Thus, more and more disputes may be settled by this noncombative approach.

Suggested Readings

Arbuckle, J. G., et al. (1985). *Environmental Law Handbook* (8th ed.). Washington, D.C.: Government Institutes. Superb overview of environmental law.

Epstein, S. S., Brown, L. O., and Pope, C. (1982). *Hazardous Waste in America*. San Francisco: Sierra Club Books. See Chapter 10 for a good overview of principles of environmental law.

Findley, R. W., and Farber, D. A. (1981). *Environmental Law: Cases and Materials*. St. Paul, Minn.: West Publishing. In-depth presentation of important cases in environmental law.

Wenner, L. M. (1976). *One Environment Under Law: A Public-Policy Dilemma*. Pacific Palisades, Calif.: Goodyear. Superb reading.

Putting It All Together: Building a Sustainable Society

What we do for ourselves dies with us. What we do for others and the world remains and is immortal.

ALBERT PINE

Images of a Sustainable Society

The year is 2050. Two executives, a husband and wife, are walking to the high-speed commuter train that will whisk them to their downtown offices. They wouldn't think of driving—it would waste fuel. Besides, they are saving alcohol fuel allotments for an upcoming ski trip.

On their way to work they talk about the changes that have taken place in the United States and the rest of the world since their parents' college days in the 1980s. No longer do families have two or three cars. One fuel-efficient vehicle is the norm. Many people don't even own vehicles. When they need one for an occasional trip, they rent it. Mass transit has improved nationwide, making the private automobile unnecessary. High-speed trains connect all the major cities. Jets, which burn much more fuel than high-speed trains, are rare; they're mostly reserved for international trips. In the cities, commuter trains have replaced many of the old superhighways.

The city the executives live in hardly resembles the one their parents used to gripe about. Most families have "gone solar." With climbing oil prices, the solar industry went wild after 2000. Any home that could be converted to passive solar was. Solar panels were installed for hot water. Virtually all homes were retrofitted with insulation and storm windows to prevent heat loss. As a result of the shrinking population and energy conservation, many local power plants shut down. The public utility companies wisely invested in solar energy and other renewable energy sources.

Figure 22-1 A flock of snow geese rising from Gray Lodge State Refuge in California.

Recycling has become as ingrained as the throw-away philosophy that dominated the 1980s. Every household has separate receptacles for glass, aluminum, plastics, paper, and organic trash. Separating trash and recycling it have saved enormous amounts of energy and cut down on municipal waste disposal. Water is recycled more and more at sewage treatment plants or is simply piped to aquifer recharge zones, where it can be naturally purified and returned for eventual reuse. Hazardous wastes have been cut back substantially by lowered consumption and by modifications in industrial processes, reuse, recycling, and incineration. They tiny amounts remaining are stabilized and stored in well-monitered burial sites.

The U.S. population has fallen. Some demographers think it will stabilize at 180 million around 2100. The decline has meant some economic dislocations, but it has also brought many benefits. Nearby streams run clean, the air is much cleaner, parks are less crowded, and wildlife is staging a comeback in forests and wilderness areas.

In outlying rural areas, farmers grow a diversity of crops without pesticides or artificial fertilizers. Toxic pesticide residues in fish and birds are almost nonexistent. America's ducks and geese now number 100 million, up 100% from the 1970s. At times, flocks of geese nearly darken the sky (Figure 22-1).

American agriculture has changed over the years, too. Today, 10% of the farmland is planted in sunflowers, the oil of which is burned like the diesel fuel used in the earlier days. Sunflower oil provides all the fuel farmers need. Farmlands also yield large quantities of alcohol for transportation. The food they produce is mostly for domestic use. U.S. food exports almost completely dried

up as much of the rest of the world stopped population growth and made tremendous strides toward agricultural self-sufficiency.

Farmers routinely protect their soil from erosion. No longer is half the farmland eroding at a rate faster than it can be replaced. Through concerted conservation efforts, soil erosion is lower than the soil replacement. The United States is building back its soils. Erosion control has increased agricultural output, stopped the continuous filling of reservoirs, and cut dredging costs in navigable rivers like the Mississippi. Water conservation programs on farms, such as drip irrigation and lined ditches, have cut irrigation water demands by half.

Drastic changes have come about through careful planning and shifts in basic attitudes. People now have a deep respect for nature and understand that society must abide by its rules. And most people feel a deep commitment to future generations. The American Environmental Party has dominated the political scene since the late 1990s, when rising oil and mineral prices, among others, began to cripple the American economy. The Environmental Party burst onto the scene with a platform of much-needed changes, which the American public gladly endorsed. Their ecological measures included population control, use of renewable resources, conservation, and recycling. Today, their candidate sits in the highest office, spending a good portion of her time advising other nations how to match U.S. achievements.

The transition to a sustainable society has also occurred in many other nations. Some, like West Germany and Sweden, made significant strides before Americans caught on to the idea. Other nations—Great Britain, Italy, even the Soviet Union—made the steady transition to sustain-

(a)   (b)

Figure 22-2   Energy conservation in the United States. (*a*) This 1962 Cadillac coupe gets 12 miles per gallon, whereas the Volkswagen GTI (*b*) gets 45 miles per gallon.

able economies. Many developing countries had a rough go of it. Some, like Bangladesh, fell into ruin. Rampant population growth, illiteracy, and poverty made it more difficult for others to make the shift, but progress was made. Today, many countries have stemmed the tide of population growth. In Africa efforts are under way to reduce population and build sustainable agriculture and industry while protecting the wildlife and forests. Tropical nations have begun to replant rain forests. Small islands of natural vegetation were left intact when forests were cut down in the 1980s and 1990s. These island parks now spread out in all directions, reclaiming the land so carelessly conquered by short-sighted business interests.

The Means of Transition to a Sustainable Society

This book takes form around three central topics—population, resources, and pollution—and offers many suggestions to build a sustainable society of the kind described above. Together, these suggestions form a battle plan of sorts, aimed at transforming a fairly wasteful society bolstered by nonrenewable resources into a conservation-minded yet prosperous society that relies heavily on renewable resources. To achieve such a goal requires some fundamental changes in the institutions and beliefs we embrace today. What will successfully direct us toward our goal is a vision of sustainability—images of a society we can build that can persist thousands of years without destroying the biosphere. Sustainability must replace growthmania (Chapter 20).

The key to sustainability lies in conservation, recycling,

renewable resource use, and population control. These must be widely adopted if human civilization is to make the earth its long-term home. Historians 100 years from now will tell the tale either of a modern society that saw the need to change and made the smooth transition to a sustainable society or one that fought the changes, persisted in its frontier notions, and possibly failed because of its insistence that the old rules could work forever.

First Steps: Some Encouraging Signs

In many ways, the transition to a sustainable society has already begun in the United States and abroad. For example, many people are simplifying their life-styles, either because materialism has lost its appeal or because economic forces leave them no other choice. Many Americans have also turned to smaller, more fuel-efficient cars and public transportation because of high oil prices (Figure 22-2). Since 1978 per capita gas consumption has fallen over 15% because of improved gas mileage and personal actions—people driving slower and driving less. The average new American automobile goes 29% further on a gallon of gas than it did in 1973. As older vehicles are retired, per capita gas consumption is likely to fall even more.

What about the decline in oil prices in 1986? Detroit reports an increase in the sale of large automobiles, but many analysts believe that conservation ethic is well established and that conservation will continue to gain momentum in years to come. Many people have also come to appreciate their smaller, more fuel-efficient cars for aesthetic reasons.

One measure of the United States' dependency on energy is the amount of energy required to produce $1

Figure 22-3 Brazilian autos are powered by ethanol. By converting to alcohol and other renewable fuels, Brazil hopes to reduce pollution and that country's dependency on costly foreign oil.

of GNP (Chapter 20). Since 1973 the energy needed to produce $1 of GNP has fallen 25%. Researchers from Lawrence Livermore Laboratory in Berkeley, California, attribute half of that gain to technical solutions such as the improved efficiency of machines. The remaining half has been produced by a consumer belt-tightening and a decline in manufacturing and rise in service industries.

Americans have become more energy conscious in their cities and homes. More and more builders are installing better insulation and domestic solar collectors for heating water. The National Association of Home Builders reports that home buyers list energy efficiency as a priority more than any other factor. Energy-efficient appliances are becoming more widespread. Several states have adopted appliance efficiency standards. California, among them, has plans to cut the average electrical consumption in new refrigerators sold in the state by 50% by 1992. Manufacturers are likely to make these models available elsewhere.

U.S. domestic energy consumption has dropped about 20% from its peak in the late 1970s. Portland, Oregon, has adopted one of the nation's toughest building codes, requiring insulation in new as well as old homes, apartments, and office buildings. City officials predict that insulation alone will cut energy consumption in Portland about 35% by 1995.

People throughout the world have made some dramatic improvements in energy efficiency. In fact, in many areas Americans lag behind the Europeans and the Japanese. Brazil more than most countries has set the pace of the transition to a sustainable energy system. By 1990 Brazil hopes to eliminate most of its oil imports. Energy will come from hydroelectric power, wood, and alcohol. Brazil is building a society whose homes, industries, and automobiles will be fueled by renewable energy, showing the whole world that it can be done (Figure 22-3).

Environmental protection has also increased in the last two decades. A general awareness of environmental issues can be found in rich as well as poor nations. Outside of the United States there are an estimated 3000 groups interested in environmental issues. The number of governmental environmental protection agencies in the developing nations increased tenfold between 1972 and 1980.

In the United States, according to estimates made by the Internal Revenue Service, 12,000 nonprofit organizations are involved in the critical issues of energy, population, resources, and the environment. Awareness has resulted in tougher laws to cut air and water pollution.

Each year more and more companies are turning from the old attitude that it pays to pollute to a new philosophy that pollution prevention pays. The Dow Chemical Company, for example, invested $2.7 million to recover hydrogen and harmful chlorine gas once released into the atmosphere from its chemical plant in Hemlock, Michigan. The plant now saves approximately $900,000 a year.

On a broader scale, world population growth has slowed in the last two decades, dropping from 2.5% 20 years ago to 1.7% today. Even though population growth continues at a fast pace in many Third World nations, it has all but come to a stop in many developed nations. Some Third World countries are recognizing the need for population control and have taken measures to stop the rampant growth.

Figure 22-4 Fishing boats hauling in fish from San Francisco Bay. Even renewable resources can be exhausted by overharvesting.

What's Needed: More of the Same Positive Changes

Despite these gains and many others too numerous to list here, much work is needed to build a sustainable society. Foremost on the list are attitudinal changes. The frontier mentality must be replaced by a sustainable mentality. Feelings of insignificance must be replaced by the positive attitude that what we do makes a difference. We must see that our children learn about their responsibilities to the biosphere and future generations. Such changes can lead to new economic expectations and new ways to do business. And they will lead to political changes with far-reaching impacts on all of human society.

As a future parent, teacher, scientist, journalist, business executive, accountant, or political leader, you can play a big role in the transition. You have glimpsed the sometimes frightening story of modern civilization and have had a chance to think about changes. You can begin to pass on your ideas and work to see them bear fruit. You can live a life consistent with sustainable ethics. In short, you can teach others directly and indirectly by your example.

Protecting Our Renewable Resource Base through Land Use Planning

New attitudes and personal changes will go a long way toward solving our problems, but they are just a start. Larger changes must come about to ensure the long-term future of our vital resources. In need of special protection are the renewable resources, which will form the foun-

dation of tomorrow's civilization. Farmland, pastures, forests, fisheries, and wild species should be viewed as irreplaceable resources. Many of us forget that renewable resources can be irretrievably lost by careless actions (Figure 22-4). Overfishing, deforestation, and intensive farming can all destroy the renewable resource base that is needed for the future of humankind.

Historically, the marketplace has determined use of this resource base. But the market often seeks immediate gains at the expense of future generations. Agricultural land conversion provides a prime example. On the outskirts of many growing cities, bulldozers now rip up prime farmland to clear the way for tract housing, shopping centers, and highways. The short-term value of suburban development outweighs the long-term value of agriculture. Such is the market's way of prioritizing resources. For the long-term future, however, such actions can be dangerous.

To stop the unnecessary destruction of resources, nationwide land use planning is needed. **Land use planning** is a process in which government officials plot strategies to put our land to the best use, preserving farmland and open space, regulating where people live and do business, and how water pipes, electrical lines, and roadways will go.

The Japanese provide a model that many countries could adopt to protect their land. In 1968 the entire country was placed under a nationwide land use planning program. Lands were divided into three classes—urban, agricultural, and "other." Several years later, the zoning classifications were expanded to include forests, natural parks, and nature reserves. The success of the Japanese plan lies in protecting land from the market system, which, left on its own, appropriates land irrespective of its intrinsic value.

Many European nations have adopted similar programs. In Belgium, France, the Netherlands, and West Germany, for instance, national guidelines for land use planning were established in the 1960s. Administered by local governments, these guidelines protect farmland, prevent urban sprawl, and help to establish **greenbelts**— undeveloped areas in or around cities and towns. The Netherlands has perhaps the best program of them all. Its national planning program affects not only land but also water and energy.

Land use planning in the United States is rudimentary at best. So far, except for establishing national parks, wilderness areas, national forests, and wildlife preserves, the federal government has done little to systematically protect its land. Most zoning occurs on the community level, and much of that is inadequate. On the local level, planners primarily concern themselves with restrictions on land use for commercial purposes—housing developments and industrial development. As a result of community-level planning, states become a patchwork quilt of conflicting rules and regulations. One result is that companies often deliberately locate in areas with lenient rules and regulations. Areas in the same state that try to protect their air and water suffer. Statewide land use planning could bring some order to the resulting chaos. But statewide land use planning is an idea that is slow in coming. Oregon recently passed such a program. A number of companies have chosen to locate in Oregon despite its tough environmental standards. Even though the rules may be stricter than those of other states, many companies prefer Oregon because they know where they stand. They have confidence that laws will not tighten and force drastic changes in the way they do business.

The main tool of land use planning for years has been **zoning**, classifying land according to use. In a city, zoning helps separate potentially noisy, odiferous, or hazardous activities from residential areas. When used properly, zoning can also protect farmland and other lands from urban development. In rural Black Hawk County in Iowa, for instance, the zoning laws provide permits for well-conceived housing developments on farmland with lower productivity. Prime farmland cannot be used for housing.

New approaches are being adopted, especially to protect farmland. One of those is **differential tax assessment laws**, under which land is assessed for taxes according to its value for farming, regardless of potential value for housing development or other uses. In years past farmers often sold their land when city planners began taxing it as if it were residential. High taxes make farming unprofitable and forced farmers off the land. Currently, most states have laws that permit differential taxation.

Another technique to keep farmers from selling their land to developers is for states to buy up the development rights for important lands. To do this, two assessments of the land are made—of its value as farmland and of its value for development. The difference between the two is the **development right**. States may buy the development rights from the farmer and hold them in perpetuity. The land must then be used for farming, no matter how many times it changes hands.

Land use planning is essential in the developing nations as well. Urbanization in these countries is a major problem, and millions of hectares of farmland fall to the bulldozer each year as cities expand. In some areas land reform is badly needed. Wealthy landowners in many Latin-American countries, for example, graze their cattle in rich valleys while peasants scratch out a living on the erodible hillsides. Hilly terrain that should be protected from erosion is being torn up by plows and is eroding away by rainfall. Lester Brown, an expert on world resource management, argues that "sensible land use hinges on reform of these feudal land-holding systems."

A Sustainable Transportation System

The End of a Love Affair Americans have been engaged in a dangerous love affair with their automobiles. Today, 25% of U.S. energy is consumed by the transportation sector. The American passion for automobiles has spread throughout the world, so much so that the global automobile fleet expanded from 50 million in 1950 to over 450 million in 1985. Today, in the United States, there is one car for every two people. In Western Europe the ratio is one to three. Automobile travel accounts for 90% of the motorized passenger transport in the United States and 78% in Europe.

The world's love affair will probably end in your lifetime because of declining oil supplies. Even liquid fuels from coal, oil shale, and fuel farms will not save the auto. Faced with inadequate fuel supplies, some experts believe, nations will be forced to ration their liquid fuels. Agriculture, cooking, and mass transit will receive the highest priority. In Stockholm, the Office of Future Studies has proposed that the private automobile be phased out. It recommends greatly expanding the mass transit system, because it is inherently more efficient, and expanding the fleet of rental vehicles, which can be used for vacations and other special occasions.

Improving Efficiency Improvement in efficiency can prolong the lifespan of the automobile. In 1982 the average new American automobile got about 9 kilometers per liter of gasoline (22 miles per gallon). By 1986, this figure had improved to 10.8 kilometers per liter (26 miles per gallon), which was still not as good as that for many other

Table 22-1 Automobile Fuel Economy in Selected Countries in 1982

Country	Autos	Fleet Average	New Cars
	(Millions)	(Miles per gallon/km per liter[1])	
Australia	6.3	19/7.9	24/10
Brazil	9.7	20/8.3	24/10
Canada	10.6	18/7.5	27/11
East Germany	2.4	27/11	32/13.3
France	17.8	27/11	32/13.3
Italy	17.7	24/10	31/12.8
Japan	39.0	31/12.8	30/12.4
Soviet Union	8.0	26/10.8	29/12
United Kingdom	15.6	22/9.1	28/11.6
United States	125.4	16/6.6	22/9.1
West Germany	23.2	22/9.1	28/11.6
Other	77.0	n.a.	n.a.
Total	353.0	21[2]/8.7	25[3]/10.4

[1]Actual mileage on the road. Data may not be strictly comparable due to differing national testing procedures.
[2]Based on 80% of the cars in the world.
[3]Based on 70% of the new cars in the world.
Source: Adapted from Worldwatch Institute.

countries back in 1982 (Table 22-1). In the United States, best mileage was achieved by a German vehicle, the diesel Volkswagen Rabbit. It averaged 25 kilometers per liter (60 miles per gallon) on the highway. The British Leyland, a four-passenger prototype vehicle, leaves the Rabbit wanting. It gets 34 kilometers per liter (83 miles per gallon). A Japanese vehicle currently gets the same mileage.

Rapid improvements in gasoline mileage could greatly stretch the available fuel supplies. New foams and plastics can reduce the risk of smaller, energy-efficient vehicles. The alleged dangers of smaller cars can also be mitigated by tough drunk-driving laws, enforcement of speed limits, and better driver education.

From Road to Rails and Buses No matter how much automobile fuel economy improves, the car can never compare to bus and train transportation (Table 22-2). In urban centers buses and trains can achieve a fuel efficiency of about 62 passenger kilometers per liter (150 passenger miles per gallon) of fuel. Intercity train and bus transport increases efficiency to 82 passenger kilometers per liter of fuel—2.5 times better than the most efficient car today.

Personal transportation is inherently inefficient. Cars carrying a single passenger burn much more fuel per

Table 22-2 Fuel Efficiency by Passenger Transportation Mode in Western Europe

	(kilojoules per passenger kilometer/mile[1])
Van pool	400/640
Rail	400/640
Bus	450/720
Car pool	650/1,040
Automobile	1,800/2,880
Airline	3,800/6,080

[1]A kilojoule is 1000 joules, a unit of energy or work.
Source: Worldwatch Institute.

passenger mile than buses and trains carrying hundreds of people. Air travel is even worse than the automobile. Personal transportation is also an inefficient use of land. Far larger numbers of people can be moved on railways and bus lines than on highways clogged with automobiles.

Faced with declining fossil fuel reserves, many cities will turn to mass transit. It is just a matter of time. The bicycle could supplement buses and high-speed trains. Few modes of transportation can measure up to the bicycle in fuel efficiency. Weighing around 30 pounds, it is often powered by the excess calories consumed by its rider. For decades, the bicycle has been a major means of transportation in many European and Asian countries. Following suit, some cities in the United States have laid out extensive bike paths for commuters (Figure 22-5). Davis, California, is a leader in promoting bicycle transportation. Today, one-fourth of all commuter transport within the city is by bicycle. Some streets are closed entirely to automobile transport, and 65 kilometers (40 miles) of bike lanes and paths have been established.

Bicycles won't replace cars, buses, and trains, but they can greatly augment these forms of transportation. Useful for short trips, under 8 kilometers (5 miles), the bicycle moves at the same speed as most urban traffic. Because of vast differences in cities, however, the bicycle can't be equally exploited. In San Francisco the terrain is too hilly for widespread bicycle commuting. In Los Angeles the terrain is flat, but the city is too spread out. Denver, on the other hand, offers great opportunities for people living within 8 kilometers of work to commute. Quiet side streets and bike paths make it possible for commuters to zip to work faster than they could on a bus, in some instances.

Successful transportation systems must be flexible. Buses, bicycles, and trains can provide much of our transportation needs. They have the flexibility to get to work, dart to the store to pick up a can of cranberry sauce, or connect us to a neighboring city. More flexibility can be achieved by introducing other efficient means of transportation like car pools and van pools. They provide the door-to-door service to which many people are accustomed and save fuel at the same time. To promote car and van pooling, some cities have offered free parking. Some companies provide vehicles for "poolers." In some cities special bus lanes are usually open to vehicles with two or more passengers, making the car or van pool a quicker way to get to work.

Economic Changes Accompanying a Shift to Mass Transit
Automobiles are big business. In fact, the automobile industry is the world's largest manufacturing industry. Declining oil supplies and the necessary shift to more efficient forms of transportation will cut into this economically important industry. Suppliers of rubber, glass, steel, and parts will also feel the impacts of the shrinking market, as will the service sector—gas stations, automobile dealerships, and repair services. Twenty cents of every dollar spent in the United States is directly or indirectly connected to the automobile industry and its suppliers. Eighteen cents of every tax dollar the federal government collects comes from automobile manufacturers and their suppliers.

Shifting toward a sustainable transportation system will change this picture over the years. But it will not cut it

Figure 22-5 The bicycle is an efficient and economical alternative to the automobile for some commuters.

off completely. Steel and glass will be used for building buses and trains. Employment will shift from automobile manufacturing and repair to making and repairing larger vehicles. Some workers, however, will inevitably be forced to find employment in new areas.

Toward an Appropriate Technology

Ethical changes are needed to make the shift to a sustainable society. So are changes in individual behavior and land use. But these must be accompanied by changes in the way people interact with the environment, especially through industry. In this section we explore technology and look at a new system that promises to help build a sustainable society.

Technology has played a major role in human civilization (Chapter 2). Human evolutionary history, in fact, is largely a history of changing technology. Until quite recently human civilization has generally seen only the benefits of its tools. As such, technology is often viewed as the answer to what ails us. Technological advances can make mining and processing of ores more efficient, allowing us to use lower-grade ore deposits while keeping the cost down. Pollution control technologies such as the catalytic converter used in cars can help reduce pollution in our cities. New products from the chemical industry may replace dangerous products.

No doubt technology has benefited humankind. But in some forms, such as nuclear weapons and fossil fuel combustion, technology poses a threat to our existence. The challenge facing modern civilization is not how to achieve greater technological mastery but how to redirect technology's use to make it less risky, cleaner, and more humane.

John Naisbitt, author of the best-selling book *Megatrends*, points out that in the 1960s and 1970s many Americans began to rebel against conventional technology—the large, impersonal factories that spewed out air pollution, produced goods by assembly lines, and reduced human labor to near meaninglessness. This revolt was caused by a shift in attitudes, which has stimulated the search for ways to remake these technologies.

We may be standing on the brink of a quiet revolution in technology, the second industrial revolution. It would be highlighted by increased workplace democracy, with workers having a bigger say in the operations of business. The tools themselves may change. Robots may take over repetitive and dangerous jobs. Proponents of a sustainable future argue that further changes are needed; technology must be redesigned. Small to medium-sized machines that are easy to repair will replace large, complex machines requiring highly trained experts, especially in Third World nations. Needed, too, are production methods that use locally available energy and materials sparingly and produce little pollution. This technology, called **appropriate technology**, is specifically adapted to the setting in which it is used (Table 22-3). In many ways it is different from the technology that emerged during the Industrial Revolution.

Appropriate technology is a concept popularized by the late E. F. Schumacher in his classic book, *Small Is Beautiful*. He emphasizes that appropriate technology fits well in developing countries as well as highly industrialized countries. Its chief advantages are that it puts people to work in a meaningful way, requires less money to construct and operate, is efficient on a small scale, uses locally available resources, and is more compatible with the environment because of the low energy requirements and minimal pollution.

In developing nations without the capital and energy resources needed to support modern industries, appropriate technology may be the key to economic development. Countries such as India and China have an abundance of people who can be employed by factories using appropriate technology (Figure 22-6). Highly automated factories that use fewer people to produce their goods would waste the human labor potential and would require large amounts of capital.

Table 22-3 Characteristics of Appropriate Technology

Machines are small to medium-sized.

Human labor is favored over automation.

Machines are easy to understand and repair.

Production is decentralized.

Factories use local resources.

Factories use renewable resources whenever possible.

Equipment uses energy and materials efficiently.

Production facilities are relatively free of pollution.

Production is less capital intensive than conventional technology.

Management stresses meaningful work, allowing workers to perform a variety of tasks.

Products are generally for local consumption.

Products are durable.

The means of production are compatible with local culture.

Appropriate technology can find a niche on farms throughout the world to replace conventional technology, which is costly and wasteful of indigenous labor. For example, a tractor is an inappropriate use of technology in rural India. Although it increases production, it tends to put people out of work. These people then move to already overpopulated cities in search of employment, creating a serious environmental problem in burgeoning cities. In addition, the cost of tractors, repair, and energy are prohibitive in poor, rural regions of developing countries. Gandhi put it best when he said that the poor of the world cannot be helped by mass production, only by production of the masses. What will work in India, Latin America, and Africa are slightly improved methods of agriculture that keep farm workers employed while using a minimum amount of energy. A well-designed metal plow produced from local resources and easily repaired by farmers, for instance, would utilize abundant human labor.

Appropriate technology in developed countries should not be viewed as a step backward but as a step forward. It is the wise use of people, resources, and energy. Some modern-day examples include solar panels for domestic and industrial heating; passive solar design for heating buildings; energy from the wind instead of from coal; bicycles for making short trips; microcomputers to control energy consumption in homes; and waterless toilets to convert human wastes into a humuslike substance good for gardening.

In developed countries the shift to appropriate technology will eliminate some jobs that have been a part of the economy for decades. Auto and steel workers and

Figure 22-6 Indian woman in a factory. Appropriate technology uses abundant labor in developing countries to manufacture goods for local consumption.

miners will be especially hard hit. But many new jobs will emerge and already have. There will be a need for energy auditors to help improve energy conservation in homes and factories. Demand for experts in solar and wind energy will increase. The need for family planning experts and a host of other workers to help maintain a sustainable society will also rise.

Appropriate technology is not a panacea, the one solution to the world's problems; but it is an essential part of a sustainable future. Combined with changes in attitude, shifts in political systems, and fundamental changes in education, appropriate technology will be part of a new world order—exciting and filled with opportunity for realizing our full potential.

Some see things as they are and say why? I dream of things that never were and say why not?

GEORGE BERNARD SHAW

Summary

A sustainable society is based on conservation, recycling, renewable resources, and population control. To achieve such a society will require some fundamental changes in the institutions and beliefs we embrace today. Sustainability must replace growthmania.

In many ways the transition to a sustainable society is already under way. Some people have simplified their life-styles and sought ways to live within the limits posed by the earth. Environmental protection groups are found throughout the world. Industry has taken a more responsible attitude. Despite these and many other gains, much more is needed to build a sustainable society. The frontier mentality must be replaced by a sustainable mentality. Feelings of insignificance must be replaced with the positive attitude that we do make a difference. We must see that our children learn about their responsibilities

to the biosphere and future generations. Such changes can lead to new economic expectations and new ways to do business. And they will mean political changes with far-reaching effects.

Land use planning is needed to protect renewable resources, but historically the marketplace has determined how land is used. To stop the unnecessary loss of resources, statewide—perhaps even nationwide—land use planning must be adopted. Japan and many European nations have national plans that could be emulated.

The chief tool of land use planning has been zoning, classifying land according to use. New approaches are being adopted, especially to protect farmland. One of those is **differential tax assessment laws**, which allow city officials to tax farmland according to its agricultural value, regardless of its potential for development. Some states purchase the **development rights**, that is, the difference between a land's assessed value for farming and its assessed value for development. States hold the development rights in perpetuity, ensuring that the land must be farmed.

Land use planning is also important in developing nations, because rapidly growing populations, largely found in urban centers, are threatening wildlife and good farmland.

A sustainable transportation system will look sharply different from the current wasteful network based primarily on automobiles and jet aircraft. Mass transit by bus and train will probably replace much of the automobile traffic, both in cities and between them. Improved efficiency in vehicles can help lengthen the lifespan of the auto, but in the long term the auto will probably go the way of the dinosaur.

Ethical changes and changes in individual behavior are needed to make the shift to a sustainable society. But these changes must be accompanied by changes from the current technology to **appropriate technology**. Appropriate technology puts people to work in a meaningful way, requires less money to construct and operate, is efficient on a small scale, and is more compatible with the environment because of its low energy requirements. In developing nations, lacking the capital and energy resources needed to run modern industries, appropriate technology may be the key to economic development. In developed nations appropriate technology represents a wise use of people, resources, and energy. Appropriate technology is an essential part of a sustainable future. Combined with changes in attitude, shifts in political systems, and fundamental changes in education, it will help create a new society.

Discussion Questions

1. Describe how a sustainable society would be different from that of today in terms of people's attitudes, agriculture, transportation, housing, and industry.

2. What major changes are needed to create a sustainable society?

3. What are the advantages of national land use planning? How would you go about devising a plan for the United States?

4. What is appropriate technology? What advantages does it offer to developed and developing nations?

Suggested Readings

Brown, L. R. (1981). *Building a Sustainable Society*. New York: Norton. A book you must read from cover to cover.

Brown, L. R., et al. (1987). *State of the World 1987*. New York: Norton. An important summary of ways to achieve a sustainable future.

Kunofsky, J., and Orman, L. (1985). Greenbelts and the Well-Planned City. *Sierra* 70 (6): 42–48. An interesting look at alternatives to urban development.

Millbrath, L. W. (1984). *Environmentalists: Vanguard for a New Society*. Albany, N.Y.: State University of New York Press. See Chapters 4–6, which deal with social change.

Schumacher, E. F. (1973). *Small Is Beautiful: Economics As If People Mattered*. New York: Harper and Row. Superb reading.

Environmental Publications

The following journals, magazines and other publications will help you learn more about specific environmental issues and stay abreast of current changes. The address of the publication is listed so you can contact it for subscription costs.

American Forests. Monthly. American Forestry Association, 1319 18th Street NW, Washington, DC 20036. Promotes public appreciation of natural resources.

The Amicus Journal. Natural Resources Defense Council, 122 East 42nd Street, New York, NY 10168. Well-written, engaging articles on variety of issues.

Audubon. Bimonthly. National Audubon Society, 950 Third Avenue, New York, NY 10022. Conservation and environmental concerns; covers more than bird watching.

BioScience. Monthly. American Institute of Biological Sciences, 1401 Wilson Boulevard, Arlington, VA 22209. Both popular and technical; major coverage of biological aspects of the environment.

Bulletin of the Atomic Scientists. Ten times a year. Educational Foundation for Nuclear Science, 5801 South Kenwood, Chicago, IL 60637. Increasingly concerned with environmental issues in relation to nuclear power, nuclear testing, and nuclear war.

Code of Federal Regulations. Office of the Federal Register, U.S. Government Printing Office, Washington, DC 20402. Covers federal regulations in agriculture, aliens, energy, energy conservation, food and drugs, minerals, parks, national forests, environmental protection, public health, public lands, transportation, and wildlife.

The CoEvolution Quarterly. P.O. Box 428, Sausalito, CA 94965. Environment and self-sufficiency. Also publishes *The New Whole Earth Catalog.*

Conservation Foundation Letter. Monthly. Conservation Foundation, 1717 Massachusetts Avenue NW, Washington, DC 20036. Concise, solid summaries of important issues.

Demographic Yearbook. Department of International Economic and Social Affairs, Statistical Office, United Nations Publishing Service, United Nations, NY 10017. Information on populations, including growth rate, population size, and mortality.

Design and Environment. Quarterly. RC Publications, 6400 Goldsboro Road NW, Washington, DC 20034. Concerned with technology and the environment.

Earth Shelter Digest. Six times a year. 479 Fort Road, St. Paul, MN 55102. Current information on earth-sheltered housing.

The Ecologist. Ten times a year. Ecostems, Ltd., 73 Molesworth Street, Wadebridge, Cornwall PL27 7DS, United Kingdom. International viewpoint on environmental issues.

Environment. Ten times a year. 4000 Albemarle Street NW, Washington, DC 20016. In-depth articles on important issues.

Environmental Abstracts. Monthly. Environment Information Centers/Intelligence, 48 West 38th Street, New York, NY 10018. Basic bibliographic reference; in most libraries.

Environmental Action. Monthly. Environmental Action, Inc., 1525 New Hampshire Avenue NW, Washington, DC 20036. Political, social-action orientation. Environmental issues covered from a broad spectrum of viewpoints.

Environmental Quality. Yearly. Council on Environmental Quality, 722 Jackson Place NW, Washington, DC 20006. Report of environmental problems and progress in environmental protection.

Environmental Science & Technology. Monthly. American Chemical Society, 1155 16th Street NW, Washington, DC 20036. A basic reference for current technological developments. Emphasizes air, water, and solid waste chemistry.

EPA Journal. Monthly. Environmental Protection Agency, 1961 Stout, Room 117, Washington, DC 20003. Environmental issues and EPA activity updates.

Family Planning Perspectives. Bimonthly. Planned Parenthood–World Population, Editorial Offices, 666 Fifth Avenue, New York, NY 10019. Free. Detailed information on population problems.

FDA Consumer. Ten times a year. U.S. Department of Health and Human Services, Public Health Service, 5600 Fishers Lane, Rockville, MD 20857. Excellent information on food additives and health issues.

The Futurist. Bimonthly. World Future Society, 4916 St. Elmo Avenue, Bethesda, MD 20814. Covers broad range of social problems, including some major issues.

Journal of Environmental Education. Quarterly. Haldref Publications, 4000 Albemarle Street NW, Washington, DC 20016. For educators.

Living Wilderness. Quarterly. Wilderness Society, 1901 Pennsylvania Avenue NW, Washington, DC 20006. Articles on wilderness, forestry, and related issues.

Monthly Energy Review. National Energy Information Center, EI-20, Energy Information Administration, Room 1F-048, Forrestal Building, Washington, DC 20585. Monthly updates on U.S. energy production and consumption.

National Parks and Conservation Magazine. Monthly. National Parks and Conservation Association, 1701 18th Street NW, Washington, DC 20009. Park and wildlife issues.

National Wildlife. Bimonthly. National Wildlife Federation, 1412 16th Street NW, Washington, DC 20036. Wildlife emphasis; action oriented.

Natural History. Ten times a year. American Museum of Natural History, Central Park West at 79th Street, New York, NY 10024. Popular. Regular coverage of environmental issues.

Nature. Weekly. Macmillan Journals, Ltd., Brunel Road, Basingstoke, Hants RG21 2X5, United Kingdom. British Publication, similar to *Science.*

New Scientist. Weekly. 1-19 New Oxford Street, London WE1 A 1 NG, United Kingdom. General science; good coverage of environmental issues and technological breakthroughs.

Not Man Apart. Monthly. Friends of the Earth, 1045 Sansome Street, San Francisco, CA 94111. National and international environmental issues.

Population and Vital Statistics Report. Quarterly. United Nations, Publications Sales Section, New York, NY 10017. Up-to-date world figures.

Population Bulletin. Bimonthly. Population Reference Bureau, Inc., 1337 Connecticut Avenue NW, Washington, DC 20036. Nontechnical coverage of human population issues.

Population Bulletin. Irregular. United Nations, Publications Sales Section, New York, NY 10017. Statistical summaries.

Population Reports. Population Information Program, Johns Hopkins University, Hampton House, 624 North Broadway, Baltimore, MD 21205. Up-to-date information on birth control and population.

Resources. Four times a year. Resources for the Future, Inc., 1755 Massachusetts Avenue NW, Washington, DC 20036. Recent research and findings on resource use and development.

Statistical Yearbook. Department of International Economic and Social Affairs, Statistical Office, United Nations Publishing Service, United Nations, NY 10017. Wide range of information, including gross domestic products, world exports, food production, housing, forestry, and energy.

Science. Weekly. American Association for the Advancement of Science, 1515 Massachusetts Avenue NW, Washington, DC 20005. Excellent but technical information on important environmental issues.

Science for Society—A Bibliography. Annually. American Association for the Advancement of Science, Education Department, 1515 Massachusetts Avenue NW, Washington, DC 20005. Environmental bibliography.

Science News. Weekly. Science Service, Inc., 1719 N Street NW, Washington, DC 20036. Popular; summarizes scientific developments.

Scientific American. Monthly. 415 Madison Avenue, New York, NY 10017. Covers all scientific issues, with many articles on the environment.

The Sierra Club Bulletin. Monthly. Sierra Club, 730 Polk Street, San Francisco, CA 94109. Citizen action viewpoint; covers a wide range of environmental issues.

Technology Review. Eight times a year. Massachusetts Institute of Technology, Room 10-140, Cambridge, MA 02139. Sophisticated. Frequent coverage of environmental material and science policy.

UNESCO Courier. Eleven issues per year. The United Nations Educational, Scientific, and Cultural Organization, United Nations, New York, NY 10017. Covers broad issues.

United States Population Data Sheet. Published annually. Population Reference Bureau, Box 35012, Washington, DC 20013. Superb source.

World Population Data Sheet. Published annually. Population Reference Bureau, Box 35012, Washington, DC 20013. Superb source.

Worldwatch Papers. Worldwatch Institute, 1776 Massachusetts Avenue NW, Washington, DC 20036. Designed to give early warning on major environmental problems.

Yearbook of World Energy Statistics. Department of International Economic and Social Affairs, Statistical Office, United Nations Publishing Service, United Nations, NY 10017. Detailed information on worldwide energy production.

Environmental and Governmental Organizations

Environmental Organizations

American Forestry Association, 1319 18th Street NW, Washington, DC 20036. Focuses on forest and soil conservation, but concerned with air and water pollution and preserving and creating parklands.

Animal Protection Institute of America, P.O. Box 22505, Sacramento, CA 94822. Education and information on humane treatment of animals. Has concentrated on whale, porpoise, and seal slaughter, leg-hold traps, and dog and cat population problems.

Center for Environmental Education, 624 Ninth Street NW, Washington, DC 20001. Dedicated to citizen involvement in improvement of environmental quality. Special emphasis on whales and marine ecosystems. Initiated a campaign to reauthorize the Endangered Species Act.

Center for Planet Management, Box 541, Boulder, CO 80302. Promotes sustainable ethics and renewable resource use. Educational.

Center for Renewable Resources, 1001 Connecticut Avenue NW, Washington, DC 20036. Educates the public and policymakers; conducts policy research.

Center for Science in the Public Interest, 1755 S Street NW, Washington, DC 20006. Public-interest scientists concerned especially with food and nutrition issues but also with the environment and the effects of science and technology on society.

Center for the Study of Responsive Law, P.O. Box 19367, Washington, DC 20036. Research and education organization working in public interest.

Citizens for a Better Environment, 33 East Congress, Suite 523, Chicago, IL 60605. Works to reduce pollution and promote energy conservation and renewable energy.

Clean Water Action Project, 317 Pennsylvania Avenue NW, Suite 200, Washington, DC 20005. National citizen-action organization working for strict pollution controls and safe drinking water. Seeks to preserve national wetlands.

Common Cause, 2030 M Street NW, Washington, DC 20036. One of the most important citizen groups in the country. Over 200,000 members active in many political issues.

The Conservation Foundation, 1255 23rd Street NW, Washington, DC 20037. Resource conservation; analysis of ecological impact of foreign aid.

The Cousteau Society, 930 West 21st Street, Norfolk, VA 23517. Concerned with environmental matters, education, research, and evaluation. Plans to construct an evaluation center to digest scientific environmental data and to monitor the accuracy of public announcements made by industry or by the government.

Critical Mass Energy Project, 215 Pennsylvania Avenue SE, Washington, DC 20003. Sponsors national conferences on nuclear energy and alternative energy; promotes safe and efficient energy.

Defenders of Wildlife, 1244 19th Street NW, Washington, DC 20036. Works to protect all wildlife. Education, lobbying, and research.

Ducks Unlimited, 1 Waterfowl Way, Long Grove, IL 60047. Conservationists in the United States, Canada, Mexico, and New Zealand interested in migrators and wildlife habitat conservation. Has acquired or protected millions of acres of important waterfowl breeding habitats.

Environmental Action, 1525 New Hampshire Avenue NW, Washington, DC 20036. Lobbies for legislative protection and reform.

Environmental Defense Fund, 444 Park Avenue South, New York, NY 10016. Lawyers, scientists, and laypeople working to link law and science together for environmental defense.

The Environmental Law Institute, 1616 P Street NW, Suite 200, Washington, DC 20036. Joint project of the Conservation Foundation and the Public Law Education Institute; conducts research and education in environmental law.

Environmental Policy Center, 317 Pennsylvania Avenue SE, Washington, DC 20003. Lobbies for water policy and energy development.

Environmental Task Force, 1346 Connecticut Avenue NW, Suite 912, Washington, DC 20036. Strengthens environmental movement by promoting cooperation among other environmental groups.

Foundation on Economic Trends, 1130 17th Street NW, Washington, DC 20036. Studies energy, economic, and health issues and disseminates information.

Friends of the Earth, 1045 Sansome Street, San Francisco, CA 94111. Powerful lobbying group.

The Fund for Animals, 200 West 57th Street, New York, NY 10019. Preserves wildlife and promotes humane treatment of animals.

Greenpeace, 1611 Connecticut Avenue NW, Washington, DC 20007. Environmental activists seeking to protect the environment, whales, and seals. Active in the fight against nuclear power and nuclear war.

Institute for Local Self-Reliance, 2425 18th Street NW, Washington, DC 20009. Promotes appropriate technologies for communities, promotes decentralized self-reliance.

International Planned Parenthood Federation, 105 Madison Avenue, 7th Floor, New York, NY 10016. Committed to informed voluntary family planning. Seeks to persuade governments to establish family planning programs. Provides information, education, and services.

Izaak Walton League of America, 1701 North Fort Meyer Drive, Suite 1100, Arlington, VA 22209. Works for wise resource use and the development and protection of outdoor recreation.

John Muir Institute for Environmental Studies, 743 Wilson Street, Napa, CA 94559. Research and education on environmental issues.

Keep America Beautiful, 99 Park Avenue, New York, NY 10016. Public service organization; works to improve the physical quality of life. Sponsors community programs for the improvement of waste handling. Provides assistance, materials, and advice for community grass-roots efforts.

League for Ecological Democracy, Box 1858, San Pedro, CA 90733. Working to develop an ecological society.

League of Conservation Voters, 320 Fourth Street NE, Washington, DC 20002. Nonpartisan; part of Friends of the Earth. Promotes and supports congressional candidates who have sound environmental platforms. Notifies the public of roll-call votes on environmental issues.

League of Women Voters of the United States, 1730 M Street NW, Washington, DC 20036. Outstanding membership organization committed to political responsibility and an informed, active citizenry.

National Audubon Society, 950 Third Avenue, New York, NY 10022. Research, education, and lobbying. Operates wildlife sanctuaries across the country; conducts research to aid endangered species.

National Parks and Conservation Association, 1701 18th Street NW, Washington, DC 20009. Works to acquire and protect public parklands. Active in general environmental issues.

National Recreation and Park Association, 3101 Park Center Drive, 12th Floor, Alexandria, VA 22302. Recreation and park development and conservation.

National Recycling Coalition, 45 Rockefeller Plaza, Room 2350, New York, NY 10110. Individuals and groups united to encourage recovery, reuse, and conservation of energy and materials and to promote recycling.

National Wildlife Federation, 1412 16th Street NW, Washington, DC 20036. Education and research. Promotes citizen and government action.

Natural Resources Defense Council, Inc., 122 East 42nd Street, New York, NY 10168. Works to protect natural resources and environmental quality.

The Nature Conservancy, 1800 North Kent Street, Suite 800, Arlington, VA 22209. Membership organization. Works to preserve natural areas. Often acquires endangered property and holds it until a public agency can buy and protect it.

Negative Population Growth, 16 East 42nd Street, Suite 1042, New York, NY 10017. Promotes population reduction.

Population Crisis Committee, 1120 19th Street NW, Suite 550, Washington, DC 20036. Promotes public understanding and action on the world's population crisis.

Population-Environment Balance, 1325 G Street NW, Suite 1003, Washington, DC 20005. Promotes national policy of stationary population growth, strong economy, and sustainable resource use.

Population Institute, 110 Maryland Avenue NE, Suite 207, Washington, DC 20002. Seeks to educate people on global overpopulation and solutions.

Population Reference Bureau, 1337 Connecticut Avenue NW, Washington, DC 20036. Publishes current information on population.

Public Interest Research Group, 1346 Connecticut Avenue NW, No. 415, Washington, DC 20036. Research and education on the environment.

Resources for the Future, 1775 Massachusetts Avenue NW, Washington, DC 20036. Conducts research and education on environment and natural resources. Provides grants to other research institutions.

Scientists' Institute for Public Information, 355 Lexington Avenue, New York, NY 10017. Scientists of all disciplines disseminate objective scientific information on social issues related to science and technology.

Sierra Club, 730 Polk Street, San Francisco, CA 94109. Educators, publishers, and lobbyists devoted to the protection of national wilderness and scenic resources.

Solar Lobby, 1001 Connecticut Avenue NW, Suite 638, Washington, DC 20036. Dedicated to alternative energy sources; lobbies for solar energy.

Union of Concerned Scientists, 26 Church Street, Cambridge, MA 02238. Research, education, and lobbying; especially concerned with nuclear safety.

The Wilderness Society, 1400 I Street NW, Washington, DC 20005. Main goal is to promote acquisition and protection of wilderness and primitive areas by the federal government.

Wildlife Society, 5410 Grosvenor Lane, Bethesda, MD 20814. Wildlife preservation.

World Environment Center, 605 Third Avenue, 17th Floor, New York, NY 10158. Established by the United Nations, with support of the U.N. Environment Program. Worldwide network to foster public understanding of global environmental problems and international cooperation. Tracks down environment data anywhere in the world.

Worldwatch Institute, 1776 Massachusetts Avenue NW, Washington, DC 20036. Research, education, and early warning on important environmental problems.

World Wildlife Fund, 1255 23rd Street NW, Washington, DC 20037. Research and education.

Zero Population Growth, 1601 Connecticut Avenue NW, Washington, DC 20009. Works for family planning in effort to stabilize population growth.

See also *Conservation Directory*. National Wildlife Foundation, 1412 16th Street NW, Washington, DC 20036; *World Directory of Environmental Organizations*. San Francisco: Sequoia Institute, 1976.

Governmental Agencies

Bureau of Land Management, Interior Building, Room 5660, Washington, DC 20240.

Bureau of Mines, Columbian Plaza, 2401 E Street NW, Washington, DC 20506.

Bureau of Outdoor Recreation, Interior Building, Room 4410, Washington, DC 20240.

Bureau of Reclamation, Interior Building, Room 7654, Washington, DC 20240.

Conservation and Renewable Energy Inquiry and Referral Service, P.O. Box 8900, Silver Spring, MD 20907. Call toll free for information on energy conservation and renewable energy sources: 1-800-523-2929 outside of Pennsylvania; 1-800-462-4983 in Pennsylvania.

Council on Environmental Quality, 722 Jackson Place NW, Washington, DC 20006.

Department of Agriculture, Washington, DC 20250.

Department of Energy, Forrestal Building, 1000 Independence Avenue SW, Washington, DC 20585.

Department of the Interior, Interior Building, Washington, DC 20240.

Department of Transportation, 400 7th Street SW, Washington, DC 20590.

Environmental Protection Agency, 401 M Street SW, Washington, DC 20460.

Federal Power Commission, 825 North Capitol Street NE, Washington, DC 20426.

Fish and Wildlife Service, Department of the Interior, Interior Building, Room 3256, Washington, DC 20240.

Food and Drug Administration, Department of Health and Human Services, 5600 Fishers Lane, Rockville, MD 20857.

Forest Service, South Agriculture Building, Independence Avenue between 12th and 14th Streets SW, Washington, DC 20250.

Geological Survey, U.S. Geological Survey National Center, 12201 Sunrise Valley Drive, Reston, VA 22092.

National Academy of Sciences, 2101 Constitution Avenue NW, Washington, DC 20418.

National Center for Appropriate Technology, P.O. Box 3838, Butte, MT 59701.

National Oceanic and Atmospheric Administration, Washington Science Center, Building 5, 6010 Executive Boulevard, Rockville, MD 20852.

National Park Service, Interior Building, Room 3256, Washington, DC 20240.

National Technical Information Service, Department of Commerce, Sills Building, 5285 Port Royal Road, Springfield, VA 22161.

Nuclear Regulatory Commission, 1717 H Street NW, Washington, DC 20555.

Solar Energy Research Institute, 1617 Cole Boulevard, Golden, CO 80401.

Superintendent of Documents, U.S. Government Printing Office, Washington, DC 20402.

Water Resources Council, 2120 L Street NW, Washington, DC 20423.

Glossary

Abiotic factors Nonliving components of the ecosystem, including chemical and physical factors such as availability of nitrogen, temperature, and rainfall.

Accelerated erosion Loss of soil due to wind or water in land disturbed by human activities.

Accelerated extinction Elimination of species due to human activities such as habitat destruction, commercial hunting, sport hunting, and pollution.

Acid mine drainage Sulfuric acid that drains from mines, especially abandoned underground coal mines in the East (Appalachia). Created by the chemical reaction between oxygen, water, and iron sulfides found in coal and surrounding rocks.

Acid precipitation Rain or snow that has a lower pH than precipitation from unpolluted skies.

Active solar Capturing and storage of the sun's energy through special collection devices (solar panels) that absorb heat and transfer it to air, water, or some other medium, which is then pumped to a storage site (usually a water tank) for later use. Contrast with *passive solar*.

Actual risk An accurate measure of the hazard posed by a certain technology or action.

Acute effects In general, effects that occur shortly after exposure to toxic agents. Contrast with *chronic effects*.

Acute toxicity Poisoning generally caused by short-term exposure to high levels of one or more agents. Symptoms appear soon after exposure.

Adaptation A genetically determined structural or functional characteristic of an organism that enhances its chances of reproducing and passing on its genes.

Advanced industrial society Post-World War II *industrial society* characterized by great rises is production and consumption, increased energy demand, and a shift toward synthetics and nonrenewable resources.

Age-specific fertility rate Number of live births per 1000 women of a specific age group.

Agricultural land conversion Transformation of farmland to other purposes, primarily cities, highways, airports, and the like.

Agricultural society A group of people living in villages or towns and relying on domestic animals and crops grown in nearby fields. Characterized by specialization of work roles.

Algal bloom Rapid growth of algae in surface waters due to increase in inorganic nutrients, usually either nitrogen or phosphorus.

Alien species (or foreign species) Any species introduced into or living in a new habitat. Also known as an exotic.

Alpha particles Positively charged particles consisting of two protons and two neutrons, emitted from radioactive nuclei.

Alveoli Small sacs in the lungs where exchange of oxygen and carbon dioxide between air and blood occurs.

Ambient air quality standard Maximum permissible concentration of a pollutant in the air around us. Contrast with *emissions standard*.

Annuals Plants that grow from seeds—for example, domestic corn and radishes.

Antagonism In toxicology, when two chemical or physical agents (often toxins) counteract each other to produce a lesser response than would be expected if individual effects were added together.

Anthropogenic hazard A danger created by humans.

Appropriate technology A term coined by the late E.F. Schumacher to refer to technology that is "appropriate" for the economy, resources, and culture of a region. It is characterized by small- to medium-sized machines, maximum human labor, ease of understanding, meaningful employment, use of local resources, decentralized production, production of durable products, emphasis on renewable resources, especially energy, and compatibility with the environment and culture.

Aquaculture Cultivation of fish and other aquatic organisms in freshwater ponds, lakes, irrigation ditches, and other bodies of water.

Aquifer Underground stratum of porous material (sandstone) containing water (groundwater), which may be withdrawn from wells for human use.

Aquifer recharge zone Region in which water from rain or snow percolates into an aquifer, replenishing the supply of groundwater.

Asbestos One of several naturally occurring silicate fibers. Useful in society as an insulator but deadly to breathe even in small amounts. Causes mesothelioma, asbestosis, and lung cancer.

Asbestosis Lung disease characterized by buildup of scar tissue in the lungs. Caused by inhalation of asbestos.

Asthma Lung disorder characterized by constriction and excessive mucus production in the bronchioles, resulting in periodic difficulty in breathing, shortness of breath, coughing. Usually caused by allergy and often aggravated by air pollution.

Atmosphere Layer of air surrounding earth.

Atom A basic unit of matter consisting of a nucleus of positively charged protons and uncharged neutrons, and an outer cloud of electrons orbiting the nucleus.

Auxins Plant hormones responsible for stimulating growth.

Bacteria A group of single-celled organisms, each surrounded by a cell wall and containing circular DNA. Responsible for some diseases and many beneficial functions, such as the decay of organic materials and nutrient recycling.

Barrier islands Small, sandy islands off a coast, separated from the mainland by lagoons or bays.

Beach drift Wave-caused movement of sand along a beach.

Beta particles Negatively charged particles emitted from nuclei of radioactive elements when a neutron is converted to a proton.

Big Bang Theory of the universe's formation. States that all matter in the universe was infinitely compressed 15 to 20 billion years ago and then exploded, sending energy and matter out into space. The matter was in the form of subatomic particles which formed atoms as the universe cooled over millions of years.

Biochemical oxygen demand (BOD) Measure of oxygen depletion of water (largely from bacterial decay) due to presence of biodegradable organic pollutants. Gives scientists an indication of how much organic matter is in water.

Bioconcentration Ability of an organism to selectively accumulate certain chemicals, elements, or substances within its body or within certain cells.

Biogas A gas containing methane and carbon dioxide. Produced by anaerobic decay of organic matter, especially manure and crop residues.

Biogeochemical cycle Complex cyclical transfer of nutrients from the environment to organisms and back to the environment. Examples include the carbon, nitrogen, and phosphorus cycles.

Biological control Use of naturally occurring predators, parasites, bacteria, and viruses to control pests. Also called food chain control.

Biological extinction Disappearance of a species from part or all of its range.

Biological magnification Buildup of chemical elements or substances in organisms in successively higher trophic levels. Also called biomagnification.

Biomass As measured by ecologists, the dried weight of all organic matter in the ecosystem. In the energy field, any form of organic material (from both plants and animals) from which energy can be derived by burning or bioconversion such as fermentation. Includes wood, cow dung, agricultural crop residues, forestry residues, scrap paper.

Biomass pyramid See *pyramid of biomass*.

Biome One of several immense terrestrial regions, each characterized throughout its extent by similar plants, animals, climate, and soil type.

Biosphere All the life-supporting regions (ecosystems) of the earth and all the interactions that occur between organisms and between organisms and the environment.

Biotic factor The biological component of the ecosystem, consisting of populations of plants, animals, and microorganisms in complex communities.

Biotic (reproductive) potential Maximum reproductive potential of a species.

Birth control Any measure designed to reduce births, including contraception and abortion.

Birth defect An anatomical (structural) or physiological (functional) defect in a newborn.

Bloom See *algal bloom*.

Breeder reactor Fission reactor that produces electricity and also converts abundant but nonfissile uranium-238 into fissile plutonium-239, which can be used in other fission reactors.

Broad-spectrum pesticide (or biocide) Chemical agent effective in controlling a large number of pests.

Bronchitis Persistent inflammation of the bronchi caused by smoking and air pollutants. Symptoms include mucus buildup, chronic cough, and throat irritation.

Brown-air cities Newer, relatively nonindustrialized cities whose polluted skies contain photochemical oxidants (especially ozone) and nitrogen oxides, largely from automobiles and power plants. Tend to have dry, sunny climates. Contrast with *gray-air cities*.

Cancer Uncontrolled proliferation of cells in humans and other living organisms. In humans, includes more than 100 different types afflicting individuals of all races and ages.

Carbon cycle The cycling of carbon between organisms and the environment.

Carcinogen A chemical or physical agent that causes cancer to develop, often decades after the original exposure.

Carrying capacity Maximum population size that a given ecosystem can support for an indefinite period or on a sustainable basis.

Catalyst Substance that accelerates chemical reactions but is not used up in the process. Enzymes are biological catalysts. Also see *catalytic converter*.

Catalytic converter Device attached to the exhaust system of automobiles and trucks to rid the exhaust gases of harmful pollutants.

Cation Any one of many kinds of positively charged ions.

Cellular respiration Process by which a cell breaks down glucose and other organic molecules to acquire energy. Also called oxidative metabolism.

Chlorofluoromethanes See *fluorocarbons.*

Chlorophyll Pigment of plant cells that absorbs sunlight, thus allowing plants to capture solar energy.

Chromosomes Genetic material of organisms, containing DNA and protein. Carries the genetic information that controls all cellular activity.

Chronic bronchitis Persistent inflammation of the bronchi due to pollutants in ambient air and tobacco smoke. Characterized by persistent cough.

Chronic effects In general, the delayed health results of toxic agents—for example, as emphysema, bronchitis, and cancer. Contrast with *acute effects.*

Chronic obstructive lung disease Any one of several lung diseases characterized by obstruction of breathing. Includes emphysema, bronchitis, and diseases with symptoms of both of these.

Chronic toxicity Poisoning generally caused by long-term exposures to low levels of one or more toxic agents. Symptoms appear long after exposure. Examples: emphysema and cancer.

Clear-cutting Removal of all trees from a forested area.

Climate The average weather conditions—temperature, solar radiation, precipitation, and humidity.

Climax community or ecosystem See *mature community.*

Closed system A system that can exchange energy, but does not exchange matter, with the surrounding environment. Example: the earth. Contrast with *open system.*

Coal gasification Production of combustible organic gases (mostly methane) by applying heat and steam to coal in an oxygen-enriched environment. Carried out in surface vessels or *in situ.*

Coal liquefaction Production of synthetic oil from coal.

Coastal wetlands Wet or flooded regions along coastlines, including mangrove swamps, salt marshes, bays, and lagoons. Contrast with *inland wetlands.*

Co-evolution Process whereby two species evolve adaptations as a result of extensive interactions with each other.

Cogeneration Production of two or more forms of useful energy from one process. For example, production of electricity and steam heat from combustion of coal. Increases energy efficiency.

Coliform bacterium Common bacterium found in the intestinal tracts of humans and other species. Used in water quality analysis to determine the extent of fecal contamination.

Common law Body of rules and principles based on judicial precedent rather than legislative enactments. Founded on an innate sense of justice, good conscience, and reason. Flexible and adaptable. Contrast with *statutory law.*

Commons Any resource used in common by many people, such as air, water, and grazing land.

Community Also called a biological community. The populations of plants, animals, and microorganisms living and interacting in a given locality.

Composting Aerobic decay of organic matter to generate a humus-like substance used to supplement soil.

Confusion technique (of pest control) Release of insect sex-attractant pheromones identical to pheromones released by normal breeding females to attract males for mating. Release in large quantities confuses males as to the location of the females, thus minimizing the chances of males finding females and helping to control pest populations.

Conservation A strategy to reduce the use of resources, especially through increased efficiency, reuse, recycling, and decreased demand.

Consumer (or consumer organism) An organism in the ecosystem that feeds on autotrophs and/or heterotrophs. Synonym: heterotroph.

Continental drift Movement of the earth's tectonic plates on a semiliquid layer of mantle, forcing continents to shift position over hundreds of thousands of years.

Contour farming Soil erosion control technique in which row crops (corn) are planted along the contour lines in sloping or hilly fields rather than up and down the hills.

Contraceptive Any device or chemical substance used to prevent conception.

Control group In scientific experimentation, a group that is untreated and compared with a treated, or experimental, group.

Control rods Special rods containing neutron-absorbing materials. Inserted into a reactor core to control the rate of fission or to shut down fission reactions.

Convergent evolution The independent evolution of similar traits among unrelated organisms resulting from similar selective pressures.

Cosmic radiation High-energy electromagnetic radiation similar to cosmic rays but originating from periodic solar flare-ups. Possesses extraordinary ability to penetrate materials, including cement walls.

Cost–benefit analysis Way of determining the economic, social, and environmental costs and benefits of a proposed action such as construction of a dam or highway. Still a crude analytical tool because of the difficulty of measuring environmental costs.

Critical population size Population level below which a species cannot successfully reproduce.

Crop rotation Alternating crops in fields to help restore soil fertility and also control pests.

Cross-media contamination The movement of pollution from one medium, such as air, to another, such as water.

Crude birth rate Number of births per 1000 people in a population at the midpoint of the year.

Crude death rate Number of deaths per 1000 people in a population at midyear.

Cultural control (of pests) Techniques to control pest populations not involving chemical pesticides, environmental controls, or genetic controls. Examples: cultivation to control weeds and manual removal of insects from crops.

Cultural eutrophication *Eutrophication* (see definition) due largely to human activities.

Daughter nuclei Atomic nuclei that are produced during fission of uranium.

DDT An organochlorine insecticide used first to control malaria-carrying mosquitos and lice and later to control a variety of insect pests, but now banned in the United States because of its persistence in the environment and its ability to bioaccumulate. Dichlorodiphenyltrichloroethane.

Decibel (dB) A unit to measure the loudness of sound.

Decomposer Also microconsumer. An organism that breaks down nonliving organic material. Examples: bacteria and fungi.

Decomposer food chain A specific nutrient and energy pathway in an ecosystem in which decomposer organisms (bacteria and fungi) consume dead plants and animals as well as animal wastes. Essential for the return of nutrients to soil and carbon dioxide to the atmosphere. Also called detritus food chain.

Deforestation Destruction of forests by clear-cutting.

Demographic transition A phenomenon witnessed in populations of industrializing nations. As industrialization proceeds and wealth accumulates, crude birth rate and crude death rate decline, resulting in zero or low population growth. Decline in death rate usually precedes the decline in birth rate, producing a period of rapid growth before stabilization.

Demography The science of population.

Desert Biome located throughout the world. Often found on the downwind side of mountain ranges. Characterized by low humidity, high summertime temperatures, and plants and animals especially adapted to lack of water.

Desertification The formation of desert in arid and semiarid regions from overgrazing, deforestation, poor agricultural practices, and climate change. Found today in Africa, the Middle East, and the southwestern United States.

Detoxification Rendering a substance harmless by reacting it with another chemical, chemically modifying it, or destroying the molecule through combustion or thermal decomposition.

Detritus Any organic waste from plants and animals.

Detritus feeders Organisms in the decomposer food chain that feed primarily on organic waste (detritus), such as fallen leaves.

Detritus food chain See *decomposer food chain*.

Deuterium An isotope of hydrogen whose nucleus contains one proton and one neutron (a hydrogen atom has only one proton).

Developed country A convenient term that describes industrialized nations, generally characterized by high standard of living, low population growth rate, low infant mortality, excessive material consumption, high per capita energy consumption, high per capita income, urban population, and low illiteracy.

Developing country Same as *less developed country*.

Dioxin A large group of highly toxic, carcinogenic compounds containing some herbicides (2,4-D and 2,4,5-T) and Agent Orange. Once disposed of by mixing with waste crankcase oil that was spread on dirt roads to control dust.

Diversity A measure of the number of different species in an ecosystem.

DNA (deoxyribonucleic acid) A long-chained organic molecule that is found in chromosomes and carries the genetic information that controls cellular function and is the basis of heredity.

Dose–response curve Graphical representation of the effects of varying doses of chemical or physical agents.

Doubling time The length of time it takes some measured entity (population) to double in size at a given growth rate.

Ecological backlashes Ecological effects of seemingly harmless activities—for example, the *greenhouse effect*.

Ecological equivalents Organisms that occupy similar ecological niches in different regions of the world.

Ecological niche See *niche*.

Ecological system See *ecosystem*.

Ecology Study of living organisms and their relationships to one another and the environment.

Economic depletion Reduction in the supply of a resource to the point at which it is no longer economically feasible to continue mining, extracting, or harvesting it.

Economic externality A cost (environmental damage, illness) of manufacturing, road building, or other action that is not taken into account when determing the total cost of production or construction. A cost generally passed on to the general public and taxpayers; external cost.

Ecosphere See *biosphere*.

Ecosystem Short for ecological system. A community of organisms occupying a given region within a biome. Also, the physical and chemical environment of that community and all the interactions between organisms and between organisms and their environment.

Ecosystem stability Dynamic equilibrium of the ecosystem. Also a characteristic of ecosystems causing them to return to their previous state (resilience) and their resistance to change (inertia).

Ecotone Transition zone between adjacent ecosystems.

Element A substance, such as oxygen, gold, and carbon, that is distinguished from all other elements by the number of protons in its atomic nucleus. The atoms of an element cannot be decomposed by chemical means.

Emigration Movement of people out of a country to establish residence elsewhere.

Emissions offset policy Strategy to control air pollution in areas meeting federal ambient air quality standards, whereby new factories must secure emissions reductions from existing factories to begin operation; thus the overall pollution level does not increase.

Emissions standard The maximum amount of a pollutant permitted to be released from a *point source* (see definition).

Emphysema A progressive, debilitating lung disease caused by smoking and pollution at work and in the environment. Characterized by gradual breakdown of the *alveoli* (see definition) and difficulty in catching one's breath.

Endangered species A plant, animal, or microorganism that is in immediate danger of biological extinction. See *threatened* and *rare species*.

Energy The capacity to do work. Found in many forms, including heat, light, sound, electricity, coal, oil, and gasoline.

Energy pyramid See *pyramid of energy*.

Energy quality The amount of useful work acquired from a given form of energy. High-quality energy forms are concentrated (e.g., oil and coal); low-quality energy forms are less concentrated (e.g., solar heat).

Energy system The complete production–consumption process for energy resources, including exploration, mining, refining, transportation, and waste disposal.

Entropy A measure of disorder. The second law of thermodynamics applied to matter says that all systems proceed to maximum disorder (maximum entropy).

Environment All the biological and nonbiological factors that affect an organism's life.

Environmental control (of pests) Methods designed to alter the abiotic and biotic environment of pests, making it inhospitable or intolerable. Examples include increasing crop diversity, altering time of planting, and altering soil nutrient levels.

Environmental impact statement (EIS or ES) Document prepared primarily to outline potential impacts of projects supported in part or in their entirety by federal funds.

Environmental phase (of the nutrient cycle) Part of the nutrient or biogeochemical cycle in which the nutrient is deposited or cycles through the environment (air, water, and soil).

Environmental resistance Abiotic and biotic factors that can potentially reduce population size.

Environmental science The interdisciplinary study of the complex and interconnected issues of population, resources, and pollution.

Epilimnion Upper, warm waters of a lake. Contrast with *hypolimnion*.

Estuarine zones *Coastal wetlands* and *estuaries*.

Estuary Coastal regions such as inlets or mouths of rivers where salt and fresh water mix.

Ethanol Grain alcohol, or ethyl alcohol, produced by fermentation of organic matter. Can be used as a fuel for a variety of vehicles and as a chemical feedstock.

Eukaryotes The first aerobic cells complete with nuclei and energy-releasing organelles.

Eutrophication Accumulation of nutrients in a lake or pond due to human intervention (cultural eutrophication) or natural causes (natural eutrophication). Contributes to process of *succession* (see definition).

Evapotranspiration Evaporation of water from soil and transpiration of water from plants.

Evolution A long-term process of change in organisms caused by random genetic changes that favor the survival and reproduction of the organism possessing the genetic change. Through evolution, organisms become better adapted to their environment.

Exclusion principle Ecological law holding that no two species can occupy the exact same *niche*.

Experimental group In scientific experimentation, a group that is treated and compared with an untreated, or control, group.

Exponential curve See *J curve*.

Exponential growth Increase in any measurable thing by a fixed percentage. When plotted on graph paper, it forms a J-shaped curve.

Externality A spillover effect that benefits or harms others. The source of the effect (say, pollution) does not pay for the effect.

Extinction See *biological extinction*.

Fallout Radioactive materials produced during an atomic detonation and later deposited from the air.

Fall overturn Annual cycle in deep lakes in temperate climates, in which the warm surface water and cool subsurface water mix.

Family planning Process by which couples determine the number and spacing of children.

Feedlot Fenced area where cattle are raised in close confinement to minimize energy loss and maximize weight gain.

First-generation pesticides Earliest known chemical pesticides such as ashes, sulfur, ground tobacco, and hydrogen cyanide. Contrast with *second-* and *third-generation pesticides*.

First-law efficiency A measure of the efficiency of energy use. Total amount of useful work derived from a system divided by the total amount of energy put into a system.

First law of thermodynamics Also called the law of conservation of energy. States that energy is neither created nor destroyed; it can only be transformed from one form to another.

Fission Splitting of atomic nuclei when they are struck by neutrons or other subatomic particles.

Fission fragments See *daughter nuclei*.

Floodplain Low-lying region along river or stream, periodically subject to natural flooding. Common site for human habitation and farming.

Fluorocarbons Organic molecules consisting of chlorine and fluorine covalently bonded to carbon. CCl_3F (Freon-11) and CCl_2F_2 (Freon-12). Used as spray-can propellants and coolants. Previously thought to be inert, but now known to destroy the stratospheric ozone layer. Also called chlorofluoromethanes and freon gases.

Fly ash Mineral matter escaping with smokestack gases from combustion of coal.

Food chain A specific nutrient and energy pathway in ecosystems proceeding from producer to consumer. Part of a bigger network called the food web. See *decomposer food chain* and *grazer food chain*.

Food web Complex intermeshing of individual food chains in an ecosystem.

Foreign species See *alien species*.

Fossil fuel Any one of the organic fuels (coal, natural gas, oil, tar sands, and oil shale) derived from once-living plants or animals.

Freons See *fluorocarbons*.

Frontier mentality A mind-set that views humans as "above" all other forms of life rather than as an integral part of nature and sees the world as an unlimited supply of resources for human use regardless of the impacts on other species. Implicit in this view are the notions that bigger is better, continued material wealth will improve life, and nature must be subdued.

Fuel rods Rods packed with small pellets of radioactive fuel (usually a mixture of fissionable uranium-235 and uranium-238) for use in fission reactors.

Gaia hypothesis Term coined by James Lovelock to describe the earth's capacity to maintain the physical and chemical conditions necessary for life.

Galaxy Grouping of billions of *stars*, gas, and dust, such as the Milky Way Galaxy.

Gamma rays A high-energy form of radiation given off by certain *radionuclides*. Can easily penetrate the skin and damage cells.

Gasohol Liquid fuel for vehicles, containing nine parts gasoline and one part ethanol.

Gene Segment of the DNA that either codes for proteins produced by the cell (structural gene) or regulates structural genes.

Gene pool Sum total of all the genes and their alternate forms in a population.

Generalists Organisms that have a broad *niche*, usually feeding on a variety of food materials and sometimes adapted to a large number of habitats.

Genetic control (of pests) Development of plants and animals genetically resistant to pests through breeding programs and genetic engineering. Also, introduction of sterilized males of pest species (see *sterile-male technique*).

Genetic engineering Isolation and production of genes that are then inserted in bacteria or other organisms. Can be used to produce insulin and other hormones. May someday also be used to treat genetic diseases.

Geopressurized zone Aquifer containing superheated, pressurized water and steam trapped by impermeable rock strata and heated by underlying magma.

Geothermal energy Energy derived from the earth's heat that comes from decay of naturally occurring radioactive materials in the earth's crust, magma, and friction caused by movement of tectonic plates.

GNP See *gross national product.*

Gradualism Theory of evolution holding that species evolve over long periods. Contrast with *punctuated equilibrium.*

Grasslands Biome found in both temperate and tropical regions and characterized by periodic drought, flat or slightly rolling terrain, and large grazers that feed off the lush grasses.

Gray-air cities Older industrial cities characterized by predominantly sulfur dioxide and particulate pollution. Contrast with *brown-air cities.*

Grazer food chain A specific nutrient and energy pathway starting with plants that are consumed by grazers (herbivores).

Greenhouse effect Mechanism that explains atmospheric heating caused by increasing carbon dioxide. Carbon dioxide is believed to act like the glass in a greenhouse, permitting visible light to penetrate but impeding the escape of infrared radiation, or heat.

Green Revolution Developments in plant genetics in the late '50s and early '60s resulting in high-yield varieties producing three to five times more grain than previous plants but requiring intensive irrigation and fertilizer use.

Gross national product (GNP) Total national output of goods and services valued at market prices, including net exports and private investment.

Gross primary productivity The total amount of sunlight converted into chemical-bond energy by a plant. This measure does not take into account how much energy a plant uses for normal cellular functions. See *net primary productivity.*

Groundwater Water below the earth's surface in the saturated zone.

Habitat The specific region in which an organism lives.

Half-life Time required for one-half of a given amount of radioactive material to decay, producing one-half the original mass. Can also be used to describe the length of residence of chemicals in tissues. Biological half-life refers to the time it takes for one-half of a given amount of a substance to be excreted or catabolized.

Hard path A term coined by Amory Lovins to describe large, centralized energy systems such as coal, oil, or nuclear power, characterized by extensive power distribution, central control, and lack of renewability.

Hazardous waste Any potentially harmful solid, liquid, or gaseous waste product of manufacturing or other human activities.

Herbicide Chemical agent used to control weeds.

Herbivore Heterotrophic organism that feeds exclusively on plants.

Heteroculture Agriculture in which several plant species are grown simultaneously to reduce insect infestation and disease.

Heterotroph An organism that feeds on other organisms such as plants and animals. It cannot make its own foodstuffs.

Hot-rock zones Most widespread geothermal resource. Regions where bedrock is heated by underlying magma.

Humus Mixture of decaying organic matter and inorganic matter that increases soil fertility, aeration, and water retention.

Hunting-and-gathering society People that lived as nomads or in semipermanent sites from the beginning of human evolution until approximately 5000 B.C. Some remnant populations still survive. They gathered seeds, fruits, roots, and other plant products and hunted indigenous species for food.

Hybrid Offspring produced by cross-mating of two different strains or varieties of plants or animals.

Hydrocarbons Organic molecules containing hydrogen and carbon. Released during the incomplete combustion of organic fuels. React with nitrogen oxides and sunlight to form photochemical oxidants in photochemical smog.

Hydroelectric power Electricity produced in turbines powered by running water.

Hydrological cycle The movement of water through the environment from atmosphere to earth and back again. Major events include evaporation and precipitation. Also called the water cycle.

Hydrosphere The watery portion of the planet. Contrast with *atmosphere* and *lithosphere*.

Hydrothermal convection zone Rock strata containing large amounts of water heated by underlying magma and driven to the surface through cracks and fissures in overlying rock layers. Forms hot springs and geysers.

Hypolimnion Deep, cold waters of a lake. Contrast with *epilimnion*.

Hypothesis Tentative explanation for a natural phenomenon.

Immature ecosystem An early successional community characterized by low species diversity and low stability. Contrast with *mature ecosystem*.

Immigration Movement of people into a country to set up residence there.

Indoor air pollution Generally refers to air pollutants in homes from internal sources such as smokers, fireplaces, wood stoves, carpets, paneling, furniture, foam insulation, and cooking stoves.

Induced abortion Surgical procedure to interrupt pregnancy by removing the embryo or fetus from the uterus. In the first trimester, generally carried out by vacuum aspiration. Contrast with *spontaneous abortion*.

Industrial smog Air pollution from industrial cities (gray-air cities), consisting mostly of particulates and sulfur oxides. Contrast with *photochemical smog*.

Industrial society Group of people living in urban or rural environments that are characterized by mechanization of industrial production and agriculture. Widespread machine labor causes high energy demands and pollution. Increasing control over natural processes leads to feelings that humans are apart from nature and superior to it.

Inertia Tendency of an ecosystem to resist change.

Infant mortality rate Number of infants under 1 year of age dying per 1000 births in any given year.

Infectious disease Generally, a disease caused by a virus, bacterium, or parasite that can be transmitted from one organism to another (example: viral hepatitis).

Infrared radiation Heat, an electromagnetic radiation of wavelength outside the red end of the visible spectrum.

Inland wetlands Wet or flooded regions along inland surface waters. Includes marshes, bogs, and river outflow lands. Contrast with *coastal wetlands*.

In-migration Movement of people into a state or region within a country to set up residence.

Inorganic fertilizer Synthetic plant nutrient added to the soil to replace lost nutrients. Major components include nitrogen, phosphorus, and potassium. Also called artificial fertilizer or synthetic fertilizer.

Input approach A method of solving an environmental problem by reducing the inputs. For example, reducing consumption and increasing product durability can cut production of solid wastes, pollution, or hazardous wastes.

Insecticide One form of pesticide used specifically to control insect populations.

Integrated pest management Pest control with minimum risk to humans and the environment through use of a variety of control techniques (including pesticides and biological controls).

Integrated wildlife or species management Control of populations through the use of many techniques, including the reintroduction of natural predators, habitat improvement, reduction in habitat destruction, establishment of preserves, reduced pollution, and captive breeding.

Interspecific competition Competition between members of different species.

Ion A particle formed when an atom loses or gains an electron.

Ionizing radiation Electromagnetic radiation with the capacity to form ions in body tissues and other substances.

Isotopes Atoms of the same element that differ in their atomic weight because of variations in the number of neutrons in their nuclei.

J curve A graphical representation of exponential growth.

Juvenile hormone Chemical substance in insects that stimulates growth through early life stages. Used with some success as an insecticide. When applied to infested fields, JH alters normal growth and development of insect pests, resulting in their death.

Kerogen Solid, insoluble organic material found in oil shale.

Kilowatt One thousand watts. See *watt*.

Kinetic energy The energy of objects in motion.

Kwashiorkor Dietary deficiency caused by insufficient protein intake and common in children one to three years of age in less developed countries. Characterized by growth retardation, wasting of muscles in limbs, and accumulation of fluids in the body, especially in feet, legs, hands, and face.

Lag effect The tendency for a population to continue growing even after it has reached replacement-level fertility. Caused by an expanding number of women reaching reproductive age.

Land use planning Process whereby land uses are matched with the needs of the community and environmental considerations—for example, need for open space and agricultural land and for control of water and air pollution.

Laterite Soil found in some tropical rain forests. Rich in iron and aluminum but generally of poor fertility. Turns bricklike if exposed to sunlight.

Less developed country Term describing the nonindustrialized nations, generally characterized by low standard of living, high population growth rate, high infant mortality, low material consumption, low per capita energy consumption, low per capita income, rural population, and high illiteracy.

Light year Astronomical unit that measures the distance that light can travel in a year.

Light water reactor Most common fission reactor for generating electricity. Water bathes the core of the reactor and is used to generate steam, which turns the turbines that generate electricity. Contrast with *liquid metal fast breeder*.

Limiting factor A chemical or physical factor that determines whether an organism can survive in a given ecosystem. In most ecosystems, rainfall is the limiting factor.

Limnetic zone Open water zone of lakes through which sunlight penetrates; contains algae and other microscopic organisms that feed on dissolved nutrients.

Liquefaction Production of liquid fuel from coal.

Liquid metal fast breeder Fission reactor that uses liquid metals such as sodium as a coolant.

Lithosphere Crust of the earth. Contrast with *hydrosphere* and *atmosphere*.

Littoral drift Movement of beach sand parallel to the shoreline. Caused by waves and longshore currents parallel to the beach.

Littoral zone Shallow waters along a lakeshore where rooted vegetation often grows.

Macronutrient A chemical substance needed by living organisms in large quantities (for example, carbon, oxygen, hydrogen, and nitrogen). Contrast with *micronutrient*.

Magma Molten rock beneath the earth's crust.

Malnourishment A dietary deficiency caused by lack of vital nutrients and vitamins.

Manganese nodules Nodular accumulations of manganese and other minerals such as iron and copper found on the ocean floor at depths of 300 to 6000 meters. Particularly abundant in the Pacific Ocean.

Marasmus A dietary deficiency caused by insufficient intake of protein and calories and occurring primarily in infants under the age of 1, usually as the result of discontinuation of breast feeding.

Mariculture Cultivation of fish and other aquatic organisms in salt water (estuaries and bays).

Mature community A community that remains more or less the same over a long period of time. Climax stage of succession. Also called a climax community.

Mature ecosystem An ecosystem in the climax stage of succession, characterized by high species diversity and high stability. Contrast with *immature ecosystem*.

Measure of economic welfare Proposed standard that takes into account the accumulated wealth of a nation.

Megawatt Measure of electrical power equal to a million watts, or 1000 kilowatts. See *watt*.

Mesothelioma A tumor of the lining of the lung (pleura). Caused by asbestos.

Metalimnion See *thermocline*.

Metastasis Movement of cancer cells to another location where new tumors are formed.

Methyl mercury Water-soluble organic form of mercury formed by bacteria in aquatic ecosystems from inorganic (insoluble) mercury pollution. Able to undergo biological magnification.

Microconsumers Bacteria and single-celled fungi that are part of the decomposer food chain.

Micronutrient An element needed by organisms, but only in small quantities, such as copper, iron, and zinc. Contrast with *macronutrient*.

Migration Movement of people across state and national boundaries to set up new residence. See *immigration, emigration, in-migration,* and *out-migration*.

Mill tailings Residue from uranium processing plants. Spent uranium ore that is contaminated with radioactivity.

Mineral A chemical element (e.g., gold) or inorganic compound (e.g., iron ore) existing naturally.

Minimum tillage Reduced plowing and cultivating of cropland between and during growing seasons to help reduce soil erosion and save energy. Also called conservation tillage.

Molecule Particle consisting of two or more atoms bonded together. The atoms in a molecule can be of the same element but are usually of different elements.

Monoculture Cultivation of one plant species (such as wheat) over a large area. Highly susceptible to disease and insects.

Mutagen A chemical or physical agent capable of damaging the genetic material (DNA and chromosomes) of living organisms in both germ cells and somatic cells.

Mutation In general, any damage to the DNA and chromosomes.

Narrow-spectrum pesticide A chemical agent effective in controlling a small number of pests.

Natural erosion Loss of soil occurring at a slow rate but not caused by human activities. A natural event in all terrestrial ecosystems.

Natural eutrophication See *eutrophication*.

Natural gas Gaseous fuel containing 50%–90% methane and lesser amounts of other burnable organic gases such as propane and butane.

Natural hazards Dangers that result from normal meteorologic, atmospheric, oceanic, biological, and geological phenomena.

Natural resource See *resource*.

Natural selection Process in which slight variations in organisms (adaptations) are preserved if they are useful and help the organism to better respond to its environment.

Negative feedback Control mechanism present in the ecosystem and in all organisms. Information in the form of chemical, physical, and biological agents influences processes, causing them to shut down or reduce their activity.

Net energy See *net useful energy production*.

Net migration Number of immigrants minus the number of emigrants. Can be expressed as a rate by determining immigration and emigration rates.

Net primary productivity Gross primary productivity (the total amount of energy that plants produce) minus the energy plants use during cellular respiration.

Net useful energy production Amount of useful energy extracted from an *energy system*.

Niche Also called an ecological niche. An organism's place in the ecosystem: where it lives, what it consumes, what consumes it, and how it interacts with all biotic and abiotic factors.

Nitrate (NO_3^-) Inorganic anion containing three oxygen atoms and one nitrogen atom linked by covalent bonds.

Nitrite (NO_2^-) Inorganic anion containing two oxygen atoms and one nitrogen atom. Combines with hemoglobin and may cause serious health impairment and death in children.

Nitrogen cycle The cycling of nitrogen between organisms and the environment.

Nitrogen fixation Conversion of atmospheric nitrogen (a gas) into nitrate and ammonium ions (inorganic form), which can be used by plants.

Nitrogen oxides Nitric oxide (NO) and nitrogen dioxide (NO_2), produced during combustion when atmospheric nitrogen (N_2) combines with oxygen. Can be converted into nitric acid (HNO_3). All are harmful to humans and other organisms.

Noise An unwanted or unpleasant sound.

Nonattainment area Region that violates EPA air pollution standards.

Nonpoint source (of pollution) Diffuse source of pollution such as an eroding field, urban and suburban lands, and forests. Contrast with *point source*.

Nonrenewable resource Resource that is not replaced or regenerated naturally within a reasonable period (fossil fuel, mineral).

Nuclear fall Hypothesis suggesting that the effects on the earth's climate of dust and smoke released in nuclear explosions would be more temporary and less severe than predicted by the nuclear winter hypothesis. Contrast with *nuclear winter*.

Nuclear fission Splitting of an atomic nucleus when neutrons strike the nucleus. Products are two or more smaller nuclei, neutrons (which can cause further fission reactions), and an enormous amount of heat and radiation energy.

Nuclear fusion Joining of two small atomic nuclei (such as hydrogen and deuterium) to form a new and larger nucleus (such as helium) accompanied by an enormous release of energy. Source of light and heat from the sun.

Nuclear power (or energy) Energy from the fission or fusion of atomic nuclei.

Nuclear winter Hypothesis suggesting that dust from nuclear explosions and smoke from burning cities would reduce solar radiation, resulting in a dramatic decrease in global temperature. Contrast with *nuclear fall*.

Nutrient cycle Same as *biogeochemical cycle*.

Off-road vehicle (ORV) Any vehicle used cross-country, especially in a recreational capacity (four-wheel-drive vehicles, dune buggies, all-terrain vehicles, snowmobiles, and trail bikes).

Oil See *petroleum*.

Oil shale A fine-grained sedimentary rock called marlstone and containing an organic substance known as kerogen. When heated, it gives off shale oil, which is much like crude oil.

Omnivore An organism that eats both plants and animals.

Open system A system that freely exchanges energy and matter with the environment. Example: any living organism. Contrast with *closed system*.

Opportunity costs Costs of lost money-making opportunities (and potentially higher income) incurred when we make a decision to invest our money in a particular way.

Ore Rock bearing important minerals—for example, uranium ore.

Ore deposit A valuable mineral located in high concentration in a given region.

Organic farming Agricultural system in which natural fertilizers (manure and crop residues), crop rotation, contour planting, biological insect control measures, and other techniques are used to ensure soil fertility, erosion control, and pest control.

Organic fertilizer Material such as plant and animal wastes added to cropland and pastures to improve soil. Provides valuable soil nutrients and increases the organic content of soil (thus increasing moisture content).

Organismic phase The part of the nutrient cycle in which nutrients are located in organisms—plants, animals, bacteria, fungi, or others.

Out-migration Movement of people out of a state or region within a country to set up residence elsewhere in that country.

Output approach A method of solving an environmental problem by controlling the outputs. For example, composting or burning trash reduces the land requirements for solid waste disposal. Control devices reduce air and water pollution.

Overgrazing Excessive consumption of producer organisms (plants) by grazers such as deer, rabbits, and domestic livestock. Indication that the ecosystem is out of balance.

Overpopulation A condition resulting when the number of organisms in an ecosystem exceeds its ability to assimilate wastes and provide resources. Creates physical and mental stress on a species as a result of competition for limited resources and deterioration of the environment.

Oxidants Oxidizing chemicals (for example, ozone) found in the atmosphere.

Oxygen-demanding wastes Organic wastes that are broken down in water by aerobic bacteria. Aerobic breakdown causes the oxygen levels to drop.

Ozone (O_3) Inorganic molecule found in the atmosphere, where it is a pollutant because of its harmful effects on living tissue and rubber. Also found in the stratosphere, where it helps screen ultraviolet light. Used in some advanced sewage treatment plants.

Ozone layer Thin layer of ozone molecules in the stratosphere. Absorbs ultraviolet light and converts it to infrared radiation. Effectively screens out 99% of the ultraviolet light.

Paradigm A major theoretical construct that is central to a field of study. For example, the theory of evolution and the structure of DNA are two paradigms that are central to biological science.

Particulates Solid particles (dust, pollen, soot) or water droplets in the atmosphere.

Passive solar Capture and retention of the sun's energy within a building through south-facing windows and some form of heat storage in the building (brick or cement floors and walls). Contrast with *active solar.*

PCBs See *polychlorinated biphenyls.*

Perennial A plant that grows from the same root structure year after year (for example, rose bushes).

Permafrost Permanently frozen ground found in the tundra.

Permanent threshold shift Loss of hearing after continued exposure to noise. Contrast with *temporary threshold shift.*

Pesticide A general term referring to a chemical, physical, or biological agent that kills organisms we classify as pests, such as insects and rodents. Also called biocide.

Petroleum A viscous liquid containing numerous burnable hydrocarbons. Distilled into a variety of useful fuels (fuel oil, gasoline, and diesel) and petrochemicals (chemicals that can be used as a chemical feedstock for the production of drugs, plastics, and other substances).

pH Measure of acidity on a scale from 0 to 14, with pH 7 being neutral, numbers greater than 7 being basic, and number less than 7 being acidic.

Pheromone Chemical substance given off by insects and other species. Sex-attractant pheromones released into the atmosphere in small quantity by female insects attract males at breeding time. Can be used in pest control. See *pheromone traps* and *confusion technique.*

Pheromone traps Traps containing pheromones to attract insect pests and pesticide to kill pests or a sticky substance to immobilize them. These traps may be used to pinpoint the emergence of insects, allowing conventional pesticides to be used in moderation.

Photochemical oxidants Ozone and a variety of oxygenated organic compounds produced when sunlight, hydrocarbons, and nitrogen oxides react in the atmosphere.

Photochemical reaction A chemical reaction that occurs in the atmosphere involving sunlight or heat, pollutants, and sometimes natural atmospheric chemicals.

Photochemical smog A complex mixture of *photochemical oxidants* and nitrogen oxides. Usually has a brownish-orange color.

Photosynthesis A two-part process involving (1) the capture of sunlight and its conversion into cellular energy and (2) the production of organic molecules such as glucose and amino acids from carbon dioxide, water, and energy from the sun.

Photovoltaic cell Thin wafer of silicon or other material that emits electrons when struck by sunlight, thus generating an electrical current. Also solar cell.

Pioneer community The first community to become established in a once-lifeless environment during *primary succession.*

Pitch (or frequency) Measure of the frequency of a sound in cycles per second (hertz, Hz)—compressional sound waves passing a given point per second. The higher the cps, the higher the pitch.

Pneumoconiosis (black lung) A debilitating lung disease caused by prolonged inhalation of coal and other mineral dusts. Results in a decreased elasticity and gradual breakdown of alveoli in the lungs. Eventually leads to death.

Point source (of pollution) Easily discernible source of pollution such as a factory. Contrast with *nonpoint source.*

Pollution Any physical, chemical, or biological alteration of air, water, or land that is harmful to living organisms.

Polychlorinated biphenyls (PCBs) Group of at least 50 organic compounds, used for many years as insulation in electrical equipment. Capable of biological magnification. Disrupts reproduction in gulls and possibly other organisms high on the food chain.

Population A group of organisms of the same species living within a specified region.

Population control In human populations, all methods of reducing birth rate, primarily through pregnancy prevention and abortion. In an ecological sense, regulation of population size by a myriad of abiotic and biotic factors.

Population crash (dieback) Sudden decrease in population that results when an organism exceeds the carrying capacity of its environment.

Population growth rate Rate at which a population increases on a yearly basis, expressed as a percentage. For world population: GR = (crude birth rate − crude death rate) × 100. For a given country, population growth rate must also take into account the net migration rate.

Population histogram Graphical representation of population by age and sex.

Positive feedback Control mechanism in ecosystems and organisms in which information influences some process, causing it to increase.

Potential energy Stored energy.

Predator An organism that actively hunts its prey.

Presbycusis Loss of hearing with age through natural deterioration of the organ of Corti, the sound receptor in the ear. Contrast with *sociocusis.*

Prey Organism (e.g., deer) attacked and killed by predator.

Primary air pollutant A pollutant that has not undergone any chemical transformation; emitted by either a natural or an anthropogenic source.

Primary consumer First consuming organism in a given food chain. A grazer in grazer food chains or a decomposer organism or insect in decomposer food chains. Belongs to the second trophic level.

Primary succession The sequential development of biotic communities where none previously existed.

Primary treatment (of sewage) First step in sewage treatment to remove large solid objects by screens (filters) and sediment and organic matter in settling chambers. See *secondary* and *tertiary treatment.*

Proactive government One that is concerned with long-range problems and lasting solutions. Contrast with *reactive government.*

Producer (autotroph or producer organism) One of the organisms that produces the organic matter cycling through the ecosystem. Producers include plants and photosynthetic algae.

Productivity The rate of conversion of sunlight by plants into chemical-bond energy (covalent bonds in organic molecules). See *gross* and *net primary productivity*.

Profundal zone Deeper lake water, into which sunlight does not penetrate. Below the *limnetic zone*.

Prospective law One designed to address future problems and generate long-lasting solutions. Contrast with *retrospective law*.

Punctuated equilibrium A theory of evolution stating that species are fairly stable for long periods and that new species evolve rapidly over short periods of thousands of years that punctuate the equilibrium. Contrast with *gradualism*.

Pyramid of biomass Graphical representation of the amount of biomass (organic matter) at each trophic level in an ecosystem.

Pyramid of numbers Graphical representation of the number of organisms of different species at each trophic level in an ecosystem.

Quad One quadrillion (10^{15}) BTUs of heat.

Rad (radiation absorbed dose) Measure of the amount of energy deposited in a tissue or some other medium struck by radiation. One rad = 100 ergs of energy deposited in one gram of tissue.

Radioactive waste Any solid or liquid waste material containing radioactivity. Produced by research labs, hospitals, nuclear weapons factories, and fission reactors.

Radioactivity Radiation released from unstable nuclei. See *alpha* and *beta particles* and *gamma rays*.

Radionuclides Radioactive forms (isotopes) of elements.

Rain shadow Arid downwind (leeward) side of mountain range.

Rangeland Grazing land for cattle, sheep, and other domestic livestock.

Range of tolerance Range of physical and chemical factors in which an organism can survive. When the upper or lower limits of this range are exceeded, growth, reproduction, and survival are threatened.

Reactive government A government that lives and acts for today, addressing present-day problems as they arise. Shows little or no concern for long-term issues and solutions. Contrast with *proactive government*.

Reactor core Assemblage of fuel rods and control rods inside a reactor vessel. Bathed by water to help control the rate of fission and absorb the heat.

Real price (or cost) The price of a commodity or service in fixed dollars—that is, the value of a dollar at an earlier time. Helpful way to determine whether a resource has experienced a real increase in cost or whether higher costs are simply due to inflation.

Reclamation As used here, the process of returning land to its prior use. Common usage: to convert deserts and other areas into habitable, productive land.

Recycling A strategy to reduce resource use by returning used or waste materials from the consumption phase to the production phase of the economy.

Reduction factors Abiotic and biotic factors that tend to decrease population growth and help balance populations and ecosystems, offsetting growth factors.

Relative humidity The amount of moisture in a given quantity of air divided by the amount the air could hold at that temperature. Expressed as a percentage.

Rem (roentgen equivalent man) Measure that accounts for the damage done by a given type of radiation. One *rad* = one rem for X rays, gamma rays, and beta particles, but one rad = 10 to 20 rems for alpha particles, because they do more damage.

Renewable resource A resource replaced by natural ecological cycles (water, plants, animals) or natural chemical or physical processes (sunlight, wind).

Replacement-level fertility Number of children a couple must have to replace themselves in the population.

Reproductive age Age during which most women bear their offspring (ages 14–44).

Reproductive isolation Any of many mechanisms that prevent species from interbreeding or producing viable offspring.

Reserve Deposit of energy or minerals that is economically and geologically feasible to remove with current and foreseeable technology.

Residence time Length of time a chemical spends in the environment.

Resilience Ability of an ecosystem to return to normal after a disturbance.

Resource (in general) Anything used by organisms to meet their needs, including air, water, minerals, plants, fuels, and animals.

Resource (as a measurement of a mineral or fuel) Total amount of a mineral or fuel on earth. Generally, only a small fraction can be recovered. Compare with *reserve*.

Retorting Process of removing kerogen from oil shale, usually by burning or heating the shale. Can be carried out in surface vessels (surface retorting) or underground in fractured shale (*in situ* retorting).

Retrospective law One that attempts to solve a problem without giving much attention to potential future problems. Contrast with *prospective law*.

Reverse osmosis Means of purifying water for pollution control and desalination. Water is forced through porous membranes; pores allow passage of water molecules but not impurities.

Risk acceptability A measure of how acceptable a hazard is to a population.

Risk assessment The science of determining what hazards a society is exposed to from natural and human causes and the probability and severity of those risks.

Risk probability The likelihood a hazardous event will occur.

Risk severity A measure of the total damage a hazardous event would cause.

Salinization Deposition of salts in irrigated soils, making soil unfit for most crops. Caused by rising water table due to inadequate drainage of irrigated soils.

Saltwater intrusion Movement of salt water from oceans or saltwater aquifers into freshwater aquifers, caused by depletion of the freshwater aquifers or low precipitation or both.

Sanitary landfill Solid waste disposal site where garbage is dumped and covered daily with a layer of dirt to reduce odors, insects, and rats.

Scrubber Pollution control device that removes particulates and sulfur oxides from smokestacks by passing exhaust gases through fine spray of water containing lime.

Secondary consumer Second consuming organism in food chain. Belongs to the third trophic level.

Secondary pollutant A chemical pollutant from a natural or anthropogenic source that undergoes chemical change as a result of reacting with another pollutant, sunlight, atmospheric moisture, or some other environmental agent.

Secondary succession The sequential development of biotic communities occuring after the complete or partial destruction of an existing community by natural or anthropogenic forces.

Secondary treatment (of sewage) After *primary treatment*, removal of biodegradable organic matter from sewage using bacteria and other microconsumers in activated sludge or trickle filters. Also removes some of the phosphorus (30%) and nitrate (50%). See also *tertiary treatment*.

Second-generation pesticides Synthetic organic chemicals such as DDT that replaced older pesticides such as sulfur, ground tobacco, and ashes. Generally resistant to bacterial breakdown.

Second-law efficiency Measure of the efficiency of energy use, taking into account the unavoidable loss (described by the second law of thermodynamics) of energy during energy conversions. Calculated by dividing the minimum amount of energy required to perform a task by the actual amount used.

Second law of thermodynamics States that when energy is converted from one form to another, it is degraded; that is, it is converted from a concentrated to a less concentrated form. The amount of useful energy decreases during such conversions.

Secured landfill One lined by clay and synthetic liners in an effort to prevent leakage.

Sediment Soil particles, sand, and other mineral matter eroded from land and carried in surface waters.

Selective advantage An advantage one member of a species has over others by virtue of some adaptation it has acquired.

Selective cutting Restricted removal of trees. Especially useful for mixed hardwood stands. Contrast with *clear-cutting* and *shelter-wood cutting*.

Sewage treatment plant Facility where human solid and liquid wastes from homes, hospitals, and industries are treated, primarily to remove organic matter, nitrates, and phosphates.

Shale oil Thick, heavy oil formed when shale is heated (retorted). Can be refined to produce fuel oil, kerosene, diesel fuel, and other petroleum products and petrochemicals.

Shelterbelts Rows of trees and shrubs planted alongside fields to reduce wind erosion and retain snow to increase soil mois-

ture. May also be used to reduce heat loss from wind and thus conserve energy around homes and farms.

Shelter-wood cutting Three-step process spread out over years: (1) removal of poor-quality trees to improve growth of commercially valuable trees and allow new seedlings to become established, (2) removal of commercially valuable trees once seedlings are established, and (3) cutting remaining mature trees grown from seedlings.

Sigmoidal curve An S-shaped curve.

Simplified ecosystem One with lowered species diversity, usually as a result of human intervention.

Sinkhole Hole created by sudden collapse of the earth's surface due to groundwater overdraft. A form of subsidence.

Slash-and-burn agriculture Farming practice in which small plots are cleared of vegetation by cutting and burning. Crops are grown until the soil is depleted; then the land is abandoned. This allows the natural vegetation and soil to recover. Common practice of early agricultural societies living in the tropics.

Sludge Solid organic material produced during sewage treatment.

Smelter A factory where ores are melted to separate impurities from the valuable minerals.

Smog Originally referred to a grayish haze (combination of smoke and fog) found in industrial cities. Also pertains to pollution called photochemical smog, found in newer cities. See *industrial smog*.

Social Darwinism The application (or misapplication) of the theory of evolution to social behavior.

Sociocusis Hearing loss from human activities. Contrast with *presbycusis*.

Soft path A term coined by Amory Lovins to describe such practices as conservation, efficient use of energy, and renewable energy systems such as solar and wind. Characterized by high labor intensity, decentralized energy production, and small-scale technology. Contrast with *hard path*.

Soil horizons Layers found in most soils.

Solar collector Device to absorb sunlight and convert it into heat.

Solar energy Energy derived from the sun (heat) and natural phenomena driven by the sun (wind, biomass, running water).

Solar system Group of planets revolving around a star.

Sonic boom A high-energy wake creating an explosive boom that trails after jets traveling faster than the speed of sound.

Spaceship earth Metaphor introduced in the 1960s to foster a better appreciation of the finite nature of earth's resources and the ecological cycles that replenish oxygen and other important nutrients.

Specialist Organism that has a narrow niche, usually feeding on one or a few food materials and adapted to a particular habitat.

Speciation Formation of new species.

Species A group of plants, animals, or microorganisms that have a high degree of similarity and generally can interbreed only among themselves.

Species diversity Measure of the number of different species in a biological community.

Spontaneous abortion Loss of an embryo or fetus from the uterus not caused by surgery. Generally the result of chromosomal abnormalities. Contrast with *induced abortion.*

Spring overturn Annual cycle in deep lakes in temperate climates in which surface and subsurface waters mix.

SST (supersonic transport) Jet that travels faster than the speed of sound.

Stable runoff Amount of *surface runoff* that can be counted on from year to year.

Star Spherical cloud of hot gas, such as the sun, fueled by *nuclear* fusion reactions in its core.

Statutory law Law enacted by Congress or a state legislature. Contrast with *common law.*

Steady-state economy Economic system characterized by relatively constant GNP, dedication to essential goods and services, and maximum reliance on recycling, conservation, and use of renewable resources. Also spaceship, or sustainable, economy.

Sterile-male technique Pest control strategy whereby males of the pest species are grown in captivity, sterilized, then released en masse in infested areas at breeding time. Sterile males far exceed normal wild males and mate with normal females, resulting in infertile matings and control of the pest.

Sterilization A highly successful procedure in males and females to prevent pregnancy. In males the ducts (vas deferens) that carry sperm from the testicles are cut and tied (vasectomy); in females the Fallopian tubes, or oviducts, which transport ova from the ovary to the uterus, are cut and tied (tubal ligation). Sterilization is not to be confused with castration in males (complete removal of the gonads).

Stratosphere Outer region of the earth's atmosphere, found outside the troposphere, extending 7 to 25 miles above the earth's surface. Outermost layer of the stratosphere contains the ozone layer.

Streambed aggradation Deposition of sediment in streams or rivers, thereby reducing their water-carrying capacity.

Streambed channelization An ecologically unsound way of reducing flooding by deepening and straightening of streams, accompanied by removal of trees and other vegetation along the banks.

Strip cropping Soil conservation technique in which alternating crop varieties are planted in huge strips across fields to reduce wind and water erosion of soil.

Subsidence Sinking of land caused by collapse of underground mines or depletion of groundwater.

Succession The natural replacement of one biotic community by another. See *primary* and *secondary succession.*

Sulfur dioxide (SO₂) Colorless gas produced during combustion of fossil fuels contaminated with organic and inorganic sulfur compounds. Can be converted into sulfuric acid in the atmosphere.

Sulfur oxides (SOₓ) Sulfur dioxide and sulfur trioxide, common air pollutants arising from combustion of coal, oil, gasoline, and diesel fuel. Also produced by natural sources such as bacterial decay and hot springs. Sulfur dioxide reacts with oxygen to form sulfur trioxide, which may react with water to form sulfuric acid.

Supply and demand theory Economic theory explaining the price of goods and services. The supply of and demand for goods and services are primary price determinants. High demand diminishes supply, creating competition for existing goods and services, thus driving up prices.

Surface mining Any of several mining techniques in which all the dirt and rock overlying a desirable mineral (coal, for example) are first removed, exposing the mineral.

Surface runoff Water flowing in streams and over the ground during rainstorm or snowmelt.

Sustainable ethics (mentality) A mind-set that views humans as a part of nature and earth as a limited supply of resources, which must be carefully managed to prevent irreparable damage. Obligations to future generations require us to exercise restraint to ensure adequate resources and a clean and healthy environment.

Sustainable society One based on sustainable ethics. Lives within the limits imposed by nature. Based on maximum use of renewable resources, recycling, conservation, and population control.

Sustained yield concept Use of renewable natural resources, such as forests and grassland, that will not cause their destruction and will ensure continued use.

Sympatric speciation Formation of new species without geographical isolation. Common in plants.

Synergism The acting of two or more agents (often toxins) together to produce an effect larger than expected based on knowledge of the effect of each alone.

Synfuel See *synthetic fuel.*

Synthetic fertilizer Same as *inorganic fertilizer.*

Synthetic fuel Gaseous or liquid organic fuel derived from coal, oil shale, or tar sands.

Taiga Biome found south of the tundra across North America, Europe, and Asia, characterized by coniferous forests, soil that thaws during the summer months, abundant precipitation, and high species diversity.

Tar sands Also known as oil sands or bituminous sands. Sand impregnated with a viscous, petroleumlike substance, bitumen, which can be driven off by heat, producing a synthetic oil.

Technological fix A purely technological answer to a problem. Also called a technical fix.

Tectonic plates Huge segments of the earth's crust that often contain entire continents or parts of them and that float on an underlying semiliquid layer.

Temperate deciduous forest Biome located in the eastern United States, Europe, and northeastern China below the taiga. Characterized by deciduous and nondeciduous trees, warm growing season, abundant rainfall, and a rich species diversity.

Temperature inversion Alteration in the normal atmospheric temperature profile so that air temperature increases with altitude rather than decreases.

Temporary threshold shift Momentary dulling of the sense of hearing after exposure to loud sounds. Can lead to *permanent threshold shift.*

Teratogen A chemical or physical agent capable of causing birth defects.

Terracing Construction of small earthen embankments on hilly or mountainous terrain to reduce the velocity of water flowing across the soil and reduce soil erosion.

Tertiary treatment (of sewage) Removal of nitrates, phosphates, chlorinated compounds, salts, acids, metals, and toxic organics after *secondary treatment.*

Thermal pollution Heat added to air or water that adversely affects living organisms and may alter climate.

Thermocline Sharp transition between upper, warm waters (epilimnion) and deeper, cold waters (hypolimnion) of a lake. Also called metalimnion.

Thermodynamics The study of energy conversions. See the *first* and *second laws of thermodynamics.*

Third-generation pesticides Newer chemical agents to control pests, such as pheromones and insect hormones.

Threshold level A level of exposure below which no effect is observed or measured.

Throughput approach A method of solving an environmental problem by recycling and reuse. For example, recycling or reusing hazardous wastes reduces their output.

Time preference A measure of the value of an immediate gain in comparison with a long-term gain.

Total fertility rate Average number of children that would be born alive to a woman if she were to pass through all her childbearing years conforming to the age-specific fertility rates of a given year.

Toxin A chemical, physical, or biological agent that causes disease or some alteration of the normal structure and function of an organism. Impairments may be slight or severe. Onset of effects may be immediate or delayed.

Transpiration Escape of water from plants through pores (stomata) in the leaves.

Tree farms Private forests devoted to maximum timber growth and relying heavily on herbicides, insecticides, and fertilizers.

Tritium (hydrogen-3) Radioactive isotope of hydrogen whose nucleus contains two neutrons and one proton. Can be used in fusion reactors.

Trophic level Describes the position of the organism in the food chain.

Tropical rain forest Lush forests near the equator with high annual rainfall, high average temperature, and notoriously nutrient-poor soil. Possibly the richest ecosystem on earth.

Tundra (alpine) Life zone found on mountaintops. Closely resembles the *arctic tundra* in terms of precipitation, temperature, growing season, plants, and animals. Extraordinarily fragile.

Tundra (arctic) First major life zone or biome south of the North Pole. Vast region on far northern borders of North America, Europe, and Asia. Characterized by lack of trees, low precipitation, and low temperatures.

Ultimate production Total amount of a nonrenewable resource that could ultimately be extracted at a reasonable price.

Ultraviolet (UV) light or radiation Electromagnetic radiation from sun and special lamps. Causes sunburn and mutations in bacteria and other living cells.

Undernourishment A lack of calories in the diet. Contrast with *malnourishment.*

Variation Genetically based differences in behavior, structure, or function in a population.

Water cycle See *hydrological cycle.*

Waterlogging High water table causing saturation of soils due to poor soil drainage and irrigation. Decreases soil oxygen and kills plants.

Watershed Land area drained by a given stream or river.

Water table Top of the zone of saturation.

Watt Unit of power indicating rate at which electrical work is being performed.

Wave power Energy derived from sea waves.

Wet cooling tower Device used for cooling water from power plants. Hot water flows through rising air, which draws off heat. Cool water is then returned to the system.

Wetlands Land areas along fresh water (*inland wetlands*) and salt water (*coastal wetlands*) that are flooded all or part of the time.

Wilderness An area where the biological community is relatively undisturbed by humans. Seen by developers as an untapped supply of resources such as timber and minerals, seen by environmentalists as a haven for escape from hectic urban life, an area for reflection and solitude.

Wilderness area An area established by the U.S. Congress under the Wilderness Act (1964) where timber cutting and use of motorized vehicles are prohibited. Most are located in national forests.

Wind energy Energy captured from the wind to generate electricity or pump water. An indirect form of solar energy.

Wind generators Windmills that produce electrical energy.

Zero population growth A condition in which population is not increasing; the *population growth rate* is zero.

Photo and Text Credits

Part I Opener   Ric Ergenbright

Chapter 1 Figures

1-1   NASA
1-2   Cleveland Public Library
       Newspaper Enterprise Assoc.
1-3   © Pam Hujanen/Video
       Dimensions
1-4   From Meadows et al. DYNAM-
       ICS OF GROWTH IN A FINITE
       WORLD. © 1974, Wright-Allen
       Press, Cambridge, MA.

Chapter 2 Figures

2-4   From D. Goldsmith. THE
       EVOLVING UNIVERSE, Second
       Edition. © 1985, The Benja-
       min/Cummings Publishing
       Company, Inc., Menlo Park,
       California. Used with
       permission.
2-5   Lick Observatory
2-6   From D. Goldsmith. THE
       EVOLVING UNIVERSE, Second
       Edition.
2-7   © 1985, The Benjamin/Cum-
       mings Publishing Company,
       Inc., Menlo Park, California.
       Used with permission.
2-9   Hale L. Wedberg, San Diego
       State University
2-10   E. S. Barghoon, SCIENCE
       1977; 198: 396–398, Fig. 1. ©
       1977 by the American Associa-
       tion for the Advancement of
       Science
2-11a Carolina Biological Supply Co.
2-11b Warren Rosenburg/BPS
2-12   From N. A. Campbell. BIOL-
       OGY. © 1987, The Benjamin/
       Cummings Publishing Com-
       pany, Inc., Menlo Park, Califor-
       nia. Used with permission.
2-13   The Granger Collection, New
       York.

2-14   From K. D. Johnson, D. L.
2-15   Rayle, and H. L. Wedberg.
2-16   BIOLOGY: AN INTRODUC-
       TION. © 1984, The Benjamin/
       Cummings Publishing Com-
       pany, Inc., Menlo Park, Califor-
       nia. Used with permission.
2-17a © Alan G. Nelson/Animals
       Animals
2-17b © Gary Milburn/Tom Stack
       and Associates.
2-17c © M. Austerman/Animals
       Animals
2-18   From K. D. Johnson, D. L.
       Rayle, and H. L. Wedberg.
       BIOLOGY: AN INTRODUC-
       TION. © 1984, The Benjamin/
       Cummings Publishing Com-
       pany, Inc., Menlo Park, Califor-
       nia. Used with permission.
2-19a Marjorie Shostak/Anthro-Photo
2-19b Marjorie Shostak/Anthro-Photo
2-21   Jean Whitney/Atoz Images
2-22   Pittsburg Photographic Library
       of Carnegie
2-23   USDA—Soil Conservation
       Service
Essay Anthony Bannister

Chapter Supplement Figures

S2-1a From K. D. Johnson, D. L.
       Rayle, and H. L. Wedberg.
       BIOLOGY: AN INTRODUC-
       TION. © 1984, The Benjamin/
       Cummings Publishing Com-
       pany, Inc., Menlo Park, Califor-
       nia. Used with permission.
S2-1b From K. D. Johnson, D. L.
       Rayle, and H. L. Wedberg.
       BIOLOGY: AN INTRODUC-
       TION. © 1984, The Benjamin/
       Cummings Publishing Com-
       pany, Inc., Menlo Park, Califor-
       nia. Used with permission.
S2-3   N. Simionescu
S2-4   E. H. Newcomb, University of
       Wisconsin, Madison/BPS

S2-5   From K. D. Johnson, D. L.
       Rayle, and H. L. Wedberg.
       BIOLOGY: AN INTRODUC-
       TION. © 1984, The Benjamin/
       Cummings Publishing Com-
       pany, Inc., Menlo Park, Califor-
       nia. Used with permission.
S2-7a G. F. Bahr, Air Forces Institute
       of Pathology
S2-7b J. R. Paulsen and U. K. Lae-
       mmli, CELL 12 (1977): 817–
       828. Used with permission.

Chapter 3 Figures

3-7a   National Parks & Wildlife Ser-
       vice, Sydney, Australia
3-7b   W. Perry Conway
3-11   Modified and redrawn from
       R. L. Smith (1974). ECOLOGY
       AND FIELD BIOLOGY. Second
       Edition, Harper and Row, New
       York.
3-15   Modified and redrawn from
       B. J. Nebel (1981). ENVIRON-
       MENTAL SCIENCE. Prentice-
       Hall, Englewood Cliffs, NJ
       07362.
3-18   From FUNDAMENTALS OF
       ECOLOGY. Third Edition by
       Eugene P. Odum, © 1971 by
       W. B. Saunders Company.
       Reprinted by permission of
       CBS College Publishing.

Table
3-1   From FUNDAMENTALS OF
       ECOLOGY. Third Edition by
       Eugene P. Odum, © 1971 by
       W. B. Saunders Company.
       Reprinted by permission of
       CBS College Publishing.

Chapter Supplement Figure

S3-1   Tim Thompson/Aperture
       Photobank

Chapter 4 Figures

4-1	Florida State Archives
4-9a	Australian News and Information Bureau
4-9b	Australian News and Information Bureau
4-11	W. Perry Conway
4-12	Ron Willocks/Aerie Nature Series

Table

4-1   From "The Strategy of Ecosystem Development," Odum, E., SCIENCE. Vol. 164, pp. 262–270, 18 April 1969, © 1969 by AAAS. Reprinted with permission of the American Association for the Advancement of Science and Dr. Eugene Odum.

Chapter Supplement Figure

S4-1   AP Wide World Photos

Tables

S4-1   From P. Goodwin (1981).
S4-2   NUCLEAR WAR: THE FACTS
S4-3   ON OUR SURVIVAL. New York: Rutledge Press. Reprinted with permission.

Part II Opener   Dr. James McClintock

Chapter 5 Figures

5-1	© Frank D. Smith/Jerobaum, Inc.
5-2	UNICEF/Maggie Murray-Lee
5-8	Modified and redrawn from Jeanne C. Bigarre (1979). "The Sunning of America: Migration to the Sunbelt." POPULATION BULLETIN Vol. 34 (1).
5-10	Modified from Haupt, A. and Kane, T. (1978) POPULATION HANDBOOK. Washington, D.C.: Population Reference Bureau. Reprinted with permission.
5-11	Modified and redrawn with permission from Population Reference Bureau (1982). U.S. POPULATION: WHERE WE ARE; WHERE WE'RE GOING. Washington D.C., Population Reference Bureau.

Chapter 6 Figures

6-1   Modified and redrawn with
6-2   permission from THE LIMITS
6-3   TO GROWTH: A REPORT FOR THE CLUB OF ROME'S PROJECT ON THE PREDICAMENT OF MANKIND, by Donella H. Meadows, Dennis L. Meadows, Jorgen Randers, William W. Behrens, III. A Potomac Associates book published by Universe Books, N.Y., 1972. Graphics by Potomac Associates.

6-4	AP/Wide World Photos
6-5	UNICEF/Abigail Heyman
6-8	AP/Wide World Photos

Table

6-1   Modified from A. Haupt and T. Kane. (1978). POPULATION HANDBOOK. Washington, D.C.: Population Reference Bureau.

Part III Opener   Photograph by Ansel Adams. Courtesy of the Ansel Adams Publishing Rights Trust. All rights reserved.

Chapter 7 Figures

7-1	FAO
7-2	UNICEF/Horst Max Cerni (81)
7-3	USDA photo/Tim McCabe
7-5	UN photo/John Isaac
7-8	Wayne Miller/Magnum Photos, Inc.
7-9	Modified and redrawn with permission from L. R. Brown (1982). "Fuel Farms: Croplands of the Future?" THE FUTURIST 14 (3): 16–28. Published by the World Future Society, 4916 St. Elmo Avenue, Washington, D.C. 20014
7-10	USDA
7-11	USDA—Soil Conservation Service
7-12a	United Nations/Bill Graham
7-12b	USDA—Soil Conservation Service
7-13a	USDA—Soil Conservation Service
7-13b	FAO photo/F. Mattioli

Table

7-1   Reprinted with permission from W. Reichert (1982). "Agriculture's Diminishing Diversity." ENVIRONMENT 24 (6): 6–11; 33–38. A publication of the Helen Dwight Reid Educational Foundation.

Chapter Supplement Figures

S7-4	USDA—Soil Conservation Service
S7-5	© Grant Heilman
S7-6	USDA—Soil Conservation Service
S7-7	USDA—Soil Conservation Service
S7-8	USDA—Soil Conservation Service

Chapter 8 Figures

8-4	Reprinted with permission from Kelly et al. (1981). THE GREAT WHALE BOOK. Center for Environmental Education, Washington, D.C. 20001.
8-5	John Launois/Black Star
8-9	USFWS Photo/Gary R. Falirer
8-10	S. W. Woo, U.C. Davis, courtesy USFWS
8-11	Carl Koford/Photo Researchers, Inc.
8-12	Courtesy of Multimedia Publications, Ltd.
8-13	USDA/Agricultural Research Services
8-14	Courtesy of Tennessee Wildlife Resources Agency
8-15	© Janet Robertson
Case Study	Ray Coppinger, Hampshire College

Table

8-1   Reprinted with permission of the Center for Environmental Education, Washington, D.C. 20001.

Chapter 9 Figures

9-1	© Ric Ergenbright
9-2	Bureau of Land Management (USDI)
9-4	USDA—Soil Conservation Service
9-6a	U.S. Forest Service
9-6b	Hank Lebo/Jeroboam, Inc.
9-7	From CONSERVATION OF NATURAL RESOURCES;. Guy-Harold Smith, © 1965. Reprinted with permission of John Wiley and Sons, Inc.
9-8a	U.S. Forest Service
9-8b	U.S. Forest Service
9-8c	Steve Botti, National Park Service
9-9	Photograph by Ansel Adams. Courtesy of the Ansel Adams Publishing Rights Trust. All rights reserved.
Essay	Bureau of Land Management (USDI)

Chapter 10 Figures

10-1	U.S. Geological Survey
10-6	Modified and redrawn from A. N. Strahler and A. H. Strahler (1973). ENVIRONMENTAL GEOSCIENCE. Hamilton Publishing Company, Santa Barbara, California. © 1973 by John Wiley and Sons.
10-7	USDA—Soil Conservation Service
10-10	Doug Lee Photography
10-11	Water Services of America

Chapter 11 Figures

11-1   © Douglas Beaman
11-5   Dr. W. Laqueur, Veterans Administration Hospital, Beckley, W. V., and NIOSH
11-6b   U.S. Geological Survey 187
11-10   © David Burkhalter/Tom Stack and Associates

Chapter 12 Figures

12-1   Washington Public Power Supply System
12-4   © Doug Lee
12-5   U.S. Department of Energy
12-12   Courtesy Solar Station
12-13b   W. Perry Conway
12-14   Emilio A. Mercado/Jeroboam, Inc.
12-15   U.S. Forest Service
12-17   From Kendall and Nadis' ENERGY STRATEGIES: TOWARD A SOLAR FUTURE, © 1980, Union of Concerned Scientists. Reprinted with permission from Ballinger Publishing Company.
Essay   TASS from Sovfoto

Tables

12-2   From Kendall and Nadis'
12-4   ENERGY STRATEGIES: TOWARD A SOLAR FUTURE, © 1980, Union of Concerned Scientists. Reprinted with permission from Ballinger Publishing Company.

Chapter Supplement Figure

S12-3   Gilles Peress/Magnum Photos, Inc.

Chapter 13 Figures

13-9   NOAA
13-10   Golden Goat Recovery Systems

Part IV Opener   Dan Morrill

Chapter 14 Figures

14-1   © Gamma-Liaison (Bartholomew)
14-2   From "Cancer and Industrial Chemical Production," D. L. Davis and B. H. Magee, SCIENCE, Vol. 206, pp. 1356–1358, 21 December 1979. © 1979 by AAAS. Modified and redrawn with permission of the American Association for the Advancement of Science and the Authors.
14-4   Modified and redrawn with permission of W. G. Thilly and H. L. Lieber (1980). "Genetic Toxicology," in TOXICOLOGY, Doull, Klaassen, and Amdur, eds. Macmillan: New York.
14-6   Modified and redrawn with permission from R. D. Harbison (1980). "Teratogens," in TOXICOLOGY, Doull, Klaassen, and Amdur, eds. Macmillan: New York.
14-7   C. D. Klaassen and J. Doull (1980). "Evaluation of Safety: Toxicologic Evidence," in TOXICOLOGY, Doull, Klaassen, and Amdur, eds. MacMillan: New York.
14-10   Reuters/Bettmann Newsphotos
14-13   Bruce Larson/Tacoma News Tribune
Viewpoint   © Jennifer W. Lester

Chapter 15 Figures

15-3a   J. W. Goodspeed/Freelance Photographers Guild
15-3b   Dave Baird/Tom Stack & Associates
15-8   Courtesy of William W. Kellogg. CLIMATE CHANGE AND SOCIETY. (1980). Westview Press: Boulder, Colorado.

Chapter Supplement Figures

Acid Rain
S15-5   From "Acid Precipitation and Sulfate Deposition in Florida," Brezonik et al., SCIENCE, Vol. 208, 30 May 1980, © by AAAS. Reprinted with permission of the American Association for the Advancement of Science.
S15-7   Ted Spiegel/Black Star

Indoor Pollution
S15-1   From T. D. Sterling and E.
S15-2   Sterling (1979). "Carbon Monoxide Levels in Kitchens and Homes with Gas Cookers." J. AMER. POLLUTION CONTROL ASSOC. 29(3): 238–241. Reprinted with permission.

Noise Pollution
S15-1   James T. Coit/Jeroboam, Inc.

Chapter Supplement Table

Noise Pollution
S15-1   From ENVIRONMENTAL SCIENCE, Second Edition by Amos Turk, Jonathan Turk, Janet T. Wittes, and Robert Wittes. © 1978 by W. B. Saunders Publishing Company. Reprinted with permission of CBS College Publishing.

Chapter 16 Figures

16-1a   Dave Baird/Tom Stack & Associates
16-1b   USDA—Soil Conservation Service
16-7   Courtesy of Groundwater Technology, Inc.
16-9   Hank Lebo/Jeroboam, Inc.
16-10   The Des Moines Register
16-12   Bureau of Reclamation

Chapter 17 Figures

17-1   Modified and redrawn with permission from A. A. Boraiko and F. Ward (1980). "The Pesticide Dilemma." NATIONAL GEOGRAPHIC 157(2), p. 149.
17-3   Fred Ward/Black Star
17-5   Grant Heilman
17-6   AP/Wide World Photos
17-7   USDA
17-8   USDA photo/Larry Lana

Chapter 18 Figures

18-1a   Michael A. Leonard
18-1b   FPG/David M. Doody
18-2a   Joe Traver/Gamma-Liaison
18-2b   Ron Schifferle/Niagara Gazette
18-6   Courtesy of the U.S. EPA, MSB-MERL, Edison, N.J.
18-8   Richard Nichols/Gamma-Liaison

Chapter Supplement Figure

S18-3   © Louie Psihoyos/Contact

Part V Opener   Bruce Davidson/Magnum Photos

Chapter 19 Figures

19-1   Dennis A. Noonan
19-4   A. B. Joyce/Photo Researchers, Inc.

Chapter 20 Figures

20-1   FAO photo/J. Van Acker
20-5   © Grant Heilman

Chapter 21 Figures

21-1   © Rex Weyler/Greenpeace
21-2   © Scott Reuman/Keystone Science School
21-3   Illustrator's Stock Photo
21-4   Reuters/Bettmann Newsphotos
21-5   © Forrest Anderson/Gamma-Liaison

Chapter 22 Figures

22-1	© Frans Lanting
22-2a	The Bettmann Archive
22-2b	Volkswagen of America, Inc.
22-3	© Pascal Maitre/Gamma-Liaison
22-4	© Yoram Lehmann/Peter Arnold, Inc.
22-5	© Frank Siteman/Jeroboam, Inc.
22-6	© The Financial Times, Ltd./Gamma-Liaison

Color Photo Credits

Gallery 1

1 NASA

Gallery 2 Biomes

1 Stock Imagery
2 Tom Till
3 Tom Till
4 G. T. Bernard/Animals Animals
5 Tom Till
6 W. Perry Conway
7 E. R. Dagginger/Animals Animals
8 David Muench
9 W. Perry Conway
10 Tom Till
11 S. Belyavoi/Tass Sovfoto
12 David Muench
13 C. W. Perkins/Animals Animals

Gallery 3 Endangered Species

1 Frans Lanting
2 C. C. Lockwood/Animals Animals
3 Tom McHugh/Photo Researchers, Inc.
4 Michael Fogden/Animals Animals
5 Tom Stack/Tom Stack & Associates
6 Jeff Fotte/Bruce Coleman, Inc.
7 Art Wolfe/Aperture

8 W. Perry Conway
9 Zoological Society of San Diego
10 Zoological Society of San Diego
11 Zoological Society of San Diego
12 Ron Garrison/Zoological Society of San Diego

Gallery 4

1 Gary Randall/Tom Stack & Associates
2 Joel W. Rogers/Aperture
3 Gesig Gerster/Photo Researchers, Inc.
4 Fiona Funquist/Tom Stack & Associates
5 Tom Stack/Tom Stack & Associates
6 New York State Department of Health Division Laboratories
7 Gary Milburn/Tom Stack & Associates
8 Gary Milburn/Tom Stack & Associates
9 Dan Morrill
10 Walt Anderson/Tom Stack & Associates
11 Russ Kinne/Photo Researchers, Inc.
12 Suzi Barnes/Tom Stack & Associates
13 Porterfield-Chickering/Photo Researchers, Inc.
14 Russ Kinne/Photo Researchers, Inc.

Index